Telephone: Bourton-on-the-Water 20352 Std 0451

𝔖𝔱𝔲𝔡𝔦𝔬 𝔄𝔫𝔱𝔦𝔮𝔲𝔢𝔰 𝔏𝔱𝔡.

(Reg. Office Co. No. 669865)

V.A.T. Reg. No. 274 9510 37

𝔅𝔬𝔲𝔯𝔱𝔬𝔫=𝔬𝔫=𝔱𝔥𝔢=𝔚𝔞𝔱𝔢𝔯

Glos.

Brass   Silver   Copper

𝔓𝔢𝔯𝔦𝔬𝔡 𝔞𝔫𝔡 ℭ𝔬𝔫𝔱𝔢𝔪𝔭𝔬𝔯𝔞𝔯𝔶 𝔉𝔲𝔯𝔫𝔦𝔱𝔲𝔯𝔢

A fine large bronze of horse & rider — stamped 'BONHEUR' — one of many fine bronzes at the time of going to press.

3

MILLER'S
ANTIQUES
PRICE GUIDE
1985
(Volume VI)

Compiled and Edited by

Martin and Judith Miller

ISBN 0-905879-34-1

Printed and bound in Great Britain by William Clowes (Beccles) Limited, Beccles and London

PUBLISHED BY M.J.M. PUBLICATIONS LTD.
THE GRANGE · BENENDEN · CRANBROOK · KENT
Telephone Cranbrook (0580) 240454

Peter Semus Antiques

Just 3 miles to the west of Brighton, Sussex are the warehouses of Peter Semus. A wide range of stock is carried along with the following services.

- **CONTAINER SALES SERVICE:** Full container loads to any destination: merchandise can be either totally refinished or just clean.

- **CUSTOM FURNITURE MAKING:** Conversion furniture such as Bureau Bookcases, Breakfront Bookcases, Desks, Chests, Cabinets. Individual "One off" items undertaken.

- **INDIVIDUAL SALES:** There is no obligation to buy entire shipments; customers for one or two pieces are very welcome.

- **REFINISHING SERVICE:** Any item bought here can be restored in our own extensive workshops. Loose leathers for desk tops available.

- **LONDON AND SOUTHERN SHIPPING:** This separate division specialises in Overseas Packing and Shipping; collections made anywhere nationwide; one piece or whole container; Antiques or Household.

Peter Semus Antiques

Peter's basic philosophy is to offer a wide range of customer services budgeted according to each clients' requirements. For example; if the customer is a retailer who wishes everything totally refinished ready for sale or is a wholesaler who has clients who want to refinish themselves, the operation is flexible enough to satisfy both people.

Likewise the Shipping Service can look after individual pieces; clients who want to roam the country seeking their requirements; household removals to any destination; parties who want vacationary trips around Stately Homes combined with "Antiquing".

The refinishing shop handles routine repairs to extensive conversion work such as Breakfront Bookcases, Double Dome Queen Anne style Bureau Bookcases and extending tables. The best selling items are Linen Presses, Chests on Chests, Bureau Bookcases and Bow Chests.

Please give Peter the chance to discuss your exact requirements so hopefully the best all round package can be put together for you.

Contact Peter at the Warehouse, Gladstone Road, Portslade, Sussex BN4 1LJ.
Telephone (0273) 420154/202989.

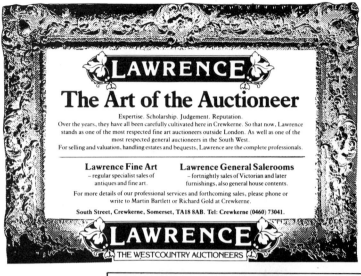

Auctioneers
in the South of England

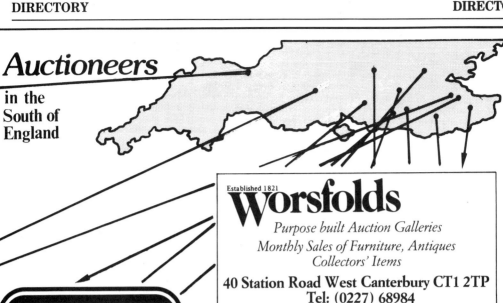

Established 1821
Worsfolds

Purpose built Auction Galleries
Monthly Sales of Furniture, Antiques
Collectors' Items

40 Station Road West Canterbury CT1 2TP
Tel: (0227) 68984

BUTLER & HATCH WATERMAN

THE AUCTION SALE ROOMS
MARINE WALK STREET
HYTHE, KENT
(0303) 66022

Estate Agents & Surveyors

BUTLER & HATCH WATERMAN

Incorporated Valuers & Auctioneers

AUCTIONEERS

Pauline Chalk FSVA, T R Lawrence FRICS, FRVA
A F Beggs FRICS, B G Gilbertson ARICS, ACIArb

THE AUCTION SALE ROOM
102 HIGH STREET
TENTERDEN, KENT
(05806) 2083

FIRST ESTABLISHED 1830   **BHW**   BRANCHES IN KENT & SUSSEX

Fryer's Auction Galleries
Terminus Road, Bexhill-on-Sea, Sussex Telephone: Bexhill (0424) 212994

Gorringes Auction Galleries

Member of the Society **SOFAA** of Fine Art Auctioneers

MONTHLY AUCTION SALES
Period Furniture, Porcelain, Glass, Objects of Virtu, Silver Plate
Jewellery, Books, Works of Art, Oriental Carpets
Valuations for Insurance, Probate, Family Division and Sale by Auction
Auction Sales conducted in Private Residences

15 NORTH STREET, LEWES, SUSSEX
Tel: LEWES (079 16) 2503 and 2382

Stephen R. Thomas
AUCTIONEERS & VALUERS
General sales of antiques held every Thursday
evening throughout the year at 6.00 p.m.
Fine art and selected antiques sales held quarterly.
Viewing: Wednesdays 6.00 p.m. to 9.00 p.m. and
sale days from 11.00 a.m.
400-600 lots sold every week. Catalogues available.
at
THE KATHERINE WHEEL HOTEL
EGHAM HIGH STREET, EGHAM, SURREY
TEL: EGHAM 31122
Saleroom open 10-5 weekdays. Entries invited.
£2 per lot. No commission charged

Established 1759
Dreweatt
Watson & Barton

Regular Specialist Antique Sales

Members of the Society of Fine Art Auctioneers

Donnington Priory Salerooms
Donnington Newbury Berkshire RG13 2JE
Tel: (0635) 31234   Telex 848580

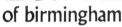

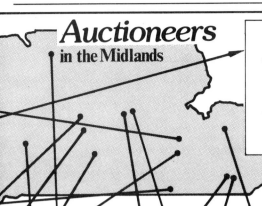

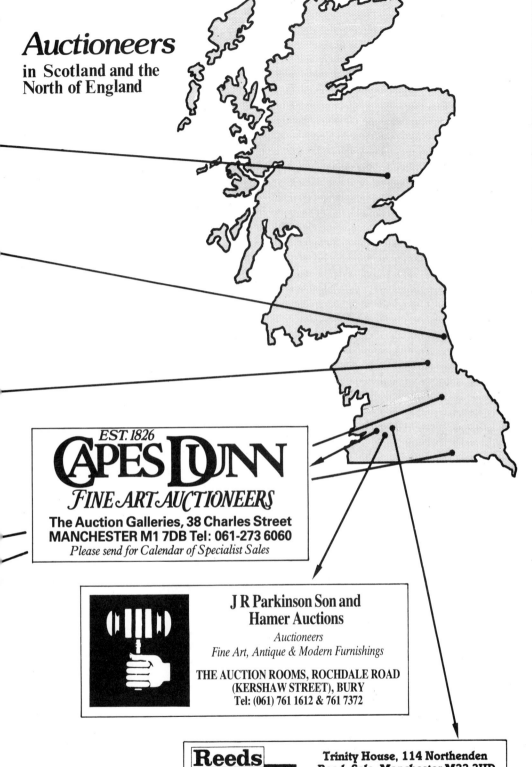

Auctioneers
in Scotland and the North of England

DIRECTORY OF AUCTIONEERS

This directory is by no means complete. Any auctioneer who holds frequent sales should contact us for inclusion in the 1986 edition. Entries must be received by April 1985. There is, of course, no charge for this listing.

LONDON
Bonhams, Montpelier Galleries
Montpelier St., Knightsbridge, S.W.7
Tel: 01-584 9161 & 01-589 4577

Borough Auctions
6 Park St., London Bridge, S.E.1
Tel: 01-407 9577 (day)
      01-981 2079 (evening)

Camden Auctions
The Saleroom, Hoppers Road
Winchmore Hill, N.21
Tel: 01-886 1550

Christie's, Manson & Woods Ltd.
8 King Street, St. James's, S.W.1
Tel: 01-839 9060

Christie's South Kensington Ltd.
85 Old Brompton Rd., S.W.7
Tel: 01-581 2231

Forrest & Co.
79-85 Cobbold Rd., Leytonstone, E.11
Tel: 01-534 2931

Stanley Gibbons Auctions Ltd.
Drury House, Russell St., W.C.2
Tel: 01-836 8444

Glendining & Co.
Blenstock House, 7 Blenheim St., New
Bond St., W.1
Tel: 01-493 2445

Harmers of London Stamp
Auctioneers Ltd.
41 New Bond St., W.1
Tel: 01-629 0218

Harvey's Auctions Ltd.
14, 16 and 18 Neal St., W.C.2
Tel: 01-240 1464/5/6/7

Jackson-Stops & Staff
14 Curzon St., W.1
Tel: 01-499 6291

Lefevre & Partners (Auctioneers) Ltd.
The Persian Carpet Galleries
152 Brompton Rd., S.W.3
Tel: 01-584 5516

London Bridge Auctions
6 Park St., S.E.1
Tel: 01-407 9577

Lots Road Chelsea Auction Galleries
71 Lots Rd., S.W.10
Tel: 01-352 2349/01-351 5748

Phillips
Blenstock House
7 Blenheim St., W.1
Tel: 01-629 6602

Rippon Boswell & Co.
The Arcade, Sth. Kensington Station
S.W.7
Tel: 01-589 4242

Robson Lowe at Christies
10 King St., S.W.1
Tel: 01-839 4034/5

Sotheby Parke Bernet & Co.
34-35 New Bond St., W.1
Tel: 01-493 8080

Sovereign Auctions Ltd.
101 Hoe St., E.17
Tel: 01-521 5456 & 01-520 3215

West London Auctions
7-21 King St., W.3
Tel: 01-993 1355/6

AVON
Aldridges, Bath
The Auction Galleries, 130-132
Walcot St., Bath
Tel: (0225) 62830 & 62839

Davis, Champion & Payne
Chartered Surveyors
42 High St., Chipping Sodbury, Bristol
Tel: (0454) 312848/313033

Hodell Pritchard
Sixways, Clevedon
Tel: (0272) 876699

Lalonde Bros. & Parham
71 Oakfield Road, Clifton, Bristol
Tel: (0272) 734052

The Mart Assembly Rooms
34-36 Baker St., Weston-super-Mare
Tel: (0934) 28419

Osmond Tricks & Son
Regent Street Auction Room, Clifton
Bristol
Tel: (0272) 737201

Phillips & Jolly's Auction Rooms of Bath
1 Old King St., Bath
Tel: (0225) 310609 & 310709

Taviner's Auction Rooms
Prewett St., Redcliffe, Bristol
Tel: (0272) 25996

BEDFORDSHIRE
Peacock, The Auction Centre
26 Newnham St., Bedford
Tel: (0234) 66366

BERKSHIRE
Buckland & Sons
Dolphin Hotel, Slough
Tel: (0753) 885451

Chancellors
31 High St., Ascot
Tel: (0990) 27101

V & V Chattel Auctioneers
105 London St. and
6 Station Rd., Reading
Tel: (0734) 594748

Dreweatt, Watson & Barton
Donnington Priory, Donnington
Newbury
Tel: (0635) 31234

Martin & Pole
5a & 7 Broad St., Wokingham
Tel: (0734) 780777

Neates
108 High St., Hungerford
Tel: (04886) 2808

Nicholas
12 High St., Streatley, Reading
Tel: (0491) 872318

Thimbleby & Shorland
31 Great Knollys St., Reading
Tel: (0734) 54438

BUCKINGHAMSHIRE
Buckland & Sons
Bridgwood, East Common Rd.
Gerrards Cross
Tel: (02813) 85451

Pretty & Ellis
The Amersham Auction Rooms
125 Station Rd., Amersham
Tel: (02403) 4627

CAMBRIDGESHIRE
Cheffins Grain & Chalk
2 Clifton Rd. and
49-53 Regent St., Cambridge
Tel: (0223) 558721

George Comins & Sons
3 Chequer Lane, Ely
Tel: (0353) 2265

Ekins Dilley & Handley
The Salerooms, St. Ives, Huntingdon
Tel: (0480) 68144

Grounds & Co.
2 Nene Quay, Wisbech
Tel: (0945) 585041

Kimbolton Auctions
The Auction Rooms, Kimbolton
Tel: (0480) 861233

Hammond & Co.
Cambridge Place, Cambridge
Tel: (0223) 356067

Raymond Munns, F.R.I.C.S.
25 High St., Willingham
Tel: (0954) 60447

Norman, Wright & Hodgkinson
Abbey Road, Bourne
Tel: (07782) 2567

CHESHIRE
Bridgford & Sons
The Alderley Saleroom
1 Heyes Lane, Alderley Edge
Tel: (0625) 585347

Brocklehursts
King Edward St., Macclesfield
Tel: (0625) 27555

Andrew, Hilditch & Son
19 The Square, Sandach
Tel: (09367) 2048 & 7246

Jackson-Stops & Staff
25 Nicholas St., Chester
Tel: (0244) 28361

Frank R. Marshall & Co.
Marshall House, Church Hill
Knutsford
Tel: (0565) 53461

David Morrison & Son
Central Auction Galleries, 1 Market
St., Altrincham
Tel: (061928) 9200

Reeds Rains
Trinity House, 114 Northenden Rd.
Sale
and
Warren House, 17 Warren St.
Stockport
Tel: (061962) 9237

Phillips of Chester
Bold Place, Chester
Tel: (0244) 315333

Sotheby's
Booth Mansion, 28 Westergate St.
Saltney, Chester
Tel: (0244) 315531

Wright Manley
Beeston Sales Centre, 63 High St.
Tarporley
Tel: (0829) 260318

CLEVELAND
Norman Hope & Partners
2 South Road, Hartlepool
Tel: (0429) 67828

Lithgow Sons & Partners
The Auction Houses, Station Road
Stokesley, Middlesbrough
Tel: (0642) 710158 & 710326

CORNWALL
Colwills
26 Fore St., St. Columb.
Tel: (0637) 880275/734

W. H. Cornish
Central Auction Rooms, Castle St.
Truro
Tel: (0872) 2968

W. H. Lane & Son
Fine Art Auctioneers, Central Auction
Rooms, Penzance
Tel: (0736) 61447/8

David Lay, A.S.V.A.
7 Morrab Rd., Penzance
Tel: (0736) 68308

May, Whetter & Grose
Cornubia Hall, Par
Tel: (072681) 2271

CUMBRIA
Tiffen, King & Nicholson
12 Lowther St., Carlisle
Tel: (0228) 25259

Mossops
Loughrigg Villa, Kelsick Rd.
Ambleside
Tel: (09663) 3015

James Thompson
64 Main St., Kirkby Lonsdale
Tel: (0468) 71555

Thomson, Roddick & Laurie
24 Lowther St., Carlisle
Tel: (0228) 28939 & 39636

DERBYSHIRE
Robert E. Spark & Co.
Matlock Auction Gallery, Olde
Englishe Rd., Dale Rd., Matlock
Tel: (0629) 2451

DEVON
Bearnes
Rainbow, Avenue Rd., Torquay
Tel: (0803) 26277

Peter J. Eley
Western House, 98-100 High St.
Sidmouth
Tel: (03955) 2552

Robin A. Fenner & Co.
51 Bannawell St., Tavistock
Tel: (0822) 4974

Gribble, Booth & Taylor
West St., Axminster
Tel: (0297) 32323

Charles Head & Son
113 Fore St., Kingsbridge
Tel: (0548) 2352

Michael G. Matthews
Devon Fine Art Auction House,
Dowell Street, Honiton
Tel: (0404) 41872/3137

Michael Newman
Fine Art Auctioneers, Central Auction
Rooms, Kinterbury House, St.
Andrew's Cross, Plymouth
Tel: (0752) 669298

Phillips
Alphin Brook Rd., Alphington, Exeter
Tel: (0392) 39025/6

Rendells
13 Market St., Newton Abbot
Tel: (0626) 3881

John Smale & Co.
19 Cross St., Barnstaple
Tel: (0271) 2000/2916

Spencer-Thomas & Woolland
Harbour Road Salerooms, Seaton
Tel: (0297) 22453

David Symonds
The Estate Office, High Street,
Crediton
Tel: (03632) 2700/4100

Laurence & Martin Taylor
Honiton Galleries, 63 High St.
Honiton
Tel: (0404) 2404

Taylor, Lane & Creber
The Western Auction Rooms, 38
North Hill, Plymouth
Tel: (0752) 266295

Ward & Chowen
1 Church Lane, Tavistock
Tel: (0822) 2458

Whitton & Laing
32 Okehampton St., Exeter
Tel: (0392) 52621

John Wood & Co.
Seaton Salerooms, Harbour Rd.
Seaton
Tel: (0297) 20290

DORSET
S. W. Cottee & Son
The Market, East St., Wareham
Tel: (09295) 2826

Hy. Duke & Son
Fine Art Salerooms, Weymouth Ave.
Dorchester
Tel: (0305) 65080

House & Son
Lansdowne House, Christchurch Rd.
Bournemouth
Tel: (0202) 26232

John Jeffery Auctioneers
Minster House, The Commons
Shaftesbury
Tel: (0747) 3331-2

Riddetts of Bournemouth
Richmond Hill, Bournemouth Sq.
Bournemouth
Tel: (0202) 25686

GREATER LONDON
Bonsor Penningtons
82 Eden St., Kingston, Surrey
Tel: 01-546 0022

Croydon Auction Rooms (Rosan &
Co.)
144-150 London Rd., Croydon
Tel: 01-688 1123/4/5

Parkins
18 Malden Rd., Cheam, Surrey
Tel: 01-644 6633 & 6127

E. Reeves Ltd.
104/120 Church St., Croydon
Tel: 01-688 3136

COUNTY DURHAM
G. H. Edkins & Son
122 Newgate St., Bishop Auckland
Tel: (0388) 603095

G. Tarn Bainbridge & Son
Northern Rock House, High Row
Darlington
Tel: (0325) 62633 & 62553

Thomas Watson & Son
Northumberland St., Darlington
Tel: (0325) 462555/462559

ESSEX
Abridge Auction Rooms
High Rd., Abridge, Romford
Tel: (037881) 2107/3113

Ambrose, 149 High Road, Loughton
Tel: 01-508 2121

Cooper Hirst
Goldlay House, Parkway, Chelmsford
Tel: (0245) 58141

Elam's
15-17 West Rd., Westcliff-on-Sea
Tel: (0702) 48404

Spurgeon & Gilchrist
1st Floor, Tokenhouse Chambers
Rosemary Rd., Clacton-on-Sea
Tel: (0255) 422472

John Stacey & Sons
Leigh Auction Rooms, 86-90 Pall Mall
Leigh-on-Sea
Tel: (0702) 77051

Vosts' Fine Art Auctioneers
Layer Marney, Colchester
Tel: (0206) 331005

Edwin Watson & Son
1 Market St., Saffron Walden
Tel: (0799) 22058

J. M. Welch & Son
Old Town Hall, Great Dunmow
Tel: (0371) 2117/8

GLOUCESTERSHIRE
G. H. Bayley & Sons
Vittoria House, Vittoria Walk
Cheltenham
Tel: (0242) 21102

Bruton, Knowles & Co.
111 Eastgate St., Gloucester
Tel: (0425) 21267

Cheltenham Galleries
1a Crescent Place, Cheltenham
Tel: (0242) 584310

Jackson-Stops & Staff
Dollar St. House, Cirencester
Tel: (0285) 3334

Mallams
26 Grosvenor St., Cheltenham
Tel: (0242) 35712

Moore, Allen & Innocent
33 Castle St., Cirencester
Tel: (0285) 2862

Sandoe Luce Panes
Chipping Manor Salerooms
Wotton-under-Edge
Tel: (045385) 3193

Specialised Postcard Auctions
12 Suffolk Rd., Cheltenham
Tel: (0242) 580323

HAMPSHIRE

Allen & May
18 Bridge St., Andover
Tel: (0264) 3417 & 63331

Austin & Wyatt
79 High St., Fareham
Tel: (0329) 234211/4

Michael G. Baker, F.S.V.A.
4 Latimer St., Romsey
Tel: (0794) 513331

Elliott & Green
40 High St., Lymington
Tel: (0590) 77225

Fox & Sons
5 & 7 Salisbury St., Fordingbridge
Tel: (0425) 52121

Hants. & Berks. Auctions
40 George St., Kingsclere
Tel: (0635) 298181

Jacobs & Hunt
Lavant St., Petersfield
Tel: (0730) 2744/5

Martin & Stratford
The Auction Mart, Market Square
Alton
Tel: (0420) 84402

D. M. Nesbit & Co.
7 Clarendon Rd., Southsea
Tel: (0705) 820785/6

Ormiston, Knight & Payne
54 Southampton Rd., Ringwood
Tel: (04254) 3333

Pearsons
Walcote Chambers, High St.,
Winchester
Tel: (0962) 64444

Whiteheads
34 High St., Petersfield
Tel: (0730) 2691/2

HEREFORD & WORCESTER

Banks & Silvers
66 Foregate St., Worcester
Tel: (0905) 23456

Blinkhorn & Co.
41-43 High St., Broadway
Tel: (0386) 852456

Coles, Knapp & Kennedy
Georgian Rooms & Tudor House, High
St., Hereford
Tel: (0989) 62227/63553/4

Maurice Fellows
6 The Tything, Worcester
Tel: (0905) 27755

Andrew Grant, F.R.I.C.S.
59/60 Foregate St., Worcester
Tel: (0905) 52310

Arthur G. Griffiths & Son
57 Foregate St., Worcester
Tel: (0905) 26464

Philip Laney & Jolly
12a Worcester Rd., Gt. Malvern
Tel: (06845) 63121/2

J. G. Lear & Son
46 Foregate St., Worcester
Tel: (0905) 25184/25494

Phipps & Pritchard
Bank Buildings, Kidderminster
Tel: (0562) 2244/6 & 2187

Russell, Baldwin & Bright
Fine Art Saleroom, Ryelands Rd.
Leominster
Tel: (0568) 3897

Stooke, Hill & Co.
3 Broad St., Leominster
Tel: (0568) 3407

HERTFORDSHIRE

George Jackson & Son
Paynes Park House, Paynes Park
Hitchin
Tel: (0462) 55212

Norris & Duvall
106 Fore St., Hertford
Tel: (0992) 52249

G. E. Sworder & Sons
Chequers, 19 North St., Bishops
Stortford
Tel: (0279) 52441

Watsons
Water Lane, Bishops Stortford
Tel: (0279) 52361/4

HUMBERSIDE NORTH

Gilbert Baitson, F.S.V.A.
The Edwardian Auction Galleries, 194
Anlaby Rd., Hull
Tel: (0482) 223355/6

Broader & Spencer
18 Quay Road, Bridlington
Tel: (0262) 70355/6

Dee & Atkinson
The Exchange, Driffield
Tel: (0377) 43151

H. Evans & Son
1 Parliament St., Hull
Tel: (0482) 23033

HUMBERSIDE SOUTH

Dickinson, Davy & Markham
10 Wrawby St., Brigg
Tel: (0652) 53666

ISLE OF MAN

Chrystalls Auctions
St. James Chambers, Athol St.
Tel: (0624) 3986

ISLE OF WIGHT

Way, Riddett & Co.
Town Hall Chambers, Lind St., Ryde
Tel: (0983) 62255

KENT

Alberts Auctions & Co.
Maiden Lane, Crayford, Dartford
Tel: (0322) 528868

B. & J. Auction Galleries
22 Mortimer St., Herne Bay
Tel: (02273) 3479/66653

Bracketts
27-29 High St., Tunbridge Wells
Tel: (0892) 33733

Burrows & Day
39-41 Bank St., Ashford
Tel: (0233) 24321

Butler & Hatch Waterman
102 High St., Tenterden
Tel: (05806) 3233/2083

also at:
86 High St., Hythe
Tel: (0303) 66032/3

Geering & Colyer
Highgate, Hawkhurst
Tel: (05805) 3181

Hobbs Parker
9 Tufton St., Ashford
Tel: (0233) 22222

John Hogbin & Son
53 High St., Tenterden
Tel: (05806) 3200

Ibbett, Mosely, Card & Co.
125 High St., Sevenoaks
Tel: (0732) 452246

Kent Sales
Kent House, 4 New Rd., S. Darenth
Tel: (0322) 864919

Parsons, Welch & Cowell
129 High St., Sevenoaks
Tel: (0732) 451211/4

Daniel Smith
24-26 Dover Rd., Folkestone
Tel: (0303) 41967

Stewart, Gore
100-102 Northdown Rd., Margate
Tel: (0843) 21528/9

James B. Terson & Son
27-29 Castle St., Dover
Tel: (0304) 202173

Ward & Partners
16 High St., Hythe
Tel: (0303) 67473

Worsfold's
40 Station Rd. West, Canterbury
Tel: (0227) 68984

LANCASHIRE

Artingstall & Hind
378-380 Deansgate, Knott Mill
Manchester
Tel: 061-834 4559

Capes Dunn & Co.
The Auction Galleries, 38 Charles St.
Manchester
Tel: 061-273 6060

Entwistle Green
The Galleries, Kingsway, Ansdell
Lytham St. Annes
Tel: (0253) 735442

Hothersall, Forrest, McKenna & Son
Bank Salerooms, Harris Court
Clitheroe
Tel: (0200) 25446/22695

J. R. Parkinson Son & Hamer
The Auction Room, Rochdale Rd.
Bury
Tel: 061-761 1612/7372

John E. Pinder & Son
Stone Bridge, Longridge, Preston
PR3 3AH
Tel: (077478) 2282

LEICESTERSHIRE

Gilding (Fine Arts)
Gumley, Market Harborough
Tel: (053753) 2847

Walker Walton Hanson
4 Market Place, Oakham
Tel: (0572) 3377

Warner, Sheppard & Wade
The Warner Auction Rooms, 16/18
Halford St., Leicester
Tel: (0533) 21613

LINCOLNSHIRE

Messrs. Brogden & Co.
39/38 Silver St., Lincoln
Tel: (0522) 31321

William H. Brown
Fine Art Dept., Westgate Hall
Westgate, Grantham
Tel: (0476) 68861

Earl & Lawrence
55 Northgate, Sleaford
Tel: (0529) 302946

James Eley & Son
1 Main Ridge West, Boston
Tel: (0205) 61687

Golding
45 High St., Grantham
Tel: (0476) 5456

Thomas Mawer & Son
63 Monks St., Lincoln
Tel: (0522) 24984 & 22215

Vergettes
38 St. Mary's St., Stamford
Tel: (0780) 52136

MERSEYSIDE

Ball & Percival
132 Lord St. and
21 Hoghton st., Southport
Tel: (0704) 36900

Kingsley Galleries
3-4 The Quadrant, Hoylake, Wirral
Tel: 051-632 5821

Outhwaite & Litherland
Kingsway Galleries, Fontenoy St.,
Liverpool
Tel: 051-236 6561/3

Eldon E. Worrall
15 Seel St., Liverpool
Tel: 051-709 2950

NORFOLK

Noel D. Abel
32 Norwich Rd., Watton
Tel: (0953) 881204

Clowes, Nash & Thurgar
6 Tombland, Norwich
Tel: (0603) 27261

Ewings
Market Place, Reepham, Norwich
Tel: (0603) 870473

Thos. Wm. Gaze & Son
Roydon Rd., Diss
Tel: (0379) 2291

Charles Hawkins & Sons
Lynn Rd., Downham Market
Tel: (0366) 382112/3

Nigel F. Hedge
28B Market Place, North Walsham
Tel: (0692) 402881

Hilham's
53 Springfield Rd., Gorleston-on-Sea
Tel: (0493) 62152

James – Norwich Auctions Ltd.
33 Timberhill, Norwich
Tel: (0603) 24817/25369

G. A. Key
8 Market Place, Aylsham
Tel: (026373) 3195

Long & Beck
2 Oak St., Fakenham
Tel: (0328) 2231

Hanbury Williams
34 Church St., Cromer
Tel: (0263) 513247

NORTHAMPTONSHIRE

M. B. Carney
Brackley Auction Rooms, Hill St.
Brackley
Tel: (0280) 702641

Goldsmith & Bass
15 Market Place, Oundle
Tel: (0832) 72349

R. L. Lowery & Partners
24 Bridge St., Northampton
Tel: (0604) 21561

Northampton Auction Galleries
Old Albion Brewery, Commercial St.
Northampton
Tel: (0604) 37263/4

T. W. Arnold Corby & Co.
30-32 Brook St., Raunds
Tel: (0933) 623722/3

Southam & Sons
Corn Exchange, Thrapston, Kettering
Tel: (08012) 2409

H. Wilford Ltd.
Midland Rd., Wellingborough
Tel: (0933) 222760/222762

NOTTINGHAMSHIRE

Edward Bailey & Son
17 Northgate, Newark
Tel: (0636) 703141 & 77154

Furniture & General Auctions
Corn Exchange, Cattle Market
London Rd., Nottingham
Tel: (0602) 866261

Neales of Nottingham
192 Mansfield Rd., Nottingham
Tel: (0602) 624141

Walker Walton Hanson (Auctions)
The Nottingham Auction Mart
Byard Lane, Bridlesmith Gate
Nottingham NG1 2GL
Tel: (0602) 54272

C. B. Sheppard & Son
The Auction Gallery
Chatsworth St., Sutton-in Ashfield
Tel: (0773) 872419

Henry Spencer & Sons Ltd.
20 The Square, Retford
Tel: (0777) 706767

OXFORDSHIRE

Green & Co.
33 Market Place, Wantage
Tel: (02357) 3561/2

Holloways
49 Parsons St., Banbury
Tel: (0295) 53197

William A. Honour & Co.
112 High St., Thame
Tel: (084421) 2383/4

Mallams, Fine Art Auctioneers
24 St. Michael's St., Oxford
Tel: (0865) 241358

E. P. Messenger & Son
Pevensey House Salerooms
Manorsfield Rd., Bicester
Tel: (08692) 45985

Phillips Inc. Brooks
39 Park End St., Oxford
Tel: (0865) 723524/5

Simmons & Lawrence
32 Bell St., Henley-on-Thames
Tel: (0491) 571111

SHROPSHIRE

Bowen Son & Watson
The Oswestry Auction Rooms
35 Bailey St., Oswestry
Tel: (0691) 652367

also at:
Ellesmere
Tel: (0691) 712534

Cooper & Green
3 Barker St., Shrewsbury
Tel: (0743) 50081

John German Ralph Pay
43 High St., Shrewsbury
Tel: (0743) 69661/4

Hall, Wateridge & Owen
Welsh Bridge Salerooms, Shrewsbury
Tel: (0743) 60212

McCartney, Morris & Barker
25 Corve St., Ludlow
Tel: (0584) 2636

Nock, Deighton & Son
10 Broad St., Ludlow
Tel: (0584) 2364/3760

Perry & Phillips
Newmarket Salerooms, Newmarket
Buildings, Listley St., Bridgnorth
Tel: (07462) 2248

SOMERSET

Cooper & Tanner Ltd.
14 North Parade, Frome
Tel: (0373) 62045

Dores
The Auction Mart, Vicarage St.,
Frome
Tel: (0373) 62257

King, Miles & Co.
The Old Palace Saleroom, Priory Rd.
Wells
Tel: (0749) 73002

Lawrence Fine Art of Crewkerne
South St., Crewkerne
Tel: (0460) 73041

The London Cigarette Card Co. Ltd.
Sutton Rd., Somerton
Tel: (0458) 73452

Phillips, Sanders & Studds
32 The Avenue, Minehead
Tel: (0643) 2281/3

Priory Saleroom
Winchester St., Taunton
Tel: (0823) 77121

Wellington Salerooms
Mantle St., Wellington
Tel: (082347) 4815

STAFFORDSHIRE

Bagshaws
17 High St., Uttoxeter
Tel: (08893) 2811

John German, Ralph Pay
The Rotunda, 131a High St.,
Burton-on-Trent
Tel: (0283) 42051

Hall & Lloyd, Auctioneers
Stafford
Tel: (0785) 58176

Louis Taylor & Sons
Percy Street, Hanley, Stoke-on-Trent
Tel: (0782) 260222

Wintertons
St. Mary's Chambers, Lichfield
Tel: (05432) 23256

SUFFOLK

Abbotts (incorp. Spear & Sons)
The Hill, Wickham Market
Woodbridge
Tel: (0728) 746321

H. A. Adnams
The Auction Room, St. Edmunds Rd.
Southwold
Tel: (0502) 723292

Oxborrows, Arnott & Calver
14 Church St., Woodbridge
Tel: (03943) 2244/5

Boardman – Fine Art Auctioneers
Station Road Corner, Haverhill
Tel: (0440) 703784

Diamond, Mills & Co.
117 Hamilton Rd., Felixstowe
Tel: (03942) 2281/2

Robert Dove & Partners
Dover House, Wolsey St., Ipswich
Tel: (0473) 55137

Durrant's
10 New Market, Beccles
Tel: (0502) 712122

James – in Suffolk
16a The Traverse, Bury St. Edmunds
Tel: (0284) 702415

January
Rothsay Sale Rooms, 124 High St.
Newmarket
Tel: (0638) 668679

Lacy Scott, Fine Art
Angel Hill, Bury St. Edmunds
Tel: (0284) 63531

Terry Marshall
The Old Schoolroom, High St.
Lavenham
Tel: (0787) 76773/247548

Neal Sons & Fletcher
26 Church St., Woodbridge
Tel: (03943) 2263/4

Notleys
Royal Thoroughfare, Lowestoft
Tel: (0502) 2024/5

Olivers
23-24 Market Hill, Sudbury
Tel: (0787) 72247

Tuohy & Son
Denmark House, 18 High St.
Aldeburgh
Tel: (072885) 2066

H. C. Wolton & Son
6 Whiting St., Bury St. Edmunds
Tel: (0284) 61336

SURREY

Clarke, Gammon
45 High St., Guildford
Tel: (0483) 72266

Cubitt & West
Millmead, Guildford
Tel: (0483) 504030

Lawrences
Fine Art Auctioneers
Norfolk House, 80 High St.
Bletchingley
Tel: (0883) 843323

Messenger May & Baverstock
93 High St., Godalming
Tel: (04868) 23567

Stephen R. Thomas
15 Milton Rd., Egham
Tel: (0784) 31122

Wentworth Auction Galleries
21 Station Approach, Virginia Water
Tel: (09904) 3711

White & Sons
104 High St., Dorking
Tel: (0306) 887654

Harold Williams Bennett & Partners
2-3 South Parade, Merstham, Redhill
Tel: (07374) 2234/5

P. F. Windibank
18-20 Reigate Rd., Dorking
Tel: (0306) 884556

SUSSEX – EAST

Burstow & Hewett
Abbey Auction Galleries and
Granary Sale Rooms, Battle
Tel: (04246) 2374

Burtenshaw Walker
66 High St., Lewes
Tel: (07916) 4225

Clifford Dann & Partners
Fine Art Auction Galleries
20-21 High St., Lewes
Tel: (07916) 77022

Rowland Gorringe & Co
15 North St., Lewes
Tel: (07916) 2503

Graves, Son & Pilcher
71 Church Rd., Hove
Tel: (0273) 735266

Edgar Horn
46-50 South St., Eastbourne
Tel: (0323) 22801

Raymond P. Inman
Auction Galleries
35 & 40 Temple St., Brighton
Tel: (0273) 774777

Lewes Auction Rooms Julian Dawson,
56 High St., Lewes
Tel: (07916) 78221

Meads of Brighton
St. Nicholas Rd., Brighton
Tel: (0273) 202997

Vidler & Co.
Rye Auction Galleries
Cinque Ports St., Rye
Tel: (0797) 222124

Wallis & Wallis
Regency House, Albion St., Lewes
Tel: (07916) 3137

SUSSEX – WEST

T. Bannister & Co.
Market Place, Haywards Heath
Tel: (0444) 412402

Sussex Auction Galleries
Bradley & Vaughan
59 Perrymount Rd., Haywards Heath
Tel: (0444) 414935

Horsham Auction Galleries
31 The Carfax, Horsham
Tel: (0403) 53837

R. H. Ellis & Sons
44-46 High St., Worthing
Tel: (0903) 38999

Fox & Sons, Jordan & Cook
41 Chapel Rd. and
33 South St., Worthing
Tel: (0903) 205565

G. Knight & Son
West St., Midhurst
Tel: (073081) 2456/8

Sotheby's in Sussex
Station Rd., Pulborough
Tel: (07982) 3831

Stride & Son
Southdown House, St. John's St.
Chichester
Tel: (0243) 782626

Turner, Rudge & Turner
29 High St., East Grinstead
Tel: (0342) 24101

Wyatt & Son
59 East St., Chichester
Tel: (0243) 786581

TYNE & WEAR

Anderson & Garland
Fine Art Salerooms, Anderson House
Market St., Newcastle-upon-Tyne
Tel: (0632) 326278

Glover, Humble & Partners
Coates Institute, Ponteland
Tel: (0661) 22041

Thomas N. Miller
18-22 Gallowgate
Newcastle-upon-Tyne
Tel: (0632) 325617

WARWICKSHIRE

John Briggs & Calder
133 Long St., Atherstone
Tel: (08277) 2206 & 3100

Colliers, Bigwood & Bewlay
The Old School, Tiddington
Stratford-upon-Avon
Tel: (0789) 69415

Henley-in-Arden Auction Sales Ltd.
92 High St., Henley-in-Arden
Tel: (05642) 3211

Locke & England
1 & 2 Euston Place, Leamington Spa
Tel: (0926) 27988

Seaman of Rugby
Auction House, 132 Railway Terrace
Rugby
Tel: (0788) 2367

WEST MIDLANDS

Allsop Sellers
8 Hagley Rd., Stourbridge
Tel: (03843) 2122

Biddle & Webb
Icknield Square, Ladywood
Middleway, Birmingham
Tel: 021-455 8042

Cecil Carriss & Son
20-22 High St., Kings Heath
Birmingham 14
Tel: 021-444 5311

Codsal Antique Auctions
Codsal, Wolverhampton
Tel: (0902) 66728

Collins, Son & Harvey
44 High St., Erdington, Birmingham
Tel: 021-382 8870

Frank H. Fellows & Sons
Bedford House, 88 Hagley Rd.
Edgbaston, Birmingham
Tel: 021-454 1261/1219

Giles Haywood
The Auction House, St. John's Road,
Stourbridge
Tel: (03843) 70891

James & Lister Lea
11 Newhall St., Birmingham
Tel: 021-236 1751

Phillips
The Old House, Station Rd., Knowle
Solihull
Tel: (05645) 6151

Walker Barnett & Hill
3 Waterloo Rd., Wolverhampton
Tel: (0902) 771511

Weller & Dufty Ltd.
141 Bromsgrove St., Birmingham
Tel: 021-692 1414

WILTSHIRE

Allen & Harris
Saleroom & Auctioneers Dept.
The Planks (off The Square)
Old Town, Swindon
Tel: (0793) 615915

Berry, Powell & Shackell
46 Market Place, Chippenham
Tel: (0249) 3361

Dennis Pocock & Son
20 High St., Marlborough
Tel: (0672) 53471

Farrant & Wightman
Blagrove House, 2/3 Newport St.
Old Town, Swindon
Tel: (0793) 33301

Geoffrey Taylor & Co.
30 St. John St., Devizes
Tel: (0380) 2321

Woolley & Wallis
The Castle Auction Mart, Castle St.
Salisbury
Tel: (0722) 21711

YORKSHIRE – NORTH

Boulton & Cooper Ltd.
Forsyth House, Market Place, Malton
Tel: (0653) 2151

H. C. Chapman & Son
The Auction Mart, North St.
Scarborough
Tel: (0723) 372424

Dee & Atkinson
The Exchange, Driffield
Tel: (0377) 43151

Lawson, Larg
St. Trinity House, King's Square
York
Tel: (0904) 21532

Morphets of Harrogate
4 Albert St., Harrogate
Tel: (0423) 502282

M. Philip H. Scott
Church Wynd, Burneston, Bedale
Tel: (0677) 23325

Renton & Renton
16 Albert St., Harrogate
Tel: (0423) 61531

Stephenson & Son
43 Gowthorpe, Selby
Tel: (0757) 706707

G. A. Suffield & Co.
27 Flowergate, Whitby
Tel: (0947) 603433

Geoffrey Summersgill, A.S.V.A.
8 Front St., Acomb, York
Tel: (0904) 791131

Tennant's
26-27 Market Pl., Leyburn
Tel: (0969) 23451

Ward Price & Co.
Royal Auction Rooms, Queen St.
Scarborough
Tel: (0723) 365455

YORKSHIRE – SOUTH

Eadon Lockwood & Riddle
2 St. James' St., Sheffield
Tel: (0742) 71277

Stanilands
28 Nether Hall Rd., Doncaster
Tel: (0302) 67766/27121

YORKSHIRE –WEST

Dacre, Son & Hartley
1-5 The Grove, Ilkley
Tel: (0943) 600655

Ernest R. de Rome
12 New John St., Bradford
Tel: (0274) 734116

Eddisons
Auction Rooms, 4-6 High St.
Huddersfield
Tel: (0484) 33151

Ilkley Auction Galleries
Riddings Rd., Ilkley
Tel: (0943) 600456

Laidlaws
Crown Court Salerooms
(off Wood St.), Wakefield
Tel: (0924) 375301

W. Mackay Audsley
11 Morris Lane, Kirkstall, Leeds 5
Tel: (0532) 758787

Phillips at Hepper House
17a East Parade, Leeds
Tel: (0532) 448011

John H. Raby & Son
Salem Auction Rooms
21 St. Mary's Rd., Bradford
Tel: (0274) 491121

Chas. E. H. Yates & Son
The Salerooms, Otley Rd., Guiseley
Tel: (0943) 74165

CHANNEL ISLANDS

Langlois Ltd.
Don St., St. Helier, Jersey
Tel: (0534) 33441

F. Le Gallais & Sons
Bath St., St. Helier, Jersey
Tel: (0534) 30202

SCOTLAND

John Anderson, Auctioneers
33 Cross St., Fraserburgh
Aberdeenshire
Tel: (03462) 2878

Christie's & Edmiston's Ltd.
164-166 Bath St., Glasgow
Tel: 041-332 8134

B. L. Fenton & Sons
Forebank Auction Halls, 84 Victoria
Rd., Dundee
Tel: (0382) 26227

Frasers (Auctioneers)
28-30 Church St., Inverness
Tel: (0463) 232395

J. & J. Howe
24 Commercial St., Alyth, Perthshire
Tel: (08283) 2594

Thomas Love & Sons Ltd.
St. John's Place, Perth, Perthshire
PH1 5SU
Tel: (0738) 24111

John Milne
9 North Silver St., Aberdeen
Tel: (0224) 50336/7

Robert Paterson & Son
8 Orchard St., Paisley, Renfrewshire
Tel: 041-889 2435

Phillips in Scotland
98 Sauchiehall St., Glasgow
Tel: 041-332 3386

also at:
65 George St., Edinburgh
Tel: 031-225 2266

L. S. Smellie & Sons Ltd.
Within the Furniture Market, Lower
Auchingramont Rd., Hamilton
Tel: (0698) 282007

Taylor's Auction Rooms
11 Panmure Row, Montrose, Angus
Tel: (0674) 2775

WALES

T. Brackstone & Co.
19 Princes Drive, Colwyn Bay, Clwyd
Tel: (0492) 30481

K. Hugh Dodd & Partners
9 Chester St., Mold, Clwyd
Tel: (0352) 2552

John Francis, Thomas Jones & Son
Curiosity Salerooms, King St.
Carmarthen
Tel: (0267) 33456

V. King Thomas, Lloyd Jones &
Williams
Bangor House, High St., Lampeter
Dyfed
Tel: (0570) 422550

Rennie, Taylor, Miles & Escott
1 Agincourt St., Monmouth
Tel: (0600) 2916

C. Wesley Haslam & Son
St. Helens Place, High St., Rhyl
Clwyd
Tel: (0745) 4467

Wingett's Auction Gallery
29 Holt St., Wrexham, Clwyd
Tel: (0978) 353553

Acknowledgements

The publishers would like to acknowledge the great assistance given by our consultant editors:

POTTERY: **Jonathan Horne,** *66b & c Kensington Church Street, London W8.*
David Clark, *Elias Clark Antiques Ltd., 1 The Cobbles, High Street, Bletchingley, Surrey.*

PORCELAIN: **Gordon Lang,** *Sotheby's, 34 & 35 New Bond Street, London W1.*
Lars Tharp, *Sotheby's in Sussex, Station Road, Pulborough, West Sussex.*
Nicholas Long, *Studio Antiques, Bourton-on-the-Water, Glos.*

WORCESTER: **Henry Sandon,** *11 Perrywood Close, Worcester.*

GOSS & CRESTED WARE: **Nicholas Pine,** *Goss & Crested China Ltd., 62 Murray Road, Horndean, Hants.*

FURNITURE: **Chris King,** *Sotheby's in Sussex, Station Road, Pulborough, W. Sussex.*
Richard Davidson, *Richard Davidson Antiques, Lombard Street, Petworth, Sussex.*

OAK: **Victor Chinnery,** *Bennetts, Oare, Nr. Marlborough, Wilts.*
COUNTRY: **Mike Golding,** *Huntingdon Antiques, The Old Forge, Church Street, Stow-on-the-Wold, Glos.*

TREEN: **Graham Child,** *Sotheby's, 34 & 35 New Bond Street, London W1.*

CLOCKS: **Richard Price,** *Bonhams, Montpelier Galleries, Montpelier Street, Knightsbridge, London SW7.*

GLASS: **Wing Cdr. R. G. Thomas,** *Somervale Antiques, 6 Radstock Road, Midsomer Norton, Bath, Avon.*

ART NOUVEAU &
ART DECO: **Keith Baker,** *Phillips, Blenstock House, 7 Blenheim Street, New Bond Street, London W1.*
Eric Knowles, *Bonhams, Montpelier Galleries, Montpelier Street, Knightsbridge, London SW7.*

SILVER: **Peter Waldron,** *Sotheby's, 34 & 35 New Bond Street, London W1.*

CARPETS & TEXTILES: **Victoria Mather,** *Sotheby's, 34 & 35 New Bond Street, London W1.*

DOLLS, TOYS &
COLLECTABLES: **Hilary Kay,** *Sotheby's, 34 & 35 New Bond Street, London W1.*
FISHING: **Nicholas Marchant-Lane,** *Salter's Cottage, Bramshott, Liphook, Hants.*

ARMS & ARMOUR: **Roy Butler,** *Wallis & Wallis, Regency House, Albion Street, Lewes, E. Sussex.*

PINE FURNITURE &
KITCHENALIA: **Ann Lingard,** *Rope Walk Antiques, Rye, Sussex.*

Key to Illustrations

Each illustration and descriptive caption is accompanied by a letter-code. By reference to the following list of Auctioneers (denoted by ★) and Dealers (●), the source of any item may be immediately determined. In no way does this constitute or imply a contract or binding offer on the part of any of our contributors to supply or sell the goods illustrated, or similar articles, at the prices stated.

A	★	Aldridges of Bath Ltd., The Auction Galleries, 130–132 Walcot Street, Bath. Tel: (0225) 62830 & 62839
AAR	★	Abridge Auction Rooms, Market Place, Abridge, Essex. Tel: (037) 881 2107
Ad	●	Adams Antiques, 47 Chalk Farm Road, London NW1. Tel: 01-267 9241
AG	★	Anderson & Garland, Anderson House, Market Street, Newcastle-upon-Tyne. Tel: (0632) 326278
AGr	★	Andrew Grant, 59/60 Foregate Street, Worcester. Tel: (0905) 52310
AL	●	Ann Lingard, Rope Walk Antiques, Rye, Sussex. Tel: (0797) 223486
AMB	★	Ambrose (Auctioneers), 149 High Road, Loughton, Essex. Tel: 01-508 2121
AP	●	Antony Preston Antiques Ltd., The Square, Stow-on-the-Wold, Glos. Tel: (0451) 31586

APC	●	The Antique Porcelain Co., 149 New Bond Street, London W1. Tel: 01-629 1254
AS	★	Andrew Sharpe & Partners, Ilkley Auction Galleries, Riddings Road, Ilkley, West Yorkshire. Tel: (0943) 600456
ASA	●	A. S. Antiques, 26 Broad Street, Pendleton, Salford 6, Lancashire. Tel: (061) 737 5938
B	★	Boardman, Station Road Corner, Haverhill, Suffolk. Tel: (0440) 703784
BA	★	Bannister & Co., T., Market Place, Haywards Heath, Sussex. Tel: (0444) 412402
BAC	●	Bacchus Antiques, 27 Grange Avenue, Hale, Nr. Altrincham, Cheshire. Tel: (061) 980 4747
BAG	●	Baggott Church Street Ltd., Church Street, Stow-on-the-Wold, Glos. Tel: (0451) 30370
BC	★	Boulton & Cooper Ltd., St. Michael's House, Malton, Yorks. Tel: (0653) 2151

BD	★ Burrows & Day, 39/41 Bank Street, Ashford, Kent. Tel: (0233) 24321
Bea	★ Bearnes, Rainbow, Avenue Road, Torquay, Devon. Tel: (0803) 26277
Bed	● Bed of Roses Antiques, 12 Prestbury Road, Cheltenham, Glos. Tel: (0242) 31918
BEL	● Bell Antiques, 68 Harold Street, Grimsby, S. Humberside. Tel: (0472) 695110
BHW	★ Butler & Hatch Waterman, High Street, Tenterden, Kent. Tel: (05806) 3233. (Also at High Street, Hythe, Kent.)
BM	★ Brown & Merry, 9 High Street, Woburn Sands, Milton Keynes, Bucks. Tel: (0908) 583231
Bon	★ Bonhams, Montpelier Galleries, Montpelier Street, Knightsbridge, London SW7. Tel: 01-584 9161
BR	★ Bracketts, 27–29 High Street, Tunbridge Wells, Kent. Tel: (0892) 33733
Bro	★ Brocklehursts, The Longden & Cook Partnership, King Edward Street, Macclesfield, Cheshire. Tel: (0625) 27555
BS	★ Banks & Silvers, 66 Foregate Street, Worcester. Tel: (0905) 23456
BWe	★ Biddle & Webb of Birmingham, Ladywood Middleway, Birmingham. Tel: (021) 455 8042
C	★ Christie, Manson & Woods Ltd., 8 King Street, London SW1. Tel: 01-839 9060
CAm	★ Christie's, Amsterdam, Cornelis Schuytstraat 57, 1071 (JG) Amsterdam, Holland. Tel: (020) 64 20 11
CBB	★ Colliers, Bigwood & Bewlay, The Old School, Tiddington, Stratford-upon-Avon, Warwickshire. Tel: (0789) 69415
CBE	★ Chamberlaine-Brothers & Edwards, Montpellier Circus, Cheltenham, Glos. Tel: (0242) 513439
CCL	● Chelsea Clocks, Antiquarius, 135 King's Road, London SW3. Tel: 01-352 8646. (Also at 479 Fulham Road, London SW6. Tel: 01-731 5704)
CD	★ Clifford Dann, Auction Galleries, 20–21 High Street, Lewes, Sussex. Tel: (07916) 77022
CDC	★ Capes, Dunn & Co., The Auction Galleries, 38 Charles Street, Manchester. Tel: (061) 273 6060
CEC	★ Clive Emson & Co., 16 High Street, Hythe, Kent. Tel: (0303) 67473 (Now Ward & Partners.)
CEd	★ Christie's & Edmiston's Ltd., 164–166 Bath Street, Glasgow. Tel: (041) 332 8134/7
CG	★ Christie's Geneva, 8 Place de la Taconnerie, 1204, Geneva. Tel: (022) 28 25 44
CGC	★ Cheffins, Grain & Chalk, 49–53 Regent Street, Cambridge. Tel: (0223) 58721/6
CH	★ Chancellors & Co., 31 High Street, Ascot, Berkshire. Tel: (0990) 27101
CKK	★ Coles, Knapp & Kennedy, Tudor House, High Street, Ross-on-Wye, Herefordshire. Tel: (0989) 63553
CLG	★ Clarke, Gammon, 45 High Street, Guildford, Surrey. Tel: (0483) 72266
CNY	★ Christie, Manson & Woods International Inc., 502 Park Avenue, New York, N.Y. 10022, U.S.A.
CoH	★ Cooper Hirst, F.R.I.C.S., Goldlay House, Parkway, Chelmsford, Essex. Tel: (0245) 58141
CSK	★ Christie's (South Kensington), 85 Old Brompton Road, London SW7. Tel: 01-581 2231
CW	★ Cubitt & West, Fine Art Auction Galleries, Millmead, Guildford, Surrey. Tel: (0483) 504030
DA	★ Dee & Atkinson, The Exchange, Driffield, Yorkshire. Tel: (0377) 43151
DDM	★ Dickinson, Davy & Markham, 10 Wrawby Street, Brigg, S. Humberside. Tel: (0652) 53666
DL	● Dunsdale Lodge Antiques, Brasted Road, Westerham, Kent. Tel: (0959) 62160
DLJ	★ Douglas L. January & Partners, 124 High Street, Newmarket, Suffolk. Tel: (0638) 668679
DS	★ David Symonds, F.S.V.A., The Estate Office, High Street, Crediton, Devon. Tel: (03632) 2700 & 4100
DSH	★ Dacre, Son & Hartley, 1–5 The Grove, Ilkley, Yorks. Tel: (0943) 600655
DWB	★ Dreweatt, Watson & Barton, Donnington Priory, Donnington, Newbury, Berks. Tel: (0635) 31234
EBB	★ Edwards, Bigwood & Bewlay, The Old School, Tiddington, Stratford-upon-Avon, Warwickshire. Tel: (0789) 69415
EC	● Elias Clark Antiques Ltd., 1 The Cobbles, High Street, Bletchingley, Surrey. Tel: (0883) 843714
EEW	★ Eldon E. Worrall, 15 Seel Street, Liverpool. Tel: (051) 709 2950
EG	★ Elliott & Green, 40 High Street, Lymington, Hampshire. Tel: (0590) 77222
EH	★ Edgar Horn, 47 Cornfield Road, Eastbourne, Sussex. Tel: (0323) 22801
EV	● Earle D. Vandekar of Knightsbridge Ltd., 138 Brompton Road, London SW3. Tel: 01-589 8481 & 3398
EWS	★ E. Watson & Sons, The Market, Burwash Road, Heathfield, Sussex. Tel: (04352) 2132
FHF	★ Frank H. Fellows & Sons, Bedford House, 88 Hagley Road, Edgbaston, Birmingham. Tel: (021) 454 1261/1219
Fr	★ Fryer's Auction Galleries, Terminus Road, Bexhill-on-Sea, Sussex. Tel: (0424) 212994
FRM	★ Frank R. Marshall & Co., Chelford Agricultural Centre, Chelford, Cheshire. Tel: (0625) 861122
FW	★ Farrant & Wightman, Blagrove House, 2/3 Newport Street Old Town, Swindon, Wilts. Tel: (0793) 33301
G & CC	● Goss & Crested China Ltd., 62 Murray Road, Horndean, Hants. Tel: (0705) 597440
GBT	★ Gribble, Booth & Taylor, West Street, Axminster, Devon. Tel: (0297) 32323
GC	★ Geering & Colyer, Auctioneers, Highgate, Hawkhurst, Kent. Tel: (05805) 3463/3181
GCA	● Gerald Clark Antiques, 1 High Street, Mill Hill Village, London NW7. Tel: 01-906 0342
GH	★ Giles Haywood, The Auction House, St. John's Road, Stourbridge, West Midlands. Tel: (03843) 70891
GM	★ George Mealy & Sons, The Square, Castlecomer, Co. Kilkenny. Tel: (056) 41229
GR	★ Green & Co., 33 Market Place, Wantage, Oxon. Tel: (02357) 3561
GSP	★ Graves, Son & Pilcher, 71 Church Road, Hove, Sussex. Tel: (0273) 735266
GT	★ Garrod Turner, 50 St. Nicholas Street, Ipswich. Tel: (0473) 54664
GTB	★ G. Tarn Bainbridge & Son, Northern Rock House, High Row, Darlington, Co. Durham. Tel: (0325) 462633 & 462553
H	● Huntington Antiques, The Old Forge, Church Street, Stow-on-the-Wold, Glos. Tel: (0451) 30842
HAL	● Hallidays Antiques Ltd., The Old College, Dorchester-on-Thames, Oxon. Tel: (0865) 340028/68
HC	★ H. C. Chapman & Son, The Auction Mart, North Street, Scarborough, Yorks. Tel: (0723) 372424
HFM	★ Hothersall, Forrest, McKenna & Son, Bank Salerooms, Clitheroe, Lancs. Tel: (0200) 25446 & 22695
HG	● Hay Galleries, 4 High Town, Hay-on-Wye, Hereford. Tel: (0497) 820356
HGA	★ Hatton Garden Auctions Ltd., 36 Hatton Garden, London EC1. Tel: 01-242 6452
HOF	● Hoff Antiques Ltd., 66a Kensington Church Street, London W8. Tel: 01-229 5516
HOL	★ Holloway's, Auctioneers & Valuers, 49 Parsons Street, Banbury, Oxon. Tel: (0295) 53197
HSS	★ Henry Spencer & Sons, 20 The Square, Retford, Notts. Tel: (0777) 708633
Hu	● Humphry Antiques, East Street, Petworth, W. Sussex. Tel: (0798) 43053
HWO	★ Hall, Wateridge & Owen, Welsh Bridge Salerooms, Shrewsbury, Shropshire. Tel: (0743) 60212
HyD	★ Hy Duke & Son, 40 South Street, Dorchester, Dorset. Tel: (0305) 65080
JB	● Joanna Booth, 247 King's Road, London SW3. Tel: 01-352 8998
JD	★ Julian Dawson, 56 High Street, Lewes, Sussex. Tel: (07916) 78221
JF	★ John Francis (Thomas Jones & Sons), King Street, Carmarthen. Tel: (0267) 233456/7
JH	★ Jacobs & Hunt, Lavant Street, Petersfield, Hants. Tel: (0730) 62744
JHo	● Jonathan Horne, 66b & c Kensington Church Street, London W8. Tel: 01-221 5658
JHR	★ John H. Raby & Son, The Estate Office, 21 St. Mary's Road, Manningham, Bradford. Tel: (0274) 491121
JHS	★ John Hogbin & Son, 53 High Street, Tenterden, Kent. Tel: (05806) 3200

JMG	• Jamie Maxtone Graham, Nithside, Closeburn, Thornhill, Dumfries, Scotland. Tel: (08484) 382
JRB	★ J. R. Bridgford & Sons, 1 Heyes Lane, Alderley Edge, Cheshire. Tel: (0625) 585347
JSA	• Jean Sewell (Antiques) Ltd., 3 Campden Street, Kensington Church Street, London W8. Tel: 01-727 3122
JT	• Jeanne Temple Antiques, Stockwell House, 1 Stockwell Lane, Wavendon, Milton Keynes. Tel: (0908) 583597
KK	• Klaber & Klaber, 2a Bedford Gardens, Kensington Church Street, London W8. Tel: 01-727 4573
KS	★ Kent Sales, Kent House, 4 New Road, South Darenth, Kent. Tel: (0322) 864919
L	★ Lawrences, South Street, Crewkerne, Somerset. Tel: (0460) 73041
LA	• Leominster Antiques, 87 Etnam Street, Leominster, Herefordshire. Tel: (0568) 3217
LAM	★ Lambrays, The Platt, Wadebridge, Cornwall. Tel: (020 881) 3593
Lan	★ Langlois, Don Street, St. Helier, Jersey, Channel Islands. Tel: (0534) 22441
LAY	★ David Lay, A.S.V.A., 7 Morrab Road, Penzance, Cornwall. Tel: (0736) 61414
LBP	★ Lalonde Bros. & Parham, 71 Oakfield Road, Bristol, Avon. Tel: (0272) 734052
LE	★ Locke & England, The Auction Rooms, Walton House, 11 The Parade, Royal Leamington Spa. Tel: (0926) 27988
LeG	★ Le Gallais & Sons, Bath Street, St. Helier, Jersey, Channel Islands. Tel: (0534) 30202
LJ	★ Louis Johnson & Co. Ltd., Oswald House, 63 Bridge Street, Morpeth, Northumberland. Tel: (0670) 513025 & 55210
LM	★ Lucas & Madley, West Gate Auction Galleries, 54 Machen Place, Cardiff. Tel: (0222) 374320
LMT	★ Laurence & Martin Taylor, 63 High Street, Honiton, Devon. Tel: (0404) 2404/5
LR	• Leonard Russell, 21 King's Avenue, Newhaven, Sussex. Tel: (0273) 515153
LRG	★ Lots Road Galleries, 71 Lots Road, Chelsea, London SW10. Tel: 01-352 2349
LS	★ Lacy Scott, 1a Angel Hill, Bury St. Edmunds, Suffolk. Tel: (0284) 63531
LT	★ Louis Taylor & Sons, Percy Street, Hanley, Stoke-on-Trent. Tel: (0782) 260222
M	★ Morphets of Harrogate, 4–6 Albert Street, Harrogate, N. Yorks. Tel: (0423) 502282
MA	• Mercury Antiques, 1 Ladbroke Road, London W11. Tel: 01-727 5106
MAL	★ Mallams, The Oxford Salerooms, 24 St. Michael's Street, Oxford. Tel: (0865) 241358
McC	★ McCartney, Morris & Barker, 25 Corve Street, Ludlow, Shropshire. Tel: (0584) 2636
Mea	★ Meads of Brighton, St. Nicholas Road, Brighton, Sussex. Tel: (0273) 202997
MGM	★ Michael G. Matthews, "The Mount", Pine Park Road, Honiton, Devon. Tel: (0404) 41872
MIL	★ Miller & Co., Lemon Quay Auction Rooms, Lemon Quay, Truro, Cornwall. Tel: (0872) 74211
MMB	★ Messenger, May Baverstock, Fine Art Salerooms, 93 High Street, Godalming, Surrey. Tel: (04868) 23567
MN	★ Michael Newman, Kinterbury House, St. Andrew's Cross, Plymouth, Devon. Tel: (0752) 669298
MS	• Mike Sturge, Collectors Shop, 17 Market Buildings Arcade, Maidstone, Kent. Tel: (0622) 54702
Ms	★ Messengers, Pevensey House Salerooms, Manorsfield, Bicester, Oxon. Tel: (0869) 245985
MWG	★ May Whetter & Grose, Cornubia Hall, Par, Cornwall. Tel: (072 681) 2271
N	★ Neales of Nottingham, 192 Mansfield Road, Nottingham. Tel: (0602) 624141
NAG	★ Northampton Auction Galleries, The Old Albion Brewery, Commercial Street, Northampton. Tel: (0604) 37263
ND	★ Nock, Deighton & Son, 10 Broad Street, Ludlow, Shropshire. Tel: (0584) 2364
Nes	★ D. M. Nesbit & Co., 7 Clarendon Road, Southsea, Hants. Tel: (0705) 820785
NML	• Nicholas Marchant-Lane, Salters Cottage, Bramshott, Liphook, Hants. Tel: (0428) 723990
NWH	★ Norman Wright & Hodgkinson, 1 Abbey Road, Bourne, Lincs. Tel: (0778) 422567

O	★ Olivers, 23–24 Market Hill, Sudbury, Suffolk. Tel: (0787) 72247
OC	• Olwen Carthew, 109 Kirkdale, London SE26. Tel: 01-699 1363
OL	★ Outhwaite & Litherland, Kingsway Galleries, Fontenoy Street, Liverpool. Tel: (051) 236 6561
OT	★ Osmond, Tricks & Son, Regent Street Auction Rooms, Clifton, Bristol. Tel: (0272) 737201
P	★ Phillips, Blenstock House, 7 Blenheim Street, New Bond Street, London W1. Tel: 01-629 6602
PB	★ Phillips, inc. Brooks, 39 Park End Street, Oxford. Tel: (0865) 723524
PE	★ Peter Eley, F.S.V.A., Western House, 98–100 High Street, Sidmouth, Devon. Tel: (03955) 2552
Pea	★ Pearsons, Walcote Chambers, High Street, Winchester, Hants. Tel: (0962) 64444
PH	• M. Deardon, Pennard House, East Pennard, Shepton Mallet, Somerset. Tel: (074 986) 266
PHM	★ Phillips, Marylebone, Hayes Place, Lisson Grove, London NW1. Tel: 01-723 2647
PK	★ Phillips (Knowle), The Old House, Station Road, Knowle, Solihull, W. Midlands. Tel: (056 45) 6151
PLJ	★ Philip, Laney & Jolly, 12a Worcester Road, Malvern, Wilts. Tel: (06845) 61169 & 63121
PSH	★ J. R. Parkinson, Son & Hamer Auctions, The Auction Rooms, Rochdale Road, Bury, Lancs. Tel: (061 761) 1612 & 7372
PWC	★ Parsons, Welch & Cowell, 49 London Road, Sevenoaks, Kent. Tel: (0732) 451211/4.
PW	★ Phillips (West 2), 10 Salem Road, London W2. Tel: 01-221 5303
RBB	★ Russell Baldwin & Bright, Auctioneers, Ryelands Road, Leominster, Herefordshire. Tel: (0568) 3897
R de R	• Rogers de Rin, 76 Royal Hospital Road, Paradise Walk, London SW3. Tel: 01-352 9007
RDV	★ Robert Dove & Partners, Dover House, Wolsey Street, Ipswich, Suffolk. Tel: (0473) 55137
Re	★ Reeds, Rains, Trinity House, 114 Northenden Road, Sale, Cheshire. Tel: (061 962) 9237
S	★ Sotheby, Parke Bernet & Co., 34–35 New Bond Street, London W1. Tel: 01-493 8080
SA	• Studio Antiques Ltd., Bourton-on-the-Water, Glos. Tel: (0451) 20352
SC	★ Sotheby's, Chester, Booth Mansion, Watergate Street, Chester. Tel: (0244) 315531
SD	★ Slater, Dann & Co., Regency House, 67 Birmingham Road, Sutton Coldfield, W. Midlands. Tel: (021 354) 2286
SHS	★ Seth Hughes & Son, St. George's Crescent, Wrexham, Clwyd. Tel: (0978) 265123
SL	★ Simmons & Lawrence, 32 Bell Street, Henley-on-Thames, Oxon. Tel: (0491) 571111
Som	• Somervale Antiques, 6 Radstock Road, Midsomer Norton, Bath, Avon. Tel: (0761) 412686
SOU	★ Southam & Sons, Corn Exchange, Thrapston, Nr. Kettering, Northants. Tel: (08012) 2409
SPA	★ Specialised Postcard Auctions, 12 Suffolk Road, Cheltenham, Glos. Tel: (0242) 580323/583314
SRO	• Simon Spero, 109 Kensington Church Street, London W8. Tel: 01-727 7413
SS	★ Sotheby's in Sussex, Station Road, Pulborough, W. Sussex. Tel: (07982) 3831
SuB	• Susan Becker, Antiques, 18 Lower Richmond Road, Putney, London SW15. Tel: 01-788 9082
SWO	★ Sworder, Chequers, 19 North Street, Bishops Stortford, Herts. Tel: (0279) 52441
T	★ Tennant's, 26–27 Market Place, Leyburn, N. Yorkshire. Tel: (0969) 23451
TAY	★ Taylor's, Honiton Galleries, 205 High Street, Honiton, Devon. Tel: (0404) 2404
TKN	★ Tiffen, King, Nicholson, 12 Lowther Street, Carlisle, Cumbria. Tel: (0228) 25259
TL	★ Thomas Love & Sons Ltd., South St. John's Place, Perth, Scotland. Tel: (0738) 24111
TM	★ Thos. Mawer & Son, 63 Monk's Road, Lincoln. Tel: (0522) 24984
TR	★ Tyrone R. Roberts, Auctioneers, High Street, Heacham, King's Lynn, Norfolk. Tel: (0485) 70067
TW	★ Thomas Watson & Son, Northumberland Street, Darlington, Co. Durham. Tel: (0325) 462555 & 462559
V	★ Vidler & Co., Rye Auction Galleries, Cinque Ports Street, Rye, E. Sussex. Tel: (0797) 222124

VV   ★ V. & V. Chattel Auctioneers, 6 Station Road, Reading, Berks. Tel: (0734) 53211

VWC   ● Vintage Wireless Co., Tudor House, Cossham Street, Mangotsfield, Bristol, Avon. Tel: (0272) 565472

W   ● Woodstock, 1563/1565 London Road, Norbury, London SW16. Tel: 01-764 0270. (Also at Furniture Cave, 533 King's Road, London SW3.)

WAG   ★ Worthing Auction Galleries, Chatsworth Road, Worthing, Sussex. Tel: (0903) 205565

Wal   ★ Wallis & Wallis, Regency House, 1 Albion Street, Lewes, Sussex. Tel: (07916) 3137

WAT   ★ Watson, Edwin & Son, 1 Market Street, Saffron Walden, Essex. Tel: (0799) 22058

WaW   ★ Warren & Wignall, The Mill, Earnshaw Bridge, Leyland Lane, Leyland. Tel: (07744) 53252

WAY   ★ Way, Riddett & Co., Town Hall Chambers, Ryde, Isle of Wight. Tel: (0983) 62255

WBH   ★ Walker, Barnett & Hill, 3 Waterloo Road, Wolverhampton. Tel: (0902) 771511

WD   ★ Weller & Dufty Ltd., 141 Bromsgrove Street, Birmingham. Tel: (021 692) 1414

WH   ● Wych House Antiques, Wych Hill, Woking, Surrey. Tel: (04862) 64635

WHB   ★ William H. Brown, Westgate Hall, Westgate, Grantham, Lincs. Tel: (0476) 68861

WHL   ★ W. H. Lane & Son (now Michael Newman – code MN), Kinterbury House, St. Andrew's Cross, Plymouth, Devon. Tel: (0752) 669298

WIL   ★ Wilson, Peter & Co., Victoria Gallery, Market Street, Nantwich, Cheshire. Tel: (0270) 623878

WL   ★ Whitton & Laing, 32 Okehampton Street, Exeter, Devon. Tel: (0392) 52621

WLS   ● Paul Wilson, Perth St. West, Hull, Humberside. Tel: (0482) 447923

WM   ★ Wright-Manley (W. T. Witter), 56 High Street, Nantwich, Cheshire. Tel: (0270) 625410

Wor   ★ Worsfolds (Canterbury), Auction Galleries, 40 Station Road West, Canterbury, Kent. Tel: (0227) 68984

WP   ★ Ward & Partners, 16 High Street, Hythe, Kent. Tel: (0303) 67473

WSH   ★ Warner, Sheppard & Wade, 16–18 Halford Street, Leicester. Tel: (0533) 21613 (Warner Auction Rooms)

WSW   ★ Wyatt & Son (with Whiteheads), 59 East Street, Chichester, W. Sussex. Tel: (0243) 786581

WW   ★ Woolley & Wallis, The Castle Auction Mart, Castle Street, Salisbury, Wilts. Tel: (0722) 21711

WWH   ★ Walker, Walton, Hanson, Byard Lane, Nottingham. Tel: (0602) 586161

A27 ANTIQUES WAREHOUSE

DITTONS ROAD INDUSTRIAL ESTATE
A27 TRUNK ROAD
POLEGATE, EAST SUSSEX

Tel: (03212) 7167

11,000 square feet period Victorian and shipping furniture and quality stripped pine. Re-finishing and upholstery service container packing and shipping.

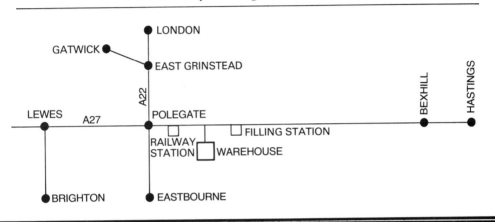

22

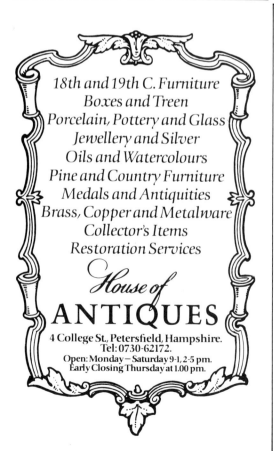

24

29

Colin Macleod's
Antiques Warehouse

Formerly Canadiana Exports.

139 Goldsmith Avenue, Portsmouth PO4 8QZ. Tel: 0705 816278.

COLIN MACLEOD'S 'ANTIQUES WAREHOUSE' has recently been enlarged to include refurbished top floor showrooms.

THE WAREHOUSE carries more than 9,000 sq ft of antiques and shipping goods.

THE GROUND FLOOR is stocked with a selection of Wardrobes, French Provincial, Armoires and Country Furniture plus Good Decorator Items from time to time.

THE SECOND FLOOR showroom is primarily Shipping Oak.

THE TOP FLOOR showroom is stocked with Commercial Mahogany, Walnut, Inlaid Furniture and Accessories.

COLIN MACLEOD is pleased to offer a FULLY COMPREHENSIVE CONTAINER SERVICE comprising EXPERT PACKING–SHIPPING–COLLECTION & DOCUMENTATION.

COLIN MACLEOD looks forward to assisting you with a personal courier service to ensure that your UK visit is both a pleasant and a profitable one.

ON YOUR NEXT INTERNATIONAL BUYING TRIP ENSURE THAT COLIN MACLEODS 'ANTIQUES WAREHOUSE' & 'ANTIQUES CENTRE' ARE INCLUDED ON YOUR SCHEDULE OF MAJOR CALLS.

LONDON
PORTSMOUTH   BRIGHTON

DURING YOUR UK VISIT a fully furnished, two bedroomed Maisonette is available for your accomodation, as an additional service, should this facility be required.

REGULAR SHIPMENTS ARRIVING FROM FRANCE, SPAIN & THE FAR EAST.

Colin Macleod's
Antiques Centre

159/161 Goldsmith Avenue, Portsmouth PO4 8BL. Tel: 0705 734173.

TWO MINUTES FROM 'THE ANTIQUES WAREHOUSE' you will find 'COLIN MACLEODS ANTIQUES CENTRE'.

'THE ANTIQUES CENTRE' comprises a further 10,000 sq ft of warehouse space occupied by eleven active dealers.

FULL FURNITURE STRIPPING, POLISHING & UPHOLSTERY SERVICES.

FACILITIES FOR PACKING TWENTY FOOT AND FORTY FOOT CONTAINERS.

Warehouse Manager DAVID ARTHUR will be pleased to give you every assistance.

PORTSMOUTH
THE ANTIQUES CENTRE OF THE SOUTH

CONTENTS

A fine late 16th C. Paduan bronze statuette of Hercules, attributed to Francesco Segala, sold for £26,000 at Christie's on 15th May, 1984.

31

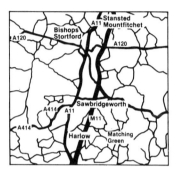
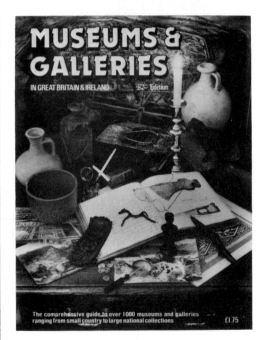

A very rare Florentine 'oak-leaf' jug with wide strap-handle and short spout attached to the narrow neck by a twisted loop, painted in dark blue impasto outlined in manganese with stylized birds and 'oak' leaves, 27.5cm., first half 15th C., some damage. **£18,000-20,000**   *S*

A Florentine double-handled jar, painted in blue with, on one side, a panel showing a stylized bird and foliage, and on the other, a fleur-de-lis, 23cm., mid-15th C., one handle remade. **£8,000-12,000**   *S*

A London delft polychrome Royalist caudle cup, with a portrait of Charles II dated 1662 glaze flaking to rim, 7.5cm. high. **£42,000-44,000**   *C*

The Review of the Season
by Anne Bouillot

For a firm that started life selling books in 1733, it is fitting that Sotheby's greatest coup in the year should also concern the sale of a book, The Gospels of Henry the Lion, a magnificent 12th C. German manuscript of the four New Testament gospels, which the crusading Henry (c.1129-1195) presented to Brunswick Cathedral. The winning bid of over £8,000,000 – the highest price ever paid for a work of art at auction, came from a consortium of West German federal and local government, financial and cultural interests determined to return the manuscript to Lower Saxony where it was painted by the monk Herimann in about 1175.

Irish interests and in particular those of Mrs. Aileen Plunkett accounted for Christie's most important house sale of the year at Luttrellstown Castle outside Dublin. Over a thousand people a day attended the three-day view and of the many lots which far exceeded their estimate, just two will serve to introduce other growth areas which deserve special mention this year.

An important documentary Faenza dish, decorated with 3 saints, inscribed on the reverse 'Baldasare Manare/fan', 21.5cm., c.1535, restored on the rim. **£21,000-24,000**   *S*

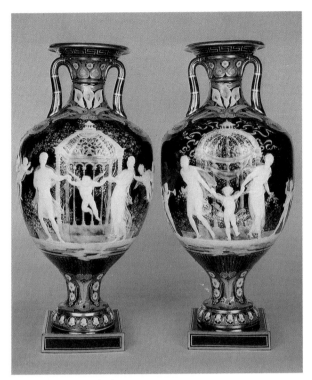

A rare Mintons 'majolica' Blackamoor, the black boy wearing a feather skirt and native jewellery, holding cymbals, a tazza balanced on his head, the whole in typical and colourful 'majolica' glazes, impressed mark, shape number 1766 and date code for 1873, repairs and chips, 40¼in. **£6,500-7,500** *S*

A pair of Mintons polychrome pate-sur-pate two-handled oviform vases by Louis Marc Solon, the bodies decorated in white slip on dark brown grounds, on square bases enriched with gilt lines, signed L. Solon, impressed Mintons marks and with impressed 1946 and 1722 numerals, 54cm. high, c.1890. **£21,000-23,000** *C*

(below)
A rare Mintons 'majolica' peacock after a model by P. Comolera, moulded signature, standing proudly on a tall rocky mound trailed with fruiting and flowering blackberry and ivy, clumps of foliage and fungi, its plumage naturalistically textured, the whole coloured in bright 'majolica' glazes, 60in., c.1875, minor damage. **£19,000-21,000** *S*

French furniture

A commode made for the bedchamber of Louis XV at the Chateau of Fontainebleau, confirmed to be a pair with commode F70 in the Wallace Collection by infra-red photographs taken by Scotland Yard Forensic Laboratories of the obliterated inventory mark on the back, realised £64,120 at Luttrellstown.

Far more attention has been paid this year to furniture in the French style, whether from France, Britain or elsewhere as in the case of the 74″ wide 19th C. Louis XV style kingwood parquetry inlaid and ormolu mounted bureau plat bearing the label A/C Lysberg, Hansen and Theup, Beedgade, Kobenhaun, Denmark, which sold for £2,900 at Gorringes Auction Galleries in Lewes.

Textiles

Also at Luttrellstown Castle, pairs of pink sheets with white applique flower borders were selling at £212 a pair and even without any provenance at all, Victorian fringed chenille tablecloths have been selling at auction in the provinces for £50 each.

Much prettier was the Polonaise of black cotton printed with a design of flowers with low neck, tight bodice, straight sleeves trimmed with lace and festooned skirt, c.1785, on which Bonhams put an estimate of £300/£500, only to see it sell for £2,800.

Metal

Quantifying the intrinsic value of antique silver now that the market has returned to an even keel after the volatility of 1979/80 needs some care. However, with the bullion price hovering around £5.50 to £6.00 per oz. of 925 standard

A pair of Meissen figures of woodpeckers (Grunspecht) modelled by J. J. Kändler, with red, black and green feather markings perched on tree-stumps with coloured insects, restoration to beaks and some extremities, 27.5cm. high, 1735-40. **£13,000-16,000**   *C*

(below)
A brilliantly enamelled pair of 'famille-rose' hawks, each perched on a rough rockwork base freely splashed in blue enamel, the yellow legs and claws with iron red scale-markings, the short powerful beak washed in puce, the remainder of the long feathers of the wings and tail in vivid colours and the down on the body finely mottled in puce, 26.7cm. and 25.4cm., Qianlong. **£13,000-15,000**   *S*

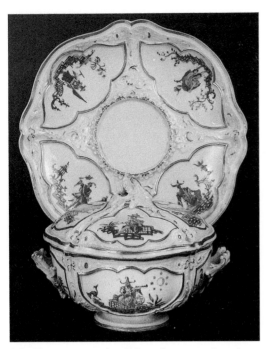

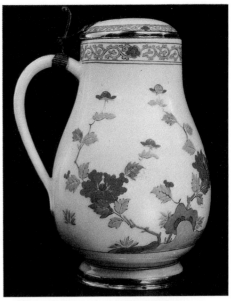

A Le Nove rococo two-handled ecuelle, cover and stand painted with Chinoiserie figures on stepped terraces and scrolled supports within moulded shaped quatrefoil cartouches edged in gilt, (minor chip to finial and hair-crack in tureen), the stand 22cm. diam., in contemporary fitted case, c.1765. £5,000-6,000   C

An early Meissen tankard and cover with contemporary silver-gilt mounts, painted in iron-red, turquoise, blue and gold, the borders with formal scrolling branches with iron-red flower-heads at intervals, the hinged cover with pierced scroll thumbpiece and with plain mount to the footrim, blue enamel crossed swords mark, the silver unmarked, 21 cm. high, 1725-1728. £8,500-9,500   C

A pair of Louis XV pots pourris each formed from two hemispherical bowls with gilt-bronze mounts, painted with polychrome flowers on a white ground, restored, 23.5cm. high, mid-18th C. £6,000-7,000   S

A rare Meissen cylindrical tankard painted in the manner of C. F. Herold with a panel of figures and buildings by a harbour in colours, enclosed by an elaborate border of quatrelobed panels of harbour scenes alternately in iron-red and purple within scrollwork in gilding, iron-red, purple and lustre, and a Dresden silver cover, 18cm., about 1735. £9,000-11,000   S

A rare Schrezheim box and cover in the form of a tortoise, decorated with manganese scales, yellow eyes and collar, minor restoration to head, tail re-stuck, 25cm., about 1770. **£6,000-8,000**   *S*

hallmarked, named early 20th C. silver is roughly £10 an oz., named Victorian £20 and named Georgian £25, which is not quite the multiplier of five it was before the scare.

Other metals to move faster than silver within their groups range from the cast iron spiral staircase by Hayward Bros., c.1880, rising to a height of 141″ which Neale's of Nottingham sold for £380, although it was still in situ, to the pair of 18th C. French bronze and ormolu chenets, 14½″ high, one as a lion cut poodle, the other a persian cat, which Michael Newman of Plymouth sold for £3,800.

A 'girl in a swing' cream-jug, painted with scattered flower-sprays, the underside left unglazed (minute chip to lip), 8cm. high, c.1750.
£13,000-15,000   *C*

(right)

A Meissen group of the Dutch or Tyrolean dancers modelled by J. F. Eberlein, the youth with iron-red hat with puce-ribbon, blue jacket reserved with white scrolls and fringed with gilding, black stockings and iron-red shoes with puce rosettes, his companion with flowered skirt reserved with iron-red and gold rosettes, fringed in purple and lined with iron-red with green stockings and black shoes, blue crossed swords mark under the base, 15.5cm. high, c.1736. **£11,000-13,000** *C*

A pair of Meissen groups of monkeys, modelled by J. J. Kaendler, one holding an apple and tied to a tree, a young monkey rests in her lap, crossed swords in underglaze blue, one cracked, some restoration, 18.5cm., mid-18th C. **£6,000-7,000** *S*

(below)

An important and early Meissen Chinoiserie arbour figure modelled by Johann Gottlieb Kirchner, delicately painted with sprays of flowers in an elaborate pierced rockwork arbour, with puce and iron-red flower heads and green leaves in relief, the trays and shells enriched in Böttger-lustre (repairs to shell bowl on his head and four of the flower bowls, damages to flowers and branches), 45.5cm. high, 1730-35. **£37,000-40,000** *C*

And while those ubiquitous Victorian bronze statues of no particular pedigree are also reportedly picking up, it should be pointed out that there are two sectors in the market where great care should be exercised since they are still inclined to be patchy: carpets and rugs and clocks and watches.

Sotheby's Pulborough also draw attention to the steady rise in value of Indian Tulwars, Russian Shasquas, Eastern Shamshirs and Turkish Yataghans – single-edged curved weapons like scimitars – and Indian Katars, Javanese Kris and Caucasian Kindjals, or double-edged daggers, ranging in price from approximately one hundred pounds to one thousand.

If edged weapons represent one of the newer areas of general collecting, then following the publication in 1863 of Chaffers celebrated *Marks and Monograms on Pottery and Porcelain*, ceramics is one of the oldest and currently a market leader.

The upward trend in prices paid for early English pottery is now followed by a rise in the value of English porcelain and Sotheby's Pulborough instance the early 19th C. Chamberlains Worcester dessert service, each of the 27 pieces brightly decorated with the Dragon in Compartments pattern which they sold for £4,620.

A fine and very rare engraved Ming sacrificial saucer dish, interior with 2 anhua dragons, lightly domed base covered with a tinted white glaze, 19.3cm., 15th C. **£18,000-22,000**   *S*

A very rare late Yuan moulded blue and white dish, painted in underglaze blue of strong inky tone, the centre with formal design of four barbed quatrefoil panels of bold outline, the reverse with a freely drawn lotus scroll with loosely petalled blooms and characteristic spiky leaves and the base unglazed, 46.3cm., mid-14th century. **£69,000-72,000**   *S*

40

A pair of Imari figures of smiling Bijn dressed in long flowing kimono and with a kushi in their hair, their robes painted in underglaze blue, iron-red, orange and gilt with a ho-o and a butterfly among flowering chrysanthemum, peony, plum and cherry blossom and foliage above a garden terrace, their hair and eyes painted black, Genroku period, 44.7cm. high.
£5,000-6,000 *C*

A magnificent Kakiemon large gourd-shaped vase decorated in turquoise, cerulean blue, yellow ochre and iron-red enamels, the body with tree-peonies, chrysanthemums and other flowers and rocks, drawn with an occasional delicate black outline, beneath a narrow red band of stylized plum blossom at the waist, the upper lobe surmounted by a band of red stylized leaf design, the foot with twin narrow red lines and the lower 3.5cm. of the body left undecorated beneath a third red line, probably Kanbun-Enpo period (1661-1681), 43cm. high, 20cm. maximum diameter.
£45,000-50,000 *C*

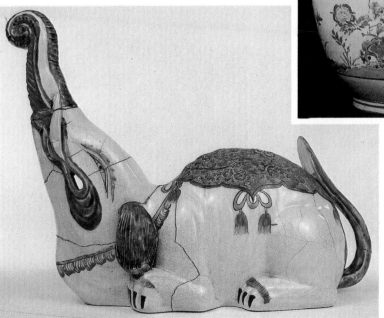

A rare Kakiemon model of an elephant, decorated in red, blue, green and yellow enamels, with partial black outline, (numerous firing cracks, the larger ones with gold lacquer naoshi), probably Tenwa-Genroku period (1681-1703), 32cm. long, 23.8cm. high.
£16,000-18,000 *C*

An important early Ming large red lacquer square tray carved with two scholars drinking tea at the window of a multi-storeyed pavilion with servants at its ground floor and two mounted dignitaries approaching from a terrace followed by their servant bearing provisions on a pole over his shoulder amongst pine, sterculia and rockwork, the foot with key-pattern arranged in connected pairs of squared spirals, the red lacquer all with a black guideline, the base underside black-lacquered, its centre carved and gilt with a Xuande six-character mark in a horizontal line, first half of the 15th C., black lacquer box, 39.5cm. square. **£70,000-80,000**   *C*

A Cizhou carved slender oviform vase, meiping, crisply carved through a creamy white slip and thin translucent overglaze with two panels of peony sprays within scalloped borders on a ground of breaking waves (minor chips and flaking), Song/Jin Dynasty, 40cm. high. **£7,000-10,000**   *C*

(left)
An important underglaze copper-red pear-shaped vase, painted in a strong opaque copper-red fired to a somewhat reddish-brown tone with an elaborate design, the thick short foot fired orange on the underside and painted with dense formal scrolls on the outside face, long overlapping strongly-drawn plantain leaves rising to the sharply everted rim, the rim itself painted on the upper face with a thin band of formal scrolls similar to that on the foot rim, the body and foot thickly potted but the neck and rim unusually crisp and thin, second half of the 14th C., 32.6cm. high, 21cm. diam. **£400,000-450,000**   *C*

A rare 14th C. blue and white dish, in cobalt with 'heaping and piling', the underside encircled by a matching lotus scroll, the unglazed base suffused with iron spots and chatter marks, radiating towards wedge-shaped rootrim, Yuan Dynasty, 15¾in. **£47,000-50,000**   *S*

A Sancai buff pottery equestrienne group, a female attendant mounted on a horse, she with biscuit head and high looped hair with black and red pigments remaining, wearing long robes under splashed green and ochre glazes and a straw-glazed shawl, the horse's body under a widely-crackled straw glaze dappled with large bright ochre splashes, (glaze flaked on the horse's head, repainting on the legs and tail and some restoration), Tang Dynasty, 37cm. high. **£14,000-17,000** *C*

An early Ming blue and white saucer-dish, painted in a strong dark blue irregularly fired almost black at the centre, with five large lotus heads and a single leaf in profile, the inside of the rim with a narrow band of breaking and boiling waves, the exterior with a similar continuous meander of inky-blue flower-heads below a thin border of small flower-head scrolls, Yongle, 38.3cm. diam. **£22,000-26,000** *C*

Demand for any good tea, dessert or dinner service is in fact exceptionally strong and, at £4,700, the late 19th C. Meissen porcelain dinner service of 72 pieces in the Marcolini pattern sold by Reeds Rains of Sale makes an interesting comparison with the Pulborough set.

The number of services still extant means that bargains are available and while the £520

An important Ming bronze figure of a caparisonned elephant, his broad rectangular saddle-cloth engraved on each side with a five-clawed dragon encompassing a flaming pearl amongst clouds and surmounted by a quatrefoil supporting a bowed ribboned holder on his back (with some wear to the gilding, mainly on the tusks), 16th C., 35.5cm. long, 27cm. high. **£16,000-20,000** *C*

A rare imperial famille rose Canton enamel and gilt copper double-gourd vase, the upper lobe made separately, enamels damaged, also flaked within the foot around the body join, blue enamel Qianlong six-character mark within a double square and of the period, 55.5cm. high. **£13,000-16,000** *C*

A fine Regency ormolu candelabrum in the style of Vulliamy, with gadrooned dish finial on vine-entwined stem supported by three addorsed models of cranes, shells, acanthus and displayed eagles and mounted with a coat-of-arms on stepped triangular plinth, c.1810, 84cm. high. **£10,000-12,000**   *C*

A fine early George III library staircase with two flights and half landing, the risers pierced, the moulded handrail on turned bannisters, the terminals fluted and the main supports of cluster column form, 310cm. high, 126cm. wide, 171.5cm. deep. **£45,000-50,000**   *C*

obtained by Henry Spencer & Sons for a 19th C. Coalport tea service of 41 pieces could be called typical, the collector willing to take a chance on Limoges for example could still show a profit. Anderson & Garland sold two Limoges dessert services of 17 pieces, each decorated with floral sprays, at a four month interval, the first for £80 but the second fetching £155.

Bargain of the year turned out to be the 14th C. Ming vase decorated with under-glaze copper-red peonies which a Glasgow couple inherited from their uncle, who had bought it in the 1940s from a dealer for £40.

A Singapore collector successfully bid £390,000 for it at Christie's (which meant a total bill for him of £425,000 by the way).

And while it is appreciated that an export licence will be required from the Department of Trade if the collector is to take the vase home with him, it is not generally realised that the exportation of any antique fetching £8,000 or more at auction in the United Kingdom is subject to the scrutiny of the Reviewing Committee on the Export of Works of Art before a licence may be granted.

(right)
A fine pair of early George II giltwood window seats, each on six square tapering legs carved with pendant bell-flowers and headed by recessed fluting and flower heads on block feet, 146cm. wide, 61cm. high, 61cm. deep. **£25,000-£30,000**   *C*

Miller's Antiques Price Guide 1985

Major Country House Sales
Anne Bouillot
"Wiggle Your Paddles"

Only a totally unexpected fusion of the unpredictable with the imponderable at Elveden Hall on the borders of Norfolk in the Spring of 1984 could explain the transformation of Christie's contents sale into a nuclear happening that rocked the fine arts world to its foundations.

After the 1st Earl of Iveagh bought the Hall in 1894 from the estate of the Maharajah Duleep Singh, whom the British had deposed in the Punjab, he had the house duplicated to form an East Wing and then joined it to the Indian or West Wing by a central block containing a galleried Indian Hall built of an immense quantity of Carrera marble.

(right)
A fine and rare late 17th C. lapis lazuli table cabinet, the front entirely panelled with richly coloured lapis within ebonised and parcel-gilt moulded and beaded borders, fitted with numerous drawers and secret drawers, the top, sides and base of ebony; on Charles II giltwood stand, 107cm. wide, 45cm. deep, 172.5cm. high.
£95,000-105,000   *C*

(below)
A fine Roman ebony mother-of-pearl and ivory exhibition cabinet on stand by Giovanni, Battista Gatti, set with semi-precious stones, the doors enclosing an arrangement of ten long and short mahogany lined drawers, with a pair of small drawers below, the panelled sides similarly inlaid within a border of porphry and lapis, the stand with a long drawer and trestle supports joined by a pole stretcher, cabinet 77cm. high by 89cm. wide, Stand 88cm. high by 107cm. wide, signed Roma, dated 1870. **£50,000-55,000**   *S*

(below)
An important Pietra Dura cabinet on stand by Bernhard Ludwig of Vienna, applied with silvered metal and brass repoussé swags of ribbon tied flowers, above 10 double panelled doors, centred by an architectural doorway above a drawer, the sides inset with semi precious stones, 11ft. 3in. high, 7ft. 10½in. wide, c.1880. **£100,000-120,000**   *S*

An important pair of silver Renaissance revival throne chairs, each with down-swept arms with massive claw and ball feet, German, possibly Hanau, c.1880. **£15,000-18,000** *S*

A fine pair of large rectangular Japanese lacquer cabinets, the interiors fitted with a pair of sliding doors above three rounded rectangular shallow trays, decorated in gold, silver, red and black, (both with some damage), Meiji period, 166.5cm. high, 98cm. wide, 45.7cm. deep. **£80,000-90,000** *C*

Twelve Geo. III chairs. **£90,000-100,000** *C*

An important George III mahogany breakfront bookcase, 318cm. wide, 283cm. high, 43cm. deep. **£10,000-15,000** *C*

An important Charles II ebony, ivory and marquetry centre-table, inlaid in stained ivory and engraved and scorched woods with an urn of tulips, oak leaves and acorns with flowering and bird spandrels and a stylized oak leaf border, with one frieze drawer, on turned legs joined by a shaped stretcher, 108cm. wide, 77cm. high, 69cm. deep. **£35,000-40,000**   *C*

(top right)
An early George III mahogany secretaire cabinet known as the D'Arcy Cabinet, the upper part with an open chinoiserie fret cupboard with fret doors and with a shallow folio drawer below with a second open-fronted fretted cupboard and with a secretaire below, the stand with a gothic panelled frieze, 184cm. high, 71cm. wide, 32cm. deep, c.1765.
£200,000-250,000   *S*

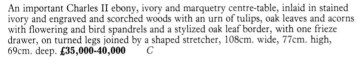

Although the Guinness family has not lived there since 1939, the house has never been opened to the public and it was therefore felt, when Christie's started to catalogue the contents and determine the estimates six months prior to the auction, that some members of the public might possibly take advantage of the view days to look the property over.

There was no way of knowing then of course that the subsequent release of a series of television and film spectaculars set on the sub-continent would arouse such universal interest in India that over 15,000 people would visit Elveden Hall by car, coach and – nice touch this – helicopter during the three-day view.

(below)
A pair of gilt-bronze mounted mahogany console dessertes in the style of J. H. Riesener, the white marble tops with rounded corners, each containing a drawer faced with inter-laced foliage and fluting, with galleried white marble shelf stretchers, 94cm. high, 105cm. wide. **£23,000-26,000**   *S*

A scarlet and gold lacquer bureau-cabinet, the shaped bevelled mirror-glazed doors enclosing a fitted interior with a fall-flap enclosing a fitted interior including a well, above two short and two graduated long drawers on bun feet, the lower part early 18th C., 212cm. high, 87cm. wide. **£18,000-20,000**   *C*

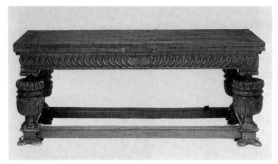

An oak draw-leaf refectory table, the mitre-framed top with two draw leaves over a heavily gadroon-carved frieze with leaf clasp corners with moulded cap stretchers, raised on shaped square moulded feet, 2ft. 9½in. high, 6ft. 11¾in. closed, 13ft. 1¾in. open (85cm. by 121cm. by 400cm.). **£4,000-6,000** in restored condition **£10,000+** in original state. *S*

Even more surprising was the fact that an equal number of potential bidders attended fourteen separate sales spread over a four-day period, an average of 1,200 per sale.

To eliminate the risk of missing bids from such large crowds, the auctioneers issued numbered paddles

A small James I oak buffet, with three open shelves, the stepped moulded frieze inlaid with diamond banding, the back support formed with a slightly tapering stop-fluted pilaster, 3ft. 7¾in. high, 3ft. 10½in. wide (111cm. by 118.5cm.) c.1620. **£10,000-14,000** *S*

(left)
A William IV rosewood and specimen wood centre table, inlaid with an ivory plaque with the Garter motto, surrounded by concentric rings, inlaid with fillets of various woods including maple, satinwood, ebony and amaranth, 51½in. (131cm.) wide. **£3,500-4,500** *C*

(below)
A good Jupe's patent expanding dining table, the circular eight segment top swivelling and with sixteen leaves, 2ft. 5in. high, 5ft. 2in. diameter (closed), (73cm. by 158cm.), 8ft. diameter, (244cm.) open (approx.), stamped Johnstone Jupe & Co., 6-7 Bond Street, London, and numbered 10715, with cabinet for the leaves, 1835-1838. **£35,000-45,000** *S*

to be held aloft at crucial moments, but, even so, "wiggle your paddles" was a caution the auctioneers had to repeat more than once. From Lot 1, which doubled its estimate to sell for £6,000, the pace was set and most of the other items doubled, if not trebled, their pre-sale estimates as well.

A fine Louis XVI ormolu-mounted mahogany bureau plat, with rectangular leather-lined top with ribbed and matted border, the angle clasp mounted with roundels fitted with two frieze drawers mounted with drapery swag handles and navette-shaped lockplates cast with eagles' masks and foliage, the panelled ends with a leather-lined slide, probably Russian, 130cm. wide, 75cm. high, 72cm. deep.
£25,000-30,000   *C*

The most dramatic over-reaction occurred during the carpet sale which had been relegated to a minor slot since Sothebys had an important sale in New York the same week and Lord Iveagh's 230 carpets had, after all, been bought almost as job lots from London department stores – 44 from Harvey Nichols in 1894, 61 from Libertys in 1902, for example.

A fine Regency penwork sofa table, the top with canted corners and a central band of Grecian ladies dancing and making music and with a central figure reclining in a vine-clad bower, with a pair of drawers, the vine-decorated lyre supports with a faceted pole stretcher and hipped sabre legs, 72cm. high, 152cm. long open, 58.5cm. deep, c.1810 decoration restored.
£18,000-20,000   *S*

A fine Queen Anne gilt-gesso side table, the moulded rectangular top with re-entrant corners and carved with foliate strapwork around a central cartouche of an eagle killing a serpent, with foliate frieze and shaped apron carved with a spreading cartouche on a pounced ground, the cabriole legs headed by acanthus on stylized claw-and-ball feet, 94cm. wide.
£25,000-30,000   *C*

A fine George II mahogany settee, en suite, with triple serpentine stuffed back, out-scrolled arms and upholstered seats, the scrolled ends of the arm-supports, seatrails and legs carved similarly to the chairs, 216cm. long, c.1745.
£125,000-200,000 *S*

In the event, all the carpets sold for an average five times estimate while, at £45,000, a 26′ × 18′ floral carpet which Christie's attributed to Ushak (W. Turkey), but the purchaser described as Mahal (W. Persia), attained a multiplier of 30.

The atmosphere at the carpet sale was undoubtedly heightened by the way in which the tapestries had been sold immediately before. Nobody could fail to be impressed by the way in which the tapestries were illuminated by arc lights as they were unfurled over the marble gallery of the Indian Hall. The most expensive lot at £85,000 was a Louis XIV Gobelins chancellerie tapestry woven with the arms of France and Navarre together with those of the Chancellor of France from 1699 to 1714.

(below)
A rare suite of parcel-gilt beechwood seat furniture, comprising a sofa and ten armchairs, the pierced central splats carved with flowerheads and leaves with caned seats and turned tapering legs, c.1800, possibly Spanish.
£12,000-14,000 *S*

(below)
A set of four William and Mary walnut chairs and a pair of similar armchairs, the tall arched backs with three acanthus-carved pierced splats, the sprung seats on gadrooned tapering legs joined by a moulded X-stretcher, c.1690, some restoration, finials replaced. **£8,000-9,000** *S*

A fine William and Mary walnut bureau bookcase, the double-domed upper part with a pair of mirrored doors, applied with shaped boletchon mouldings, enclosing a finely fitted interior, including adjustable shelves, folio holders, pigeon holes and six drawers above two candle slides, the lower part with a fall front enclosing a fitted interior and wells above two short and three long drawers, with herringbone bandings throughout, on ball feet, 202cm. by 104cm., late 17th C. **£14,000-16,000** *SC*

(below)
A very fine Victorian marquetry side cabinet, in the manner of Holland & Sons, the top veneered with a trellis parquetry design and crossbanded in kingwood above a pair of panelled doors, flanked by amboyna pilasters with finely cast floral swag mounts and serpentine glazed end cupboards, the whole with ormolu foliate mouldings, 208cm. wide. **£4,500-5,500** *Bon*

(below)
An important Louis XVI Vernis Martin armoire, by Francois Duhamel, with ormolu-galleried coved frieze lacquered with musical trophies in colours on a blue-green ground, the corners mounted with ormolu swagged shells, the centre with an ormolu plaque of scrolls and foliage, fitted with two doors in the front and a door at each side enclosing shelves, stamped DUHAMEL twice and JME, 84cm. wide. **£60,000-70,000** *C*

(left)
A rare important pair of North Italian marquetry games tables, tops open to reveal inlaid interior with a reserve, one with Neptune and a cherub, the other with a figure of Plenty working a treadmill, inlaid frieze, 80cm. signed Luigi Galinelli, dated 1808. **£18,000-20,000** *S*

A chancellor's economic expertise will certainly be required to determine whether the £6m. realised against the £2.5m. forecast is a one-off phenomenon and, once the provenance element is discounted, whether prices will generally regain more realistic levels.

Future sales of J.F. Herring Senior's equestrian portraits could well provide a pointer. Those on offer at Elveden Hall were valued at between £8,000/£10,000 each, but sold for between £26,000/£30,000.

Less than a month earlier, Christie's estimate of the value of the remaining contents of Belton House at £1.5m. had proved to be extremely accurate.

A red lacquer secretaire en pente, with gilt-bronze mounts, in the style of Dubois, the sloping front enclosing a fitted interior with three wells, the exterior faced with pictorial scenes in imitation of Chinese lacquer in shades of gilt and black on red, 94cm. high, by 102cm. wide. **£18,000-20,000** *S*

(below)
An Edwardian painted satinwood Carlton-House writing table, the horseshoe-shaped superstructure containing drawers and cupboards above a pull-out leather-lined writing surface, the drawers with turned ivory handles and the whole painted with swags of flowers and oval vignettes of ladies gardening, 99cm. high, by 137cm. wide, c.1905. **£4,500-5,500** *S*

A good pair of late George III painted and rosewood side tables, the D-shaped tops with a wide satinwood cross-banded border painted with flowers, the panelled frieze divided by lions' heads, with gilt paw feet, 86cm. high, 85cm. wide, c.1810. **£12,000-14,000** *S*

A highly important George III satinwood and marquetry semi-elliptical commode, attributed to Ince and Mayhew, the top with three applied painted ovals, the front divided by panels with six pilasters mounted with well-chased ormolu ram's head and ring capitals, the lunette-inlaid frieze with a drawer above three doors, the centre enclosing three mahogany drawers flanked by cupboards, 184cm. wide, 93.5cm. high, 74cm. deep. **£140,000-180,000** *C*

A rare and fine Queen Anne figured maple chest of drawers, with rectangular top with moulded edge over four graduated thumb-moulded drawers flanked by fluted quarter-columns above a moulded base, on cabriole legs with trifid feet, 40in. high, 35½in. wide, 21½in. deep, Pennsylvania 1750-1770. **£7,000-10,000**   *CNY*

A fine Vernis Martin gilt-bronze mounted mahogany secretaire cabinet, with bevelled glass doors flanked by a pair of slightly lower side sections, the lower part of inverted breakfront form and with a secretaire painted with arcadian lovers and flanked by a pair of doors, the whole richly mounted throughout with crisply cast gilt-bronze, 239cm. high by 142cm. wide, c.1890. **£5,000-6,000**   *S*

(below)
A fine William and Mary walnut and seaweed marquetry cabinet-on-cabinet, the panelled cupboard doors with glazed bevelled mirror backs and twelve various-sized drawers inscribed 'The property of King George I and II George Spencer Duke of Marlborough and Rich Bartholomew Esq.', the base with a pair of cupboard doors on bracket feet with two sets of gilt-brass carrying handles, 112cm. wide. **£40,000-45,000**   *C*

A good Chinese coromandel lacquer cabinet on stand, the doors enclosing short and long drawers, the exterior with mountain landscapes, the sides with peonies in colours on a gilt ground, 49½in. high, 31in. wide, mid 18th C. **£4,000-5,000**   *S*

53

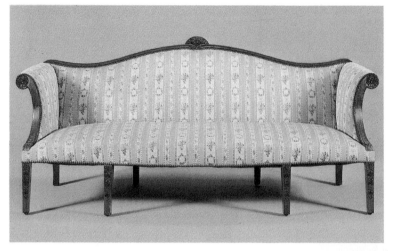

(below)
A fine Chippendale mahogany gaming table, the top opening to a baize-lined playing surface with dished counter holders and corner candlestick holders, on five cabriole legs with ball and claw feet, marked on inside of back frame 'MWM', hidden drawer behind swing gate missing, 71.1cm. high, 81.9cm. wide, 42.5cm. deep (closed), New York 1765-1785. **£25,000-32,000** *CNY*

A rare and important Federal carved mahogany sofa, with moulded serpentine crest rail flanked by outward scrolling arms carved with rosette terminals and water leaves, on square tapering legs carved with clusters of grapes pendant from bow knots, 72.4cm. high, 221cm. long, Salem, Massachusetts, 1794-1800. **£22,000-35,000** *CNY*

(below)
A fine Federal inlaid mahogany and birch veneer secretary, in two parts: the upper with double rounded-arch pattern glazed doors enclosing an adjustable shelved interior above double doors centering three rectangular panels; the lower section with hinged writing flap above a case with four graduated drawers on French feet, 219.7cm. high, 104.1cm. wide, 50.8cm deep, New Hampshire 1790-1815. **£8,500-11,500** *CNY*

As a result of negotiations which took place in 1983 when Lord Brownlow, the owner of Belton, and his Trustees decided they could no longer bear the heavy cost of maintaining the house, it was gifted to the National Trust, which, in turn, acquired about two-thirds of the contents, valued at £5m., with the assistance of a substantial grant from the National Heritage Memorial Fund.

A fine Empire mahogany veneer and gilt and painted wood card table, the rectangular hinged top with canted corners, 29in. high, 36½in. wide, New York, c.1825. **£18,000-25,000** *CNY*

A fine Federal inlaid mahogany pembroke table, the oval top with 2 drop leaves. veneered drawer, 28½in. high, 22¼in. wide, 28in. long, New York 1790-1870. **£7,000-8,500** *CNY*

A Chippendale mahogany card table, some damage, 28¼in. high, 34½in. wide, Philadelphia 1765-85. **£21,000-29,000** *CNY*

The remaining contents Christie's were instructed to sell had been removed to Belton in 1920 on the disposal of two other family houses and were not therefore an integral part of the Belton contents.

Nevertheless, both the National Trust, with the aid of an unexpected donation, and Lord Brownlow made successful purchases, the Trust paying top price of £95,000 for an Italian lapis lazuli table cabinet on Charles II giltwood stand and Lord Brownlow paying £20,000 for a Louis XV kingwood and purpleheart table à ecrire attributed to BRVB.

Frank Partridge, Lord Brownlow's grandson, who was the underbidder on so many items at Elveden Hall, secured a fine mid-18th C. walnut and parcel-gilt cabinet-on-chest from Schleswig-Holstein for £26,000 while the biggest pair of library steps ever seen outside Althorp – a staircase with two flights and half-landing that had been rescued from the stables – fetched £45,000.

The highlight of the silver section, a pair of Queen Anne sconces, made by Phillip Rollos, c.1710, 55oz., realised top estimate of £25,000.

An important collection of 100 lots of silver which Lady Juliet de Chair inherited from her Father's Fitzwilliam collection was included in the sale of contents which Christie's conducted at St. Osyth's Priory, Essex. At £98,000, four George II candlesticks on square bases,

An important and rare Queen Anne inlaid walnut armchair, with triple line-inlaid crest rail, stiles and splat, the shaped arms with ram's horn scroll terminals above a trapezoidal slip seat, on beaded cabriole legs with slipper feet joined by a flat serpentine H-shaped stretcher, old restoration to sides of front feet, 111.7cm. high, 68.6cm. wide, Newport, Rhode Island 1730-1750.
£21,000-29,000 *CNY*

(bottom right) A fine Federal inlaid mahogany lady's secretary, in two parts: the upper with shaped pediment over two diamond-pattern glazed doors enclosing a blue painted interior with two shelves, the lower section with hinged writing flap above an apron with single long drawer, 165.7cm. high, 82.9cm. wide, 48.6cm. deep, Boston, Massachusetts, 1790-1810.
£14,000-20,000 *CNY*

(below)
An important Empire mahogany and marble-top centre table, with mosaic marble top inlaid with 4 playing-cards, 29¼in. high, 41½in. diam., attributed to Anthony G. Querville, Philadelphia 1825-35.
14,000-20,000 *CNY*

A fine inlaid cherrywood desk and bookcase, in two parts: the upper part enclosing two shelves; the lower section with a compartmented interior, 99½in. high, 46in. wide, Rowan County, North Carolina 1800-1820. **£11,500-14,500** *CNY*

An early George III red-japanned musical bracket clock, the 8-inch dial signed Step: Rimbault London and with pendulum and calendar apertures, lower mask spandrels, Strike/Silent and Music/Silent dials in the upper corners and Minuet/Rigodon selector dial in the arch, the three train movement with verge escapement and bob pendulum, the music played on eight bells with the pin drum at right angles to the plates, the backplate signed Stephen Rimbault London and engraved with acanthus scrolls, in a bell-top case with urn finials, giltwood foliate frets and leaf-scroll feet, the whole decorated in gilt heightened with black on a vermilion ground with chinoiserie scenes, figures, masks and flowers divided by delicately drawn latticework panels, 70cm. high. **£8,000-10,000**   S

*Rimbault was a renowned maker of musical clocks, many of them for the foreign market.

each with a detachable pair of two-light branches in scroll form, 307oz., by George Wickes 1733, led the way with four unmarked Paul de Lamerie candlesticks, c.1740, 88oz., making £10,000.

Representative of Mr. Somerset de Chair's particular interest in Chinese works of art was a pair of unglazed buff pottery figures of wrestlers from the Tang Dynasty, which seems to have been a bargain at £4,500, but how unfortunate that the understated elegance of the huang-hua-li cupboard of the Ch'ing dynasty remained unappreciated, even at a modest £3,000. This type of furniture is relatively unknown in the U.K. although anyone who first became

A fine and rare Queen Anne walnut tall-case clock, with three brass ball and steeple finials above moulded cornice over a glazed square door enclosing a brass dial with second, minute and hour hands and day-of-the-month indicator, signed 'Christopher Witt Germantown fecit', 216.5cm. high, 53.3cm. wide, 25.4cm. deep, Pennsylvania 1720-1730. **£7,000-11,000**   CNY

A fine James II circular monteith, on rim foot, the sides chased with broad panels and flat-chased with scenes of figures and exotic birds in the Chinese taste, with vertical matted panels and plain circles between, the shaped border with applied foliage, engraved on the underneath with initials IMT to MT, 1687, maker's mark B in script, 27cm. diam., 35oz.
£50,000-60,000   *C*

There has always been a great demand for the finest James II chinoiserie pieces. Good contemporary decoration of this type triples the value of a piece.

A fine George II plain tapering cylindrical tankard, on moulded foot, with leaf-capped double scroll handle, the domed cover with corkscrew thumbpiece, engraved with a coat-of-arms within baroque cartouche, by Paul de Lamerie, 1727, 23.5cm. high, 62oz.
£40,000-45,000   *C*

Only three other tankards by de Lamerie appear to be recorded: one of 1716, now in the Sterling and Francine Clark Art Institute, and a pair of 1732 exhibited at South Kensington in 1862.

A very fine and rare lower Rhenish walnut group of The Lamentation, the Virgin fainting to the ground, her robe forming numerous angular folds as she is supported on either side by the Magdalene and St. John, another of the Holy Women raising her arms in distress behind, the whole with traces of original colour and gilding beneath later overpainting, 21½in. (52cm.) wide, late 15th C. **£18,000-20,000**   *S*

An important early 16th C. upper Swabian polychrome limewood statue of St. Sebastian tied to a tree, attributed to the Meister der Biberacher Sippe, left hand, big toe and right little finger missing; five toes restored, 70cm. high. **£40,000-45,000**   *C*

A pine figure of a female saint, perhaps the Magdalene or one of the Holy Women, restoration dated 1640, Styria, late 14th C., 42½in. high. **30,000-35,000**   *S*

A 19th C. French bronze group of an Arab falconer on horseback, cast from a model by Pierre Jules Mêne, on an oval naturalistic base cast with ferns and signed P. J. Mêne, numbered on the back 223, spurs replaced, 77.5cm. high. **£7,000-8,000**   *C*

acquainted with it through the superb pieces from the earlier Ming Dynasty, which Christie's sold in New York in June 1982, could only describe it as a revelation.

There was also some good oak at St. Osyth's with a 17th C. buffet contributing £2,400 to the overall total of £585,000, but it was Sotheby's which claimed an oak record at their sale of the contents of Rooksnest in Lambourn, Berkshire.

An extravagantly carved late 16th C. Elizabethan tester bed bearing the Tudor Royal arms sold for £19,000, an auction record for an oak bed. Probably made in Devonshire, it was sold from the Morgan Williams Collection at St. Donat's Castle, Llantwit Major, for £300 in 1921.

Another piece from St. Donat's was the oak food cupboard in the medieval style, actually constructed in the 19th C., using 16th C. panels, which a Swiss dealer bought for £6,600.

(below)
A fine pair of bronze vases, after the Medici and Borghese vases, from the Zoffoli workshops, 34.3cm. high, second half 18th C., black marble bases. **£4,000-6,000**   *S*

The Medici and Borghese vases were much admired in the 18th C. and were often paired together.

(right)
A late 19th C. French bronze group of Ugolino and his sons, after Jean Baptiste Carpeaux, on an octagonal naturalistic base inscribed B. Carpeau ROMAE 1860, rectangular wooden base, 44cm. high. **£3,000-3,500**   *C*

(centre) A fine silver hexagonal censer and shallow domed cover, with hawk finial, the body inset with six shaped kinji panels inlaid in Shibayama style with dragon handles, the silvered-metal base supported by a three-clawed dragon, finial repaired, signed Haruaki, 30cm. high, late 19th C. **£2,500-3,000**

(left and right) A very fine pair of Ando cloisonné enamel slender oviform vases, the rim with a band of hanabishi design, silver rims, late Meiji period, 30.3cm. high. **£3,000-3,500**

(centre left) A fine small cloisonné enamel globular vase, with tall slender neck, decorated with sparrows and butterflies among flowers below hanabishi designs, gilt metal rims, rim with slight dent, minute scratch on body, signed on a square silver tablet, Kyoto Namikawa (Yasuyuki), 8.9cm. high, c.1900 **£2,000-2,500**

(centre right) A very fine small rounded rectangular cloisonné enamel vase, decorated with autumn flowers and foliage (aki-no-nanakusa), fitted with silver rims, unsigned but probably by Namikawa, c.1900, wood stand, 12.4cm. high. **£800£1,200**   *C*

(left)
A fine black lacquered Kon-ito-Sugake-Odoshi Yokohagi-Do, comprising a kabuto with a russet iron eighteen-plate sujibachi with five-stage gilt tehen kanamono, the mabizashi and fukigaeshi with gilt fukurin, the latter bearing gilt usagimon, and with an unusual ox-horn folding crescent maedate; with a russet-iron mempo, black lacquer ko-sode, shinogote, gyoyo, detachable kusazuri, shino-haidate, o-tateage-suneate and kegutsu, 19th C., in a fine leather-covered armour box. **£3,500-5,000**   *C*

(right)
A fine red-lacquered Kon-ito-Odoshi Nuinobe-Do, the kabuto comprising a two-plate momonari hachi with small fukigaeshi and a leather-covered sugake-laced five-lame Hinenojikoro, with ko-sode kebiki-laced in iro-iro-odoshi, kusarigote, detachable kusazuri, haidate and shino-suneate, 19th C., with armour box.
£3,000-3,500   *C*

61

An important Tirolese wax and metal oval relief of St. George, the head of the bearded saint modelled in wax encircled by a halo in brass, the armour of pewter, the whole mounted on a board covered with red velvet and framed by an oval brass band engraved with the dedication: Effigies S: Georiji M: Desumpta ex Antiquissima Arce Ambras in Tijroli, 44.5cm. high, first half 18th C. **£2,000-3,000**   *S*

A fine Florentine baroque silver and hardstone portable altar, centred by a silver relief of the Coronation of the Virgin, the ebony frame applied with silver and gilt metal, and striated agate, lapis lazuli and semi-precious stones, the outer border of applied and pierced silver scrollwork enriched with gilt bronze, lapis lazuli and grey and pink agate interspersed with stylized buds set with carnelians, 78cm. high, early 18th C., in fitted leather-covered wooden case. **£10,000-12,000**   *S*

An Indian casket, of shaped oblong form, the cover and sides chased throughout with scrolling foliage and Hindu motifs, the base flat-chased with further Hindu motifs and a flowering vine, South Indian, second half 19th C., 22ct., bearing London Assay Office marks for 1980, in fitted velvet-lined wood case, 13½in. long, 80oz. **£25,000-30,000**   *C*

A fine Sicilian rectangular casket, with gilt metal mounts, veneered in tortoise-shell and set with panels of agate encrusted with acanthus carved from coral and mother-of-pearl, on four gilt bronze putti feet, red velvet lining, 59cm., c.1700, Trapani. **£15,000-18,000**   *S*

A Reichsadler humpen, enamelled with the crowned Imperial double-headed eagle, its outstretched wings bearing the Quationes Imperii flanking an orb, the reverse inscribed Das Heilige Römische Reich mit Sampt Seinen Glidern 1601, Germany 1601, 29cm. high. **£7,000-8,000**   *C*

A fine Beilby-enamelled ale glass, the deep funnel bowl decorated with an armorial crest of a bird, the reverse with pendant barley ear, the bowl supported on a double-series opaque-twist stem, conical foot, 18.5cm., c.1770. **£4,500-5,500**   *S*

(below)
A rare airtwist landscape goblet, attributed to William Beilby, the waisted bucket bowl enamelled with a pastoral scene, the reverse with a butterfly hovering over a foliate-spray, on a double-series airtwist stem and conical foot, two chips to foot rim, 17.3cm. high, c.1765-70. **£4,500-5,500**   *C*

A dated 'Jagd' humpen, enamelled in colours with three huntsmen, hounds attacking a bear, and chasing a boar, the rim with blue cloud scrolls above an inscription, the foot dated 1717, with kick-in base and later pewter mount to the foot rim, crack to base, Franconia or Thuringia, 21.5cm. high. **£2,000-3,000**   *C*

An important pair of Stourbridge decanters, the club-shaped bodies wide flute cut with alternate amber flashed panels, engraved with floral decoration, star cut bases, similarly cut and decorated spire stoppers, probably Richardsons, 24cm. high, c.1850. **£450-500**   *Som*

A rare purple amethyst ovoid decanter, with gilt circle and 'Rum' with gilt lozenge stopper, probably Ricketts of Bristol, 19.5cm. high, c.1800. **£280-330**   *Som*

A massive purple amethyst bowl, with gadrooned body and foot rim, probably American, 12.5cm. high, 13.7cm. diam., c.1800. **£200-250**   *Som*

A gilt blue glass scent bottle, diamond facet cut, decorated on one side with figures in a garden, the reverse with a bouquet of flowers, gadrooned gold cap, probably London, Giles' workshop, 8cm. high, c.1765. **£600-650**   *Som*

A set of four wine/spirit bottles, in amber, amethyst, green and blue, with silver mounts and silver/cork stoppers, 31.5cm. average height, c.1840. **£450-500** *Som*

A dark amber bottle glass wine bottle, with loop handle, probably Nailsea, 21.2cm. high, c.1810. **£280-320** *Som*

A fine engraved, enamelled and intercalaire glass vase, enamelled to simulate shrimp tails, embellished with gilt, engraved E. Gallé fect Nanceius no. 180. 10.7cm. high. **£1,400-1,600** *CG.*

A pair of Bristol blue square spirit bottles, with canted corners and pouring necks, with simulated gilt wine labels for rum and brandy, gilt lozenge stoppers, 17cm. high. c.1800. **£380-420** *Som*

(left)
A green crown glass Nailsea flask, with opaque white dashes, 17cm. high, c. 1810. **£180-220** *Som*

A crown glass green Nailsea jug, with opaque white stringing round the rim, 17cm. high, c.1810. **£180-220** *Som*

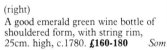

(left)
A good set of three facet cut amethyst
bottles, with cut stoppers, in a plated
stand, marked "Elkington & Co.",
bottles 24.5cm. high, c.1840.
£450-500 *Som*

(right)
A good emerald green wine bottle of
shouldered form, with string rim,
25cm. high, c.1780. **£160-180** *Som*

A rare blue Irish runner, the heavy ovoid
bowl with sliced vescia and printy cutting on
a hollow conical stem, 11cm. high, c.1800.
£120-140 *Som*

(right)
A rare Apsley Pellatt amber flashed
scent bottle, with diamond cut panels
and cut mushroom stopper, the body
with moulded picture of the three
graces, lens cut on the reverse side,
embossed mark "Pellatt & Co.
Patentee" 8cm. high, (less stopper)
c.1830. **£200-240** *Som*

(left)
A turquoise green wine glass,
the ovoid bowl on a Wrythen
Balustroid stem with centre ball knop
plain conical foot, 13.5cm. high,
c.1760. **£400-500** *Som*

A tall etched and overlay glass table lamp and shade, the
slender base and domed shade of yellow glass and overlaid
in tones of orange and amber with trailing autumnal sycamore
branches, signed Gallé in the overlay on the shade and
engraved on the base, 60cm. high. **£6,000-8,000**   *CG*

(below)
A mould blown glass vase, by Emile Gallé
of baluster form, the yellow white ground
with amber-leaves and plums, signed Gallé
in the overlay, 40cm. high, c.1900.
£3,000-4,000   *CAms*

An important enamelled and applied glass bottle
and stopper of gourd form, the clear glass enamelled
and applied with a large carved beetle with gilt-foil
inclusions, the yellow and orange stopper formed as
a curved stalk and leaf engraved Daum Nancy,
24cm. high. **£17,000-19,000**   *CG*

A guild of handicraft oak cabinet,
designed by C.R. Ashbee, with two
drawers below a pair of doors inlaid in
fruit woods with stylized flowers, the
inner face veneered in satinwood and
painted and gilt with flowers, silver
lamp-fitting above, a writing-flap
extending onto hinged supports, and a
pair of doors enclosing a fitted shelf,
the hinge and key plates pierced with
stylized flowers, 160cm. high, by
105.5cm. wide, by 55cm. deep,
stamped 'The Guild of Handicraft
Ltd. Essex House Bow E.', c.1900.
£20,000-25,000   *S*

A Gordon Russell walnut and
mahogany fall-front writing cabinet,
the panelled fall-front inlaid in ebony
with fine stringing, enclosing a writing
compartment, above three drawers
edged with ebony stringing and with
ebony knobs, on octagonal legs linked
by cross-stretchers, 136cm. high, by
120cm. wide, by 47.5cm. deep, affixed
paper label 'This piece of furniture
design no. 570 was made throughout
in The Russell Workshops Broadway,
Worcestershire, Designer: Gordon
Russell/Foreman: Edgar Turner/
Cabinet Maker: T. Lees/Metal
Worker: D. Keen/Timber used:
English Walnut and White
Mahogany/Date: 15/2/27.
£2,500-3,000   *S*

A large Larchc gilt-bronze inkwell, modelled naked figure seated erect on draped rocks, hinged inkwell concealed within the rockwork, 48cm., signed in the maquette 'Raoul Larche', foundry mark 'Siot Decauville Paris Fondeur', numbered 'K 503', c.1900. **£4,000-5,000**   S

An ebony and ivory inlaid mantel clock, designed by Josef Maria Olbrich, constructed in cherry wood, circular dark fruitwood face inlaid with ivory numerals, hinged door opening to reveal original movement, by George Karp, Darmstadt, Key, 26.75cm., interior with affixed plate with clock-maker's details, c. 1902. **£16,000-20,000**   S

Panels also figure in the fine Henry VIII oak chest, the four front panels of profile portrait roundels, c.1540, which sold for £8,000.

Now, if the Elveden House auction is considered to be as "rich" as the homemade cake on sale in the refreshment tent there,

(right) Raoul Larchc gilt-bronze figure of Loie Fuller, 45.75cm. 'Siot Decauville Fondeur Paris', c.1900. **£11,000-13,000**   S

A Liberty & Co. 'Cymric' copper, mother-of-pearl and lapis clock, the design attributed to Archibald Knox, with copper numerals pierced and cast with entrelacs and set with mother-of-pearl lapis cabochons, key, 24.5cm. maker's mark, stamped 'Cymric 5191', Birmingham, 1903. **£6,500-7,500**   S

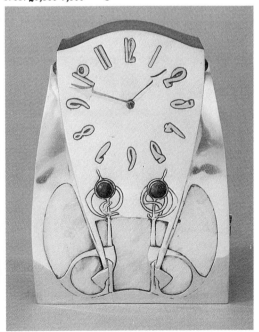

A rare "Citta Di Carte"/"Bosco" Trompe L'Oeil printed four panel screen, by Piero Fornasetti, c.1952. Recto printed in colours depicting a city of cards with jesters, the verso with genre scenes in shades of blue, unsigned, each panel 217×50cm. on casters; together with a declaration signed by Fornasetti that the "City of Cards" was designed and executed by him in 1952 and was the first screen he created. **£95,000-115,000** *CNY*

(centre)
A fine and rare Ebene De Macassar, marquetry, giltwood and marble commode, by Sue et Mare incorporating doors decorated to a design by Mathurin Meheut, c.1925. Of curved rectangular form veneered in ebene de macassar surmounted by highly figured black and white marble top above two doors inlaid with stained woods depicting a stylized underwater scene of two turtles paddling amidst all manner of aquatic flora and fauna, the boldly scalloped lower edge caught up over bulbous lobed giltwood feet terminating in swirls, the interior fitted with drawers and shelves in beige-stained bird's-eye maple, unsigned, 84.5cm. high, 173cm. wide, 66cm. deep. **£123,000-135,000** *CNY*

(bottom left)
A carved and polychrome painted pine breakfront cabinet, designed by Gerhard Munthe, deeply carved with reliefs of Nordic warriors, gods, beasts and foliage, vibrantly painted in red, yellow, blue and green, hammered metal hardware, unsigned, 230.5cm. high, 76.5cm. wide, 63.5cm. depth of cornice. **£14,000-21,000** *CNY*

A library wing armchair, the decoration includes representations of Anubis, Sebek, the nursing Isis and Osiris in a sunboat on the arm sides, 97.5cm. high. **£100,000-115,000** *CNY*

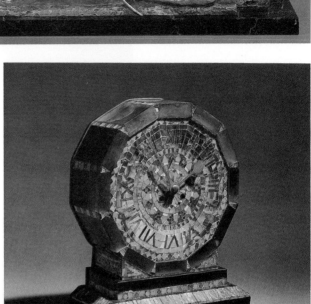

Kora, a gilt and cold-painted bronze and ivory figure of an exotic dancer, cast and carved from a model by Demêtre Chiparus, French, early 20th C., 61cm. high, including stepped red marble plinth signed DH. Chiparus and ETLING-PARIS. **£6,000-9,000**   *CNY*

(top left)
A rare silvered, gilt and cold-painted bronze and ivory figure of a fashionable lady, cast and carved from a model by Demêtre Chiparus, French, early 20th C., stamped 54cm. high, including elaborate stepped brown onyx base signed Chiparus. **£21,000-25,000**   *CNY*
(top right)
Penthesilia, a silvered-bronze figure of a female archer, cast from a model by Marcel Bouraine, French, early 20th C., inscribed Susse^{ts} Ed^{ts} Paris – cire perdue and impressed with the Susse Freres foundry seal – 86.4cm. long, including green marble base. **£6,000-9,000**   *CNY*
(bottom right)
A fine mosaic Favrile glass mantel clock, by Tiffany Studios, the twelve-sided dial inset with Roman chapters within radiating concentric bands of green, gold and blue tesserae, the border comprised of twelve clear glass tiles intersected by triangular green and gold tesserae, the tiered foot similarly decorated, the reverse mounted with a metal plate, 33.4cm. high, with replaced mechanism. **£87,000-100,000**   *CNY*

(right)
A gilt and cold painted bronze and ivory figure of a ballerina, 'Tanara', signed D.H. Chiparus and inscribed ETLING. PARIS, 7⅝in. high (19.3cm.). **£4,000-5,000**   *CNY*

(right)
A Markling guage one clockwork
0-4-0 locomotive, with lever brake,
simulated whistle, lacking lamp,
slightly retouched, with matching
four-wheeled tender, 12½in. long
over buffers, (32cm.), German, in
contemporary wooden box, c.1902.
£400-600 *S*

(left) A good and unusual Carete hand-painted four-seat open
tourer, with simulated buttoned-seats, opening rear doors,
rubber-tyred wheels, forward/reverse lever, hand brake,
nickel-plated lamps, 32.5cm. long, with original cardboard
box bearing Gamages 12/6d. label, envelope for additional
tyres and key, German, c.1910. **£8,000-9,000** *S*

(centre left)
A fine and unusual Carette fifty tinplate open tourer,
the lithographed vehicle with side lamps, rubber-tyred
wheels, steering wheel and clockwork mechanism driving the
rear axle, 20cm. long, contained in original cardboard box
base, German, c.1906. **£4,000-5,000** *S*

A rare Marklin gauge one tinplate
bogie kaiser-wagen, hand-painted
in navy-blue and white lined gold
and turquoise with fitted interior,
(slightly re-touched in places),
(no. D4020, German,) 28cm. long
over buffers, c.1901.
£600-700 *S*

A good and rare Marklin tinplate
'Rocket' gauge one train-set,
comprising 2-0-2 locomotive No.
1829, spirit-fired with two outside
cylinders, (re-touched), tender with
water barrel, open passenger
coaches and luggage car, contained
in original cardboard box with lid
and, (non-original), funnel and can.
German, c.1909.
£20,000-30,000 *S*

72

(above left)
A 'Cottage Garden' large pottery wall plaque, by Clarice Cliff, with deep well, painted with hollyhocks and marigolds in a stylized garden before a cottage with smoking chimney, in shades of blue, green, orange, brown, black and yellow on a cream ground, printed marks, C., 18in.
£1,400-2,000

(above right)
A large pottery wall plaque, by Clarice Cliff, with deep well, painted with hollyhocks and marigolds in a stylized garden beneath a foreground tree, in shades of blue, green, orange, brown, black and yellow on cream ground, printed marks, D., 18in. **£1,100-1,400**   *CNY*

(left)
A pair of Gruber leaded glass doors, in four sections, in panels of frosted opalescent, smoked and painted glass, bronze framework, 245cm. by 180cm., painted signature 'J. Gruber', 1920's.
£2,200-2,400   *S*

(bottom left)
A good Martin Brothers bird, with splayed webbed feet and smug expression, two talons chipped, 34.8cm., incised marks, the head dated 10-1895, the base dated 1-1894, fixed wood base.
£3,000-3,200   *S*

(below)
A Poertzel bronze and ivory group of a pierrot and partner, cold-painted details, oval mottled black marble base, 37cm., bronze base marked 'Prof. Poertzel', 1930's.
£2,800-3,000   *S*

(below)
A Marcolin painted and gilt-bronze and carved ivory figure, inspired from Paul Poiret, parcel gilt, green onyx base, 33cm., marked 'O. Marcolin', c.1925.
£1,700-1,900   *S*

An exceptionally rare swivel-head two-faced bisque doll, probably by Bru Jeune et Cie., impressed 3 indistinctly, one face gently smiling with closed mouth, fixed blue glass eyes with black eye lining and delicately painted eyelashes, fine feathered brows, the other face swivelling round to show the same smiling face only with closed eyes finely painted, the wig of ash-blonde mohair, with 3 stamped inside, the fully gusseted kid body filled with sawdust and the hands with separately stitched fingers, some sawdust missing, tiny chip on tip of nose of one face and chip to one neck base, unclothed, French, 35.5cm. c.1870.
£1,800-2,200 *S*

A fine and rare Emile Jumeau bisque talking doll, impressed DEPOSE E 8 J with open/closed mouth, hanb-cut glass paper-weight eyes, jointed composition body, pull-string for voice box, JUMEAU Medaille D'Or Paris, French, 19in., 1880, with other clothes. **£4,000-5,000** *S*

(below) An exceptionally fine and rare William and Mary wooden doll, painted black eyes, the remains of a black silk beauty spot clearly visible on the forehead; with well carved ears, a wisp of auburn real hair and nailed-on stitched linen wig, legs peg-jointed at hips and knees, wooden forearms, three fingers broken, left arm loose, two small patches flaked on left cheek, English, 42.5cm., c.1690. **£16,000-18,000** *S*

(below)
A fine and rare George I wooden doll, the gesso-covered head finely painted, with black glass eyes, the hips and knees peg-jointed, one wooden pin missing on left leg, missing wig, tip of nose rubbed, English, 41cm., c.1725.
£12,000-14,000 *S*

Tandem tricycle, probably built in Coventry, frame no. 189, non-tangential driving wheels of 40in. (100cm.) diameter, front wheel 25in. (63cm.) diameter, steered by rack and pinion actuated by the right hand forward twist grip, the left hand grip actuates the brake, twin original leather saddles, one damaged, tread plates are finished in brass, with solid tyres, c.1888.
£4,000-5,000 *CSK*

(right)
A 1917 Ford agricultural tractor, powered by the renowned Ford 4 cylinder S.V. engine, with magneto ignition. **£2,000-3,000** *P*
A good example of this famous tractor which, in its day represented a considerable advance over the more ponderous agricultural ploughing engines then in use.
Despite their long production run, few examples of these sturdy and workmanlike vehicles remain.

F.N. 448c.c. four-cylinder solo motorcycle, reg. no. PB 4127, frame no. 113, engine no. 1330, the Belgian Fabrique Nationale d'Armes de Guerre was almost certainly the first firm to build a commercially successful four-cylinder motorcycle, though sadly the production of true motorcycles faded away in 1957, leaving only a range of mopeds.
This is a typical early example with cylinders of 50mm. bore and 57mm. stroke, a three-speed gear with hand change, Bosch magneto ignition and rod-operated braking on the rear wheel, the wheels are shod with 2.75×21 tyres, c.1908. **£7,000-8,000** *CSK*

75

1914 Rolls-Royce 40/50 H.P. Alpine Eagle Sporting Torpedo, coachwork by Portholme, Huntingdon, reg. no. LR 4846, chassis no. 17 RB, engine no. 77 Z, engine, six-cylinder, side-valve, bi-block, bore 114.3mm., stroke 120.7mm., capacity 7,428c.c.: magneto and coil ignition; four-speed gearbox, right-hand change: shaft and bevel drive: foot and hand brakes on rear wheels: suspension semi-elliptic front, cantilever rear: wheelbase 3.43m. (135½in.): tyre size 895×135: price new in England approx. £1,150. **£80,000-90,000** *CSK*

1923 Rolls-Royce twenty single Landaulette, coachwork by Hamshaw, Leicester, reg. no. XO 1816, chassis no. 58-S-l, engine no. G.301, engine, six-cylinder, overhead-valve, monobloc, bore 76.2mm., stroke 114.3mm., capacity 3,127c.c.: coil ignition: three-speed gearbox, central change: spiral bevel final drive: foot and hand brakes on rear wheels: suspension semi-elliptic front and rear: wheelbase 3.27m. (129in.): tyre size 32×4½in.: price new in England (chassis) £1,100. **£25,000-30,000** *CSK*

1905 Rolls-Royce light twenty replica four-seater Tonneau, coachwork by Harrington, Hove, reconstructed from two decaying specimens, reg. no. M.9974, chassis no. 26350, engine, four-cylinder, overhead-inlet-valve, bi-block, bore 101.6mm., stroke 127mm., capacity 3,994c.c.: magneto and coil ignition: four-speed gearbox with overdrive top, right-hand change: shaft and bevel drive: footbrake on transmission, handbrake on rear wheels: suspension semi-elliptic front, semi-elliptic and transverse rear: wheelbase 2.69m. (106in.): tyre size 815×105: price new in England, £735. **£60,000-70,000** *CSK*

1957 Maserati 250F lightweight single-seater racing car, not regd., chassis no. 2527, engine, six-cylinder, twin overhead camshafts, monobloc, bore 84mm., stroke 75mm., capacity 2,494c.c.: five-speed gearbox in unit with rear axle: spur-gear final drive: four-wheel hydraulic brakes: suspension independent: wheelbase 2.28m. **£110,000-130,000** *CSK*

1958 Lotus 16 single-seater Grand Prix racing car, not regd., chassis no. 362, engine no. FPF 1071, engine, four-cylinder, twin overhead camshafts, monobloc, 86.4×83.8mm. (91×83.8mm.) capacity 1,960c.c., magneto ignition: four-speed gearbox: bevel drive: four-wheel hydraulic disc brakes: suspension independent: wheelbase 2.27m. **£40,000-50,000** *CSK*

then remember that the lots at Rooksnest ranged from £19,000 to £1 while the three principal lots at Hungershall Lodge, Royal Tunbridge Wells, which Phillips were instructed to sell for the executor of Lady Evans went for £6,800, £6,000 and £5,800 – respectively a fine William and Mary walnut and floral marquetry longcase clock by

(left) 1956 Ferrari 508-128B-250 Tour de France two-seater Berlinetta, coachwork by Scaglietti, Modena, reg. no. SPY 250, chassis and engine nos. 0557 GT, engine, twelve-cylinder, twin overhead camshafts, vee, bore 73mm., stroke 58.8mm., capacity 2,953c.c.: four-speed all-synchromesh gearbox: wheelbase 2.6m. **£60,000-70,000** *CSK*

(right) 1934 Rolls-Royce 40-50 H.P. Phantom II Sedanca De Ville coachwork by Barker, London, engine, six-cylinder, overhead valve, bi-block, bore 108mm., stroke 139.7mm., capacity 7,668c.c.: 4-speed synchromesh gearbox, right-hand change: footbrake mechanical servo on 4 wheels, wheelbase 3.8m., tyre size 7.00×19: price new in England (approx.), £2,700. **£50,000-60,000** *CSK*

77

1912 Rolls-Royce 40-50
H.P. Silver Ghost semi-
open drive limousine,
coachwork by Hooper,
London, reg. no. R.1252,
chassis no. 1721, engine
no. 87 M, engine, six-
cylinder, side-valve,
capacity 7,428 c.c.: three-
speed gearbox, wheelbase
3.65m. (143½ in.): tyre
size 895×135: price new
in England (approx.)
£1,400. **£85,000-
95,000**   *CSK*

A 1926 Rolls-Royce 40/50
H.P. Phantom I two-seater
coupe cabriolet, coachwork
by Barker, London, chassis
number 21 SS, engine
number EU 85, registration
number YN 9160, engine,
six cylinder, overhead
valve, bi-block, bore
108mm., stroke 139.7mm.,
capacity 7,668cc.; magneto
and coil ignition, four-speed
gearbox, right-hand change,
spiral bevel final drive,
footbrake mechanical servo
on four wheels, handbrake
on rear wheels, suspension
semi-elliptic front, cantilever rear, wheelbase 3.8m.
(149.6in.), tyre size
7.00×21. **£30,000-
35,000**   *CSK*

1938 Rolls-Royce 40-50
H.P. Phantom III touring
limousine, coachwork, by
Thrupp and Maberly,
London, reg. no. ANV
688, chassis no. 3 DL 76,
engine no. B.88C, engine,
twelve-cylinder, overhead
valve, vee, capacity
7,340c.c.: four-speed
synchromesh gearbox;
suspension independent
coil front, semi-elliptic
rear, wheelbase 3.62m.
(142in.): tyre size
7.00×18: price new in
England, £2,960.
£60,000-70,000   *CSK*

A fine silk Qum carpet, the pale beige field with a series of
elaborate scrolling ivory floral panels, in a pale beige
flowering and scrolling vine border between gold and ivory
scrolling vine stripes, 326cm. by 213cm.
£10,000-12,000　　C

A fine antique silk Heriz prayer rug, with two
irises flanked by elaborate columns of chevron
and stellar design, supporting a rust-red mihrab
with rows of palmette vine, with a large
elaborate pendant floral stylized mosque lamp
with palmette and ivory band of curl-hooked
vine above, with minor indigo key-pattern and
plain outer stripe, one tiny area of damage at
top, one small area of very slight wear, 183cm.
by 124cm., 19th C. **£9,000-10,000**　　C

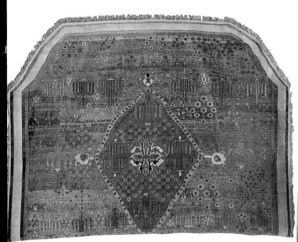

fine and unusual antique octagonal Serapi carpet, with large
ylized floral sprays and matrices around a similar medallion, with
endants at each corner, areas of slight wear, added tassel fringe, a
w small areas of repair, several slight stains, 442cm. by 422cm.
0,000-12,000　　C

An Esfahan Sanaye part silk hunting rug, the field with
scenes of mounted huntsmen in pursuit of wild animals,
the border with animals and trees, single guard stripes,
with a signature panel at one end, 244cm. by 152cm.,
modern. **£6,000-7,000**　　S

A Mereze prayer rug, the indigo mehrab with polychrome stripes, diced and honeycomb botehs, the ivory stylized bird and vine border with twin guard stripes, 152cm. by 114cm., c.1880. **£5,000-6,000**   *S*

John Martin, London, a very pretty 19th C. satinwood and marquetry bonheur du jour and a pair of good quality Edwardian satinwood and inlaid side cabinets, one stamped Edwards and Roberts.

A Konya Ladik runner, the madder field with four quatrefoil medallions, all surrounded by hooked guls, and flowerheads, the saffron border with stylized palmettes and vines, single guard stripes, 361cm. by 122cm., c.1800. **£4,000-6,000**   *S*

A fine Isfahan carpet, the ivory field with palmettes, flowerheads, feathery leaves and scrolling vine around a large rust-red and blue tracery vine and palmette medallion with pendants, 356cm. by 274cm. **£11,000-13,000**   *C*

(right)
A Kashan carpet, with a central indigo pole medallion all surrounded by scrolling vines bearing palmettes serrated leaves and floral sprays, floral spandrels, the border with four inner and three outer guard stripes, 12ft. by 8ft. 9in. **£2,500-4,000**   *SC*

80

81

BRITISH ANTIQUE EXPORTERS LTD

WHOLESALERS   EXPORTERS   PACKERS   SHIPPERS

HEAD OFFICE: QUEEN ELIZABETH AVENUE, BURGESS HILL, WEST SUSSEX, RH15 9RX   ENGLAND

TELEPHONE BURGESS HILL (04446) 45577   CABLES BRITISHANTIQUES BURGESS HILL   TELEX 87688

To: Auctioneers,wholesalers and
    retailers of antique furniture,
    porcelain and decorative items.

Dear Sirs,
We offer the most comprehensive service available in the U.K.

As wholesale exporters, we sell 20ft. and 40ft. container-loads of antique furniture, porcelain and decorative items of the Georgian Victorian, Edwardian and I930's periods. Our buyers are strategically placed throughout the U.K. in order to take full advantage of regional pricing. You can purchase a container from us for as little as £5,000. This would be filled with mostly I870 to I920's furniture and chinaware; you could expect to pay approximately £7,000 to £I0,000 for a quality shipment of Georgian, and Victorian furniture and porcelain. Our terms are   £500 deposit, the balance at time of arrival of the container. If the merchandise should not be to your liking, for any reason whatsoever, we offer you your money back in full, less one-way freight.

If you wish to visit the U.K. yourself and purchase individually from your own sources, we will collect,pack and ship your merchandise with speed and efficiency within 5 days. Our rates are competitive and our packing is the finest available anywhere in the world. Our courier- finder service is second to none and we have knowledgeable couriers who are equipped with a car and the knowledge of where the best buys are.

If your business is buying English antiques, we are your contact. We assure you of our best attention at all times.

Yours faithfully
BRITISH ANTIQUE EXPORTERS LTD.

N. Lefton
Chairman and Managing Director.

DIRECTORS N LEFTON (Chairman & Managing). P V LEFTON. THE RT. HON THE VISCOUNT EXMOUTH. A FIELD, MSC FBOA DCLP FSMC FAAD
REGISTERED OFFICE BURGESS HILL   REGISTERED NO 863406 ENGLAND
BANKERS NATIONAL WESTMINSTER BANK PLC, 155 NORTH STREET, BRIGHTON, SUSSEX   THE CHASE MANHATTAN BANK, N.A. 410 PARK AVENUE, NEW YORK

THERE ARE A GREAT MANY ANTIQUE SHIPPERS IN BRITAIN

but few, if any, who are as quality conscious as Norman Lefton, Chairman and Managing Director of British Antique Exporters Ltd. of Burgess Hill, Nr. Brighton, Sussex. Twenty years' experience of shipping goods to all parts of the globe have confirmed his original belief that the way to build clients' confidence in his services is to supply them only with goods which are in first class saleable condition. To this end, he employs a staff of over 50, from highly skilled, antique restorers, polishers and packers to representative buyers and executives. Through their knowledgeable hands passes each piece of furniture before it leaves the B.A.E. warehouses, ensuring that the overseas buyer will only receive the best and most saleable merchandise for their particular market. This attention to detail is obvious on a visit to the Burgess Hill warehouses where potential customers can view what must be the most varied assortment of Georgian, Victorian, Edwardian and 1930's furniture in the UK. One cannot fail to be impressed by, not only the varied range·of merchandise but also the fact that each piece is in showroom condition awaiting shipment.

BRITISH ANTIQUE EXPORTERS LTD

QUEEN ELIZABETH AVENUE
BURGESS HILL
WEST SUSSEX, RH15 9RX, ENGLAND
Telex 87688
Cables BRITISH ANTIQUES BURGESS HILL

Member of L.A.P.A.D.A.
Guild of Master Craftsmen

Telephone BURGESS HILL (04446) 45577

As one would expect, packing is considered somewhat of an art at B.A.E. and the manager in charge of the works ensures that each piece will reach its final destination in the condition a customer would wish. B.A.E. set a very high standard and, as a further means of improving each container load Helyn O'Hare, who also deals with customer/container liaison, invites each customer to return detailed information on the saleability of each piece in the container thereby ensuring successful future shipments. This feedback of information is the all important factor which guarantees the profitability of future containers. "By this method" Mr. Lefton explains, "we have established that an average £7000 container will immediately it is unpacked at its final destination realise in the region of £10000 to £14000 for our clients selling the goods on a quick wholesale turnover basis". When visiting the warehouses various container loads can be seen in the course of completion. The intending buyer can then judge for himself which type of container load would best be suited to his market. In an average 20-foot container B.A.E. put approximately 150 to 200 pieces carefully selected to suit the particular destination. There are always at least 10 outstanding or unusual items in each shipment, but every piece included looks as though it has something special about it.

Based at Burgess Hill 7 miles from Brighton and on a direct rail link with London 39 miles (only 40 minutes journey) the Company is ideally situated to ship containers to all parts of the world. The showrooms, restoration and packing departments are open to overseas buyers and no visit to purchase antiques for re-sale in other countries is complete without a visit to their Burgess Hill premises where a welcome is always found.

WANTED

SPECTACULAR SHIPPING PIECES

We are looking for The Unusual, The Outrageous,
The High Quality, The Spectacular pieces of Shipping Furniture
from Desks, Hall Stands, Washstands, Clocks, Cabinets to
Wardrobes.
We will pay
maximum possible prices
to obtain The Unusual.

FOR SALE

CONTAINER LOADS OF ANTIQUES TO WORLD WIDE DESTINATIONS

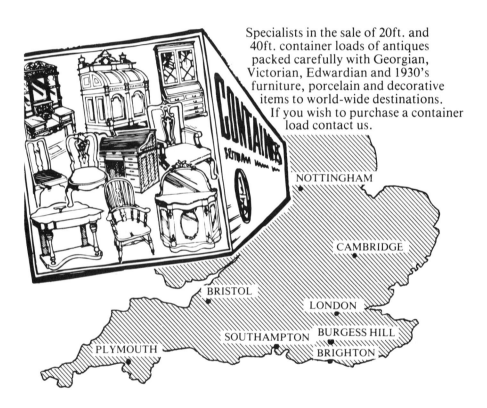

Specialists in the sale of 20ft. and 40ft. container loads of antiques packed carefully with Georgian, Victorian, Edwardian and 1930's furniture, porcelain and decorative items to world-wide destinations. If you wish to purchase a container load contact us.

POTTERY — MARKET TRENDS

English Delftware — The market in blue and white delft has been quite strong over the period with two possible exceptions. The first is some late 17th C. **chinoiserie pieces** as doubts have been expressed as to provenance. Any hint that they may have been produced in Holland immediately depresses price. The second is the minor blue and white pieces.

Prices of polychrome delft rocketed at the time of the first and second Lipski sales but seem since then to have levelled out. This has particularly affected the more primitive pieces, such as the naturalistic subjects: birds and flowers.

ENGLISH POTTERY
Rustic influenced figures, such as **Ralph Wood** are very strong. **Cow Creamers** are scarce, due to vulnerability and are now highly desirable. Prices which had remained static are now rising sharply. This is also helped by great American

interest in most early English pottery of primitive or rustic nature.

Animal figures continue in popularity and steadily increase in price. Good early ones are becoming increasingly scarce.

Toby Jugs — Rare early and/or finely potted examples have always been desirable. There has been very little on the market and anything unusual has caused great excitement. Again there is strong American interest in early, rare Toby jugs.

This year has seen a greater interest in **English majolica** with staggering prices paid for the more adventurous models, particularly **Minton**.

CONTINENTAL POTTERY
Dutch: It continues to be slightly flat with the exception of very rare or early pieces.

German: Both stoneware and faience have continued to increase steadily over the past two to three years. Rare pieces of **Sieburg** and

Raeren are highly prized. If there is anything exceptional about the piece, it can easily make two or three times normal price.

Westerwald continues to prove a difficult seller. It still seems to be suffering from the glut of more ordinary pieces.

French: There have been some very good sales in France with high prices paid for anything of quality. The prices of **Strasbourg** and **Marseilles** in particular are very strong.

Italian: This has not seen much change this year, with both Italian and Sicilian pottery maintaining the same steady level. With one or two notable exceptions there hasn't been much of real interest in the last 12 months.

A Faenza cup-shaped bowl, the blue reserved in white with affronte dolphins, vases of fruit and foliage masks, restoration to lower part of body, 15 cm. diam., c. 1530. **£1,300-1,500**   *C*

A large Cologne stoneware bellarmine flagon, the narrow neck crisply sprigged beneath a flange with a traditional wide-eyed mask, the beard extending over the continuous horizontal grooving, covered in a variegated glaze ranging from brown to green, body cracks and reparation, 48 cm., 16th/17th C. **£850-950**   *SS*

A German stoneware bellarmine, 8 in., c. 1630. **£260-280**   *JHo*

A massive Talavera circular bowl, painted with 2 horsemen, the exterior with 3 horses and a dog barking at a horse among trees, rim chips, 54 cm. diam., mid 17th C. **£1,900-2,100**   *C*

A German stoneware bellarmine, 9 in., c. 1680. **£190-220**   *JHo*

A delft broth-bowl in the white, with a pierced strainer on the interior, set on a small flared foot, cracks, chips, 5 in., c. 1670-80. **£150-250**   *S*

A bellarmine stoneware jug, the bulbous body moulded with a circular design below a typical bearded face, covered in mottled brown glaze, 21 cm., 17th C. **£230-£300**   *Bea*

A Bristol delft blue and white barber's bowl, the centre painted with the tools of his trade, with an indentation and 2 pierced holes for hanging, cracked and chipped and with glaze flaking to rim, 25.5 cm. wide, c. 1720. **£900-1,000** *C*

A Bristol delft blue and white deep bowl, the interior with a flower-spray and a band of stylised flowerheads, rim chip and chips to foot, 34 cm. diam., c. 1720. **£600-£700** *C*

A delftware barber's bowl of circular outline, inscribed 'Sir Your Quarter's Up' in blue about painted razors, scissors and comb, the boucheed rim moulded with thumb-piece grip and pierced with suspension holes, Bristol or Lambeth, 25.6 cm., early 1700's. **£3,000-4,000** *SS*

The 'quarter' of the text is, intentionally perhaps, ambivalent: while it may refer to the barber's fee of one farthing (or to the time allowed for a shave) a more gruesome interpretation, suggested by the alternative use of this piece as a bleeding bowl, might be paraphrased 'You are Bled to the Brink'. For a dated piece of similar form bearing painted implements see Garner & Archer English Delftware, pl. 53A.

A rare delftware punchbowl, finely painted in the centre in pale tones of blue with the scene of 'The Taking of Portobello', within a border of floral scrolls, brown-edged rim, the exterior decorated with a 3-part rhyme in shaped panels, probably Liverpool, repaired, 10½ in., c. 1740-45. **£1,600-1,800** *S*

Although Frank Britton illustrates an engraving of 'The Taking of Charges' in English Delftware in the Bristol Collection, p. 160, fig. 16, he notes that no print has yet been recorded which shows all the features of the bombardment of Portobello from contemporary descriptions.

A Liverpool delft polychrome ship bowl, the exterior with trailing flowering branches enriched in yellow, iron-red and green, minor rim chips and flaking to rims, 23.5 cm. diam, c. 1750. **£5,000-£6,000** *C*

The 1st edition of Lloyd's Register in 1764 records a ship called 'The Love' being built in Liverpool in 1748, the owners were Parker & Co. and in 1764 the master was Richard Parker. Joseph Haile, however, is not mentioned.

An English delftware punchbowl of large form, the powder-blue exterior reserved with 3 octagonal panels containing chrysanthemum sprigs between 3 smaller barbed panels of hibiscus, with a brown ended rim, the white interior decorated with an upper and a lower three-lined band, probably Wincanton, foot chip, 32 cm. diam., c. 1740. **£1,700-2,000** *SS*

Though not mentioned in the transcript this bowl was used as an exhibit by the late Louis Lipski in his brief paper to the English Ceramics Circle on Wincanton delftware, see E.C.C. Transactions, Vol. 4, 27/5/1957.

A rare Wedgwood 'marbled' bowl, the brown, ochre, white and pale blue clays wedged and thrown to form well defined striations, the foot rim with a moulded key pattern border, impressed mark, hair cracks, 15 in., early 19th C. **£250-300** *S*

A rare pink lustre Sunderland bowl and cover, 5 in., c. 1835-40. **£365-£385** *EC*

A Bristol delft blue and white colander bowl, the exterior painted with gallants and companions in continuous hilly landscape with sponged trees, minor rim chips, 23 cm. diam., c. 1750. **£750-850** *C*

A Spode pottery pot pourri, cover and inner lid, the ruby ground reserved with colourful birds perched among flowers painted in yellow, green, blue, purple and red, pattern no. 3009 in red, 24.5 cm., early 19th C. **£140-180** *SS*

A Pratt jug of Admiral Nelson/ Captain Berry, 5 in., c. 1790. **£190-£200**　*GCA*

A Prattware Nelson/Captain Berry jug, in yellow, blue, ochre and brown glazes of the typical Pratt palette, 6¼ in., c. 1797. **£150-185** *LR*

A rare creamware jug, depicting battle scene, with figure, possibly George III, with serpent handle, in coloured enamels, 8½ in., c. 1795. **£275-325**　*LR*

A Pratt jug of Admiral Jervis/Royal Family, 5¾ in., c. 1799. **£220-240** *GCA*

A Pratt commemorative jug of Nelson, 6¼ in., c. 1805. **£350-375** *EC*

A brightly coloured pottery commemorative jug of Sir Francis Burdett, 4¾ in., c. 1810. **£185-£200**　*EC*

A Lord Rodney commemorative mug, 5 in., c. 1790. **£350-375**　*EC*

A Sunderland lustre Crimean commemorative jug, printed with French and English soldiers, 8½ in., c. 1855. **£120-160**　*LR*

A creamware freemason's jug, marked John Grundy 1821, with polychrome decoration, 7½ in. **£145-165**　*GCA*

A rare pottery commemorative jug of Princess Charlotte, 6½ in., c. 1815. **£250-275**　*EC*

A creamware cylindrical commemorative mug, transfer printed in black by Morris with an inscribed oval portrait of Earl St. Vincent KB Admiral of the Blue, 15.5 cm. high, c. 1797. **£400-500**　*C*

A set of 4 graduated Sunderland lustre jugs, transfer printed in black with sailing ships, nautical instruments and verses, with loop handles, 1 spout chipped, 9 in.-4¾ in. **£250-300**　*WW*

A Staffordshire church, 11 in., c. 1850. **£90-100** *DL*
This is made more unusual by its large size.

A Victorian Staffordshire church spill vase, 5 in., c. 1840. **£100-120** *GCA*

A Staffordshire church spill vase, 5½ in., c. 1840. **£90-110** *GCA*

An unusual early 19th C. church, 9 in. **£600-700** *JHo*

An unusual ornate Victorian Staffordshire castle spill vase with cherubs, 10¾ in., c. 1840. **£120-£135** *GCA*

A Victorian Staffordshire Warwick Castle spill vase, 8¾ in., c. 1845. **£90-110** *GCA*

An unusual gazebo pastille burner, 3¾ in., c. 1835. **£195-210** *GCA*

An unusual Staffordshire pastille burner, with upturned eaves, 6 in., c. 1845. **£310-330** *DL*

A large Gothic-style gazebo pastille burner, 9 in., c. 1835. **£225-245** *GCA*

A rare Continental pagoda pastille burner, probably Paris, 5½ in., c. 1830. **£225-245** *GCA*

A money box, modelled as a cottage with blue gabled roof above an ochre doorway and windows flanked by a man and woman, the walls modelled with flowering vines, on rectangular sponged base, 5½ in. high, late 19th C. **£110-150** *CSK*

A rare temple-style pastille burner, 3¾ in., c. 1825. **£245-275** *GCA*

A Staffordshire house money box, 5 in., c. 1845. **£60-75** *GCA*

A Staffordshire farmhouse money box, 4¼ in., c. 1845. **£80-95** *GCA*

An unusual Newcastle 'St. Anthony's' cow creamer, 4¾ in., c. 1790. **£435-455** *DL*
Recognised by blue/green underglaze colours round the eyes.

A cow creamer and milkmaid, in grey, ochre and green glazes, 5½ in., c. 1780. **£385-425** *GCA*

A Staffordshire cow creamer, in enamel colours, 5¼ in., c. 1830. **£225-250** *LR*

A Yorkshire-type cow creamer with calf, in brown, yellow and blue mottled glazes, restored cover, 4½ in., c. 1790. **£330-360** *LR*
Perfect £450-525

A rare Yorkshire cow creamer, 4¾ in., c. 1800. **£475-525** *EC*

A Yorkshire cow with attendant and dog, in blue, ochre, beige and black glazes, slight restoration, 5½ in., c. 1785. **£450-500** *LR*
Perfect £550-600

A Staffordshire cow creamer, in ochre, brown and green glazes, cover missing, slight restoration, 5½ in., c. 1790. **£375-425** *LR*

POTTERY: COW CREAMERS

The price of cow creamers depends upon age, type and complexity.
Whieldon cow creamers are probably the most expensive. They are thinly potted and readily damaged and consequently few survive. They are to be distinguished by their rich tortoiseshell lead glaze coloured by the inclusion of different metallic oxides. These early cow creamers have a glassy appearance, the later Staffordshire and North of England products have a more primitive look, the potters relying on sponging simple high fixed oxides for decorative effect. Generally speaking neatness of potting and a harmonious colouring make a piece expensive. Other considerations are the presence of a milkmaid – 'hobbled' legs also add to value.

A Yorkshire cow, with lady and calf, in unusual buff and rust, 5¾ in., early 19th C. **£600-650** *JHo*

A Staffordshire cow creamer, in mainly sponged raspberry and black with green glazed base, 6 in., c. 1790. **£325-375** *LR*

A Staffordshire cow creamer, sponged in ochre and grey-brown, with vertical stripes, replacement lid, 5½ in., c. 1790. **£400-450** *LR*

A Swansea cow creamer, in iron-red with purple lustre patching, 5¾ in., c. 1830. **£200-230** *LR*

A Yorkshire patched cow creamer, restored, 6¼ in., c. 1790. **£375-425** *LR*
Perfect £550-600

A Yorkshire-type cow creamer, in coloured glazes, 5¼ in., c. 1790. **£425-450** *DL*
These are becoming increasingly popular.

A slipware cup, 3½ in., first half 18th C. **£550-600**   *JHo*

A slipcast stirrup cup, almost life size, 5¼ in., early 19th C. **£400-£450**   *JHo*

A Liverpool delft blue and white teabowl and saucer, painted with a house on a rocky wooded island with a sailing boat moored beside, saucer cracked and with glaze flaking, c. 1760. **£800-900**   *C*

A rare and unusual Victorian Staffordshire seated hare, 10 in. wide, c. 1845. **£750-800**   *GCA*

A pair of Wedgwood two-handled cups and saucers, with impressed marks, the matching plate inscribed 'Chrysanthemum No. 5', one cup chipped, 8 in. diam., c. 1820. **£70-100**   *BD*

A Marseilles (Robert) faience cup and saucer, painted en camaieu vert, the rims gilt with foliage and flowerheads, minute rim chips, c. 1760. **£250-300**   *C*

A Ralph Wood pottery ewe, 4 in., c. 1770. **£450-500**   *EC*

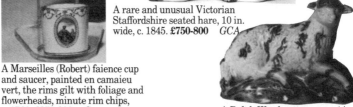

A rare Yorkshire ram, 4 in., c. 1795. **£380-425**   *EC*

A pair of Wedgwood black basaltes 'Water' ewers, after a model by Flaxman, impressed mark and incised 236, 15¾ in., mid 19th C. **£800-900**   *S*

A Bayreuth dated polychrome pear-shaped ewer, with crowned MS mirror monogram in blue, with the date 1737 within a tied floral cartouche, IF mark in sepia, chip to upper rim and foot, 16 cm. high, c. 1737. **£3,000-3,500**   *C*

An Enoch Wood pottery lion, 8¾ in., c. 1810. **£800-850**   *EC*

A small Newcastle pottery sheep, 2¾ in., c. 1800. **£175-200**   *EC*

A pair of Enoch Wood well-modelled figures of lions, facing right and left, on marbled bases modelled with stiff turquoise leaves, outlined in gilt, 9¾ in. high. **£2,200-2,600**   *CSK*

Two Ralph Wood lions, their coats splashed in brown and olive-green, on concave rectangular green washed bases, one with restoration to 2 feet and base, 28 cm. wide, c. 1775. **£1,500-1,800**   *C*

A well-coloured Enoch Wood lion, with paw on globe of the world, 9 in., c. 1800. **£700-800**   *GCA*

A pair of Victorian Staffordshire lion spill vases, 6½ in., c. 1850. **£375-425** *GCA*

A Ralph Wood Jnr. model of a stag at lodge, on black plinth, having green and pink husk border, repair to antlers, 8½ in. wide by 12 in. high. **£1,700-2,000** *A*

A rare pair of Victorian Staffordshire circus ponies, 5½ in., c. 1850. **£275-295** *GCA*

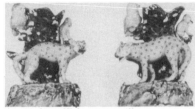

A pair of rare Walton-type spill vases, modelled as leopards standing before trees, a monkey and bird on raised green mound bases modelled with flower sprays, 5½ in. high. **£1,400-1,600** *CSK*

A pair of Staffordshire bocage groups of cows and calves, 6 in., early 19th C. **£400-450** *JHo*

A Staffordshire figure of a deer, with hole in head as spill holder, 6¼ in., c. 1825. **£110-140** *LR*

A pair of Victorian Staffordshire well-modelled spill vases of a stag and doe with young, 11½ in., c. 1850. **£225-245** *GCA*

An early Staffordshire figure of a stag, with mint condition bocage, 6¼ in., c. 1820. **£300-330** *DL*

A Staffordshire figure of a stag, with bocage, 6 in., c. 1825. **£100-£140** *LR*

A pair of Staffordshire peacocks, 4¼ in., c. 1820. **£320-345** *DL*

A pair of Obadiah Sherratt cows, one with serpent, with unusual rainbow bases, with restoration to bocage, 7½ in., c. 1825. **£300-350** *LR*

Perfect **£500-600**

An unusual early Staffordshire figure of a goat, 8½ in., c. 1820. **£440-475** *DL*
Could be a Scottish copy of a Whieldon original.

A pair of rare models of a standing cockerel and hen, brightly coloured on circular coloured bases, 7½ in. high. **£700-800** *CSK*

A Ralph Wood goat, 6½ in., c. 1775-80. **£700-750** *EC*

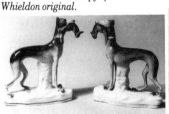

A well-modelled pair of Staffordshire greyhounds, with hares in mouths, 8½ in., c. 1845. **£210-235** *GCA*

A pair of Luneville faience blue glazed recumbent door or stair 'guardian' lions, highlighted in white and magenta, 18½ in. long overall, 14 in. high. **£650-700** *GC*

An Enoch Wood model of a retriever, 3¼ in., c. 1805. **£325-375** *EC*

THE WOOD FAMILY

Ralph Wood senior	1715-72
Ralph Wood junior	1748-95
Aaron Wood **(brother of R. Wood snr.)**	1717-85
Enoch Wood **(son of A. Wood)**	1759-1840

A pair of Staffordshire greyhounds, on blue gilded bases, 7½ in., c. 1855. **£165-185** *GCA*

An early English setter, 5¼ in. wide, c. 1810. **£235-255** *GCA*

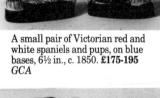

A small pair of Victorian red and white spaniels and pups, on blue bases, 6½ in., c. 1850. **£175-195** *GCA*

A medium-sized pair of Victorian Staffordshire red and white King Charles spaniels, mantel dogs, 8½ in., c. 1845. **£90-110** *GCA*

An early English seated setter, 6¼ in. wide, c. 1810. **£235-255** *GCA*

A pair of Ralph Wood-type tree vase groups with sheep and birds, on green rocky base, each group with one sheep missing, 7½ in. **£280-320** *A*

Left
A pair of Staffordshire porcellaneous spaniels, 5½ in., c. 1840. **£275-300** *DL*

A pair of Victorian Staffordshire black and white mantel dogs, 12 in., c. 1850. **£140-160** *GCA*

A bust of Milton, inscribed Ra Wood 81, 9 in., c. 1785. **£275-325** *LR*

An Enoch Wood bust of Newton, with marbled socle, 9¼ in., c. 1790. **£250-300** *LR*

A Leeds bust, 7 in., c. 1790. **£225-£280** *DL*

This bust is the same size as comparable 'Elements' busts but the turret causes some confusion.

A rare Dutch Delft bust of a Sultan, modelled as a flower-holder, with pierced shoulders, Lambertus van Eenhoorn factory marks in blue, damage to plume, 33.7 cm., c. 1700. **£1,300-1,500** *S*

An Enoch Wood bust of Minerva, in enamel colours with 'marbled' socle, impressed twice on base, 12¼ in., c. 1790. **£300-350** *LR*

A Wedgwood basalt ware bust, of Shakespeare, 13 in., c. 1840. **£250-275** *DL*

A bust of Neptune, by Enoch Wood, in coloured enamels, 11½ in., c. 1800. **£275-325** *LR*

PRICE

Prices vary from auction to auction — from dealer to dealer. The price paid in a dealer's shop will depend on
1) *what he paid for the item*
2) *what he thinks he can get for it*
3) *the extent of his knowledge*
4) *awareness of market trends.*
It is a mistake to think that you will automatically pay more in a specialist dealer's shop. He is more likely to know the 'right' price for a piece. A general dealer may undercharge but he could also overcharge.

A Staffordshire bust of Nelson, 6 in., c. 1810. **£260-285** *DL*

A rare saltglaze figure of a man, wearing a long coat and a grey tricorn, his wig en queue, raised on a mound base, chips to hat, 3¾ in., second quarter 18th C. **£2,200-£2,400** *S*

A Wedgwood basalt ware bust, of Wesley, 8½ in., c. 1840. **£210-235** *DL*

An early Staffordshire bust of Milton, in enamel colours, 9 in., c. 1800. **£240-265** *DL*

A Wedgwood basalt ware bust, of Robert Burns, 8¼ in., c. 1860. **£150-£175** *DL*

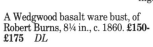

A Wedgwood bronzed black basalt bust, of Minerva, on socle, 19 in. high. **£150-200** *GSP*

A Staffordshire bust, possibly William Cobbett, in enamel colours, 8 in., c. 1820. **£120-180** LR

A Staffordshire figure of the Virgin Mary, with incised brown hair and with a crown and veil and wearing a low-cut ribbed and striped dress and flowing yellow robe, 24 cm. high, c. 1790. **£400-500** C

A fine quality late 18th C. figure of 'Flora', in Pratt colours, 11 in. **£400-450** JHo

A rare Astbury-Whieldon figure of a bagpiper, wearing a green-glazed jacket, his hair tied en queue and glazed in manganese brown, his eyes picked out in brown slip, the mound base and tree stump patched in green, grey-blue and yellow-brown, repaired, some damage, 6 in., c. 1740-45. **£1,500-£1,700** S

A late 18th C. figure from the Four Seasons, 7¾ in. **£90-100** JHo

An unusual Prattware candlestick figure, of a Turk, in blue, ochre, black glazes, 9¾ in., c. 1800-1810. **£100-150** LR

A late 18th C. figure of 'Venus', 8 in. **£90-100** JHo

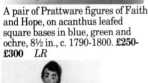

A Prattware figure of Winter, 8½ in., c. 1790. **£125-165** LR

A pair of Prattware figures of Faith and Hope, on acanthus leafed square bases in blue, green and ochre, 8½ in., c. 1790-1800. **£250-£300** LR

Two figures from the Four Seasons: (l.) Autumn by Wood and Caldwell, 9 in., c. 1815. **£250-300** (r.) Winter by Enoch Wood, 8½ in., c. 1800. **£400-450** LR

A rare Prattware version of Ralph Wood's Roman Charity, in translucent glazes, 8¼ in., c. 1790. **£450-500** LR

Only group which Wood had 4 figures on one piece.

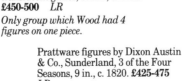

A Prattware figure of Autumn, in translucent glazes, 7¼ in., c. 1790-1800. **£125-150** LR

Prattware figures by Dixon Austin & Co., Sunderland, 3 of the Four Seasons, 9 in., c. 1820. **£425-475** LR

A Pratt figure of a musician, in Pratt colours, 9½ in., late 18th C. **£250-280** *JHo*

A Leeds-type coloured glaze figure of the Orator, 9½ in., c. 1790. **£360-£390** *DL*

These figures are sometimes known as Ralph Wood type.

An early Staffordshire figure of a sailor, 7¾ in., c. 1790. **£400-450** *DL*

An early Staffordshire Dandies group, 8½ in., c. 1800. **£430-450** *DL*

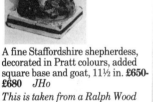

A fine Staffordshire shepherdess, decorated in Pratt colours, added square base and goat, 11½ in. **£650-£680** *JHo*

This is taken from a Ralph Wood model.

A pair of Neale-type figures of musicians, in enamel colours, 6 in., c. 1790. **£550-595** *DL*

A Staffordshire figure of John Liston as Paul Pry, 5½ in., c. 1825. **£150-200** *LR*

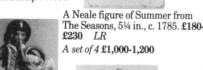

A Neale figure of Summer from The Seasons, 5¼ in., c. 1785. **£180-£230** *LR*

A set of 4 **£1,000-1,200**

A Staffordshire musicians group, 7 in., c. 1810. **£320-375** *EC*

A Yorkshire figure of the Lost Sheep, ochre, blue and green glazes, 9 in., c. 1790. **£250-300** *LR*

A Neale pottery figure of 'Hygieia', 7¾ in., c. 1795. **£110-125** *EC*

A Yorkshire figure of a soldier, holding a sabre, in brown plumed helmet, blue jacket, yellow breeches and brown boots, standing before a green tree stump on a tapering circular base, moulded with key-pattern, repair to sabre and base, 22 cm. high, c. 1800. **£550-650** *C*

A rare figure of The Shipwrecked Sailor, in Yorkshire colouring, 5 in., c. 1820. **£150-180** *LR*

An early Staffordshire Neale-type hairdressing group, in enamel colours, 6½ in., c. 1790. **£350-375** *DL*

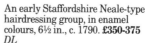

A Herculaneum figure, reputed to be a Liverpool volunteer, sword missing, 8¼ in., c. 1800. **£500-£600** *JHo*

A Wedgwood figure known as Simon, impressed Wedgwood, 9¾ in., c. 1800. **£275-295** *DL*

Wedgwood commissioned a large number of wares from small factories, and if their work came up to his standard it was impressed with his mark.

An unusual figure of 'St. Luke', 7¼ in., c. 1810. **£175-200** *EC*

A small Staffordshire figure of a sailor, in enamel colours, 5¾ in., c. 1800. **£160-175** *DL*

A pottery figure of Cupid, disguised as a fruit seller, painted by Absolom of Yarmouth, 7 in., c. 1805. **£185-210** *EC*

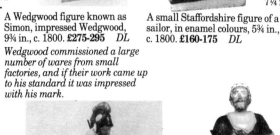

A Ralph Wood figure of Apollo, with Ralph Wood impressed numeral '41', 8¾ in., c. 1780. **£450-490** *DL*

A Ralph Wood group of St. George and the dragon, of conventional type, astride a streaked brown horse, St. George wearing a pale yellow tunic and blue spotted shawl, St. George's arms and legs restored and horse's tail, minor chips to base, 27 cm. high, c. 1775. **£850-950** *C*

A Ralph Wood Jnr. figure of Jupiter, underglaze and enamel colours, 11 in., c. 1795. **£225-275** *LR*

A pair of Ralph Wood the younger figures, 'Elijah' and the 'Widow of Sarepta', in enamel colours, 11 in., c. 1790. **£400-440** *DL*

A Staffordshire Parson and Clerk group by Enoch Wood, in enamel colours, 9½ in., c. 1800. **£275-325** *LR*

A 'St. George and the Dragon' group by Enoch Wood, in coloured enamels, some restoration, 13¾ in., c. 1790-1800. **£400-450** *LR*

This group by Ralph Wood in translucent glazes is not as rare as this present example.

A Ralph Wood Jnr. group, 'Rural Pastime', in coloured enamels, some restoration, 7¾ in., c. 1785-90. **£325-400** *LR*

A Wood and Caldwell figure of Britannia, in enamels with silver lustre helmet, shield and breastplate, impressed mark, Burslem in copperplate underneath, trident missing, 9½ in., c. 1810. **£300-350** *LR*

A Staffordshire group of Vicar and Moses, in enamel colours, slight restoration, 9 in., c. 1840. **£150-£200** *LR*

From the Ralph Wood original. Ralph Wood version in running glazes **£600-800**

An Enoch Wood group, Hercules with the Cretan bull, in enamel colours, 5½ in., c. 1800. **£300-350** *LR*

An Obadiah Sherratt group, The Flight into Egypt, 7¾ in., c. 1825. **£650-700**   *EC*

A Staffordshire figure of 'Christs Agony' by Obadiah Sherratt, 9¼ in., c. 1830. **£475-550**   *LR*

An Enoch Wood figure group of 'Scuffle', 6¾ in., c. 1805. **£350-385** *EC*

POINTERS TO REPRODUCTIONS

The Marriage Act group has been copied quite extensively. If the man in the bower group faces to the left (i.e. inwards), it tends to suggest a Kent and Parr reproduction. If he is looking to the right (i.e. outwards), it is more likely to be an Obadiah Sherratt group.

Vermicular bases also point to an Obadiah Sherratt group but these have been copied.

A pair of Staffordshire saints, 'S. John' and 'S. Mark', by Obadiah Sherratt, 8½ in., c. 1825. **£300-350** *LR*

An Enoch Wood figure of The Woman at the Village Pump, 6¼ in., c. 1820. **£300-350**   *LR*

An Enoch Wood figure of Jupiter, 11 in., c. 1805. **£350-400**   *EC*

A pair of Staffordshire figures of 'Elijah &' 'Widow', with lustre, by Obadiah Sherratt, 11½ in., c. 1830. **£400-450** *LR*

An early Staffordshire musician group, 7½ in., c. 1810. **£345-365** *DL*

101

A pair of Walton musicians, marked c. 1815, 6¼ in., **£375-400** *DL*

An Obadiah Sherratt bull-baiting group, of conventional type, the roped bull with ochre and black markings and grey hoofs and horns, being savaged by a yellow dog and tossing a brown dog over his shoulder, a man standing at the side in sponged green jacket and blue trousers, minor damages to dogs, man's hat and 3 feet at base, 35 cm. wide, c. 1835. **£2,000-£2,200**   *C*

An Obadiah Sherratt group, The Christening, with castle spill vases and bocage to either side, slight faults, 7 in. **£2,000-2,200**   *A*

An Obadiah Sherratt highly coloured figure of Venus, with typical bracket feet, 9¾ in., c. 1825. **£390-425**   *DL*

An Obadiah Sherratt anvil marriage group, on oblong base with shaped feet, castle spill vases and bocage to either side, slight faults, 7 in. **£2,000-2,200**   *A*

An Obadiah Sherratt performing bear group, decorated in bright enamel colours, with bocage background and with monkey figure to centre, restored, 8 in. high. **£1,900-2,200**   *A*

A Walton-type bocage tithe group, 7¼ in., c. 1815. **£450-480**   *DL*
Watch cheap prices for bocage groups – bocage often totally restored.

OBADIAH SHERRATT
(1755-1845)

- **Sherratt worked at Hot Lane, Burslem from c.1815-28 and then moved to Waterloo Road**
- **Sherratt specialised in 'social comment' groups**
- **some Derby copies were tried at the factory but they tend to be crude and not of high value**
- **highly collected are the 'Teetotal' groups (the word teetotal was not coined until 1833)**
- **these groups are very detailed and hence some damage and restoration is acceptable**
- **it used to be thought that the footed groups were early – but the teetotal groups are usually footed and they are certainly late**
- **Sherratt's 'bull baiting' and 'Red Barn Murder' groups have great appeal**
- **after Sherratt's death the factory was continued by his wife and son Hamlet until the late 1850's**
- **many models were produced at this time using old moulds – these tend not to have the same detail and can have less vivid colours**

A Walton figure of Spring, marked, 6 in., c. 1825. **£110-150**   *LR*
Beware of figures with Walton mark but without serifs – these are late reproductions.

A Walton group, 'Return from Egypt', impressed WALTON on a scroll, restoration, minor chips, 7½ in., c. 1820. **£400-500**   *S*

An Obadiah Sherratt tithe pig group, 5¾ in., c. 1820. **£575-625** *GCA*

A Salt figure of a female archer, 8 in., c. 1810. **£275-325** *EC*

A Walton-type performing bear group, 7 by 7 in. **£1,200-1,400** *A*

A Staffordshire musicians group, 7¼ in., c. 1810. **£300-350** *EC*

JOHN WALTON

- **John Walton worked from c. 1805-1850**
- **is known mainly for sentimental figures with bocage backgrounds**
- **bocage tended to support the figures in the kiln**
- **uses some excellent vivid colours**
- **work is often marked with an impressed name on a scroll at the rear**
- **any animal groups with amusing lions are very desirable**

A Staffordshire pottery 'Gretna Green' group, painted in bright enamel colours, some restoration, 20.5 cm. **£300-350** *Bea*

A Staffordshire pottery figure of Charity, 7½ in., c. 1815. **£285-325** *EC*

A Staffordshire group, possibly by Tittensor, 4¾ in., c. 1800. **£225-275** *JHo*

A pair of Walton marked groups of the 'Flight into Egypt' and 'Return from Egypt', on mound bases with bocage supports, some restoration, 8 in. **£700-800** *A*

A Staffordshire group of rural musicians, with 6 sheep and a swan, slight damage, 8 in., c. 1815. **£250-300** *LR*
Perfect £350-375
The price is helped by the large number of animals for one group.

A rare Staffordshire group 'Jolly Traveller', in coloured enamels, 7 in., c. 1825-30. **£400-450** *LR*

A bocage group of 'Tenderness', 8 in., early 19th C. **£325-375** *JHo*

A pair of Staffordshire musician figures, with wreath bocages, on open scrollwork bases, 7½ in., c. 1820. **£400-450** *LR*

A Staffordshire pottery gardeners group spill vase, 7¼ in., c. 1810. **£340-385**   *EC*

A pair of Staffordshire early 19th C. musicians, in good condition, 6 in. **£300-350**   *JHo*
These figures are at a premium as so many 19th C. bocage group figures are damaged.

A Staffordshire tithe pig/spill group, 8½ in., c. 1810. **£375-450**   *LR*

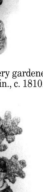

A rare Staffordshire group of a hairdresser, naively entitled 'Barber & Mate', decorated in coloured enamels in al fresco setting, restored, 9¾ in., c. 1810. **£425-475**   *LR*

A Staffordshire pottery tithe pig group, 7 in., c. 1810. **£400-435**   *EC*

A pair of Staffordshire spill vases, in the form of rural musicians, with animals, on rocky bases, 6 in., c. 1810. **£250-300**   *LR*

An unrecorded figure of Victoria, the shaped gilt scroll moulded base entitled 'England' in gilt capitals, 11¼ in. high. **£120-160**   *CSK*

A Victorian Staffordshire figure pair of Victoria and Albert, with enamel blue, 8¾ in., c. 1850. **£175-£195**   *DL*

A pair of Victorian Staffordshire figures 'Going to Market' and 'Returning Home', 9 in., c. 1845. **£185-225**   *GCA*

All numbers refer to the coding system used in P. D. Gordon Pugh's book 'Staffordshire Portrait Figures of the Victorian Era'.

An early pair of Victorian Staffordshire equestrian figures of Victoria and Albert, with restoration, 8½ in., c. 1840. (A.38/104, 105). **£250-275**   *DL*

A well-coloured group of the Prince of Wales and the Princess Royal asleep, watched over by a Guardian Angel, outlined in gilt on oval gilt-lined base, 9 in. high (A.55/164). **£60-80**   *CSK*

A rare figure of Victoria standing crowned, holding the Princess Royal in her arms, on oval gilt lined base, 7½ in. high (A.14/27). **£130-150**   *CSK*

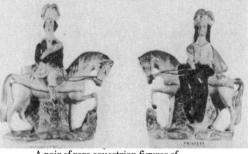

A pair of rare equestrian figures of the Prince of Wales and the Princess Royal, sitting on dun-coloured horses, 10¾ in. high (A.65/198, 199). **£220-260** *CSK*

A rare candlestick group of Victoria and Albert, surmounted by a vase above the Prince of Wales in a rowing boat on shaped gilt-lined base, 9¾ in. high (A.55/165). **£85-105** *CSK*

A Victorian Staffordshire vase group entitled 'King Charles & Cromwell', one hand missing, 14½ in. (A.97/260). **£60-80** *WHL*

A pair of rare white and gilt equestrian figures of Prince Frederick William and the Princess Royal, the oval bases named in gilt capitals, 13¾ in. high (A.68/208, 209). **£350-400** *CSK*

A Staffordshire figure of 'Wellington', 11 in. (B.2/17). **£80-£100** *WHB*

A Staffordshire portrait figure of the Duke of Wellington, wearing pink waistcoat and black jacket, head repaired, 12½ in. (B.2). **£65-85** *WW*

A good group depicting the Act of Union between England and Ireland, modelled with an angel above 2 national figures, slight damage, 12¼ in., 1882 (B.16/56). **£40-60** *WHL*

This figure forms the centrepiece to a pair Gladstone and Parnell. It was issued to commemorate the signing of the Kilmainham Peace Treaty.

Left
A rare 18th C. Wedgwood Triton candlestick, the solid white jasper figure with solid blue cornucopia, cape and rock work bases, stamped Wedgwood twice, chip to sconce, 11¼ in. **£600-650** *DWB*

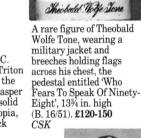

A rare figure of Theobald Wolfe Tone, wearing a military jacket and breeches holding flags across his chest, the pedestal entitled 'Who Fears To Speak Of Ninety-Eight', 13¾ in. high (B.16/51). **£120-150** *CSK*

A pair of equestrian figures of Marshal Arnaud and Lord Raglan on dun-coloured horses, on oval gilt-lined bases named in black capitals, 10¼ in. high (C.64/164, 165). **£400-500** *CSK*

A pair of equestrian figures of Omar Pasha and Abd-ul-Medjid, on dun-coloured horses, both wearing iron-red fez and blue coats, the oval gilt-lined bases named in black capitals, 10½ in. high (C.64/166, 167). **£350-400** *CSK*

A rare figure of Napoleon standing in black cocked hat and full military uniform, 21¼ in. high (similar to C.23A/61A). **£350-400** *CSK*

A well-modelled group of Napoleon and Albert, the rectangular base name in puce capitals, 14 in. high (C.77/225). **£400-450** *CSK*

A portrait figure of Hamlet, wearing a black cape and holding the skull of Yorick, the base inscribed 'Alas Poor Yorick', head repaired, 10¾ in. (E.13/32). **£65-75** *WW*

A very rare figure of Lady Isabelle Burton, on a camel on shaped gilt-lined base, 8¾ in. high (C. 95/279). **£160-200** *CSK*

A Victorian Staffordshire figure of 'Britain's Glory', 10¾ in., c. 1850 (C.69/186). **£140-150** *DL*

A rare white and gilt group of an English and French officer standing, the oval gilt-lined base entitled England and France in gilt capitals, 12 in. high (C.83A/239). **£300-350** *CSK*

A pair of Staffordshire equestrian portrait figures of Napier and Garibaldi, wearing red shirts, titled in black capitals, head repaired, cracked, 9¼ in. high (C.104/283, 282). **£110-150** *WW*

A pair of rare equestrian figures of King William I of Prussia and Prince Frederick William, on grey horses, the oval bases named in gilt script, 14½ in. high (C.108/310, 311). **£350-400** *CSK*

A very rare group of Mr. Van Amburgh, the lion tamer, dressed in theatrical Roman costume, standing between a lion and lioness and patting their heads, a leopard clambering to peer over his shoulder and a lamb standing at his feet, titled in gilt script, minor chip, 5¾ in., c. 1840 (E.200). **£3,500-4,500** *S*

This group differs from other similar examples in that it has the figure of a lamb rather than a lion-cub resting at the tamer's feet. It is reported that a lamb featured in the act, had been trained to lie down with a lion.

A Staffordshire portrait bust of General Booth, in underglaze blue and iron-red, small chip to peak of cap, 13 in., c. 1900 (D.55). **£400-600** *S*

A rare group of Mlle Ella, standing on top of an iron-red stool wearing a plumed hat and blue bodice, flanked by 2 dancers, on green and yellow marbled stepped base, 10 in. high (E.91/180). **£95-115** *CSK*

A Victorian Staffordshire cottage 'Palmer's House', 8 in., c. 1856 (G.18B/43). **£350-390** *DL*

A Victorian Staffordshire cottage, 'Potash Farm', 5½ in. (G.20/44). **£140-160** *DL*

A Victorian Staffordshire 'Stanfield Hall, 5½ in., c. 1849 (G.24/46a). **£140-160** *DL*

A rare Staffordshire portrait figure of William Huntington, picked out in colours on a shaped square base, chair chipped, slight flaking, 8½ in. (21.5 cm.), 1850-60 (D.24A/50). **£250-300** *SC*

A rare figure of a cricketer standing in iron-red cap, on oval gilt-lined base (possibly George Parr) 13¾ in. high (F.7/13). **£300-£350** *CSK*

A Staffordshire portrait figure of Emily Sandford, wearing a blue bodice and green skirt, standing by a pedestal and holding a manuscript, titled in gilt script, 9½ in., c. 1849 (G.23/47). **£400-500** *S*

Emily Sandford was the mistress of the murderer James Rush who, in 1849, was convicted of the murder of Isaac Jeremy at Stanfield Hall. He was hanged at Norwich Castle on 21st April that year.

A rare pair of Staffordshire portrait figures of F. G. Manning and Maria Manning, each entitled in gilt script, 9¾ and 9¼ in., c. 1849 (G.40/41). **£900-1,000** *S*

Frederick George Manning and his wife Maria were executed in November 1849 for the murder of Patrick O'Connor, Maria's former lover. Having been invited to supper at their Bermondsey house, O'Connor was killed and buried under the kitchen floor.

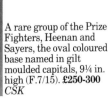

A Staffordshire figure of the poetess Eliza Cook, painted in bright enamel colours, inscribed on the base in gold, 26 cm. (H.10/36). **£220-280** *Bea*

A rare group of the Prize Fighters, Heenan and Sayers, the oval coloured base named in gilt moulded capitals, 9¼ in. high (F.7/15). **£250-300** *CSK*

STAFFORDSHIRE PORTRAIT FIGURES

'Prince of Wales & the Princess Royal', 7¾ in.	(A47/143)	£300-400
Princess Royal standing, 6¼ in.	(A47/135)	£60-90
'Princess' Royal in pony cart in colours, 8 in.	(A51/148)	£400-500
Victoria & Prince of Wales, Albert & Princess Royal, 9½ in.	(A56/172/173)	£350-400
Prince of Wales standing, 6 in.	(A58/180)	£30-40
'Prince of Wales' standing, 14½ in.	(A60/186)	£120-160
'Prince of Wales' seated in kilt, 15 in.	(A60/187)	£80-120
Pair Equestrian 'Prince' & 'Princess of Wales', 11 in.	(A65/200,201)	£150-200
Equestrian 'Princess of Wales', 13½ in.	(A68/213)	£80-120
Equestrian 'Prince Frederick William' & 'Princess Royal'	(A68/210,211)	£250-300
Princess Alice & Prince Louis of Hesse, 8 in.	(A69/216)	£80-120
'Prince & Princess of Wales', 10¼ in.	(A72/219)	£130-180
Princess Louise with Marquis of Lorne, 7¾ in.	(c.f.A74/223)	£50-60
'Prince of Wales' standing, 9¼ in.	(A76/226)	£65-75
'Duchess of Edinburgh', 17½ in. and Duke of Edinburgh, 16½ in.	(A79/231) (A81/236)	£90-130
'Duke of Clarence' and 'Princess May', 15¾ in.	(A82/237,238)	£180-220
'Edward VII' and 'Alexandra', 14¼ in.	(A85/244/245)	£120-160
'Sir Robert Peel' standing, 7½ in.	(B1/1)	£280-350
'Richard Cobden', 7½ in.	(B1/6)	£300-400
'Lord Shaftesbury', 7¼ in.	(B1/7)	£180-250
Wellington seated, 11½ in.	(B4/25)	£60-90
'Beaconsfield', 12 in.	(B13/40)	£120-160
'Gladstone', 11 in.	(B14/46)	£120-160
Thomas Sexton, 15 in.	(B17A/58)	£120-160
'Uncle Tom & Eva', 8¾ in.	(B26/76)	£80-100
A Pair 'Uncle Tom' & 'Aunt Chloe', 8¾ in.	(B26/81,82)	£250-300
'Uncle Tom's Cabin' A Group of Tom & Eva, 9 in.	(B29/88)	£140-180
Equestrian 'Duke of Cambridge'	(B59/155)	£40-80
Napoleon, 8 in.	(C11/19)	£45-65
Nelson, 7½ in.	(c.f.C11/22)	£120-160
'Death of Nelson', 8¾ in.	(C11/21)	£90-140
'Death of Nelson'	(C12/33)	£80-120
Napoleon, 9 in.	(C12/39)	£70-90
Equestrian Napoleon in colours, 5½ in.	(C14A/42A)	£60-80
Napoleon on Horseback, gilt on white, 8¼ in.	(C17/51)	£70-90
Napoleon in colours, 7 in.	(C17/54)	£80-100
Equestrian 'Abd-ul Mehjid' in colours, 7½ in.	(C31/73)	£120-140
Abd-ul-Medjid, Victoria & Napoleon III, a group entitled 'Turkey England France'	(C32/75)	£140-180
Eugenie & the Prince Imperial, 7¾ in.	(C34/79)	£50-80
Field Marshal 'Lord Raglan', 15¼ in.	(C38/153)	£180-220
Princess Eugenie 'Empress of France' & the Prince Imperial, 7¾ in.	(C40/100)	£350-400
'Admiral Dundas' standing, 15½ in.	(C41/103)	£200-250
'Sir Charles Napier', 16 in.	(C42/102)	£180-250
'Sir Charles Napier' standing named in yellow, 16 in.	(c.f.C42/104)	£100-140
Florence Nightingale, 5¼ in.	(C55/142A)	£40-60
'Duke' and 'Duchess of Cambridge' equestrian, 14 in.	(C59/157,158)	£140-180
'Omar Pasha' and 'Marshall Arnaud' on horseback	(C64/166,164)	£200-250
'Omar Pasha' on horseback in colours, 10¾ in.	(C65/166A)	£100-150
'Highland Jessie' and Wounded Soldier, 14 in.	(C89/265)	£150-180
'Volunteer Rifles' 2 elderly soldiers, 11¾ in.	(C93/276)	£280-340
British Lion seated on top of Napoleon III, 9½ in.	(C93/277)	£120-160
'Garibaldi' beside his horse, 14¾ in.	(C97/282)	£350-450
Garibaldi, 10¼ in.	(C98/284)	£80-120
Equestrian Wolseley and 'Connaught', 14 in.	(C115/328, 329)	£90-140
'Kitchener', 13¾ in., 'Gordon', 14 in. and 'Gordon', 17 in.	(C119/335,337, 339)	£300-350
'Baden-Powell', 16½ in.	(C133/365)	£80-120
'Moody' and 'Sankey', 12¼ in.	(c.f.D4/9,10)	£100-150
Rev. Charles 'Spurgeon', 12½ in.	(D22/44)	£80-120
J. Bryon standing with bible, 10¾ in.	(D23/46)	£140-180
Jenny Marston as Perdita & Frederick Robinson as Florizel in Winters Tale, 12 in.	(E1A/2)	£100-120
Charlotte Cushman as Romeo and Susan Cushman as Juliet, 10¾ in.	(E1A/1)	£250-300
Kemble as Hamlet and Mrs. Siddons as Lady Macbeth, 8½ in.	(E7/19)	£60-90
Falstaff and a Soldier drinking, 6 in.	(E10/27)	£90-120
Arbour Group possible Lorenzo & Jessica, 10 in.	(E13/36)	£70-90
David Garrick as Richard III, 7 in.	(E13/37)	£50-70
Harwood as Selim and Rosa Henry as Zuleika, 10¾ in.	(E28/61)	£120-180
Thomas Rice as Jim Crow in colours, 6 in.	(E37/73)	£300-380
Charles Sherwood Stratton as Tom Thumb, 5½ in.	(E50/87)	£250-300
Jules Perrot as Diavolina in colours, 11 in.	(E51/89)	£300-400
An actor in colours, 6½ in.	(E68/129)	£350-400
Jules Perrot as Albrecht, standing, 6½ in.	(E68/132)	£60-90
Dancing Jules Perrot and Carlotta Grisi, 9¼ in.	(E68/132,133)	£150-200
Mr. Hemming as Prince Almansor with castle and elephant, 6½ in.	(E80/156)	£200-250
Androcles seated with the lion, 8¼ in.	(E100/197)	£80-120
Harlequin, 7¼ in.	(E126/248)	£120-180
Conrad, 8½ in.	(E139/287)	£80-120
Louisa Woolford, tightrope walker, 12¼ in.	(E146/305)	£450-550
Equestrian 'Dick Turpin' and 'Tom King', 10 in.	(G3/5,6)	£90-130
Equestrian 'Dick Turpin' and 'Tom King', 11¾ in.	(G4/15,16)	£200-250
'Jemmy Wood' standing, 11 in.	(G16/32)	£80-100
'Jemmy Wood' standing, 7½ in.	(G16/33)	£100-150
'Stanfield Hall', 8½ in.	(G20/46)	£200-250
'Potash Farm', 6 in.	(G23/44A)	£60-90
'Potash Farm' mistitled Stanfield Hall, 5½ in.	(G23/44B)	£100-150
Thomas Smith and William Collier, an Arbour Group, 13½ in.	(G27/54)	£120-180
'Shakespeare', 14 in.	(H2/3)	£140-180
Milton Shakespeare & clock, 9¼ in.	(H5/15)	£140-180
Pair 'Milton' and 'Shakespeare' in white & gilt	(H5/7,8)	£100-120
Lord 'Byron' seated, 7½ in.	(H7/17)	£120-160
Sir Walter Scott and his dog Maida	(H18/57)	£300-350
Group 'Mr. & Mrs. Caudle', 6¼ in.	(H24/73)	£60-80
'Sancho Panza' on Donkey, 8 in.	(H26/76)	£45-65
'Edward Morgan' standing by table and jug, 11¼ in.	(I2/2)	£150-200
William 'Wallace' and 'Bruce', 15½ in.	(I6/12/13)	£140-180
'Grace Darling' and 'Her Father', 7¼ in.	(I18/39)	£200-250

A Castelli small plate, painted in the Grue workshop, minor rim glaze chips, 17.5 cm. diam., first quarter of the 18th C. **£800-900** *C*

A Deruta polychrome circular portrait charger, the ribbon scroll inscribed 'Lorenza. Bella' within an a quartieri border of scale pattern and symmetrical foliage divided by navettes, repaired, 36.5 cm. diam., c. 1540. **£1,000-1,200** *C*

A Faenza dish, decorated in the centre with a portrait of an elderly man wearing blue drapery on a yellow ground, chip and slight restoration on rim, crack, 24.5 cm., second quarter of 16th C. **£7,000-£8,000** *S*

A Gubbio dish, decorated in the centre in gold and red lustre and blue, rim damaged, 20.5 cm., second quarter 16th C. **£3,000-£4,000** *S*

A Deruta a quartieri conical dish with raised central boss, decorated in blue, green and gold and copper lustre, the rim extensively chipped and worn, restoration to glaze at centre, 23 cm. diam., c. 1525. **£900-£1,200** *C*

A Faenza a quartieri crespina, with raised centre, with ochre and green ground, on a blue ground reserved with scrolling foliage in yellow and ochre, with waved blue rim, slight chips, 26.5 cm. diam., c. 1540. **£1,700-2,000** *C*

A Faenza ('Casa Pirota') tondino, decorated with a figure of a saint, possibly St. Apollonia, in blue and ochre on a yellow ground, on a berettino ground, the wide rim with palmettes, fish and scrolls in white and blue on a dark blue ground, minor rim chips, 24.3 cm., second quarter 16th C. **£7,000-£8,000** *S*

An important Gubbio roundel, probably from the workshop of Maestro Giorgio Andreoli, decorated in gold and red lustre, green and shades of blue, the reverse with scrolls in gold lustre, pierced for suspension, minor rim chips, 22 cm., c. 1515. **£4,000-5,000** *S*

The arms are possibly those of a cardinal created during the pontificate of Julius II (1503-13) or related in some way to the della Rovere family.

A Deruta dish decorated in blue, yellow, green and ochre with St. Francis kneeling below a church on a rocky mountain receiving the Stigmata, minor rim chips, 40 cm., c. 1530-40. **£5,500-6,000** *S*

A Faenza portrait dish painted in yellow, ochre, manganese, turquoise and blue with a girl in profile to the left, her hair braided and tied with a ribbon, with striped and brocaded sleeves and herringbone bodice, C mark, 28.5 cm. diam., c. 1500. **£4,000-£4,500** *C*

A Gubbio lustre dish, the recessed centre with St. Francis holding a cross in blue and olive green, reserved on a gold and lustre ground, the deep blue border reserved in gold and ruby lustre with lyre-pattern and formal scrolling foliage, Z mark in ruby lustre, broken in 4 pieces and riveted, 26 cm. diam., c. 1525. **£3,000-4,000** *C*

An Urbina Istoriato tazza, painted with the Finding of Moses, slight frits to rim, 25.5 cm. diam., c. 1540. **£2,500-3,000**   *C*

A Holics shaped oval table plateau, manganese H. mark, chip to foot, 51 cm. wide, c. 1755. **£600-700**   *C*

A Ludwigsburg two-handled shaped oval tray, the rococo-scroll handles edged in colours, blue interlaced C's and a Z mark, minor chips to handles, 37 cm. wide, c. 1765. **£1,400-1,600**   *C*

A North German dish, painted with a yellow bird perched on a branch of flowering peony and lesser flowers and with an insect in a further flower-spray above, probably Hannoversch-Munden, minor rim chips, 37 cm. diam., c. 1760. **£1,300-1,400**   *C*

A Rouen shaped circular plate, painted in a 'famille verte' palette with a peacock perched on a flowering plant, minor rim chips, 25 cm. diam., c. 1740. **£1,100-1,500** *C*

An Istoriato plate, painted with Leda and the Swan, in an extensive river landscape with Zeus appearing in a cloudburst clutching a thunderbolt, minor rim chips, inscribed on the reverse in manganese, C. in a shaped square, 23 cm. diam., 16th C. **£1,000-1,200**   *C*

An Hispano Moresque charger with central boss, lightly moulded with scalloped panel, picked out in copper lustre and cobalt blue, pierced for suspension, slight chips, 16¼ in. (41 cm.), 16th C. **£500-600** *SC*

A Venice 'Istoriato' dish, decorated with the creation of Eve, she stands beside God the Father who points to the sleeping Adam, rim damaged, 35.5 cm., c. 1570, later gilt-wood frame. **£1,800-2,200**   *S*

A Netherlandish maiolica dish, painted in green-yellow, blue and ochre with a concentric design and with blue-dash rim, the reverse covered in a honey-coloured glaze, probably Antwerp, rim chips, 24.5 cm. diam., 16th C. **£2,600-£3,000**   *C*

A Proskau shaped oblong-octagonal dish, the centre with sponged blue and puce, the corners painted with puce and yellow shells, with brown rim, blue P mark, 19.5 cm. wide, c. 1770. **£500-600**   *C*

A Palissy-type dish on a short foot, the bowl pierced and moulded with masks and foliage, all picked out in green, blue and manganese glazes, probably Saintonge, cracked, 20 cm., late 16th/early 17th C. **£700-800**   *S*

Miller's is a price GUIDE Not a price LIST

The price ranges given reflect the average price a purchaser should pay for similar items. Condition, rarity of design or pattern, size, colour, pedigree, restoration and many other factors must be taken into account when assessing values.

A Winterthur armorial plate decorated in green, blue, yellow and manganese with, around the rim, a bunch of grapes, a pomegranate (?), a pear and a plum, cracked, 32.5 cm., 1681. **£2,300-2,500** *S*

A combed slipware dish, 13 in., c. 1800. **£500-550** *JHo*

A Bristol delftware 'Adam and Eve' charger, with blue-dashed rim enclosing the 2 manganese figures before a manganese Tree-of-Life, bearing yellow fruit and green leaves, a blue and yellow snake encoiling the trunk, riveted, 33.5 cm., late 17th C. **£600-800** *SS*

A Bristol delft inscribed and dated grace plate, the powdered manganese ground reserved with a central hexagonal cartouche inscribed in blue 2/Give thanks/before thou eat/(1746), minor glaze flaking to rim, 17.5 cm. diam., c. 1746. **£1,800-2,000** *C*

A Wedgwood creamware trial dessert plate for The Catherine the Great Service, the centre painted in soft colours with Westcowes Castle, in the Isle of Wight, within a border of radiating brown false gadroons and dot-pattern to the well, the shaped border with trailing berried bryony and a brown line rim, two minute rim chips at 2 and 6 o'clock, 22.5 cm. diam., c. 1773. **£9,000-10,000** *C*

The completed service was made to the order of Catherine the Great of Russia between 1773-74, intended for the Palace of Chesman at La Grenouillière, each piece bearing the crest of a green frog. The service comprised 952 pieces, according to Bentley who catalogued the service in June 1774, for its exhibition prior to its delivery to Russia. Each piece was painted at the Chelsea enamelling works with a different named view, but since the cost of production proved to be so high, it was decided to execute the service in purple monochrome. The trial plates, to which this example belongs, were painted in polychrome without the frog crest.

An 'Adam and Eve' charger, depicting the 2 figures flanking a fruiting 'sponged' tree, a serpent coiled around the trunk, painted in blue, copper-green, yellow and ochre, 'blue-dash' rim, probably Bristol, glaze flaking on rim and reverse, 12 in., early 18th C. **£1,000-1,300** *S*

A Bristol delft blue and white charger, freely painted in washed blues with a galleon at full sail, 33.5 cm. diam., c. 1700. **£2,300-2,500** *C*

A Strasbourg plate, painted with carefully drawn flowers in bright colours within gilt dentil rim, blue PH monogram mark of Paul Hannong, two minute rim chips, 28 cm. diam., c. 1750. **£1,400-1,800** *C*

A Bristol delft blue-dash Royalist portrait charger, showing George I with a yellow cloak, flanked by blue sponged trees and the initials GR, on a green grassy mound, within a blue-dash rim, cracks to rim, 34 cm. diam., c. 1715. **£1,200-£1,500** *C*

Two 'Adam and Eve' chargers, painted in dark blue, yellow and iron-red, the foliage 'sponged' in bright green, 'blue-dash' rims, probably Bristol, both restored, 13 in. approx., early 18th C. **£700-£800** *S*

A Bristol delft blue plate, painted in manganese with 3 ships on a billowing sea with a large fish swimming beneath, minor chips and glaze flaking to rim, 22 cm. diam., c. 1750. **£900-1,000** *C*

A Bristol delft blue and white plate, early 18th C. **£120-140** *JHo*

A Bristol delft polychrome dish, star cracked, rim chip, 13¼ in. (33.7 cm.), mid 18th C. **£250-300** *SC*

A Bristol delft blue and white plate, 8 in., dated 1728. **£400-450** *JHo*

A pair of Bristol delft polychrome dishes, each decorated with a building on an island, within a barbed panel, slight glaze chips, one cracked, 13 in. (33 cm.), mid 18th C. **£450-500** *SC*

A Bristol delft blue and white inscribed and dated plate, with the initials PIA 1725 within a herringbone surround and border, slight rim chips, 22.5 cm. diam., c. 1725. **£450-500** *C*

A Bristol delft polychrome dish, decorated with iron-red flowers, glaze chips, 13 in. (33 cm.), mid 18th C. **£250-300** *SC*

A Dublin delft blue and white dish, painted with the arms of Dalrymple above the motto 'Firm', the rim painted in the Chinese manner, repaired, 32 cm., mid 18th C. **£250-300** *Bea*

A Bristol delft polychrome dish, trellis band rim reserved with foliate panels, numeral 4 in blue, 12¾ in. (32.7 cm.), mid 18th C. **£600-700** *SC*

A Lambeth delft blue and white inscribed and dated oval plaque, the reverse inscribed LAM 1716 in blue, the top pierced for hanging, minor glaze flaking to rim, 23.5 cm. wide, c. 1716. **£1,350-1,550** *C*

A Bristol delft polychrome dish, rim chips, 13 in. (33 cm.), mid 18th C. **£250-300** *SC*

A Bristol delft polychrome dish, 13 in. **£800-900** *JHo*

MILLER'S *Antiques Price Guide builds up year by year to form the most comprehensive photo-reference system available. The first five volumes contain over 40,000 completely different photographs.*

A pair of Dublin delft pierced oval dishes, painted in blue with central Chinese figures carrying flower vases in baskets, both marked 'W' in blue, rim chips, 10¼ in., c. 1755. **£800-900** *S*

A Lambeth delft blue-dash charger, painted with 3 tulips in ochre and copper-green colours, restored, 13½ in. **£2,000-2,500**   *AGr*

A Lambeth delft teapot stand, on 3 shaped feet, painted with hillocks and buildings in the Chinese taste, in iron-red, green and yellow colours, 1 repaired foot, 5½ in. diam. **£700-900**   *AGr*

A Liverpool delft blue and white plate, with chinoiserie design, 8½ in., c. 1760. **£120-140**   *JHo*

Three Liverpool delft blue and white inscribed and dated plates, painted in a bright blue and dated 1754 within elaborate trellis-pattern and sgraffiato flowerhead wells, one cracked, minor rim chips, 22 cm. diam., c. 1754. **£600-700**   *C*

A Lambeth delft blue and white merryman plate, the centre inscribed with the second rhyme '2 Leet him diu what he can' (sic) within a border of further concentric blue lines, minor glaze flaking to rim, 22 cm. diam., c. 1720. **£300-350**   *C*

A Brislington delft Adam and Eve charger, painted in green, yellow, blue and manganese on an eggshell blue ground within an everted blue-dash rim, the back covered in a lead glaze, repaired, 40.5 cm. **£7,000-8,000**   *Bea*

A delftware plate, The Taking of Portobello, decorated in pale tones of blue with the scene of three of Vernon's fleet attacking the Spanish fortress, the town in the distance beyond another castellated building on the right, within a border of foliage and berries, brown edged rim, the reverse with 'whiplashes', probably Liverpool, chips on rim, 8½ in., c. 1740-45. **£1,400-1,600**   *S*

After his boastful parliamentary speech, Vernon was given command of six ships of the line with instructions to 'destroy the Spanish settlements in the West Indies and distress their shipping by every method whatever'. His squadron arrived at Portobello on the night of 20th November 1739, and the next day bombarded the castle at the entrance to the harbour. On the following day the town surrendered, with British casualties of no more than six killed and thirteen wounded.

A rare Lambeth delft dated armorial dish of embossed silver form, centred on the arms of the Grocers Company, and surmounted by the initials IHM and dated 1651, 15 in. **£12,000-14,000**   *AGr*

Ex. Garner collection.

The initials are those of Sir James Houblon and Marie, his wife. Houblon's son was the first Governor of the Bank of England, and Master of the Grocers' Company.

A Liverpool delft blue and white inscribed and dated ship plate, the reverse inscribed Francis Gott 1752, glaze flaking to rim, 22 cm. diam., c. 1752. **£2,100-2,400**   *C*

Lloyd's Register of 1764 records only one 'Diadem', built in France in 1750 for Tivitoe & Co., the master was Evan Johnson, there is apparently no record of Francis Gott.

A very rare delft sweetmeat dish, probably London, the border with 6 fan-shaped compartments painted in blue and black, the centre painted with a half-length portrait of William III wearing a crown and ermine robes, flanked by initials WR, 24.5 cm., c. 1690. **£900-1,100**   *P*

A Liverpool delft blue and white plate, with chinoiserie design, 9 in., c. 1760. **£120-140** *JHo*

A set of three delft polychrome 9 in. plates and another 10 in., decorated with parrot figure and flowers, some damage. **£200-250** *A*

This type of decoration is frequently seen on Liverpool delftware.

A London delft blue and white inscribed and dated Royalist portrait plate, painted with half-portraits of William III and Queen Mary in their coronation robes, within a double blue line cartouche, chip and glaze flaking to rim, 21.5 cm. diam., c. 1691. **£3,500-4,000** *C*

A London delft blue and white Royalist portrait plate, with a portrait of George II in his coronation robes and holding a sceptre, inscribed G2R, cracked and chipped, 22.5 cm. diam., c. 1727. **£2,700-3,000** *C*

No similar example would seem to be recorded.

A pair of delft blue and white plates, the central shaped medallion containing a deer in a landscape within a lapet border decorated with stylised flowers, very slight glaze chips to rims, 35 cm., early 18th C. **£350-400** *Bea*

A London delft blue and white Royalist portrait plate, with King William and Queen Mary in their coronation robes, flanked by the initials WMR, extensively cracked and riveted, 21 cm. diam., c. 1690. **£800-900** *C*

A pair of delft polychrome plates, painted with peacocks and sponged in manganese, with damage, 9 in. diam., probably Bristol, early 18th C. **£1,800-2,000** *A*

A pair of delft 'Merryman' plates, each painted with an encircling band of blue leaves on a green stem, one inscribed 'To Entertain his Guests', the other 'With wine & Merry Jests', minor glaze chips to rims, 22 cm., dated 1717. **£2,000-£2,500** *Bea*

A purple lustre dish with ship 'Duke of Wellington – 131 guns', impressed mark Scott, 6½ in. diam., c. 1850. **£80-90** *DL*

A near-pair of Dutch Delft plates, painted in blue with the Peacock pattern, 26 cm., mid 18th C. **£130-£180** *SS*

A Dutch Delft fluted circular dish, with raised centre, painted in yellow, blue and green with a peacock, the border with a wreath of tulips and other flowers, 35.5 cm., late 17th C. **£200-250** *L*

A Dutch Delft portrait dish, painted in shades of blue with the busts of King William III and Queen Mary beneath blue drapery with tassels, the border with birds amongst rockwork, 34.7 cm., c. 1680. **£800-1,000** *S*

A Palermo waisted cylindrical albarello, painted with a bishop saint, the reverse with martial trophies, some restoration, 31 cm. high, early 17th C. **£700-800** *C*

A Savona two-handled blue and white drug vase and cover, the handles formed as camels' heads, cover repaired, rim chips, 29 cm. high, c. 1700. **£1,100-1,300** *C*

A pair of dated North Italian albarelli, decorated in shades of blue with a blue scale border above a label, the waisted foot with date '1710', minor chips, 17.5 cm., 1710. **£600-700** *S*

A Palermo a quartieri albarello, Syo de Suco Aceto, named in blue gothic script upon a scroll above yellow, ochre and blue foliage reserved on a turquoise ground, slight rim chips, 29.5 cm. high, late 16th C. **£1,400-1,600** *C*

A pair of Savona maiolica albarelli, painted in orangey yellows, blue and manganese, lighthouse mark in manganese and blue, probably Chiodo workshop, 17 cm., mid 18th C. **£500-600** *SS*

A similar piece of Savona pottery, apparently painted by the same hand, is in the Glaisher Collection, Fitzwilliam Museum.

A Sienna albarello, decorated in ochre, green, white, yellow and blue, small patch of glaze missing on shoulder, 16.7 cm., early 16th C. **£3,500-4,500** *S*

A Sicilian drug jar, of ovoid form, 9 in., 17th C. **£350-450** *DWB*

MAKE THE MOST OF MILLER'S

Miller's is completely different each year. Each edition contains completely NEW photographs. This is not an updated publication. We never repeat the same photograph.

An English miniature drug jar for P:STOM:CU GUM, minor chips and glaze flaking, 8.5 cm. high, c. 1740. **£600-700** *C*

A dated Tuscan oviform wet-drug jar, the multicoloured striped handle dated at the base 1563, probably Montelupo, rim and glaze chips, 23 cm. high. **£1,100-1,300** *C*

A massive Talavera two-handled oviform jar, minor chips to glaze, 57 cm. high, late 16th or early 17th C. **£1,600-2,000** *C*

The hunting subjects on this are after engravings published collectively at Antwerp in 1578, entitled Venationes, ferarum, avium, piscium, from drawings by Johannes Stradanus.

A large Sicilian albarello, decorated in blue and ochre, in a panel reserved on a ground of floral scrolls, 37 cm., 17th C. **£1,600-£2,000** *S*

A pair of 18th C. tinglaze earthenware drug jars, 13 in. high. **£300-350**   *A*

Two Dutch Delft tobacco jars, each decorated in blue with a Red Indian seated smoking a pipe beside a vase inscribed respectively 'Havana' and 'Violet', with sailing ships in the background, brass covers fitted for electricity, mark in blue of the 'De drie Klokken' factory, rims worn, 26 cm. **£900-1,000**   *S*

A red pottery jar and cover, decorated with rolls of clay and flowerheads applied to the surface in the form of stylised symmetrical blossom trees, covered in a galina glaze, slight damage, 22 cm. high. **£600-700**   *Bea*

A large jug, pinched-in spout and handle in the form of 3 snakes, painted with 2 of the Elders observing Susanna bathing in a pool of water, Urbino or Venice, restored, 30.5 cm., late 16th C. **£1,900-2,300**   *S*

Three Lambeth delft albarelli with blue bands, 6 in., 5¾ in. and 5 in. high. **£80-125** each   *AGr*

A large Faenza jug, decorated in blue, green and ochre, patches of glaze and tip of spout restored, 31 cm., late 15th C. **£7,000-9,000** *S*

A Hanau 'Enghalskrug' with hinged pewter cover bearing the initials 'SLW', painted in blue and yellow with the symbols of the carpenter's trade, minor chips to rims and glaze cracks to foot, 26.5 cm., last quarter 18th C. **£1,100-1,300**   *S*

A Gleinitz parrot-shaped jug and cover, decorated in green, yellow, brown and ochre, 25 cm., late 18th/early 19th C. **£950-1,150**   *S*

A Westerwald pale grey stoneware tall jug, the neck with 3 bands of beading enriched in blue, the lower half modelled as 3 animal legs on shaped trefoil base, chips, 34 cm. high, 17th C. **£1,100-1,300**   *C*

A Nottingham stoneware 'carved jug' with globular double-walled body, the outer wall incised and pierced with stylised foliage, below a reeded cylindrical neck, ribbed loop handle, the whole covered with a lustrous saltglaze, small chips on rim, 4 in., c. 1700. **£1,100-1,300**   *S*

A proof, probably for a trade card for James Morley at the Pot-House in Nottingham, includes a 'Carved Jug'. This is reproduced by Oswald, Hildyard and Hughes in English Brown Stoneware, 1670-1900, p. 103, pl. 57. The latest date recorded on a piece of carved ware of this type is 1703 see Oswald, Hildyard and Hughes, op. cit. p. 293, Fig. X, No. 3.

A Staffordshire saltglaze owl jug and cover, lightly enriched in brown and joined by loops of studwork, the domed cover with raised features and brown eyes and nose, the back of the head with bands of raised studwork, crack round base of neck, minor chipping to some studwork, 19 cm. high, c. 1720. **£16,000-18,000**   *C*

An Enoch Wood jug depicting smokers and drinkers, in blue, green and yellow glazes, 7¾ in., c. 1785. **£250-300**   *LR*

A Prattware Bacchus jug, with Pan on reverse, in coloured glazes, 11½ in., c. 1800. **£270-320**   *LR*

A rare and interesting set of 3 graduated stoneware jugs, each sprigged against the off-white ground with crisp deep blue reliefs of a head and shoulders portrait of Queen Caroline, one handle repaired, small chips, 5, 6 and 7 in., c. 1820. **£250-300**   *S*

A copper lustre jug, the Adam Buck prints with yellow background, ¼ in., c. 1845. **£130-145**   *DL*

A gaily coloured Scottish pottery jug, 6½ in., c. 1805. **£150-175**   *EC*

A Wedgwood pearlware jug, with coloured transfer printed botanical subjects, 7 in. **£250-300**   *A*

A pearlware jug, with coloured transfer of a man o' war, reverse with compass, 7 in., c. 1815. **£60-90**   *LR*

A pearlware moulded jug, decorated in coloured enamels, 5 in., c. 1820. **£50-70**   *LR*

A Wedgwood hunting jug, in ochre and blue, 8 in., c. 1830. **£100-120**   *DL*

A Ralph Wood 'Fair Hebe' jug, impressed Voyez 1789, 8 in. **£250-£285**   *DL*

A Swansea pottery jug, in silver shape, 5½ in., c. 1820-25. **£95-110**   *EC*

A copper and purple lustre jug, with Charity, in transfer printed colours, 5½ in., c. 1825. **£80-100**   *LR*

A platinum lustre jug, with flower and leaf decoration, 4½ in., c. 1825. **£50-70**   *LR*

A small yellow ground platinum lustre jug, with black transfer rural scene, 5 in., c. 1820. **£150-200**   *LR*

A Sunderland purple lustre jug, with the Weir Bridge, 8¼ in., c. 1840. **£145-160**   *DL*

A Mason's Patent ironstone jug and basin set, jug 11 in. high, c. 1830. **£175-195**   *GCA*

A Ralph Wood Toby jug of the usual model, wearing a bright blue coat, manganese breeches and dark treacle brown hat, 24.5 cm. **£450-£500**   *P*

A Walton Toby jug, impressed mark on base, 10¼ in., c. 1820. **£375-395**   *DL*

INFLATIONARY TIMES!

In the 1950's Sunderland lustre jugs used to be priced roughly £1 to an inch. This has certainly changed. Lustre now is valued on historical interest of subject; rarity of shape, quality of print or painting, and of course condition. A great deal of lustre ware has been damaged and repaired.

A Sunderland purple lustre jug, with the 'Gardeners Arms', 8¾ in., c. 1840. **£170-190**   *DL*

A rare early Toby jug, in Pratt colours, with double base, 10¼ in., c. 1785. **£560-700**   *EC*

A good Ralph Wood Toby jug, with cup up to lips, 9¾ in., c. 1780. **£600-£650**   *DL*

TOBY JUGS

There are many contradictory theories about the inspiration of this jug in the form of a drinking figure in a three cornered hat. Some claim the honour for Sir Toby Belch, of 'Twelfth Night', and others Uncle Toby in 'Tristram Shandy' by Sterne. It is more likely however that the character came from a print published in 1761 of Toby Philpot illustrating a popular song 'The Brown Jug'. By far the most desirable 'Tobys' were made by Ralph Wood but most of the pottery factories produced them in quite substantial quantities. For the collector there are many varieties: 'The Nightwatchman', 'The Drunken Parson', 'Prince Hal', 'Hearty Good Fellow', 'Admiral Jarvis', 'Martha Gunn' etc. On these early jugs, crisp modelling, good colouring and any unusual features all increase value. Many Toby jugs were produced depicting characters from the First World War and also later of Churchill. As most of these were limited editions, their rarity leads to reasonably high prices today.

A platinum lustre jug, with birds and flowers, 5½ in., c. 1825. **£60-80** *LR*

A rare miniature Toby jug, with ochre-trimmed blue jacket, yellow breeches and brown tricorn, standing on a green glazed mound base, chip on foot, small crack on handle, 3½ in., late 18th C. **£200-£250**   *S*

A Ralph Wood 'long faced' Toby jug, in translucent glazes, 11 in., c. 1780. **£675-£725**   *LR*

Ralph Wood jugs usually have unglazed bases, barrel between legs never Ralph Wood – usually Leeds.

A Prattware 'Hearty Good Fellow' jug, 11 in., c. 1795. **£575-625**   *EC*

A 'Planter' Toby jug, in underglaze colours, 11¼ in., c. 1775-85. **£850-£950**   *JHo*

An early type Toby jug, with stepped base, minor repair, 9¼ in., c. 1765. **£375-425**   *JHo*

A Toby jug, modelled as a toper, wearing a blue coat with ochre collar, striped waistcoat, ochre breeches and black shoes, probably Yorkshire, 7¾ in., late 18th C. **£360-400**   *S*

A Prattware 'long faced type' Toby jug, in Pratt palette, 10½ in., c. 1790. **£350-400**   *LR*

A Yorkshire Toby jug, in Pratt colours, 7¾ in., c. 1800. **£425-475** *EC*

A 'Sailor' Toby jug, decorated in enamel colours, some repair, 11½ in., c. 1800. **£450-550**   *JHo*
More unusual type – more desirable.

An Enoch Wood 'Planter' Toby jug, 11½ in., c. 1800. **£500-550**   *EC*

A Staffordshire sailor Toby jug, 10¼ in., c. 1810. **£200-225**   *DL*

A Toby jug, Dr. Johnson, also known as The Unfrocked Parson, with coloured coat, by Enoch Wood, some restoration, 6¼ in., c. 1790-1800. **£400-450**   *LR*
Perfect **£500-550**

A Toby jug, Dr. Johnson, by Enoch Wood, complete with measure, 8½ in., c. 1790-1800. **£275-325** *LR*

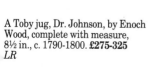

A silver-mounted stoneware cylindrical mug, covered in a rich brown glaze, with moulded rings to the base, the silver mount suspending a band of leaves, chip to foot rim, 21.5 cm. high, c. 1720. **£700-900** *C*

A rare 'Turner's Patent' mug, of porcellaneous stoneware, painted with Imari-style panels in bright colours embellished in gilding, mark in red, faint star crack, 15.3 cm., early 1800's. **£350-400** *SS*

A creamware inscribed and dated cylindrical mug, painted with the inscription 'May Shoemakers flourish/ And Trade increase/ And Victory gain/ Everlasting Peace', the reverse with a shoemaker seated on a bench making a shoe and inscribed above George Selby 1804, beneath an iron-red linc, small star crack to base and minute glaze flaking to rim, 13.5 cm. high, c. 1804. **£700-800** *C*

A purple lustre mug, with the Weir Bridge, 4¾ in., c. 1840. **£85-95** *DL*

An English pearlware pipe, painted in muddy brown and blue with a twisted rope and dot pattern, the mouthpiece and bowl edged in ochre, hair crack, 28.8 cm., c. 1800. **£200-300** *SS*

A Prattware pipe in typical palette, of 'The Old Farmer', supposedly George III, 5½ in., c. 1800-10. **£250-£300** *LR*

A Prattware pipe in the form of a sailor, 6½ in., c. 1800. **£275-325** *LR*

A Prattware pipe in the form of a hand, 4½ in., c. 1810. **£150-200** *LR*

A Castelli rectangular plaque, painted in the Grue workshop, 18.5 by 25.5 cm., c. 1730. **£1,100-1,300** *C*

A Castelli mythological plaque, painted in the Grue workshop, with Bacchus crowning Ariadne, ebonised and giltwood frame, 25 by 32 cm., c. 1740. **£1,200-1,500** *C*

A Castelli plaque, painted in the typical palette of shades of ochre, blue and green, wooden frame, the faience 20 by 27 cm., 35.5 by 43 cm. overall, 18th C. **£1,300-1,500** *S*

A Castelli rectangular plaque, painted in the Grue workshop, dated on the reverse 1752, minor rim chips, 20.5 by 26.5 cm. **£900-£1,000** *C*

A Dutch Delft plaque, decorated in shades of blue, probably representing a scene from the story of 'The Prodigal Son', giltwood frame, plaque ground down on two sides on the reverse, 30 by 37.5 cm., mid 18th C. **£3,000-£3,500** *S*

A Pratt Bacchus plaque, 7 in. diam., c. 1780. **£275-325** *GCA*

A Staffordshire plaque, in enamel colours, 7 in., c. 1810. **£365-425** *EC*

A Prattware pottery plaque, depicting Flora, in coloured glazes of green, ochre, yellow and slate-grey, 8½ in., c. 1790. **£150-200** *LR*

A pearlware portrait plaque of Sarah Siddons, coloured in enamels, 4¾ in., c. 1810. **£120-160** *LR*

A purple lustre plaque, with green borders, with black transfer print of dancers, makers mark Falconer B. & Co., 8½ in. wide, c. 1850. **£80-£100** *LR*

(*t.*) An unusual Sunderland lustre plaque, printed and sparsely painted with 'Victoria and Albert Yacht', the rim in pink and copper lustre, rim chip, 8 by 9 in., mid 19th C. **£80-100**

(*b.*) An amusing Dixon Phillips & Co. plaque, transfer printed in black, within a splashed pink and copper lustre rim, impressed mark, 7½ by 8¼ in., c. 1840-65. **£80-100** *S*

A Sunderland purple lustre plaque, with coloured transfer of a man o' war with billowing sails, 9½ in. wide, c. 1850. **£90-120** *LR*

(*t.*) A Sunderland lustre plaque, of Crimean interest, printed and naively painted with an English sailor and a French sailor shaking hands below the inscription 'May They Ever Be United', the rim with splashed lilac and copper lustre, 8 by 8¾ in., c. 1855. **£80-100**

(*b.*) A rare Sunderland lustre plaque, printed and naively painted with 'The Star of Tasmania', the rim with splashed pink lustre within a brown scroll border, 8½ by 9½ in., mid 19th C. **£110-130** *S*

A Sunderland purple lustre plaque, with coloured transfer entitled 'A frigate in full sail', 9¼ in. wide, c. 1850. **£90-120** *LR*

A Sunderland lustre plaque, with a coloured transfer of Italianate rural scene, makers transfer mark for Samuel Moore on reverse and impressed mark, 8½ in., c. 1850. **£45-65** *LR*

A Lambeth delftware white glazed posset pot and cover, 7 in., late 17th/early 18th C. **£4,000-5,000** *AGr*

A pair of small pot lids, The Ins and The Outs, both with double line borders (15, 16). **£140-170** *CSK*

The Bride, a small lid with purple lined border (97). **£180-220** *CSK*

(*l.*) Eastern lady dressing hair, an unusual medium lid with border and margin (Ball 99). **£50-60**

(*r.*) Nelson Crescent, Ramsgate, an extra large lid (Ball 43), with base, glaze flaw. **£55-65** *S*

Lady Fastening Shoe, a small lid with line border. **£80-100** *CSK*

Wellington, with clasped hands, a large lid (Ball 160b), slight staining. **£80-90** *S*

A Bristol delft blue and white miniature chamber pot, painted with trailing flowering branches and grasses beneath a key-pattern border, minute chip to underside of rim, 12 cm. wide, c. 1715. **£4,000-£4,500** *C*

No similar example would seem to be recorded.

A Staffordshire copper lustre chamber pot, in mint condition, 9 in. diam., c. 1860. **£300-350** *DL*

Anything unusual in lustre is rare and desirable.
Very popular with the American market.
Condition is vital in the lustre market.

(*l.*) The New Jetty and Pier, Margate, an extra large lid (Ball 39), with base. **£70-80**

(*r.*) Sandown Castle, Kent, a medium lid (Ball 44), printed retailer's mark for Tatnell & Son. **£140-160** *S*

The Great Exhibition of 1851 – Closing Ceremony (141), damaged flange only. **£600-800** *P*

A large Mettlach circular plaque, incised and signed by M. Hein, on a pale blue ground, impressed mark including number 1418, 19 in. (48 cm.), c. 1900. **£500-600** *SC*

(*t.l.*) Bear, Lion and Cock, a small lid (Ball 19). **£65-75**

(*t.r.*) Polar Bears, a rare and early small lid, with gilt line border (Ball 18), gilding slightly rubbed. **£180-£250**

(*b.*) Shakespeare's birthplace, interior, two medium lids, one with a leaf and scroll border (Ball 227). **£150-180** *S*

Lady with Hawk, a small lid (106). **£60-80** *CSK*

(*l.*) Napoleon III and Empress Eugenie, a large lid (Ball 156), with base, some discolouration. **£140-£160**

(*r.*) Grand International Buildings of 1851, a large lid (Ball 133). **£60-£70** *S*

The late Duke of Wellington, a large lid with marbled border (161A). **£75-85** *CSK*

The Allied Generals: a medium lid with laurel leaf border and registration mark (168). **£75-95** *CSK*

Admiral Sir Charles Napier, C.B. (167), large, with border. **£400-500** *P*

Embarking For The East, a medium lid with chain border (206). **£60-70** *CSK*

Ann Hathaway's Cottage (228), gold lined border and flange, with similarly decorated base. **£400-500** *P*

(*t.l.*) The Fisher Boy, a small lid (Ball 341). **£55-75**

(*t.r.*) Windsor Castle and St. George's Chapel, a small lid (Ball 177). **£140-160**

(*c.*) Floral Subject, a miniature lid (Ball 131/19), with shaped pot. **£140-160**

(*b.l.*) The Old Water-Mill, a small lid with a marbled border (Ball 318). **£60-80**

(*b.r.*) The Faithful Shepherd, a small lid with marbled border (Ball 309). **£80-100** *S*

'The Village Wakes', No. 232A, with dog and monkey, scroll border, 3½ in. diam. with pot. **£90-100** *MN*

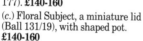

The Village Wakes', No. 232A, with dog and monkey, very slight chip to underside of rim, 3 in. diam. with pot. **£60-70** *MN*

The Buffalo Hunt (243), repair to flange and small crack. **£800-1,000** *P*

'Christmas Eve', No. 238, a black and white border, 3½ in. with pot. **£120-140** *MN*

Dangerous Skating, with six steps, with dotted border, 249A, 2¾ in. **£50-60** *MN*

Seashore Study and Tyrolean Village Scene, two small rectangular lids (Ball 393 and 397), with bases. **£120-140** *S*

A plate, bearing: The Last In (412), narrow malachite border, gold line decoration, the reverse with Pratt, Prince Albert stamp. **£300-350** *P*

Napirima Trinidad, a large lid with double line border and title (225). **£80-90** *CSK*

POT LIDS

Alas! poor Bruin	(1)	£40-50	hairline crack	(212)	£20-25
The Bear Pit, with dome	(6)	£50-60	Harbour of Hong-Kong	(221)	£60-80
The Bear Pit, no dome	(6)	£30-50	Ning Po River	(222)	£30-40
Bears at School	(9)	£40-50	Rifle Contest, Wimbledon 1864	(224)	£40-50
Bears on rocks, small	(10)	£35-45	Shakespeare's Birthplace —		
Bears on rocks, medium	(10)	£35-45	Exterior	(226)	£30-35
Shooting Bears	(13)	£25-30	Holy Trinity Church	(229)	£50-55
Arctic Expedition in Search of			Children of Flora	(237)	£60-65
Sir John Franklin	(17)	£150-250	The Swing, restored	(239)	£20-25
Pegwell Bay — Lobster Fishing	(24)	£20-30	The Bullfight, late issue	(244)	£35-45
Pegwell Bay —			The Enthusiast	(245)	£25-40
Established 1760	(25)	£50-70	Master of the Hounds	(247)	£30-40
Pegwell Bay — Four Shrimpers	(26)	£30-40	Chiefs return from Deer		
Belle Vue Tavern — with			Stalking	(248)	£45-55
Carriage	(28)	£30-40	Dangerous Skating, cracked	(249)	£20-30
Belle Vue — Pegwell Bay	(30)	£60-70	A False Move	(251)	£150-200
Pegwell Bay — Shrimping	(33)	£100-120	A Pair	(252)	£40-50
Pegwell Bay and Ramsgate,			The Best Card	(254)	£25-30
restored	(37)	£20-30	Hide and Seek	(255)	£25-35
Landing the Fare —			A Fix	(256)	£35-45
Pegwell Bay	(38)	£45-55	The Sportsman	(259)	£20-30
Royal Harbour — Ramsgate	(42)	£30-35	The Game Bag	(260)	£30-40
Walmer Castle	(47)	£150-180	Pheasant Shooting, mottled		
Pretty Kettle of Fish	(48)	£25-35	border	(261)	£140-180
Hauling in the Trawl	(53)	£25-35	Children Sailing Boats in Tub	(263)	£80-100
The Fish Market	(57)	£35-45	Good Dog	(265)	£80-100
The Fish Barrow	(58)	£45-55	Deerhound Guarding Cradle,		
The Shrimpers	(63)	£20-30	moulded border	(269)	£50-60
An Eastern Report	(98)	£80-100	Both Alike	(272)	£50-60
Grand Exhibition 1851	(135)	£40-50	Country Quarters, restored	(273)	£25-35
The Crystal Palace	(137)	£150-180	The Snow-Drift	(276)	£35-45
The Crystal Palace — Interior,			H.R.H. Prince of Wales visiting		
hairline crack	(139)	£100-120	the Tomb of Washington	(310)	£80-120
Dublin Industrial Exhibition			I See You my Boy	(311)	£35-45
1853	(143)	£180-220	French Street Scene, medium	(312)	£25-35
L'Exposition Universalle de			French Street Scene, large	(312)	£40-50
1867, damaged	(145)	£40-50	The Breakfast Party, mottled		
Paris Exhibition 1878	(148)	£25-35	border, decorated base	(314)	£200-250
England's Pride, black			The Breakfast Party, marbled		
background	(149)	£70-90	border	(314)	£100-140
Queen Victoria on Balcony	(150)	£180-220	Lady, Boy and Goats, restored	(316)	£25-35
Queen Victoria and Prince			Lend a Bite	(317)	£35-40
Consort, restored	(152)	£70-90	The Queen God Bless Her	(319)	£80-100
Queen Victoria and Prince			The Farriers	(324)	£40-50
Albert, fancy border, gilt			The Times	(327)	£30-40
apple green flange similar			Uncle Toby, chipped	(328)	£10-15
base, initialled RA.	(152)	£550-650	The Second Appeal	(330B)	£70-90
The Late Prince Consort	(153)	£50-70	Strasburg	(331)	£35-45
Albert Edward Prince of Wales			Transplanting Rice	(332)	£45-55
and Princess Alexandra on			Vue de la Ville de Strasbourg,		
their Marriage in 1863	(157)	£70-90	Prise du Port	(333)	£35-45
Wellington — with clasped			Fording the Stream	(335)	£25-30
hands, with order	(160)	£180-220	The Flute Player	(337)	£30-40
Wellington — with clasped			On Guard	(340)	£30-35
hands	(160A)	£120-150	Tam-o'-Shanter and Souter		
Tria Juncta in Uno	(164)	£250-300	Johnny, damaged	(346)	£35-45
Dr. Johnson, chipped	(175)	£18-22	Tam-o'-Shanter	(347)	£120-160
Buckingham Palace	(176)	£250-300	The Poultry Woman	(349)	£45-55
Drayton Manor	(179)	£70-90	Preparing for the Ride	(351)	£35-45
Osborne House	(182)	£50-80	The Quarry	(352)	£200-250
Strathfieldsaye	(188)	£100-120	The Picnic, damaged	(354)	£25-30
Albert Memorial	(191)	£40-50	Royal Coat of Arms, restored	(355A)	£70-90
St. Paul's Cathedral	(192)	£350-400	Letter from The Diggings,		
Thames Embankment, restored	(197)	£10-20	medium	(360)	£50-60
Chapel Royal	(198)	£40-50	Letter From the Diggings,		
Trafalgar Square	(201)	£40-45	large, mottled border,		
Holborn Viaduct	(202)	£50-60	restored	(360)	£35-45
New St. Thomas's Hospital	(203)	£50-60	The Wolf and the Lamb	(361)	£35-45
Embarking for the East,			Charity	(362)	£40-50
with chain border	(206)	£70-80	The Waterfall	(365)	£30-35
Battle of the Nile	(210)	£50-60	The Travellers Departure,		
War — After Wouvermann,			green border and similar base	(396)	£55-65

**All numbers refer to the
coding system used in 'Price
Guide to Pot Lids' by A. Ball.**

A Davenport stone china part dinner service, decorated in underglaze blue and coloured in the 'famille rose' style, comprising: 5 dishes, 2 sauce tureens, covers and stands, a carving dish, a soup tureen stand, 3 serving dishes in sizes, a shell-shaped dish, 48 plates and 12 bowls, blue printed Davenport Stone China and anchor marks, pattern No. 7, c. 1820. **£3,500-4,000**   *C*

A pair of rare Prattware vases, bearing prints of 'Chinese River Scene with Junks' (Ball 440), the rim with formal border, 5½ in., third quarter 19th C. **£1,300-1,500** *S*

A Mason's ironstone china part dinner service, painted in an Imari palette, lightly enriched in gilding, comprising: 2 soup tureens, covers and stands (one base cracked), 4 sauce tureens and covers, 2 vegetable dishes and covers, 12 dishes, 10 soup plates (one with rim chip), 12 dinner plates, 2 dessert plates and 6 side plates, impressed Patent Ironstone China in a circle, some pieces with shield mark flanked by Royal supporters and impressed Ironstone China, c. 1820. **£3,000-3,500**   *C*

An Ashworth dessert service, hand-painted with botanical specimens, with turquoise borders, comprising: a pair of tall tazze, 4 low tazze, 11 plates, pattern No. 9992, impressed mark, c. 1860-80. **£250-£300**   *WW*

A Mason's ironstone dessert service, in iron-red, underglaze blue and gilding, comprising: a pair of fan-shaped dishes, 4 shaped rectangular dishes, a shell-shaped dish and 17 plates, impressed mark, some chips, repairs and wear, plate 8½ in., c. 1820. **£700-£900**   *S*

A fine Davenport stone china dinner service, painted in blue and coloured in 'famille rose', comprising: a soup tureen, cover and stand, 4 tureens, 2 covers and stands, a gravy boat and stand, 2 baking dishes, 7 serving dishes, 28 meat plates, 9 soup plates and 17 plates, printed anchor marks. **£3,500-4,000**   *P*

An Ashworth's ironstone china dinner service, decorated with deep blue bands, heightened in iron-red, green, pink and gilding, comprising: 6 meat dishes, 22 side plates, 25 dinner plates, 12 soup plates, 2 tureens and covers, 2 sauce tureens, covers and stands, impressed marks, c. 1860. **£2,200-£3,000**   *SS*

A Prattware dessert service, each piece colour-printed with 'The Last ...n' after Mulready, 'The Truant' after Webster, 'The Hop Queen' after Withrington, 'The Bully' after Mulready, 'The Blind Fiddler' after Wilkie or 'Highland Music' after Landseer (Ball 412, 413, 414, 415, ...17 or 418), comprising: 18 plates, circular tazze, 2 oval tazze, another oval tazze, larger, and a fruit stand, the majority with printed titles, fruit stand and several handles repaired, plate ...½ in., third quarter 19th C. **£600-700**   *S*

A Minton ironstone dinner service, each piece printed in underglaze blue and picked out in iron-red, comprising: 5 tureens, covers and ladles, one with stand, 3 serving dishes, 11 meat plates, 12 soup plates, 10 cheese plates and 11 side plates, printed and impressed marks, c. 1850. **£1,000-1,200**   *SC*

A mid 19th C. Dimmock & Co. pearlware Japonica pattern part dinner service, comprising: 50 meat plates, 6 vegetable and sauce tureens, 10 soup dishes, 22 plates and 4 stands. **£2,000-2,500**   *A*

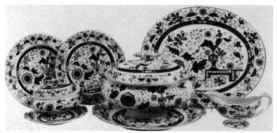

An Ashworth's ironstone dinner service, decorated with an Imari pattern, comprising: soup tureen, cover and stand, 4 tureens and covers, 2 sauceboats, 9 serving dishes, 18 soup plates, 36 meat plates and 18 side plates, printed Royal Arms marks in puce, impressed marks, 1862-80. **£1,300-£2,000** SC

On the death of C. J. Mason, Ashworth's took over the Mason's factory including their ironstone. After using this mark c. 1862-80, they returned to using the Mason's mark.

A John Rogers & Son blue and white part dinner service, transfer printed with figures amongst classical ruins, comprising: a soup tureen and cover, 24 plates, 4 stands and a meat platter, impressed mark, several items with slight damage or staining, platter 21 in., c. 1820. **£600-700** S

A Hicks & Meigh ironstone part dinner service, printed and painted in colours with shaped puce cell-pattern bands within shaped and moulded rims, comprising: a soup tureen, cover and stand, 2 sauce tureens, stands and 2 covers, 3 vegetable dishes and covers, a salad bowl, 11 serving dishes, 12 soup plates, 27 dinner plates (one cracked), 16 side plates, printed Royal coat-of-arms, Stone China and no. 23 marks, c. 1820. **£8,500-£9,500** C

An extensive Spode 'stone china' dinner service, decorated in underglaze blue, iron-red and gilding with floral sprays, comprising: 6 tureens, covers and stands, 4 vegetable dishes and 3 covers, 22 soup plates, 51 dinner plates, 15 dessert plates, 3 pudding dishes, a fruit bowl, 15 meat and serving platters in sizes, printed mark in underglaze blue, painted pattern number 2086, some chips, cracks and repairs, c. 1820. **£8,000-£9,000** S

A Spode new stone part dinner and dessert service, painted in a bright 'famille rose' palette, comprising: soup tureen, cover and stand (base cracked), 9 dishes, 2 vegetable dishes and covers, a small deep oval dish, 12 soup plates, 29 dinner plates (one with star crack to base), 21 dessert plates, pattern no. 2038, c. 1820. **£7,000-8,000** C

A Staffordshire ornithological dessert service, with broad pink ground border heightened with grasses in raised gilding, comprising: 2 high footed dishes, 4 low footed dishes and 12 plates, pattern no. 4/9511 in puce, c. 1860. **£700-800** SC

A Spode 'pheasant' pattern 'stone china' dinner service, transfer printed in underglaze blue and painted in bright enamels, comprising: a soup tureen and cover, 2 sauce tureens, covers and stands, 4 vegetable dishes and covers, 15 soup plates, 49 dinner plates, 10 side plates, 24 dessert plates, 10 serving dishes in three sizes, a strainer and a venison dish, the majority with printed 'Stone China' mark, painted pattern number 2240, some repairs, chips, c. 1830. **£6,500-7,000** S

A Wedgwood pearlware dessert service, each piece moulded and coloured in pastel shades of pink, green and yellow, comprising: a fruit stand, 2 cream tureens, covers and stands, 5 dishes and 14 plates, impressed mark, some damage and repairs, plate 8 in., early 19th C. **£1,500-1,700** S

A Wedgwood 'Queensware' part supper set, each piece crested in sepia without a ducal coronet, a unicorn's head above the initials 'HM' in sepia and blue, probably for Marden of Marden, Hereford, comprising: a dish and cover, 2 fitted fan-shaped dishes and covers and 6 plates, impressed WEDGWOOD and workman's initials, one cover cracked, one dish repaired, some wear, c. 1790. **£500-£600** S

A Wedgwood dessert service, stone colour, each piece modelled in the form of vine leaves and tendrils, comprising: an oval basket on foot with gilt branch handles, 2 oblong dishes, a large oval leaf dish, 4 vine leaf dishes and 23 plates, impressed Wedgwood mark. **£1,100-1,300** *L*

A fine Wedgwood caneware tea service, each piece crisply applied in olive-brown, comprising: a teapot and cover with silver mount to the spout, a sucrier and cover, a jug, a bowl and 6 teacups and saucers, all impressed WEDGWOOD. **£1,000-1,200** *P*
For the moulded pattern see W. Mankowitz Wedgwood, pl. 103 left.

A Wedgwood dinner service, painted with flowering branches in red, blue, green and gold, comprising: soup tureen, vegetable dish and cover, 3 fan-shaped dishes and covers, 3 pie dishes, 2 sauce tureens and one cover, circular strainer and stand, 7 meat dishes, 7 soup plates, 38 meat plates, 30 pudding plates and 8 cheese plates, impressed marks. **£650-750** *L*

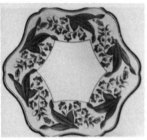

A Wedgwood pearlware dessert service, decorated with a broad yellow border painted in pink with floral sprays, comprising: one comport, one rectangular dish, 2 petal-shaped dishes and 10 plates, impressed 'Wedgwood', early 19th C. **£500-600** *SS*

A Wedgwood dessert service, each piece painted by A. Halland, signed, with game subjects within broad cobalt blue borders heightened in gilding, comprising: 12 plates, 2 heart-shaped dishes, 2 diamond-shaped dishes and an oval dish, green printed vase mark, red retailer's mark and printed titles, pattern no. 5506 in puce, c. 1870. **£1,000-1,200** *SS*

A Wedgwood part dessert service, in Imari pattern, 22 pieces. **£600-£750** *DWB*

A Westerwald stoneware cylindrical mug, modelled in low relief in blue, hinged pewter cover with ball billet, engraved I.G.B. 1602, 23 cm., 18th C. **£200-250** *L*

A W. Smith & Co. 'Wedgewood' service, printed in black with 'Select Views', comprising 162 pieces, printed and impressed marks, some plates and soup plates cracked, mid 19th C. **£2,000-2,500** *WW*

W. Smith & Co. of Stockton on Tees used this 'Wedgewood' mark from about 1826 until the middle of the 19th C. They catered mainly for the export market and no doubt hoped to confuse foreign buyers by adopting a mis-spelling of the well-known English factory.

A stoneware flagon, fitted with a pewter cover, 25 cm. **£120-150** *Bea*

A Raeren 'Krug' by Peter Emens, dated 1585 and the initials PE, pewter cover, minor chips, 29.5 cm., c. 1585. **£1,200-1,500** *S*

A Westerwald stoneware tankard, with hinged pewter cover, painted in a pale blue wash on a mottled grey ground, 18.5 cm., 18th C. **£200-300** *Bea*

A stoneware tankard, dipped in an orange glaze, with hinged pewter cover, 16.5 cm. **£120-150** *Bea*

A dated silver-mounted Raeren stoneware jug, the elaborately decorated silver mounts in Renaissance style, minute chips, dated 1597, 26 cm. **£800-900** *S*

A Bunzlau stoneware jug, covered with a warm brown glaze, with hinged pewter cover inscribed E.S.1725, with ball billet, pewter foot rim, 30 cm. **£400-500** *L*

A Dutch Delft jug, painted in blue in Chinese taste, with pewter hinged cover with ball billet and engraved M.D.1708, within a foliage wreath, 24 cm., early 18th C. **£250-300** *L*

A Westerwald flagon, with crisp decoration, 10¼ in., late 16th C. **£1,000-1,200** *JHo*

An early 18th C. Westerwald tankard, with contemporary pewter lid, 7¼ in. **£225-250** *JHo*

An early 18th C. Westerwald tankard, with Adam and Eve decoration, 5¾ in. **£225-250** *JHo*

A 16th C. Siegburg tankard, with coat-of-arms of town and contemporary pewter mount, 11 in., c. 1570. **£2,000-2,200** *JHo*

A Kreussen tankard, modelled in relief in colours on a brown glazed ground, with scroll motifs in yellow, white and blue and a border of tulips at the base, hinged pewter cover with ball billet, inscribed 'A.S. P.R.H. 1712', pewter foot rim, loose. **£950-1,050** *L*

A Westerwald blue and grey stoneware cylindrical pewter-mounted tankard, 27 cm. high, c. 1700. **£400-500** *C*

A Bayreuth pewter-mounted tankard, with manganese ground, painted in shades of ochre, green and blue, B.P.F. in blue, minor cracks and chips, 22.3 cm., c. 1760. **£500-600** *S*

A North German faience tankard, the hinged pewter cover surmounted by a ball-shaped thumb-stop, decorated in colours with a goat trying to climb a tree, S in iron-red, probably Dorotheenthal, 22.5 cm., c. 1781. **£1,000-1,200** *S*

A Bayreuth tankard, painted in soft tones of green, manganese, blue and yellow, blue line borders and manganese dashed handle, later pewter mounts, BP in manganese, two cracks, 25 cm., c. 1760. **£700-800** *S*

An Erfurt faience tankard, painted in colours, the hinged pewter cover initialled M.M.H. and dated 1768, 20 cm. **£350-400** *P*

A German faience cylindrical tankard, with hinged pewter cover, boldly painted in colours, 22.5 cm. **£300-350** *P*

A Whieldon hexagonal teapot and cover, with stylised serpent handle and moulded spout, the cover with recumbent dog finial, covered in a green glaze streaked with yellow and brown, spout and cover chipped, rim of teapot restored and cracked, 15 cm. high, c. 1760. **£1,600-1,800** *C*

A Staffordshire saltglazed stoneware teapot and cover, crabstock spout and handle, hair crack, 18 cm., c. 1760. **£500-600** *SS*

A creamware oviform teapot and cover, painted in the manner of David Rhodes, with a bouquet of flowers and with scattered flower sprays, between beaded rims, the cover with flowerhead finial, perhaps Leeds, cracks to body, chips to spout, rim and interior of cover, 13 cm. high, c. 1770. **£350-£400** *C*

A rare Marseilles teapot and cover, decorated with sprays of flowers in green, blue, manganese and ochre painted on a yellow ground, Veuve Perrin factory, spout chipped, 24 cm., c. 1760. **£500-700** *S*

A Westerwald teapot and cover, the grey body decorated with applied moulds, minute chips to cover, 27 incised, 13 cm., 18th C. **£800-900** *S*

A rare Staffordshire saltglaze 'house' teapot and cover, in the white, the sides moulded with 3 storeys and figures in doorways below Royal coats-of-arms, applied with a serpent spout and 'notched' handle, very minor chips and hair cracks, 6¼ in., c. 1745-50. **£850-£950** *S*

The 'notched' handle is characteristic of wares made by Thomas and John Wedgwood of the Big House, Burslem. Compare with the examples illustrated by Arnold Mountford in Staffordshire Salt-glazed Stoneware, pls. 89 and 90.

A coloured saltglaze teapot, 5 in., c. 1760. **£600-650** *DL*

Coloured saltglaze is increasingly sought after – particularly by the American market.

A creamware tankard, decorated in red and black, with chinoiserie decoration, with restoration, 6¼ in., c. 1770. **£225-260** *JHo*

A creamware teapot, with unusual brown slip, probably Cockpit Hill, 5½ in., c. 1765. **£550-650** *JHo*

A Wedgwood creamware punch pot and cover, transfer printed in black with two cartouches, one of peasants smoking and drinking punch, the other of drunken gentlemen arguing, on a gilt vermiculé scrolling foliage and strapwork ground, impressed mark, slight chip to spout, 32 cm. wide, c. 1770. **£3,200-3,600** *C*

A Staffordshire saltglaze baluster jug and cover, covered in a Littler's blue glaze and gilt with an Oriental standing among shrubs, crack to base, chip to inside of cover, 20.5 cm. high, c. 1755. **£4,600-5,000** *C*

A Delft teapot and cover, the spout and handle with scrolls and dashes, in green, yellow, blue and brown enamels, 12.5 cm., mid 18th C. **£400-500** *Bea*

A rare Dutch Delft polychrome teapot and cover, the ribbed body of pumpkin form reserved on a green ground, set with a blue spout and chinoiserie handle, and surmounted by a comical spotted dog, body crack, 12 cm., mid 18th C. **£450-500** *SS*

A Liverpool delft tile, with manganese decoration, mid 18th C. **£30-35** *JHo*

A Liverpool delft tile, with manganese decoration, mid 18th C. **£25-30** *JHo*

A Liverpool delft tile with manganese decoration, mid 18th C. **£30-35** *JHo*

An English delft biblical tile, c. 1760. **£20-25** *JHo*

An English delft biblical tile, c. 1760. **£20-25** *JHo*

A rare pair of Liverpool delft tiles, painted in green, yellow, blue and red and delineated in manganese, chips, 5 in. square approx., third quarter 18th C. **£300-400** *S*

An English delft biblical tile, c. 1760. **£20-25** *JHo*

A pair of Liverpool delft tiles, painted with bright yellow birds with blue wing feathers and purple tails, chips, 5 in. square approx., third quarter 18th C. **£250-300** *S*

Four Liverpool delft tiles by Sadler, one signed, c. 1760-70. **£250-300** *DWB*

Six Liverpool 'Fazackerley' tiles, chips, some damage, 5 in. square approx., third quarter 18th C. **£250-350** *S*

A Liverpool delft tile of a goat, c. 1760. **£60-70** *JHo*

A Liverpool delft tile of two sheep. **£80-100** *JHo*

A Bristol delft bianco-sopra-bianco floral tile, c. 1750-60. **£60-80** *JHo*

A Bristol delft bianco-sopra-bianco tile, with blue and white scene, c. 1750-60. **£70-80** *JHo*

An important Hungarian stove tile, made to fit a corner, moulded with a portrait of Ferdinand I, King of Hungary, holding a crowned shield bearing his arms, on the side the coat-of-arms of his wife Anna of Hungary, all on a green ground and picked out in blue, yellow and manganese, Neusol, 21.5 by 21.5 by 10 cm., c. 1540-50. **£1,400-1,600** *S*

Two Dutch Delft polychrome plover tureens and covers, naturally modelled and painted, one cover restored, one base cracked and chipped, one with the mark of Jacobus Holder of the Greek A, the other with an IP monogram of either Johannes Pennis of Jacobus Pijnacker of the Porcelain Dish, 14 cm. long, mid 18th C. **£1,300-£1,400** *C*

A Frankfurt oviform vase, painted in the Transitional Chinese style, minor glaze chips, 37 cm. high, c. 1690. **£900-1,100** *C*

A Wedgwood pottery tile picture of a milkmaid, carrying her stool and pail, before a rustic gate, 'Josiah Wedgwood' signature, 138 by 92 cm. (58 tiles), c. 1880. **£900-£1,100** *SS*

A rare Whieldon-type gull tureen, 3 in., c. 1780. **£370-390** *DL*

An early Staffordshire pottery pigeon tureen, with good underglaze colours, 5 in. high, c. 1790. **£400-450** *DL*

A Strasbourg melon tureen and cover, painted in yellow and green, restored, 21 cm. long, c. 1750. **£550-£750** *C*

A Bristol delft bianco-sopra-bianco bird tile, c. 1750-60. **£160-180** *JHo*

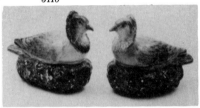

A pair of creamware tureens, modelled as nun pigeons, on nest bases, decorated in natural colours, slight faults, 8 by 5¾ in., c. 1790. **£1,000-1,200** *A*

A Victorian Staffordshire hen tureen, on ochre basket base, 5½ in., c. 1850. **£85-110** *GCA*

A Holics circular rose tureen and cover, the petals painted in puce, the handles modelled as gnarled branches, with foliage terminals, black fish mark to cover and HE monogram and S. to the base, restoration to handles and some repairs, 23 cm. wide, c. 1765. **£900-£1,200** *C*

Trompe l'oeil subjects are very rare in Holics but reflect the dominant influence of Strasbourg.

Two London delft blue and white flower vases, in the form of a child's head, with hair painted in streaked blue, with blue wavy line to the shoulder and the head pierced with holes, glaze flaking to nose, hair and base, 16.5 cm. high, c. 1685. **£2,000-3,000** *C*

The only other examples recorded were inscribed and dated 1685.

A pair of blue Wedgwood classical urn vases, 10¼ in., c. 1850. **£240-£265**   *DL*

A Wedgwood rosso antico pastille burner, c. 1805. **£150-180**   *WIL*

A pair of Wedgwood three-colour jasper ovoid vases and covers, with 2 lilac ground figure medallions on a pale green ground, 11½ in. high. **£450-500**   *MMB*

A near pair of Wedgwood pottery vases, impressed 'Wedgwood', 17.2 and 18 cm., c. 1860. **£200-250**   *SS*

A Wedgwood black jasper dip Portland vase, the base with a Phrygian head, impressed Wedgwood, 11 in., early 19th C. **£700-800**   *S*

An early 19th C. Dixon Austin & Co. watch holder, in Pratt colours, marked on front, with 2 holes to nail to mantel, 11 in. **£450-500**   *JHo*

An unusual ornate Victorian Staffordshire watch stand and spill vase, 10 in., c. 1835. **£110-125**   *GCA*

A rare Victorian Staffordshire cupid bedecked watch holder, 11¼ in., c. 1840. **£120-135**   *GCA*

A Victorian Staffordshire church watch stand and spill vase, 10¼ in., c. 1840. **£100-120**   *GCA*

A large Wedgwood blue jasper dip pot pourri vase and cover, impressed mark, 14¾ in., late 19th C. **£500-600**   *S*

A Wemyss black and white pig, impressed Wemyss, 6¼ in., c. 1900-20. **£150-200**   *RdeR*

WEMYSS WARE
c. 1880-1930

Wemyss has seen a steady rise in popularity over the last year, with unusual pieces like the carp tureen and cover selling in the Sotheby sale for more than three times top estimate.

A very rare Robert Heron & Son Wemyss ware carp tureen and cover, modelled by Karel Nekola, its scales and fins coloured in tones of bright pink shading to grey-green and heightened in bright yellow, the cover with a smaller fish handle, impressed mark and initials, small restoration to one fin, 18½ in. long, c. 1900. **£4,000-£5,000**   *RdeR*

This example took such time and precision, it was uneconomic for production. The powder pigment mixed with gum arabic solution explains the underglaze shading. The technique was costly and time-consuming and Nekola destroyed the mould.

A Wemyss preserve jar and cover, painted with strawberries, middle period, 4½ in. **£40-50** *RdeR*

A Wemyss ware 'goose flower-holder', the stylised bird with smiling expression, its plumage painted in tones of green, blue, lilac and yellow, impressed mark, 7¾ in., c. 1900. **£500-600** *S*

A Wemyss Gordon plate, well painted with oranges, painted by Joseph Nekola, 8 in. **£50-100** *RdeR*

A rare Wemyss vase, of diamond section, painted on each facet with stylised fuchsia and foliate scrolls in blue, green and ochre, painted mark, 22 in., c. 1900. **£350-450** *S*

For a similar vase attributed to Karel Nekola see Exhibition of Wemyss Ware, Rogers de Rin, at Sotheby's, Belgravia, 1976, cat. no. 323.

A rare Wemyss ring stand, painted with roses, 3¼ in. **£75-100** *RdeR*

A Wemyss preserve jar and cover, painted with flowering blackberries, with red rim, impressed Wemyss, 6¼ in. **£100-£150** *RdeR*

A large Wemyss brush vase, painted with roses, by Karel Nekola impressed Wemyss, 11 in. **£100-150** *RdeR*

A Wemyss brush vase, painted with buttercup, impressed Wemyss, 6¼ in. **£50-100** *RdeR*

WEMYSS WARE, c. 1883-1930

Robert Methven Heron introduced a group of continental artists into his Fife pottery in the 1880's. The very characteristic nature of Wemyss derives from their influence although roses, apples and cherries had been stiffly painted before.

Most of the artists returned home but Karel Nekola remained. Wemyss was always wanted by the rich and the ware was well supported by Scottish lairds.

Wemyss was fired at low temperatures to produce a biscuit body which would absorb the delicate brush strokes. Then it was dipped in a soft lead glaze and fired again at a low temperature. This accounts for the fragility of Wemyss and the relative rarity of exceptional quality pieces.

Nekola trained James Sharp, David Grinton, John Brown, Hugh and Christina McKinnon

and they were later joined by Nekola's sons Carl and Joseph.

Karel Nekola tended to paint the large important pieces and also the commemorative pieces from Queen Victoria's Jubilee in 1897 until the Coronation of George V in 1911. He died in 1915.

Edwin Sandiland became chief decorator in 1916. The change in public taste after the First World War, with the introduction of the Art Deco movement, saw a move away from the traditional Wemyss designs. Various new designs were tried but by the time Edwin Sandiland died in 1928, the end was in sight. The Fife Pottery closed in 1930.

The Bovey Tracy pottery in Devon bought the rights and moulds of the Fife pottery and gave employment to Joseph Nekola, who continued the familiar decorations to a high standard until his death in 1952. Royal Doulton subsequently acquired the rights.

A large Wemyss sponged colouring black and white pig, early Scottish, 17 in. wide, c. 1885-90. **£300-700** *RdeR*
Very early because of wrinkles and pink ears and nose.

A Wemyss small shamrock pig, painted Wemyss mark, 6½ in. **£100-120**   *RdeR*

A Wemyss sleeping pig, impressed Wemyss, painted by Karel Nekola, 6½ in., c. 1883-1926. **£250-350** *RdeR*

A Wemyss stylised tulip mug, impressed Wemyss, 6 in. **£100-200** *RdeR*

A Wemyss cup and cover, commemorating the Coronation of Edward VII, impressed mark WEMYSS, T. Goode & Co. in green script, 9 in. (22.8 cm.), c. 1902. **£500-600**   *RdeR*

A small Wemyss three-handled loving cup, painted with apples, impresssed Wemyss, 4 in. **£100-£250**   *RdeR*

A Wemyss brown cockerel tyg, 7½ in. **£200-350**   *RdeR*

A large Wemyss tyg, freely painted with trails of full-blown pink cabbage roses, the rim and foot with green line borders, painted mark, 9¼ in., early 20th C. **£450-£550**   *S*

A Wemyss mug, painted with cherries, with red rim, 5½ in., c. 1885-1900. **£150-200**   *RdeR*
Period of best paintings.

A Wemyss pomade pot, painted with roses, 3 in. **£65-100**   *RdeR*

A Wemyss preserve jar, painted with bees, impressed Wemyss, 6 in. **£50-75**   *RdeR*

A Wemyss dog bowl, painted with apples, 'Qui aime Jean, aime son chien', 6½ in. diam. **£150-200** *RdeR*

A pair of Wemyss candlesticks, painted with thistles, impressed Wemyss, 7 in. **£100-200** *RdeR*

Many candlesticks destroyed or at the best damaged. Hence perfect pieces at a premium.

PRICES

The never-ending problem of fixing prices for antiques! A price can be affected by so many factors, for example:
- *condition*
- *desirability*
- *rarity*
- *size*
- *colour*
- *provenance*
- *restoration*
- *the sale of a prestigious collection*
- *collection label*
- *appearance of a new reference book*
- *new specialist sale at major auction house*
- *mentioned on television*
- *the fact that two people present at auction are determined to have the piece*
- *where you buy it*

One also has to contend with the fact that an antique is not only a 'thing of beauty' but a commodity. The price can again be affected by:—
- *supply and demand*
- *international finance — currency fluctuation*
- *fashion*
- *inflation*
- *the fact that a museum has vast sums of money to spend*

A Wemyss thistle inkwell, 6 in. wide, impressed Wemyss. **£40-80** *RdeR*

Some Wemyss gets discoloured, e.g. an inkwell if it has been used as it is porous. This would detract from value.

A Wemyss match holder, painted with roses, 3½ in. **£50-85** *RdeR*

A Strasbourg surtout de table, painted with deutsche Blumen and edged in puce, the trunk with leaves and acorns naturally coloured, some repairs to branches, 30 cm. high, c. 1750. **£2,000-3,000** *C*

No example of such elaborate construction would appear to be recorded.

A Castel Durante hand-warmer, in the shape of a book, the covers decorated with musical and military trophies, one inscribed SPQR, in shades of brown on a dark blue ground, and tied with two green bows, minor chips, 12.8 cm., mid 16th C. **£2,500-3,000** *S*

An Urbino salt cellar, applied with three leaf-and paw-feet, decorated on the well and rim with Hercules and a naked female figure seated in a rocky landscape, one foot repaired, 18.5 cm., c. 1550-70. **£3,000-3,500** *S*

A Palissy Ajoure tazza, enriched in blue, aubergine, yellow and ochre, the reverse marbled, rim chip, cracked and restored, 22.5 cm. diam., late 16th C. **£700-800** *C*

A Höchst circular saucepan and cover, with flowers in relief painted in a bright palette with indianische Blumen, the handle naturally coloured, puce wheel mark, minor chips to foliage, 19 cm. wide, c. 1740. **£2,500-3,000** *C*

Cf. Margrit Bauer: Europäische Fayencen, no. 223 and 224, for other wares with similar 'rustic' handles so typical of Höchst faience.

An Albissola tazza, painted with equestrian figures and birds, in landscape vignettes with trees, manganese falcon and F mark of Falco, crack, rim chips, 34.5 cm. diam., c. 1760. **£450-500** *C*

A rare Yorkshire bough pot, in ochre, blue, green and red, 7½ in., c. 1800. **£425-475**   *GCA*

A large Mintons 'majolica' jardiniere and stand, glazed in unusually colourful tones of blue, green, ochre, brown and plum, the circular stand matching, impressed mark, shape number 650, date code for 1883, crack in stand, minor glaze chips, stand 18¾ in. **£1,200-£1,500**   *S*

An unusual Mintons 'majolica' centre bowl, the whole in tones of blue, green, brown and ochre with a turquoise interior, on a wave moulded base, impressed mark, shape number 1551 and date code for 1881, minor damage, 25 cm. **£650-750**   *S*

An unusual Minton 'majolica' centrepiece, in typical 'majolica' glazes, impressed ermine mark and date code for 1859, basket repaired, 18½ in. **£300-350**   *S*

MILLER'S *Antiques Price Guide builds up year by year to form the most comprehensive photo-reference system available. The first five volumes contain over 40,000 completely different photographs.*

A Bristol flower brick, painted in blue with repeated scene of two European ladies, chips, 14.6 cm. long, c. 1750. **£750-850**   *SS*

A Mintons 'majolica' centrepiece, the whole decorated with typical 'majolica' glazes, impressed mark, shape number 1204 and dated code for 1875, 22¾ in. **£1,800-2,000**   *S*

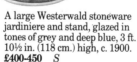

A large Westerwald stoneware jardiniere and stand, glazed in tones of grey and deep blue, 3 ft. 10½ in. (118 cm.) high, c. 1900. **£400-450**   *S*

A Wedgwood 'majolica' tobacco jar, applied with portrait medallions of Sir Walter Raleigh, the cover bearing the words 'Tobacco, introduced by Sir Walter Raleigh 1585', impressed factory and registration marks and date code for 1870, 18 cm. **£350-400**   *SS*

An unusual pearlware flowerpot, bat-printed in puce with a woman and child between green leaf moulded corners, and on four ball feet upon a black washed square base, base detached, 22 cm., c. 1800. **£150-200**   *SS*

A Mintons faience jardiniere and stand, the jardiniere with spirally moulded blue body and rams mask handles, between polychrome floral garlands moulded in relief, stand crack, 16 in. diam. **£750-850**   *HyD*

A Minton conservatory stool, in green and yellow on an aubergine frame, impressed mark Minton, 47 cm. **£600-650**   *L*

A rare redware scent bottle or tea jar, the shoulders moulded with fluting, stepped foot, silver-mounted neck and screwed silver cover, 4¾ in. overall, 18th C. **£1,200-1,400**   *S*

A rare solid agate ware money box, probably Yorkshire, with birds, squirrels and a fox, 6¼ in., c. 1860. **£380-420** *LR*

A Staffordshire saltglaze rectangular tea caddy, the sides moulded with flowering tea plants and inscribed CIA or TE herb and HerbTeng (sic.) beneath a loop and dot pattern border, 9.5 cm. high, c. 1755. **£550-650** *C*

A pair of Staffordshire saltglaze wall pockets of cornucopia form, each moulded with a half length figure of Flora, picked out in bright colours, one with a small repair and damage on rim, 10½ in., c. 1760-70. **£850-950** *S*

For an undecorated example see Mountford, Staffordshire Salt-glazed Stoneware, pl. 156. Mountford notes that in the Thomas and John Wedgwood crate-book there is a record of them having sold '10 Corna Copiaes' for 34d. in September 1770.

A set of 4 furniture rests, or window rests, 4¼ in., c. 1815. **£250-£270** *DL*

It's unusual to have a matched set of 4.

An early English pottery watering pot, the front with an apron of a rich brown glaze covering the pale red body, chip to rose and foot and crack to body, 35.5 cm. high, 17th C. **£1,200-1,500** *C*

According to a manuscript note sold with the pot, this was excavated in Old Pye Street, Westminster.

A Mason's ironstone inkstand, decorated in 'famille rose' colours, with flower panels reserved on a rich mazarine blue ground, printed mark in black, some repair, 13¼ in. (33.5 cm.), 1815-20. **£500-£600** *SC*

A very rare slipware bird whistle group, in tortoiseshell glazes, most likely Brameld or Rockingham, 9 in., c. 1830. **£550-600** *DL*

A very rare London delft candlestick in the , after a metal original, broad drip-pan and flattened nozzle, the column with a double groove at the neck, restoration on nozzle, small chips, 7 in., mid 17th C. **£7,000-8,000** *S*

An 18th C. Marseilles faience casket, in the form of an armoire, painted with classical romantic scenes and a coat-of-arms, the shelved interior painted with sprays of flowers in colours and gilt, fleur de lys mark, 14½ by 11 in. **£800-900** *M*

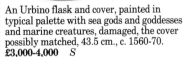

An Urbino flask and cover, painted in typical palette with sea gods and goddesses and marine creatures, damaged, the cover possibly matched, 43.5 cm., c. 1560-70. **£3,000-4,000** *S*

An early 19th C. coffee coloured Stilton dish and cover, 11½ in., c. 1825. **£145-165** *GCA*

A rare pair of Wedgwood and Bentley vase-candlesticks and reversible covers, slip decorated to simulate veined agate in tones of brown, ochre and slate-blue, impressed mark, one restored, small chips, 9¼ in., c. 1775. **£1,200-£1,300** *S*

A Belleek circular 2-handled basket, impressed ribbon marks, 9½ in. diam., late 19th C. **£550-650** *WIL*

Besides the marks impressed on a ribbon, the basketwork made up of groups of three interlacing central strands is said to be an early sign.

A Belleek floral encrusted basket, ribbon mark, 8 in., c. 1900. **£700-£1,000** *DWB*

The body of Belleek is a type of Parian (see Glossary).

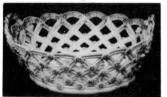

A Caughley chestnut basket, printed 'Pine Cone' pattern in underglaze blue, restored, printed 'C' mark, 8½ in. long. **£150-250** *McC*

*See Godden 'Caughley & Worcester Porcelains 1775-1800' plate 90 for the printed mark on a similar basket.

A Derby basket, with unusual spectacle border, with applied yellow flowers, restoration, 8¼ in., c. 1760. **£450-500** *MA*

Note the influence of Sèvres decorative style of exotic birds in parkland also found on the contemporary wares of Chelsea and Worcester.

A Belleek oval 2-handled lattice basket, with domed cover, delicately tinted in pink and yellow, impressed ribbon mark, 8¾ in. wide, c. 1900. **£700-1,000** *N*

Some of the early wares are covered in iridescent pink and yellow lustres. These pigments were thinly applied and have suffered through rubbing or perhaps from the fugitive nature of the enamel.

PORCELAIN — MARKET TRENDS
ENGLISH

English blue and white porcelain continues to prove strong and demand for rare and unusual pieces continues to push prices higher. This unprecedented demand for blue and white has caused many polychrome prices to seem low and this may be an area for wise buys.

One of the most dramatic changes over the period is the long overdue rise in the price of the early **Chelsea** wares, particularly the botanical or so-called Hans Sloane plates. This escalation in price has pulled in its wake the **Bow** versions of the same type.

Rare pieces or those of exceptional quality or desirability now command extraordinary prices even in a damaged state. It has finally dawned on collectors that it is becoming nearly impossible to find perfect examples.

One area of little movement is figure subjects from all English factories. They now seem grossly underpriced and should enjoy a revival of interest within the next few years.

Small academic pieces of **Liverpool** porcelain are enjoying an unprecedented boom. The **Liverpool** factories need far more research and it would seem likely that prices may harden as new facts are published.

Standard or conventional **Royal Worcester**, which saw a tremendous increase in interest in the last five to 10 years seems to have peaked but again rare and unusual pieces continue to increase in value.

CONTINENTAL

Meissen figures, unless of great rarity, would seem to have been rather flat over the past two years. 19th C. **Meissen** has not seen much movement over the period as 18th C. wares were undervalued in comparison.

The more obscure German factories such as **Limbach, Ansbach, Kloster Veilsdorf** still command disproportionate interest to their aesthetic appeal.

French porcelain prices, particularly of Sèvres, are quite erratic, probably caused by uncertainty of attribution and dating.

It will be interesting to watch **Mennecy, Chantilly** and other soft-paste French factories as wares prior to 1760 are not overpriced at the moment (with the obvious exception of Oriental or chinoiserie Chantilly wares and St. Cloud wares which have always fetched relatively high prices).

Italian porcelain has had a quiet season, with little of any merit coming onto the market.

A Belleek basket, impressed mark on ribbon, 6¼ in. (15.8 cm.), late 19th C. **£150-200** *SC*

A Bow blue and white circular basket in Worcester style, painted with the 'Pine Cone' pattern, shaded crescent mark, 8½ in., c. 1770. **£450-550** *S*

It is unusual to find a hand-painted version of this pattern which was printed on Worcester and Caughley.

A Derby basket, applied with flowers, one handle damaged, 8½ in. wide, c. 1760. **£250-270** *MA*

Unusual sparse floral decoration. This is really more of a Chelsea shape.

(l.) A Coalbrookdale basket, the peach coloured ground with gilt, and decorated and encrusted with flowers, 5⅜ in. high. **£150-180** *GC*

A very rare Derby blue and white basket, damaged, 7½ in. wide, c. 1770. **£140-160** *MA*

A Spode oval basket, with twist handles, decorated with flowers on a gilt ground, pattern 711, mark and number in buff, 4¼ in. **£500-£550** *DWB*

See Leonard Whiter's book on Spode for the dating of pattern numbers.

A Champion's Bristol quatrefoil 2-handled bowl, painted 'en grisaille', moulded and gilt with radiating leaves, 18 cm. wide, c. 1775. **£600-800** *C*

A Coalport punch bowl, painted with flower sprays within gilt borders on a 'gros bleu' ground, slight rubbing, 10¼ in. (26 cm.), early 19th C. **£250-300** *SC*

A Philip Christian's Liverpool blue and white bowl, painted with islands, divided by sprays of prunus, the interior with flowering branches, rim chip, 21 cm. diam., c. 1765. **£180-220** *C*

A Wedgwood dragon lustre bowl, the interior gilt against mottled blue ground, the exterior against orange lustre ground, pattern no. Z4825, 9 in. diam., c. 1920. **£180-£220** *WW*

Similar but less saleable subjects were made by Carltonware and Rosenthal.

A Minton basket, 12 in., c. 1840. **£500-600** *SuB*

A Bow blue and white bowl, 4½ in. diam., c. 1750. **£270-300** *SRO*

BRISTOL c. 1770-81

- **William Cookworthy transferred his Plymouth factory to Bristol in 1770**
- **the body had a tendency to slight tears and firing cracks**
- **early wares extremely difficult to differentiate from Plymouth — both show same firing imperfections, such as smoky ivory glaze and wreathing in the body**
- **Champion took over the works in 1773**
- **towards mid and late 1770's the dominant decorative style was neo-classical with particular reliance on delicate swags and scattered flowers**
- **later pieces showed little imperfections in enamel and potting**
- **later Bristol colours are sharp and gilding is of excellent quality**

A Chelsea octagonal bowl, painted in a pale Kakiemon palette, the interior with scattered flowerheads, minute crack and chips to rim, 15.5 cm. diam., c. 1752. **£650-750** *C*

Direct copy of an Arita Kakiemon bowl dating from the late 17th C. (See Glossary).

A Mintons polychrome pâte-sur-pâte bowl, decorated with sea creatures swimming against a deep blue-green ground and behind gilt netting, marks and date code for 1881, 10½ in. **£480-520** *S*

A Meissen table centrepiece, 16 in. wide. **£550-650** *DA*

A Chelsea leaf-shaped bowl, the stalk handle with leaf terminals, the sides painted in Kakiemon palette, the interior with scattered flowerheads, the centre with grasses, the interior rubbed, the feet with stilt marks lacking glaze, 19.5 cm. wide, c. 1750. **£4,500-5,000** *C*

The red anchor period.

A Meissen oval bowl, moulded on the exterior with basketwork, the interior painted in Kakiemon palette, the rim with 2 upright handles with mask terminals, handles restored, crossed swords in underglaze blue, impressed numerals, 25 cm., c. 1740. **£500-700** *S*

A Meissen bowl, with finely painted panels of army encampments and a battle, the interior with a fruiting branch and scattered insects, minor chip on rim, 20 cm., mid 18th C. **£1,200-£1,800** *S*

A Wedgwood fairyland lustre bowl, with polychrome and gilt landscape and fairy decoration, 9 in. diam. **£480-520** *DSH*

The accuracy of the registering of the design to the background colours increases the desirability of this type.

A Wedgwood fairyland lustre 'Imperial' bowl, the interior with the 'Fairy with Large Hat' pattern, the exterior with the 'Woodland Bridge', design against a blue ground, Z4968, 6¼ in., 1920's. **£350-400** *S*

A Wedgwood fairyland lustre octagonal bowl, the exterior decorated with 'Dana' landscape panels within black and gilt marbled borders, printed gilt urn and Z5125, England, 9 in. wide, c. 1920. **£700-800** *AG*

A Wedgwood fairyland lustre bowl, decorated with 'Poplar trees' pattern, gilt Portland vase mark, painted mark Z4968, 24 cm. diam. **£480-550** *Bon*

A Wedgwood sunset fairyland lustre octagonal bowl, the interior decorated with the 'Jumping Faun' pattern, against an orange ground, the exterior with the 'Feather Hat' variation of the 'Woodland Elves' design, printed urn mark, Z4851, 8½ in., c. 1929. **£700-800** *S*

A Wedgwood fairyland lustre punchbowl, the interior decorated with the 'Woodland Bridge' design against a daylight background around a central 'Mermaid' medallion, the exterior with the 'Poplar trees' design, pattern no. 4968, 28.3 cm. diam. **£800-1,000** *Bea*

A Wedgwood fairyland lustre punchbowl, decorated with woodland bridges, elves and birds in flight, the exterior with poplar trees, 9½ in. diam., c. 1920. **£400-£500** *M*

A Wedgwood fairyland lustre 'Antique Centre' bowl, the interior decorated with the 'Spider and Web' pattern, the exterior with the 'Woodland Bridge' design, against daylight and midnight grounds, printed urn mark, Z4968, 8½ in., 1920's. **£800-1,000** *S*

A Chelsea gold-mounted bonbonnière, the cover set with polished agate, 5.5 cm. wide, c. 1765. **£1,500-1,600** *C*

A 'Girl-in-a-Swing' gold and enamel mounted egg-shaped bonbonnière, the gold mount with the inscription 'L'Espoir de ta Fidelite Fait ma seul Felicite', some rubbing, 5 cm. high, 1749-54. **£1,700-2,000** *C*

A Wedgwood fairyland lustre dish, decorated with the 'Imps on a Bridge and Tree House' design, with lush green and blue foliage and flowers, a shaded pink sky and orange enamel and gilt details, printed urn mark, 13¼ in., 1920's. **£1,200-1,600** *S*

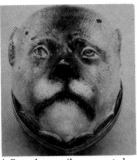

A Copenhagen silver-mounted snuff box, in the form of a pug dog's head, 5.5 cm., second half 18th C. **£400-500** *S*

A Mennecy snuff box, painted in colours with flowers, insects and fruit, with silver mounts, 7.3 cm., c. 1740-50. **£1,800-2,000** *S*

A Meissen gold-mounted snuff box, the exterior moulded with Ozier and painted with deutsche Blumen, the interior to the cover stippled by J. M. Hinrici with a lady in green dress and blue cloak before a purple curtain, 8 cm. wide, c. 1745. **£3,500-4,000** *C*

A Meissen snuff box, painted in colours with flower sprays and a grasshopper, butterflies, a snail and a ladybird, gilt metal mounts, crack, 6.7 cm., 1755-65. **£500-700** *S*

A rare German porcelain snuff box, in the form of a walnut, probably Meissen, chip to cover, minor wear, 6.5 cm., mid 18th C. **£600-700** *S*

A Vienna 'Wickelkind', with contemporary silver gilt mounts, 12 cm., c. 1830. **£500-650** *S*

A Nymphenburg snuff box, the interior of the cover painted with a portrait of Kurfürstin Maria Anna von Bayern, 8.5 cm., c. 1760. **£3,500-4,000** *S*

MAKE THE MOST OF MILLER'S

CONDITION *is absolutely vital when assessing the value of an antique. Damaged pieces on the whole appreciate much less than perfect examples. However a rare desirable piece may command a high price even when damaged.*

A St. Cloud lamb bonbonnière, with silver mounts, replacement cover, 6.3 cm., mid 18th C. **£250-£300** *S*

A rare Mennecy bonbonnière, in the form of an egg, sprigged overall with sprays of flowers and picked out in a typical palette, silver-plated mounts, 5.4 cm., mid 18th C. **£1,300-1,500** *S*

A documentary Schrezheim snuff box, in the shape of a leather trunk with gilt handles, the interior of the cover painted in trompe l'oeil to imitate letters and other papers, silver gilt mounts, slightly rubbed, 8.3 cm., c. 1770. **£3,500-4,000** *S*

● *The attribution of any porcelain to the Schrezheim factory has always raised considerable difficulties. It is known for certain that Jean Baptiste Boux, a wine merchant, was granted the franchise for porcelain manufacture at Schrezheim as early as 1752 by the Prince-Elector of Trier and that by 1766, with the aid of 20 employees, he was producing both porcelain and faience.*

A Vienna snuff box, painted in Meissen style, contemporary gilt metal mounts, shield mark in underglaze blue, crack to one side, minor chip to cover, 7.8 by 6.2 cm., 1750-60. **£1,400-1,600** *S*

A St. Cloud 'Magot' bonbonnière, with silver gilt mounts, representing the Chinese god of plenty, Pu Tai, 6.3 cm., c. 1740. **£1,300-1,500** *S*

A pair of Minton candlestick figures, with the original ormolu candlesticks, one neck repaired, 10½ in. high overall, c. 1840. **£1,400-1,800** *S*

A pair of Minton candlestick figures, each modelled as a maiden or a gallant in richly coloured and gilt rustic clothes, one hand and leg restored, 8½ in., c. 1830-40. **£1,300-£1,700** *S*

A Meissen candlestick, painted in colours with birds in branches and insects, the scrollwork picked out in pink, turquoise and gilding, crossed swords and a dot in underglaze blue, 24.3 cm., c. 1760. **£500-600** *S*

A pair of Dresden 5-light wall brackets, restorations to branches, 53 cm., last quarter 19th C. **£1,500-£2,000** *C*

A pair of 'Sèvres-style' candlesticks, each with a youthful satyr supporting a gilt metal mounted nozzle, glazed overall in bright turquoise, heightened with gilding, interlaced L's in blue enamel, 11¾ in. (29.7 cm.). **£200-300** *SC*

Two Meissen 2-light candelabra, modelled as young men seated between scrolling branches, trailed with coloured flowers and supporting the leafy nozzles, blue crossed swords marks, minor chips and repairs, 20 cm. high, c. 1750. **£1,800-2,200** *C*

A pair of ormolu mounted 'Sèvres' cassolettes, painted in 'Teniers' style, within 'jewelled' and gilt borders on a gros bleu ground, some 'jewelling' missing, 12¼ in. (31.2 cm.), late 19th C. **£700-900** *SC*

A pair of Coalport Parian ormolu-mounted candelabra, modelled in 'Sèvres' style, the stepped base with flower panels reserved on a blue celeste ground, small repairs, printed retailer's mark for Daniell enclosing CBD, 19 in. (48.3 cm.), late 19th C. **£800-1,000** *SC*
See Parian in Glossary of Terms.

A pair of Minton 2-light candelabra, each stem formed from 3 intertwined dolphins, the tails supporting foliate scroll branches in a predominantly green palette with gilt details, minor chips and restoration, 12¾ in., c. 1830. **£1,000-1,500** *S*

A Meissen 3-light candelabrum, modelled as 'Winter' from a set of the Seasons, crossed swords in underglaze blue, some restoration, 30 cm., mid 18th C. **£1,800-2,200** *S*

A French clockcase and stand, probably 'Michel-Isaac Aaron, Chantilly', in the form of an Eastern warrior in colourful traditional robes, the rectangular base painted with flowers against a blue ground, MA in underglaze blue, the movement stamped 'Laval', chips, 49.5 cm., mid 19th C. **£1,200-1,800** *S*

A Dresden clockcase, the children emblematic of the seasons, crossed swords and star in underglaze blue, 1 ft. 7¼ in. (49 cm.), late 19th C. £800-1,000   S

A Paris clock garniture, the clock with floral panels and vases painted with panels of lovers in Hungarian dress, the reverse with flowers, reserved on blue ground, the clock on rosewood-marquetry stand, 1 ft. 4 in. (40.5 cm.), and 1 ft. 5 in. (43 cm.), mid 19th C. £800-900 S

A Thuringian clock garniture, painted in pastel shades and flower encrusted, the candelabra 18 in., late 19th C. £500-600   TW

A Meissen rococo baluster clock case and stand, surmounted by a nymph, the base with the head and shoulders of Time, fitted with an English watch movement with elaborate engraved and pierced back plate by Arl Dobson of London, blue crossed swords mark, the putti on the base with left leg missing, minor chips, 43 cm. high, c. 1760. £3,000-4,000   C

A Vienna porcelain mantel clock, with 8-day chiming movement, with polychrome painted reserves by Johner on gold and dark blue ground, 18¼ in., late 19th C. £1,100-1,300   DSH

An English porcelain pastille burner, 5½ in., c. 1835. £370-395 DL

A Staffordshire porcellaneous cottage, 7 in. high, c. 1840. £275-£295   DL

An English octagonal porcelain pastille burner, probably Samuel Alcock, 4¼ in., c. 1835. £175-195 DL

An English porcelain pastille burner, with birds and bees on front and sides, 5¼ in., c. 1835. £450-485   DL

An English porcelain pastille burner, probably Coalport due to pattern number, restored, 5 in., c. 1835. £370-395   DL

A rare Staffordshire porcelain rustic pastille burner, in the form of a farmhouse, with dilapidated lean-to, encrusted with coloured flowers, a dog lying beside his kennel, minor chips, 27 cm. long, 1830's. £2,500-3,000   SS

A rare Ansbach coffee can, Hague decorated, c. 1770. £220-250   KK

143

An English porcelain white and gilt pastille burner, 5¼ in., c. 1835. **£270-295** *DL*

A Chantilly shaped hexafoil tea bowl, decorated in the Kakiemon manner with storks, quails and flowering plants, beneath the chocolate rim, iron-red hunting horn mark, c. 1740. **£550-650** *C*

The Chantilly hunting horn mark is frequently copied by Samson of Paris from 1860.

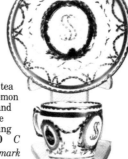

A Champion's Bristol coffee cup and saucer from the Sarah Smith service, the cup with the floral initials SS flanked by 2 coats-of-arms, the saucer with some rubbing to gilding, blue X mark, c. 1774. **£400-450** *C*

A Berlin cabinet cup, cover and stand, painted with a portrait of Hindenburg, within an oval and shaped yellow cartouche reserved with flowering foliage, the stand with a dagger, within a yellow border inscribed 'Generalfieldmarschall Paul von Hindenburg und von Beneckendorff', blue sceptre and iron-red KPM marks, 1915-18. **£350-450** *C*

A Berlin cabinet cup and saucer, painted in puce monochrome with a battle scene of 5 soldiers in a trench, the reverse with 2 oval panels of green scale-pattern, beneath a gilt band border entwined with floral swags, blue sceptre, iron-red KPM and Iron Cross marks, 1915-18. **£150-200** *C*

A Bow white prunus moulded coffee can, c. 1758. **£70-90** *SRO*

A Chelsea raised anchor prunus moulded flared beaker, 3⅛ in., c. 1749-50. **£1,200-1,300** *HOF*

Actually has raised anchor mark — rare on a beaker. Both early Chelsea and Bow copied the exportwares from Te Hua (De Hua) on Fukien (or Fujian) so called 'Blanc-de-Chine'. (See Donnelly in Bibliography and also Glossary.)

A Capodimonte (Carlo III) coffee cup, painted by Giovanni Caselli, with peaches, pears and a melon in a landscape and with gilt border to the interior, blue fleur-de-lys mark handle riveted, c. 1750. **£600-800** *C*

Capodimonte is the name of Carlo III's palace at Naples and was adopted by the manufactory. The fleur-de-lys was the mark used on the early wares made between 1743-59. The common misconception that the crowned N was the mark of this factory — it was in fact the mark of the Naples factory founded in 1771. Volkstedt Rudolstadt also used the crowned N at the end of the 19th C.

CHELSEA TRIANGLE PERIOD 1745-49

- **wares scarce and costly**
- **many based on silver prototypes and 'Blanc de Chine' ware**
- **mainly left undecorated**
- **body comparatively thick, slightly chalky with 'glassy' glaze**

A pair of Chelsea Kakiemon pattern tea bowls and saucers, painted in turquoise, iron-red and gilt, after Arita originals, one tea bowl and one saucer with minute rim chip, c. 1750-52. **£1,000-1,500** *C*

A Chelsea octagonal fable tea bowl and saucer, finely painted by J. H. O'Neale, with 'The Stork and the Wolf', minute short hair crack to saucer, c. 1752. **£4,800-5,200** *HOF*

A Chelsea octagonal tea bowl and a saucer, painted in the Kakiemon palette with a ho-ho bird in flight, with hedges, prunus and bamboo, the saucer restored, c. 1750. **£400-£450** *C*

RAISED ANCHOR PERIOD 1749-52

- paste now improved
- shapes still derived from silver, although Meissen influence noticeable
- mostly restrained decoration, either Kakiemon or sparse floral work (often to cover flaws)
- often difficult to distinguish from wares from 'Girl in a Swing' factory
- the most collectable ware of this and the Red Anchor period was fable decoration by J. H. O'Neale
- the creamy almost waxy appearance of glaze is virtually indistinguishable from red anchor glaze, apart from higher content of earlier body

---

A Chelsea scolopendrium moulded cinquefoil tea bowl and a saucer, the saucer with extended firing cracks and crazing, the saucer with raised anchor mark, c. 1750. **£600-£800** *C*

A Chelsea artichoke moulded tea bowl and saucer, boldly painted with scattered fruit within gilt dentil rims, gold anchor marks, c. 1760. **£600-700** *C*

A Chelsea-Derby tea cup and saucer, painted by James Banford, in puce camaieu, within a raised green and gilt swag border, interlaced D and anchor in gold, 5¼ in. diam., c. 1775. **£350-450** *N*

A pair of Chelsea-Derby custard cups and covers, painted with polychrome floral swags, suspended from blue borders beneath gilt rims, interlaced D and anchor in gold, 3⅛ in. high, c. 1775. **£450-550** *N*

Cozzi tea bowl and saucer, each decorated in colours with a dwarf standing in a garden and a fantastic bird, red anchor mark, saucer cracked, c. 1765-70. **£750-850** *S*

A rare Derby polychrome tea bowl and saucer, c. 1768. **£150-170** *SRO*

A Chinese porcelain cup and saucer, decorated in Europe with raised gilded figures, French silver-gilt mounts and lining to cup, fleur-de-lys control marks, Paris, saucer 13 cm. diam., c. 1720. **£300-400** *S*

Raised gilding is commonly attributed to a German origin. There is a growing school of thought that considers that raised gilding was also practised in France not only on Saint-Cloud porcelain but on other porcelain and enamel objects.

Three Derby polychrome tea cups, with floral decoration, c. 1756. (*l.*) **£200-250** (*c.*) **£160-200** (*r.*) with slight fault on handle **£250-300** *MA*

A Fulda cup and saucer, painted in iron-red with landscapes including buildings and classical ruins, gilt rims, X in underglaze blue, A incised, minor wear to rims, mid 18th C. **£1,200-1,600** *S*

A Derby tea cup and saucer, with deep blue ground and gilding, c. 1760. **£320-350** *KK*

A Fulda cup, cover and stand, decorated with a blue urn standing on a grassy ground, surrounded by insects, gilt rim, FF beneath on electoral hat in underglaze blue, incised IK probably for the repairer, Knittel, minor wear to gilding, 1781-89. **£800-1,200** *S*

A Ginori blanc-de-Chine libation cup, moulded with sprigs of prunus, 10.5 cm. wide, mid 18th C. **£120-£180** *C*

See 'Blanc-de-Chine' in Glossary.

HÖCHST

- factory was founded in 1746 by the painter A. F. von Löwenfinck from Meissen
- porcelain was produced from 1750
- milk-white in colour, almost tin-glazed appearance
- early wares tended to have poor translucency and be somewhat heavy
- from 1758-65 the style reminiscent of the French 'Louis Seize' style came into fashion
- this style was continued and developed by J. P. Melchior who was chief modeller 1767-79
- the base of figures from 1765 tends to be in the form of a distinctive grassy mound, executed in dark café-au-lait and green stripes
- the factory closed in 1796

A documentary Höchst cup and a saucer, painted by Louis Victor Gerverot, with figures in rural pursuits, the cup with double scroll handle, gilt rims, wheel mark in underglaze blue, 'gerv.' and painter's mark in purple, impressed IE, incised PI, 1765-70, some wear to gilding, possibly matched. **£1,000-1,200** *S*

Louis Victor Gerverot, 1747-1829, was born in Luneville. He was a painter at Sèvres from 1764-65. He is recorded as having worked in Niderviller, Fulda, Ludwigsburg, Ansbach-Bruckberg, Höchst, Frankenthal, Offenbach, Weesp, Schrezheim and for Wedgwood in about 1786. From 1795-1814 he was a director at Fürstenberg.

A pair of Le Nove coffee cups and saucers, painted with figures and buildings in river landscapes in rectangular panels, and with scattered gilt flowers and gilt rims, one saucer with incised Z mark, c. 1775. **£250-350** *C*

A Chaffer's Liverpool blue and white tea bowl and saucer, c. 1760-62. **£250-270** *SRO*

A Christian's Liverpool blue and white tea cup and saucer, nicks in both pieces, c. 1768. **£140-155** *KF*

A Chaffer's Liverpool blue and white hexagonal tea bowl, c. 1758. **£250-280** *SRO*

A Christian's Liverpool blue and white tea cup and saucer, c. 1765. **£165-185** *SRO*

A Christian's Liverpool blue and white tea bowl and saucer, c. 1765-68. **£160-180**   *SRO*

LIVERPOOL

Much discussion has taken place over the last few years as to how many factories in Liverpool were actually producing porcelain in the 18th Century. Three factories — Chaffers, Christian's and Penningtons were the most influential from c. 1754 until the end of the century. Recent research would indicate that there may have been more than one Pennington factory. The accepted dates for the factories:—

- Richard Chaffers & Co., c. 1754-65
- Samuel Gilbody, c. 1754-61
- William Ball, c. 1755-69
- William Reid & Co., c. 1756-61
- Philip Christian & Co., c. 1765-76
- Seth Pennington, c. 1770-99
- Wolfe & Co., c. 1795-1800

Some points on the different factories

- Chaffers & Co. — produced first a bone ash and later a soapstone porcelain, mainly blue and white ware, much good painting, some polychrome wares are of very high quality
- Samuel Gilbody — rarest of Liverpool porcelains, with soft glaze colours which tend to sink into glaze; very difficult factory to correctly attribute wares
- William Ball — blue and white slightly more common from this factory, decoration very Bow-like, glaze can be confused with Longton Hall but frequently has a greenish-blue appearance
- William Reid & Co. — mainly blue and white specimens, quite crude in appearance, often sanded, chinoiserie based decoration, sometimes resembling contemporary style on Liverpool delftware
- Philip Christian & Co. — underglaze blue tends to be of a greyish tone: some fine painting; flatware is rare but bowls were something of a speciality
- Seth Pennington — large amount of copies of Christian's wares, standard never reached earlier factories, mainly blue and white wares
- Wolfe & Co. — polychrome wares normally use chinoiserie decoration, blue and white wares extremely rare

A rare William Ball Liverpool blue and white tea bowl and saucer, c. 1758. **£280-320**   *SRO*

A William Ball blue and white tea bowl and saucer, with rare chinoiserie design, c. 1760. **£650-£720**   *KK*

A William Ball Liverpool tea bowl and saucer, with iron-red, blue and gilt, damaged, c. 1756. **£90-100** *MA*

A rare Lowestoft moulded 'Hughes' pattern blue and white tea bowl and saucer, c. 1762. **£250-280** *SRO*

A Longton Hall blue and white octagonal tea bowl and saucer, decorated with pavilions, rocks and 'comma' scroll borders, painter's marks P in underglaze blue, slight wear, firing fault on tea bowl, c. 1755-57. **£650-750**   *S*

A Lowestoft blue and white tea cup and saucer, hair crack, c. 1765. **£300-330**   *SRO*

A rare Lowestoft blue and white tea bowl and saucer, c. 1762-64. **£200-230**   *SRO*

An unusual Lowestoft blue and white tea bowl and saucer, c. 1770-72. **£130-150** *SRO*

LOWESTOFT, c. 1757-99

- soft paste porcelain
- rather naïve form of painting
- from c. 1757-70 only blue and white ware produced
- early pieces tend to be painted in grey-blue
- the printed designs date mainly from the 1770's
- the 'kick' handle is distinctive
- the Lowestoft body tends to stain — prior to introduction of harder body?
- it is always difficult to put a date on the closing of 18th C. factories as often blanks were later decorated

---

A rare Lowestoft blue and white saucer, c. 1762-64. **£80-100** *SRO*

A Bottger tea bowl and a saucer, each decorated, probably by J. G. Höroldt, with chinoiserie, each scene enclosed by typical scrollwork borders, gilder's mark, 1720-25. **£1,000-1,200** *S*

A Meissen beaker and saucer, painted with chinoiserie panels within scrolling borders in purple, iron-red, gilding and lustre, the back of the saucer with indianische Blumen, crossed swords in blue enamel, the saucer very slightly rubbed, c. 1722-23. **£2,000-2,500** *S*

A Meissen cup and saucer, each with painted panels of single chinoiserie figures in gardens, the cup with ear-shaped handle, between coloured sprays of indianische Blumen, 1 in. gilding, saucer very slightly rubbed, c. 1720-25. **£2,000-2,500** *S*

A Meissen rare powder blue ground beaker, painted with Chinese figures amongst palm trees, c. 1730. **£1,300-1,400** *HOF*

Three early Meissen chinoiserie 2-handled beakers, painted in the workshop of J. G. Herold, with figures within Böttger-lustre, gold, puce and iron-red Laub-und-Bandelwerk cartouches, gilt 2 marks, Hermitage inventory numbers in red, one with small restored rim chip, c. 1725. **£2,000-£2,500** *C*

A Meissen cup and saucer, with scrolling wishbone handle and elaborately decorated with chinoiserie scenes, crossed swords in underglaze blue, H. in gilding, incised numeral 6, c. 1735. **£1,500-£2,000** *S*

A pair of Meissen quatrefoil cups and saucers, blue crossed swords marks and Pressnummern 23 and 24, one saucer incised 25, c. 1738. **£1,800-2,200** *C*

A pair of Meissen 'Kakiemon' cups and saucers, with brown barbed rims, crossed swords in underglaze blue, impressed repairer's mark, one handle missing, one saucer cracked, 1729-32. **£650-750** *S*

A Meissen yellow ground tea bowl and saucer, with 'en grisaille' decoration, flaw on back of saucer, c. 1738-40. **£750-850** *HOF*

The saucer with yellow ground underneath. Ship scenes on Meissen are always more popular.

pair of Meissen 'Hausmaler' tea
wls and saucers, decorated in
lours and gilding, probably by
Mayer of Pressnitz with, on the
ucers, mythological scenes, the
ntre decorated in underglaze blue
d gilding, with the so-called 'Fels
d Vogel' decor, crossed swords
d blue painter's marks in
derglaze blue, mid 18th C.
,000-1,200   *S*

Meissen cinquefoil Kakiemon
ucer, painted with the Flying Fox
ttern, within a chocolate rim,
e crossed swords mark, minor
frits, c. 1730. **£350-450**   *C*

air of Naples porcelain cups and
cers, decorated in relief with the
gement of Paris, and Aphrodite
er chariot with attendants,
ressed marks, one cup cracked.
80   *GC*

*late 18th C. examples of these
lded wares can combine stipple
ted flesh tones and use of tin
e to whiten the glaze. The more
mon 19th/20th C. examples tend
o employ this technique.*

MEISSEN

- in 1709 J. F. Böttger produced a white hard paste porcelain
- wares often decorated by outside decorators (Hausmaler)
- in 1720 kilnmaster Stozel came back to Meissen bringing with him J. G. Herold
- from 1720-50 the enamelling on Meissen was unsurpassed — starting with the wares of *Lowenfinck* — bold, flamboyant chinoiserie or Japponaise subjects, often derived from the engravings of Petruschenk, particularly on Augustus Rex wares, *J. G. Herold* — specialised in elaborate miniature chinoiserie figure subjects, *C. F. Herold* — noted for European and Levantine quay scenes
- crossed swords factory mark started in 1723
- underside of wares on later body has somewhat greyish chalky appearance
- in late 1720's a somewhat glassier, harder looking paste was introduced, different from the early ivory tones of the Böttger period
- finest Meissen figures modelled by J. J. Kändler from 1731
- best figures late 1730's and early 1740's — especially the great Commedia dell'Arte figures and groups
- other distinguished modellers who often worked in association with Kändler were Paul Reinicke and J. F. Eberlein
- cut-flower decoration (Schnittblumen) often associated with J. G. Klinger. The naturalistic flower subjects of the 1740's, epitomised by Klinger, gradually became less realistic and moved towards the so-called 'manier Blumen' of the 1750's and 1760's
- early models had been mounted on simple flat pad bases, whereas from 1750's bases were lightly moulded rococo scrolls

A Meissen cup, cover and saucer,
decorated in Sèvres style, with the
monogram 'IP' below a wreath in
blue, brown and green, and
inscribed 'Kuteuzow', reserved on a
dark blue ground, crossed swords
and a star in underglaze blue,
gilder's mark, late 18th C. **£600-
£700**   *S*

A Meissen tea cup and saucer,
painted with children playing as
soldiers in landscapes, the rim with
a purple feathered border, crossed
swords mark in blue, incised mark,
chips to footrim, mid 18th C. **£400-
£500**   *S*

A Meissen (Marcolini) bucket-
shaped chocolate cup, cover and
saucer, with rural landscapes and
buildings beneath blue bands and
gilt with C-scrolls, blue crossed
swords and star marks, and various
Pressnummern, c. 1785. **£350-450**
C

A pair of Meissen cups and saucers,
each piece painted with cupids,
reserved within a key-fret band,
foliage and ribbons, in enamel
colours and gold, crossed swords
with a dot, c. 1770. **£650-850**   *Bea*

A pair of Vincennes bleu lapis large cups and saucers (Gobelet Calabre), painted with pairs of birds within ciselé gilt cartouches, blue interlaced L enclosing the date letter B for 1754. **£3,000-4,000** *C*

The bleu lapis ground here is underglaze; bleu du roi introduced prior to 1760, whilst of similar tone, is applied overglaze.
See Vincennes and Sèvres pointer.

A Vincennes tea bowl and saucer, chip on saucer restored, c. 1750-52. **£420-450** *KK*

A Sèvres 2-handled cup, cover and stand, painted with grisaille classical busts and trophies, within ciselé gilt and seeded blue bands, divided by gilt brick pattern, blue interlaced L mark and incised repairer's mark, c. 1765. **£400-500** *C*

A Sèvres cup and saucer, with bleu celeste ground, a panel on the saucer showing a young boy holding a bird, on the cup a boy fishing, interlaced L's beneath painter's mark, date letters G in blue enamel, incised repairer's mark, 1759. **£900-1,200** *S*

A Sèvres bleu celeste coffee cup and saucer, gilt with foliage encircled with puce and reserved on the bleu celeste ground, blue interlaced L marks and the date letter F for 1758 with 2 dots, repairer's mark BP to the cup and incised cross to the saucer. **£1,200-1,800** *C*

Bleu celeste was introduced in 1752.

A Sèvres cup and saucer, with scroll handle, painted with figures in river landscapes, with buildings within cisele gilt cartouches and reserved on a blue chequered ground with gilt dots, blue interlaced L mark enclosing the date letter O for 1767, incised repairer's mark. **£700-800** *C*

A Sèvres cup and saucer, painted with white and gilt foliage scrolls on a bleu nouveau ground, vermiculé gilt, puce interlaced L marks, the cup with the date letter for 1768 and the painter's mark of Boulanger, chips to foot rim of cup. **£450-550** *C*

A rare Sèvres chinoiserie cup and saucer, in hard paste, decorated with quatrefoil panels of Orientals in colours on a gilt ground, the panels interspersed with fantastic vignettes of buildings in purple on a pink ground, marked in purple with interlaced L's below a crown, date letters AA and the painter's mark L, the saucer slightly rubbed in the centre, 1778. **£2,000-3,000** *S*

A Sèvres cup and saucer, painted in the Empire taste, with jewelling and foliage, the interior gilt, printed blue Sèvres and fleur-de-lys mark and incised marks, c. 1820. **£550-650** *C*

A Sèvres cup and saucer, painted
with sailing vessels and river
landscapes, divided by gilt foliage
scrolls and floral garlands, blue
interlaced L marks and the date
letters BB for 1779,' and painter's
mark of perhaps Léandre, various
repairer's marks. **£280-320**   *C*

A Vienna (Du Paquier) 2-handled
beaker and trembleuse saucer,
with scroll handle, pierced gallery
and shaped rim painted in
Schwarzlot, the rims gilt, the stand
17 cm. wide, c. 1740. **£2,500-3,000**
C

A Vienna large tea bowl and
saucer, painted with chinoiserie
subjects, with gilt scrolled supports
and with gilt rim, blue bee-hive
marks and various incised marks,
c. 1750. **£480-520**   *C*

A set of 3 'Sèvres' 2nd Republic
cups and stand, painted by
Lahoche, signed, with oval
portraits of ladies from the court of
Louis XVI: Mme. Dubarry, Marie
Lescinska and the Duchesse du
Maine, within leaves in tooled
gilding, incised repairers' marks
and printed marks in green for
1848. **£250-350**   *SS*

A pair of Vienna (Du Paquier)
2-handled beakers, precisely
painted with coloured flowers and
with gilt rim, c. 1730. **£800-1,000**
C

VIENNA

- factory founded by C. I. du
  Paquier in 1719 with the help
  of Stolzel and Hunger from
  Meissen
- the body of du Paquier wares
  has a distinctive smoky tone
- decoration tends to cover
  much of the body and can be
  more elaborate than Meissen
- with an extensive use of trellis
  work or 'gitterwerk'
- the 'State' period of the
  factory ran from 1744-84
- the style of this period was
  baroque, with scrollwork and
  lattice-like gilding
- plain bases were used from
  mid 1760's
- excellent figure modelling
  was undertaken by J. J.
  Niedermayer from 1747-84
- Konrad von Sorgenthal
  became director from
  1784-1804
- the style became far less
  based on rococo and much
  simpler in taste, but with
  good strong colours and
  raised gilding
- factory closed in 1864

A Tournai blue and white tea bowl
and saucer, chips, c. 1760. **£50-55**
KK

A Venice (Vezzi) octagonal tea
bowl, the lower half moulded with
stiff leaves, beneath alternating
panels of foliage, in lime-green and
puce, the interior with a flower
spray and puce band, incised with
white scrolls, iron-red Ven, a mark
and incised M and P, rim chip,
c. 1725. **£3,800-4,200**   *C*

A pair of Vienna coffee cups and
saucers, with gilt C-scrolled borders,
blue bee-hive marks and various
impressed numbers, c. 1765. **£700-800**
C

An early Doccia Stampino blue and white
rectangular tea caddy, the sides stencilled
with flowering branches issuing from
rockwork (fire crack in base), c. 1750,
12.5 cm. high. **£200-300**   *C*

A German tea caddy and cover, painted in colours with a variety of birds perched in trees and scattered winged insects, the rims gilt, 14.5 cm. **£480-540** *P*

A Meissen Hausmalerei tea caddy, with original underglaze blue panels, decorated probably at Augsburg in the Auffenwerth workshop, with alternate gold panels and panels of chinoiserie figures in bright colours, crossed swords mark in underglaze blue, 10 cm. **£500-600** *P*

A Ludwigsburg ornithological flattened gourd shaped tea caddy, with moulded scale pattern and C-scrolled shoulder, painter's mark HL and various impressed numbers, rim repaired, 12 cm. high, c. 1770. **£320-420** *C*

c.f. Lahnstein/Landenberger: op. cit. p. 123 for a similar caddy with similar flowers after drawings by G. Fr. Riedel.

A Meissen quatrefoil tea caddy, blue crossed swords mark, later gilt metal cover, 10 cm. high, c. 1730. **£2,500-3,000** *C*

A Bow chocolate pot and cover, with serpent's head spout and scroll handle at right angles, painted in the Kakiemon style, slight chip to cover, damage to spout, 21.5 cm. high, c. 1755. **£900-1,100** *C*

A Bristol barrel-shaped tea pot and cover, painted with a red parrot in a gilt cage, within a turquoise border, Richard Champion's factory, minute rim chips and minor damage to finial and minute chip to cover, 12.5 cm. high, c. 1775. **£850-1,050** *C*

A Meissen tea caddy with cover, rubbed, 18th C. **£250-300** *DWB*
Painted with manier Blumen, c. 1745-50.

A rare Vienna hexafoil tea caddy, cover and stopper, moulded in relief with the Eight Chinese Immortals, enriched with gilding, impressed mark, 17 cm. high. **£900-1,200** *C*
Shield early State period.

A Meissen turquoise ground tea caddy and cover, the shoulder and cover with puce butterflies, blue crossed swords mark, Pressnummern 49, gilder's mark Z to each piece, 12.5 cm. high, c. 1740. **£2,300-2,800** *C*

A Derby fluted pear-shaped coffee pot and cover, painted with bouquets and scattered flowers, the cover with butterflies, Wm. Duesbury & Co., minute crack to spout, 23 cm. high, c. 1758. **£1,200-£1,800** *C*

A Liverpool globular tea pot and cover, painted in a vibrant sticky blue, William Ball's factory, minute chips to spout and one small chip to underside of cover, 12 cm. high, c. 1758. **£1,800-2,200** C

A Bloor Derby miniature veilleuse, the tea pot and cover set on a pierced cylindrical stand and shallow base, the whole with a blue ground and formal gilt borders, circular thumb-printed mark, hair crack in base, 4¾ in., 1820-40. **£550-650** S

A rare Derby coffee pot and cover, printed in blue with a boy riding a buffalo, in an Oriental landscape, crack, 20 cm., c. 1760. **£750-950** SS

An early Meissen K.P.M. tea pot and cover, with contemporary Augsburg silver-gilt mounts, painted with a man-of-war flying large flags and with European figures on a foreshore, within quatrefoil lustre iron-red and gold Laub-und-Bandelwerk cartouches, K.P.M. above crossed swords in blue, gilder's mark 2., the cover with gilder's mark 3, the mounts by Elias Adam,, 16.5 cm. wide, c. 1725-28. **£8,000-12,000** C

The European subjects on this tea pot are among the earliest to be found on Meissen wares.

A Höchst tea pot and cover, the shoulder and cover with puce trellis, within green swags, blue crowned wheel mark and impressed IN, repair to edge of cover and tip of spout, 11 cm. high, c. 1760. **£650-750** C

A Frankenthal tea pot and cover, painted in colours with, on one side, a shepherdess resting under a tree, her sheep on the reverse, CT beneath crown, cover cracked, 12.5 cm., c. 1775. **£550-650** S

A Meissen tea pot and a cover, with fish-moulded spout and wishbone handle, the body painted with a continuous landscape of merchants by a harbour, cover surmounted by a passion fruit knop, rubbed, crossed swords in underglaze blue, 11 cm., c. 1740. **£580-680** S

A Meissen tea pot and cover, with gilt Gitterwerk and puce and iron-red scroll cartouches, blue crossed swords and gilt 59 marks, crack in handle, 15 cm. wide, c. 1740. **£900-£1,200** C

A Meissen coffee pot and cover, the scroll handle painted with Indianische Blumen, painted with shaped panels of chinoiserie figures, gilder's no. 3 to the base, replacement finial, cover repaired, minute chip to spout, 21 cm. high, c. 1725. **£3,000-4,000** C

A Meissen coffee pot and cover, blue crossed swords mark, spout and handle restored, 24 cm. high, c. 1755. **£250-350** C

A Meissen tea pot and cover, of quatrefoil form with faceted spout and angular scrolling handle, painted in colours with scattered floral sprays, butterflies and insects, crossed swords in blue, chip on rim, 13.5 cm., c. 1735. **£500-600** S

A Newhall straight sided oval tea pot, in Imari colours, pattern 570, star crack, 6¼ in. **£150-170**   *MA*

A Meissen coffee pot and cover, blue crossed swords and dot mark, restoration to finial, 24.5 cm. high, c. 1745. **£250-350**   *C*

A Meissen coffee pot and cover, with scroll-moulded spout and handle, painted with views within a border of flowers, foliage, flower-baskets and purple scrolls, crossed swords in underglaze blue, chips to cover, 25 cm., mid 18th C. **£600-800** *S*

It has been suggested that this coffee pot was painted by John Baptist Balthasar Bornemann (Borrmann).

A Meissen tea kettle, cover and stand, the kettle with ormolu mounts and quatrefoil panels painted with figures in landscapes, within gilt borders on a purple ground, open on one side to take a burner, the cover attached by a gilt-metal chain, crossed swords in underglaze blue on the stand, minor crack on stand, 38 cm., mid 18th C. **£2,000-2,500**   *S*

A Newhall double ogee tea pot, pattern 173, lid damage, slight chip on spout, 7 in., c. 1785. **£50-60** *MA*

A Tournai coffee pot and cover, painted in colours with a parrot perched in a tree on each side, the parrots named in gilding on the base, incised marks, 26 cm., late 18th C. **£800-1,200**   *S*

A Newhall silver shape tea pot, pattern 366, hair crack, chips on lid, 6 in. **£90-110**   *MA*

A Rockingham miniature tea pot and cover, applied with trailing garden flowers, puce griffin mark finial chipped, minor chipping to flowers, 7 cm. high, c. 1835. **£480-£550**   *C*

TOURNAI

- founded in 1751 by F. J. Peterinck
- produced soft-paste porcelain which is strongly reminiscent and difficult to distinguish from Mennecy
- early body tends to be a little greyish becoming more yellow later
- early wares were imitations of Meissen, then in the 1760's copied Sèvres
- much porcelain sold 'in the white' and decorated elsewhere
- as with many other European factories, the Louis XVI style was followed in the 1780's
- amalgamated with the Saint-Amand-les-Eaux factory
- closed in the mid 18th C.

A Spode tea pot of unusual small size, 4½ in., c. 1805. **£170-190** *MA*

A 'Vienna' tea kettle and cover painted by Kramer, with 'Tanz' and 'Werbung' between royal blue borders, shield in underglaze blue, 8 in. (20 cm.), late 19th C. **£600-800** *S*

A Newhall boat-shaped tea pot and cover, pattern 571, slight chip, 6 in., c. 1800. **£120-140**   *MA*

A Champion's Bristol part coffee set, from the 'Gainsborough' service comprising: 2 coffee cups and saucers, a milk jug and cover, and a sucrier and cover, each painted with brightly coloured flowers, milk jug and sucrier riveted, overall wear, c. 1775-78. **£300-400** S

A Coalport tête-à-tête in Sèvres style, painted 'en grisaille' with gilt scroll borders reserved on a rich aquamarine ground, comprising: tea pot and cover, sucrier and cover, cream jug, and shaped oval tray, CBD marks in gilding, 1851-61. **£500-600** SC

A 'solitaire' is a tea set on tray for one, a 'tête-à-tête' for two and a cabaret' set for more than two.

A 19th C. Coalport tea service, 37 pieces. **£550-650** CW

A 'Coalport' porcelain tea service, each piece with a band of alternate blue and white panels painted in gold, with a pendant foliate design, comprising: tea pot and cover, milk jug, sugar basin and cover, slop basin, plate, 10 tea cups, 7 coffee cups and 3 saucers, slight damage, late 26 cm., 1835-40. **£180-220** Bea

A Caughley part tea service, painted with blue and gilt comprising: a tea pot and cover, a milk jug, a sugar bowl and cover, 2 saucer dishes, 3 coffee cups, 3 tea bowls and 2 saucers, blue S mark, puce mark, c. 1785-95. **£180-220** CSK

A Copeland and Garrett breakfast set, painted with brightly coloured birds, within moulded and gilt foliate scrolls against an azure ground, comprising: 6 breakfast cups and 6 saucers, 6 plates and a small bowl, printed mark, painted pattern number 5697, 3 items cracked, 1833-47. **£800-900** S

Use the Index!
Because certain items might fit easily into any of a number of categories, the quickest and surest method of locating any entry is by reference to the index at the back of the book. This has been fully cross-referenced for absolute simplicity.

A Royal Copenhagen coffee service, with osier moulded and gilt rims, comprising: coffee pot and cover, sucrier and cover, 11 cups, 14 saucers, creamer and cover, milk jug, water jug, 3 dishes and 2 odd covers, underglaze blue wavy line, early 19th C. **£400-500** SS

A Derby part solitaire, painted in the manner of Zachariah Boreman, in puce camaieu, comprising a tea cup and saucer (crack to base of handle), a sugar bowl and cover and shaped quatrefoil tray, Crown, crossed batons and D marks in puce, Wm. Duesbury & Co., c. 1785. **£1,200-1,800** C

A Derby 'Old Japan' pattern tea and coffee set, comprising: a tea pot, cover and stand, a milk jug, a sugar bowl and cover, a slop bowl, 12 coffee cans, 12 tea cups and 12 saucers, painted crowned crossed batons and D in red, various painted numerals, one cup repaired with rivets, several other items with cracks and chips, c. 1820. **£1,200-1,800** S

A Meissen travelling service, painted with Teniers figures comprising: a samovar and cover, a tea caddy and cover, a sugar bowl and cover, 2 teaspoons, 2 coffee cups, 2 tea cups and 2 saucers, blue crossed swords marks and various Pressnummern, in contemporary fitted leather case, restoration to the samovar and the handle of one coffee cup, c. 1750. **£3,800-4,500** C

A Derby part tea service, painted with cornflowers within gilt borders, comprising: a tea pot and cover, a milk jug, a slop bowl, 2 dishes, 8 coffee cups, 2 tea cups and 11 saucers, Crown, crossed batons and D marks in puce, c. 1790. **£500-£600**   *CSK*

A Newhall part coffee service, printed in the manner of Adam Buck, comprising: milk jug, bowl and 2 coffee cans and saucers, pattern no. 1277. **£200-300**   *T*

A composite Sèvres tea service, with feuille de choux borders, painted in blue and gilt, comprising: tea pot and cover, sugar bowl and cover, milk jug, 12 cups and saucers, some pieces marked with interlaced L's, various date letters and painter's marks, tea pot and sugar bowl restored, 18th C. **£1,200-1,800**   *S*

A pair of Meissen cups and saucers, with a pink scale ground, enriched with gilt florettes, enclosing fruit and flower reserves and a small Meissen milk jug and cover and tea caddy en suite, crossed swords in underglaze blue, impressed and incised numerals, chips to saucers, damage to cover, mid 18th C. **£800-£1,200**   *S*

An outside decorated Meissen and Dresden tea and coffee set, comprising: a gilt-metal mounted tea kettle and cover on stand complete with burner and cover, a coffee pot and cover, a sugar bowl and cover, a milk jug, 5 cups, 5 saucers and shaped rectangular tray, some items with cancelled crossed swords in underglaze blue, other items with erased crowned D mark, slight wear, tray 1 ft. 5½ in. (44.3 cm.), late 19th C. **£2,000-£2,500**   *S*

A Rockingham tea and coffee service, decorated in grey and gilding, comprising: sucrier and cover, milk jug, slop basin, 11 tea cups, 6 coffee cups, 11 saucers, 12 plates, saucers with griffin marks in puce, 1830-42. **£350-450**   *SC*

A composite Sèvres tea service, decorated with swags and garlands of flowers in blue, gilt dentil rims, comprising: tea pot and cover, sugar bowl and cover, milk jug, 6 cups and saucers, some marked with interlaced L's, various date letters and painters' marks, incised marks, 18th C. **£1,800-£2,200**   *S*

A Meissen part Jagd service, with puce and gilt rococo supports and with gilt foliage rim, comprising: a coffee pot and cover, a sugar bowl and cover, a cream jug, 2 coffee cups and a tea cup, blue crossed swords and dot marks and various Pressnummern, c. 1770. **£1,000-£1,200**   *C*

A Miles Mason part tea service, painted with iron-red flowers, divided by pink ribbons on a gilt vermicular ground, a tea pot cover and stand, a sugar bowl and cover, a slop bowl, 2 dishes, 6 coffee cups, 9 tea cups and 12 saucers, pattern 483, c. 1810. **£750-850**   *CSK*

A Rockingham breakfast and tea service, glazed in rich brown, gilt rims, printed griffin mark in iron-red, including 'Manufacturer to the Queen', some staining, 1842-46. **£500-600**   *SC*

A rare Oude Amstel porcelain coffee service, comprising: coffee pot and cover, 9 coffee cans and stands, a cylindrical jug and a tea pot and cover, all marked 'Amstel' in underglaze blue script, one can initialled 'R(?)B' in underglaze blue, coffee pot cracked, coffee pot and cover 26.5 cm., 1780's. **£2,500-£3,000**   *SS*

A German box fairing, 10.3 cm.
£20-30 *Bea*

A German china fairing, entitled
'Paddling his own canoe', 11 cm.
high. **£30-40** *Bea*

A German china fairing, entitled
'Open your mouth and shut your
eyes', incised no. 2861, some
damage. **£100-200** *Bea*

FAIRINGS

Now Marm Say When, damaged	£30-40
A fairing type group depicting a blacksmith repairing the hoops in a lady's dress, damaged	£20-25
Ready to Start, damaged	£20-30
The Orphans	£70-80
Tug of War, restored	£30-40
Good Templars, restored	£40-50
Hark Tom, Somebody's Coming, restored	£40-50
Five o'clock Tea, restored	£45-55
Good Night	£30-35
When a Man is Married his Troubles Begin and God Bless our Home, both restored	£35-45
Shall we Sleep First or How?	£35-45
Necessity Knows no Law	£50-60
Little Red Riding Hood	£40-50
Tug of War, restored and The Last in Bed to put out the Light, damaged	£40-50
A matchstriker modelled with a boy and a puppy and a similar matchstriker	£40-50
I am Starting for a Long Journey, and I am off With Him	£40-50
Two matchstrikers modelled with children	£30-50
A Brothel Series figure, damaged	£15-25
A matchholder modelled as an Artist figure and another figure	£35-45
A figure of a man replacing his boot, another of a lady from the Brothel Series and one other	£20-25
A pin holder modelled with a child and a puppy on a dressing table	£25-30
Two dressing table style pin boxes and covers	£40-50
Five o'clock Tea, damaged	£45-55
...or, Three Legs I'll Charge 2d., restored	£35-40
Oysters Sir?	£50-60
Now Ma'rm say When, damaged	£40-50
(Happy Father!) What two, yes Sir, two little beauties!!, brightly decorated	£60-70
An awkward interruption, restored	£30-40
Tug of War, damaged	£30-40
The Decided Smash	£70-90
Pluck, restored	£30-40
A long pull and a strong pull, restored	£70-80
Three o'clock in the morning	£20-30
Kiss me Quick	£30-40
Come Along these Flowers	

Don't Smell very good, restored	£30-40
The Power of Love, damaged	£40-50
Sir, where is your gloves if you think to go out with me, good condition	£150-180
The Last in Bed to put out the Light, damaged	£15-20
Love's First Lesson	£35-45
The Wedding Night and The Old Welsh Spinning Wheel, both reproductions	£5-10
Nothing Venture, Nothing Have	£45-55
A pastoral visit by the Rev. John Jones	£25-35
Returning at one o'clock in the morning, restored	£25-30
I am Starting for a long journey, and I am off with him, both restored	£25-35
Good Templars, restored, and an uncaptioned fairing of two cats	£20-25
Shall we Sleep first or how? and When a man is married his troubles begin	£20-25
Welsh Tea Party, two examples	£35-40
Ladies of Llangollen and Jenny Jones and Ned Morgan, uncaptioned	£25-35
The Spoils of War, slight damage	£40-50
Tug of War, damaged	£30-40
The Organ Boy, good condition	£150-180
The Murder, untitled, good condition	£40-50
The Spoils of War	£60-70
Two fairing type groups of girls riding cycles, repaired	£15-20
Beware of a collision, restored	£100-120
To Epsom, head restored to front nearside rider	£200-250
The Power of Love	£45-55
Kiss me Quick, slight damage	£35-45
Be Good and if you can't be Good, be Careful	£50-60
Married for Money	£40-50
Sarah's young man, small chip to hat	£45-55
Returning at one o'clock in the morning	£20-30
The Last in Bed to put out the Light, two examples, both damaged	£25-30
Shall we Sleep first or How? and Twelve Months after Marriage, both damaged	£20-30
The Wedding Night, slight damage to candlestick	£45-55
Twelve Months after Marriage	£30-40

18th C. DERBY

- some early white jugs incised with the letter 'D' have been attributed to the Derby factory under the direction of John Heath and Andrew Planché, believed to start c. 1750
- early Derby is soft paste and is generally lighter than Bow and Chelsea
- very rare to find crazing on early Derby, the glaze was tight fitting and thinner than Chelsea
- glaze often kept away from the bottom edge or edge was trimmed, hence the term 'dry-edge'
- c. 1755, three (or more) pieces of clay put on bottom of figure to keep it clear of kiln furniture, giving 'patch' or 'pad' marks — which now have darker appearance
- Duesbury had joined Heath and Planché in 1756
- Duesbury's early works display quite restrained decoration, with much of the body left plain, following the Meissen style
- Derby can be regarded as the English Meissen
- the porcelain of this period has an excellent body, sometimes with faintly bluish appearance

A Derby cow and calf group, 5¾ in., c. 1800. **£250-280**   *DL*
Bocage in mint condition adds considerably to the value.

A Derby fox, 3 in., c. 1800. **£275-£295**   *DL*

- Chelsea-Derby figures almost always made at Derby
- 1770's saw the introduction of unglazed white biscuit Derby figures
- this points to the move away from the academic Meissen style towards the more fashionable French taste
- 1770-84 known as the Chelsea-Derby period
- in 1770's a leading exponent of the neo-classical style, and comparable to contemporary wares of Champion's Bristol
- body of 1770's is frequently of silky appearance and of bluish-white tone
- 1780's Derby body very smooth and glaze white, the painting on such pieces was superb, particularly landscapes, Jockey Hill and Zachariah Boreman
- 1780's and 1790's noted for exceptional botanical painting of the period especially by 'Quaker' Pegg and John Brewer
- around 1800 the body degenerated, was somewhat thicker, the glaze tended to crackle and allow discolouration

A rare Frankenthal figure of a wild boar, on a base mottled in green, CT beneath crown and above 77 in underglaze blue, damage to both ears, shrub and one leg, 13.5 cm., 1777. **£3,500-4,000**   *S*

A Meissen cockatoo, decorated in yellow and white, on a tree stump base, 14½ in. high, late 19th C. **£300-400**   *Pea*

Whilst Meissen tree stumps were left in the white in the 18th C. and early 19th C., in the mid and late 19th C. they were painted overall in semi-naturalistic russet tones.

A large Meissen cockerel, the brightly coloured bird standing upon a bundle of sticks, crossed swords in underglaze blue, incised '1661', restoration, 39 cm., 19th C. **£300-500**   *SS*

A pair of Meissen foxes, in shades of brown, black and red, traces of crossed swords in blue, minor chips, 10.5 cm., mid 18th C. **£1,500-2,000**   *S*

A rare Longton Hall figure of an owl in the white, 5 in., c. 1755. **£5,500-6,000**   *DWB*

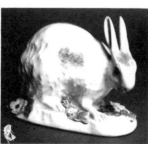

A Meissen hare, shallow glaze chip on base, ears partly restored, 4 in. wide, c. 1745. **£1,250-1,350**   *HOF*

A Meissen figure of a Bolognese terrier, with pink and brown eyes, its coat grey and brown, blue crossed swords mark, slight chip to tail, 22 cm. high, c. 1880. **£550-600**   *C*

A pair of Meissen groups of billing doves, modelled by J. J. Kändler, in the white, traces of crossed swords in blue, 2 beaks damaged, 14 cm., mid 18th C. **£700-900** *S*

An English porcelain model of a rabbit, painted in pink and black, gold line encircling the base, probably Minton, impressed M under the base, 5.5 cm. long, mid 19th C. **£150-200** *Bea*

Two Plymouth white figures of pheasants, on shaped circular bases, beneath a toffee glaze, William Cookworthy's factory, beaks and tails restored, some chipping to flowers and branches, 20 cm. high, c. 1768. **£1,500-2,000** *C*

A pair of Staffordshire porcellaneous figures of a unicorn and a lion, unicorn restored, 9 cm. high, c. 1850. **£120-180** *SS*

A pair of porcelain pointers, 4½ in., c. 1830. **£225-250** *GCA*

An English porcelain mouse, 3 in. wide, c. 1835. **£100-125** *DL*

A Nymphenburg figure of a parrot, modelled by Dominicus Auliczek, its plumage realistically painted in green, yellow, iron-red and blue, impressed Bavarian shield mark and I D, 15.5 cm. high, c. 1765. **£3,000-3,500** *C*

A rare Belleek standing figure of a young woman, the circular pedestal impressed Belleek Pottery, printed mark a hound, a harp and Belleek, 43 cm. **£2,500-3,000** *L*

A pair of Berlin figures, each as a vintager standing behind a floral painted basket, sceptre in underglaze blue, printed orb and KPM in red, handles on one basket missing, chips, 22.5 and 22 cm., c. 1880. **£300-400** *S*

A Belleek-style porcelain group, of 3 women representing Peace, The Arts and Industry, 27 cm., mid 19th C. **£180-220** *Bea*

NYMPHENBURG

- factory founded in the late 1740's but the main production started in 1753
- J. J. Ringler was employed as arcanist
- from 1757 a fine milky-white porcelain was produced
- the porcelain is of great quality and virtually flawless
- F. A. Bustelli modelled some excellent figures from 1754-63 which perfectly expressed the German rococo movement
- the models are the epitome of movement and crispness and are invariably set on sparingly moulded rococo pad bases
- note light construction of these slip-cast figures
- J. P. Melchior, previously at Frankenthal and Höchst, was chief modeller from 1797-1810
- on finest pieces the mark is often incorporated as part of the design
- the factory still exists

Two rare complementary Bow figures of Harlequin and Columbine, modelled after Meissen originals, slight damage to Harlequin, restoration to Columbine, 4¾ in., c. 1755. **£1,500-£1,800** *S*

BOW FIGURES

- the earliest Bow figures had simple pad bases in common with Chelsea and Derby
- figures tend to be less sophisticated than those from the Chelsea factory
- from 1750-54 many figures were modelled by the 'Muses modeller'
- these figures have quite thick glaze and low square bases
- best period runs from 1750-59
- the influence of Meissen can be seen in the figures from c. 1755 on
- many figures left in the white
- rococo bases appeared in late 1750's, earlier bases of c. 1760 in common with Chelsea are relatively restrained
- by 1760 'C & S' scroll decoration was in great demand as were large shell bases, which are often thought of as a trade mark of Bow (although other factories did use them)
- by 1760's typical colours used are blue, emerald-green, yellow and a good red
- from c. 1765 greater use of underglaze blue as a ground colour, like contemporaries at Longton Hall
- late 1760's figures elevated on more elaborate and pierced bases, generally applied with flowers
- figures with elaborate bocage are typical
- figures tend now to copy Chelsea gold anchor groups
- figures with an underglaze blue crescent tend to be Bow (Worcester produced very few figures)

A Bow figure of Neptune, restored, 7¾ in., c. 1760. **£270-295** *DL*

A rare Bow figure of the Hurdy Gurdy player, after Meissen model by Kändler and Reinicke, from the Cris de Paris, some restoration, 5½ in., c. 1755-65. **£670-750** *KK*

A Bow figure of Earth, modelled as a nymph in a pink and yellow cloak, holding a cornucopia and standing on a mound base with a lion at her feet, arm damaged, 7½ in., c. 1760. **£250-300** *S*

A rare Bow blackamoor sweetmeat figure, the lady wearing a purple bodice and red-lined blue veiled head-dress, restoration to basket, chip on base, 7 in., c. 1760. **£600-£700** *S*

A Bow new dancer, modelled as a youth in plumed yellow hat, yellow-lined pink jacket and striped yellow trousers, left hand repaired, 18 cm. high, c. 1758. **£400-500** *C*

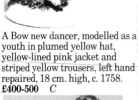

A Bow figure of Matrimony, in pink, yellow and pale blue, arms, neck and tree-stump restored, 18.5 cm. high, c. 1760. **£400-500** *C*

A Bow Bacchanalian group, modelled as 2 naked putti garlanded with fruiting vine, one seated astride a goat suckling its kid, on a high scrolling base, edged in purple, blue and gilding, goat's tail missing, 8 in., c. 1760-65. **£1,000-1,200** *S*

A Bow figure of a blackamoor attendant, in predominantly pink and yellow clothes, with a blue sash and pale blue trousers, restoration to neck, arm and hand and 2 feet of base, 19 cm. high, c. 1760. **£320-380** *C*

A Bow figure of a drummer, in yellow-lined pink jacket and striped breeches, the stand moulded and painted with martial trophies, restoration to figure and pedestal, 25 cm. high, c. 1760. **£650-700** *C*

A Bow figure of a gardener's companion, painted in a vibrant palette, in blue, yellow and pink, on a moulded mound base, enriched in blue and puce, hat and some flowers restored, 17 cm. high, c. 1762. **£600-£700** *C*

A Bow figure of a nun, seated reading her breviary, in blue habit, yellow-lined black veil and black scapula, anchor and dagger mark in iron-red, firing crack to back of base, 19.8 cm. high, c. 1768. **£400-£500** *C*

A Bow figure of a lady in Turkish dress, in yellow, puce, gilt and blue flowered clothes, anchor and dagger mark in iron-red, minor chips, 19.5 cm. high, c. 1765. **£550-650** *C*

A rare Bow figure of Mars, the god in lilac, green and red classical armour and plumed helmet, a recumbent mule and a cannon at his feet, painted anchor and dagger mark in red, minor damage, 8 in., c. 1760-65. **£450-550** *S*

A Cozzi figure possibly representing Charity, with slight damage to head, 8 cm., c. 1775. **£500-700** *S*

A Bristol white figure of Water, from a set of the Elements, minor chipping to left hand and wreath, 26.5 cm. high, c. 1770-75. **£500-600** *C*

A Capodimonte (Carlo III) figure of a nymph, emblematic of Summer, modelled by Gricci, her dress with gilt florets and stylised border in green and puce, edged with gilding blue fleur-de-lys, 13.5 cm. high, c. 1750. **£3,500-4,500** *C*
This figure has the typical disproportionate head so often associated with Gricci's figures.

CHELSEA FIGURES

- **triangle period (1745-49) figures are extremely rare**
- **the raised anchor period (c. 1749-52) figures are again scarce — many were left in the white**
- **the finest figures were made in the red anchor period (c. 1753-57). These figures are beautifully proportioned and exquisitely enamelled — the colours are always used sparingly. They were often direct copies of Meissen but due to the soft paste porcelain seem to have a 'softer' appearance. They lack the brilliant whiteness and brittleness of the German counterparts. Virtually no gilding appears until c. 1759.**
- **this heralded the beginning of the gold anchor period (c. 1758-70). The glaze was now thicker, gilding which appears in the early gold anchor period became less restrained following the current fashion at Sèvres. Figures were frequently backed by heavy bocages and stood on heavy scroll bases**

A Chelsea figure emblematic of Earth, modelled as a young lady in long yellow robe and floral dress holding a cornucopia with a lion recumbent at her feet, gold anchor mark, 8½ in. high, c. 1760. **£450-550** *CSK*

A Chelsea figure of a shepherd, with flowering pink and yellow cloak, iron-red tunic and turquoise breeches, gold anchor mark, some restoration, 29 cm. high, c. 1765. **£450-550** *C*

A pair of Chelsea figures of a gardener and companion, she with gold anchor mark at back, both some restoration, 23.5 cm. high, c. 1765. **£750-950** *C*

A Derby figure of a Ranelagh dancer, in pale yellow flowered cloak, pink hose and yellow breeches, Wm. Duesbury & Co., restoration to neck, left hand and thigh, 28 cm. high, c. 1756. **£500-£600** *C*

A Derby figure of a bagpiper, in blue bonnet, pink jacket, turquoise cloak and iron-red breeches, playing his instrument, Wm. Duesbury & Co., restoration to hands, instrument, cloak and neck, 16.5 cm. high, c. 1758. **£380-450** *C*

A Derby figure of a huntsman, gold anchor mark, 6¾ in., c. 1764. **£300-350** *DL*
Can be wrongly classified as Chelsea due to misleading mark.

A Derby figure of Mars, in gilt scale pattern cuirass and yellow and white cloak and chiton, with a shield and a pink flag at his side, Wm. Duesbury & Co., minor chips to flag, 17 cm. high, c. 1760. **£350-£450** *C*

A pair of Derby figures 'Ranlegh Dancers', 12½ in., c. 1765. **£750-790** *DL*

A Derby figure of Jupiter, draped in yellow-lined pink clothes, seated in a chariot with an eagle before him, Wm. Duesbury & Co., some restoration to left hand, eagle and chariot's wheel, 25 cm. high, c. 1765. **£400-500** *C*

A Derby figure of a Turk, left forearm and hand restored, 5½ in., c. 1765. **£180-195** *KK*

A pair of Derby figures of Mercury and Fame, draped in turquoise, purple and pink flowered clothes, Wm. Duesbury & Co., restored, 22 and 21.5 cm. high, c. 1765. **£450-£550** *C*

A Derby figure of a young man, in turquoise coat and yellow breeches, beating a tambourine and standing before a flowering bush, 7½ in. high, c. 1768. **£380-420** *CSK*

A pair of Derby figures of a shepherd and shepherdess, restored, 9½ in., c. 1765. **£550-595** *DL*

Two Derby figures of Neptune and Venus, each set on a rocky mound base applied with numerous colourful shells, coral and weeds below a large dolphin, chips, repairs and some restoration, 9¾ in., c. 1770. **£900-1,200** *S*

A Derby porcelain figure, in a green jacket and decorative breeches, with a spirit barrel slung over his shoulder, restored, 7⅜ in. high. **£150-250** *GC*

A Derby figure of John Wilkes, after Pierre Stephan, his right hand on scrolls, inscribed 'MAGNA CARTA' and 'THE BILL OF RIGHTS', a putto at his feet holding a book inscribed in gilt 'JN O WILKES ESQ', chip to nose, 13 in., c. 1770-75. **£350-450** *DW*

A Frankenthal group of marital discord (die Zweitracht in der Ehe), modelled by Karl Gottlieb Luck, the husband seated in drunken disarray being chastised by his wife, blue crowned CT and 6 mark, 18 cm. wide, c. 1770. **£2,500-3,000** *C*

A pair of French coloured biscuit figures, of a barbarian and his companion, painted crossed swords, some damage and restoration, 1 ft. 6 in. and 1 ft. 6¼ in. (46 and 46.5 cm.), mid to late 19th C. **£350-400** *S*

A pair of Gardner figures, painted in colours, impressed St. George and factory mark, Moscow, 14.5 cm. high, c. 1850. **£300-380** *C*

A Gardner biscuit group of a laundress, with child beside her playing the squeezebox, red factory mark and numbered 132, Moscow, 4½ in. (11.5 cm.), c. 1880. **£350-400** *S*

FRANKENTHAL

- Paul A. Hannong started producing porcelain in Frankenthal in 1755, under the patronage of the Elector Carl Theodor
- glaze has a quite distinctive quality as it tends to 'soak in' the enamel colours
- high quality porcelain produced under Modellmeister J. W. Lanz, who favoured striped gilt grounds and green and dark puce
- K. G. Lück and his brother or cousin J. F. Lück came to Frankenthal from Meissen in 1758
- K. G. Lück's work tends to be quite fussy and often on grassy mounds, with rococo edges picked out in gilding
- in the late 18th C. a fine range of figures produced by J. P. Melchior and A. Bauer
- Melchior also worked at Höchst
- Frankenthal utility ware is noted for the quality of the painting, particularly flower painting
- factory closed in 1799
- moulds from the factory were used in many 19th C. German factories

A pair of French biscuit porcelain figures, each dressed in colourful 18th C. costume, 34.5 cm., late 19th C. **£250-300** *Bea*

A Gardner biscuit porcelain figure of a man eating bread, wearing a black coat and blue trousers, impressed and red factory mark, Moscow, 5 in. (13 cm.), c. 1880. **£300-380** *S*

A Frankenthal figure of a girl milking a goat, horns and one ear restored, 4½ in., c. 1770. **£850-930** *KK*

A Frankenthal group of marital concord (die Eintracht in der Ehe), modelled by Karl Gottlieb Luck, embracing, blue crowned CT mark and AB monogram of Adam Bergdoll, minor damage to tree stump, 17 cm. wide, c. 1770. **£2,500-3,000** *C*

A pair of Giles Jeune coloured biscuit figures, applied blue tablet mark, one restored, 9½ in. and 10 in. (24.5 cm. and 25.5 cm.), mid to late 19th C. **£300-400** *S*

A Gardner biscuit figure of a dancing man, wearing a black hat and grey coat with green belt, impressed St. George and printed Gardner mark under Imperial Warrant, Moscow, 25 cm. high, c. 1870. **£250-300** *C*

A Gardner biscuit porcelain figure of an old woman making thread, factory mark in red, impressed St. George and the Dragon, numbered 99 and 3, Moscow, 5 in. (13 cm.), c. 1880. **£250-300**   *S*

An Höchst figure of a young girl, modelled by J. P. Melchoir standing in yellow lined white cape and red striped skirt, blue wheel mark and incised DN, M85, N88, 11 cm. high, c. 1765. **£500-700**   *C*

A pair of Le Nove figures of a lady and a gentleman, their clothes in puce, green, yellow and pink, restorations to her arm and right leg and damages to his hands, 15 cm. high, c. 1790. **£1,200-1,600** *C*

An Höchst figure of a Chinese musician, playing the serpent and standing on a dark green square base with canted corners, probably modelled by the 'Chinesen Meister', wheel mark in underglaze blue, incised mark, serpent and right foot damaged, drapery restored, 18.5 cm., c. 1765. **£700-800**   *S*

A Liverpool blue and white figure of a Chinese Immortal, enriched in underglaze blue, Richard Chaffer's Factory, 15 cm. high, c. 1760. **£800-1,200** *C*

No similar example of this figure would appear to be recorded although in paste and glaze it is closest to the steatitic wares made at Richard Chaffer's factory in Liverpool.

A rare Longton Hall figure of a toper, seated on a tree stump and resting on a barrel, he wears a plumed hat, purple jacket and yellow breeches, restored, 5 in., c. 1755. **£550-650**   *S*

Four Limbach figures of musicians, wearing mostly pale puce clothes, on scroll moulded mound bases, some damage, 14.5 cm. high, c. 1775. **£2,400-2,800**   *C*

A Ludwigsburg figure of a butcher about to cut up a pig, iron-red coat, yellow breeches and black shoes, blue crowned interlaced C mark and incised CS, 11.5 cm. wide, c. 1765. **£400-600**   *C*

LUDWIGSBURG

- porcelain factory was founded in 1758
- J. J. Ringler directed the factory from 1759-99
- best period was from 1765-75
- porcelain has a distinctly greyish tone which is generally poorer than contemporary German factories
- specialised in producing figures
- most desirable are the 'Venetian fair groups' produced by Jean-Jacob Louis
- in 1770's figures of a more classical nature were produced
- the later figures were of a much poorer quality
- quality of the flower painting is of a fairly undistinguished nature
- the factory closed in 1824

A rare pair of Longton Hall seated figures of a boy and girl, emblematic of Spring and Summer, she with a yellow bodice, he with a mauve jacket and black breeches, the scrolling bases edged in green and purple, the boy repaired, 5 in., c. 1756. **£1,500-1,800**   *S*

A Ludwigsburg figure of a peasant, wearing a purple bodice above a yellow skirt, the mound base mottled in green and brown, interlaced C's in underglaze blue, painter's mark in iron-red, impressed and incised numerals and letters, damage to nose, 15 cm., c. 1765. **£400-500**   *S*

A Ludwigsburg figure of a spinet player, from the series of the 'Kleine Musiksoli' modelled by J. C. W. Beyer, the lady playing a spinet with green-glazed case, interlaced C's beneath crown, L in iron-red, PZ and SZ incised, one corner of base repaired, 10 cm., 1765-70. **£750-850**   *S*

A Ludwigsburg figure of a young girl holding a puppy, she wears a lilac jacket piped in green, indistinct interlaced C's mark in blue, 11.2 cm. **£580-680**   *P*

A Böttger pagoda figure, seated in black cap, yellow-lined purple-spotted cloak and iron-red breeches, firing crack extended and re-stuck, 10 cm. high, c. 1720. **£1,800-2,200**   *C*

A Ludwigsburg figure of a Vestal Virgin, wearing a floral patterned skirt beneath a yellow-lined purple cloak, interlaced C's in underglaze blue, painter's mark in iron-red, various incised marks and numerals, 14.5 cm., c. 1770. **£600-£800**   *S*

A pair of Meissen figures of cooks, in blue bodices, both seated on brown and brickwork bases, blue crossed swords mark on the back of her base, the knife in her left hand damaged, 18 cm. high, c. 1745. **£3,000-3,500**   *C*

A Meissen figure of Christ crucified, naturalistically painted in iron-red with blood from His wounds and suspended from a wooden cross, 25.5 cm. overall, the porcelain 18.3 cm., c. 1743. **£1,000-£1,200**   *S*

A Meissen figure of Harlequin with a passglass, modelled by J. J. Kändler, holding bagpipes made from the skin of a goat with head and horns, painted in colours, the plain rockwork base with a tricorn hat, blue crossed swords mark at the back, 14.5 cm. high. **£2,800-£3,500**   *C*

A Meissen figure of a sower, modelled by J. J. Kändler, in white scarf, green bodice, yellow apron and white skirt, traces of blue crossed swords mark on base, restored through waist, 21.5 cm. high, c. 1745. **£550-650**   *C*

A Meissen figure of a sower, modelled by J. J. Kändler, in brown jacket, cream breeches, holding seeds in his apron, the mound base applied with coloured flowers, traces of blue crossed swords marks on base, restoration to his hat and right arm, 21.5 cm., c. 1745. **£1,200-£1,800**   *C*

A Meissen figure of the doctor, from the Weissenfels series of Commedia dell'Arte figures, modelled by Peter Reinicke, with a black hat, white cloak over an iron-red and gilt coat, white breeches and black shoes, traces of mark in blue, one hand damaged, 14 cm., c. 1745. **£3,200-3,800**   *S*

A Meissen figure of a young boy with nodding head, modelled by J. J. Kändler, with a yellow-lined puce gown, blue crossed swords mark at back, minor chips to his hat, 21.5 cm. high, c. 1750. **£2,000-£2,500**   *C*

Four Meissen miniature busts emblematic of the Seasons, blue crossed swords marks on the back of Winter, 8.5 cm. high, c. 1750. **£450-550**   *C*

A Meissen Italian comedy scent bottle, with gold mounts, formed as a figure of Harlequin in yellow hat, iron-red and yellow and puce-scaled quartered suit, contemporary stopper with blue crossed swords mark at back, 7 cm. high, 1745-50. **£1,800-2,500**   *C*

A Meissen group of Africa, modelled by J. J. Kändler, represented as a negress on the back of a lion, her dress of coloured feathers and a white cloak with gilt edges, crossed swords in blue, sceptre and some leaves damaged, 19 cm., c. 1745-50. **£1,200-1,600** S

A Meissen figure of a sultan riding on a rhinoceros, modelled by J. J. Kändler, right shoulder and wrist restored, 24 cm. wide, c. 1750. **£3,500-£4,000** C

A Meissen figure of a Russian peasant woman, in blue-lined flowered robe and maroon underskirt on mound base, traces of blue crossed swords mark on base, chip to top of hat, repaired through neck and shoulders, 15 cm. high, c. 1750. **£700-800** C

A Meissen figure of a seated lutenist, modelled by J. J. Kändler or P. Reinicke, with a gilt-edged white jacket over a purple waistcoat and black breeches, crossed swords in underglaze blue, one hand restored, 13 cm., c. 1750. **£650-750** S

A Meissen figure of a button seller, he with breeches of lemon, white jacket and waistcoat, indistinct blue crossed swords on reverse footrim, probably modelled by J. J. Kändler and P. Reinicke, 23 cm., c. 1754. **£750-950** Bon

A pair of Meissen figures of children, in puce, green and yellow, blue crossed swords marks, repair to his staff and cockerel's crest, and to her hat and neck, 15 cm. high, c. 1750. **£500-600** C

A Meissen group of 4 Bacchanalian putti, scantily clothed and decorated in colours enriched with gilding, the oval grasswork base moulded and gilt with C scrolls, blue crossed swords and incised 2499 marks, minor chips, 16.5 cm. high, mid 19th C. **£300-400** C

A Meissen sweetmeat figure of a young woman, in blue hat, puce-edged collar, yellow waistcoat and flowered skirt, blue crossed swords mark at back, minor chips to foliage, 14.5 cm. high, c. 1750. **£650-750** C

A Meissen figure of a bird seller, from the Cris de Paris series, modelled by P. Reinicke and J. J. Kändler in yellow and puce, blue crossed swords mark at back, repair to the top of his hat and through neck, 12.5 cm. high, c. 1755. **£3,200-3,800** C

A pair of Marcolini Meissen biscuit figures, of a man and a lady, on ribbed columnar plinths supported on square bases, with laurel wreaths picked out in gilding, crossed swords, stars and dots in underglaze blue, x incised, one toe and 2 fingers missing, 37 cm., early 19th C. **£600-700** S

A Meissen figure of female monkey, modelled by J. J. Kändler, traces of blue crossed swords mark on base, her right arm re-stuck, 13 cm. high, c. 1755. **£500-600** C

A Meissen figure of a man, a dog at his feet, outside decorated, cancelled crossed swords and a star in blue, 16.5 cm., mid 19th C. **£200-300** S

A Mennecy figure of a seated Magot, painted in Kakiemon style, with red flowers on a yellow ground, marked D.V. beneath one foot, restored, 11.3 cm., c. 1740. **£1,000-1,200** *S*

A Minton figure of a Grand Turk, wearing richly coloured and gilt robes, one feather missing, 5¼ in., c. 1830. **£500-600** *S*

The figure corresponds to design no. 90 in the Minton Pattern Book.

A rare Minton figure of a woman force-feeding a goose, 4 in., c. 1835. **£155-175** *DL*

This figure is flat backed.

A rare pair of Minton figures, 7¾ in., c. 1835. **£750-850** *DL*

The present pair are typical of the stiffly modelled and perhaps over-decorated figures of the 1830's.

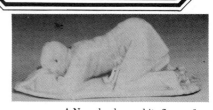

A Nymphenburg white figure of a kneeling Chinese, modelled by F. A. Bustelli, impressed Bavarian shield mark, some damage, 15 cm., c. 1762. **£5,000-5,500** *C*

A large parian bust of Apollo, waisted socle base, 22½ in. (57.2 cm.), c. 1860. **£250-320** *SC*

MAKE THE MOST OF MILLER'S

When buying or selling, it must always be remembered that prices can be greatly affected by the condition of any piece.
Unless otherwise stated, all goods shown in Miller's are of good merchantable quality, and the valuations given reflect this fact.
Pieces offered for sale in exceptionally fine condition or in poor condition may reasonably be expected to be priced considerably higher or lower respectively than the estimates given herein.

A Copeland parian figure of Beatrice, wearing a gilt-trimmed robe, after a model by Edward Papworth Junior, impressed marks including title, 22 in. (55.8 cm.), c. 1860. **£150-200** *SC*

A parian group, of an angel with 2 children, sculpted by John Hancock, signed, incised artist's name and dated 1855, 57 cm. **£250-£300** *SS*

A Nymphenburg porcelain figure of an Oriental, wearing a yellow jacket with purple sash, 12.5 cm., the porcelain 18th C., probably later decorated. **£380-440** *S*

A figure of a woman selling fish, from the Cris de St. Petersbourg series, wearing a green scarf, puce bodice and beige skirt with black network, incised Cyrillic letters P S, Imperial Porcelain Factory, St. Petersburg, 21.5 cm. high, c. 1790. **£700-900**   *C*

A Plymouth figure of Winter, 5¾ in., c. 1770. **£370-400** *KK*

A St. Petersburg figure of a street vendor, wearing a green hat, blue coat and red striped trousers, the base with Russian inscription and date 1820, Nr. 4, by the Imperial Porcelain Factory, 28 cm. high. **£400-500**   *C*

A St. Petersburg figure of a dancing peasant boy, wearing a pink shirt and blue trousers, red factory mark of the Brothers Kornilov, 17.5 cm. high, c. 1840. **£180-220**   *C*

A Samson group, depicting a lady with attendants, pseudo crossed swords marks in underglaze blue, slight damage, 15¼ in. (38.5 cm.), late 19th C. **£400-500**   *SC*

A Rudolstadt nodding mandarin figure, after a Meissen original, anchor mark in blue, impressed numerals, 11½ in. (29.3 cm.), late 19th C. **£800-1,200**   *SC*

USE THE INDEX!

Because certain items might fit easily into any of a number of categories, the quickest and surest method of locating any entry is by reference to the fully cross-referenced index at the back of the book. This is particularly true this year when certain sections, e.g. Worcester Porcelain and Oak Furniture have been featured in isolation.

A Samson 'Gold Anchor' pastoral group, after a Chelsea original, gold anchor, slight restoration, 36 cm., late 19th C. **£300-400**   *SS*

A Vienna figure of a young woman singing, seated in pale orange flowered dress, holding sheets of music, blue beehive mark and impressed F, repaired at neck, minor chips, 15 cm. high, c. 1775. **£250-350**   *C*

A Samson group of 'Uncle Toby' from Laurence Sterne's Tristram Shandy, 13 in. high, spurious Chelsea-Derby mark in gold, late 19th C. **£350-450**   *T*

A Vienna figure of a young shepherdess, in green hat and puce and white flowered dress, on moulded base edged with gilt, blue beehive mark and impressed Q, various painters' marks, minor chips, 15 cm., c. 1775. **£250-300**   *C*

A rare Rockingham figure of a boy, wearing a pink jacket and yellow hat, the details gilt, impressed 'Rockingham Works Brameld', incised No. 26, painted Cl.2 in red, chip on hat, 5½ in., c. 1830. **£1,000-£1,500** *S*

Similar models were also produced at the Derby and Minton factories.

A large Volkstedt group, in colourful 19th C. evening dress, painted in bright enamel colours and gold, 31.5 cm. high, late 19th C. **£200-300** *Bea*

A Vienna figure of Harlequin, in green hat and orange and yellow costume, blue beehive mark and impressed W, repairs to bird cages, hat and left foot, 18 cm. high, c. 1780. **£400-500** *C*

A Zurich figure of a girl, she is wearing a skirt with stripes and flowers, a pink and blue bodice, Z and 2 dots in underglaze blue, restoration to hen and one chicken, 13.2 cm., c. 1773. **£1,400-1,800** *S*

The same group was made at Meissen and Höchst. For an illustration of all three models see S. Ducret, Die Züricher Porzellanmanufaktur, col. II, fig. 336.

A Bow 'Botanical' plate, painted in the centre with purple grapes, encircled by winged insects, brown-edged rim, some wear, chips on rim, 9 in., c. 1755-58. **£200-300** *S*

A rare Zurich group of the Nativity, painted in purple, brown, grey and pale green, Z and .. in blue, 23 cm., late 18th C. **£3,000-£4,000** *S*

For a similar group, see Ducret, Die Züricher Porzellanmanufaktur, Vol. II, pl. 395, see also p. 233 et seq. This group appears to have been made up from 28 different moulds.

A Zurich figure of a boy, he is wearing a large black hat, a white shirt, an ochre coloured jacket and pale blue breeches, Z in underglaze blue, hat restored, 13.3 cm., c. 1775. **£1,400-1,800** *S*

A rare Ansbach soup plate, decorated in 'famille rose' style, with 2 birds in a garden, all in orange, purple, green, blue, yellow and gilding, marked A in underglaze blue, 3 impressed, 23.3 cm., c. 1765. **£1,200-1,800** *S*

A pair of Bow plates, each painted with the same full-blown tulip specimen, dragonflies and butterflies, fire specking and minor wear, 9 in., c. 1755-58. **£3,000-3,500** *S*

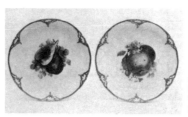

A set of 12 Berlin dessert plates, sceptre in underglaze blue, printed orb and K.P.M., 8½ in. (21.7 cm.), c. 1900. **£1,000-1,200** *S*

A Bow plate, vigorously painted with a Turk's Cap Lily, Lilium martagon, attracting a dragonfly and moths, slight wear, 2 small hair cracks on rim, 9 in., c. 1755-58. **£650-750** *S*

A Bow octagonal dish, painted with a branch of yellow roses, a ladybird and a gnat, within a brown-edged rim, 27.5 cm. **£1,000-1,500** *L*

A Caughley blue and white strainer, printed with the Fisherman pattern, 3½ in., c. 1770. **£120-140** *SA*

A set of 3 Caughley plates, indented rims and flutes wells, painted with Chantilly sprigs and blue borders in underglaze blue, impressed 'Salopian', 7¾ in. diam. **£200-280** *McC*

A Caughley blue and white plate of the 'Weir' pattern, 8¼ in., c. 1770. **£90-100** *SA*

BOW PORCELAIN

- probably the first porcelain factory in England
- although the date normally given for the opening of the factory is c. 1747, many experts now believe it was established much earlier, c. 1744-45
- very similar soft-paste body to early Lowestoft
- the early body had a creamy tint but very difficult in some cases to distinguish from early Derby. Figure in question of Kitty Clive which is very difficult to distinguish from Bow figures, relies almost totally on difference between the treatment of the clothes and applied flowers on the base
- painter's numerals sometimes in footrings — another confusion with Lowestoft
- body heavy for its size and very porous, prone to discolourations
- paste is thick and heavy and subject to fire cracking
- translucency poor
- tended to warp in the kiln
- after 1765 quality markedly deteriorated
- factory closed in 1776

CAUGHLEY

- factory ran from 1772-99, when it was purchased by the Coalport management
- painted wares tend to be earlier than printed ones
- Caughley body of the soapstone type
- often shows orange to transmitted light, but in some cases can even show slightly greenish which adds to the confusion with Worcester
- glaze is good and close fitting, although when gathered in pools, may have greeny-blue tint
- from 1780's many pieces heightened in gilding, some blue and white Chinese export wares were similarly gilded in England
- main marks: impressed 'Salopian', 'S' was painted on hand-painted designs, 'S' was printed on blue printed designs, although an 'X' or an 'O' was sometimes hand-painted beside it, one of the most common marks was the capital C. Hatched crescents never appeared on Caughley, they were purely a Worcester mark
- Caughley is often confused with Worcester, they have many patterns in common, e.g. 'The Cormorant and Fisherman' and 'Fence' patterns

A Bow dish, painted with a spray of bright yellow flowers, probably a Dyer's Greenweed, Genista tinctoria, brown edged rim, indistinct incised marks, some wear, small hair crack on reverse, 10½ in., c. 1755-58. **£1,000-1,500** *S*

A rare Bow sycamore-leaf shaped dish, naturalistically moulded and painted in bright enamels, numeral 5 on the reverse, minor chips on rim, 7¾ in., c. 1762. **£1,000-1,500** *S*

A rare Caughley plate, painted in blue camaieu, after drawings by Paul Sandby, within bead and linked grain borders in gilding, rubbed, 8¼ in. (21 cm.), c. 1785. **£150-180** *SC*

A Caughley blue and white shell-shaped dish, printed with the Fisherman pattern, slight repair, 7 in., c. 1770. **£130-150** *SA*

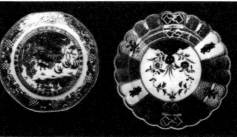

A Chelsea octagonal saucer, painted in the 'Kakiemon' style with 'The Flaming Tortoise' pattern, c. 1750-52. **£550-600**   *C*

(*l.*) A Caughley powder blue dessert plate, with scalloped rim and 6 reserves to the border, centre reserve painted with shrub and insect, in underglaze blue, 8 in. diam. **£180-240**

(*r.*) A Caughley plate, printed Willow Nankin pattern, unmarked, 7 in. diam. **£100-140**   *McC*

A pair of Salopian porcelain shaped square gilded and enamelled Kylin pattern dessert dishes, impressed mark — probably decorated by Chamberlain in Worcester, 8¾ in. (22.25 cm.), c. 1790. **£280-360**   *LBP*

(*l. & r.*) A pair of Chelsea fluted dishes, within chocolate line rims, red anchor marks, 24 cm. diam., c. 1753. **£1,500-2,000**   *C*

(*c.*) A Chelsea soup plate, with a moulded diaper and flower and scroll-pattern border reserved with 3 shaped panels edged in puce and painted with figures in an estuary, one minute rim chip, slight rubbing to centre, red anchor mark, 24 cm. diam., c. 1753. **£500-600**   *C*

A Chelsea leaf dish, painted with two-tone green border, puce vein and posy decoration to centre, crabstock handle, red anchor mark. **£150-250**   *WLH*

A Chelsea peony-flower dish, modelled with overlapping petals edged in purple in the centre, overlaid with a green leaf veined in brown, the stalk handle terminating in a bud, red anchor mark, small hair cracks and chips, 9 in., c. 1752-56. **£1,100-1,300**   *S*

A Chelsea plate, brown-edged lobed rim, red anchor mark, restoration on rim, hair cracks, 8½ in., c. 1755-56. **£500-600**   *S*

A Chelsea plate, painted with an 'Antholyza', restored on rim, worn; and another, decorated with an 'Anonis', restored on rim, worn, red anchor marks, both 8½ in., both c. 1755-56. **£600-700**   *S*

A Chelsea 'Hans Sloane' plate, painted with botanical specimens including 'South African gooseberry' and a blue-flowered plant resembling 'Speedwell', brown-edged rim, red anchor mark, crack, chip on rim, 9¼ in., c. 1754-56. **£350-400**   *S*

A pair of Chelsea plates, with 'feather-moulded' rims picked out in brown and blue, red anchor marks, some pitting, some wear, 8¼ in., c. 1756. **£350-450**   *S*

A Chelsea plate, painted with a spray of 'Hypericum' type, with a brown-edged lobed rim, red anchor mark, small restored hair crack on rim, fire specking, 9¼ in., c. 1754-56. **£500-600**   *S*

A Chelsea oval dish, painted with 4 reserves each depicting exotic birds in a garden, in purple, orange, green and yellow enamels and gold, gold anchor and spur marks to the base, chipping to foot rim, 36 cm., c. 1758-60. **£800-1,200**   *Bea*

A pair of Chelsea oval dishes, with brown and turquoise 'feathered' rims, brown anchor marks, some wear, 10½ in., c. 1756. **£1,200-1,600** *S*

An interesting Coalport plate, painted with a silhouette of children, said to be members of the 'Angerstein' family, the apricot-ground rim with gilt and black borders, 9¼ in., c. 1805-10. **£250-£300**   *S*

A pair of Coalport plates, painted and signed by 'J.H. Plant' with named views of 'Near Dover' and 'Buttermere' reserved on a blue scale ground, green printed marks, 8⅞ in. (22.5 cm.), c. 1900. **£250-300**   *SC*

A Chelsea yellow ground plate, the yellow border edged with gilt scrolling foliage, puce anchor mark, slight rubbing, ground colour perhaps later, 21 cm. diam., c. 1758. **£350-400**   *C*

Two Coalport commemorative plates, printed in blue, one with a portrait of 'Dewey' beneath the inscription 'Manila' dated May, 1898, the other with a portrait of 'Sampson' beneath 'Santiago' dated July, 1898, green printed marks, hairline crack, 10¼ in. (26 cm.). **£120-180**   *SC*

Two Coalport plates, painted and signed by 'P.H. Simpson', named on the reverse within an acid etched gilt and ivory coloured band and apple-green and gilt scroll-work on the other, 8¾ in. (22.8 cm.), c. 1920. **£150-200** *SC*

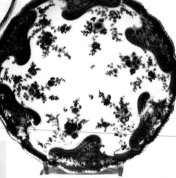

A pair of Chelsea claret-ground saucer dishes, with shaped gilt dentil rims, gold anchor marks, 20 cm. diam., c. 1763. **£1,000-1,500** *C*

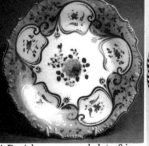

A Daniel green ground plate, 9 in., c. 1825. **£85-95**   *MA*

Four Coalport plates, with gilt piecrust rims, each painted and signed by 'P. Simpson' with a named view including 'Barnard Castle', 'Rhuddlan Castle' and 'Dover Castle' within shaped green, salmon-pink and grey borders, green printed marks, 10¾ in. (27.3 cm.), c. 1930. **£350-400**   *SC*

A Daniel pink ground plate, 9 in., c. 1825. **£65-75** *MA*

A Derby crown porcelain company plate, painted by 'J. Platts', the blue-ground rim gilt by 'Lambert' with foliate scrolls and formal borders, printed and impressed marks, gilder's monogram, 9¼ in., c. 1880. **£250-300** *S*

An affixed contemporary paper label identifies the pattern as 954, recorded in pattern book 2: see J. Twitchett and B. Bailey, Royal Crown Derby, p. 148.

A Derby 'vine-leaf' dish, painted with a central spray and sprigs of coloured flowers in the manner of the 'Cotton Stem' painter, brown-edged rim, base misshapen, slight wear, 11 in., c. 1758-60. **£350-450** *S*

A pair of Royal Doulton plates, painted and signed by 'Frederick Hancock' each titled on the reverse within beaded gilt borders, purple printed marks including date code for 1887, 9 in. (22.8 cm.). **£180-220** *SC*

A Derby yellow-bordered botanical plate, pattern no. 216, probably by 'John Brewer', painted with 'Cypripedium calceolus, Ladies Slipper', crown, crossed batons and D, and pattern no. 216 in blue enamel, 9 in. (22.8 cm.), c. 1795-1800. **£250-300** *SC*

See Derby Pointer.

A Frankenthal plate, with partridge in centre, with pink scale borders, with coloured flowers, 9¼ in., c. 1756-59. **£700-800** *HOF*

This is an early piece of Frankenthal with the lion mark.

A pair of Höchst plates, with pierced basketwork borders picked out in purple, impressed wheel mark, incised Nl, 23 cm., c. 1765. **£800-900** *S*

A Liverpool William Reid-type blue and white shell-shaped dish, 4¼ in., c. 1755. **£450-500** *SRO*

A Longton Hall 'strawberry-moulded' plate, painted in the manner of the 'Trembly Rose Painter', with coloured flowers enclosed by fruiting strawberry leaves edged in green and with purple veining, slight wear, 9 in., and a soup plate, en suite, cracked and chipped, 9¼ in., both c. 1754-57. **£550-650** *S*

A Liverpool Pennington's plate, printed with 'The Fisherman' pattern, 8 in., c. 1790. **£45-55** *MA*

A Liverpool William Ball-type saucer-dish, painted in bright underglaze blue, minor wear, 7¼ in., c. 1758. **£2,200-2,800** *S*

A Meissen dish, decorated in Imari style with, in the centre, 'indianische Blumen', the reverse with flowers, leaves and prunus blossom, crossed swords in underglaze blue, 25.5 cm., c. 1730. **£1,000-1,500** *S*

A pair of Ludwigsburg dishes, blue crowned interlaced C's mark and various impressed marks, one with rim chip, 33 cm. wide, c. 1765-70. **£480-540** *C*

A Meissen plate, decorated in Chinese style in underglaze blue with birds, rocks and flowering plants, crossed swords and Z in underglaze blue, 24.3 cm., c. 1730. **£1,800-2,200** *S*

A Longton Hall leaf dish, modelled as a leaf strongly coloured in green, the veins and twisted loop handle picked out in puce, 15 cm. **£220-280** *P*

LONGTON HALL

- factory founded by William Jenkinson in c. 1749
- in 1751 he was joined by Wm. Littler and Wm. Nicklin
- earliest pieces the 'Snowman' figures and some blue and white wares
- painting tends to have a primitive, slightly crude, look
- the figures, in particular, tend to have a stiff, lumpy appearance
- the porcelain is of the glassy soft-paste type
- the glaze can tend to have a greenish-grey appearance
- pieces often thickly potted
- Duesbury worked at Longton Hall before going to Derby
- the 'middle period' of the factory from c. 1754-57 saw the best quality porcelain produced
- specialised in wares of vegetable form, some of ungainly appearance, unlike the more sophisticated wares of Chelsea
- much of the output of the middle period was moulded
- two famous painters from the period are the 'Castle painter' and the 'trembly rose' painter
- Sadler's black printed wares are extremely rare and sought after
- the porcelain is generally unmarked
- if marked it is usually 2 crossed L's with dots below
- very similar in some ways to Plymouth — it is thought that Longton Hall moulds were sold to Cookworthy
- the factory closed in 1760 — all wares are now rare

A Meissen plate, painted by Johann Christoph Horn, with elaborate gilt and black borders, the ground with scattered insects and deutsche Blumen in colours, and another Meissen plate, en suite, the central panel unsigned, gilt borders slightly rubbed, crossed swords in underglaze blue, impressed 16 and ii, 23.2 cm., c. 1740. **£3,000-3,500** *S*

Johann Christoph Horn was employed at the Meissen factory from 1720 until 1760.

A Meissen dish, decorated in Kakiemon style, brown line rim, crossed swords in underglaze blue, incised repairer's mark, enamel slightly flaked, 15.5 cm., c. 1730-35. **£1,200-1,800** *S*

Four Meissen plates, moulded with Sulkowsky-ozier borders, decorated in Kakiemon style with the so-called 'fliegender Hund' pattern, some slightly rubbed, crossed swords in underglaze blue, repairer's mark on footrim, 23 cm., c. 1735. **£1,800-2,200** *S*

A Meissen Imari saucer-dish, reserved on a ground of scrolling gilt and iron-red foliage, blue crossed swords and K of Kretschmar mark, 24.5 cm. diam., c. 1735. **£2,800-3,200** *C*

A pair of Meissen plates, painted in the Imari manner, with pink lustre, blue crossed swords and 4 marks, 22.5 cm. diam., c. 1735. **£1,500-1,800** *C*

A Nantgarw plate from the MacIntosh service, brightly painted in London, with an exotic bird with purple plumage, the rim gilt with C-scrolls and shells reserving 4 floral panels, impressed NANTGARW/C.W., 9⅜ in., c. 1817-33. **£1,000-1,500** S

A London decorated Nantgarw plate, painted in Sèvres style, the rim with 4 elongated oval panels of flowers, reserved on a blue ground, gilt with oeil-de-perdrix, impressed NANTGARW/C.W., 9⅝ in., c. 1818-22. **£1,000-1,200** S

W. D. John tentatively attributes the decoration of the Kenyon service to T. Martin Randall, see Nangarw Porcelain, p. 105.

A London decorated Nantgarw dish, painted in a distinctive palette, with C-scroll moulded rim, slight wear, 8¼ in., c. 1817-22. **£350-400** S

A pair of London decorated Nantgarw plates, painted probably in the atelier of Robins and Randall, with C-scroll moulded rims, impressed NANT GARW/C.W. marks, hair crack in one, 8½ in., c. 1820. **£450-550** S

Two London decorated Nantgarw plates, each painted probably by Robins and Randall, with C-scroll moulded rims, some wear, each impressed NANT GARW/C.W., 8⅝ in., c. 1817-22. **£350-450** S

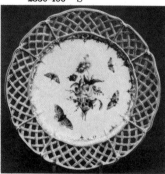

A Nymphenburg dessert plate, with pierced basketwork border, picked out in blue and gilding, with a gilt foliate scroll border, shield mark and 72 impressed, incised mark, chip on rim, 23.7 cm., c. 1760. **£1,200-1,600** S

A pair of Sèvres plates, from the du Barry service, the border with blue and gold vases of flowers and gilt loops suspending floral garlands, 24 cm. diam., c. 1771. **£1,000-1,200**

Seven Paris (Darte) plates, painted in bright palette with wild birds and animals, named on the reverses, the royal blue borders variously gilt with stylised floral foliage, 4 with red stencil marks, 23 cm. diam., c. 1825. **£2,800-3,200** C

A Rockingham plate, with hand-painted flowers, with sharks tooth border, slightly damaged, crack, with red mark, 9 in., c. 1826-30. **£40-45** MA

ORDER

The English and Continental porcelain section is ordered in alphabetical category order. Each category is then divided into alphabetical factory order and each factory is chronologically ordered.

Sèvres Compotier, from the service made for Catherine II, with bleu céleste ground, painted with cameos, with a band of tooled gilt scrollwork, the centre showing the crowned initials of the Empress, interlaced L's, date letters AA and painter's mark for Foure in blue enamel, 2000 in gilding for Henry-François Vincent jeune, 20 incised, repaired, restored on rim, 22 cm., 1778. **£900-1,100** S

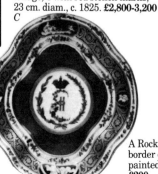

A Rockingham pin tray, with gilt centre within a border of encrusted flowering stems, naturalistically painted, cl.2 in gold, mark in puce, 3⅝ in. wide. **£150-200** T

A Swansea pottery shell-shaped dish, painted by Thomas Pardoe in an Imari palette, with a central spray of flowers, within a scrolling border, impressed SWANSEA and C, minor cracks, 8¼ in., c. 1800-05. **£250-350** *S*

A Spode plate, painted with a view of Fonthill Abbey, 8½ in., c. 1800. **£300-330** *KK*

A Spode plate, on apple-green ground, with named birds, Sedge, Little Bittern, Peregrine Falcon and Kite, 9¾ in., c. 1810. **£170-190** *MA*

A Swansea 'Japan' pattern plate, decorated in an Imari palette with pattern no. 232, reserved on a gros bleu and gilt ground, slight wear, printed SWANSEA mark and patt. no. in red, 8¼ in., c. 1814-22. **£200-£280** *S*

SWANSEA PORCELAIN

- factory produced high quality soft-paste porcelain from 1814-22
- factory started by Dillwyn, Billingsley and Walker
- superb translucent body, excellent glaze
- in many ways one of the best porcelain bodies produced in the British Isles
- also noted for delicacy of flower painting, usually attributed to Billingsley although much was obviously done by other decorators including Pollard and Morris
- a close study of marked pieces will give one an idea of Billingsley's work but unless actually signed by him pieces should be marked 'possibly by Billingsley'
- on pieces moulded with the floral cartouches the moulding can be detected on the other side of the rim, unlike the heavier Coalport wares which later utilised same moulds
- especially notable are figure and bird paintings by T. Baxter
- the Swansea mark often faked, particularly on French porcelain at the end of the 19th, beginning of the 20th C.
- in 1816 Billingsley left to start up again at Nantgarw
- many pieces were decorated in London studios

A Swansea plate, brightly painted in the manner of Henry Morris, with gilt edged rim, slight wear, indistinct printed SWANSEA mark, 8⅜ in., c. 1817-22. **£320-380** *S*

A Swansea plate, decorated probably by William Pollard, with a C-scroll moulded rim and a formal green and gilt border, gilding rubbed on rim, printed SWANSEA marks in red, 8¼ in., c. 1820-22. **£250-300** *S*

Two Swansea plates, with C-scroll moulded rims, painted probably by William Pollard, with finely gilt formal borders, some wear, printed SWANSEA marks in red, 8¼ in., c. 1820-22. **£480-580** *S*

See Swansea pointer.

A Tournai saucer dish, with wavy rim, painted with a variety of cut fruit, wine bottles and birds in a garden, 23 cm., c. 1765. **£380-440** *P*

A Swansea plate, decorated in an Imari palette, the rim with petal-shaped floral panels, reserved on a ground of gilt whorls and within a green border, some wear, 9½ in., and a smaller Swansea plate, en suite, 8⅛ in., printed SWANSEA marks in red, both c. 1814-22. **£250-300** *S*

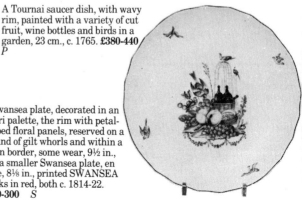

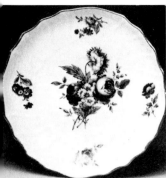

Four Cozzi dishes, with spirally moulded borders, each decorated with sprays of coloured flowers, minor chips, red anchor mark, 21.5 cm., c. 1760. **£1,000-1,200** S

(*l.*) A pair of Cozzi dishes, with gilt rims, red anchor mark, 29.5 cm., c. 1760. **£550-600**

(*r.*) Three Cozzi leaf-shaped dishes, decorated with sprays of coloured flowers, gilt rims, anchor mark, 16 cm., c. 1760. **£700-800** S

Three Venice (Cozzi) dishes, 27.5 cm. wide, c. 1760. **£780-880** C

A Venice (Cozzi) saucer-dish, painted in an Imari palette, 23 cm. diam., and an oval sauce tureen and cover, en suite, finial missing, base cracked, c. 1760. **£250-300** C

A dish, applied with upright handles, painted in pale colours in the centre, the curved rim with panels of deer in landscapes, enclosed by purple borders, probably Vienna, 29.5 cm., c. 1744. **£1,000-1,200** S

A pair of Vienna plaques, painted with classical scenes, within formal borders, late 19th C. **£500-600** CDC

A Vienna porcelain plaque, painted by Dressel, painted in colours upon a solid gilt ground, within a magenta arabesque border, the reverse signed 'F. Russ', entitled 'Studienkopf', beehive mark in underglaze blue, 41 cm. diam., in a gilt outer frame. **£480-540** HSS

A 'Vienna' circular plaque, painted by A. Kraüse, with the triumphal procession of Alexander attended by Fame and Victory, reserved on a matt gilt ground, bearing grotesques and trophies of war, titled 'Vienna', shield in underglaze blue, 48.3 cm., c. 1870. **£750-950** S

A 'Vienna' tray, painted after Rubens, with 'Die Opferschau' inscribed on the reverse, with a blue border gilt with stylised foliage, blue beehive mark, 42 cm. wide, c. 1880. **£750-950** C

A Vienna octagonal plate, painted with classical scenes, late 19th C. **£350-450** MMB

A pair of Derby green ground bough pots, with painted views of Caernarvon Castle and Welshpool, chip on one foot, c. 1830. **£450-£500** JSA

A pair of Derby turquoise ground combé-shaped bough pots, painted by Zachariah Boreman, with river landscapes, within gilt oval cartouches, gold anchor marks, Wm. Duesbury & Co., one with minute chip to foot, 23.5 cm. wide, 1775. **£1,000-1,500** C

A George Frederick Bowers porcelain jug, printed in black with 2 views, titled 'Light Cavalry Charge at Balaclava' and 'Sebastopol Attack and Capture of Malakhoff by the French' and inscribed in gilding 'P.J. Charles, Liverpool, 1855', black printed mark, 19 cm. **£100-150** SS

A Coalport porcelain 2-handled oval jardiniere, painted with reserves with exotic birds and flowers, leaf gilding on royal blue ground, 8 in. high. **£300-350** *Re*

COALPORT (Rose & Co.)

- factory was founded in the early 1790's by John Rose when he left Caughley
- early blue and white wares very close in style and feeling to Caughley products
- note particularly the somewhat clear royal blue tone of the cobalt
- Rose purchased the Caughley works in 1799 and ran them until he had them demolished in 1814
- produced hard paste porcelain certainly after 1800, before then produced soapstone porcelain, this was quite similar to Caughley but does not have the yellow-brown translucency
- early wares heavy, with greyish appearance
- in this period quite similar to Newhall and Chamberlains
- the highly decorated Japan wares were of exceptional quality as are some of the flower painted examples

- in around 1811 firm taken over by John Rose, William Clark and Charles Maddison
- in 1820 a new leadless glaze was invented and they also began to use Billingsley's frit paste, whereas original Welsh plates were thinly potted, Coalport were much heavier and less crisp
- in 1820 Rose also bought moulds from Nantgarw and Swansea and Billingsley came to work at Coalport
- best period for the Coalport factory began in 1820 when the factory produced a brilliantly white hard felspar porcelain, with a high level of translucency
- the rococo wares of the late 1820's and 30's are often confused with Rockingham
- after 1820, CD, CD monogram, C.Dale, Coalbrookdale and Coalport were all marks used, before this date the marks tend to vary and much was unmarked
- in 1840's and 1850's Coalport perfected many fine ground colours: maroon, green and pink
- these often rivalled Sèvres especially in 1850's and 1860's and are close to the Minton example of this period
- Coalport also at this time produced some Chelsea copies, with fake marks — these are very rare
- the Coalport factory is still in existence today

A Bristol baluster milk jug, from the Smyth service, with the floral and gilt monogram RS within a gilt oval cartouche, flanked by 2 classical busts 'en grisaille' in similar cartouches suspended by berried swags, Richard Champion's Factory, blue X and gilt 3 mark, 10.5 cm. high, c. 1776. **£600-700** *C*

From a service made for Sir Robert Smyth, 5th Bt. of Berechurch Hall, near Colchester, Essex, given to his bride Miss Blake of Hanover Square in 1776.

A Caughley cabbage leaf mask jug, printed in underglaze blue, inscribed 'Nothing good within I have Be not so free to every Knave My Master only I supply let begging Fellows go & buy', with monograms T.B. above and the date 1792 below, 19 cm. **£300-400** *L*

A Caughley cream jug, printed in underglaze blue with a fenced garden on a river bank, in Chinese style, crescent mark, 8.8 cm. **£90-£120** *L*

A Cassel pear-shaped hot milk jug and cover, painted with exotic birds, blue lion rampant mark, painter's mark D., lacks tip of handle, 14.5 cm. high, 1770-75. **£2,500-3,000** *C*

A Derby jug, painted in soft colours with exotic birds, the spout painted with purple scrollwork, the handle similarly decorated, slight wear, 6¾ in., c. 1758-60. **£650-750** *S*

A Caughley mask jug with rare fox print, printed with roses and with a running fox beneath the handle, in underglaze blue, the unglazed base with printed 'S' mark, slight firing crack to base of handle, 8½ in. **£750-850** *McC*

A Derby boat-shaped cream jug, painted by Robert Brewer, with 2 named landscapes, 'Near Leghorn' and 'View Near Glasgow', crown, crossed batons, dots, D with titles and 71 in iron-red. **£250-300**   *N*

A Derby cream jug, taken from silver shape of 1790's, with pad feet, 5¼ in., c. 1815. **£60-70**   *MA*

A Derby jug, the spout moulded with the head of Admiral Rodney, above an oval gilt medallion inscribed 'April 12th 1782' and flanked by flower sprays, puce mark, 8½ in. high. **£550-600**   *CSK*

Lowestoft sparrow beak jug, with polychrome decoration, 3½ in., 1785. **£130-145**   *KK*

A Fulda jug, moulded on the rim with rococo scrollwork, picked out in purple, painted in colours with a spray of flowers, handle and foot damaged, cross in underglaze blue, 26 cm., c. 1770. **£1,200-1,800**   *S*

A Herculaneum cream jug, with floral decoration, 4¼ in., c. 1815. **£80-90**   *MA*

A Meissen cream jug, the panels of chinoiserie figures painted in the manner of A. F. von Lowenfinck and reserved on a yellow ground, crossed swords in underglaze blue, chip on rim, 11 cm., c. 1730. **£900-1,200**   *S*

A Liverpool blue and white baluster cream jug, with 2 Orientals on a rocky wooded river island, the interior with a trellis border, William Ball's Factory, 8 cm. high, c. 1758. **£550-650**   *C*

A late 18th C. Liverpool helmet-shaped cream jug, with 'biting snake' handle, 4 in. **£250-300**   *LBP*

A Meissen hot milk jug and domed cover, blue crossed swords mark and impressed Dreher's mark of Schiefer, 15.5 cm. high, c. 1730. **£4,000-4,500**   *C*

A Meissen 'Hausmaler' milk jug and cover, decorated in underglaze blue with the so-called 'Fels und Vogel Decor', overpainted probably by F. Mayer of Pressnitz, with an angel recumbent on a rainbow and a flying putto holding a torch by his side, crossed swords and blue painter's marks in underglaze blue, incised X, knop repaired, 18 cm., mid 18th C. **£280-340**   *S*

A Newhall cream jug, of obconical shape, pattern 144, 5 in., c. 1785. **£85-95**   *MA*

A Meissen cream jug, 3 in., c. 1768. **£170-200**   *KK*

A Lowestoft blue and white flared mug, painted with chinoiserie figures, temples and bridges, 3½ in., c. 1785. **£200-230** *JSA*

A Lowestoft mug, inscribed in brown 'A Trifle from Lowestoft', between greyish-blue and brown foliate borders, scrolling handle, 2 minor chips on rim, 3½ in., c. 1795. **£1,000-1,200** *S*

A Chelsea tankard, painted with flowers, red anchor mark, 11 cm. **£900-1,100** *P*

A Pennington's Liverpool tankard, decorated in iron-red and blue, 5¾ in., c. 1780. **£190-200** *MA*

A Pennington's Liverpool Imari-style mug, painted in inky cobalt-blue, iron-red and gilding, below a hatched diaper border, grooved strap handle with kick-out terminal, slight staining, 24.6 cm., c. 1780. **£150-200** *SS*

A Longton Hall polychrome bell-shaped mug, with Chinese figures and large 'talking' bird, 3¾ in., c. 1755. **£1,500-1,600** *HOF*

This type of barrel-shaped tankard with 'barbed' ear-form handle is typical of middle period.

CHELSEA POINTS TO NOTE

- some red anchor marks usually neat and very small and not in prominent position
- later brown and gold anchor marks are larger and more thickly written
- paste varies from white to greenish when seen by transmitted light
- on red anchor ware, look out for 'moons' caused by frit in the kiln, also seen by transmitted light
- three spur marks often found on the base, left by kiln supports, also a feature of Arita porcelain (not to be confused with Derby pad marks)
- glaze on early pieces is reasonably opaque, this later becomes clearer and more glassy; later still it becomes thicker when it tends to craze
- body on later gold anchor wares and figures often has a dry, brownish appearance

A Chelsea mug, with a reeded handle, painted in colours with an elaborate bouquet of flowers, slightly rubbed, the reverse with scattered sprigs, red anchor mark, 14.5 cm. **£550-650** *P*

A Derby Bacchantes head mug, with gilt moulded handle and rim, crown over batons and 'D' in puce, repaired, 4 in., early 19th C. **£120-180** *WW*

A Derby mug, moulded with a mask of Jupiter, with turquoise twist strap handle, crown over 'D' and batons in puce, handle cracked, 4 in., late 18th/early 19th C. **£100-150** *WW*

A rare Chaffer's Liverpool phosphatic polychrome tankard, 5 in., c. 1754-55. **£850-950** *SR*

A fine Berlin plaque, painted after Titian with 'venetianisches Mädchen' Belvedere Gallerie, in a purple robe which falls off one shoulder to reveal a breast, inscribed 'en grisaille', impressed sceptre mark and KPM, 16½ by 13¼ in. (42 by 33.7 cm.), third quarter 19th C. **£4,000-4,500** *SC*

A Berlin plaque, painted after Murillo, giltwood frame, impressed sceptre and incised KPM, 15¾ by 13¾ in. (40 by 35 cm.), third quarter 19th C. **£3,500-4,500** *SC*

A Berlin plaque, painted by H. Stadler after Gerard Dou, with an old woman, impressed sceptre and KPM mark, in carved giltwood frame, 26.5 by 21.5 cm., c. 1880. **£1,000-1,400** *L*

Berlin plaque, painted with 'Maternal Joy', signed J. Jakobides, impressed KPM and sceptre mark, in gilt gesso frame, the reverse with exhibition label, 30.5 by 29 cm. **£1,800-2,400** *P*

A Carl Magnus Hutschenreuter plaque, painted by Ed Baerschneider, signed, with 'L'Aurora' after Guido Reni, impressed mark, framed, 16.8 by 36 cm., late 19th C. **£1,200-1,800** *S*

A Dresden plaque, painted after Leotard with La Belle Chocolatière, the maid wearing pink cap, olive-green bodice and blue skirt, blue crossed swords mark, carved giltwood frame, 27.5 by 21 cm., second half 19th C. **£900-1,100** *C*

Berlin porcelain oval plaque, impressed sceptre and KPM marks, 7 by 9 in. **£700-800** *GSP*

A Fürstenburg plaque, with gilt moulded frame, probably painted by J. L. B. Junge, F in underglaze blue, incised 4, restoration to 2 scrolls, 15.2 by 13.3 cm., c. 1768. **£4,000-5,000** *S*

Berlin plaque, painted with a dungeon scene, impressed KPM and sceptre, 22 by 27.5 cm., mid 19th C. **£350-450** *SS*

An interesting Mintons plaque, painted by E. Broughton, signed and dated 1877, of a girl wearing a pink quilted jacket, with contemporary ebonised and giltwood frame, painted retailer's mark for T. Goode & Co., London, affixed paper label for Mintons and T. Goode & Co., at the Paris Exhibition, 1877, 12½ by 8½ in. **£700-800** *S*

A Meissen plaque, painted in a soft palette with Flora, a garland in her hair and wearing pink drapery, crossed swords mark in underglaze blue, incised numerals, contemporary giltwood frame, 17 by 12⅛ in., late 19th C. **£3,000-4,000** *N*

A Mintons plaque, painted by
Edith Mapleston, signed on the
reverse, in a pastel palette, with a
small child reaching to post a letter
and lifted by a girl with flaxen
hair, reserved on a blue ground,
contemporary ebonised and
giltwood frame, impressed mark,
retailer's mark for T. Goode & Co.,
London, 14¾ by 10 in., c. 1880.
£400-500 *S*

A 'Vienna' rectangular porcelain
plaque, painted by Herrn Schmitt,
after Murillo, with the Virgin
Mary, holding the Child, St.
Elizabeth kneeling with St. John,
blue beehive mark, 48.5 by
41.5 cm., c. 1880. **£1,800-2,200** *C*

A porcelain plaque, the painting
attributed to Jabez Aston, framed,
10½ by 8½ in. (26.7 by 21.6 cm.),
c. 1840. **£350-450** *SC*

A plaque, the painting
attributed to Aston,
framed, repaired, 9½
by 7¾ in. (24.2 by
19.7 cm.), c. 1840.
£100-200 *SC*

A Sèvres plaque, painted in
colours, the shaped border enriched
with gilding, crowned interlaced L
mark enclosing the date letter V
for 1774 and the painter's mark LB
for Le Bel, 2 chips to rim, gilding
rubbed, 40 cm. high. **£4,500-5,500**
C

*Plaques made to stand on their
own, as distinct from those intended
from the outset to be fitted to pieces
of furniture, are very rare at Sèvres.
Although both Le Bel brothers
would seem to have used the LB
mark, the date of the present lot and
the quality of the execution place it
clearly in the oeuvre of Jean-Etinne,
known as l'aine. At this time he was
working in the Attelier Particulier
(sic).*

A 'Vienna' circular wall plaque,
painted with a nude maiden
reclining on the back of a winged
beast, the rim gilt, blue beehive
mark, 42.5 cm. diam., c. 1880.
£500-600 *C*

A 'Sèvres' circular plaque, painted
by Leber, signed, with the Battle of
Tolbiach in 496 AD, framed,
painted interlaced L's,, 1 ft. 5¼ in.
(44 cm.), mid to late 19th C. **£550-
650** *S*

A 'Vienna' plaque, painted by
'Ferdi', with 'The Smoker', titled in
dramatic chiaoscuro effect, 43 by
27 cm., late 19th C. **£280-340** *SS*

A Vienna plaque, painted by
R. Dittrick, with 'The Three Fates',
13 by 8 in. **£1,200-1,800** *Re*

A French plaque, painted by
H. Desprez, framed, 28 by 58 cm.,
late 19th C. **£1,000-1,500** *S*

A Bow large sauceboat, with
enamel colours, fire crack, 8½ in.,
c. 1754. **£220-245** *KK*

A Derby blue and white dolphin
ewer, with small chips, 5¼ in.,
c. 1768-70. **£110-130** *KK*

A Bow moulded blue and white
sauceboat, 5 in. wide, c. 1762. **£160-
190** *SRO*

A Belleek honey pot and cover, in
the form of a beehive, with
shamrocks and flying bees, picked
out in naturalistic colours, black
printed dog and harp mark, 6¼ in.
(15.8 cm.), c. 1900. **£180-240** *SC*

A rare Longton Hall blue and
white flower pot, chips, cracks,
2¼ in., c. 1756-58. **£600-660** *KK*

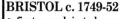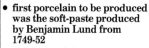

A Bow blue and white sauceboat,
chips to foot rim, 5¾ n., c. 1756.
£180-200 *KK*

A rare Caughley pounce pot, of
capstan shape, printed with small
fruit, flowers and insects in
underglaze blue, unmarked, 3½ in.
high. **£700-800** *McC*

A Derby polychrome leaf moulded
sauceboat, 5 in. wide, c. 1758. **£240-
£280** *SRO*

A Lund's Bristol sauceboat, the
sides painted in a blurred blue,
with an Oriental in a fenced garden
and a pagoda on a river island, the
interior with flowering branches
and emblems, 20 cm. wide, c. 1750.
£1,800-2,200 *C*
*The pattern would seem to be
unrecorded.*

A Caughley silver shape creamer,
with chip restored, 3¼ in., c. 1790.
80-90 *KK*

Longton Hall sauceboat, of silver
shape, with tall lip moulded with
rolls, painted in a delicate palette
with flowering shrubs, the interior
with a flower spray, the circular
foot with scattered foliage
disguising faults in the glaze,
minute chip to lip and foot, 22 cm.
wide, c. 1752. **£800-900** *C*

BRISTOL c. 1749-52

- **first porcelain to be produced
  was the soft-paste produced
  by Benjamin Lund from
  1749-52**
- **these porcelains are very rare
  but examples sometimes
  show the relief moulded
  marks 'Bristol' or 'Bristoll'**
- **mostly underglaze blue ware
  with chinoiserie decoration**
- **the glaze was tight fitting
  although it had a tendency to
  pool and bubble**
- **the blue often looks watery
  where it has run in the firing**
- **in 1752 Bristol moulds were
  sold to Worcester**
- **it is extremely difficult to
  differentiate late Lund's
  Bristol from early Worcester**

A Lund's Bristol sauceboat, of
silver shape, painted in underglaze
blue, in scroll moulded panels with
a figure crossing a bridge between
2 islands, the interior with flower
sprays and ribboned emblems,
scrolling handle, small chip on rim,
7 in., c. 1750. **£1,500-2,000** *S*

A Liverpool blue and white
William Ball small sauceboat,
handle made up, 4 in., c. 1756.
£130-140 *MA*

A pair of Sèvres saucières, with flowers reserved on a bleu céleste ground, minor chips and rubbing to gilding, painted interlaced L's, the porcelain late 18th C., the decoration mid 19th C., 9 in. (22.5 cm.). **£500-600**   *S*

A Chelsea double scent bottle, modelled as a greyhound seated behind a vase painted with flowers, the stopper formed as a bird, on an oval base painted with a bouquet and flower sprays, within a gilt dentil rim, minute chips to base, 7.5 cm. high, c. 1756. **£2,000-2,500** *C*

A Chelsea scent bottle and stopper, the stopper formed as a posy of flowers, the underside with a gilt flower spray within a green dentil rim, gilt metal mounts, slight chipping to stopper, 7.5 cm. high, c. 1760. **£900-£1,100**   *C*

(*l.*) A Liverpool gadrooned oval sauceboat, with stalk and serpent handle, painted with a border of scrolling foliage on a blue ground, William Ball's Factory, small extended fire crack to one side, 18.5 cm. wide, c. 1755. **£750-850**

(*c.*) A Liverpool blue and white sauceboat, the interior with an Oriental with a dog chasing a deer, William Reid's Factory, minute chip to rim, 18 cm. wide, c. 1758. **£2,000-2,500**

(*r.*) A Liverpool blue and white sauceboat, painted with an Oriental fishing by a fence in a woodland island garden, the interior with a river island within a loop pattern border, William Ball's Factory, 16.5 cm. wide, c. 1755. **£750-850**   *C*

Although attributed here to the Liverpool factory of William Reid, these wares remain the subject of considerable discussion; the Shelton factory of John Baddeley and the Pomona Potworks at Newcastle-under-Lyme must be considered as possible alternatives.

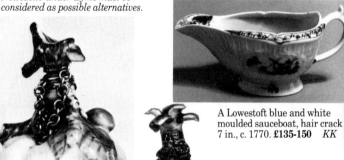

A Chelsea scent bottle and stopper, naturally modelled and coloured as a peach, gold mounts, 6.5 cm. high, c. 1755. **£1,500-1,800**   *C*

A Chelsea scent bottle and stopper of 'Girl in a Swing' type, modelled as Cupid holding a globe, the base inscribed in black 'je soutiens le monde', minor restoration to foliage and chip repaired to base, 8.5 cm. high, c. 1755. **£700-800**   *C*

A Chelsea scent bottle and a stopper, modelled as a lady in white clothes, holding a muff, on a base painted with flowers, within a gilt loop pattern rim, gold mounts, minute chips to foot, 8.5 cm. high, c. 1755. **£1,000-1,200**   *C*

A Chaffer's Liverpool polychrome moulded sauceboat, 5½ in. wide, c. 1760. **£400-450**   *SRO*

Two documentary Lowestoft blue and white sauceboats, with crisply moulded Hughes-type floral cartouches, enclosing chinoiseries with fishermen, the moulding including the initials 'I H' and the date 1762, 8½ in. **£1,000-1,500**   *S*

The initials 'I H' on Lowestoft moulded pieces are thought to stand for James Hughes, who is recorded as a 'China Painter' — see Christopher Spencer, Early Lowestoft, p. 52.

A Lowestoft blue and white moulded sauceboat, hair crack 7 in., c. 1770. **£135-150**   *KK*

A Chelsea scent bottle and stopper, modelled as a bouquet of flowers, tied by a pink ribbon, the stopper formed as a 2-tier posy, slight chipping, later gold mounts, 8 cm. high, c. 1756. **£900-1,100**   *C*

184

A rare 'Girl in a Swing' etui, surmounted by the head of Columbine, wearing a black domino with rose diamond eyes, the case painted with scattered floral sprigs, gold mounts, small hair crack in case, 4⅞ in., c. 1754. **£1,000-£1,200** *S*

A scent bottle and stopper of 'Girl in a Swing' type, modelled as a Polish soldier, in pink jacket and yellow breeches, silver mounts, 7 cm. high, c. 1755. **£2,400-2,800** *C*

A Chelsea scent bottle and stopper of 'Girl in a Swing' type, the stopper formed as a female bust with grapes in her hair, restoration to top of pump, minor chips to foliage, repairs to base, 9 cm. high, c. 1755. **£500-600** *C*

A Chelsea scent bottle and stopper of 'Girl in a Swing' type, modelled as 2 putti by an alchemist's forge, the stopper formed as flames, the oval base inscribed in red 'mon feu ne peut s'etaindre', 9 cm. high, c. 1755. **£1,200-1,800** *C*

'GIRL IN A SWING' FACTORY

- **probably a small factory closely associated with the Chelsea factory**
- **it was possibly only in existence for a few years in the late 1740's/early 1750's**
- **very few useful pieces have yet been attributed to the factory**
- **pieces now quite rare**

A scent bottle and stopper of 'Girl in a Swing' type, modelled as 2 putti supporting an oval fountain, the stopper formed as a dolphin, silver-gilt mounts, 10.5 cm., c. 1755. **£1,500-£1,800** *C*

A Meissen scent bottle and stopper, in yellow, puce and green, the youth's head forming the stopper, the underside of the base with a band of purple flowers and green foliage, minor restoration to dog's neck, blue crossed swords mark to base, 9.5 cm. high, c. 1750. **£550-£650** *C*

A double scent bottle of 'Girl in a Swing' type, modelled as 2 billing doves perched on a rose bush, the stoppers a finch and 2 billing doves, on a base edged with green gadroons, gold mount, minor chip to one stopper and minute chip to base, 6 cm. high, c. 1755. **£2,800-£3,200** *C*

A Caughley blue and white painted miniature part dinner service, comprising: 4 graduated meat dishes, 2 plates and a soup tureen with cover, handle missing, c. 1785. **£600-900** *A*

A scent bottle and stopper of 'Girl in a Swing' type, modelled as a Chinese family, wearing pale pink, yellow and turquoise, on a base inscribed 'L'Amour Comble Les Desirs', gold mount, minute chipping to foliage and finial, 9 cm. high, c. 1755. **£4,500-5,500** *C*

A Coalport Japan pattern dinner service, painted in Imari palette and gilt, comprising: a tureen, cover and stand, 9 soup plates, 26 plates, 2 dishes, 2 vegetable dishes and covers. **£7,000-8,000** *WW*

A service of the same design is in the Brighton Pavilion.

185

A Coalport botanical part dessert service, painted with named flowers, comprising: a centre-piece, 4 dishes, a lozenge-shaped dish and 11 plates, some rubbing, c. 1815. **£3,500-4,500** *C*

ORDER
The English and Continental porcelain section is ordered in alphabetical category order. Each category is then divided into alphabetical factory order and each factory is chronologically ordered.

A Caughley blue and white miniature part dinner service, comprising: 2 sauce tureens and covers, one cover chipped, 2 sauceboats, one foot chipped, the other cracked, 4 dishes and 21 plates, 3 with minute rim chips, most pieces with blue S mark, c. 1785. **£2,500-3,000** *C*

A Coalport part dinner service, made to the order of the Coldstream Guards, the centres with the Regimental Badge, the borders moulded with blue C-scrolls, edged in gilding, comprising: a sauce tureen, cover and 3 stands, 5 vegetable dishes, covers and 3 stands, 2 meat dishes, one chipped, 12 dishes, 20 soup plates, one chipped, 61 plates, one damaged, some pieces with puce printed retailer's mark of Nixon & Son, Windsor, c. 1850, some later replacements. **£2,000-2,500** *C*

A Coalport part dinner service, having blue and gilt waved borders, each item bearing family crest in colour, supplied by A. B. Daniell & Sons, 46 Wigmore Street, London, W., 60 pieces in all, slight faults. **£550-650** *A*

A miniature Coalport type dinner service, comprising: a tureen and cover, a vegetable dish and cover, 4 dishes and 11 plates, c. 1830-40. **£350-450** *S*

A green ground dessert service of Coalport type, comprising: 2 tureens, covers and stands, 12 dishes, 23 plates and a fruit stand, several pieces cracked or repaired, one plate restored, c. 1840. **£2,500-£3,000** *S*

A Copelands part service, of Mecklenburg-Strelitz type after the Chelsea original, with royal blue grounds, comprising: a pair of ice pails, covers and liners, 4 jardinières, 3 tureens and covers, one cracked, 8 dishes, 4 cake stands, one with top tier detached, 9 coffee cans, printed Copelands China, England marks and retailer's mark for T. Goode & Co., London, early 20th C. **£1,800-2,200** *C*

A Crown Derby Imari pattern dinner service, in underglaze blue, iron-red and gilding, comprising: 52 plates, 6 dishes and a drainer dish, printed marks in iron-red and impressed marks, date cypher for 1887. **£800-1,000** *SC*

A rare Crown Derby 'replica' plate of the Gladstone service, the centre painted by Count G. Holtzendorff and monogrammed 'GH' with a named view of 'Winfield House' (sic), enclosed by a rich blue ground, signed on the reverse by J. Rouse Senr., slight rubbing, impressed mark DERBY, printed marks in iron-red, crowned monogram, and registration diamond, script marks in red comprising named view 'Rouse' and 'replica', 9¼ in. (23.5 cm.), 1883. **£1,000-1,200** *SC*

Twitchett & Bailey record that the original service which was presented to Gladstone at Hawarden Castle on 22nd December 1883 comprised 26 pieces and that only 17 duplicates or replicas were made.

A Copeland and Garrett and Copeland topographical dessert service, each piece painted with a landscape view, named on the reverse, reserved on a green ground within a gilt foliate scroll rim, comprising: 23 plates, 6 dishes and a fruit stand, slight wear, printed garland and initials marks, pattern number 5750, c. 1847. **£2,000-2,200** *S*

A Royal Crown Derby dessert service, decorated in an Imari palette, comprising: 12 plates, 4 dishes and a fruit stand, slight wear, printed crowned initials mark, painted pattern number 9009, date codes for 1898 and 1906. **£700-800** *S*

A Ridgway dessert service, printed and painted with named botanical specimens, comprising: a comport, 9 dishes and 20 plates, some pieces stained or damaged, printed specimen names, c. 1820. **£1,000-£1,400** *S*

A Samson dessert service, decorated in Chinese 'famille verte' style, 14 plates, 8 in., 6 dishes, 11½ in. **£400-500** *DWB*

An extensive Meissen part service for dinner and dessert, comprising: a soup tureen and cover, a sauceboat and fixed stand, a cushion-shaped dish, 6 tazze, 231 plates, some damaged, blue crossed swords marks and impressed numerals, 20th C. **£10,000-12,000** *C*

RIDGWAY

- one of the most important factories manufacturing English bone china
- most of the early Ridgway porcelain from 1808-30 is unmarked; some, however, do have pattern numbers which are fractional, as did Coalport, with which it is often confused
- the quality of the early porcelain is excellent, brilliant white and with no crazing in the glaze
- there were many skilled flower painters employed at the Cauldon Place works including George Hancock, Thomas Brentnall, Joseph Bancroft
- the development of the Ridgway factory is as follows:–
  John Ridgway & Company, 1830-55
  John Ridgway, Bates & Company, 1856-58
  Bates, Brown-Westhead & Moore, 1859-61
  Brown-Westhead, Moore & Company, 1862-1905
  Cauldon Ltd., 1906-20
  Cauldon Potteries Ltd., 1920-62

A Minton Imari pattern breakfast service, comprising: 4 dishes, muffin dishes and covers, 6 plates, slop bowl, 6 large tea cups and saucers, 6 small tea cups, coffee cups and saucers, 3 egg cups, patt. no. 615 in gilding, c. 1820. **£1,100-£1,300** *SC*

A Minton pierced dessert service, with an azure ground rim reserved with gilt scroll-edged panels, comprising: 12 plates, 2 tazze and 2 fruit stands, 2 items repaired, painted pattern number A2754, impressed date codes for 1857 and 1858. **£1,100-1,300** *S*

An English porcelain dessert service, possibly Ridgway, each piece painted within pierced gilt and blue borders, comprising: a comport, a tureen and stand, 6 dishes and 13 plates, some damage, gilt pattern no. 3/234, c. 1830-40. **£300-400** *SS*

A Vienna part dinner service, comprising: a tureen, cover and stand, 6 dishes, one with rim chips, 2 soup plates, some rim chips, 54 inner plates, some with rim chips, blue beehive marks and various painters' marks, c. 1770. **£4,500-5,000** *C*

A Minton dessert service, decorated by Joseph Smith, against a blue ground with gold rim, comprising: 2 tureens, covers and stands, 2 jugs, 8 comports, 16 plates, some damage, date code for 1868. **£1,300-£1,500** *Bea*

A Rockingham-style part service, with turquoise and gilt rims and rose and yellow central sprays, comprising: 3 serving plates and 7 side plates. **£50-80** *LRG*

A fine English porcelain part dessert service, with wild flowers in pale enamel colours within a gold painted deep blue border, signed A. Wagg, comprising: 3 dishes and 6 plates. **£400-450** *Bea*

A rare dessert service, painted with scenes from the life and times of Dr. Syntax, after Rowlandson, comprising: 2 tureens and covers on fixed stands, comport, 8 dishes and 18 plates, very slight damage, c. 1815. **£5,000-5,500** *SC*

A Bow white prunus-moulded miniature sugar bowl and cover, minute chip to inside rim of cover, 7 cm. diam., c. 1755. **£500-550** *C*

A rare Chelsea 'rose' box and cover, naturalistically modelled with overlapping petals 'feathered' in tones of puce, handle repaired, red anchor period, 3¼ in., c. 1755. **£750-850** *S*

A Doccia sugar box and cover, decorated alla Sassonia, with gilt scrollwork borders enriched in iron-red, purple and sepia, flower knop, restoration to flower petals, 14.5 cm., mid 18th C. **£750-950** *S*

A Meissen sugar basin and cover, with recumbent lion finial, painted with figures in continuous harbour landscapes, blue crossed swords and gilder's mark 7, 11.5 cm. wide, c. 1735. **£4,000-5,000** *C*

DOCCIA

- **factory started by Carlo Ginori, near Florence in 1735**
- **hybrid hard paste porcelain of pronounced greyish-white appearance**
- **body liable to firecracks**
- **often decorated with mythological, religious and hunting subjects**
- **glaze can have a 'smudgy' look**
- **used strong enamel colours**
- **from 1757-91 the factory was directed by Lorenzo Ginori, glaze and body improved considerably**
- **figures often in the white and sometimes decorated with an iron-red colour exclusive to the factory**
- **porcelain often confused with Capodimonte, although Doccia is hard paste and Capodimonte soft-paste**
- **around 1770 figures covered in a white tin-glaze, often firecracked**
- **factory still exists**

An early Meissen sugar box and cover, with typical panels of chinoiseries in the manner of J. G. Herold, and indianische Blumen, with iron-red trellis and scrolls, crossed swords and K.P.M. in underglaze blue, 83 in gilding on both pieces, chip on footrim, hair crack, 11 cm., 1722-23. **£2,600-£3,400** *S*

A Meissen sugar bowl and cover, painted with figures in a continuous river landscape, with gilt scrollwork borders and flower finial, chip to rim of bowl, blue crossed swords and 52A gilder's mark on each piece, 12 cm. diam., c. 1740. **£1,000-1,200** *C*

A Meissen sugar caster, the ribbed body with ozier-moulded border and decorated with coloured flowers, pears and chestnuts, crossed swords in underglaze blue, rim chipped on interior, 18.5 cm., mid 18th C. **£800-£900** *S*

An Ansbach tureen, painted with groups of fruit and vegetables flanked by gilt-edged green scrolls and with gilt vertical lines, entwined with flowering plants, blue A mark and incised S twice, 39.5 cm. wide, c. 1770. **£500-600** *C*

A Meissen sugar bowl and cover, painted in coloured enamels in the manner of C. F. Herold, the cover with gilt scroll border and faceted gilt knop, gilding rubbed, H. in gilding, impressed 31, 10.7 cm., c. 1740. **£1,500-2,000** *S*

A Newhall sugar box and cover, with painted flowers, pattern 376, one handle restored, 5¼ in., c. 1795. **£100-110** *MA*

A rare Chelsea partridge tureen and cover, red anchor period, marked on both tureen and cover, marked with numerals, 5¾ in. wide, c. 1754-55. **£1,850-1,950** *HOF*

These tureens were not made for serving such delicacies as partridge but for desserts.

A Clignacourt Paris sauce tureen, cover and stand, with a panel of chinoiserie figures painted 'en grisaille', gilt monogram of Louis-Stanislas-Xavier, knop repaired, 18.5 cm. wide by 11.5 cm. high, c. 1775-85. **£250-350** *SS*

A Bristol ecuelle, cover and stand, painted 'en grisaille', with gilt line borders and gilt dentil rims, Richard Champion's Factory, the stand 16.5 cm. wide, c. 1775. **£500-£600** *C*

A Kuznetzov tureen and cover, in the form of a duck, painted in blue and purple, factory mark in blue, 20 cm. (8 in.), late 19th C. **£130-180** *S*

A Meissen bowl and cover, decorated in colours with groups of chinoiserie figures, the rims with gilt borders, crossed swords in underglaze blue, 15.3 cm., c. 1735-40. **£1,300-1,500** *S*

A Meissen chinoiserie wochenterrine and cover, with silver-gilt mounts, with shaped gilt Böttger-lustre, iron-red and puce Laub-und-Bandelwerk cartouches with indianische Blumen in colours, with silver-gilt liner and foot rim, hair crack in base, the porcelain 1725-28, the mounts possibly contemporary, 23 cm. wide. **£2,300-2,800** *C*

A pair of Meissen powdered-purple ground Kakiemon ecuelles, covers and stands, restorations to both tureens and one cover, blue crossed swords marks, the stands 17.5 cm. diam., c. 1735. **£900-1,200** *C*

A Meissen ecuelle, cover and stand, with trefoil cartouches surrounded by puce and gilt scrolled foliage, blue crossed swords marks, Pressnummer 21, minor chips to rim, the stand 23 cm. diam., c. 1755. **£1,000-1,200** *C*

A rare Meissen tureen and cover, the sides pierced with scrollwork, the interior burnished gilt and crisply moulded with 'indianische Blumen', swords mark in underglaze blue, incised numerals, some chipping, 10 in. (25.5 cm.), late 19th C. **£2,000-2,300** *SC*

A German oval jagd tureen and cover, in the Meissen style, the base with Frauenkopf handles, with oval gilt and puce flowered cartouches, divided by gilt flower sprays and yellow shaped panels edged in gilt, cancelled blue crossed swords mark, hair crack in base, chips to handles, 37.5 cm. wide, 18th C. **£600-800** *C*

A Sèvres turquoise ground ecuelle, cover and stand, blue interlaced L marks enclosing the date letter U for 1773 and the painter's mark of Le Bel and gilder's mark of Vande, the stand 20 cm. wide. **£1,500-1,700** *C*

SÈVRES

- most decoration of these early years has a somewhat tentative appearance and few pieces show the sharpness of German contemporaries
- the vases and other hollow wares including ice pails and flower holders epitomised the rococo style predominant at the court
- Sèvres plaques were inset into furniture from 1760's
- Sèvres managed to discover the secret of hard paste porcelain at the same time as Cookworthy at Plymouth in 1768
- 'jewelled porcelain' was introduced in 1773, using a technique of fusing enamels over gilt or silver foil

A Sèvres bleu celeste ecuelle, cover and stand, painted with bouquets of pink, white and yellow roses within ciselé surrounds on turquoise grounds, interlaced L marks in blue with the date letter Y for 1776 and the painter's mark apparently that of Tandart, the stand 20 cm. wide. **£1,000-1,500** *C*

A Belleek multiple vase centrepiece, printed dog and harp mark, some restoration, 33.2 cm. **£160-220** *Bea*

A Belleek 'croaking' frog vase, its eyes delineated in black, the glaze of yellowish tone, printed dog and harp mark in black, 5 in. (12.7 cm.) c. 1900. **£200-250** *SC*

A Coalport vase, in green and gilt, with pierced double scroll handles and quatrelobed foot, gold anchor mark, 27.5 cm. **£200-250** *L*

A Berlin large gilt ground vase, sceptre mark in blue, 47.5 cm. **£1,200-1,400** *P*

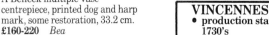

A set of 3 Coalport vases, painted with bouquets of flowers and insects, with green and gilt scroll handles and borders, with encrusted flowers, supported by green and gilt scrolls, 18.5 and 20 cm. **£300-400** *L*

VINCENNES

- production started in the late 1730's
- early production was generally of indifferent quality
- and probably inferior to the contemporary productions of St. Cloud and Mennecy
- towards end of 1740's probably influenced by Meissen introduced coloured grounds
- 1750's lightly tooled gilding was used to heighten their reserve panels
- coloured grounds:–
  'gros bleu' from late 1740's
  'bleu celeste' from 1752
  'jaune jonquille' from 1753
  'rose pompadour' from 1757
- factory had moved from Vincennes to Sèvres in 1756

A rare pair of Chelsea Kakiemon-style vases and covers, painted with panels of prunus, pine and bamboo, symbolising the 'Three Friends', divided by iron-red panel with turquoise scrolling foliage, re anchor marks inside necks, repaired and damaged, one knop missing, vases 9¾ in., c. 1752-55. **£800-1,000** *S*

An unusual Belleek vase, in the form of a large pink bordered tulip, printed mark, 13 in. **£700-800** *DWB*

A rare garniture of 3 Chelsea-Derby vases and covers, the covers and feet with pink-scale decoration, handles on covers retored, 2 handles repaired, 14 and 11¾ in., c. 1770. **£1,300-1,500** *S*

A Coalport limited edition diamond jubilee vase and cover, painted with respective portrait medallion of youthful and elderly monarch, printed marks in gilt and numbered 4 from a limited edition of 50, cover and rim with restoration, 21 in. high (53 cm.). **£1,100-1,500** *Bon*

A garniture of 3 Coalport (John Rose) vases, the reverse with an overall pattern of gilt flowerheads and black dots, the necks with gilt overlapping diamond pattern, one foot restored, 20 to 22.5 cm. high, c. 1810. **£700-800** *C*

A Coalport vase and cover, in Sèvres style, with burnished gilt borders reserved on a bleu celeste ground, CBD monogram in gilding, 11⅜ in. (28.8 cm.), 1851-61. **£350-£400** *SC*

A Coalport vase and cover, reserved on pale yellow and gros bleu grounds, green printed mark, 11⅜ in. (28.8 cm.), c. 1900. **£150-£200** *SC*

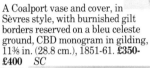

A Coalport (John Rose) oviform 2-handled vase, with gilt flower-sprays and foliage between elaborate gilt and white borders, 24 cm. high, c. 1810. **£350-400** *C*

A Coalport blue ground vase, painted 'en grisaille' by Thomas Baxter, from a drawing by F. Van Mieris, on a knopped stem and gilt square base, signed 'Baxter Pinxt, 1808', the underneath of the foot inscribed 'G. Phillips Jun. 135 Oxford Street', one handle repaired, 37 cm. high, c. 1808. **£800-900** *C*

A Derby frill vase, 7 in. with cover, c. 1765. **£110-140** *HyD*

Frill vases of this type were also made at Bow, Longton Hall and later by Samson.

A Coalport (John Rose) pink ground vase, the flared rim and circular foot gilt with flowerheads and stylised anthemion and with gilt line rims, 19.5 cm. high, c. 1810. **£400-500** *C*

A pair of Bloor Derby vases, reserved on a royal blue ground with ornate gilt scrolls some wear , thumb-print circular mark, 9 in., c. 1830. **£900-1,000** *S*

A Royal Crown Derby 'jewelled' vase, painted by Leroy, signed, with a royal blue ground, the neck and foot with further gilt bands and 'jewelling' over a green ground, printed crowned initials mark, numbered F1484/1485, 5¼ in., c. 1910. **£600-700** *S*

A pair of Royal Crown Derby vases and covers, with royal blue grounds, printed crowned initials mark, incised shape number 1563, dated code for 1911, one knop repaired, hair crack in one base, 16¼ in. **£1,000-1,200** *S*

A Derby pot pourri vase and cover, on a green scale pattern ground, on a rockwork base applied with partridges, flowers and a hound, Wm. Duesbury & Co., chips to flowers and birds, finial damaged, cover cracked and chipped, 34 cm. high, c. 1765. **£2,000-2,500** *C*

A pair of Royal Crown Derby apple-green ground vases and covers, each painted by A. F. Wood, one signed with initials, printed crowned initials mark, date code for 1905, 5½ in. **£650-750** *S*

A Royal Crown Derby 'jewelled' vase and cover, painted by A. Gregory, signed, within ornate raised gilt borders against a midnight blue ground with further formal borders, heightened in white and turquoise enamel 'jewelling', printed crowned initials mark and date code for 1909, knop repaired, 10¾ in. **£700-800** *S*

A pair of large Dresden vases, covers and stands, marks in underglaze blue, repairs, chips, 86.5 cm., late 19th C. **£3,500-4,500** *S*

A rare pair of Herculaneum 'Empire' vases, the matt blue ground bodies sprigged with beige reliefs, square black bases, printed factory marks including Liver Birds in puce, 12¾ in., c. 1815-20. **£1,200-1,400** *S*

A label attached to these vases notes that they were a present from King Charles XIV of Sweden to the architect Luistow, who designed the palace at Christiania.

A pair of Dresden vases, covers and stands, in the manner of Helena Wolfsohn, with turquoise blue ground heightened with flowers within gilt borders, crowned Dresden mark in blue, 46 cm. high, c. 1900. **£500-600** *HSS*

A pair of Dresden vases and covers, with rose pink ground, late 19th C./early 20th C. **£500-600** *WHL*

A Liverpool blue and white vase and cover, Richard Chaffer's Factory, minute chip to cover, 10.5 cm. high, c. 1762. **£700-800** *C*

A Loosdrecht vase and cover, incised M.O.L. and a star, 24 cm. **£400-500** *P*

A pair of Meissen baluster pot pourri vases and covers, enriched with gilding, blue crossed swords marks, one finial re-stuck, chips, 21.5 cm. high, c. 1745. **£2,200-2,500** *C*

A Meissen deckelpokal and octagonal cover, with shaped quatrefoil lustre gold, iron-red and puce Laub-und-Bandelwerk cartouches, blue crossed swords mark and gilder's number 5 on each piece, repair to finial, hair crack to the body, 18 cm. high, c. 1730. **£1,800-2,000** *C*

A fine Meissen beaker, painted in colours with Watteauesque scenes and sprigs of deutsche Blumen, all beneath a gilt scrollwork border, crossed swords in underglaze blue, 11.8 cm., mid 18th C. **£1,300-1,500** *S*

A pair of fine Meissen vases, decorated with named views of the royal Saxon castles, Schloss Moritzburg and Schloss Pillnitz, crossed swords and I in underglaze blue, impressed and incised numerals and letters, 'Pillnitz' and 'Moritzburg' in black enamel, 27.5 cm., late 18th/early 19th C. **£3,500-4,000** *S*

A pair of Meissen vases, with gilt scroll borders against a deep blue ground, crossed swords in underglaze blue, incised and impressed numerals, 5½ in. (14.2 cm.), late 19th C. **£350-400** *S*

A Meissen vase, the neck and foot with formal gilt borders and pale green grounds, crossed swords in underglaze blue, 58.5 cm., third quarter of the 19th C. **£550-650** *S*

A Meissen 'Schneeballen' vase and cover, applied overall with numerous florets and a golden oriole and a wagtail, crossed swords in underglaze blue, small chips, 1 ft. 10 in. (56 cm.), c. 1880. **£1,200-£1,500** *S*

A garniture of 3 Minton 'Wellington' vases, painted in the manner of Thomas Steel, the green ground with further gilt motifs in the style of Thomas Till, one stem repaired, 12 and 13½ in., c. 1830-35. **£1,300-1,500** *S*

A pair of Minton 'Dresden' green ground pot pourri vases and covers, with elaborately moulded ochre and gilt C-scroll and foliage cartouches on apple-green grounds, gilt with flower sprays, one vase with hair cracks, one putto's leg restored, minor chips to garlands, 45 cm. high, c. 1838. **£1,000-1,200** *C*

A Minton vase, with a royal blue ground, the neck with a band of medallions and grotesques, the circular foot moulded with vine above a square base, some restoration, the figures at the shoulder now missing and replaced with gilt metal shell motifs, 21¼ in., c. 1855-60. **£450-550** *S*
The design for this vase in the Minton pattern book is numbered 666.

A pair of Minton 'cloisonne' vases, decorated in colourful enamels and gilding against a turquoise ground, in imitation of Chinese cloisonné, impressed mark, shape number 1592 and date code for 1871, 11 in. **£350-450** *S*

A pair of Mintons polychrome pâte-sur-pâte vases in the Persian taste, elaborately decorated in variously coloured slips, on brown grounds enriched with gilt dashes, impressed and gilt Mintons' marks, one vase with restoration to the body, 58 cm. high, c. 1880. **£1,400-£1,800** *C*

A Mintons polychrome pâte-sur-pâte vase, decorated by Lawrence Birks, decorated in white slip, on salmon-pink grounds, enriched with gilding, LB monogram, impressed and gilt Mintons marks and date code for 1888, 44.5 cm. high. **£1,700-1,900** *C*

A Plymouth polychrome vase, with birds, butterflies and insects, mark for 4, badly damaged, 7½ in., c. 1770. **£200-250** *MA*
Perfect **£1,200-1,500**

A Mintons pâte-sur-pâte vase, decorated by L. Solon, signed, in white relief against a deep blue ground, printed globe mark, firing fault in glaze, 8½ in., c. 1900. **£400-£450** *S*

A pair of large flower-encrusted bottle vases and covers, probably Ridgway, with a deep blue ground with gilt sprigs, painted crossed swords in blue, chips, 18½ in., mid 19th C. **£700-800**   *S*

PLYMOUTH

- factory ran from c. 1768-70
- a hard-paste porcelain body patented by William Cookworthy
- high proportion of kiln wastage
- had a tendency to firing flaws and smokiness as a result of improper technique in kiln and many imperfections in the glaze
- very black underglaze blue
- most recognised products are the bell-shaped tankards painted with dishevelled birds in the manner of the mysterious Monsieur Soqui
- the shell salt, also known at Worcester, Derby and Bow, most commonly found piece
- Cookworthy transferred the factory to Bristol c. 1770

A Rockingham baluster pot pourri vase and pierced cover, painted with a view of Eton Hall, puce griffin mark and C4 in gold, flowers chipped, cover repaired, 24 cm. high, c. 1835. **£800-900**   *C*

A pair of Sèvres (Charles X) brown ground vases, the dark brown grounds in imitation of porphyry, reserved and decorated in ochre, heightened in sepia and black, blue interlaced L, fleur-de-lys and Sèvres marks, 25.5 cm. high, c. 1825. **£1,500-1,800**   *C*

A pair of Sèvres-pattern gilt metal mounted vases, the royal blue grounds reserved and decorated in colours by J. Lothe, 47 cm. high. **£1,000-1,200**   *C*

A pair of Samson armorial export-style vases and covers, on grounds of 'famille rose' scattered sprays, enclosed by 'bianco sopra bianco' foliage, within iron-red and gilt spearhead borders, pseudo seal marks in red, 17¾ in. (45 cm.), late 19th C. **£800-900**   *SC*

A pair of ormolu-mounted Sèvres-style vases, of ovoid form, painted by H. Desprez, signed, the deep blue ground necks and feet with chased gold trophies, scrolls and flowers, 118 cm. **£4,500-5,500**   *P*

A pair of Sèvres-pattern gros bleu ground ormolu-mounted vases and covers, with gilt foliage and turquoise jewelled cartouches, 27.5 cm. high, last quarter of the 19th C. **£1,500-£1,700**   *C*

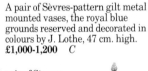

A Sèvres-pattern turquoise ground jewelled and ormolu-mounted garniture-du-cheminee, the turquoise grounds enriched with bands of jewelling, signed Ab: Schil à Sèvres, the central vase fitted and adapted for electricity, one with small hair crack to lower part, 38 and 45 cm. high, last quarter of the 19th C. **£2,700-3,000**   *C*

A pair of 'Sèvres' gilt bronze mounted and 'jewelled' vases and covers, with pink grounds, one cover restored, 33.5 cm., mid 19th C. **£1,000-1,200**   *S*

A pair of Sèvres-pattern turquoise ground vases and covers, enriched with jewelling and gilding, imitation blue interlaced L marks and initials, 24.5 cm. high, last quarter of the 19th C. **£600-800**   *C*

A pair of Sèvres-pattern turquoise ground ormolu-mounted vases and covers, enriched with gilding beneath a band of jewelling, imitation blue interlaced L marks, 46 cm. high, last quarter of the 19th C. **£2,600-2,800**   *C*

A pair of Sèvres pâte-sur-pâte vases, each decorated by J. Gély, signed, with white birds chasing blue butterflies amongst trails of ivy and pink foxgloves, against a pale celadon ground, printed marks, incised numerals, 33.5 cm., date code for 1875. **£1,100-1,300** *S*

Léopold-Jules Joseph Gély worked at Sèvres from 1851 until 1889.

A pair of Sèvres vases and covers, painted with Watteauesque lovers, on a bleu de roi ground, interlaced L's in blue, 34.5 cm. high, second half 19th C. **£900-1,000** *HSS*

A pair of Spode spill vases, decorated in pattern 1227, 4½ in. high, c. 1820. **£1,000-1,200** *EV*

A rare Cozzi Venice vase, 6¼ in., c. 1765. **£350-390** *KK*

A garniture of 3 Spode vases, marked '967' pattern, decorated in blue, gilt, rust and green, 7 and 5½ in. **£600-700** *A*

A pair of Spode vases, decorated in underglaze blue, iron-red, green and gilding, one with painted mark, pattern number 967, one cracked, 4½ in., c. 1825. **£250-£300** *S*

A pair of Wedgwood fairyland lustre 'Candlemas' vases, decorated with panels of candles with human heads, between borders of elves tugging on bell ropes, printed urn mark, Z5157, 10¼ in., 1920's. **£1,500-2,000** *S*

A Wedgwood fairyland lustre vase, decorated with the 'Candlemas' design, printed urn mark, Z5157, gilding rubbed, 8¾ in., 1920's. **£300-400** *S*

A pair of Wedgwood fairyland lustre vases, with the design 'Torches', printed Portland vase mark in gilding, inscribed Z5360, 10⅞ in. (27.7 cm.), 1920's. **£1,000-£1,500** *SC*

A 'Vienna' vase, cover and stand, painted with 2 panels of the Graces and Cupid reserved on a polychrome ground, gilding rubbed, shield in blue, 33.5 cm., late 19th C. **£300-400** *S*

ORDER

The English and Continental porcelain section is ordered in alphabetical category order. Each category is then divided into alphabetical factory order and each factory is chronologically ordered.

A pair of Wedgwood flame fairyland lustre vases, each decorated with 'tree serpent and torches', printed urn mark, Z5360, incised shape number 3149, 12½ in., 1920's. **£1,500-2,000** *S*

A pair of Wedgwood fairyland lustre vases, each printed in gilding over mottled lustrous coloured glazes with the 'Candlemas' design, printed Portland vase mark in gilding, inscribed in black Z5157, 7⅞ in. (20 cm.), 1920's. **£700-900** *SC*

A rare Lowestoft blue and white large size moulded butter boat, 3⅞ in., c. 1780. **£200-225** *MA*

A Meissen bottle, painted in Kakiemon style, with panels of a red tiger and bamboo, prunus, birds and flowers, on a turquoise ground, chip on foot rim, some wear, crossed swords in blue, Johanneum number $\frac{N.382}{W}$, 20.2 cm., c. 1730. **£5,500-6,500** *S*

A pair of English porcelain vases, the Brunswick green ground, reserved with gilt edged floral cartouches, restored, 24 cm., c. 1820. **£100-140** *SS*

A Wedgwood flame fairyland lustre vase, decorated with the 'ship and tree' panels of the 'sycamore tree' design, above a 'flaming wheel' border, all in bright colours against a shaded orange ground, printed urn mark, incised shape number 2033, 12¼ in., 1920's. **£1,000-1,500** *S*

A German silver-mounted pipe bowl, modelled as a man in yellow shirt, with gilt trim, 7 cm. long, 18th C. **£800-900** *C*

A Vienna (Du Paquier) deep oval bourdalou, painted by J. P. Dannhofer, modelled with a Frauenkopf beneath the lip, the handle with a similar mask, both enriched with silver lustre, restored and with hair crack around base of handle, 20 cm. wide, the porcelain c. 1730. **£1,100-1,400** *C*

A Meissen cane handle, modelled by Johann Friedrich Lücke, with a painted 'Kauffahrtei' scene in typical palette, some scratches to glaze, 7.8 cm., 1748-57. **£850-£950** *S*

A rare Meissen bottle, painted in colours, minor chips on rim, Johanneum number , 20.3 cm., c. 1728-30. **£6,000-7,000** *S*

A Meissen cane handle, painted in colours with vignettes of Watteauesque figures, including Harlequin and a companion, later gold mounts, 9.5 cm., mid 18th C. **£900-1,100** *S*

The vignette of Harlequin derives from an engraving by Thomassin after Watteau.

A rare Meissen model of a barn, painted in tones of red-brown and the thatch with mossy-green tints, 18th C. **£1,500-2,000** *S*

A rare Meissen cane handle, painted in the manner of J. E. Stadler in typical palette, with chinoiserie figures in a garden between underglaze blue line borders, 5 cm., c. 1725-30. **£1,500-2,000** *S*

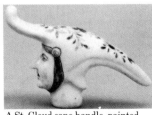

A St. Cloud cane handle, painted with oriental flowers in colours, 12.5 cm., c. 1740-50. **£450-550** *S*

An interesting Italian cane handle of T-shape, painted with panels of pastoral scenes in the manner of Giovanni Caselli, enclosed by moulded borders of scrolls and flowers, incised G, probably Capodimonte, 11.5 cm., c. 1755-59. **£1,100-1,500** *S*

An Easter-egg, painted with flowerheads and laurel branches and gilt with the monogram of Empress Alexandra Feodorovna, with pink silk ribbon, 8.8 cm. high, c. 1910. **£280-340**   *C*

A Bow white prunus-moulded egg cup, 7 cm. high, c. 1760. **£500-600**   *C*

MAKE THE MOST OF MILLER'S

Miller's is completely different each year. Each edition contains completely NEW photographs. This is not an updated publication. We never repeat the same photograph.

A Meissen allegorical ewer, after a model by J. J. Kändler, emblematic of Water, some restoration, crossed swords mark in underglaze blue, 24¾ in. (63 cm.), mid to late 19th C. **£1,000-1,500**   *SC*

BERLIN

- first factory started by W. K. Wegely in 1752
- body hard to distinguish from Meissen
- particularly close the Cupids in Disguise and the Commedia dell'Arte figures
- closed in 1757 at the start of Seven Years War
- a second factory was started in 1761 by J. E. Gotzkowsky
- many artists came from Meissen, including F. E. Meyer
- porcelain has a distinctly creamy tone
- painting was in the restrained rococo manner
- pieces with puce scale borders and delicate flower painting
- derived from fashion for Sèvres — in common with most major German factories
- from 1770 the porcelain has a much colder more brilliant white tone
- the factory became influenced by the neo-classical movement in common with Fürstenburg and Meissen
- figure modelling was perfected by the brothers Friedrich Elias Meyer and Wilhelm Christian Meyer — note the characteristic small heads and elongated bodies
- c. 1775 figure bases became more architectural in design, notably oval and square pedestals
- in the early 19th C. the 'Empire' style of Sèvres and Vienna was copied
- as the 19th C. progressed Berlin tended to follow the prevailing trends

A rare Berlin Easter-egg, decorated with a painted view of Schloss Sanssoucis painted in colours, on a gilt ground, with gilt metal mount, minor scratching, 6.5 cm., c. 1825-30. **£1,600-1,800**   *S*

A Sèvres 'egg' casket, mounted in ormolu with hinged lid, the blue ground with painted panels and gilt decoration, 9 in. high. **£400-£500**   *DA*
Signed by P. Poche and given to the British Ambassador by the last Tsar of Russia.

A pair of Berlin ewers, painted with mythological subjects including the Triumph of Bacchus and the Chariot of Apollo, some damage, sceptre in underglaze blue, 1 ft. 11¼ in. (59 cm.), c. 1860. **£1,000-1,500**   *S*

A rare Böttger porcelain ewer, moulded on the sides with sprays of flowers and applied around the base with a band of acanthus leaves, painted in the manner of Franz Ferdinand Mayer of Pressnitz, the gilt spout in Chinese style, gilt scrolling handle, marked 12 in gilding, handle repaired, foot rim chipped, 25.7 cm., the porcelain c. 1715, the decoration mid 18th C. **£1,500-2,000**   *S*

WORCESTER PORCELAIN

Worcester has not only the longest continuous history of porcelain production in England but one of the most complicated.

Founded in June 1751 by 15 partners headed by Dr. John Wall, the Worcester Porcelain Company took over an earlier factory producing soft paste porcelain in Bristol — Miller and Lund's factory. The body, made with soaprock from the Lizard in Cornwall, did not crack nor craze and was found particularly suitable for teawares and sauceboats, the main production for the first few years. It is difficult to tell the difference between the wares from Bristol and early Worcester and the use of the description of Bristol/Worcester is safer. These early pieces, often silver shape, are very beautiful and highly appreciated nowadays, especially any pieces with the very rare moulded mark of the word Bristol. Wares of the 1750's range from blue and white and onglaze paintings in the Chinoiserie style to Meissen styles and frequently the blue and white is marked with the so-called painter's marks. Early onglaze printing was introduced by about 1755 with 'smoky primitive' prints, to be improved by 1757 with the strong jet enamel prints typified by the King of Prussia portraits. By 1758 underglaze blue printing had been introduced and this was to become more important a feature of production in the 1770's and 80's. Most Worcester blue and white from 1760 was marked with the crescent mark, painted in the case of painted wares and printed with hatched lines in the case of printed wares.

In the 1760's the introduction of fine coloured grounds, particularly the use of blue scale with onglaze paintings of fabulous birds and fine gilding moves the production into a different league and such pieces have always been very collectable, although their values have not gone up in recent years as greatly as have the Bristol/Worcester styles and they may well be undervalued at present. Some very exotic pieces were decorated by Giles in London on Worcester 'blanks' and in general pieces with underglaze blue and onglaze colours are marked with a fretted square mark and those with only onglaze decoration have no factory mark or occasionally a version of the Meissen crossed swords with a 9 in the hilts or copies of other factory marks. Perhaps the finest painting

was done by Donaldson and O'Neale around 1770.

In 1776 Dr. Wall died and the factory was continued by William Davis until 1783 when it was bought by the Flight family. In these periods the quality of production took a downward turn, with a concentration on blue printing, the blue becoming brighter and more violet toned in colour and the translucence of the body turning yellow and orange from its earlier green. A new mark of a disguised numeral is seen, as well as the continuing use of the crescent on underglaze blue pieces, although a certain amount of better ware was still being produced. In 1792 the Flights were joined by Martin Barr and the firm is called Flight and Barr (frequently found mark of an incised B) until 1804 when it changed to Barr Flight and Barr, then in 1813 to Flight Barr and Barr, which title continues to 1840. A steady improvement is seen from 1792 and the quality of making and decorating reaches its height in the 1810's and 20's, when such great craftsmen as William Billingsley and Thomas Baxter were associated.

Meanwhile in about 1787 Robert Chamberlain, who had worked for Dr. Wall, set up his own factory in the Diglis area of Worcester, where the works still are. At first he decorated ware bought from Caughley and occasionally from Flight, then he began to produce his own by the mid 1790's. The Chamberlain factory grew in strength through the 19th century and were great competitors of Flight and Barr until 1840 when the two firms merged — 'a marriage of convenience and not of love'. The Flight and Barr factory site was given over to the making of tiles until 1852 while production of the bone china body and some stone china continued at the Diglis factory, the firm being known as Chamberlain and Company. In 1852 a new partnership was formed called Kerr and Binns and produced some charming wares in the Victorian classical style until 1862 when a new partnership headed by R. W. Binns formed a joint stock company, the Worcester Royal Porcelain Company Limited and the famous mark of a crowned circle was introduced. Through the second half of the 19th century Royal Worcester produced a fine quality of bone china and parian wares and the superb modeller James

Hadley designed magnificent figures and vases which were decorated by a range of decorators second to none in the industry. Of particular interest are the wares in the style of the Japanesque or Aesthetic Movement and the incredible pieces hand pierced by George Owen.

In 1889 Royal Worcester acquired the rival Worcester factory of George Grainger and Company Limited which had been formed by Thomas Grainger in the St. Martin's Gate area of the city in 1801 or shortly afterwards and production continued at the old site until 1902 when it was sold. Grainger's wares can be delightful and a forthcoming book should put the factory on the map, one problem being that many of the earliest pieces are unmarked. The Grainger workmen joined Royal Worcester and formed a marvellous group of decorators, headed by such outstanding painters as John and Harry Stinton (Highland Cattle subjects), James Stinton (Game Birds), Charles Baldwyn (Swans and other birds), William Hawkins (still life), Harry Davis (Landscapes and Sheep) and Richard Sebright (Fruit). James Hadley had left Royal Worcester to set up his own factory in 1896 and shortly after he died Hadley's was bought by Royal Worcester in 1905. Another outside factory in Worcester was that of Locke and Company (1895-1904) but these wares do not count as Royal Worcester as the firms did not merge and they are not as good in quality as those of the main company.

In the 1930's Royal Worcester used the models of a large number of young free lance designers, many of them women. Many of the models were in the style of the Art Deco movement and were not popular with the public, very few of some being sold and these are now very collectable. The only successful free lance modellers of the 1930's were Doris Lindner, who produced small animals, especially dogs and later went on to model magnificent large equestrian studies, Freda Doughty (studies of children) and her sister Dorothy Doughty who modelled life size studies of birds on flowers, mostly for the American market and these were made in limited editions. Since the last war Royal Worcester has continued to produce fine quality useful and ornamental wares both in bone china and hard paste porcelain.

by **Henry Sandon**

A ladle or caddy spoon of Chinese rice spoon shape, painted with the 'Maltese Cross Flower' pattern, crescent mark, 13.8 cm. long, c. 1770. **£300-400** *P*

While once reasonably common these are now rarely found, especially in perfect condition. Like all small spoons, they are very delicate and easily broken near the florette, so the survival factor is limited.

A Worcester blue and white cylindrical mustard pot and cover, 1770. **£750-850** *C*

A Worcester blue and white salt mustard spoon, the bowl with a flowerhead within a cell-pattern border, one minute rim chip, 10 cm. long, c. 1770. **£350-400**

All early porcelain spoons are now rare, especially in good condition. The especial danger point is the junction of handle and bowl, which is a thin and fragile part.

A Worcester blue and white cylindrical mug, with grooved loop handle, painted with 'The Gardener' pattern, blue crescent mark, 12 cm. high, c. 1768. **£750-£850**   *C*

A Worcester mug of 'scratch-cross' type, painted in underglaze blue with the 'Plantation' pattern, the reverse with a flowering plant, workman's mark in blue, incised cross mark below handle, 9 cm., c. 1754. **£350-450**   *P*

A Worcester blue and white sauceboat, of silver shape, the moulded panels painted with Chinese fishing boats and islands, the centre with a flower spray, workman's mark, 18 cm. long, c. 1755. **£1,100-1,500**   *P*

The pattern is not recorded by Branyan, French and Sandon although two other examples have since been noted.

A first period Worcester sauceboat, the ground moulded with basketweave, painted in underglaze blue with 'Man with a Bomb' pattern, the interior decorated with a foliage spray and cell diaper spout, open crescent mark, 7½ in. long, 3½ in. wide. **£350-450**   *CLG*

A rare Worcester blue and white small moulded cream boat, of Chelsea ewer type, painted with 'The Chelsea Ewer Sprays', cracked and small chip, 4 in. wide, c. 1770. **£160-180**   *JSA*

Even though this piece is damaged, it is of sufficient rarity to make it desirable, an indication that damage to 18th C. blue and white is not such a worry to collectors as it once was.

A Worcester blue and white sauceboat, very similar to the previous lot and with the same very rare pattern, workman's mark, 17 cm., c. 1755. **£500-600**   *P*

Early silver shaped sauceboats are among Worcester's most delightful productions. Generally they have different modelling on each side and a matching pair would be a great rarity nowadays.

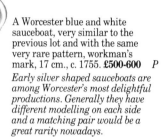

A Worcester shell-shaped pickle dish, painted with the 'Two Peony Rock Bird' pattern, workman's mark, 10 cm., c. 1757. **£350-400**   *P*

A rare Worcester blue and white basin, painted with a fantastic oriental island scene, some wear, 11 in., c. 1760. **£800-900**   *S*

A similar bowl is illustrated by Branyan, French and Sandon in Worcester Blue and White Porcelain, 1751-90, p. 113, No. B.34. These large basins should have a bottle or jug to be complete as wash sets and are then very desirable. The blue and white painting is usually very clear at this period but can become blurred later.

A Worcester blue and white shell/pickle dish, with 'The Two Peony Rock Bird' pattern, workman's mark, 4½ in. wide, c. 1758. **£380-£420**   *MA*

A Worcester blue and white coffee pot, painted with the 'Rock Strata' pattern, chip to finial, 8¾ in., c. 1775. **£480-530**   *JSA*

Coffee pots are rarer objects than tea pots but this is not necessarily reflected in its price, especially where, as here, the pattern is a fairly common one.

A Worcester blue and white fluted tea bowl and saucer, painted with 'The Hollow Rock Lily' pattern, foot chips to saucer, c. 1770. **£75-80**   *JSA*

A Worcester blue and white tea bowl and saucer, painted with 'The Waiting Chinaman', crescent mark, c. 1760. **£250-280**   *MA*

A Worcester blue and white tea cup and saucer, painted with 'The Bird in a ring' pattern, c. 1755-65. **£440-£490**   *KK*

A Worcester blue and white tea bowl and saucer, painted with the 'Rock Warbler' pattern, c. 1756-58. **£280-320**   *SRO*

A Worcester patty pan, painted with the 'Bare Tree and Speared Bird' pattern, Mansfield border, swastika workman's mark, 12 cm., c. 1758-60. **£350-400**   *P*

A Worcester blue and white tea pot, painted with the 'Mansfield' pattern, 5½ in., c. 1760-62. **£325-£370**   *SRO*

Worcester tea pots prior to about 1762 more generally have a pointed knob than a flower one. They will also have glaze under the flange of the cover but later ones will be unglazed.

A Worcester blue and white bowl, painted with the 'Prunus Root' pattern, workman's mark, 5 in. diam., c. 1758. **£130-140**   *MA*

A Worcester blue and white mug, painted with 'The Walk in the Garden' pattern, 3½ in., c. 1760-65. **£500-550**   *SRO*

A Worcester blue and white octagonal tea bowl, painted with 'The Prunus Root' pattern, c. 1762-65. **£125-145**   *SRO*

A Worcester spoon tray of plain oval shape, painted with the 'Arcade' pattern, with alternating arched panels, the underside of the rim with 4 Buddhist emblems, mark of a Chinese character within 2 narrow lines, 12.7 cm., c. 1765. **£1,300-1,600**   *P*

A very unusual shaped spoon tray, allied with a rare and beautifully painted pattern produced this high price.

A Worcester blue and white dish, painted with the 'Mansfield' pattern, 7⅜ in., c. 1768-70. **£120-£140**   *SRO*

A Worcester blue and white moulded tea cup and saucer, painted with 'The Fisherman and Willow Pavilion' pattern, both pieces chipped, c. 1756. **£180-200**   *SRO*

Perfect **£400-500**

This is a rare pattern and if perfect as well explains the apparent high price.

A Worcester dry mustard pot and cover, painted with 'The Prunus Root' pattern, slight chip, 5¼ in., c. 1763-65. **£580-640**   *KK*

A Worcester blue and white coffee can, with 'The Landslip' pattern, crescent mark, 2⅜ in., c. 1760. **£350-400**   *HOF*

A Worcester blue and white miniature coffee cup and saucer, painted with the 'Prunus Root' pattern, blue crescent marks, 1760-65. **£600-650** *C*

A Worcester tea pot and cover, painted in underglaze blue with 'The Cannonball' pattern, slight damage. **£200-250** *HSS*

This is one of the more common of the Worcester painted patterns but a tea pot is always a desirable object. It is becoming rare to find a perfect tea pot, undamaged at the spout or the flower finial.

A Worcester blue and white miniature baluster tea kettle and cover, painted with the 'Prunus Root' pattern, blue crescent marks, crack across base, 10 cm. high, 1760-65. **£800-900** *C*

Worcester miniatures are much rarer than Bow or Caughley examples and this shape of tea kettle only appears in miniature form.

A Worcester blue and white miniature globular tea pot and cover, painted with the 'Prunus Root' pattern, blue crescent marks, chip to spout and cover, 7 cm. high, 1760-65. **£500-550** *C*

A small Worcester cream boat, printed in blue with 'The Early Creamboat Sprays', 3¾ in. wide, c. 1757-60. **£300-350** *SRO*

These are among the earliest Worcester blue and white printing and the printing is so fine that you should look carefully to see that they are printed and not painted. The creamboat with this pattern is not particularly rare but a butter boat would be extremely rare.

A Worcester blue and white miniature flared pierced circular strainer, painted with the 'Prunus Root' pattern, the sides pierced in 3 places and resting on 3 scroll feet, blue crescent mark, 7.3 cm. diam., c. 1760-65. **£2,100-2,300** *C*

A Worcester blue and white miniature cylindrical tea caddy and cover, painted with the 'Prunus Root' pattern, blue crescent marks, 6.5 cm. high, 1760-65. **£1,900-2,100** *C*

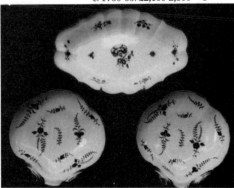

(*t*) A Caughley shaped fruit dish, with basketweave moulded border, painted 'Carnation' pattern and sprigs, with line rim in underglaze blue, impressed 'Salopian' mark, 12 in. diam. **£100-130**

(*b*) A pair of Worcester shell-shaped dishes, painted with 'The Chantilly Sprig' pattern, in underglaze blue, each with Chantilly hunting horn mark, 7¾ in. oval, c. 1788. **£280-£340** *McC*

A Worcester blue and white miniature bucket-shaped sugar bowl and cover, painted with the 'Prunus Root' pattern blue crescent marks, minute chip to cover, 5.5 cm. high, 1760-65 **£400-450** *C*

A Worcester cylindrical mug, printed in underglaze blue, with 'La Pêche' and 'La Promenade Chinoise', crescent mark in underglaze blue, firing crack to handle, 4¾ in., c. 1770-75. **£300-£350** *S*

'La Promenade Chinoise' (illustrated here) and 'La Pêche' usually appear as a pair of patterns on either side of a piece.

A Worcester blue and white mug, printed with a shooting scene 'The Man aiming a gun', 3¼ in., c. 1775-85. **£450-480** *SRO*

This is the middle of 3 sporting prints, all of which are uncommon.

A Worcester mug, of cylindrical shape, printed with the 'Parrot Pecking Fruit' pattern, second version, in underglaze blue, hatched crescent mark, 3⅜ in. high, c. 1770-85. **£280-320** *McC*

This is the much more common version of the two 'Parrot Pecking Fruit' patterns, the rare version shows the parrot perched above hanging grapes with 'Rbt. Hancock fecit' engraved on the branch. Both prints are by Robert Hancock.

A first period Worcester small mug, printed in underglaze blue, with 'The Plantation' pattern, 5.5 cm., c. 1760-65. **£200-250** *L*

This printed pattern is almost an exact copy of the painted 'Plantation' pattern and is not uncommon.

Two Worcester cress dishes and stands, with scalloped and barbed rims, printed in underglaze blue with the 'Pine Cone' pattern, hatched crescent marks in underglaze blue, one stand with minor chips on foot rim, stands 8⅜ in., c. 1775. **£400-500** *S*

This was a very popular pattern and is comparatively commonly found nowadays on plates and dishes, but a cress dish and stand is fairly rare.

A Worcester blue and white shell dish, with printed pattern, 'The Marrow', crescent mark, small firing crack, 5 in., c. 1775. **£300-350** *JSA*

The 'Marrow' pattern is only found on this shape of dish and is rare.

A Worcester mug, transfer printed in black with a named portrait of Frederick the Great, the print signed 'RH Worcester' and dated '1757', 5 in. **£1,000-1,100** *SA*

A Worcester 'King of Prussia' mask jug, printed in black with a portrait of Frederick the Great pointing to trophies of war, dated 1757, inscribed 'RH Worcester' for Robert Hancock and with the anchor rebus for Richard Holdship, the reverse with a figure of Fame blowing 2 trumpets, minor wear, 6 in., c. 1757. **£850-1,050** *S*

The King of Prussia print was the first example of transfer printing on porcelain to capture the public's imagination and led to an escalation in the use of printing. There are many variations in this print, some are dated, some not, some have different battle titles and some have the anchor rebus mark of Richard Holdship

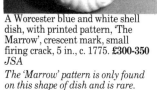

A pair of Worcester blue and white butter tub stands, transfer printed with 'The Rose centred spray group' pattern, slight damage, 19.5 cm., c. 1770. **£200-250** *Bea*

A Worcester spittoon or 'saffer-pot, printed in underglaze blue with the 'Three Flowers' pattern, moulded scroll handle, crescent mark in underglaze blue, 4⅜ in., c. 1770-75. **£450-500** *S*

A pair of Worcester cress dishes, printed 'Pine Cone' pattern and sprays, in underglaze blue, hatched crescent marks, each 7½ in. diam., c. 1775. **£350-400** *McC*

A Worcester tea and coffee service, each piece printed in underglaze blue with the 'Fisherman and Cormorant' pattern, with gilt rims, comprising: tea pot and cover, tea caddy and cover, sucrier and cover, milk jug, slop bowl, 9 tea bowls, 6 coffee cups and 11 saucers, disguised numerals in underglaze blue, c. 1775-80. **£1,200-1,400** *S*

Geoffrey Godden illustrates the difference between this pattern in 'Caughley and Worcester Porcelains' plates 229 and 230. The Worcester fisherman has a slack line and the Caughley one is taut.

A Worcester mug, transfer printed in manganese after Robert Hancock, with George III and Queen Charlotte flanking Britannia and with putti above holding laurel wreaths, 15.5 cm. high, c. 1761. **£3,500-4,500** *C*

c.f. Cyril Cook, op. cit. items 33, 54, 67, 91-113.
Taken from an engraving by James McArdell after Jeremiah Mayer. It is extremely rare to find the portraits of George III and Queen Charlotte on the same mug, in this case a delightfully shaped mug of bell form. The price reflects the extreme rarity of the combination of subjects.

A Worcester cylindrical mug, transfer printed in black by Robert Hancock after Thomas Worlidge, with a bust portrait of George II, signed 'RH Worcester' with the rebus of an anchor, star crack to base, 16 cm. high, c. 1757. **£600-700** *C*

c.f. Cyril Cook, The Life and Works of Robert Hancock, items 52 and 61.

A Worcester dated mug, by Robert Hancock, printed with the King of Prussia, signed 'R.H. Worcester', and with anchor, all the trophies and the angel with trumpets, dated 1757, 3½ in. **£650-720** *HOF*

Small sized versions of the King of Prussia print are very attractive.

A fine Worcester trio, printed in black by Hancock, with the 'Milkmaids' pattern, c. 1760-65. **£400-470** *SA*

A trio, somewhat more desirable than just a cup and saucer, comprises a tea cup (or bowl), coffee cup and saucer.

A Worcester baluster mug, transfer printed in black after Robert Hancock with 'The Milkmaids' and 'May Day', 14.5 cm. high, c. 1765. **£450-550** *C*

c.f. Cyril Cook, op. cit. items 69 and 73.
'Milkmaids' and 'May Day' usually appear as companion prints on opposite sides of a piece.

A Worcester tea bowl and saucer, printed in black by Robert Hancock, with 'The Tea Party, No. 2' and the 'Maid and the Pageboy' pattern, c. 1760. **£320-370** *SA*

A Worcester hexagonal flared cream boat, moulded with 2 sprays of coloured prunus blossom, flanked by a moulded caterpillar on a branch, an insect, pine trees on a mountain and a bird among tendrils, chips and staining to foot, minute chips to rim, 11 cm. wide, c. 1753. **£600-700** *C*

c.f. F. A. Barrett, Worcester Porcelain, pl. 7B.
An extremely rare piece and if it had been in better condition the price would have been much greater.

A Worcester baluster coffee pot and a cover, painted in the 'famille rose' palette, chip to rim, star crack to base, 17 cm. high, c. 1754. **£950-1,050** *C*

Early Worcester coffee pots of silver shape are very rare and if this piece had been in better condition its price could have been much higher.

A Worcester silver shaped oval sauceboat, painted in a 'famille verte' palette, with a green diaper pattern border reserved with iron-red flowerheads, 16.5 cm. wide, c. 1755. **£1,500-1,700** *C*

A pair of Worcester plates, painted in 'famille verte' style with birds perched in branches and chrysanthemums delineated with black 'pencilling', 8¾ in., c. 1765-70. **£1,400-1,600** *S*

Made as replacements for a Meissen 'famille verte' style service. Similar examples are illustrated by Sandon in Worcester Porcelain, pl. 58.

A rare Worcester polychrome sparrow beak jug, with 'The Red Bull' pattern, small chip, 3½ in., c. 1754. **£450-480** *KK*

A rare and early Worcester tea pot and cover, 'pencilled' in black enamel with a Chinese attendant riding an ox beneath a pine tree, painter's mark in black enamel, small hair crack, small chip on spout, 4½ in., c. 1755. **£1,000-£2,000** *S*

There has recently been an interesting escalation in the price of such pieces — a tea pot of almost identical form and pattern having been sold at auction in March 1984 for £2,100.

A Worcester fluted flared coffee cup, painted in a 'famille rose' palette and a red line rim, chip to foot, 5.5 cm. high, c. 1753. **£250-300** *C*

An early Worcester cream jug, after a silver original, painted with a Long Eliza figure on one side and a pine tree on the other, chip on foot, some wear, 3¼ in., c. 1754-55. **£550-650** *S*

A Worcester moulded cream jug, of tall Chelsea ewer shape, with puce decoration, slight fault, c. 1760. **£450-500** *MA*

A Worcester black pencilled tea bowl, with 'The Boy on the Buffalo' pattern, c. 1760. **£250-280** *JSA*

This scene, at one time thought to be Liverpool, is undoubtedly Worcester and is one of a small series of black pencilled patterns (actually painted by brush with fine lines).

A Worcester polychrome tankard, with 'The Beckoning Chinaman' pattern, faint star crack, 4¾ in., c. 1760. **£950-1,050** *MA*

A rare Worcester 'famille verte' sparrow beak jug, 2 chips restored, 3¼ in., c. 1760. **£200-220** *KK*

A Worcester tea pot and cover, painted 'en grisaille' with 2 quail among rockwork and with pink, blue and yellow flowers, beneath an iron-red and gilt C-scroll border, 14 cm. high, c. 1765. **£900-1,100** *C*

Three Worcester polychrome tea cups, printed and coloured in by hand, each with foot chips, c. 1760-65.
(*l.*) **£65-70** (*c*) **£60-65** (*r*) **£45-50** *MA*

A Worcester polychrome bell-shaped cup and saucer, with peaked handle, 'Pu Tai' pattern, c. 1760. **£500-550** *HOF*

A Worcester bell-shaped cup, with peak handle, with unusual lilac pencilled chinoiserie painting, c. 1760. **£400-470** *HOF*

A Worcester octagonal coffee cup, painted with alternate panels of insects and flowering shrubs, 5.5 cm. high, c. 1752. **£600-700**   *C*

A Worcester dish painted in the Imari style, with panels of curious flowering shrubs in pink, iron-red and gold and with sinuous pink dragons among cloud scrolls, divided by 4 blue panels, minor firing fault to rim in one place, 31.5 cm. wide, c. 1775. **£350-400** *C*

A Worcester polychrome tea cup and saucer, with 'The Fan Pattern', mock Chinese numeral mark, c. 1770. **£220-230**   *MA*

A Worcester fluted dish, painted with exotic birds in parkland, butterflies and moths, reserved on a blue scale ground, crescent marks in underglaze blue, very minor wear, 11⅞ in., c. 1770-75. **£550-600** *S*

A pair of Worcester blue scale sauce tureens, covers and stands, painted with exotic birds, blue square seal marks, the stands 21 cm. wide, c. 1770. **£3,600-4,000** *C*

A Worcester fluted flared coffee cup of tall form, chip repair to rim, 6 cm. high, c. 1752. **£350-400**   *C*

Cups of this type apparently did not have saucers.

A Worcester sparrow beak jug and cover, with a blue scale ground, fret mark in underglaze blue, 14 cm., mid 18th C. **£350-400**   *Bea*

Most Worcester sparrow beak-shaped milk jugs began their life with covers but perfect covered examples are getting rarer.

A Worcester cylindrical tankard, painted with panels of fabulous birds, framed with gold rococo scrollwork reserved on a blue scale ground, square mark, 15 cm., c. 1775. **£550-600**   *P*

A Worcester vase and cover, painted with 3 panels of exotic birds, chrysanthemums and wheatsheaf, divided by blue ground panels, gilt with prunus and foliage, below an iron-red border, square mark in underglaze blue, 23 cm., c. 1765-70. **£600-650**   *P*

Vases of this type would have been part of a garniture.

A rare Worcester vase and cover, painted on either side with a heart-shaped panel of brightly coloured exotic birds in parkland, edged with elaborate gilt trellis and scrollwork on a rich 'gros bleu' ground, pseudo seal mark in underglaze blue, 12 in., c. 1770. **£1,100-1,500**   *S*

A Worcester tea caddy and cover, from the Marchioness of Ely service, the wet blue ground gilt with elaborate scrollwork framing 2 oval panels painted in the manner of George Davis, crescent mark, cover with slight restoration, 16.5 cm., c. 1780. **£450-500**   *P*

Some Worcester patterns are ascribed to a particular person who either owned the service or a service of a similar pattern and these are called named services.

A Worcester first period blue scale tea cup and saucer, with unusual daisy pattern, c. 1768. **£220-245** *KK*

A Worcester scale blue tea bowl and saucer, with English flowers, with unusual pansy inside, with seal mark, c. 1765. **£500-550** *HOF*

This piece is earlier than usual scale blue. It also has fine light colour scale blue and very rare natural flower painting, as opposed to stylised flowers. Generally speaking, the brighter the blue the later the piece will be, the blue becoming violet tinged by the late 1780's.

A Worcester powder blue tea bowl and saucer, painted with English flowers, c. 1770. **£350-380** *SRO*

A Worcester 'blue scale' plate, painted with gilt edged mirror shaped panels, on a blue scale ground, pseudo seal mark in underglaze blue, 7¾ in. (19.7 cm.), 1770-75. **£200-250** *SC*

A pair of Worcester sauce tureens, covers and stands, painted with panels of flower sprays within gilt borders against a 'gros bleu' ground, W in underglaze blue, slight wear, stand 9½ in., c. 1770. **£1,300-1,500** *S*

Pairs of tureens, complete with stands, are rare nowadays.

A Worcester vase, decorated with rococo scrolling panels of coloured flowers, edged with gilt scrollwork and reserved on an apple-green ground, slight wear, 5¼ in., c. 1770. **£400-500** *S*

The question of the authenticity of green ground on Worcester porcelain is a very difficult one and explains the often wide ranging prices that such pieces can go for.

A Worcester 'fable' dish of shaped rectangular form, painted in the centre in the manner of J. H. O'Neale, with an ox, a goat and 2 sheep, within 4 clusters of fruit divided by birds in flight, the 'gros bleu' rim heightened with dentil gilding, crescent mark in underglaze blue, some small over-painted chips, 8⅝ in., c. 1780-85. **£800-1,000** *S*

Such pieces can be very beautiful, especially if definitely painted by O'Neale, but sometimes doubts are raised as to when they were decorated and the type of fruit painting around the border suggests a date in the 1780's.

USE THE INDEX!

Because certain items might fit easily into any of a number of categories, the quickest and surest method of locating any entry is by reference to the fully cross-referenced index at the back of the book. This is particularly true this year when certain sections, e.g. Worcester Porcelain and Oak Furniture have been featured in isolation.

A Worcester polychrome bowl, painted in 'famille verte' colours, c. 1754. **£800-900** *MA*

A Worcester quatrefoil tureen stand, with green and gilt shell handles from the Duke of Gloucester service, gold crescent mark, minute chip to one handle, 29 cm. wide, c. 1770. **£900-1,000** *C*

A Worcester dessert dish, of fluted lozenge shape, decorated in Kakiemon palette, with a 'gros bleu' border heightened with foliage and trellis in gilding, script W mark in underglaze blue, 10½ in. (26.7 cm.), c. 1770-75. **£550-£600** *SC*

A Worcester scale blue tea pot stand, 6 in., c. 1770. **£130-150** *MA*

A Worcester polychrome spoon tray, painted with a Japan pattern, seal mark, 6 in. wide, c. 1770. **£370-£420** *MA*

An interesting Worcester armorial dish or tureen stand, painted in the centre with the arms of Gresley quarterly with Bowyer in pretence, the gadrooned rim edged in blue and gilt, shell-moulded handles, some wear, chips on foot rim, 13¾ in., c. 1770-75. **£800-900** *S*

Made as a replacement for a Chinese, Yongzheng service ordered for Sir Thomas Gresley, 4th Baronet of Drakelow (c. 1699-1746). Replacements for this service were also made at Derby in about 1821; see David Howard, Chinese Armorial Porcelain, p. 330.

A Worcester spoon tray, with wet blue border, painted with oriental type flowers, 6 in., c. 1770-75. **£270-£300** *HOF*

A Worcester spoon tray, with orange Imari pattern, 6 in., c. 1770. **£520-580** *KK*

A Worcester first period spoon tray, with Giles gilding, 6 in., c. 1770. **£150-170** *KK*

A Worcester faceted tea pot and cover, painted with flower sprays, blue seal mark, 7 in. wide, c. 1770. **£150-200** *CSK*

A Worcester cabbage-leaf moulded jug, painted with large bouquets of garden flowers, 7¾ in. high, c. 1758. **£250-300** *CSK*

Ring necked jugs can be contemporary with the more common mask-spouted jugs but are more likely to be earlier.

MILLER'S *Antiques Price Guide builds up year by year to form the most comprehensive photo-reference system available. The first five volumes contain over 40,000 completely different photographs.*

A Worcester tea pot and cover, the wet blue ground with gold 'caillouté' and scrollwork, reserving 4 oval panels of ripe 'spotted' fruit and leaves, crescent mark, restored finial, 17 cm., c. 1770. **£450-550** *P*

A rare Worcester tea pot, cover and stand, painted in coloured enamels, the handle and knop picked out in purple, wear on stand, stand 5½ in., c. 1765-70. **£1,500-1,700** *S*

Worcester part tea service, painted in puce 'camaieu', comprising: tea caddy and cover, milk jug and cover, tea pot stand, spoon tray, coffee cup and saucer and a tea bowl and saucer, tea bowl cracked, c. 1775-85. **£650-750** *S*

This pattern derives from Meissen and is always beautifully decorated, but it does not seem to attract the value that it deserves.

A Worcester double-handled 'Blind Earl' moulded spoon tray, with turquoise and gold borders, 6½ in., c. 1770. **£270-300** *HOF*

The moulded pattern of rose leaves and rose buds has long been known as the 'Blind Earl' pattern after the Earl of Coventry, who lost his sight in a hunting accident. It is now certain that the pattern was in existence before the Earl went blind.

A Worcester spoon tray, of lobed hexagonal shape, painted with the 'Jabberwocky' pattern and turquoise border, 15.5 cm., c. 1770. **£700-800**   *P*

A Worcester tea service, decorated with 'cabled' turquoise borders outlined in gilding, comprising: tea pot, cover and stand, milk jug and cover, sucrier and cover, spoon tray, tea caddy, slop bowl, saucer dish, 6 tea bowls and 6 saucers, slight wear to gilding, c. 1775-80. **£900-1,000**   *S*

A Flight and Barr Worcester tea pot and stand, stand incised B, 7¼ in. **£140-160**   *MA*

Spiral shapes came into production in the 1780's and quickly took over from the earlier plainer shapes.

A Flight, Barr and Barr Worcester part service, decorated with a 'Japan' pattern, in bright enamels and gilding, comprising: 16 plates, 3 serving dishes, printed mark, impressed crown and initials, one dish repaired, some chips and wear, largest dish 16½ in., c. 1825. **£1,800-1,900**   *S*

The crest and motto are those of Booth.
Fine armorial services were made at Worcester during the periods of Flight and Barr to Flight, Barr and Barr and the quality can be superb.

A Worcester part tea and coffee service, blue and gilt borders, 35 pieces, c. 1795. **£450-500**   *DWB*

Simple decorated tea wares of this period are neat and smart and yet do not fetch the money that they deserve in view of their fine quality. Perhaps this is one field where increases are likely.

A Barr, Flight and Barr dessert service, painted in 'Imari' palette and gilt, comprising: 2 sauce tureens and covers, 4 dishes and 12 plates, impressed crowned initials mark, printed mark including 'No. 1 Coventry Street' address, one knop repaired, c. 181 **£5,000-6,000**   *S*

A very fine Flight and Barr tea pot, decorated in the Oriental manner, with rust red, blue and green flowers and foliage with gold leaf edging, c. 1803. **£350-400**   *DA*

A Chinese part tea and coffee service, gilt, in the atelier of James Giles, with festoons of flowers, comprising: tea pot and cover, sugar basin, bowl, 3 tea bowls, 5 coffee cups and a saucer, Qianlong. **£90-100**   *L*

Many Oriental white wares, as well as English, were decorated by outside decorators in London, such as James Giles. They were the equivalent of the German Hausmalerei — and some examples are still quite inexpensive.

A part Barr, Flight and Barr Worcester dessert service, painted with flowers in blue, red and pink with elaborate gilding, in the Japan style, comprising: 4 oval dishes, 3 square dishes and 16 plates, c. 1810. **£6,000-£7,000**   *McC*

A Worcester Flight, Barr and Barr tea and coffee service, white with gilt gadroon borders and a band of vines above a maroon band, comprising: a pair of tea pots, covers and stands, a cream jug, a pair of slop bowls, 6 biscuit plates, 22 saucers, 13 coffee cups, 7 tea cups, impressed mark, c. 1820-30. **£450-500**   *HyD*
Gold and white services, even with added ground colours, do not fetch the price that their quality of work demands and must be worth buying.

A pair of Flight, Barr and Barr pill vases, reserved on a gilt seaweed frond ground, square plinths, impressed FBB beneath a crown, 3½ in. (8.8 cm.), c. 1820. **850-950** *SC*

Seaweed gilding and eagle head and ring handles are typical of Flight, Barr and Barr Worcester.

A good Chamberlain's Worcester 'named view' mug, painted with a titled view of Oxford 'from the London Road', against a lilac ground below a gilt anthemion border, painted mark and title, 3½ in., c. 1810. **£800-900** *S*

A Chamberlain's Worcester flared cup, with 'Kensington Palace', the pink ground with gilding, 2¾ in., c. 1825. **£200-230** *JSA*

A Flight, Barr and Barr vase, painted in a panel possibly by Baxter or Astles, on a light green ground, the shoulders with a 'pearl' border, mark in sepia, 23 cm. **£1,200-1,300** *P*

The shape is illustrated by H. Sandon in Flight & Barr Worcester Porcelain, p. 171, pl. 165.

A Chamberlain's Worcester jug, painted with brightly coloured flowers on a gilt ground band, reserved on a dark blue ground with 'cailloute' gilding, with the initials G. R. in gold, script mark in red, 17.5 cm. **£350-400** *P*

A pair of Flight and Barr jardinières, on a canary yellow ground enriched with gilding, overall puce script Flight & Barr, Worc. Manus. to their Majs., jardinières incised '5 & 3' bases incised '2 & 3', one interior rim cracked, 17 cm., 1790's. **£1,900-£2,100** *SS*

The quality of these pieces is superb and even the damage to one has not detracted from an appreciative price.

An extensive Chamberlain's Worcester dinner service, decorated in bright enamels and gilding with the 'Dragon in compartments' pattern, comprising: 2 soup tureens, stands and one cover, 2 sauce tureens and covers, 4 vegetable dishes and covers, 3 vegetable dishes, a square bowl, 16 dishes and 62 plates, 'Chamberlains Worcester' and patt. no. 75 in purple, printed factory/retailer marks in purple and red, c. 1800-20, and 9 Kerr & Binns plates, replacements, impressed marks, some damaged overall, c. 1860. **£7,000-8,000** *S*

A Chamberlain's Worcester plate, painted with a view of 'Thorngrove, near Worcester', 9 in., c. 1815. **£270-300** *KK*

A Chamberlain's Worcester plate, painted with a view of 'Carisbrooke Castle Isle of Wight', including ..int, c. 1815. **£270-300** *KK*

A Chamberlain's Worcester ..morial part dinner service, with ..aborate grey and iron-red ..antling with the motto Regi ..triaeque Fidelis below, on a blue ..ound elaborately enriched in ..n-red and gilding, comprising: ..auce tureens, covers and fixed ..nds, 2 vegetable dishes and ..vers, 7 dishes, 34 plates, many ..ces with script mark in iron-red ..puce, some pieces cracked, ..810. **£10,000-11,000** *C*

..e arms are those of Scott or Great ..rr, Co. Stafford.

A Chamberlain's Worcester plate, with the 'Entrance to Burleigh House, Northamptonshire', c. 1820. **£420-480** *JSA*

A Worcester 'Kylin' pattern tankard, the sides with 4 panels decorated in typical palette, 5½ in., late 18th C. **£280-360**   *DWB*

A Chamberlain's Worcester crested Imari-pattern part dinner and dessert service, comprising: a soup tureen, cover and stands, a pair of sauce tureens, covers and stands, 3 vegetable dishes and covers, a salad bowl, 2 vegetable dishes, 9 dishes, 51 plates, most pieces with impressed marks, the covers with full printed marks, pattern no. 886, c. 1840. **£2,500-3,000**   *C*

A Worcester Kylin pattern fluted coffee cup, seal mark in blue, 3 in late 18th C. **£85-95**   *DWB*

The pattern is often incorrectly called 'Bengal Tiger' or 'Bishop Sumner'. If from Dr. Wall's factor in Worcester it should be called 'Kylin' and the green is a deep 'famille verte' colour; if from Chamberlain it should be called 'Dragon in compartments'; the green is more yellow and there is often the pattern number 75 unde the base.

A tea pot and a cover, the blue scale ground reserving rococo panels, painted in Kakiemon style, crescent mark, 16.5 cm., c. 1775. **£400-500**   *P*

A rare Chamberlain's Worcester vase and cover, the body painted with flowers against a grey background, within a gilt border, rare mark inside cover 'Chamberlains Worcester Porcelain Manufacturers to H.R.H. The Prince Regent' surmounted by Prince of Wales feathers, 24 cm. **£900-1,100**   *P*

A milk jug and cover, with blue scale ground, painted in Kakiemon style, square mark, 13.5 cm., c. 1770. **£400-500**   *P*

Formerly in the Dr. Knowles Boney collection.

A pair of Chamberlain's Worceste bottles, with bulbous reticulated panels and narrow necks, painted with birds and fruit, marked to base, 5¼ in., c. 1845-51. **£350-400** *A*

A Grainger's Worcester oviform jug, painted with the Birmingham, Bristol and London Royal Mail coach, the reverse with the repeated initials JR, script mark Grainger & Co. Worcester, in iron-red, crack to base, 21.5 cm. high, c. 1810. **£1,800-2,000** *JSA*

Grainger's factory in Worcester (1801-1902) produced some superb porcelains and their wares should not be thought of as the poor relation of Flight and Chamberlain.

A sucrier and a cover with flower finial, with blue scale ground, painted in Kakiemon style, squar mark, 11 cm., c. 1775. **£350-400**

A pair of Kerr and Binns Worcest porcelain bottle vases and covers, the compressed form decorated in Limoges enamel technique by Thomas Bott, red printed mark ar artist's signature and initials in blue, one underside with simulate marble detail, 11½ in. (29 cm.), c. 1855. **£600-800** *Bon*

Thomas Bott (1829-70) joined Ker and Binns in 1853 after initial wo as a glass enameller with Richardson's of Wordsley near Stourbridge. He is recognised as th inventor of the Limoges enamel technique which proved popular b always expensive. It is believed tha the formidable pressure of work w largely responsible for his untimel end.

A rare Chamberlain's Worcester honey pot and cover, modelled as a hive with 3 bees moulded in relief, decorated with alternating apricot and white gilt-edged panels, 4¼ in., early 19th C. **£500-600**   *S*

A similar honey pot is illustrated by G. A. Godden in Chamberlain-Worcester Porcelain, p. 244, pl. 292. The author notes that these pots could be included as part of a breakfast service or sold separately.

rare Royal Worcester cache pot,
corated in enamels and gilding,
ssibly by James and Thomas
allowhill, with a Japanese lady
d gentleman wearing colourful
aditional robes, impressed
owned circle mark, printed
tailer's mark for A.B. Daniel and
n, 46 Wigmore Street, slight
bbing to gilding, 4¾ in., c. 1875.
50-450   *S*

A plaque, painted and signed by
T. S. Callowhill, Worcester and
dated 1872, with 'Limoges type'
enamelling, framed, 11¼ by 9⅛ in.
(28.6 by 23.2 cm.), 1872. **£500-600**
SC

(*l.*) A Royal Worcester vase, pierced
by George Owen, 7 in. **£1,700-1,900**

(*r.*) A Royal Worcester vase and
cover, pierced by George Owen,
12 in. **£3,600-4,000**   *SuB*

Royal Worcester Tazza, pierced
the manner of George Owen, and
t with formal bands and seeding,
nted crown circle mark, shape
mber 2490, date code for 1911,
 in. over handles. **£600-700**   *S*

*orge Owen's reticulating was in a
ss of its own — of enormous
ficulty and superb beauty. Not all
pieces were signed, especially his
lier work, but the lack of a
nature has a great effect upon the
ue of a piece.*

A Grainger Lee &
Co. Worcester vase,
painted with a
view of 'Brownsea
Castle', 8¼ in.
£150-165   *KK*

A Royal Worcester ewer,
pierced by George Owen,
painted by E. Phillips,
with swags of roses below
a pierced border, printed
crowned circle mark,
shape number 789, gilt
signature, date code for
1931, 6¾ in. **£500-600**   *S*

A pair of Royal Worcester vases,
painted by John Stinton, signed,
shape no. 1969, date codes for 1929,
31.5 cm. **£1,300-1,500**   *P*

*John Stinton painted Highland
cattle for Worcester in such quantity
that his colleagues said he grew to
look like his subject. The quality of
painting is so fine that it is hard to
realise that he never went to
Scotland in his life but his work is
beginning to attract the sort of
appreciation that it has long
deserved. The feet of the cattle are
never to be seen in a Stinton
painting.*

A Royal Worcester plaque, with
cattle in a lane by a stream,
inscribed 'Grange Bridge,
Borrowdale', signed J. Stinton,
framed, 5¾ by 8¾ in. **£1,000-1,200**
LT

oyal Worcester vase and cover,
ated by John Stinton, signed,
 four Highland cattle in a
ty mountainous landscape, the
ils in pale green, pink and
ing, printed crowned circle
k, shape number 2010 and date
 for 1908, 16¾ in. **£1,500-1,700**

e and large piece by John
ton, perhaps the rather fussy
dles producing a lower value
 the piece deserves.

A pair of Royal Worcester
topographical oval plaques, each
painted by J. Stinton, signed, with
a scene entitled 'Glencoe' or 'On the
Llugwy', printed crowned circle
mark, painted title, date codes for
1919 and 1920, both framed, 9½ in.
£1,900-2,100   *S*

*Plaques are regarded by ceramic
painters as their ultimate challenge
and good ones must be among the
most desirable items.*

A set of 6 Royal Worcester coffee
cups and saucers, each painted by
H. Stinton, signed, with two
Highland cattle, printed crowned
circle mark, date codes for 1922
and 1923, one cup repaired, and
6 silver-gilt coffee spoons, maker's
mark of H.J. Hulbert & Co. Ltd.,
London, 1922, fitted case. **£900-
£1,100**   *S*

*Harry Stinton was the son of John
Stinton and produced almost as
much Highland cattle painting as
his father, although generally on
smaller pieces. Lovely coffee sets in
their fitted boxes were very popular
presentation gifts in the 1920's and
will be keenly sought.*

A Royal Worcester coffee pot,
signed by Harry Stinton, 9 in.
£550-650   *SuB*

A Royal Worcester cased coffee se
each piece painted with pheasant.
by James Stinton. **£600-700**   *Le(*

*This gorgeous coffee set was paint
by John Stinton's brother James,
who specialised in game birds.
Such sets must go up in value.*

An unusual Royal Worcester pot
pourri jar and cover, painted by
C. Baldwyn, signed, with 3 fan-
tailed doves and another 2 in flight
above, with eau-de-nil ground,
printed crowned circle mark, shape
number 1515, indistinct date code
possibly for 1905, slight rubbing to
gilding, 9¼ in. **£1,400-1,600**   *S*

*Doves are an unusual subject to
find for Charley Baldwyn, reflected
in the price realised.*

A Royal Worcester 'game' service,
printed and painted with a game
bird in its natural setting,
including grouse, pheasant and
partridge, within a sepia printed
border of stylised flowers,
comprising: 9 plates, a sauce
tureen, cover and stand, 2 toasted
breadcrumb dishes and an oval
serving platter with pheasant's
head and wing handles, printed
crowned circle mark, painted
pattern number W3727, date code
for 1896, tureen and one small dish
repaired, platter 17¾ in. **£700-800**
S

*Most game sets were decorated with
a printed outline, painted in by
hand. Complete sets are now
uncommon.*

A set of 6 Royal Worcester 'game'
coffee cups and saucers, each
painted by Jas. Stinton, signed,
with a game bird in its habitat,
fitted case, one cup damaged,
printed crowned circle mark,
printed or painted titles, date code
for 1938, and 6 silver-gilt coffee
spoons, mark for Mappin & Webb
Sheffield 1937. **£800-900**   *S*

A Royal Worcester vase, painted by
C. Baldwyn, signed, with a rustic
gentleman accompanied by 2 small
children, puce printed mark and
date code for 1905, shape no. 2026,
20 cm. **£250-300**   *SS*

*This vase sadly lacks its cover and
is a little unbalanced accordingly,
hence a price which is lower than
the quality of painting deserves.*

A Royal Worcester vase and cover,
painted by C. Baldwyn, signed,
with an azure ground, the reverse
with swallows, the moulded scroll
and lattice-patterned borders in
pale green, pink and gilding,
printed crowned circle mark, shape
number 2010, date code for 1902,
16½ in. **£1,500-2,000**   *S*

A gilded Worcester urn vase, w
painted scene of Arundel Castl
signed G.H. Evans, 15½ in. **£4
£500**   *JD*

A pair of Royal Worcester bottle
vases, painted by C. H. C. Baldw
signed with swans in flight on a
powder blue ground, beneath
slender trumpet necks, puce
printed mark and date code for
1904, shape no. 1748, 18 cm. **£4
£500**   *SS*

*Flying swans on a blue ground i
Charley Baldwyn's most famous
subject although his rarer gener
landscapes and birds are perha
his finest works.*

A Royal Worcester dessert service,
each piece painted and signed by
R. Sebright, with apple-green
borders reserved with pink ground
mirror shaped panels edged with
foliate scrollwork in raised gilding,
comprising: 6 dishes, 12 plates,
purple printed marks including
date code for 1923, one plate with
hairline crack. **£3,500-4,500** *SC*

*A complete Worcester dessert
service, especially painted by a
Master like Richard Sebright and
with fine ground and gilding can be
an awe-inspiring sight. Let us hope
that as many complete sets as
possible can be kept together and
not split up.*

A pair of Royal Worcester ewers,
painted by W. A. Hawkins, with a
panel of fruits and flowers, within
raised gilt trails of berried
branches, the moulded borders and
handle in apple-green, printed
crowned circle mark, shape number
1309, date code for 1907, 15½ in.
£2,100-2,500 *S*

*William Hawkins was the foreman
painter of Royal Worcester for many
years and a superb painter in his
own right.*

pair of Royal Worcester vases
d covers, each painted by
Sebright, signed, within gilt
rders against an apple-green
ound, printed crowned circle
ark, shape number 2410, date
le for 1932, covers fixed, repairs,
¾ in. **£500-600** *S*

arge Royal Worcester vase, painted
Frank Roberts, signed, with a royal
e ground, printed crowned circle
rk, shape number 1969 and date
e 4 1933, one cracked, 21½ in. **£900-
00** *S*

A pair of large Royal Worcester
vases, each painted by F. Roberts,
signed, with tooled and raised
details against a royal blue ground,
printed crowned circle mark, shape
number 1969, date code for 1919,
one cracked, 19¾ in. **£1,300-1,500**
S

A Royal Worcester 'named view'
plaque, painted and signed by
R. Rushton, with a view of 'Market
Place Rouen', purple printed mark
including date code for 1918, 7⅛ in.
(18.2 cm.). **£200-250** *SC*

A Royal Worcester pot pourri vase,
signed W.E. Jarman, 17 in. high.
£600-800 *Re*

Two Royal Worcester flower vases,
each painted, one by J. Llewellyn,
signed, with pink and red cabbage
roses amongst foliage, printed
crowned circle mark, shape number
1985, date codes for 1911 and 1917,
10¼ in. **£700-800** *S*

yal Worcester vase and cover,
ted by J. Southall, signed, with
and red cabbage roses,
htened in green and gilding,
ted crowned circle mark, shape
ber 248/H, date code for 1913,
ired, 16 in. **£160-220** *S*

A Royal Worcester jardiniere,
painted by W. Sedgley, signed, with
pink and red cabbage roses, below a
moulded and gilt border of berried
branches, printed crowned circle
mark, shape number 2644, date
code for 1918, chipped, 11½ in.
£450-550 *S*

A pair of large Royal Worcester pedestal vases, each painted by Freeman, signed, printed mark, painted shape number 1669/3, modern, 20¾ in. **£3,100-3,500**   *S*

A set of 13 Royal Worcester dessert plates and 4 oval serving dishes, painted by J. Smith, all but one plate signed, the rim gilt, printed crowned circle mark, all post 1960, plate 10¾ in. **£2,000-2,500**   *S*

A Royal Worcester miniature tea and coffee set, the majority indistinctly signed, comprising: a coffee pot and cover, a tea pot and cover, a milk jug, 2 cups, 2 saucer and 2 plates, printed crowned cir mark, various date codes, 1955/6 coffee pot 5 in. **£450-650**   *S*

Miniature pieces painted with fru generally by William Roberts are very appealing and collectable. Roberts' signature is very hard to decipher.

A pair of Royal Worcester vases and covers, each painted by T. Lochyer, signed, printed crowned circle mark, shape number 229/H, date codes for 1930 and 1932, one knop repaired, 13½ in. **£700-800**   *S*

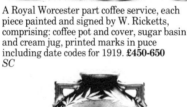

A Royal Worcester part coffee service, each piece painted and signed by W. Ricketts, comprising: coffee pot and cover, sugar basin and cream jug, printed marks in puce including date codes for 1919. **£450-650** *SC*

A pair of Royal Worcester moon flasks, each painted, possibly by Josiah Rushton, reserved on a royal blue ground with gilt leaf and berry borders, printed and moulded crowned circle marks, date code for 1875, gilding slightly rubbed, 8 in. **£550-650**   *S*

A Royal Worcester vase and cove painted by Ricketts, signed, print mark in puce, date symbol for 19: shape number 1428, 29 cm. high. **£800-900**   *HSS*

MAKE THE MOST OF MILLER'S

Miller's is completely different each year. Each edition contains completely NEW photographs. This is not an updated publication. We never repeat the same photograph.

A Royal Worcester commemorative scent bottle for Queen Victoria's Silver Jubilee, picked out in gilding, screw silver cover in the shape of a crown, printed mark in gilding, 3¼ in. (8.3 cm.), c. 1887. **£150-200**   *SC*

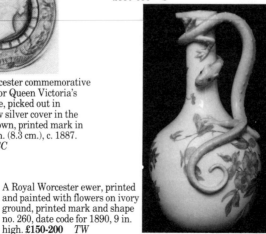

A Royal Worcester ewer, printed and painted with flowers on ivory ground, printed mark and shape no. 260, date code for 1890, 9 in. high. **£150-200**   *TW*

A Royal Worcester plaque, sig Bradley, restored, 10½ by 8½ c. 1900. **£200-225**   *DL*

Mint **£500**

Royal Worcester vase, printed
th flowers on shaded ground,
inted mark and date code for
17, 8½ in. (21.5 cm.) high. **£90-**
40   *TW*

A Royal Worcester vase, painted
with flowers in autumnal colours
on an ivory ground, enhanced in
gold, printed mark and date code
for 1900, shape no. 1024, 33.5 cm.
£200-250   *Bea*

A Royal Worcester vase, with
raised decoration, pattern no. 2033,
17 in. high, c. 1901. **£200-250**
GSP

A Royal Worcester 'metallic' vase,
with bronzed handles, decorated in
blue and raised gilding, green
printed and impressed marks and
puce printed 'Patent Metallic'
mark, 39 cm. high, c. 1880. **£210-**
£270   *C*

Royal Worcester pot pourri jar,
ver and lid, the ovoid body
inted and painted with flowers,
nted mark and date letter for
87, 7 in. (17.8 cm.) high. **£160-**
00   *TW*

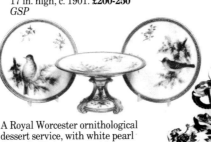

A Royal Worcester ornithological
dessert service, with white pearl
dot and gilt rims, comprising:
5 dishes and 12 plates, printed and
impressed marks, dated 1876, one
low footed dish repaired. **£950-**
£1,050   *SC*

A Royal Worcester dinner service,
printed and painted in puce and
gilt, comprising: 71 plates, 13
stands and dishes, 8 tureens and
covers, 112 pieces, a few blemishes,
with crowned wheel mark and date
letter for 1884/5/6. **£800-1,000**
PWC

*Such pieces are in the style of the
'Japanesque' or 'Aesthetic'
movement, popular in the 1880's.*

> **Miller's is a price GUIDE
> Not a price LIST.**
> *The price ranges given reflect
> the average price a purchaser
> should pay for similar items.
> Condition, rarity of design or
> pattern, size, colour,
> provenance, restoration and
> many other factors must be
> taken into account when
> assessing values.*

air of Royal Worcester
dlestick figures, modelled by
mes Hadley, toned in pale
ours and gilding, facsimile
ulded signatures, impressed
tory marks, printed registration
mber and model in purple,
 in. (26.3 cm.), c. 1886. **£650-**
0   *SC*

*mes Hadley's modelling has a
erb sense of period, with
redibly detailed hair, fingers and toes.*

A pair of Royal Worcester figures of
Bringaree Indians, after models by
James Hadley, moulded signature,
colours in tones of ivory, apricot
and pastel shades, printed and
impressed crowned circle marks,
shape number 1243, date code for
1888, stave repaired, chip ground
down, 19¼ in. **£1,500-1,700**   *S*

A rare Royal Worcester group of
Paul and Virginia, based on
characters from a novel by
Bernardin de Saint-Pierre, painted
in naturalistic enamel colours, with
the clothes in muted tones
enhanced in gold, impressed mark,
minor damage, 35.5 cm. high, mid
19th C. **£600-800**   *Bea*

A pair of Royal Worcester figures of water carriers, date cypher marks for 1903, 17½ and 16 in. high. **£600-700** *M*

A great number of water carriers were made by Royal Worcester, attesting to the interest in Near Eastern people caused by the opening up of the Suez Canal.

A Royal Worcester figure, after a model by Hadley, the Bedouin chief in tones of peach, ivory and gilding, facsimile signature on pillar, date code for 1898, crack in base, 22⅛ in. (56.2 cm.). **£650-750** *SC*

A pair of Royal Worcester figures, of a Welshman with a sack over hi shoulder and his companion holding a shallow basket, printed mark and date code for 1886, shape no, 1875, slight chip, 17 cm. **£250-£300** *Bea*

A pair of Royal Worcester figures of Cairo water carriers, picked out in peach and ivory tones, edged with a foliate design, printed marks in puce including shape number 1250, one with cracked base, 9¼ in. (23.5 cm.), c. 1891. **£350-400** *SC*

A rare pair of Royal Worcester figures of Eastern water carriers, after the models by James Hadley, decorated in tones of ivory and tooled goldwork, impressed and green printed marks, the woman with pattern no. 637, one with hair cracks to the base, the other with chips to rim of water pot, about 25 cm. high, 1877. **£1,100-1,400** *C*

Sold with an accompanying letter dated 15 April 1905, stating that these figures were made for R. W. Binns as a special commission, decorated by Bejot of Paris, and were purchased from the Royal Worcester Porcelain Museum on Mr. Binns' death.

A pair of Royal Worcester figures of a French fisherboy and girl, after original models by James Hadley, moulded signature, coloured in pale apricot and green with gilt details, printed and impressed crowned circle marks, shape number 1202, date code for 1887, basket repaired, 17¾ and 17 in. **£400-500** *S*

A pair of Worcester Grecian water carriers, decorated overall in tones of ivory and pale apricot, printed crowned circle mark, date code for 1893, 20 in. **£600-700** *S*

These figures were intended for use as Cricklite holders, popular objects before the common use of electricity.

A pair of Royal Worcester figures of 'Dancing' and 'Music', in tones of shaded gilding, printed crowned circle mark, shape numbers 1827 and 1828, date code for 1923, pipe damaged, 12½ and 12¼ in. **£400-£450** *S*

A pair of Royal Worcester figures, allegorical of Liberty and Captivity, one wearing a green and gilt dress, the other peach and green, purple printed marks including date code for 1898, impressed marks, Captivity with repaired arm, 10 and 10⅜ in. (25.4 and 26.4 cm.). **£250-300** *SC*

A Royal Worcester figure of a Grecian water carrier, her loosely draped robe in shaded gilding tinted green, printed crowned circ mark, shape number 2/125 and date code for 1920, 19¾ in. **£300-£350** *S*

A pair of Worcester figures of putti with baskets, 7½ in., c. 1870. **£300-£350**   *JD*

A pair of Worcester figures of 'Dancing' and 'Music', 'Music' lacking her flute, 13 in. **£300-400**   *JD*

A pair of Royal Worcester figures of musicians, the boy playing a pipe, the girl playing a tambourine, all picked out in pale colours, printed marks in puce including shape number 1803, boy with repaired pipe and chipped hat, 6¼ in. (16 cm.), c. 1894. **£350-450**   *SC*

Two Royal Worcester figures, by Ruth Esther van Ruyckevelt, 'Beatrice', 7½ in. high, no. 148 of a limited edition of 500 copies, and 'Caroline', 7⅛ in. high, no. 148 of a limited edition of 500 copies, with signed certificates. **£600-700**   *GC*

Examples of modern day limited editions, some of which become very desirable and fetch more at auction than their original purchase price. However some do not and it is difficult to know how such pieces are going to behave when sold at auction as secondhand within a short time of their purchase. It is a truism to say that you should purchase a piece because you like it.

A Royal Worcester figure of 'Felicity', after a model by Ruth van Ruyckevelt, printed crowned circle mark, title, facsimile signature and numbered 343 from an edition of 750, dated 1970, signed certificate and fitted box, 7 in. **£250-350**   *S*

This figure was originally one of a pair.

A pair of Royal Worcester figures of a gallant and young lady, after original models by James Hadley, moulded signature, wearing early 19th C.-style clothes in pastel colours, printed and impressed crowned circle marks, printed date code for 1884, 15 in. **£600-700**   *S*

Specialist Bibliography

Albert Amor Ltd.	...	...	Exhibition Catalogues
Barrett F. A.	...	...	Worcester Porcelain and Lund's Bristol
Branyan, French and Sandon			Worcester Blue and White Porcelain 1751-90
Binns R. W.	...	...	A Century of Potting in the City of Worcester
Binns R. W.	...	...	Worcester China 1852-97
Godden G. A.	...	...	Caughley & Worcester Porcelain 1775-1800
Godden G. A.	...	...	Chamberlain Worcester Porcelain 1788-1852
Hobson R. L.	...	...	Worcester Porcelain
Mackenna F. S.	...	...	Worcester Porcelain
Marshall H. R.	...	...	Coloured Worcester Porcelain
Sandon H.	...	...	Flight and Barr Worcester Porcelain 1783-1840
Sandon H.	...	...	Royal Worcester Porcelain from 1862
Sandon H.	...	...	Worcester Porcelain 1751-93
Twitchett and Sandon	...		Landscapes on Derby and Worcester Porcelain

WORCESTER PORCELAIN – SUMMARY OF HISTORY

Warmstry House

1751	Dr. Wall founds factory
1752	Miller & Lund factory acquired
1757	First dated transfer print
1776	Dr. Wall dies, factory continued by William Davis
1783	Thomas Flight purchases factory
1788	Visit of King George III, First Royal Warrant Granted in 1789
1792	Flight and Barr period
1804	Barr Flight and Barr period
1813	Flight Barr and Barr period
1840	Merger with Chamberlain
1852	Factory sold

A Goss cabinet, design E.
£400 *G&CC*

Ashtray, Edward VII,
Coronation. **£20** *G&CC*

Hippopotamus. **£300**
G&CC

Shetland Pony. **£130**
G&CC

Letchworth Carinated
vase. **£55** *G&CC*

GOSS CHINA

The factory of William Henry Goss commenced the production of the finest parian ware in Stoke-upon-Trent around 1860. His son Adolphus introduced crested ware in the 1890's and collecting heraldic porcelain was popular until the outbreak of the Great War. The last piece was produced in 1935.

A range of Goss cottages was produced from 1893-1925 and these are very collectable.

Damage affects the value of Goss china a great deal and substandard pieces are worth ¼ to ½ of their perfect prices.

There are over 1,500 different shapes and over 7,000 decorations which appear on them. A page of decorations is shown in this section and the price given should be added on to the price of the piece to determine the true total value of any item. Only a representative selection can be shown here and readers are recommended to 'The Price Guide to Goss China' and 'Goss China, Arms Decorations, and Their Values' by Nicholas Pine (Milestone Publications, Horndean, Hants.) should they wish to study the subject further.

St. Columb Major Cross.
£110, London Stone **£100**,
Kirk Braddan Cross **£65**
G&CC

Teapots. **£20-40**, Jugs. **£4-£10** *G&CC*

Queen Phillippa's record
chest. **£30** *G&CC*

Floral Decorations. **£40-90**
G&CC

Cardinal Beaufort's
candlestick. **£95** and
Winchester flagon. **£15**
G&CC

Four busts:– top row:
W. H. Goss. **£110**, Milton.
£110, Bunyan. **£125**,
Wordsworth. **£90** *G&CC*

Three candlesnuffers:
Monk. **£150**, Cone. **£4**,
Welsh Lady. **£50** *G&CC*

St. Ives Cross. **£200**,
Skegness Clock Tower.
£75 *G&CC*

A selection of small models, each **£4-8**
G&CC

St. Martin's Cross, Iona. **£130** *G&CC*

A selection of scarcer models, each **£15-30** *G&CC*

Welsh Hat. **£10**, with Llanfair P.G. **£40** *G&CC*

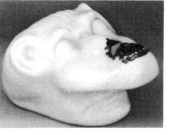

The Noze of Brazenose. **£15** *G&CC*

Peeping Tom, coloured. **£125** *G&CC*

The Balloon Seller. **£175** *G&CC*

Haddon Hall font. **£50** *G&CC*

Manx Cottage, nightlight. **£130** *G&CC*

Lorna. **£130** *G&CC*

The Rock of Ages. **£25** *G&CC*

Duck open as posy holder. **£45** *G&CC*

Irish Cruisken, International League model. **£130** *G&CC*

Toby jug. **£60** *G&CC*

Playing Card symbol ashtray. **£20** *G&CC*

The Oxford jug. **£15** *G&CC*

York Roman Ewer, small. **£4**, large. **£11** *G&CC*

Tenby Gateway. **£275** *G&CC*

219

Goss Cottages: Dr. Johnson's House. **£115**, Prince Llewellyn's House. **£95**, The Cat and Fiddle Inn, Buxton. **£195**, Shakespeare's House. **£85** *G&CC*

Kendal jug, small. **£4**, large. **£17** *G&CC*

Hats, Helmets and Boaters. **£5-35**

Ten large models. **£10-30** each *G&CC*

Crinkle dish. **£4** *G&CC*

Child's Head wall vase. **£150** *G&CC*

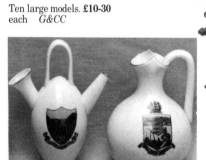

Salisbury Kettle, small. **£8**, large. **£12**, and Oxford Ewer, small. **£4**, large **£9** *G&CC*

Brass pipe rack with Goss porcelain plaque inset. **£100** *G&CC*

Late Scottie dog, 260 mm. long. **£120** *G&CC*

Teapots, kettles and jugs. **£4-12**

Small models. **£4-5** each *G&CC*

Top row: Mons Meg **£30**, Amersham Leaden Measure. **£8**, British Tank. **£30**

Bottom Row: Jersey Fish Basket. **£8**, Bournemouth Fish Cone. **£8**, Blackgang Cannon. **£7**, Limpet Shell. **£8** *G&CC*

Tea plates, cups and saucers. **£5-8** *G&CC*

More common domestic ware. **£4-18** each *G&CC*

Public School, Oxford and
Cambridge. Add £2-8
G&CC

Duke of Wellington, for
nobility. Add £3-10
G&CC

Wedding of the Prince and
Princess of Wales 1888.
Add £50   *G&CC*

GOSS DECORATIONS

Certain decorations
add considerable value
to Goss models. Some of
the more important are
listed below.

Olympic Games. Add £30-
£40   *G&CC*

Seven flags of the Allies.
Add £10-15   *G&CC*

Robin Hood's last shot.
Add £20-25   *G&CC*

George & Mary
Coronation 1911. Add
£10-20   *G&CC*

Old Kings. Add £5-15
G&CC

Oak Leaf. Add £30-50
G&CC

Late (Goss England)
transfer. Add £5-15
G&CC

Welsh Antiquities. Add
£20-70   *G&CC*

Crocuses and Proverb.
Add £5-15   *G&CC*

Seagulls. Add £10-20
G&CC

Boer War, South Africa,
1900. Add £30-40   *G&CC*

Tomatoes. Add £10-30
G&CC

Transfers. Add £15-50
G&CC

Words. Add £10-20
G&CC

CRESTED CHINA

Manufactured from
around 1870-1935, some
200 factories produced
over 6,000 different
shapes which were sold
bearing the coat-of-
arms of the town in
which they were sold.
Damage affects the
price considerably and
pieces with chips or
cracks would only be
worth ¼ to ½ the retail
price.
All the manufacturers
were in competition
with the originators and

market leaders W. H.
Goss of Stoke-Upon-
Trent. The most prolific
producers were:
Arcadian, Carlton,
Willow, Shelley, Grafton
and Savoy.
The most popular (and
sought after pieces) are
from the following
themes: Military,
Animals, Buildings,
Figures and other
unusual shapes. Small
pots and domestic ware
are only of nominal
interest and value.

Space only permits a
small selection of pieces
to be given here and
readers are
recommended to 'The
1985 Price Guide to
Crested China' by
Sandy Andrews and
Nicholas Pine should
they wish to learn more.
(Available from
Milestone Publications,
Horndean, Hants.)

Carlton Stag. £50
G&CC

221

Arcadian 'A Nap Hand'.
£100 *G&CC*

Lamps and Lanterns. **£4-£20** *G&CC*

Carlton Cat Playing
Band. **£20** *G&CC*

Shelley Paddle Steamer.
£40 *G&CC*

Dogs. **£7-35** *G&CC*

Pillar Boxes. **£6-15**
G&CC

Buildings, Monuments
and National Souvenirs.
£10-30 *G&CC*

MAKE THE MOST OF MILLER'S

When a large specialist well-publicised collection comes on the market, it tends to increase prices. Immediately after this, prices can fall slightly due to the main buyers having large stocks and the market being 'flooded'. This is usually temporary and does not affect very high quality items.

Hat Pin holders. **£5-8**
G&CC

Arcadian Boy and Girl on
Log. **£50** *G&CC*

Chess Pieces. **£4-25**
G&CC

Domestic Wares. **£4-15**
G&CC

Figures. **£15-75** *G&CC*

Shaving Mugs. **£4-7**
G&CC

Musical Instruments. **£6-£12**   *G&CC*

Baskets and Bags. **£4-8**   *G&CC*

Chairs. **£4-15**   *G&CC*

Gramophones. **£10-20**   *G&CC*

Carlton Luggage Trolley. **£30**   *G&CC*

Grandfather Clocks. **£8-12** *G&CC*

Slippers and Boots. **£4-6** *G&CC*

Arcadian Armoured Car. **£20**   *G&CC*

Arcadian Wishing Chair. **£40**, Carlton, Daniel Lambert. **£35**, Carlton, John Citizen. **£70**, Carlton, Cash Register. **£20**   *G&CC*

Shelley Bugle. **£30** *G&CC*

Corona Renault Tank. **£50** *G&CC*

Arcadian Folkestone War Memorial. **£50**   *G&CC*

A Bomb. **£5**, Hand Grenades. **£6-10**, and a Revolver. **£30**   *G&CC*

Carlton Dreadnought. **£35**, and H.M.H.S. Anglia. **£50**   *G&CC*

Transport. **£20-80** *G&CC*

The Seaside. **£4-15**   *G&CC*

Carlton Soldier. **£40** *G&CC*

Castles and Gateways.
£10-20   *G&CC*

Tanks. **£15-25**   *G&CC*

Red Cross Vans and
Armoured Cars. **£15-40**
G&CC

Guns and Howitzers. **£15-
£35**   *G&CC*

Busts. **£20-30**   *G&CC*

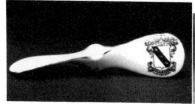

Aeroplane propeller. **£15**
G&CC

Shells. **£4-10**   *G&CC*

Arcadian Trench Dagger.
£30   *G&CC*

Aynsley Boer War Models.
£15-30   *G&CC*

Animals, Birds and Fish.
£4-20   *G&CC*

Monoplanes. **£20-40**
G&CC

Submarines. **£10-25**
G&CC

Common Ships. **£10-15**
G&CC

Carlton British Naval
Gun. **£100**   *G&CC*

Tents. **£6-20**   *G&CC*

DIFFERENTIATING MING AND QING WARES

In order to distinguish Ming porcelain from the later Qing wares it is necessary to appreciate the technical rather than the decorative differences between the two. The Qing decorators frequently copied ancestral designs with great accuracy and at first sight it is sometimes difficult to attribute certain pieces.

A good example of this is the Doucai (contrasting colours) category. The originals were produced during the Ming reign of Chenghua (1465-87) and the copies were made in the reign of the Qing emperor Kangxi. Were it not for the characteristic smoky ivory appearance of the Ming glaze one might well be at a loss to differentiate early from late.

In the first place, with certain exceptions, Ming porcelain is more heavily glazed and the depth of glaze effects a bluish or greenish tint. The glaze is rarely evenly applied and if carefully examined one can detect runs and dribbles of excess glaze. Most Qing wares are covered in a glaze of uniform thickness. Particularly characteristic is the pure white appearance achieved by the Kangxi potters by only coating the vessel or dish in a thin and even wash. The reigns of Yongzheng and Qianlong did witness some pieces (non-export) which were deliberately covered in a thick glaze in order to emulate the early 15th Century porcelains.

As far as potting is concerned there are more obvious idiosyncracies enabling easier identification.

For example, Ming vases if of sufficient size to warrant being made in two or more pieces are generally luted horizontally even on vessels which it would appear to be simpler to make in two vertical sections, Yongle and Xuande 'moon' or 'pilgrim' bottles are a case in point. Qing pilgrim bottles would invariably be made by joining two vertical halves.

The footrims on Ming wares are generally knife-pared and little effort made to remove the facets left by the blade. If not all, Qing pieces are smoothed after the trimming. The feet on Ming dishes or bowls are for the most part higher than Qing examples. They are frequently undercut immediately indicating that they have been thrown by hand and not as many Qing pieces which have been moulded by a mechanical process utilising a profile cutter. A further point concerning the footrim on Ming wares — it will generally manifest a narrow orange zone abutting the edge of the glaze. This is due to the presence of iron in the body of the porcelain which appears to oxidise more strongly in the kiln in the area most closely in contact with the glaze.

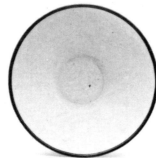

A moulded Dingyao bowl, the almost conical sides springing from a characteristic low foot rim, copper-bound at the rim, the interior decorated with floral sprays divided by thin raised lines, moulded in light relief, the ivory-tinted glaze falling unevenly on the reverse, 6¾ in. (17.2 cm.), Song Dynasty. **£1,200-1,500**   *S*

Compare the mould with very similar decoration, dated to the sixth year of Taihe in the Jin Dynasty, corresponding to A.D. 1206, illustrated in Chugoku Toji Zenshu, vol. 9, pl. 130.

DINGYAO

A northern Chinese type of porcelain produced during the Song and Yuan periods. The glaze is a rich ivory colour which appears either a pale green or brown where it has pooled. The decoration is mainly floral, either carved or moulded.

A miniature Junyao bowl, covered with a thick crackled pale lavender-coloured glaze thinning to olive-green at the rim and pooling down the sides, the interior with a wide purplish-blue crackle, the glaze on the exterior falling short of the foot rim partly glazed in brown, 6 cm. wide by 3.5 cm. high, Song Dynasty. **£200-300**   *Bon*

JUNYAO

A northern Chinese stoneware made from the Song Dynasty through to the Yuan and Ming periods. The coarse granular body is thickly applied with a blue glaze sometimes varying from lavender to deep purple. There are however a few examples of green Jun.

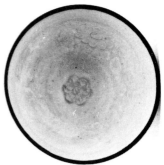

A crisply moulded Yingqing bowl, with thinly potted sides, covered overall with a slightly tinted glaze, the rim mounted in copper, 4⅛ in. (10.5 cm.), Song Dynasty, box. **£650-850**   *S*

YINGQING

A type of porcelain produced during the Song and Yuan dynasties in various regions of central and southern China. The dominant characteristic being the pale blue-green translucent glaze; Yingqing translates as misty blue, the Chinese word Qing can mean either blue or green. Designs like Dingyao are either moulded or carved floral subjects.

A good Longquan celadon bowl, covered overall with a smooth sea-green glaze, the footrim unglazed and burnt orange in the firing, 7 in. (18 cm.), Song Dynasty, box. **£2,100-2,500**   *S*

A good Zhejiang celadon bowl, the footrim of broad section enclosing an unglazed ring on the base, burnt to a reddish tone in the firing, the glaze of characteristic olive tone, 12 in. (30.5 cm.), early Ming Dynasty. **£1,300-1,600**   *S*

A pair of Northern celadon bowls, covered overall with a transparent crackled olive-green glaze, the knife-pared footrim of wedge section, unglazed, 4¼ in. (10.5 cm.), Song Dynasty. **£1,100-1,300**   *S*

A Cizhou bowl, the coarse body applied with a white slip and painted in dark ferruginous brown beneath a translucent glaze, 5¼ in. (13.3 cm.), Song/Yuan Dynasty. **£700-900** *S*

A blue and white bowl, the exterior painted with the Eight Immortals on a continuous ground of undulating waves, small chip, 9½ in. (24.2 cm.), 6 character mark and period of Jiajing. **£1,100-1,300** *S*

Taoist subjects were a favourite theme on the wares of this reign.

A Ming blue and white bowl, painted with 2 pairs of figures, the centre of the interior with a dignitary beside a deer, rim fritted, slightly restored and possibly with a small crack, unencircled Jiajing 6 character mark and of the period, 21 cm. diam. **£750-950** *C*

Compare the looser rendering of the figure subjects on the present piece with the more precise brushwork on the following Transitional deep bowl.

ORIENTAL POTTERY AND PORCELAIN
This section is alphabetically arranged by object: bowl, box, censer, etc. In each group the wares are firstly divided into Chinese followed by Japanese and then ordered chronologically.

A blue and white bowl, painted in cobalt, of good colour, with a boldly drawn lotus meander, 7½ in. (19.1 cm.), 6 character mark and period of Kangxi. **£850-950** *S*

A blue and white bowl, painted with a pair of Mandarin ducks swimming amongst flowering lotus, the reverse with sprays of orchid, 4⅛ in. (11.2 cm.), 6 character mark of Xuande, Wanli. **£900-1,000** *S*

A pair of Mandarin ducks among aquatic plants has been used as a decorative theme on ceramics from the Song Dynasty. It is found on the very earliest blue and white dating from the first half of the 14th Century.

A Transitional blue and white deep bowl, painted with 3 sages playing Go, a musician with a jin and a scholar reading a scroll, fritted, 21.5 cm. diam., c. 1640. **£900-1,200** *C*

See pointer on Transitional wares.

A blue and white potiche, pierced with 4 circular apertures to accommodate handles, painted in inky tones with birds and butterflies, 8¼ in. (21 cm.), 6 character mark of Chenghua, Transitional. **£500-600** *S*

A Junyao bowl, covered overall in a rich lavender-blue glaze suffused with white speckling, draining from the rim to a dark mushroom tone and coagulating just above the slightly splayed base on the exterior, 5⅞ in. (15 cm.), Yuan Dynasty. **£1,100-1,400** *S*

A blue and white bowl, the alternately tight and loosely petalled stylised blooms borne on slender curling stems amongst numerous foliate motifs, the interior with a central medallion of waves, 6 in. (15.3 cm.), 6 character mark and period of Wanli, box. **£3,500-4,000** *S*

A rare blue and white bowl, delicately potted with rounded sides and a slightly flared rim, the interior painted in delicate tones, with lotus flowers amongst foliage, the exterior with 3 fungus sprays within line borders, 3¾ in. (9.5 cm.), 6 character mark of Chenghua, Wanli or Tianqi. **£1,200-1,400** *S*

A blue and white bowl, the exterior decorated with a continuous scene depicting groups of scholars, 4⅝ in. (11.8 cm.), 16th C. **£700-900** *S*

blue and white bowl, the exterior inted with alternating panels of dies in a garden and groups of mboo and prunus, with a narrow vastika trellis border, slight mage, 10 in. (25.4 cm.), Kangxi. 00-600   *S*

A blue and white jardinière, the exterior painted with groups of Precious Objects, on a blossom-strewn cracked-ice ground, wood stand, 9 in. (22.8 cm.), Kangxi. **£250-350**   *S*

A blue and white bowl, the interior painted with a circular panel of 5 boys playing in a garden, the exterior with scenes of figures in interiors and gardens, 8 in. (20.3 cm.), 6 character mark and period of Kangxi. **£900-1,000**   *S*

pair of blue and white bowls, the terior of each painted with 2 oenix in flight, the interior with nedallion of rocks and bamboo, in. (11.7 cm.), Kangxi. **£450-50**   *S*

A rare pair of blue and white bowls, each painted in the centre with a stylised lingzhi spray, the exterior with a ruyi meander, the whole well painted in cobalt of vivid tones, 4¾ in. (12.1 cm.), 6 character marks of Jiajing, Kangxi, 17th C. **£800-1,000**   *S*

A blue and white bowl, the exterior painted with 4 figure scene panels in a continuous frieze, 7¾ in. (19.6 cm.), 6 character mark of Chenghua, Kangxi. **£600-700**   *S*

A 'famille verte' bowl, 7¾ in. Kangxi. **£400-600**   *WW*

famille verte' bowl, painted with wers below an iron-red lappet der, chipped, 29 cm. diam., ngxi. **£1,000-1,200**   *C*

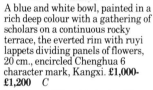

A blue and white bowl, painted in a rich deep colour with a gathering of scholars on a continuous rocky terrace, the everted rim with ruyi lappets dividing panels of flowers, 20 cm., encircled Chenghua 6 character mark, Kangxi. **£1,000-£1,200**   *C*

This form of flanged rim bowl is a characteristic Kangxi type which is invariably thinly-potted and covered in a pure white glaze. This is not so with 19th C. copies which can initially deceive.

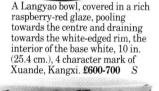

A Langyao bowl, covered in a rich raspberry-red glaze, pooling towards the centre and draining towards the white-edged rim, the interior of the base white, 10 in. (25.4 cm.), 4 character mark of Xuande, Kangxi. **£600-700**   *S*

amille verte' bowl, the interior nted in blue, green, aubergine, ow and iron-red with 3 fish, the erior with similar fish on the n white ground, 7¾ in. (19 cm.), ngxi. **£400-500**   *S*

opper-red decorated bowl, a le bat in the centre, and 4 her bats on the exterior, 6⅛ in. 6 cm.), 6 character mark and od of Yongzheng. **£400-500**   *S*

An engraved biscuit bowl, rim decorated on the exterior with spaced sprays of rose and hibiscus, in bright yellow, aubergine and pale green enamels, wreathed by dark green leaves, the interior undecorated, 5⅞ in. (15 cm.), 6 character mark and period of Kangxi. **£500-600**   *S*

A blue and white bowl, delicately painted in a linear style, with a roundel of C scrolls, encircled Yongzheng 6 character mark and of the period, 10 cm. diam. **£1,100-£1,300**   *C*

A blue glazed stem bowl, raised on a tall collared stem flared at the foot, the wide bowl, with rounded sides, covered in a dark blue glaze pooling on the stem, the interior white, 7¼ in. (18.4 cm.), seal mark and period of Yongzheng. **£200-£250** *S*

It is rare to find a stem cup of this form glazed in blue. Yongzheng stem cups with copper-red glazes have been included in the Exhibition of Ch'ing Porcelain from the Wah Kwong Collection, Hong Kong, 1973, Catalogue no. 4.

A good blue and white bowl, the exterior painted in cobalt of soft tone with a frieze of the 'Three Friends', the arching bamboo canes rooted beside ornamental rocks and the pine and prunus trees, a single line encircling the rim, 3⅜ in. (8.6 cm.), 6 character mark and period of Yongzheng. **£1,300-1,600** *S*

The Three Friends as a decorative theme, see glossary.

A 'famille rose' punch bowl, with a continuous scene of sages in a landscape, the rim encircled by a bolder blue-ground border of stylised lotus, the bright pink flowers spaced among dense foliate scrolls in green and white, another floral border in gilding, wood stand 15⅛ in. (38.4 cm.), Yongzheng. **£4,000-5,000** *S*

A pale coffee glazed square bowl, the sides evenly covered with a pale brown glaze, 11 cm. over the handles, impressed seal mark and period of Qianlong. **£170-220** *Bon*

Two 'famille rose' eggshell deep bowls and covers, enamelled in delicate tones with exotic butterflies and sprays of lingzhi, each bowl rim with one small ch[...] 9.75 cm. diam., encircled Yongzheng 6 character marks a[...] of the period. **£700-1,000** *C*

A fine pair of blue and white dragon bowls, the sides of the exterior of each well painted in cobalt of rich tone with 2 dragons, another dragon with outstretched claws within a double line medallion in the centre of the otherwise plain interior, 3¾ in. (9.5 cm.), 6 character marks and period of Yongzheng. **£5,500-6,000** *S*

A massive blue and white and underglaze red jardinière, with a continuous landscape of scholars in pavilions, riveted around the bottom and fritted, 58 cm. diam., early Qianlong. **£5,500-6,500** *C*

When this appeared at auction the original cataloguer dismissed this piece as being 19th C. or later. The detailed but nonetheless bold or sure brushwork belies his doubts. 19th C. pieces are never as strongly and surely executed.

A rare large 'famille rose' deep ov[...] basin, painted after a design by Cornelis Pronk with 'The Doctors[...] one each in 4 panels alternately wearing aubergine robes and blu[...] robes, on a yellow trellis-pattern ground below bands of iron-red shells, the exterior with swags on[...] purple trellis-pattern grounds in broad panels on a similar pink ground, below grisaille shells at t[...] shoulder and architectural wave-pattern dividing similar turquois[...] and gilt black trellis-patterns on the flaring rim, foot damaged, sid[...] pierced, 64.5 cm. wide, early Qianlong. **£7,000-8,000** *C*

A pair of blue and white bowls, each interior plain, the exterior painted with a formal frieze of the 'ba jixiang', and a band of spiral petals in blue wash encircling the base, 3⅝ in. (9.2 cm.), 6 character marks and period of Yongzheng. **£800-900** *S*

The Eight Buddhist Emblems (pa jixiang) have been used on porcelain certainly as early as the 14th C. when they are to be seen on both monochrome and blue and white wares.

A European-subject punch bowl, decorated in 'famille rose' enamels of bright tones, the interior with 2 carp amongst aquatic weeds in the centre, 10⅜ in. (26.4 cm.), Qianlong. **£1,300-1,600** *S*

rare 'famille rose' 'Jacobite' unch bowl, painted with Charles hiding in the Boscobel oak, 2 orsemen riding by in search of the Monarch, the exterior with further gures joining in the search, hair ack, 10¼ in. (26.2 cm.), Qianlong. 800-1,000 S

relatively common design on nglish delftware but extremely re on Chinese exportware.

A 'famille rose' punch bowl, the exterior enamelled with a scene depicting a tiger hunt, the animal kicking its back legs in the air to fend off the surrounding huntsmen, the interior with a cock crowing, perched on an ornamental rock, 10½ in. (26.7 cm.), Qianlong. **£1,200-1,400** S

A Chinese Imari bowl, painted in 'famille verte' enamels and underglaze blue, 14 in. (35.5 cm.), second quarter of the 18th C. **£750-£850** S

A Wucai dragon and phoenix bowl, the exterior with a frieze of 2 dragons alternating with descending phoenix, their bodies in iron-red, green, yellow and pale aubergine enamels, heightened in underglaze blue, chasing 'flaming pearls' on a ground of foliate sprigs, 5⅛ in. (13 cm.), seal mark and period of Qianlong. **£500-600** S

This type of dragon and phoenix pattern bowls are recorded throughout the Qing dynasty.

rare punch bowl for the Swedish arket, the interior painted en isaille and in white enamel with otifs from a 9 daler banknote of 62, the exterior en grisaille and t with peony, rose and exotic wers, the interior with some ar, 31 cm. diam., Qianlong. ,100-1,300 C

A blue and white barber's bowl, 10⅝ in. (27 cm.), Qianlong. **£300-£400** S

A bowl, enamelled in 'famille rose' palette with an Eastern man on horseback, holding a reversed banner of 3 fleurs-de-lys, surmounted by a seated figure of Britannia, surrounded by draped flags of various countries, inscribed below on a scroll 'For Our Country', the ground and inner border with flowers in iron-red, black and gold, 23.5 cm., Qianlong. **£1,500-2,000** L

The price reflects the fact that this is a very rare subject.

A flambé bulb bowl, covered overall with a thick glaze of brilliant streaked blue and reddish purple tones, with paler creamy mottling falling short of the unglazed foot rim, enclosing the base applied with a café-au-lait wash, 10 in. (25.4 cm.), Qianlong. **£300-400** S

A blue and white bowl, the interior painted with a scene of a sage and a boy, 13¼ in. (33.7 cm.), Qianlong. **£650-850** C

pair of copper-red decorated stem wls, the exterior covered with an en liver-red glaze, draining from rim to leave a white edge, the erior white, 7⅞ in. (19.2 cm.), l marks and period of Qianlong. 50-950 S

A large 'famille rose' punch bowl, painted with a tripod vessel, vases and scholars' utensils on blue rockwork, below a gilt iron-red wave-pattern border, divided by lappets of sepia cell-pattern in the interior, 40 cm. diam., Qianlong. **£1,600-1,800** C

A similar bowl in the collection at Burghley House is illustrated by Gordon Lang in 'the Wrestling Boys'.

arge 'famille rose' 'Hunting' ich bowl, painted with 2 large els after prints by James mour, the centre of the interior a spray of finger citrus below ar-heads, restored, 39.5 cm. m., Qianlong. **£1,600-1,900** C

A large 'famille rose' punch bowl, with a ground of gilt scrolling foliage, divided by floral and iron-red landscape vignettes at the exterior, the interior with a butterfly and a cluster of flowers, 39 cm. diam., Qianlong. **£3,500-£4,000** C

A large Chinese porcelain punch bowl, painted in Mandarin palette with figure cartouches on a gilt scroll ground, riveted, 40 cm., Qianlong. **£450-550**   *SS*

A large blue and white shallow basin, painted with a pavilion and a pagoda in a rocky river landscape, the trellis-pattern divided by flowerheads and triangular panels on the flat everted rim, 56 cm. diam., Jiaqing. **£1,500-1,700**   *C*

A 'famille rose' punch bowl, vividly painted with figures at leisure, within surrounds of bats on aubergine scale-pattern and iron-red and gilt Y-pattern grounds at the exterior, 27.5 cm. diam., late Qianlong. **£1,500-1,700**   *C*

A 'Compagnie-des-Indes' bowl, the interior painted with a polychrome oval landscape medallion of a white house, the exterior painted with 3 sepia Oriental/European landscape medallions, all under complex blue and gilt ribbon and festoon borders, 35.8 cm., c. 1800. **£2,200-2,800** *SS*

A similar but smaller bowl is illustrated by Howard & Ayres, China for the West, vol. I, plate 282, page 284. The authors point out that the only bowls of this type with an established provenance were made for the American market.

A pair of 'famille rose' octagonal jardinières, the flat rims with blue cloud-scrolls and hatched-pattern divided by lotus-heads at the angles, the short spreading feet pierced with horizontal patterns in alternate pink and pale turquoise panels, chipped, one rim repaired, 41 cm. wide, Qianlong/Jiaqing. **£4,000-5,000**   *C*

A Canton bowl, decorated in 'famille rose' palette, 15½ in. (39.5 cm.), Daoguang. **£1,100-1,3** *SC*

A massive Canton 'famille rose' bowl, 23¼ in. (59.2 cm.), Daoguang with wood stand. **£4,000-5,000**   *S*

An unusual pair of bowls, each decorated on the exterior in white slip, with scattered mons of differing design, beneath a bright translucent yellow enamel, the interior painted in underglaze blue, the rim edged in gilding, 5⅞ in. (14.8 cm.), seal marks and period of Daoguang. **£1,000-1,200** *S*

A blue and white bowl, the exterior painted with a continuous frieze of the Eight Immortals, the interior with 2 sages with Shou Lao in a landscape, 4¼ in. (10.8 cm.), seal mark and period of Daoguang. **£600-700** *S*
Compare with the Jiajing bowl painted with the same figure subjects.

A large 'famille rose' Canton enamel deep bowl, painted on the exterior with court scenes of Manchu warriors, 39.5 cm. wide, c. 1830. **£1,900-2,200** *C*

rare pair of Ming-style bowls, ainted in underglaze blue of ntense tone, 6 in. (15.2 cm.), seal arks and period of Daoguang. 700-800 *S*
he central apparently geometric evice is almost certainly a rrupted form of the crossed underbolts or double vajras troduced in the 14th C.

A yellow-ground 'famille rose' bowl, decorated with an overall multi-coloured feathery composite floral frieze on a brilliant yellow ground, the interior with the wu fu in iron-red at the centre, 7½ in. (18.3 cm.), seal mark and period of Daoguang. **£400-500** *S*

A coral-ground 'famille rose' bowl, the interior undecorated, 4¼ in. (10.7 cm.), seal mark and period of Daoguang. **£550-650** *S*

A Canton 'famille rose' bowl, 14⅓ in. (36.6 cm.), 19th C., with wood stand. **£700-800** *S*

A 'famille rose' bowl, with a pink ground incised with a feathery scroll, the interior with a double line medallion in underglaze blue, enclosing a rabbit beneath a tree in blossom, 5⅞ in. (14.8 cm.), seal mark and period of Daoguang. **£900-1,000** *S*

large blue and white jardinière, in. (53.4 cm.), 19th C. **£3,000-,500** *S*

A gilt Satsuma bowl, enamelled with an Imperial palanquin procession beneath Fujiyama, the exterior with millefiori over breaking waves, 12.6 cm., 4 character seal mark, 1890's, wood stand. **£450-550** *S*

A pair of lotus bowls, the interior covered in a rich turquoise enamel, the exterior decorated with triple tiered lotus petals in shaded cream and pink, with veining in a deeper tone, below a band of yellow stamens encircling the gilt-edged rim, 3⅝ in. (9.2 cm.), seal marks and period of Daoguang. **£250-£300** *S*

Imperial yellow glazed bowl, th a minutely crackled bright aze, except within the foot, .5 cm. diam., unenclosed aoguang seal mark and of the riod, with wood stand. **£900-,200** *C*

A Satsuma bowl, decorated inside and out with a dragon and numerous seated dignitaries, in enamel colours and gold, 27 cm., late 19th/early 20th C. **£200-250** *Bea*

A Japanese Imari circular barber's bowl, in iron-red, blue and gilt, 12¼ in. diam., early 18th C. **£600-£800** *WHB*

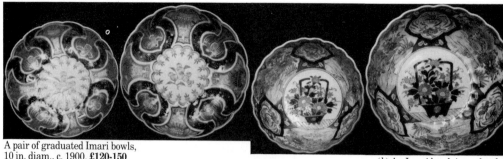

A pair of graduated Imari bowls, 10 in. diam., c. 1900. **£120-150** *TW*

(*l.*) An Imari bowl, in underglaze blue and overglaze red, green, yellow, 10 in. diam., late 19th C. **£70-90**

(*r.*) A large Imari bowl, in underglaze blue and overglaze red yellow and green, 12½ in. diam., late 19th C. **£120-150** *TW*

An inlaid Korean celadon bowl, the interior inlaid in black and white slip in mishima technique, all beneath a crackled grey-green glaze, 7¾ in. (19.1 cm.), Koryu Dynasty. **£700-900** *S*

A pair of 'famille verte' jardinières, 35 cm. diam., second half 19th C. **£2,200-2,500** *C*

A large 'famille verte' fish bowl, 18 in. (45.7 cm.), Guangxu. **£1,400-£1,800** *S*

A Canton porcelain punch bowl, in 'famille rose et verte' enamels, 39 cm. diam., 17.5 cm. deep, complete with a carved hardwood stand with scrolling feet, second or third quarter of the 19th C. **£450-£550** *HSS*

A blue and white jardinière, painted with panels of 2 spotted deer below a pine, 49 cm. diam., second half of the 19th C. **£1,800-£2,200** *C*

A pair of narcissus bowls, the exterior covered in a coral-red glaze, decorated in gilding with a frieze of shou characters, beneath a classic scroll on the everted rim, 9⅞ in. (25 cm.), 4 character marks and period of Tongzhi. **£450-650** *S*

A massive blue and white fish bowl, 24⅜ in. (62 cm.), Guangxu and rosewood stand, 35 in. (88.8 cm.) high. **£2,500-3,000** *S*

A pair of dragon bowls, engraved on the exterior with 2 dragons in pursuit of 'flaming pearls', the designs all in green enamels reserved on a yellow ground, a matching shou medallion on the interior, 4 in. (10.2 cm.), 6 character marks and period of Guangxu. **£450-550** *S*

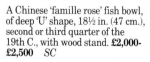

A Chinese 'famille rose' fish bowl, of deep 'U' shape, 18½ in. (47 cm.), second or third quarter of the 19th C., with wood stand. **£2,000-£2,500** *SC*

A 'famille rose' yellow ground jardinière, 16 in. (40.8 cm.), Guangxu. **£1,000-1,300** *S*

A grey pottery censer and cover, the low domed cover painted in russet and white pigment with a simple scroll pattern on the black ground, within a russet band on the rim, 9¾ in. (24.7 cm.), early Han Dynasty. **£700-1,000**   *S*

A pair of 'famille verte' jardinières, painted on the exteriors with 6 dragon roundels, 40 cm. diam., 5-legged wood stands, late 19th C. **£4,000-4,500**   *C*

A glazed pottery censer, the body covered in a finely crackled green glaze, leaving the interior, base and sections of the underside unglazed, 4½ in. (11.4 cm.), Tang Dynasty. **£800-900**   *S*

blue and white censer, painted in tones of underglaze blue with confronting dragons chasing 'flaming pearls', within double line borders, 4½ in. (11.5 cm.), 6 character mark and period of Wanli, box. **£1,400-1,800**   *S*

A Jun Yao tripod broad globular censer, with a thick opaque lavender glaze, with areas of purple and red colour, thinning to olive translucency on the upper parts, the foot ends chipped, 15.5 cm. wide, Yuan Dynasty. **£700-800**   *C*

A Chinese porcelain fish bowl, decorated with brown dragon and white peonies on yellow ground, with turquoise and pink scroll and flower borders, 17½ in. wide, on carved and giltwood stand with scrolled feet, 17 in. high, late 19th C. **£1,700-1,900**   *DSH*

ORIENTAL POTTERY AND PORCELAIN

This section is alphabetically arranged by object; bowl, box, censer, etc. In each group the wares are firstly divided into Chinese, followed by Japanese and then ordered chronologically.

A blue and white bowl, painted with 14 large squirrels, 2 small rim chips, 22 cm. diam., unenclosed Guangxu 6 character mark and of the period. **£500-600**   *C*

A finely painted Ming blue and white censer, the underglaze blue of soft rich tone, with delicate shading beneath a tinted glaze, the nianhao on the base within a double line medallion, encircled by an unglazed ring burnt orange in the firing, 4½ in. (11.5 cm.), 6 character mark and period of Zhengde. **£8,000-10,000**   *S*

A pair of large yellow ground fish bowls, the exteriors painted en grisaille, white, iron-red and green, the interiors with large iron-red fish swimming amongst green aquatic plants, 51 cm. high, 5-legged wood stands, period of Guangxu. **£5,000-6,000**   *C*

A pair of 'famille rose' fish bowls, decorated in bright colours, the interiors with goldfish and aquatic plants, 53 cm., late 19th C. **£2,000-2,500**   *Bon*

An unusual green Jun censer, covered overall with a transparent deep green glaze, thinning to mushroom on the rim, 5¾ in. (15.6 cm.) high by 6½ in. (16.5 cm.) wide, Yuan Dynasty. **£2,300-3,000**   *S*

An unusual miniature Longquan celadon tripod censer, covered overall with a thick sea-green glaze, stopping short of the feet to reveal the ware burnt orange in the firing, 2⅞ in. (7.5 cm.), Ming Dynasty, wood stand, box. **£600-700**   *S*

233

A rare glazed pottery stem cup, the translucent minutely crackled glaze of colourless tone, 2⅜ in. (6.1 cm.), Tang Dynasty. **£600-£700** *S*

A white-glazed stem cup, the interior decorated in underglaze linear white slip with 4 lhantsa characters in flaming roundels amongst formal lotus, small chips, 14.3 cm. diam., Kangxi. **£500-600** *C*

A rare glazed pottery cup, the colourless glaze falling short of the base, revealing the smooth buff body, 3 in. (7.6 cm.), Tang Dynasty, box. **£1,500-1,700** *S*

A set of 6 'famille rose' tea bowls and 5 saucers, Qianlong. **£200-£300** *S*

A set of 4 coffee cups and saucers, decorated in Mandarin palette 'famille rose' enamels, late Qianlong. **£300-350** *S*

A Canton 'famille rose' tankard, 4¾ in., Daoguang. **£220-300** *DWB*

A Ming-style blue and white stem cup, slightly reduced rim, hair crack, 10.7 cm., foot rim underside with seal mark of Qianlong and of the period. **£250-300** *SS*
If perfect **£600-800**

A Compagnie-des-Indes tea and coffee service, each piece painted in blue with the Willow pattern within gilt borders, comprising: tea pot and cover, jug and cover, slop bowl, tea bowls, 9 coffee cups, 12 saucers, 4 saucer dishes and one odd cover, Qianlong. **£450-550** *SS*

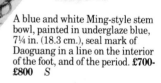

A blue and white Ming-style stem bowl, painted in underglaze blue, 7¼ in. (18.3 cm.), seal mark of Daoguang in a line on the interior of the foot, and of the period. **£700-£800** *S*

A rare Korean celadon cup and stand, the overall glaze of characteristic greyish tone, 5½ in. (13.9 cm.), Koryu Dynasty. **£1,200-£1,500** *S*

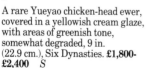

A rare Yueyao chicken-head ewer, covered in a yellowish cream glaze, with areas of greenish tone, somewhat degraded, 9 in. (22.9 cm.), Six Dynasties. **£1,800-£2,400** *S*

Related chicken-head ewers with similar loop handles but different spout and plain handle, decorated with brown spots, are illustrated by Addis, Chinese Ceramics from Datable Tombs, pl. 6, excavated from a tomb dated to A.D. 368 in Ruian county, Zhejiang province.

A rare and early Ming blue and white wine ewer body, Zhi Hu, the cobalt blue with extensive 'heaping and piling', the handle and neck missing, the top of the vase with a 19th C. metal mount, 21 cm., early 15th C. **£3,000-3,500** *Bon*

A silver-mounted Transitional blue and white pear-shaped ewer, painted with a dignitary and 2 attendants greeting a sage, rim chip, 22.5 cm. high, the porcelain mid 17th C., the mounts Amsterdam, 19th C. **£1,000-1,200** *C*

An initialled chocolate pot, decorated in 'famille rose' enamels, enriched in gilding with the repeated initials 'WMM' on a shield, 7⅝ in. (19.3 cm.), Qianlong. **£150-200** *S*

A rare 'famille rose' wine ewer, cover and stand, coloured blue and pink, minor chips, 13.5 cm., early Qianlong. **£350-400** *SS*

A blue and white covered ewer, following a Near Eastern metal shape, 13½ in. (34.3 cm.), 17th C. **£700-800** *S*

A pair of 'famille rose' covered jugs, 4½ in. (11.4 cm.), early Qianlong. **£500-600** *S*

A 'famille rose' ewer and cover, 14¼ in. (36.2 cm.), Guangxu. **£800-900** *S*

A 'famille rose' ewer, with a gilded dragon handle, the lower body painted in Mandarin palette, 10¾ in. (27.3 cm.), Qianlong. **£300-£350** *S*

A good Arita ewer, decorated in underglaze blue in Chinese Transitional style, with figures in a landscape, 25.2 cm., second half 17th C. **£500-600** *S*

A rare 'famille rose' 'tobacco-leaf' oviform ewer, domed cover and deep basin, boldly painted all over with veined blue, yellow, turquoise, lime-green and iron-red, handle replaced, spout lip bruise, some enamels rubbed, the basin 32 cm. diam., the ewer 25 cm. high, early 19th C. **£1,700-2,000** *C*

A graduated set of 3 Chinese export jugs, in 'famille rose' enamels and gold, some gilding rubbed, 23.2, 21.2 and 18.6 cm., Jiaqing. **£1,100-£1,600** *Bea*

An unusual blue and white Fujian kendi, 22.5 cm., 18th C. **£200-300** *Bon*

A rare and important pair of pottery lions, the unglazed grey ware showing traces of the original white slip, traces of red pigment and some earth adhering, 10½ in. (26.8 cm.), Han Dynasty. **£11,000-15,000** *S*

A very rare early Kakiemon-style ewer, in the form of a bijin seated on a rectangular bottle, decorated in iron-red, green, blue, yellow and black enamel, the neck repaired, 20.6 cm., second half 17th C. **£1,200-1,500** *S*

An unusual figure of a horse, the grey ware covered in a somewhat degraded white slip with traces of red pigment, 13¼ in. (33.6 cm.), Sui Dynasty. **£3,000-5,000**   *S*

A rare unglazed pottery group of an ox and cart, the grey ware showing traces of red pigment, 15 by 8 in. (38.1 by 20.3 cm.), Six Dynasties, wood stand. **£5,000-6,000**   *S*

A Japanese earthenware ewer and cover, decorated in subdued colours and raised gilding, with an overall design of Divinities, signed and inscribed, some damage, 11¼ in. (28.5 cm.), late 19th C. **£250-350**   *SC*

A chestnut-glazed pottery figure of a horse, the unglazed saddle with traces of red pigmentation, the glaze of yellowish-brown colour, with mottled darker patches on the hind quarters and lower legs, and a tassel on the front of the head splashed in green, 12¾ in. (32.4 cm.), Tang Dynasty, wood stand and box. **£5,000-6,000**   *S*

An unglazed pottery figure of a prancing horse, the pale buff pottery showing traces of red patches simulating the piebald coat and on the saddle cloth, further traces of the harness and other details in red and black, 25½ in. (64.8 cm.), Tang Dynasty. **£5,500-£6,500**   *S*

Jan Fontein and Tung Wu discuss in Unearthing China's Past, pp. 172-3, the crenellated mane, a sign of distinction of which the origin can be traced back to the 5th C. B.C. and examples found from areas as widely apart as southern Russia, Iran, Central Asia and China. They illustrate a glazed horse with mane clipped into the 'Three Flowers', always associated with persons of exalted or Imperial rank, from the tomb of a Tang General, fig. 89, and mention others from the tombs of 2 of the Crown Princes, all dating from the early 8th C. when it became particularly popular.

A glazed pottery figure of a camel, glazed in cream with the remainder of the body in rich chestnut brown, with an oval cloth spread over its back, decorated in splashed brown, cream and green, 15 in. (38.2 cm.), Tang Dynasty. **£9,000-10,000**   *S*

A nightlight, modelled as a crouching cat, painted on the biscuit with black patches and fur markings, its back with a peach-shaped aperture for the emission of smoke, cracked, ears restored, 15 cm. wide, Kangxi. **£2,000-3,000**   *C*

Two export candleholders, modelled as recumbent elephants, their bodies with sepia markings and underglaze blue strapwork, one restored, 12.5 cm. wide, Qianlong. **£2,500-3,500**   *C*

A 'famille rose' figure of an elephant, the details of the head in iron-red, the eyes in grisaille, 7½ in. (19 cm.), Qianlong. **£900-£1,000**   *S*

Two pottery figures of seated dogs, one of the dogs with dark blue patches on the degraded white slip, 11.5 and 11 cm., Tang Dynasty. **£550-650**   *Bon*

A rare Chinese enamelled biscuit porcelain cat, with black patches under an iridescent clear glaze, 22.5 cm., Qianlong/Jiaqing. **£900-£1,200** *SS*

A pair of parrots, the plumage in red, yellow, green and black, 7½ in. (19 cm.), 19th C. **£1,700-1,900** *S*

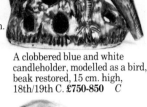

A clobbered blue and white candleholder, modelled as a bird, beak restored, 15 cm. high, 18th/19th C. **£750-850** *C*

An exportware figure of a crane, 16¾ in. (42.4 cm.), Qianlong. **£2,000-3,000** *S*

A pair of Kutani cats, wearing a colourfully enamelled collar, the fur painted with iron-red and gilt, slight restoration on one paw and ear, 22.5 cm., Meiji period. **£800-£900** *S*

A pair of exportware doves, the bases washed in a lime-green glaze, the beak, eyes and feet picked out in pink, and the white body with lightly engraved plumage, 6½ in. (16.5 cm.), Jiaqing. **£700-800** *S*

A pair of rare Arita cats, decorated in iron-red, purple-black enamel and gilding with piebald patches, one leg, one ear and one collar repaired, 13.7 cm., second half 17th C. **£2,500-3,500** *S*

A pair of figures of birds, the rockwork washed in light green enamel streaked in grisaille, the folded wings with plumage in green, yellow-orange, and black, 7¾ in. (19.7 cm.), first half 19th C. **£1,000-1,200** *S*

A Kutani cat, the fur patched in black and wearing a red sash around its neck, 11½ in. (29.3 cm.), c. 1900. **£500-600** *SC*

A pair of 'famille rose' candleholders, modelled as recumbent Buddhist lions, with vivid iron-red and gilt bodies, one foot repaired, 12.5 cm. wide, Daoguang. **£1,500-2,000** *C*

A Sancai pottery figure of a Dignitary, modelled as an Uighur Turk, covered with a bright chestnut glaze falling in rivulets and splashed in green and cream, the borders of the coat and the apron unglazed and decorated in black and red pigments, the unglazed features with facial details in matching pigments with a lobed court hat on top, 28⅝ in. (72.7 cm.), Tang Dynasty, wood stand, box. **£4,000-5,000** *S*

A Kizan earthenware elephant, being ridden by Kannon, decorated in dark coloured enamels and gilding, gilt dai Nippon Satsuma Kizan saku, Kannon with orb from one hand missing, 11 in. (28 cm.). **£800-900** *SC*

An unglazed tomb figure of a female courtier, traces of pigment, 24.5 cm., Tang Dynasty. **£600-800** *SS*

A pair of unglazed pottery figures of Dignitaries, showing traces of scrolls painted in black pigment, 31⅛ in. (79.1 cm.), Tang Dynasty. **£5,500-6,500** *S*

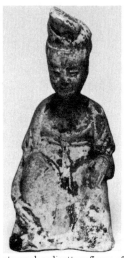

A straw-glazed pottery figure of a seated lady, 13.5 cm., Tang Dynasty. **£350-400** *Bon*

A glazed ridgetile figure of Guandi, 17¼ in. (43.7 cm.), Ming Dynasty, wood stand. **£1,100-1,400** *S*

A Ming tileworks figure of a Demon, the head glazed in green, a brown scarf around his neck, 14¼ in. (36.7 cm.), Ming Dynasty, wood stand. **£600-£700** *S*

A rare Dehua blanc-de-chine European subject group, traditionally identified as the family of Governor Duff, an early Dutch administrator of the VOC in the Far East, dog ears and bonsai branch chipped, 15.5 cm. wide, 18th C. **£2,000-2,500** *C*

VALUE POINTS FOR CHINESE PORCELAIN

- condition — This is always an important factor when dealing with porcelain. Some collectors will only buy perfect pieces — this is particularly the case with Far Eastern buyers. They will pay high prices for excellent condition. This affects the price considerably as a very good piece with a hair line crack or small chip can reduce the value by up to two thirds
- rarity — As with most aspects of antiques, rare items fetch substantially more than common counterparts. This is also important when thinking of damage, as damage to a common piece is much more likely to affect the price dramatically than a similar damage to a rare piece
- imperial v. export — Most of the high prices for Chinese porcelain seem to come from the Hong Kong salerooms. The Far Eastern buyers tend to collect the pieces made by the Chinese potters for their own market rather than exportware. Hence prices are higher

A Ming glazed pottery figure of a Dignitary, seated on a green and yellow throne, wearing an aubergine hat, damage to hands and extremities, 77 cm. high, 16th/early 17th C. **£2,600-3,000** *C*

A 'famille verte' figure of Guanyin, and a detachable base, damaged and repaired, 35 cm. high, Kangxi. **£400-500** *C*

A rare pair of glazed pottery figures of a Dignitary and a Lady, the Dignitary with a green glazed coat, the unglazed head with crisp features, his consort attired in a green glazed tunic, 33½ and 32 in. (85 and 81.3 cm.), Ming Dynasty. **£8,000-10,000** *S*

A tileworks figure of Budai, 15¾ in. (40 cm.), Ming Dynasty. **£400-500** *S*

A Zhejiang celadon figure of Guanyin, the glaze of olive-green tone, the goddess left in the biscuit and burnt to a reddish colour in the firing, 11⅜ in. (28.9 cm.), Ming Dynasty. **£1,200-1,400** *S*

A Ming 'Fa Hua' porcelain figure, seated upon a throne, perhaps representing K'uei Hsing, God of Literature, his head, hands and feet unglazed, his clothing enamelled in a rich indigo with turquoise detail, his belt touched in yellow and lilac, 14½ in. high, 16th C. **£600-700** *T*

A white-glazed figure of Budai, with a pale turquoise glaze, chipped, 18.5 cm. high, 17th C. **£250-350** *C*

A fine Dingyao small dish, the ivory-coloured glaze short of the unglazed rim, 12.2 cm., Song Dynasty. **£500-700** *Bon*

A Longquan celadon dish, the whole covered in a light green glaze, the base with an unglazed frieze showing a body burnt orange in the firing, 18½ in. (47 cm.). **£850-950** *S*

A rare blue and white dragon dish, double line in underglaze blue encircling the lipped rim, with a continuous dragon in pursuit of a 'flaming pearl' among dispersed clouds, the reverse decorated with 8 similar dragon roundels, 6½ in. (16.5 cm.), 6 character mark and period of Jiajing. **£4,000-5,000** *S*

A Ming blue and white saucer dish, the cobalt of good tone, 7⅛ in. (18.2 cm.), 4 character mark of Wanli spaced around a seal reading chua zhang chun, and of the period of Wanli. **£400-500** *S*

A large Ming celadon dish, glaze slightly worn, 43.5 cm. diam., 14th/15th C. **£1,500-1,700** *C*

A Ming Imperial yellow saucer dish, covered overall with a rich egg yolk yellow glaze draining slightly from the rim, the base glazed in white, 8⅛ in. (20.7 cm.), 6 character mark and period of Zhengde. **£3,000-4,000** *S*

An unusual pair of blue and white saucer dishes, decorated on the interior with a leaping carp rising from waves, the underside with birds perched on detached fruiting boughs, 6 in. (15.2 cm.), 4 character marks of Xuande, Wanli. **£450-650** *S*

A blue and white dish, the interior painted with 2 pairs of water birds, the reverse with 2 birds perched on trailing boughs, 5⅛ in. (13 cm.), Wanli. **£300-350** *S*

A large Ming celadon dish, centrally carved with tree peony, a single spray and 4 leaf fronds issuing from a curling stalk, wood stand, glaze crackles, 45 cm. diam., 14th/15th C. **£1,300-1,500** *C*

An engraved dragon saucer dish, in translucent emerald-green enamel applied on the biscuit in reserve on the white-glazed ground, 2 matching dragons on the underside on an incised ground of waves, 8¼ in. (20.5 cm.), 6 character mark and period of Zhengde. **£4,000-£6,000** *S*

A Kraak porselein dish, the centre painted with a figure plying a sampan across a lake, 5⅝ in. (14.3 cm.), Wanli. **£180-240** *S*

Five dishes painted with these borders are illustrated by Yeo and Martin, Chinese Blue and White Ceramics, pl. 87, nos. 165-9, and another meisande dish of slightly larger size was included in the Hong Kong O.C.S. Exhibition of Transitional Wares and Their Forerunners, 1981, Catalogue no. 26, where Kilburn mentions that a number of similar dishes were salvaged from the wreck of the Witte Lieuw, sunk in 1613, and another appears in a still-life dated 1615, but none is found in the Ardebil Collection, which was not added to after 1611.

239

A Kraak porselein blue and white
dish, 14⅝ in. (37.3 cm.), Wanli.
£500-600   *S*

A Kraak porselein dish, well
painted with a central shaped
panel of 2 deer, the reverse with
similar panels and standing on a
short foot, 11 in. (27.9 cm.), Wanli.
£400-500   *S*

A Kraak porselein dish, painted
with one white and several blue
geese on the shore of a lotus pond,
riveted, 50 cm., Wanli. **£400-500**
SS

If perfect **£700-1,000**

A blue and white dish, peony sprig
mark, 11¼ in. (28.5 cm.),
Transitional. **£500-600**   *S*

TRANSITIONAL WARES

- these wares are readily identifiable both by their form and by their style of decoration
- Forms: sleeve vases, oviform jars with domed lids, cylindrical brushpots and bottle vases are particularly common
- the cobalt used is a brilliant purplish-blue, rarely misfired
- the ground colour is of a definite bluish tone, probably because the glaze is slightly thicker than that of the wares produced in the subsequent reigns of Kangxi and Yongzheng
- the decoration is executed in a rather formal academic style, often with scholars and sages with attendants in idyllic cloud-lapped mountain landscapes
- other characteristics include the horizontal 'contoured' clouds, banana plantain used to interrupt scenes, and the method of drawing grass by means of short 'V' shaped brush strokes
- in addition, borders are decorated with narrow bands of scrolling foliage, so lightly incised as to be almost invisible or secret (anhua)
- these pieces were rarely marked although they sometimes copied earlier Ming marks

A richly enamelled 'famille verte'
dish, aiye mark, 15⅛ in. (38.4 cm.),
Kangxi. **£1,600-1,800**   *S*

A pair of plates, painted in rouge-
de-fer and gilding, with a moulded
border outlined in underglaze blue,
8¾ in. (22.3 cm.), Kangxi. **£500-600**
S

A Chinese blue and white dish,
painted with a central octagonal
panel within compartmentalised
border, frit chipping, 22 cm., late
17th C. **£60-80**   *SS*

*This is an example of a late 17th C.
revival of Kraak porselein.*

A pair of lobed polychrome dishes,
each painted in the centre with a
yellow bird perched on a flowering
chrysanthemum branch, boxes,
7⅝ in. (19.7 cm.), seal marks,
Tianqi. **£1,800-2,000**   *S*

*This hexagonal form with
indentations at the angles is a
typical late Ming shape. This type is
generally regarded as being made
for the Japanese market from about
1620-50.*

A richly decorated 'famille verte'
dish, with a group of Precious
Objects within a central medallion,
all reserved on a ground of trellis-
pattern with numerous chilong in
green, blue and aubergine and
iron-red encircled in gilding, a
seeded green-ground border strewn
with butterflies and sprigs and
reserved with stylised sprig
vignettes around the rim, aiye
mark, 15⅜ in. (39.1 cm.), Kangxi.
£1,200-1,500   *S*

A 'famille verte' saucer dish, seal mark, 13⅞ in. (35.2 cm.), Kangxi. £1,200-1,500   S

(l.) A Chinese 'Compagnie-des-Indes' dish, mark — an artemisia leaf, 15 in. diam., Kangxi. £160-200

(r.) A Chinese 'Compagnie-des-Indes' dish, mark — a pair of books, 13½ in. diam., Kangxi. £160-200 WHB

A massive 'famille verte' dish, painted with scholars and ladies in boats on a river and dismounted warriors and bannermen at its rocky bank, damaged and repaired with rivets, 65 cm. diam., encircled Chenghua 6 character mark, Kangxi, tall wood stand. £5,000-£6,000   C

Two 'famille verte' plates, chipped, one border crack, 21.5 cm. diam., encircled zhi (made to order) marks, Kangxi. £450-550   C

A pair of 'famille verte' dishes, 8 in. (20.3 cm.), ding marks, Kangxi. £1,200-1,800   S
Possibly Ching Chang.

Two 'famille verte' plates, painted with a crane in flight above a yellow deer, minor chips, 22 cm. diam., Kangxi. £800-900   C

An armorial dish, decorated in Imari palette with the crest of Thyssen, 18¾ in. (47.6 cm.), Kangxi. £1,200-1,500   S

A 'famille verte' plate, 15½ in. (39.3 cm.), Kangxi. £600-700   S

A set of 3 blue and white dishes, 14¼ in. (36.1 cm.), painted mark, Kangxi. £700-900   S

A rare pair of blue and white plates, the flared rim pierced with diaper and reserved with foliate panels enclosed by a geometric band on the rim, 8¼ in. (21 cm.), ruyi marks, Kangxi. £500-600   S

An unusual pair of blue-ground dishes, the overall richly mottled bleu soufle ground reserved with a central medallion, the figure scenes with details in copper-red, the reverse entirely plain, 14½ in. (36.8 cm.), Kangxi. £1,400-1,600 S

A pair of blue and white plates, 14⅝ in. (37.2 cm.), 6 character mark of Chenghua, Kangxi. £550-£650   S

A Chinese blue and white plate, painted with a dragon and carp leaping from waves, 27 cm., Kangxi. **£150-200**   *SS*

A pair of dishes, of almost eggshell quality, each decorated in 'famille rose' enamels, 8⅛ in. (20.7 cm.), Yongzheng. **£1,000-1,200**   *S*

A black-ground saucer dish, the flowers picked out in blue and iron-red enamels, and smaller green leaves all reserved on a rich black ground washed in translucent green enamel, the interior white, 5⅞ in. (14.9 cm.), 6 character mark and period of Yongzheng. **£1,400-£1,600**   *S*

A 'famille rose' saucer dish, interior glaze crackle, 31 cm. diam., encircled 4 character mark Da Ming Nian zhi, Yongzheng. **£900-£1,000**   *C*

A 'famille rose' saucer dish, decorated on the interior in 'boneless' style, 6¼ in. (15.7 cm.), 6 character mark and period of Yongzheng. **£500-600**   *S*

A 'famille rose' plate, 9¼ in. (23.5 cm.), Yongzheng. **£600-700**   *S*

A large 'famille verte' dish, 15½ in. (39 cm.), 18th C. **£500-600**   *S*

A pair of blue and white saucer dishes, painted with a dappled stag standing beside a darker doe on a terrace below pine and a flying bat, glaze scratched, 28 cm. diam., second quarter 18th C. **£450-550**   *C*

Probably from Fujian.

A 'famille rose' Canton enamel ruby-back dish, minor crackle and pitting, 33 cm. diam., Yongzheng. **£800-1,100**   *C*

A pair of European subject plates, each richly enamelled in 'famille rose' palette, with pink-ground diaper borders, 9 in. (22.8 cm.), early Qianlong. **£1,200-1,500**   *S*

Notice the similarity between the design layout between these 2 dishes.

A blue and white saucer dish, painted with a writhing 4-clawed dragon grasping a flaming pearl amongst fire scrolls, 15.5 cm. diam., encircled Yongzheng 6 character mark and of the period. **£1,700-2,000**   *C*

A pair of 'famille rose' black-ground plates, painted with a large yellow brocade scroll of peony, 22.5 cm. diam., Yongzheng/early Qianlong. **£900-1,100**   *C*

A 'famille rose' European subject plate, with puce cell pattern border, small rim chip, 22.5 cm. diam., early Qianlong. **£650-750**   *C*

A pair of fine Chinese Imari Pronck plates, decorated in underglaze blue, iron-red and gilt with 'La Dame au Parasol', below a cell pattern iron-red border, after engravings by Cornelius Pronck, 23.5 cm. diam., early Qianlong. **£2,000-2,300**   *C*

A pair of blue and white plates, painted with a view of Burghley House near Stamford, cracked and chipped, 22.5 cm. diam., c. 1745. **£200-300**   *C*

A set of 7 blue and white soup plates, each painted in bright cobalt with a bird darting over a flowering peony tree, 8¾ in. (22.3 cm.), early Qianlong. **£400-£500**   *S*

A set of 4 Chinese exportware plates, 29 cm., Qianlong. **£300-350** *SS*

A rare 'famille rose' dish, the centre enamelled in ruby back style, in reserve on an oxidised silver ground, 15¼ in. (38.7 cm.), early Qianlong. **£1,600-2,000**   *S*

A 'famille rose' rectangular dish, painted with cockerels in confrontation, minor fritting, 27 cm. wide, Qianlong. **£800-900** *S*

A set of 9 unusual European subject plates, the centre of each decorated in 'famille rose' enamels, 9 in. (22.8 cm.), Qianlong. **£2,600-£3,000**   *S*

An oval meat dish à la Pompadour, decorated in bright 'famille rose' enamels, 14⅞ in. (37.8 cm.), Qianlong. **£1,200-1,400**   *S*

A set of 4 'famille rose' plates, 9 in. (22.8 cm.), Qianlong. **£400-500**   *S*

A pair of 'famille rose' plates, 23 cm. diam., Qianlong. **£3,000-3,500**   *C*

A pair of blue-ground dishes, painted with a central medallion of a dragon chasing a 'flaming pearl', all on an underglaze blue wash ground, 25.8 cm., seal marks and period of Qianlong. **£1,000-1,200** *S*

A set of 12 'famille rose' plates, 9¾ in. (24.8 cm.), Qianlong. **£500-£700**   *S*

ORIENTAL POTTERY AND PORCELAIN

This section is alphabetically arranged by object: bowl, box, censer, etc. In each group the wares are firstly divided into Chinese followed by Japanese and then ordered chronologically.

A pair of armorial soup plates, decorated in 'famille rose' enamels, 8¾ in. (22.3 cm.), Qianlong. **£750-£850** *S*

A massive saucer dish, painted in iron-red and gilt, 71.5 cm. diam., unencircled iron-red Kangxi 6 character mark, late Qing Dynasty. **£1,100-1,500** *C*

An unusual Imari shaving dish, decorated in underglaze blue, iron-red, coloured enamels and gilt, 26 cm. diam., Genroku period. **£750-850** *C*

A large Imari dish, painted in underglaze blue, iron-red, coloured enamels and gilt, slightly rubbed, 53.5 cm. diam., late 17th/early 18th C. **£500-700** *C*

A set of 3 Chinese 'famille rose' rectangular panels, 12 by 8¾ in., 19th C. **£350-450** *DWB*

A pair of blue and white saucer dishes, 19.7 cm., 6 character marks of Guangxu and of the period. **£350-£450** *Bon*

A Kakiemon blue and white saucer dish, with chocolate-brown foliate rim, the base with a Fuku mark, chip to foot rim, 22.2 cm. diam., c. 1680. **£250-350** *C*

The attribution to Kakiemon is a conventional one relying to some extent on the brown edged rim and generally fine paste and glaze. It is however primarily conjectural and may well prove to be another Arita Kiln.

A large Arita blue and white dish, small rim chip, 54 cm. diam., late 17th C. **£750-850** *C*

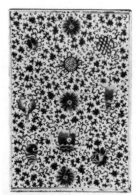

A blue and white panel, 20¼ in. (51.4 cm.), c. 1800. **£700-800** *S*

A pair of blue and white plaques, 16¾ by 12 in. (42.6 by 30.5 cm.), 19th C. **£350-400** *S*

A blue and white dish, with lilies, peonies, chrysanthemums and butterflies, 38 cm., Qing Dynasty. **£110-150** *Bon*

A Kakiemon 10-sided dish, with chocolate-brown foliate rim, decorated in iron-red, blue, turquoise and black enamels and gilt, slightly rubbed, 21.8 cm. diam., c. 1680. **£1,100-1,500** *C*

A Matsugatani-style dish, lightly moulded in relief and painted in underglaze blue, the whole raised on a tall thin foot, repair, 16.5 cm., late 17th/early 18th C. **£750-850** *S*

A fine 19th C. Japanese charger, 56 cm. wide. **£250-300** *OT*

A set of 5 Utsutsugawa-Yaki-style oval kashizara, glazed in chocolate-brown with a blue and white slip decoration of wisteria above shibagaki, Meiji period, fitted wood box with inscribed lid, 19.5 cm. wide. **£750-850** *C*

Tanaka Gohei and his son opened the kiln at Utsutsugawa in Hizen Province in 1692 which closed about 1743. Baba Fujidayu and his son re-opened a kiln nearby which lasted from 1895 to 1903, producing wares in a similar style.

A rare Arita saucer dish, decorated in underglaze blue with a Dutch riverscape in the style of van Fryton, confused Ming mark, 12.5 cm., late 17th/early 18th C. **£250-300** *S*

Arita dishes of this type were based on Dutch Delftware originals painted in the so-called 'van Fryton' style and were later copied at Bow from 1752 onwards.
A similar dish from the collection of Burghley House, Stamford, exhibited 1983, is illustrated in the catalogue, No. 38, a Delft original is illustrated, Vecht, A., Frederick van Frytom 1632-1702, pl. 44.

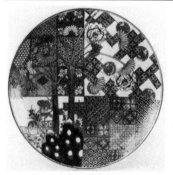

An Imari dish, painted in underglaze blue and bright overglaze enamels, 55 cm., mid/late 19th C. **£350-450** *S*

A large Imari plate, richly enamelled and gilt with overlapping landscapes, 56 cm., first half 19th C. **£900-1,000** *SS*

An Arita dish, moulded and painted in underglaze blue with a map of Japan, mark Honcho Tenpo (1830-44), 48.3 cm., late 19th C. **£1,200-1,400** *S*

An Imari plaque, decorated in underglaze blue and overglaze red and gilt, blue character mark, 11½ in. (29.5 cm.) across, late 19th C. **£70-90** *TW*

pair of Imari plaques, 18¼ in. iam., 19th C. **£300-350** *CDC*

A reticulated Zhejiang celadon garden seat, the overall glaze of characteristic olive-green colour, 16½ in. (41.9 cm.), Ming Dynasty **£2,500-3,000** *S*

An Imari circular dish, 18 in., hairline crack to rim. **£160-200** *PWC*

A pair of yellow-ground barrel-shaped garden seats, painted with dense white and grisaille leafy peony and magnolia, dividing turquoise-ground floral borders, 49 cm. high, late 19th C. **£2,500-3,000** *C*

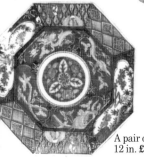

A pair of Imari octagonal dishes, 12 in. **£300-350** *PWC*

A pair of 'famille rose' yellow-ground barrel-shaped garden seats, 31 cm. wide, second half 19th C. **£2,500-3,000** *C*

An ormolu-mounted Chinese porcelain jardinière, with beaded rim and 2 lion mask handles flanking the blue and white porcelain, the porcelain Wanli, 13½ in. (34 cm.) high. **£800-1,000** *C*

A Japanese Imari jardinière, in underglaze blue, iron red and gilt, 40 cm. diam., 34 cm. high, last quarter of 19th C. **£400-500** *HSS*

JAPANESE ART PERIODS

PREHISTORY AND PROTOHISTORY
c. 7,000 B.C. Jomon culture; first recorded pottery with simple design.
c. 300 B.C. Yayoi culture; bronzes and more sophisticated pottery.
1st to 4th C. A.D. Haniwa culture; bronzes and distinctive red pottery.
220 A.D. first influence from Korea.
ASUKA PERIOD — 552-645
HAHUKO PERIOD — 672-685
NARA PERIOD — 710-794
HEIAN PERIOD — 794-1185
KAMAKURA PERIOD — 1185-1333
MUROMACHI (AHIKAGA) PERIOD — 1338-1573
MOMOYAMA PERIOD — 1573-1615
1598: Immigrant Korean potters begin kilns at Kyushu, producing the first glazed pottery.
EDO (TOKUGAWA) PERIOD — 1615-1867
1616: First porcelain made by Ninsei (1596-1666)
1661-1673: Great age of porcelain; Arita, Nabeshima, Kutani and Kakiemon.
1716-1736: Popularity of lacquering and netsuke as art forms.
MEIJI PERIOD — (1868-1912) Strong influence of Western cultures developing and growing. Japanese art appears to decline in many respects. Much trading with the West.

A Japanese porcelain jardinière, on a celadon green ground, 16 in. diam. by 12 in. high, late 19th C. **£350-450** *M*

A pair of 'famille rose' barrel-shaped garden seats, reserved on blue key-pattern grounds, 46 cm. high, late 19th C. **£2,600-3,000** *C*

A celadon jardinière, the exterior moulded with a lotus meander, covered overall in a light celadon glaze, the interior white and the base unglazed, 12½ in. (31.7 cm.), Qianlong. **£300-400** *S*

A pair of jardinières and stands, enamelled in 'famille rose' palette, 6 in. (15.5 cm.), 19th C., Guangxu. **£650-750** *S*

An Imari jardinière, the exterior painted with panels of ho-ho bird flowering plants and mons on a chrysanthemum scroll ground, 44 cm. diam. **£750-850** *L*

A green-glazed pottery jar, covered in a translucent green glaze, with large areas of silvery iridescence, parts of the interior unglazed, revealing the reddish ware beneath, 8½ in. (21.5 cm.), Han Dynasty. **£800-900** *S*

An unusual Yueyao jar, covered overall with a rich olive-green glaze pooling in the grooves, 4 rust-coloured splashes on the rim, the unglazed base encircled by 6 wedge-shaped spur marks, 5¼ in. (13.3 cm.), Western Jin Dynasty. **£1,500-2,000** *S*

A small Yueyao jar, covered in a greenish-buff glaze with some degraded sections, 2¾ in. (7 cm.), Six Dynasties. **£200-250** *S*

A rare proto-porcelain jar, a mottled olive-green kiln-gloss extending halfway down the body revealing the reddish-brown ware below, 12½ in. (31.7 cm.), Han Dynasty. **£1,500-2,000** *S*

A Sancai pottery jar, covered with bright dappled glazes of chestnut and straw, stopping short of the flattened base revealing the pinkish ware, 3 in. (7.7 cm.), Tang Dynasty. **£2,500-3,000** *S*

An unusual glazed pottery jar, the sides in green with pendent triangles in cream and a band of ochre below, falling short of the base showing the orange buff body, the bevelled edge of the wide mouth picked out in ochre, trickling into the otherwise unglazed interior, 7⅞ in. (20 cm.), Tang Dynasty. **£2,200-2,500** *S*

large blue and white Swatow jar, he base with traces of gilt lhering, 13⅜ in. (34 cm.), 16th C. **750-950** *S*

A white-glazed lobed jar of Ding type, covered overall with an ivory-tinted glaze, stopping just short of the foot, 3¾ in. (9.5 cm.) high, 4¾ in. (12 cm.) wide, Song Dynasty. **£450-550** *S*

A good Henan jar, standing on an unglazed foot of broad section, the body covered in a thick glaze of speckled greenish-brown tone, the shoulders decorated in black with 2 floral sprays fired to a metallic greyish colour, 11 in. (27.9 cm.), Song Dynasty. **£1,300-1,800** *S*

Smaller bottles with this unusual decoration are illustrated in the Royal Ontario Musuem handbook, pl. 69, and by Warren Cox, The Book of Pottery and Porcelain, vol. I, pl. 54, top right, together with a large teadust-glazed vase, fig. 345. Compare also the vase with an unglazed ring around the shoulder illustrated in Sekai Toji Zenshu, vol. II, pl. 131.

rare blue and white jar, painted underglaze blue of vivid tone, n. (20.3 cm.), 6 character mark d period of Jiajing. **£1,200-1,500**

Ming blue and white jar, 15⅜ in. cm.), Wanli. **£1,500-2,000** *S*

A rare Ming ovoid jar, decorated in enamels applied on the biscuit, the blooms with yellow petals radiating from an aubergine centre, on a green ground, a band of lappets painted in underglaze blue encircling the base and a blue and white floral border around the shoulders, 8 in. (20.3 cm.), Wanli. **£1,500-2,000** *S*

A Ming blue and white jar and cover, freely painted in cobalt of soft tone, the matching cover surmounted by a conical knop, 15¾ in. (40 cm.), c. 1500. **£950-£1,150** *S*

A good Ming blue and white jar, the exterior pencilled with 2 scaly dragons in pursuit of 'flaming pearls', the underglaze blue of bright purplish-blue tone, 4 in. (10 cm.) high by 5¼ in. (13.5 cm.), 6 character mark and period of Wanli. **£7,000-9,000** *S*

A Transitional blue and white oviform jar and a domed cover, the body painted in a violet-blue with 3 warriors, cover flange and neck rim chipped, 27.5 cm. high, mid 17th C. **£1,000-1,500** *C*

A blue and white jar, painted in inky tones of blue with 4 scaly dragons, cracked, 16¾ in. (42.5 cm.), 6 character mark of Wanli, and of the period. **£2,000-£2,500** *S*

A blue and white jar, 8⅛ in. (20.7 cm.), second quarter of 17th C. **£800-1,000** *S*

An engraved white-glazed jar, the body incised with a peony meander below a narrow zig-zag border, 4¼ in. (10.8 cm.), early 18th C. **£400-500** *S*

A copper-red and underglaze blue celadon ground jar, box, 6⅜ in. (16.2 cm.), Kangxi. **£950-1,050** *S*

A blue and white ovoid jar, wood cover, 20.5 cm., Kangxi. **£350-450** *Bon*

A 'famille verte' covered jar, of U-shape, the spandrels below the rim infilled with demi-florettes on a seeded green ground, 5⅛ in. (13 cm.), Kangxi. **£600-800** *S*

A pair of 'famille verte' jars and covers, 12 in. (30.5 cm.), Kangxi. **£900-1,100** *S*

A blue and white Potiche, the shoulders pierced for attachment of the handles, 8¾ in. (22.3 cm.), Kangxi. **£400-500** *S*

A blue and white ovoid jar, decorated with ladies and boys in a garden playing at a games table, minute rim cracks, wood stand, 20.5 cm., Kangxi. **£200-300** *Bon*

Two blue and white jars, almost forming a pair, wood covers, 8½ in. (21.6 cm.), Kangxi. **£800-1,000** *S*

A yellow-glazed ovoid jar, the interior and foot glazed in grey-white, wood cover, 22 cm., Kangxi. £600-700 *Bon*

Two blue and white oviform jars, each reserved on cracked ice grounds scattered with prunus blossoms with quatrefoil panels of archaistic vessels, scholars' utensils and vases of feathers, one wood cover, both about 19 cm. high, Kangxi. £600-700 *C*

A 'famille verte' ovoid jar, with a green seeded ground, 20.5 cm., Kangxi. £400-600 *Bon*

blue and white ovoid jar, painted with groups of figures at scholarly pursuits, 21 cm., early Kangxi. 500-600 *Bon*

A blue and white oviform jar, 20.5 cm. high, Kangxi. £700-800 *C*

Two blue and white oviform jars, wood covers, one damaged, 20.5 cm. high, Kangxi. £900-1,000 *C*

MAKE THE MOST OF MILLER'S

CONDITION *is absolutely vital when assessing the value of an antique. Damaged pieces on the whole appreciate much less than perfect examples. However a rare desirable piece may command a high price even when damaged.*

A Doucai jar, decorated in underglaze blue and overglaze enamels, crack to neck, 11 cm., seal mark and period of Qianlong. £300-£500 *SS*

An unusual flambé jar, covered overall in a purplish blue glaze liberally streaked in creamy tone. wood stand, 15 in. (38.2 cm.), Qianlong. £1,300-1,500 *S*

celadon glazed ovoid jar and ver, all covered on the exterior d interior with an even green aze, 21 cm., Qianlong seal mark d of the period. £1,300-1,600 *on*

A small blue and white jar, each facet painted with a vertically arranged stem of lingzhi fungus entwined with bamboo, 2⅝ in. (6.7 cm.), 6 character mark and period of Yongzheng. £1,000-1,200 *S*

A pair of flambé covered jars, covered in a glaze of rich reddish-purple tones attractively streaked in cream, 9 in. (22.8 cm.), 19th C. £500-600 *S*

249

A pair of Cantonese vases and covers, decorated in 'famille rose' palette with a continuous dragon dance procession, 13¼ in. (33.6 cm.), third quarter of 19th C. **£450-550** *SC*

A Chinese export 'famille rose' part tea service, comprising a tea pot, cover and stand, 3 tea bowls, 3 coffee cups and 4 saucers, some damage, Qianlong. **£250-300** *Bea*

An unusual pair of blue and white jars and covers, 15¼ in. (38.7 cm.), 19th C. **£1,400-1,600** *S*

An early Kakiemon baluster jar, decorated in iron-red, green, blue and mustard-yellow enamels, enamels rubbed and chipped, hairline star crack in base, 21.6 cm. high, c. 1670. **£1,100-1,500** *C*

A 'famille verte' tea pot and cover, painted in bright enamels, 7 in. (17.8 cm.), Kangxi. **£400-500** *S*

A fine Arita blue and white globular jar, 18.3 cm. high, c. 1680. **£500-600** *C*

A Chinese Jesuitware tea pot and cover, milk jug and tea pot stand. **£300-400** *DWB*

A 'famille rose' tea pot and cover, painted with a pair of pheasants perched on a peony bough, 6¾ in. (17.2 cm.), Yongzheng. **£200-300** *S*

A fine Arita blue and white baluster jar, painted with 2 paradise flycatchers among flowering chrysanthemum, probably from the Kakiemon k 25.5 cm. high, late 17th C. **£1,2 £1,500** *C*

A pair of Batavian ware ecuelles and covers, the honey-coloured ground reserved with shaped panels painted in underglaze blue with 'Precious Objects', 7¼ in. (18.4 cm.), Kangxi. **£500-600** *S*

Batavian was only a trading station, no porcelain was manufactured there. The same could be said for Nanking and Imari, all these terms were used by European dealers when alluding to the types of ware transhipped through these ports.

A 'European subject' tea pot and cover, painted en grisaille, Qianlong. **£500-600** *C*

A Dutch-decorated tea pot and cover, painted en grisaille with additional flesh tints and gilding, 6 in. (15.3 cm.), 18th C. **£150-250** *S*

A 'famille rose' pear-shaped coffee pot and domed cover, painted with 2 merchant ships in black and iron-red enamel, each flying the British Union Jack, the jug modelled on a German porcelain prototype, rim crack, 21.5 cm. high, Qianlong. **£650-750** *C*

A pair of blue and white covered ecuelles, painted in bright cobalt with scenes of pavilions set on the shores of a lake, 7½ in. (19.1 cm.), Kangxi. **£500-600** *S*

A pair of 'famille rose' tureens and shallow domed covers, with pear-shaped finials, painted with 2 pairs of cockerels confronted amongst peony and rockwork, one extensively damaged, 38.5 cm. diam., early Qianlong. **£3,500-£4,000** *C*

A pair of buttertubs, covers and stands, decorated in 'famille rose' palette, predominantly in pink, 6⅛ in. (15.6 cm.), Qianlong. **£1,000-£1,200** *S*

A 'famille rose' ecuelle and cover, fluted handles washed in gilding, 7⅜ in. (19.3 cm.), Qianlong. **£400-£500** *S*

A pair of 'famille rose' sauce tureens, shallow domed covers and stands, with iron-red hare-head handles, minor fritting, the stands 19.5 cm. wide, Qianlong. **£5,000-£6,000** *C*

A 'famille rose' oval tureen and domed cover, reserved on gilt cracked ice around the extremity borders, 35.5 cm. across the handles, Qianlong. **£2,000-3,000** *C*

The shape is taken from a Meissen design of about 1737, modelled by J. F. Eberlein.

A Chinese 'famille rose' tureen in the form of a water fowl, 5 in. high. **£900-1,100** *CDC*

A rare 'famille rose' European subject oval tureen, cover and stand, with iron-red upright scroll handles, the enamel delicately and thinly applied as the outlines, some enamel rubbed, handles re-attached, the stand 38 cm. wide, Qianlong. **£3,000-3,500** *C*

A 'famille rose' tureen and cover, 8⅞ in. (22.5 cm.), Qianlong. **£900-1,100** *S*

A blue and white tureen and cover, 13 in. (33 cm.), Qianlong. **£950-£1,050** *S*

A blue and white tureen and cover, 14 in. (35.6 cm.), Qianlong. **£750-£850** *S*

A 'famille rose' tureen and cover, after a Meissen original, 11 in. (28 cm.), Qianlong. **£1,500-2,000** *S*

A blue and white tureen, cover and stand, 14½ in. (36.9 cm.), Qianlong. **£800-900** *S*

A pair of soup tureens and covers, decorated in 'famille rose' enamels, with a 'prunus on cracked ice' border in iron-red and gold, with an enamelled blue diaper border edged with gilt spearhead pattern, pierced crown finials, 23 cm. diam., Qianlong. **£2,600-3,000** *L*

The form is borrowed from European faience or silver, and the sides are painted with so-called European flowers.

A blue and white tureen and cover, with double rabbit head handles and pomegranate sprig knop, 13½ in. (34.2 cm.), Qianlong. **£600-£700** *S*

Two 'famille rose' cockerel tureens and related covers, with iron-red plumage on the bodies and multi-coloured wing and tail feathers, combs and one wattle restored, 18 cm. wide, Qianlong. **£2,400-£3,000** *C*

A Canton 'famille rose' oval tureen cover and stand, with gilt ground enriched with pink and green floral meander, stand slightly chipped, one handle cracked, the stand 36 cm. wide, second quarter 19th C. **£900-1,100** *C*

An early 19th C. blue and white willow pattern tureen. **£300-350** *JD*

CHINESE PORCELAIN VALUE POINTS

- about 80% of the marks that appear on Chinese porcelain are retrospective
- if a piece bears a correct, as opposed to a retrospective, reign mark then its value compared to an unmarked but comparable specimen would probably be of the magnitude of 3 to 4 times more
- a piece of a known date but bearing the mark of an earlier reign would be adversely affected and could possibly fetch less than an unmarked piece of the same vintage
- as a rule condition will adversely affect a readily available type of ware more than a very rare or early type
- original covers or lids can raise the price considerably — especially if the vessel appears more complete with it. Hence a baluster vase, for example, would be less affected than a wine ewer

A Chinese export blue and white tureen and cover, 19th C. **£350-£400** *WW*

A pair of exportware covered urns, following a Marieberg original, picked out in cobalt enriched with gilding, all picked out in underglaze blue and gilding, 14½ in. (36.2 cm.), Qianlong. **£2,500-3,000** *S*

A rare pair of 'famille rose' neo-classical 'friendship' urns and covers, modelled closely after European ceramic prototypes, the neck and foot painted in blue enamel and gilt within moulded flutes, one cover and handle repaired, 43.5 cm. high, late Qianlong. **£5,000-6,000** *C*

A rare pair of urn-shaped vases and covers, the 2 oval panels inscribed 'Sacrée au l'audeur' and 'Ornament du Cabinet', the whole decorated in blue enamel and gilding with details in iron-red, 15½ in. (39.4 cm.), Qianlong. **£2,500-3,000** *S*

A straw-glazed stoneware amphora, covered overall with a slightly degraded straw-glaze stopping short of the foot showing the pale buff ware, 15 in. (38 cm.), Tang Dynasty. **£1,800-2,200** *S*

A rare painted grey pottery jar, painted in brown, red and buff on a white ground, 10¼ in. (26 cm.), Tang Dynasty. **£1,300-1,500** *S*

A very rare Jizhou vase, boldly decorated on one side with a pine tree reserved and carved through the brown glaze, to leave the outline in the buff-coloured ware beneath, 8⅜ in. (21.2 cm.), Song Dynasty. **£450-550** *S*

An unusual Longquan celadon vase, moulded in low relief below the thick crackled translucent olive glaze, pooling to sea-green above the foot, 12.3 cm., Song Dynasty, fitted case. **£650-750** *Bon*

A Longquan celadon vase (yuhuchun ping), covered with a bright sea-green glaze, the footrim burnt orange in the firing, 9¾ in. (24.7 cm.), 14th C. **£900-1,100** *S*

A rare Guanyao vase, covered in a creamy greyish-green glaze falling evenly to the straight foot, enclosing a glazed interior, 6 in. (15.2 cm.), Song Dynasty. **£750-850** *S*

A Cizhou vase, painted in brown over a thin white slip, cracked and rim chipped, 25 cm., Song Dynasty. **£200-300** *Bon*

A celadon-glazed carved baluster jar, shoulder star crack, 22.5 cm. high, Yuan/early Ming Dynasty. **£1,200-1,600** *C*

An unusual Yingqing vase, covered in a translucent glaze pooling slightly in the incised areas and stopping unevenly short of the base, 8¼ in. (21 cm.), Yuan Dynasty, fitted box. **£1,300-1,600** *S*

A rare and early blue and white vase, the body freely painted in deep cobalt-blue with sinuous -clawed dragon chasing a 'flaming earl', all on a milky-coloured round tinted light blue, the unglazed footrim burnt reddish in the firing, 11¼ in. (28.6 cm.), Yuan Dynasty. **£9,000-11,000** *S*

No other yuhuchun ping of this pattern appears to have been published. A bottle of this form carved with a lotus spray between double line borders is illustrated by Addis, Chinese Porcelain from the Addis Collection, pl. 1, where he suggests a date about 1300-10, as it 'seems of stylistic grounds to represent an early stage in the series of decorated bottles from Chingtechen', pre-dating the bottles with additional leaves and petals around the neck and foot such as the vase carved with lotus found in the Sinan shipwreck, which is tentatively dated to 1320-30, included in the Special Exhibition of Cultural Relics Found off Sinan Coast, National Museum of Korea, 1977, Catalogue no. 160.

Cizhou type jar, decorated in own over a cream ground, ¼ in., Yuan/Ming Dynasty. **,000-2,500** *DWB*

A blue and white vase, originally a ewer, the tapering neck with a Near Eastern metal mount, with double scroll handles joined to the base of the handle and spout, 4 character mark, wan fu you tong (May infinite happiness be heaped upon you), 12⅛ in. (30.8 cm.), Wanli. **£450-550** *S*

A pair of blue and white bottles, 11⅛ in. (28.3 cm.), Wanli. **£2,000-£2,500**   *S*

A late Ming blue and white square bottle, fritted, 26 cm. high, Wanli. **£500-700**   *C*

A rare late Ming armorial blue and white Kraak porselein square bottle, with elaborate Continental coat-of-arms, surmounted by the crest of a bird resembling a displaying phoenix, neck chipped, edge body crack, 30 cm. high, late Wanli. **£2,600-3,000**   *C*

This is a very rare piece; it must be one of the earliest coat-of-arms on Chinese porcelain. A very important reference piece, which is reflected in the price.

A blue and white vase, painted in cobalt of bright tone, the rim encircled by a blue ground classic scroll border reserved with the nianhao, 17⅞ in. (45.4 cm.), 6 character mark and period of Wanli. **£5,000-6,000**   *S*

A silver-mounted late Ming blue and white Kraak porselein double gourd bottle, the neck probably reduced, mounted with Islamic silver alloy neck top, 30 cm. high overall, Wanli. **£450-550**   *C*

A late Ming blue and white bottle, 3 areas of wax infill, 28 cm. high, early 17th C. **£1,200-1,500**   *C*

An unusual vase of double gourd form, painted in underglaze blue with auspicious characters in panels on a cell-diaper ground and applied overall with a translucent green enamel, 8¼ in. (20.9 cm.), Wanli. **£300-400**   *S*

A rolwagen vase with the same unusual decoration of a translucent green enamel covering the underglaze blue decoration, with the cyclical date corresponding to A.D. 1638, was included in the Hong Kong O.C.S. Exhibition of Transitional Wares, 1981, catalogue no. 61.

A blue and white double gourd vase, the whole well painted in inky tones of underglaze blue, cracked, 11½ in. (29.2 cm.), late Wanli. **£600-700**   *S*

Two late Ming blue and white double gourd bottles, 29 cm. high, c. 1630. **£1,000-1,400**   *C*

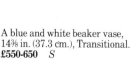

A blue and white beaker vase, 14⅜ in. (37.3 cm.), Transitional. **£550-650**   *S*

A Transitional blue and white baluster jar, minor interior chip, 27.5 cm. high, c. 1640-50. **£500-600**   *C*

A blue and white brushpot, 7⅞ in. (20 cm.), Transitional. **£1,300-1,700** S

A pair of polychrome jars and covers, 15 in. (38.2 cm.), Transitional. **£2,000-3,000** S

A blue and white bottle vase, painted in soft tones with a river landscape scene, divided by rockwork and swirling clouds, 8¾ in. (22.2 cm.), Transitional. **£500-600** S

A polychrome jar and cover, 15½ in. (38 cm.), Transitional. **£1,000-1,200** S

Very similar vases are in the Burghley Collection and are illustrated in 'The Wrestling Boys' — see Bibliography.

ORIENTAL POTTERY AND PORCELAIN

This section is alphabetically arranged by object: bowl, box, censer, etc. In each group the wares are firstly divided into Chinese followed by Japanese and then ordered chronologically.

A pair of beaker vases, decorated in light relief, picked out in celadon, underglaze blue and copper red, light chipping, 16⅝ in. (42.3 cm.), character marks and period of Kangxi. **£1,600-2,000** S

A celadon ground yen-yen vase, decorated in white slip, underglaze blue and copper-red, some damage, 17¼ in. (43.8 cm.), Kangxi. **£700-£900** S

Two large blue and white gu-shaped vases, glaze flaw inside one rim, other rim slightly fritted, 51 cm. high, Transitional/early Kangxi. **£4,000-5,000** C

A 'famille verte' yen-yen vase, 18⅜ in. (46.7 cm.), Kangxi. **£1,800-2,200** S

An amusing blue and white vase, painted with European figures on board a 3-masted sailing ship, 20⅞ in. (52.9 cm.), Kangxi. **£2,000-2,500** S

A blue and white yen-yen vase, neck crack and chip, 46.5 cm. high, Kangxi. **£400-500** C

A good 'famille verte' brushpot, 5⅛ in. (13 cm.), Kangxi. **£450-550** S

A rare celadon-ground double gourd vase, decorated in underglaze blue and copper-red, 6½ in. (16.5 cm.), Kangxi. **£1,400-1,800** S

A blue and white brushpot, some damage, 7½ in. (19 cm.), aiye mark, Kangxi. **£300-400** *S*

A 'famille verte' brushpot, 4¾ in. (12.2 cm.), Kangxi. **£600-700** *S*

A fine blue and white cylindrical brushpot, the glaze in unusually good condition, particularly on the rims, one small foot rim glaze line, 17.5 cm. diam., Kangxi. **£2,300-£2,600** *C*

A dated 'famille verte' brushpot, the reverse with a poetic inscription, dated to 1709, 5⅜ in. (13.6 cm.), Kangxi. **£2,500-3,000** *S*

A blue and white cylindrical brush-holder, rim fritted and with one flaw, 18 cm. diam., Kangxi. **£700-900** *C*

A blue and white cylindrical brushpot, minor fritting, leaf mark, 19.5 cm. diam., Kangxi, wood stand, fitted box. **£1,200-£1,500** *C*

A finely painted blue and white brushpot, 7¾ in. (19.7 cm.), early Kangxi, wood cover and stand. **£1,300-1,600** *S*

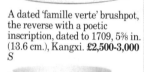

A powder blue-glazed cylindrical brushpot, with traces of gilt decoration, 18 cm. high, Kangxi. **£750-850** *C*

A celadon-glazed carved cylindrical brush-holder (bidong), incised on the exterior under a glossy pale glaze firing deeper in the recesses with 2 long slender chilong dragons in mutual pursuit amongst leafy coils of lingzhi, foot rim chips, 18 cm. diam., Kangxi. **£900-1,200** *C*

A celadon-glazed gu-shaped vase, rim chipped and polished, 47 cm. high, Kangxi. **£900-1,200** *C*

A mirror-black vase of archaic hu form, the glaze suffused throughout with a pearly lustre, 9¼ in. (23.3 cm.), Kangxi. **£750-850** *S*

A blue and white gu-shaped vase, painted in violet-blue with various landscapes, tree peony clusters and vases of flowers, reserved on a ground of blue interlocking cell-pattern, rim cracked, 52 cm. high, Kangxi. **£600-800** *C*

A large coral-ground cylindrical vase, with overlapping 'famille verte' trefoil floral lappets, the shoulder with cell-pattern, neck restored, 44.5 cm. high, Kangxi. **£1,300-1,500** *C*

A garniture of 5 'famille verte' lobed oval quatrefoil vases and 3 domed covers, one body and cover cracked and repaired, small rim chips, 30 cm. high, 27 cm. high, Kangxi. **£3,000-4,000** *C*

A pair of Chinese blue and white canister vases, painted in blue with animated episodes from an epic, restoration to one neck, aiye marks, 27.5 cm., Kangxi. **£800-90** *SS*

An underglaze red and blue beaker vase, Gu, 44 cm., Kangxi. **£600-800** SS

A Wucai baluster jar, painted in underglaze blue, green and iron-red, some enamels flaked and scratched, 32.5 cm., mid 17th C. **£900-1,000** C

A pair of Chinese reticulated blue and white vases and covers, restoration to one neck, 28.7 cm., Kangxi. **£400-500** SS

A pair of covered baluster vases, painted in bright rouge-de-fer enriched with gilding, 13¾ in. (34.9 cm.), Kangxi. **£850-950** S

A blue and white baluster jar, 13 in. (33 cm.), Kangxi. **£400-500** S

A blue and white baluster jar and cover, 16¼ in. (41.3 cm.), Kangxi. **£450-550** S

A blue and white jar and cover, 11½ in. (29.2 cm.), 4 character mark of Chenghua, Kangxi. **£800-900** S

blue and white jar, 18¼ in. (46.3 cm.), Kangxi. **£1,300-1,600**

A blue and white vase, of massively potted pear shape, 17½ in. (44.3 cm.), 4 character mark of Xuande, Kangxi. **£650-750** S

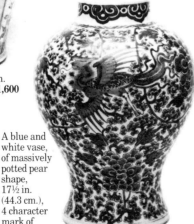

A blue and white jar, painted in greyish-blue tones, 13½ in. (34.3 cm.), Kangxi. **£600-700** S

A blue and white vase, painted with sprays of prunus blossom on a cracked ice ground, wood stand, 8¾ in. (21.3 cm.), Kangxi. **£300-400** S

An unusual Ming-style blue and white vase, with contrived 'heaping and piling', 9⅞ in. (25.1 cm.), Yongzheng. **£600-750** *S*

A 'famille verte' pear-shaped vase, moulded in relief and brightly painted primarily in iron-red, turquoise and gilt with 4 Immortals, neck rim polished, 38.5 cm. high, Yongzheng. **£650-850** *C*

A blue and white vase, the body with sprays of lotus flowers attached to scrolled leafy stems in Ming style, 4½ in. (10.9 cm.), 6 character mark and period of Yongzheng. **£4,000-5,000** *S*

A large 'famille rose' vase and cover, heightened in gilding, 31½ in. (80 cm.), Yongzheng. **£6,000-7,000** *S*

A flambé vase, covered in a streaked reddish-purple glaze draining to a colourless tone around the rim, showing the body beneath, 15⅝ in. (39.7 cm.), Qianlong. **£650-750** *S*

A pair of vases, painted in the Mandarin palette, 43.5 cm., Qianlong. **£3,000-3,500** *Bea*

A pair of 'famille rose' baluster vases and covers, each painted in underglaze blue, bright enamels and gilt, reserved on turquoise cell-pattern around the neck, old repair, 66 cm. high, the necks bound in metal, Yongzheng/early Qianlong. **£5,000-6,000** *C*

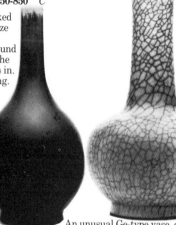

An unusual Ge-type vase, covered overall with a thick ash-grey glaze suffused with a fine black mesh crackle, the ring foot covered with a purplish wash, 9 in. (22.8 cm.), Qianlong. **£1,800-2,200** *S*

A well potted copper-red vase, covered in a liver-red glaze deepening on one side and lower body, the interior and base glaze in white, 12 in. (30.5 cm.), seal mark and period of Qianlong. **£1,400-1,700** *S*

A celadon bottle vase, brightly painted with butterflies and sprigs of flowers, the undamaged foot mounted with a silver gilt base, bearing the assay mark for London 1839, total height 44 cm., Qianlong mark. **£400-500** *Bea*

A large blue and white bottle vase, boldly painted in the 15th C. taste, neck and body crack, 53 cm. high, 18th C. **£1,500-2,000** *C*

A pair of Chinese Imari jars and covers, painted in underglaze blue, iron-red and gilding, one vase with damaged rim, covers chipped, 17 in. (43 cm.), Qianlong. **£1,800-£2,200** *SC*

A pair of ormolu-mounted celadon glazed dragon vases, touched in underglaze copper-red firing partially green, the necks and bodies with similar dark fitted patches, one body cracked, overall 35 cm. high, Qianlong 6 character seal marks, the mounts 19th C. **£950-1,050** *C*

An unusual pair of 'famille rose' vases and covers, washed in iron-red, delicately painted in pastel shades with upright panels of dignitaries and attendants, 21¼ in. (54 cm.), Qianlong. **£2,500-3,000** *S*

A pair of 'famille rose' vases, enamelled in Mandarin palette, on a biscuit stippled ground washed in lime-green enamel, 11⅞ in. (30.3 cm.), Qianlong. **£600-700** *S*

A 'famille rose' vase and cover, painted in Mandarin palette with figures around a table on a terrace, 12¼ in. (31.3 cm.), Qianlong. **£450-£550** *S*

A pair of 'famille rose' vases, painted in bright enamels of Mandarin palette, the base reserved with panels of birds in grisaille and iron-red, 6½ in. (16.5 cm.), Qianlong. **£600-700** *S*

A pair of 'Compagnie-des-Indes' covered vases, 11½ in. (29.3 cm.), Qianlong or Jiaqing. **£1,600-2,000** *S*

Two 'famille rose' hexagonal vases and one cover, with iron-red and gilt pierced hexagonal cell-pattern surrounds, one restored, 36 and 30 cm. high, Qianlong. **£800-900** *C*

Two large blue and white baluster vases and domed covers, damaged, both about 60.5 cm. high, mounted with metal collars, hinges and clasps at the tops, Qianlong/Jiaqing. **£1,800-2,200** *C*

A pair of Mandarin palette covered vases, 14⅛ in. (35.9 cm.), Qianlong. **£1,500-2,000** *S*

A pair of 'Compagnie-des-Indes' vases, each in the form of a carp, modelled in relief, applied in iron-red and enriched in gilding, 10½ in. (36.6 cm.), Qianlong. **£2,500-3,000** *S*

A 'famille rose' vase and cover, painted in Mandarin palette, 14¼ in. (36.3 cm.), Qianlong. **£650-£750** *S*

A brushpot, with gilt-edged rim, the sides decorated in 'famille rose' enamels with the Immortal Lu Dongbin confronted by the Spirit of the Willow Tree, 4½ in. (11.4 cm.), seal mark and period of Daoguang. **£400-550** *S*

The subject is believed to come from the Tang dynasty Daoist tale which forms the basis for a Yuan play, The Yueh-Yang Tower.

A pair of Chinese blue and white large bottle-shaped vases, 22 in. seal mark, 19th C. **£1,300-1,600** *DWB*

A 'famille rose' vase, decorated with a court scene on a terrace, 15¾ in. (40 cm.), Qianlong seal mark, Daoguang. **£200-300** *SC*

A simulated bamboo brushpot, with pin-pricking imitating the grain on the rim, the glaze of yellowish tone, 4½ in. (11.4 cm.), seal mark and period of Daoguang. **£400-550** *S*

A rouleau vase of large size, painted in underglaze blue and copper-red of good tone, 23½ in. (59.7 cm.), 19th C. **£450-550** *S*

A Canton vase and cover, painted in 'famille rose' palette, 25 in. (63.5 cm.), Daoguang. **£1,400-1,800** *S*

A lime-green ground 'famille rose' vase and cover, 11¼ in. (28.6 cm.), seal mark and period of Daoguang. **£600-750** *S*

A pair of polychrome jars and covers, 16 in. (40.6 cm.), 19th C., wood stands. **£900-1,100** *S*

Compare with the earlier Wucai jars.

A Canton 'famille rose' vase, 62 cm., c. 1840. **£500-600** *Bon*

A pair of Cantonese vases, painted in 'famille rose' colours, the shoulders applied with gilt chilong, one with chip to rim, 17¾ in. (45 cm.), Daoguang. **£700-800** *SC*

A pair of Canton 'famille rose' vases and covers, painted in mirror image, very slightly chipped, 54 cm. high, early 19th C. **£1,700-£2,000** *C*

The dignitary is identified as Di Ren Jie, who lived A.D. 630-700 and was a well-known figure during a very troubled period. He is particularly identified with justice and indeed held the post of Assistant at the Court of Justice. He was posthumously ennobled as Duke of the State of Liang, the title used on these vases. He is better known to Westerners as the source for Robert van Gulik in his short detective novels under the Gulik appellation of Judge Dee.

An unusual pair of Arita blue and white sake bottles (tokkuri), the tops painted with landscapes and the sides with panels of wave, floral and cell-pattern designs, one with slightly chipped spout, both about 20 cm. high, c. 1700. **£600-800** *C*

A pair of 'famille verte' vases, 23 in. (58.5 cm.), Guangxu. **£1,100-1,600** *S*

A pair of Canton 'famille rose' vases, 23½ in. (59.8 cm.), Guangxu. **£800-1,000** *S*

A massive Canton 'famille rose' vase, the interior washed in turquoise, 50¼ in. (127.6 cm.), Guangxu. **£6,000-7,000** *S*

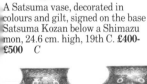

An Arita blue and white jar, 22.7 cm., c. 1680-1700. **£600-900** *Bea*

A large Arita oviform vase, painted in underglaze blue, iron-red, colours and gilt, 58.5 cm. high, late 19th C. **£1,700-2,200** *C*

A Satsuma vase, decorated in colours and gilt, signed on the base Satsuma Kozan below a Shimazu mon, 24.6 cm. high, 19th C. **£400-£500** *C*

A 'famille rose' 'hundred deer' vase, with iron-red and gilt archaistic dragon handles, the deer in white enamel, pale and dark sepia with white breasts and under-parts, the leaves in shades of green and the rocks in blue shading to green, 47.5 cm. high, late Qing Dynasty. **£1,500-2,000** *C*

A pair of large Satsuma vases, decorated in colours and gilt with shaped panels of samurai, courtiers, courtesans, vases and flowers, 48 cm. high, 19th C. **£2,500-£3,000** *C*

A good Arita vase, 27.9 cm., late 17th C. **£550-650** *S*

A pair of Imari jars and covers, in typical enamel colours, 37.5 cm., late 19th C. **£500-600** *Bea*

A pair of Imari fluted ovoid vases and covers, painted in iron-red, blue and gilt, 15 in. high. **£550-650** *WHB*

A large Kyoto-Satsuma vase, decorated in colours and gilt on a deep coral ground, signed on the base Dai Nihon Tanzan sei, next to an impressed signature Tanzan, 59.9 cm. high, Meiji period, wood stand. **£900-1,000** *C*

An Imari vase, 45.5 cm., late 19th C. **£500-600** *Bea*

A Japanese Imari large bottle vase, painted in tones of iron-red, underglaze blue and gilt, 54 cm. high, late 19th C. **£400-500** *HSS*

A Kinkozan vase, brilliantly painted and gilt on the ovoid body with 2 landscape panels, indistinct (Kin?) Kozan tsukuru mark, rim restoration, 28 cm., 1890's. **£700-£800** *SS*

A pair of large Japanese blue and white vases, each painted in washy tones of underglaze blue, with a bird perched under flowering peonies, 30⅞ in. (78.5 cm.), Meiji period. **£600-750** *SC*

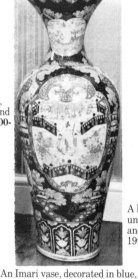

A pair of Japanese Kutani vases, decorated in tones of red, sepia and gilt, 37 cm. high, late 19th C. **£400-£500** *HSS*

A Japanese Imari vase, in cobalt-blue shades in typical palette, incorporating prunus blossoms in reserves, 29½ in. high, late 19th C. **£1,000-1,200** *Re*

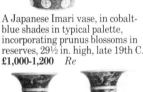

A large Imari vase and cover, in underglaze blue, overpainted in red and gilt, 3 ft. 10 in. high, late 19th C. **£3,000-3,500** *MMB*

An Imari vase, decorated in blue, red, gilt, green and puce, 4 ft. 2 in. high, late 19th C. **£600-700** *MMB*

A pair of earthenware vases, each thickly painted and gilt, signed Kinkozan, 29 cm., Meiji period. **£550-650** *S*

A pair of large blue and white vases, 96 cm., Meiji period. **£1,600-£2,000** *S*

MAKE THE MOST OF MILLER'S

Price ranges in this book reflect what one should expect to pay for a similar example. When selling one can obviously expect a figure below. This will fluctuate according to a dealer's stock, saleability at a particular time, etc. It is always advisable to approach a reputable specialist dealer or an auction house which has specialist sales.

A Fukagawa umbrella stand, decorated in underglaze blue with bamboo stems, signed Fukagawa sei, base cracked, 60 cm., Meiji period. **£550-650** *S*

An unusual and large earthenware vase and cover, decorated in Chinese style in coloured enamels and gilding, inscribed Qui ying Shifu, 63 cm., Meiji period. **£1,400-£1,700** *S*

A large Imari vase, painted in underglaze blue coloured enamels and gilt, 125.5 cm., Meiji period. **£2,500-3,000** *S*

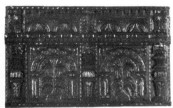

An oak tester bed, with leaf-carved fluted columnar supports, the frieze carved with fleur-de-lys above a panelled backboard, with alterations, 4 ft. 9 in. wide approx., 6 ft. 4 in. long approx. (145 by 193 cm.), mid 17th C., in need of restoration. **£3,500-4,000** *S*

In good condition, restored, £5,000-£7,000

A good small early 17th C. oak tester bed with excellent quality decoration, in sound original order, 4 ft. 8 in. wide by 7 ft. high by 5 ft. 11 in. long. **£4,500-7,000** *H*

If larger, say 5 ft. 6 in. wide by 7 ft. 6 in. long might well make £10,000 or more.

An early 17th C. oak full tester four poster double bed, with carved, arcaded and inlaid headboard, panelled tester with fine carved and inlaid frieze, excellent colour and patination, 84 in. long by 59 in. wide by 78½ in. high. **£5,000-8,000**

An oak tester bed, with panelled canopy, the double arcaded head end inlaid with vases of stylised foliage divided by caryatids, carved with masks and flowerheads, box spring and mattress, 69 in. wide by 98 in. long (175 by 244 cm.), 17th C. **£15,000-25,000** *C*

EARLY OAK FURNITURE

General Comments
- Not all English furniture of the early period was made of oak. Often native timbers are found, such as ash, elm, fruitwood, walnut and yewtree.
- High prices for exceptional pieces and articles in good order of fine colour are not uncommon, for the market is learning rapidly how to discern the best from the mediocre.
- The most desirable pieces are those which score highly in the following areas:

  Oak Colour and patination
  The best colour is a rich warm chestnut red and black, with the glossy sheen that comes from generations of polishing. Do not buy pieces that have been recently stripped and re-finished.

- **Condition**
  Damage and restoration is always to be regretted and the price must reflect this.
- **Originality**
  As far as possible the best pieces do not have replaced parts and any decoration should have been made when the piece was new, not added at a later date.
- **Rarity**
  This is often over-rated, since a relatively common form in good condition is more pleasing than a rare piece in poor condition.

When considering the values of 19th and 20th century copies, and any heavily-restored period item, it is always worth remembering how much it would cost to get the same work done today, by a competent firm of restorers or furniture-makers. In particular, the cost of seasoned timber, the cost and time spent in carving and finishing should be borne in mind, e.g.

carved panel-back armchair	£500-700
gateleg table, small	£500-700
gateleg table, large	£1,000-2,000
refectory table, 8 ft. long	£500-1,500
dining chair, carved	£250-400
dining chair, upholstered	£200-300
press cupboard, carved	£2,000-3,000
tester bedstead	£1,500-5,000

These costs must represent the minimum value of old pieces. Therefore, make up your mind whether you really want a genuine period item, and if so, what is the premium you are prepared to pay for age, originality, condition, colour, etc.

In some cases a lesser piece, or a reproduction, might offer better value.

A Charles I-style carved oak tester bed, the end board with a spindle gallery, triple panels and a foliate apron, with later carving, restored and partly made-up, 4 ft. 3 in. wide, c. 1640. **£1,100-1,500** *SS*

With a box spring and spring interior mattress.

A German oak four poster bed, the headboard profusely carved with scales and birds eating fruit, with restoration, 60 in. wide, 17th C. **£1,100-1,300** *B*

BEDS

Beds have invariably been altered. The most common change being in length — we are simply much taller now. This is regarded as acceptable generally if the bed is to be used. Size can account for considerable differences in price — a good Charles II four poster of, say, 4 ft. 7 in. wide by 6 ft. long might well be less desirable than a less good bed measuring 5 ft. 6 in. wide and 7 ft. long. 99% of bed buyers *do* want to use their 'fantasy' furniture while retaining 20th C. comfort.

A Charles II oak tester bedstead, the tester carved with a triad IMP and dated 1664, North Country, 8 ft. high, 5 ft. 9 in. wide, 7 ft. 7 in. long (224 by 175 by 232 cm.), height increased later and comprehensively restored. **£3,000-£5,000** *S*

Formerly at Horham Hall, Thaxted, Essex.
In unrestored condition **£7,000-£15,000**

An oak cradle, 33 by 37¾ in. (84 by 96 cm.), 18th C. **£550-650** *SC*

An oak cottage or child's tester bed, probably Dutch, 48 in. (122 cm.), early 19th C. **£600-800** *SC*

An oak cradle, edged with zigzag-and-dot border, carved at one end with initials FWN, 1667, on pierced rockers, 40 in. wide by 23 in. deep (102 by 58 cm.). **£1,100-1,500** *C*

A George II bureau, in figured faded oak, the fall with moulded bookrest concealing a stepped interior with pigeon holes, drawers and a well, 32½ in. wide by 39 in. high by 20 in. deep, c. 1740. **£1,500-£2,000** *HAL*

A rare Regency small oak Gothic revival library bookcase, in the manner of George Smith, 7 ft. high by 6 ft. wide (214 by 183 cm.), c. 1820. **£5,000-6,000** *S*

George Smith, A Collection of Designs for Household Furniture and Interior Decoration (1808) illustrates a Gothic bookcase as plate 101 with several features similar to this present bookcase.

An unusual Charles II oak bookcase, on turned elm feet, later glazing, 36 in. wide by 73½ in. high (91.5 by 187 cm.). **£1,800-2,200** *C*

If retaining original small-panel glazing and otherwise unrestored **£5,000**

An oak bureau, with fully fitted interior, some damage, 18th C. **£400-600** *FHF*

An early Georgian small oak bureau, the fall flap with sunken panel enclosing a fitted interior with well, on later bracket feet, 31 in. (79 cm.). **£1,700-2,000** *L*

£2,000+ *if colour very good.*

A small oak bureau, the cleated flap enclosing pigeon holes and drawers, with elm sides, top restored, 3 ft. high by 2 ft. 2½ in. wide (92 by 67 cm.), mid 18th C. **£900-1,200** *S*

In unrestored condition.

A small oak country cottage bureau, the fall front enclosing an interior fitted with 9 pigeonholes to centre, 38 in. wide, late 18th C. **£600-700** *BHW*

An oak bureau, with fall front to the well-fitted interior, 36 in. wide, late 18th C. **£500-700** *BHW*

A Georgian oak bureau, with mahogany crossbandings throughout and edged with stringing, with a shaped interior, 36 in. (91 cm.). **£800-1,000** *L*

An 18th C. oak and mahogany banded bureau, the fall front revealing shaped and fitted interior with well. **£600-800** *WM*

£1,000+ *for a better interior and unrestored condition.*

An oak Gothic revival cabinet, in the manner of A. W. N. Pugin, 3 ft. 6 in. high by 2 ft. 4 in. wide (107 by 71 cm.), c. 1840. **£750-850** *S*

A Jacobean-style oak breakfront tallboy, with 6 long drawers, flanked by 6 secret drawers enclosed by sliding panels, on block feet, 42½ in. **£600-1,100** *CSK*

Not a period design.

A small Flemish-style oak fallfront cabinet, the gadrooned frieze flanked by lions masks above a carved fallfront and over a single door, flanked by caryatid figures. **£550-650** *B*

This is a 19th C. piece, incorporating 17th C. panels.

A Dutch oak display cabinet on stand, 7 ft. high by 5 ft. 2½ in. wide (214 by 159 cm.), early 18th C. **£1,400-1,600** *S*

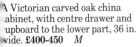

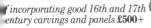

A mid Georgian oak and elm press, 73 by 55 in. (186 by 140 cm.), largely mid 18th C. **£600-900** *SC*

An 18th C. oak clothes press, 55 in. wide. **£650-750** *McC*

A Victorian carved oak china cabinet, with centre drawer and cupboard to the lower part, 36 in. wide. **£400-450** *M*

If incorporating good 16th and 17th century carvings and panels **£500+**

A Queen Anne oak escritoire, the bolection frieze fitted with a drawer, with a fitted interior, with drawers, pigeonholes and cupboards, inlaid with boxwood and ebony strings, 63 by 34½ in. (160 by 88 cm.), early 18th C. **£700-£900** *SC*

A rare Aberdeen carved oak armchair, the leaf carved cresting of almost swan-neck form, above a panelled back carved with a shield, the initials I S and the date 1668, the wedge-shaped seat with a Gothic arched apron, part of the cresting and apron lacking. **£3,500-£4,000** *S*

Excellent colour and patination contributes to value.

A good ash turner's armchair, stamped IN with elaborate turning, the back in 2 parts and with canted wings, the sloping arms with massive thistle-shaped handles, above turned legs and panelled seat, with restorations, 17th C. **£1,500-2,000** *S*

A pair of giltwood and polychrome Gothic revival armchairs, the tall arched backs centred by a crocketted finial above an ogee arched padded back, with legs studded with paterae, with stuffed seats, the backs incised with a polychrome flowering thistle and armorial devices, French, c. 1900. **£2,300-2,600** *S*

A fine 17th C. oak wainscot armchair, with unusual cresting rail, feet restored. **£750-1,100** *H*

(*l.*) A Charles II oak armchair, the panelled back carved with a stylised flowering plant, the crest rail and ears carved with scrolled leaves. **£700-800**

(*r.*) A Charles II oak armchair, the panelled back carved with stylised leaves and strapwork, with castellated ornament to the uprights. **£700-800** *BD*

In better condition **£1,000+**

(*l.*) A Charles II oak armchair, the panelled back later carved with stylised leaves within a lozenge. **£550-650**

(*r.*) A Charles II oak armchair, with plain panelled back, carved on the uprights with initials I.R. and 16 and I.R. and 14, seat squab for same. **£500-600** *BD*

In better condition **£750+**

A set of 8 splat back Lancashire oak chairs, c. 1770. **£750-850** *LA*

A rare mid 18th C. oak bacon settle, 37½ in. wide by 26 in. deep by 74 in. high, c. 1750. **£1,500-1,900** *HAL*

A set of 4 rush seat Yorkshire wavy ladderback chairs, early 19th C. **£750-900** *JHR*

A James I oak caqueteuse armchair, the moulded panelled top with an arched cresting, with a later solid single plank seat, Salisbury, c. 1620. **£500-600** *S*

Heavily restored and therefore price very low.
In good original condition **£1,500+**
With good carved decoration **£3,000+**

late 17th C. oak wainscot chair, th foliate carving to the central ck panel. **£800-1,200** *B*

A good set of late 18th C. Wigan ladderbacks, in original order. **£1,950-2,500** *H*

A lambing chair, of primitive form, partly in elm, the panel seat with drawer beneath, 24 by 55 in. high (61 by 140 cm.), 18th C. **£950- £1,050** *L*

Good colour and original condition important here.

early 18th C. oak wainscot air. **£400-500** *WIL*

good colour and design **£750+**

A 17th C.-style oak armchair, c. 1930. **£350-400** *SC*

A matched set of 8 late 18th/early 19th C. Lancashire spindle back chairs, including 2 armchairs, all with rush seats, turned front stretcher rails on pad and ball feet **£1,500-1,750** *Re*

A Scottish armchair, in ash and walnut, with burr wood veneered panel, one back support repaired, originally with a front stretcher, veneering later, c. 1680. **£350-450** *S*

et of 6 William and Mary lnut dining chairs, with minor lacements. **£3,000-4,000** *C*

A rare pair of James II walnut dining chairs. **£3,800-4,500** *C*

A fine set of 6 walnut dining chairs, with rectangular padded backs and upholstered seats, covered in 17th C. floral tapestry woven in blues and reds, edged with multi-coloured silk fringe on spirally turned legs and stretchers, two bearing labels inscribed 'Brought to Taymouth Castle/the Marquess of Breadalbane's Apartments/at Holyrood Palace/May 16 1860', two with slight variations, not period chairs. **£3,500-4,500** *C*

With 17th C. tapestries.

A set of 6 George II oak chairs, the drop-in rush seats on turned front legs with pad feet, c. 1730. **£3,500- £4,500** *S*

An 18th C. ash and elm comb back Windsor chiar. **£150-200** *TM*

Eight late 18th C. ladderback dining chairs, having rush and string seats, 2 carvers and 6 singles. **£1,500-2,000** *A*

A set of 11 oak 'Smoker's bow' armchairs and another matching, 19th C. **£800-1,200** *TM*

A 'Harlequin' set of 10 late George III elm ladderback dining chairs, including a pair of armchairs, late 18th/early 19th C. **£2,200-2,600** *S*

A good 18th C. yew tree armchair, with draught pattern Windsor back. **£400-480** *B*

A set of 4 early 19th C. yew and elm Windsor chairs, with pierced splats, turned arm supports, crinoline stretchers and turned legs. **£1,200-1,600** *DSH*

A composed set of 5 ash and elm Windsor dining chairs, including an armchair. **£500-600** *SC*

A pair of early 19th C. yew and elm Windsor armchairs, legs joined by crinoline stretchers. **£900-1,200** *Bea*

Two late 18th C. yew wood bow and spindle back elbow chairs, with pierced splats and crinoline stretchers. **£400-650** each *A*

A set of 4 George III yew and elm Windsor chairs, with pierced splats, turned legs and crinoline stretchers. **£1,500-1,800** *DSH*

A set of 6 early 19th C. yew and elm wood Windsor armchairs, of good colour, with crinoline stretchers. **£2,800-3,500** *Re*

An ash and elm comb back chair, 24½ by 19½ by 41 in., c. 1790. **£250-350** *LA*

A mid-Georgian elm Windsor armchair, with waved toprail, railed back with pierced splat, cabriole legs and pad feet. **£1,000-£1,500** *C*

Early Windsor armchairs of this style probably originated in the Thames Valley.

Six 18th C. elm comb back Windsor elbow chairs, damaged. **£1,200-£1,400** *JD*

In good order **£1,500-2,000**

A 19th C. 'Turner's Chair', carved seat having turned decoration throughout. **£80-150** *SD*

A pair of 19th C. yew and elm Windsor armchairs, 'Yorks' splat and crinoline stretchers. **£1,200-£1,500** *Bea*

rare set of 8 yew wood draught
ck Windsor armchairs, some
mped Robert Prior, Uxbridge.
800-5,500 *H*

A closely matched set of 8 late
18th C. Lancashire spindlebacks,
with Chippendale ears. **£1,800-
£2,400** *H*

A matched set of 12 late 17th C.
South Yorkshire back stools.
£8,000-12,000 *H*

ur from a set of 8 late 18th C.
1 back' spindle dining chairs
singles, 2 armchairs). **£1,800-
200** *H*

A fine matched set of 8 burr yew
wood Windsor armchairs, some
stamped 'Gabitass Worksop'.
£4,800-5,500 *H*

A small James II oak settle, the
back carved with stylised flowers,
32 by 57 in. (81 by 145 cm.), third
quarter 17th C. **£1,000-1,500** *SC*

A small Welsh oak settle, the top
ail carved and dated 1687, the
ase fully enclosed with a small
emovable lid, inserted in the seat,
he base made up later, 45 by 46 in.
115 by 117 cm.), the top 17th C.,
he base made up later. **£400-500**
C

A fine matching set of 6 plus
2 armchairs, Charles II period
chairs. **£7,000-10,000** *H*

MAKE THE MOST OF
MILLER'S

*Miller's is completely
different each year. Each
edition contains completely
NEW photographs. This is
not an updated publication.
We never repeat the same
photograph.*

A Victorian carved and moulded
oak settle, the box base having a
hinged lid carved with foliage,
raised on paw feet, 3 ft. 6 in. wide
by 3 ft. 4 in. high. **£250-300** *V*

An oak hall settle, with carved
panels above coffer seat, 19th C.
£500-600 *JF*

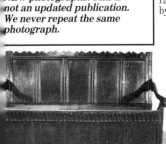

te 17th C. oak settle, later
ed seat and panelled front with
ded frieze and base, 72 in. long.
0-600 *DSH*

An oak child's rocking armchair,
Welsh, 22 by 14 in. (56 by 36 cm.),
18th C. **£200-300** *SC*

269

A late Elizabethan oak chest, with a 3 panelled frieze applied with moulded diamond bosses, 4 ft. 7 in. wide (140 cm.), c. 1600. **£1,400-£2,000** *S*

c.f. Victor Chinnery, Oak, the British Tradition, p. 362.

An oak slat back chair, 18¾ by 16½ by 39½ in., c. 1680. **£150-300** *LA*

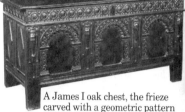

A James I oak chest, the frieze carved with a geometric pattern with blind fretwork above a triple arcaded arched front on plank feet 58 in. wide (147.5 cm.). **£1,000-£1,500** *C*

An early 17th C. panelled oak chest, the front inlaid with rectangular panels of various woods, original lock and key, 48 in. wide. **£800-1,200** *BD*

A good Carolean period oak chest, the lid to a finely carved contemporary decorated front with a frieze of tulips, leaf scrolls, flanked by rose bosses and initials W L 1671, 4 ft. 9 in. **£800-1,200** *WW*

A good oak chest, the panelled front carved with stylised foliage within archways, carved with flowerheads and designs, 28 by 50 in. (71 by 127 cm.), mid 17th C. **£800-1,200** *SC*

A small oak chest, the front carved with 2 panels with a diamond lozenge and meandering foliage, 2 ft. 10 in. wide (86 cm.), mid 17th C. **£800-1,000** *S*

An early 17th C. oak chest, the front with two arcaded panels, divided by stop-fluted uprights and on stile feet. **£800-1,200** *Bea*

A good oak chest, the front carved with lozenges, roundels and guilloche, 25 by 47 in. (64 by 120 cm.), second quarter 17th C. **£400-500** *SC*

A Charles I carved oak chest, with a key pattern frieze and triple panel front, 4 ft. 7 in. wide (140 cm.), c. 1630. **£500-800** *SS*

A carved oak chest, 50 by 21 by 24¾ in., c. 1680. **£400-600** *LA*

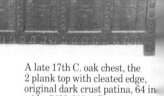

A late 17th C. oak chest, the 2 plank top with cleated edge, original dark crust patina, 64 in. wide. **£400-600** *B*

A fine mid 16th C. Gothic oak coffer. **£2,800-4,000** *H*

A late 17th C. oak chest, with moulded panelled top and sides, carved frieze, 53 in. wide. **£300-£600** *DSH*

An oak chest, 30½ by 52 in. (77 by 132 cm.), late 17th/early 18th C. **£400-600** *SC*

A small early 17th C. oak plank chest, good colour with deeply chip-carved front and moulded edge to the lid, the spandrels now missing, 34 in. wide. **£500-800** *Hu*

Charles I oak boarded chest, carved with initials and date 1638, now on block feet, 3 ft. wide (92 cm.), c. 1635. **£250-400** *SS*

German oak chest, elaborately carved with strapwork and figures, vases of flowers and fruit, fixed with iron carrying handles, carved with 3 Biblical scenes in the life of Esther and Ahasueras above inscriptions, 47 by 36 in. high (120 by 91 cm.), the chest late 16th/17th C., the top and base 18th C. **£1,500-2,500** *L*

A 16th C. late Gothic oak chest, with chip decoration and a central lozenge flanked by chip-carved roundels to the front, 46 in. wide. **£750-950** *B*

A George II period mule chest in oak, the fretted back and hinged moulded lid above drawers crossbanded and with mainly original brasswork, all on shaped ogee bracket feet, now converted entirely to drawers, the lid sealed, 64 in. wide by 21½ in. deep by 38 in. high, c. 1740. **£1,200-1,800** *HAL*

A small oak 6-plank chest, 2 ft. 7½ in. wide (80 cm.), second quarter 17th C. **£400-500** *S*

A miniature oak chest or cofr bach, the stiles forming the feet, 25 in. (64 cm.), 18th C. **£400-600** *L*

An 18th C. chest, with drawers, the panelled front with 3 fielded panels above 2 drawers, fitted with a candlebox, some repair, 51 in. **£150-300** *WHL*

An oak and mahogany chest, with 6 small simulated drawers and 4 long drawers, the rising lid and drawer fronts being crossbanded, 61 in. wide by 45 in. high by 22 in. deep. **£350-400** *BHW*

An oak chest with drawers, with plain moulded-frame panels and drawers on later bracket feet. **£250-400** *BA*

An oak chest with drawers, the panelled front carved with figure motifs and lunettes, the plain panelled top enclosing a small lidded compartment, 4 ft. 3 in. wide by 2 ft. 1 in. deep by 3 ft. 1 in. high. **£450-550** *V*

The carving all 19th C.

A George III Lancashire oak chest, with drawers, fitted with 6 false drawer fronts and 3 drawers below, with brass swan neck handles, the whole crossbanded in mahogany, 5 ft. 3 in. by 3 ft. 2 in. high. **£800-£900** *AGr*

An early 18th C. oak dower chest, with moulded hinged lid, 3 moulded panels to the front and 2 drawers in the base, on bracket feet, 51 in., c. 1740. **£250-400** *M*

An oak chest of drawers, of panelled construction, on later bracket feet, c. 1700. **£700-1,000** *WM*

A William and Mary walnut and marquetry chest, with moulded rectangular top, inlaid above 2 short and 3 graduated long drawers, on later turned oak feet, 38 in. wide (96.5 cm.). **£2,200-3,000** *C*

A Queen Anne stained walnut and yew wood chest, with crossbanded rectangular top, 2 short and 3 graduated long drawers on bracket feet, 30 in. wide (78 cm.). **£2,000-£2,500** *C*

A small early 18th C. burr yew wood chest of drawers, 2 ft. 8 in. wide. **£1,400-1,800** *H*

A William and Mary walnut and ebony and marquetry chest, on later turned supports and turned pulls, 36 by 40 in. (92 by 102 cm.), late 17th C. **£3,000-4,000** *SC*

A good mid 17th C. walnut chest in 2 parts, with pearwood veneer and ebonised mouldings, 3 ft. 8 in. high by 3 ft. 9½ in. wide (112 by 115 cm.). **£1,500-2,000** *S*

A Queen Anne walnut and marquetry chest, on later bracket feet, 38 in. (96 cm.). **£2,000-2,750** *L*

A small William and Mary burr elm crossbanded chest of drawers. **£2,200-2,800** *H*

A small William and Mary burr elm crossbanded chest of drawers. **£2,200-2,800** *H*

An early 18th C. walnut chest, of 3 long and 2 short oak lined drawers, 41 in. wide. **£400-600** *B*

A Charles II oak chest, the cleated top above drawers with mitred mouldings, on later bracket feet, 2 ft. 10 in. wide (86 cm.), c. 1680. **£500-800** *SS*

A William and Mary oak and inlaid straight front chest, with dentilled frieze, some restoration. **£500-800** *WHL*

A William and Mary style marquetry chest of drawers, 3 ft. 4 in. wide (101.5 cm.). **£1,200-1,800** *LBP*

A Charles II oak chest, split turned ornament at the sides and with panelled ends, on turned feet, 42 in. wide by 38 in. high. **£600-900** *BD*

A William and Mary oyster/walnut veneered chest, the top, sides and drawer fronts veneered with a geometric design, later bun feet, with restorations, 38 in. wide. **£2,500-3,500** *PWC*

A Charles II oak chest, the deep drawer centred by an architectural panel and flanked by fruitwood-veneered geometric panels and divided by split turnings, the cupboards below similarly panelled and enclosing three long drawers, on later turned feet, 3 ft. 11½ in. high by 3 ft. 8½ in. wide (120 by 113 cm.), c. 1665. £600-900 *S*

A Charles II oak and walnut chest, the base with a pair of panelled and welded cupboard doors centred by arches, divided by tapering pilasters on plank feet, 45 in. wide (114 cm.). £1,200-1,800 *C*

An 18th C. oak chest, top and drawer fronts crossbanded in rosewood, 36 in. £400-600 *JD*

16th/17th C. Flemish armoire, with ornate lock plates and metal hinges, with later additions, 6 ft. in. by 6 ft. £650-750 *MMB*
all original £2,500-3,000

A 17th C. walnut and oak small chest of drawers, on later bracket feet, 37 in. £800-1,200 *PWC*

A Charles II oak oyster-veneered walnut and yew wood chest, the drawers geometrically coffered and inlaid with holly lines on block feet, 38½ in. wide (98 cm.). £1,500-2,500 *C*

A Charles II oak and oyster chest of drawers, with walnut oyster-veneered panels and inlaid with roundels and arches, on bracket feet, extensively restored, 40 in. (102 cm.). £1,000-1,500 *L*

A small oak chest, pine lined with brass knobs, 22 in. wide, late 18th/early 19th C. £350-400 *WIL*

An oak chest, with rectangular mitred top, the drawers applied with geometric mouldings, on later bracket feet, with restorations, 35½ by 38 in. (90 by 97 cm.), late 17th C. £400-600 *SC*

A late Gothic oak aumbry, of panelled construction, the 3 doors including carved and pierced roundels, with 2 drawers, altered and restored, 5 ft. 3½ in. high by 4 ft. 10 in. wide (161 by 147 cm.), c. 1540. £5,000-8,000 *SS*

A carved oak 2-part cupboard, the frieze inlaid with diamond trellis and with 3 heads above a pair of recessed doors, each carved with a stag and leafy scrolls centred by a niche with a figure in Jacobean costume, carved with the initials TW IW GW TW 1656, 6 ft. 2 in. high by 5 ft. 3 in. wide (188 by 160 cm.), mid 17th C. £3,000-4,000 *S*

A Charles II oak Lancashire press cupboard, carved with meandering leaves and berries above a pair of panelled doors, outlined with chevron banding, carved Thomas Meller and Ellen Meller 1681, 6 ft. 3 in. high by 4 ft. 7 in. wide (190 by 140 cm.), c. 1680. **£2,500-3,500**   *S*

A massive carved oak early 17th C. cupboard, enclosed by 2 panel doors with grotesque figure supports, with considerable additions and restoration, 5 ft. 4 in. wide. **£1,200-£1,800**   *MIL*

An outstanding late 16th C. oak court cupboard, of small proportions, Scottish, showing French influence, 47 in. wide by 64 in. high by 24 in. deep. **£6,000-£8,000**   *H*

An oak press cupboard, the elaborately carved front dated 1648, including strapwork to the frieze, top boards replaced, 5 ft. 4 in. high by 5 ft. wide. **£2,000-£4,000**   *T*

A good early 17th C. oak livery cupboard, the doors with geometric inlaid designs within moulded strapwork, 48 in. wide. **£2,000-£3,000**   *B*

A 17th C. oak court cupboard, with fine decoration, colour and patina, 5 by 5 ft. by 22 in. deep. **£3,000-£4,000**   *H*

A carved oak court cupboard, with triple panel cupboard doors below with cocks-head hinges, 49 in. long by 23 in. wide by 62 in. high, dated 1695. **£1,000-1,500**   *OL*

A Charles I oak cupboard, now with a plank top, above leaf-carved frieze with acorn pendants, 5 ft. 2 in. high by 4 ft. 7 in. wide (157 by 140 cm.), c. 1630. **£1,200-1,800**   *S*

An oak press, the overhanging cornice carved with foliate lozenges, the base with lunette frieze and 2 panelled cupboard doors, carved with lozenges between notched borders, with restorations, 59½ in. wide (151 cm.), 17th C. **£1,200-1,800**

An oak court cupboard, dated 1667, the lower part with a frieze carved with archways, above 3-panelled cupboard doors, formerly with a top part and on stump feet, 61 by 72 in. (155 by 183 cm.), third quarter of the 17th C. **£1,000-1,500**   *SC*

An oak cupboard, the moulded cornice and the carved frieze with the date 1678 and the initials RW IW, the lower part with a pair of 4-panelled doors, restored and cornice replaced, 5 ft. 2 in. high by 7 ft. 2 in. wide (158 by 219 cm.), late 17th C. **£800-1,200**   *S*

An unusual late Elizabethan provincial plate cupboard of small proportions, the shaped frieze incised with fleur-de-lys, the display shelf with dentil mouldings and simple carved pendants, and raised on stile feet, side friezes replaced, one spandrel missing, 6 ft. 8 in. high by 3 ft. 6½ in. wide (191 by 108 cm.), c. 1600. **£8,000-£10,000** *S*

A 17th C. North Holland oak beeldenkast, carved with caryatid figures above narrative central panels to doors and above a lower part of 2 long doors, each with narrative scenes of the Old Testament and flanked by reeded columns, with Ionic capitals and foliate carved bases, 69 in. high by 63 in. wide. **£1,000-1,500** *B*

A 17th C. oak cupboard with canopy, 71 by 57 in. (180 by 145 cm.), largely late 17th C. **£1,200-1,800** *SC*

A James I carved and inlaid oak livery cupboard, the gadrooned cornice supported on a pair of birds flanking a cupboard with a pot board, the door, cornice and lower portion restored, 4 ft. ½ in. high by 4 ft. wide (123 by 122 cm.), c. 1610. **£900-1,200** *S*

n oak court or livery cupboard, e frieze carved with foliate scrolls ith turned pendants, on turned pports of double cup and cover rm, joined by base platform, with storations, 49 by 48 in. high (125 122 cm.), mid 17th C. **£600-800**

MAKE THE MOST OF MILLER'S

When buying or selling, it must always be remembered that prices can be greatly affected by the condition of any piece.
Unless otherwise stated, all goods shown in Miller's are of good merchantable quality, and the valuations given reflect this fact.
Pieces offered for sale in exceptionally fine condition or in poor condition may reasonably be expected to be priced considerably higher or lower respectively than the estimates given herein.

A small oak cupboard, the slightly projecting lower part with three short drawers and a pair of 3-panelled doors, North Wales, 5 ft. 11 in. high by 3 ft. 6½ in. wide (180 by 107 cm.), late 18th C. **£1,400-£2,000** *S*

oak Cwpwrdd tridarn, the top rt with outset turned supports, e central panel enclosing a yew od veneered fitted interior, the er part with 3 drawers above a r of cupboard doors, flanking 3 all central panels, pediment king and reduced slightly in ght, 79 by 55 in. (201 by cm.), second quarter of the h C. **£1,000-1,500** *SC*

An oak Cwpwrdd deuddarn, North Wales, late 18th C. **£1,000-1,500** *JF*

An early 18th C. oak court cupboard, the upper part with moulded overhanging cornice and bold turned pendant finials, 57 in. wide by 60 in. high. **£1,000-1,500** *BD*

275

An early 18th C. oak Cwpwrdd tridarn, the panelled back canopy with turned front supports, with pendant apple finials and 2 fielded panel doors, with later brass hardware. **£1,200-1,800** *B*

An oak court cupboard, in 17th C. style, incorporating a William III Royal carved oak coat-of-arms with foliate mantling, 13 by 15 in., applied to the central door, 47 in. **£500-800** *HyD*

Made up probably in the late 19th C.
The value rests largely in the finely carved coat-of-arms.

A Dutch ebony, rosewood and oak cupboard, with moulded cornice and shaped frieze, the base with a pair of conforming cupboard doors, separated by fielded panels above one long drawer and a plinth base, bearing a handwritten label 'from the collection of the Archer family . . .', 70 in. wide (178 cm.), 17th C. **£2,000-3,000** *C*

COURT CUPBOARDS

These early cupboards may be divided into three types:–

1) The 'open' type consisting of three tiers with turned and often carved front supports and flat back supports. These frequently have drawers fitted in the middle and upper tiers. They were made until the end of the 17th Century.

2) Livery Cupboards. This type is similar in style and construction to the above. The upper section however, is wholly or partially enclosed to store food and wine.

3) Press Cupboards. This most familiar type is completely enclosed and is constructed in two parts, the upper section being recessed. These impressive and often very large cupboards were, in many households, the most important piece of furniture and provided considerable storage space for plates, cups and other chattles.

These cupboards were all reproduced in the 19th and early 20th Centuries and many plain examples were later carved in the Victorian period.

Points to look for:–

Originality and condition
Colour and patination
Original carved decoration
Inlaid decoration

A carved oak cupboard, of ornate appearance, with original hinges, enclosing interior fitted 2 shelves, on massive bun feet, Victorian, incorporating early 17th C. carved panels and rails, 29 in. wide. **£200-£400** *BHW*

A Flemish carved oak cupboard, with a pair of panelled doors incorporating carved strapwork panels and flanked by fluted pilasters, with 2 drawers below and bun feet, 6 ft. 10½ in. high by 5 ft. wide (210 by 152 cm.), mid 17th C. **£2,000-2,500** *S*

An oak court cupboard, the upper section with a pair of panelled doors, carved and divided by femal caryatids, above a heavy gadroon moulding, the back panel carved with roundels and strapwork on moulded base and bun feet, incorporating earlier fragments, 4 ft. 11½ in. high by 4 ft. 7½ in. wide (151 by 141 cm.), c. 1900. **£600-800** *S*

A 17th C. Flemish oak standing cupboard, the reeded pillars in three-quarter relief with carved Corinthian capitals and foliate tracery, flanking a central door with arcaded decoration of raised pillars and figures above a shallow drawer beneath and bun feet, 42 in. wide. **£800-1,200** *B*

A rare 17th C. Flemish oak kast, with blind fretwork moulded cornice, the 2 upper cupboard doors each with deeply and intricately carved panels, depicting biblical scenes and flanked by 4 allegorical female figures, with 2 concealed drawers below, 89 in. high by 76 in. wide. **£6,000-8,000** *Re*

A 17th C. Flemish oak cupboard, with ebony and geometric moulded facings, 69 in. wide by 68½ in. high. **£2,000-3,000**   *Re*

Provenance: Doune Castle, Perthshire.

A provincial Dutch oak and ebonised armoire, the gadrooned frieze flanked by lion masks above 2 panelled cupboard doors flanked by fluted angles headed by strapwork on plinth base and later burr feet, 30½ in. wide (70.5 cm.), basically 17th C. **£1,200-1,800**   *C*

George III oak low dresser, crossbanded in mahogany, 6 ft. in. wide by 1 ft. 6¾ in. deep (184 by 47.5 cm.), c. 1760. **£1,000-2,000**

A George II oak low dresser. **£2,000-3,000**   *AMB*

A George III elm and oak dresser base, on square supports, 34 by 85 in. (86 by 216 cm.), early 19th C. **£1,000-1,500**   *SC*

A George II oak low dresser, 34 by 82 in. (87 by 208 cm.), first quarter of 18th C. **£1,500-2,500**   *SC*

An oak open low dresser, the slightly raised back with 5 small drawers, the 3 front supports of silhouette baluster form, with restorations, 80 by 33 in. high (202 by 84 cm.), late 17th C. **£2,000-£3,000**   *L*

A late 17th/early 18th C. small oak low dresser, the 3 drawers with geometrically moulded panels, 57 in. **£1,500-2,500**   *PWC*

A mid 18th C. oak dresser base, with an ogee-arched apron, baluster supports joined by an undertier and on block feet, 31½ in. high by 74 in. wide. **£2,000-3,000**   *Bea*

A Flemish oak and ebony press cupboard, with fielded panel construction and projecting mouldings, on later massive bun feet, restored, 6 ft. 6½ in. high by 5 ft. 3 in. wide (200 by 160 cm.), c. 1680. **£1,300-1,600**   *SS*

An early Georgian oak low dresser, with top crossbanded with walnut and outlined with ebonised and boxwood lines, 50¼ in. wide (128 cm.). **£1,200-2,000**   *C*

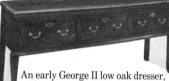

An early George II low oak dresser, with a deep moulded top above 3 frieze drawers, with mahogany crossbandings above further mouldings, 74 by 31½ in. (188 by 85 cm.). **£2,000-3,000**   *L*

An 18th C. oak low dresser, 81 in. **£1,500-2,500**   *JD*

MAKE THE MOST OF MILLER'S

When buying or selling, it must always be remembered that prices can be greatly affected by the condition of any piece.
Unless otherwise stated, all goods shown in Miller's are of good merchantable quality, and the valuations given reflect this fact.
Pieces offered for sale in exceptionally fine condition or in poor condition may reasonably be expected to be priced considerably higher or lower respectively than the estimates given herein.

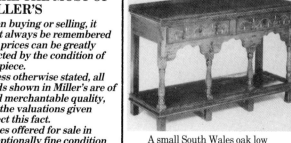

A small South Wales oak low dresser, the rectangular top with moulded edge above 2 drawers inlaid with meandering tulips, backrail added, probably made in the Vale of Glamorgan, 4 ft. 1 in. wide (125 cm.), c. 1740. **£2,000-£3,000**   *S*

A George II low oak dresser, restored, 71 in. (180 cm.). **£1,000-£1,500**   *L*

A Georgian oak dresser, the delft rack with moulded cornice, 59½ in. wide, c. 1740. **£1,500-2,500**   *DSH*
The rack and base married.

A mid 18th C. oak dresser base, with mahogany crossbanding, 31½ in. high by 78 in. wide. **£1,500-£2,500**   *Bea*

An early 18th C. oak dresser, with later plate rack, the base fitted 3 crossbanded drawers, each with brass plate handles and escutcheons, 85 in. wide. **£1,200-£1,800**   *BS*

A George II oak dresser, the upper part with moulded cornice, 72 in. wide by 82 in. high, c. 1750. **£1,500-£2,500**   *BD*

An early 19th C. oak and mahogany crossbanded dresser, of good quality and condition, 73 by 74 in. high. **£1,500-2,000**   *DWB*

An early 18th C. oak open backed Welsh dresser, the back plates illustrating hunting scenes and above deep scalloped and pierced apron and fitted lower pot shelf, 72 in. wide by 82 in. high. **£1,800-£2,500**   *WHL*

A George III oak dresser, restored, 6 ft. 5 in. high by 6 ft. 2 in. wide (195.5 by 188 cm.), c. 1770. **£1,500-£2,500**   *S*

A Georgian oak, Swansea Valley, dresser, c. 1760. **£1,500-2,500**   *JF*

A good Swansea oak dresser, with pierced fretwork frieze and apron, 4 small spice drawers to back, 6 shallow drawers below, 58 in. wide by 79 in. high, mid 18th C. **£2,000-3,000**   *Re*

An 18th C. oak dresser, with open rail pot rack below, 68 in. wide. **£1,500-2,500**   *Re*

A good early 19th C. oak pot board dresser, 5 ft. by 7 ft. 2 in. **£1,200-£1,800**   *AGr*

279

A George II oak dresser, 6 ft. 3 in. high by 6 ft. 3 in. wide (191 by 191 cm.), c. 1750. **£1,500-2,000** *SS*

An oak dresser, with open back and 5 drawers above pot rack with enclosed back, late 18th C. **£1,200-£1,800** *FHF*

A late George III oak and mahogany small dresser, 5 ft. 11 in. high by 4 ft. wide (180.5 by 122 cm.), c. 1780. **£2,000-3,000** *S*

A mid 18th C. dresser, on cabriole legs and with square feet, 72 in. **£1,200-1,800** *A*

An unusual oak dresser base, with cabriole legs and raised pot board. **£3,500-4,500** *H*

An 18th C. Shropshire dresser, crossbanded in mahogany on ball and claw feet, 74 in. **£1,500-2,500** *JD*

A Georgian oak dresser base. **£2,500-3,500** *H*

An unusual late 17th C. oak dresser base. **£3,000-4,000** *H*

A fine cabriole legged oak dresser, with matched pierced friezes and cupboards to rack. **£3,500-4,500** *H*

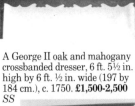

A George II oak and mahogany crossbanded dresser, 6 ft. 5½ in. high by 6 ft. ½ in. wide (197 by 184 cm.), c. 1750. **£1,500-2,500** *SS*

An early 18th C. North Wales oak dresser of fine quality. **£4,500-5,500** *H*

A rare oak and mahogany cabriole legged dresser base. **£3,500-4,500** *H*

A late 18th C. dresser, 62 in. **£1,200-1,800** *A*

A rare 17th C. cushion moulded oak dresser base. **£8,000-10,000**

An oak and mahogany banded dresser, inlaid with satinwood bands, 74 in., 18th C. **£1,000-£1,500** *CSK*
The carving later.

An oak enclosed low dresser, with applied geometric mouldings, the stiles forming the supports, with restorations, 81 by 84 in. high (206 by 84 cm.), c. 1690. **£4,000-5,000** *H*

An oak dresser, restored, 2 ft. 2 in. high by 6 ft. 6½ in. wide (80 by 199 cm.), mid 18th C. **£2,000-3,000** *S*

A mid Georgian oak dresser, 74 in. long. **£2,000-3,000** *DSH*

An 18th C. oak dresser, the rack missing, 64 in. wide. **£1,500-2,500** *M*

A good rare early George III mahogany dresser, the top of inverted breakfront outline, above a dentil cornice, on ogee bracket feet, 77 by 86 in. (196 by 219 cm.), third quarter of 18th C. **£10,000-£12,500** *SC*

An early 18th C. oak dresser, with moulded edges to the top, with fielded panels, later iron handles, 64 in. wide by 38 in. **£1,200-1,800** *BD*

An oak dresser base, on stump feet, with restorations, 36½ by 86 in. (92.5 by 218.5 cm.), early 18th C. **£1,500-1,800** *SC*

A mid 18th C. low dresser in oak, the figured surface with plate-stay above drawers and a panelled cupboard, all framed by heavy moulding, standing on stile feet, the sides also panelled, the brasswork of later date, 70 in. wide by 19½ in. deep by 31 in. high, c. 1760. **£2,000-3,000** *HAL*

An 18th C. oak dresser, the back with 6 spice drawers and open frieze with cupid bow fret motifs, brass knob handles, 60 in., with restoration. **£2,000-3,000** *GSP*
If in original condition **£3,000-£4,000**

A low oak cupboard dresser, with later back, 57 by 35½ in. high (145 by 90 cm.), late 18th C. **£1,500-£1,800** *L*

A George III oak and pine Welsh dresser, 5 ft. 6 in. wide. **£1,200-£1,800** *MIL*

A good George III oak dresser, the lower part crossbanded in oak and with chevron stringing, with 4 fluted quadrant columns, on ogee bracket feet, 6 ft. 9 in. high by 2 ft. 11 in. wide (206 by 89 cm.), late 18th C. **£4,000-5,000** *S*

A small early 18th C. oak Welsh dresser, in original condition, 51 in. wide by 5 ft. 8 in. high. **£800-1,200** *WIL*

An early 19th C. oak dresser, the outset ogee moulded cornice above 3 plate rails joined by carved sides, 84 by 66 in. (213 by 168 cm.). **£1,200-1,800** *SC*

A Georgian oak dresser, with rack back partly replaced, handles late 63 by 75 in. (160 by 191 cm.). **£1,000-1,500** *L*

An 18th C. oak dresser, the open 2-shelf rack above a base of 3 frieze drawers, of good colour and patination, 63 in. wide. **£1,000-£1,500** *B*

A fine oak cupboard dresser with rack, with an ogee cornice above a waved frieze and open plate shelves with shaped sides, 71½ by 80½ in. (182 by 205 cm.), 18th C. **£3,000-£4,000** *L*

A small oak dresser, the lower pa with 3 frieze drawers, 72 by 63 in. (183 by 160 cm.), mid 18th C. **£1,500-2,500** *SC*

An oak dresser, 37 by 83 in. (94 by 211 cm.), late 18th/early 19th C. **£1,500-2,000** *SC*

MAKE THE MOST OF MILLER'S

When buying or selling, it must always be remembered that prices can be greatly affected by the condition of any piece.
Unless otherwise stated, all goods shown in Miller's are of good merchantable quality, and the valuations given reflect this fact.
Pieces offered for sale in exceptionally fine condition or in poor condition may reasonably be expected to be priced considerably higher or lower respectively than the estimates given herein.

A Georgian large oak cupboar dresser, the lower part with mahogany crossbandings, 79 93 in. (201 by 237 cm.). **£1,000£1,500** *L*

An 18th C. delft rack in oak, the moulded fretted cornice supported on fretted uprights, flanking 3 shelves, the central cupboard with fluted decoration and inlaid door concealing further fretted shelves, 56 in. wide by 7½ in. deep by 46 in. high, c. 1770. **£700-1,000** *HAL*

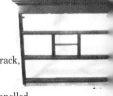

A small 17th C. oak delft rack, 41 in. wide. **£350-450** *B*

A breakfront dresser, of panelled construction, with enclosed delft rack, early 19th C. **£1,500-2,000** *WM*

A pair of oak joint stools, with moulded rectangular tops, notched friezes and waved edges on ring-turned legs joined by stretchers and turned feet, incised with initials TC, one inscribed C. Pardey, 1818, late 17th C. **£1,700-2,500** *C*

A fine James I oak joint stool. **3,000-4,000** *H*

A Charles II oak joint stool, the moulded top above a lunette carved frieze, 1 ft. 7½ in. wide (50 cm.), c. 1680. **£700-1,000** *SS*

A George II walnut stool, on 4 cabriole supports with pad feet, 18 in. square (46 cm.). **£500-650** *L*

(*l.*) A joined oak stool, with moulded top, plain frieze and tapering columnar and ringed supports, with plain stretchers, 19 in. (48 cm.), 17th C. **£300-500**

(*r.*) Another joined oak stool, 18 in. (45 cm.), 17th C. **£300-500** *L*

A fine George I walnut stool, with drop-in rectangular needlework seat, on cabriole legs and claw-and-ball feet, 24 in. wide (61 cm.). **£2,000-2,800** *C*

A late Elizabethan oak draw leaf table, the rectangular cleated top above a frieze, lightly carved with acanthus lunettes, Sussex, 4 ft. 4 in. closed, 2 ft. 9¾ in. deep by 8 ft. open (132 by 86 by 244 cm.), c. 1600. **£5,000-8,000** *S*

Cescinski & Gribble, p. 106, for a similar table at Ruckinge Church. This table is typical of the Romney Marsh, Rye and Hythe districts.

A Charles I oak joint stool, top replaced, 1 ft. 8 in. wide, c. 1630. **£400-600** *S*

A pair of French stools, each with an almost square 2-plank walnut top, with moulded edge and chamfered underside, restored, 1 ft. 2½ in. high by 1 ft. 1½ in. wide (37 by 32 cm.), second half 17th C. **£600-700** *S*

Welsh oak refectory table, the plank cleated top on 6 baluster s, joined by stretchers, 8 ft. 3 in. g by 2 ft. 5 in. deep (251 by cm.), c. 1700. **£4,000-5,000** *S*

An oak side table, possibly Dutch or German, 93½ in. wide (238 cm.), 17th C. **£5,000-8,000** *C*

A William and Mary oak refectory table, with a single plank top, restored and with later feet, 78 by 28½ in. (198 by 73 cm.). **£1,000-£1,800** *L*

ate 17th C. dining table, 77 by in. **£1,000-1,800** *A*

A Victorian 17th C.-style oak refectory table, with carved frieze and legs, made up from old timber, 29 in. by 8 ft. 6 in. **£800-1,200** *DA*

A 17th C. Dutch oak refectory table, the plank top with pegged bearers raised upon a base of 4 baluster turned legs, 9 ft. long. **£800-1,200** *B*

A good 18th C. English oak tavern table, 8 ft. long. **£2,000-3,000** *H*

An 18th C.-style oak refectory dining table, made up from old timber, 84 by 31 in. **£700-1,000** *M*

An oak refectory table, with 2-plank top, 7 ft. long by 2 ft. 2 in. wide. **£800-1,000** *MMB*

Period dining tables were never made in England with a centre stretcher in this way.

A Flemish oak draw-leaf table, the cleated top above a plain frieze with shaped apron, 2 ft. 4 in. high by 3 ft. 8 in. wide closed by 6 ft. 8 in. wide fully extended (71 by 112 by 203 cm.), mid 17th C. **£2,000-3,000** *S*

A fine Swiss walnut and oak extending refectory table, the moulded rectangular plank top fitted with iron hasps, the frieze carved with the initials CPMB within a shield, and dated 1715, 74 in. wide, shut, (188 cm.), 132 in. wide, open, (336 cm.), early 18th C. **£3,000-5,000** *C*

A Charles I oak credence table, with hinged top and broadly canted sides, on 4 inverted baluster legs and a hinged gateleg support at the back, 2 ft. 6 in. high by 3 ft. 6 in. wide (76 by 108 cm.), c. 1630. **£2,500-4,000** *H*

A Dutch oak gateleg table, with oval single-flap top on ring-turned bulbous baluster legs, joined by a plain T-shaped stretcher, 38½ in. wide open (98.5 cm.), 17th C. **£1,000-1,500** *C*

A 17th C. Dutch oak centre table, the oval top pegged to a base with a single drawer and above a shaped frieze, 43 in. wide. **£700-1,000** *B*

MAKE THE MOST OF MILLER'S
Miller's is completely different each year. Each edition contains completely NEW photographs. This is not an updated publication. We never repeat the same photograph.

A Charles II oak table stool, with lopers. **£1,000-1,600** *H*

A rare James I oak vestment chest. **£3,500-4,500** *H*

A Charles I small oak folding table, the semi-circular top with iron butterfly hinges, the flap on a gateleg support, restored, 2 ft. 5 in. high by 2 ft. 7 in. wide by 1 ft. 3½ in. deep (73.5 by 79 by 39.5 cm.), c. 1630. **£800-1,200** *S*

A William and Mary small oak, elm and fruitwood gateleg table, top restored, 2 ft. 8½ in. wide open (82.5 cm.), c. 1690. **£700-1,000** *S*

An oak gateleg table, with oval top, plain frieze and turned legs, ending in arched feet, 40 in. wide open (102 cm.), 17th C. **£800-1,200** *C*

A small 17th C. oak drop-leaf table, the oval top supported by pull-out slides, now missing, 26½ in. wide by 22 in. high and opening to 34½ in. **£800-1,200** *B*

An oak and elm gateleg table, 28 by 37 by 50 in. (71 by 94 by 127 cm.), third quarter of the 17th C. **£600-900** *SC*

A late 17th C. oak 8/10 seater gateleg table, of good colour and patination, opening to 5 ft. 6 in. by 4 ft. 6 in. **£1,500-1,800** *B*

A late 17th C. oak gateleg table, with oval top, shaped apron, turned legs and gates and turned stretchers, 38 in. wide. **£1,200-£1,800** *DSH*

An early 18th C. oak gateleg table, with oval flap top and turned legs with ball feet, 66½ by 57½ in. **£1,500-2,000** *DSH*

A large oak William and Mary gateleg dining room table, with square lower sections and braganza feet, the tip of one flap replaced, 5 ft. long (152 cm.), c. 1690. **£1,500-2,500** *S*

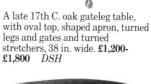

A Queen Anne oak gateleg table, 41½ by 47 in. extended (106 by 120 cm.). **£600-800** *L*

An oak gateleg table, 31 by 56 by 64 in. extended (79 by 142 by 163 cm.), late 17th C. **£1,500-2,500** *SC*

A large Carolean period oak oval twin flap top gateleg table, on turned spiral twist baluster block supports to plain stretchers and bun feet, 5 ft. by 5 ft. 8 in. **£1,000-1,500** *WW*

original condition **£2,500-4,000**

An oak gateleg dining table, 28½ by 50 by 53 in. (72 by 127 by 135 cm.), late 17th/early 18th C. **£700-1,000** *SC*

A 17th C. oak gateleg dining table, with drawer, 57 by 21 in. extending to 68 in. **£1,800-2,500** *EWS*

A Charles II oak and elm gateleg table, the oval top on bobbin-turned supports, 5 ft. 4 in. wide open (163 cm.), c. 1680. **£1,500-2,500** *S*

A late 17th C. yew wood gateleg table, 54 by 48 by 29 in. **£2,500-£3,500** *H*

285

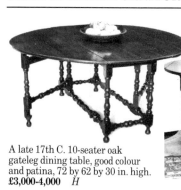

A late 17th C. 10-seater oak gateleg dining table, good colour and patina, 72 by 62 by 30 in. high. **£3,000-4,000** *H*

A Charles II 10-seater oak double gateleg table. **£5,000-7,500** *H*

An unusual 18th C. oak folding top writing table, on turned supports with gateleg action, 32 by 11 in. **£800-1,200** *JD*

A rare Charles II oak gateleg 12-seater table, with split barleytwist turnery. **£7,000-10,000** *H*

An oak side table, 31½ in. wide (80 cm.), late 17th C. **£700-1,000** *C*

An oak oval top swing-leg table, on 4 turned legs with club feet, 3 ft. 11 in. wide, mid 18th C. **£200-400** *EG*

A George I oak side table, the valanced apron flanked by baluster turned and square legs, joined by stretchers, handles replaced, 2 ft. 10 in. wide (81 cm.), c. 1720. **£400-£600** *SS*

A William and Mary burr oak side table, on twist turned supports with stretchers, top crossbanded in fruitwood, with herringbone inlay, 38 by 22 in. **£1,000-1,500** *JD*

A late 17th C. oak table, fitted with a drawer at either end, 33½ by 21 in. **£400-600** *DWB*

A George I oak secretaire table, altered and restored, 3 ft. 1¼ in. wide (95 cm.), c. 1725. **£250-400** *SS*

A William and Mary oak side table, with unusual stretchers. **£800-£1,250** *H*

An oak lowboy, 3 drawers to the arched frieze, early 18th C. **£1,200-£1,800** *DWB*

An antique oak lowboy, fitted with oak lined drawers, with crossbanding to drawer fronts, top replaced, 39½ in. wide. **£150-250** *BHW*

A good early 18th C. yew wood side table. **£1,400-1,800** *H*

An unusual William and Mary oak side table. **£900-1,250** *H*

FURNITURE – MARKET TRENDS

We have seen an extremely strong market develop over the last 12 months. Prices of furniture in the top and medium quality ranges have escalated; the former has caused a series of record prices and the latter a consistent steady rise. This has led to a mirror situation of the last boom in the early 70's when the great problem was actually finding the high quality pieces, especially those in true original condition. Shortage of supply is a problem for auctioneers, dealers and the private buyers.

The main feature of this market is that items with provenance and history sell very easily — with strong competition from both dealers and private buyers — causing extremely high prices. 'House sale hysteria' has demonstrated itself on several occasions and unexpected prices, several times auctioneers estimates, have been reached. These prices can not always be taken as representative.

Early English furniture has been particularly strong especially over continental. However there is a very much stronger interest in foreign furniture, with some record prices reached in London salerooms. The International Monetary Markets have once again had a great effect on furniture prices. A strong dollar and various American museums with vast sums of money to spend create even more demand at the top end of the market.

Good quality distressed furniture has seen a rapid escalation in value — again caused by the lack of original perfect pieces.

Prices paid for Edwardian furniture again staggers those who believe that true English furniture was only produced in the 18th Century. However they can console themselves by thinking that the highest prices paid are for the Edwardian Sheraton revival pieces. This seems to have stabilised somewhat but the best is still greatly sought after.

Furniture that is useful: desks, chairs, tables, beds (particularly larger examples), is selling far better than exotic collectors pieces. However, the obscure does have its own market.

PRICES

The never-ending problem of fixing prices for antiques! A price can be affected by so many factors, for example:

- *condition*
- *desirability*
- *rarity*
- *size*
- *colour*
- *provenance*
- *restoration*
- *the sale of a prestigious collection*
- *collection label*
- *appearance of a new reference book*
- *new specialist sale at major auction house*
- *mentioned on television*
- *the fact that two people present at auction are determined to have the piece*
- *where you buy it*

One also has to contend with the fact that an antique is not only a 'thing of beauty' but a commodity. The price can again be affected by:—

- *supply and demand*
- *international finance — currency fluctuation*
- *fashion*
- *inflation*
- *the fact that a museum has vast sums of money to spend*

GUIDE TO STYLES

Dates	Monarch	Period	Woods
1603-1625	James I	Jacobean	
1625-1649	Charles I	Carolean	Oak period
1649-1660	Commonwealth	Cromwellian	up to c. 1670
1660-1685	Charles II	Restoration	
1685-1689	James II	Restoration	
1689-1694	William and Mary	William and Mary	
1694-1702	William III	William III	Walnut period
1702-1714	Anne	Queen Anne	1670-1735
1714-1727	George I	Early Georgian	
1727-1760	George II	Early Georgian	Early mahogany period
1760-1811	George III	Late Georgian	1735-1770
1812-1820	George III	Regency	Late mahogany period
1820-1830	George IV	Regency	1770-1810
1830-1837	William IV	William IV	
1837-1901	Victoria	Victorian	
1901-1910	Edward VII	Edwardian	

A George III mahogany tester bed, canopy with restorations, 7 ft. 10 in. high by 5 ft. 2½ in. wide by 6 ft. 8 in. long (239 by 159 by 203 cm.), c. 1790. **£4,000-5,000**　*S*

A fine late 18th C. rosewood tester double bed, the arched headboard with gadrooned decoration and finely carved foliate tracery, 60 in. wide, 4 ft. 6 in. wide at base. **£650-£750**　*B*

Price indicates a late 18th C. copy, if 'right' value would be **£2,000-£3,000+**

A late Regency painted satinwood cradle, the height adjustable, 40½ in. (103 cm.) wide. **£1,800-£2,200**　*C*

A George IV mahogany tester bed, with box mattress, and drapes, 91 in. high by 67 in. wide by 90 in. long (321 by 171 by 229 cm.), second quarter of 19th C. **£4,000-£4,500**   *SC*

A mahogany single tester bed, with box mattress and drapes, 81½ in. long by 41 in. wide (207 by 104 cm.), second half of 19th C. **£600-800**   *SC*

A Regency ebonised and parcel-gilt bonheur du jour, the raised superstructure with mirror-backed open centre flanked by 2 drawers, painted to simulate specimen marbles, adapted and redecorated, 27½ in. (70 cm.) wide. **£1,800-2,200**   *C*

A Victorian inlaid walnut bonheur du jour. **£1,400-1,600**   *AMB*

A George IV mahogany tester bed, with an upholstered canopy surmounted by flambeau finials, 55 in. (140 cm.) wide, second quarter of 19th C. **£1,500-1,800**   *SC*

Points to note on mahogany tester beds:
Domed and carved canopies.
Quality of carving on posts: wheatears, husks, reeding, etc.
Original drapes.
N.B. Beware many late 19th C. copies.

A French 19th C. rosewood and kingwood double bed, embellished with gilt metal mounts, 4 ft. 10 in. by 6 ft. 4 in., c. 1860. **£1,200-1,500**   *BHW*

An unusual William IV rosewood-veneered writing cabinet, the superstructure with a pair of leafy corbels flanking a pivoting panel, which enclosed numerous drawers and pigeonholes and is 'locked' in conjunction with the slide and fitted frieze drawer below, 3 ft. 11½ in. high by 3 ft. 7 in. wide (121 by 109 cm.), c. 1830. **£900-1,100**   *S*

A Louis XVI-style grey-painted lit-de-repos, the arched head and end boards upholstered in pink satin, with ribbon-tied crestings re-supported, box-spring, mattress and 2 bolsters, 78 in. (201 cm.) long, late 19th C. **£600-900**   *C*

A Portuguese hardwood bed, incorporating fragments from an altar piece, 48 in. wide. **£700-900**   *Bea*

A George III satinwood and rosewood bonheur du jour, the hinged writing flap crossbanded with faded rosewood, 25 in. (63 cm.) wide. **£4,500-5,000**   *C*

A good marquetry and satinwood side cabinet, crossbanded in rosewood, stamped Edwards & Roberts, 4 ft. 6 in. by 3 ft. 6 in. (138 by 107 cm.), c. 1880. **£2,600-3,000**   *S*

A 19th C. amboyna table, in French style by W. Williamson & Sons, Guildford, the drawers and cupboard set with Sèvres-style porcelain plaques, 31 by 42 in. high. **£2,200-2,600**   *DWB*

A Victorian thuya, ormolu and porcelain-mounted bonheur du jour, with porcelain cherub plaques flanked by cupboards, inset with oval plaques of Marie Antoinette and Mme. Elisabeth, 135 cm. wide, c. 1870. **£1,600-2,000**   *Bon*

A Victorian burr yew inlaid and crossbanded bonheur de jour, 34 in. **£1,000-1,200**   *A*

An inlaid rosewood bonheur du jour, 3 ft. 11 in. high by 2 ft. 7 in. wide (120 by 79 cm.), c. 1900. **£600-£800**   *S*

A harewood bonheur du jour, with a hinged writing surface, crossbanded throughout in tulipwood, 41 by 28 in. (104 by 71 cm.), 20th C. **£500-600**   *SC*

A satinwood bonheur du jour, the superstructure with an arched three-quarter galleried open shelf and 8 cedar-lined small drawers surrounding 2 cupboard doors, the base with flap painted with peacock feathers and roses, 23 in. (58 cm.) wide, late 19th C. **£2,000-2,500**   *C*

An Edwardian mahogany writing table, by Edwards and Roberts, the drawers with blind fret decoration, 36 by 21 in. **£600-700**   *JD*

A French Directoire-style bonheur du jour. **£500-700**   *CDC*

A 19th C. French ebony-veneered cabinet, in Louis XVI style, having cast gilt brass mounts and brass line inlay, the leather inset writing slide and a frieze drawer with vitruvian scrolling, 3 ft. **£1,500-£1,800**   *WW*

A Louis XV/XVI Transitional kingwood bonheur du jour, attributed to Charles Topino, with a frieze writing drawer, fitted with metal pen tray and ink holders, inlaid throughout, 3 ft. 1½ in. high by 2 ft. ½ in. wide (95 by 62 cm.), c. 1775. **£6,000-8,000**   *S*

A 19th C. French Louis XV-style serpentine bonheur du jour, in kingwood crossbanded walnut, set with 6 Sèvres-style porcelain plaques, 4 ft. wide. **£1,500-1,800** *GC*

A Napoleon III boulle bonheur du jour, the lower section with a velvet-lined writing slide above a shaped frieze drawer, the whole inlaid with engraved brass foliate scrolls on a red tortoiseshell ground, 83 cm. wide. **£1,200-1,500** *Bon*

A French porcelain mounted writing desk, in rosewood and tulipwood, 29 by 50 in. high (74 by 127 cm.), 19th C. **£2,000-2,500** *L*

A 19th C. marquetry inlaid walnut bonheur du jour, the superstructure with central mirror, the sloping fall-front below enclosing an interior of pigeonholes, 2 ft. 8 in. wide by 4 ft. 7 in. high. **£1,400-£1,600** *CDC*

A mahogany Empire-style bonheur du jour, the marble top with pierced brass gallery, 30 in., c. 1900. **£900-1,100** *JD*

A Louis XVI-style mahogany and brass-mounted bureau, the fall with a Vernis Martin-style panel, 3 ft. 4 in. high by 2 ft. 8½ in. wide (102 by 82 cm.), c. 1900. **£900-1,100** *SS*

A Dutch satinwood and rosewood bonheur du jour, 31 in. (79 cm.) wide. **£800-1,200** *C*

A French ormolu-mounted rosewood and mahogany writing desk, 36 in., 20th C. **£700-800** *GSP*

A George II mahogany bookcase, 7 ft. 9 in. high by 4 ft. 7 in. wide (226 by 140.5 cm.), c. 1740. **£4,000-£5,000** *S*

A George III small mahogany library bookcase, 39½ in. wide. **£2,000-2,500** *PWC*

A George III mahogany and satinwood bookcase, with crossbanded and inlaid panel doors, 56½ in. **£1,500-2,000** *GM*

A George III mahogany bookcase, the moulded cornice above astragal glazed doors concealing adjustable shelves, 96 in. high by 49 in. wide by 20 in. deep, c. 1800. **£3,000-£3,500** *HAL*

A late George III rosewood bookcase, 7 ft. 2½ in. high by 5 ft. 8 in. wide (220 by 173 cm.), c. 1810. **£4,000-5,000** *S*

A George III mahogany bookcase, the moulded cornice inlaid with a line of satinwood, brasswork early but replaced, 62 in. wide by 87 in. high by 17 in. deep, c. 1800. **£3,000-£3,500** *HAL*

A Regency bookcase, 42½ in. (108 cm.) wide. **£5,500-6,500** *C*

A George III mahogany bookcase, 67½ in. wide. **£900-1,200** *GM*

A George III-style mahogany dual bow-front cabinet bookcase, inlaid with ebony stringing and reeded lozenge medallions, 6 ft. 10½ in. high by 3 ft. 3 in. wide (210 by 99 cm.), c. 1930. **£800-1,200** *SS*

A pair of Regency small figured mahogany bookcases, the lower part with panelled door concealing shelves and drawers mounted on unusual turned feet, originally with glazing bars, 73 in. high by 24 in. wide by 14 in. deep, c. 1830. **£3,000-4,000** *HAL*

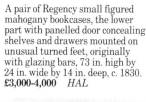

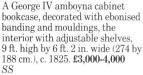

A George IV small mahogany library bookcase, 7 ft. 2 in. high by 5 ft. 5¾ in. wide (218.5 by 167 cm.), c. 1820. **£4,500-5,500** *S*

A Regency mahogany cabinet bookcase, 8 ft. 2 in. high by 7 ft. wide (249 by 214 cm.), c. 1810. **£4,000-5,000** *SS*

A George IV amboyna cabinet bookcase, decorated with ebonised banding and mouldings, the interior with adjustable shelves, 9 ft. high by 6 ft. 2 in. wide (274 by 188 cm.), c. 1825. **£3,000-4,000** *SS*

A 19th C. mahogany and inlaid library bookcase, with marquetry decoration, 74½ in. wide by 98 in. high. **£2,500-3,000** *DSH*

A pair of mahogany library book cabinets, with ebonised mouldings, 6 ft. 11 in. high by 4 ft. 5½ in. wide (211 by 136 cm.), c. 1840. **£1,800-£2,500** *S*

A small Georgian mahogany bookcase, 4 ft. 10 in. by 6 ft. 10 in. **£2,000-2,500** *AGr*

A pair of Regency mahogany library bookcases, 7 ft. 10½ in. high by 3 ft. 11 in. wide (240 by 119 cm.), c. 1810. **£20,000-25,000** *S*

A Victorian mahogany bookcase, with ogee moulded cornice, 122 cm. wide. **£600-800** *Bon*

A Victorian mahogany library bookcase, with carved scrollwork pediment, 4 ft. wide by 8 ft. 6 in. high. **£600-800** *CDC*

A pair of mahogany bookcases, each with an ogee-moulded cornice above a pair of glazed doors with lancet bars and flanked by panelle pilasters with lotus-scroll capitals and bases, 8 ft. 2 in. high by 4 ft. 11 in. wide (249 by 150 cm.), c. 1840. **£4,000-5,000** *S*

BOOKCASES

- the small bookcase really became fashionable with the demand for finer, smaller furniture during the Regency period
- these pieces tend to be in great demand and hence expensive mainly because of their small size and craftsmanship
- many are simple to reproduce and a large number of much later copies are around
- some look very similar to side cabinets and were often made to match
- dwarf bookcases no matter how modern are always in great demand and period examples tend to be expensive

A good pair of walnut bookcases, in well-figured and burr veneers, with gilt metal mounts and mouldings throughout, 7 ft. (213 cm.) high. **£6,000-7,000** *S*

An Edwardian mahogany and marquetry bookcase, 98 by 55 in. (249 by 140 cm.), early 20th C. **£2,000-2,500** *SC*

A Victorian oak and pollard oak bookcase, 149 cm. wide. **£700-90** *Bon*

A fine Victorian red mahogany library bookcase, 72 in. wide by 93 in. high. **£2,000-2,500** *PSH*

A stained oak display cabinet, 36 by 76 in. high. **£150-200** *WP*

A large early Victorian rosewood bookcase, 5 ft. 9 in. wide by 7 ft. 9 in. tall. **£800-1,200** *Fr*

A mahogany breakfront bookcase, the moulded top with Greek key and Chinese blind fretwork and centred by a broken triangular pediment, the lower part with a slide, 8 ft. 2 in. high by 7 ft. 7 in. wide (249 by 231 cm.), c. 1770, centre wings later. **£6,000-7,000** *S*

BREAKFRONT BOOKCASES

- originally bookshelves in libraries were fixtures
- freestanding bookcases were developed in the 17th C. and perfected in the 18th C.
- bookcases were made for the rich and have always been collectable
- one should also always check height as many bookcases were made for higher ceilings than present room heights allow
- it is vital to remember the 18th C. love of proportion — if the groove for the first shelf is 6 in. from the bottom, the groove for the top shelf will be 6 in. from the top
- many breakfront bookcases started life as breakfront wardrobes
- tell-tale signs can be seen where about 8-10 in. have been cut off the depth

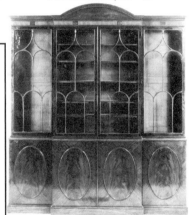

A George III mahogany breakfront library bookcase, the cornice with arched centre section above a fluted frieze set with paterae, 9 ft. high by 8 ft. 2 in. wide (275 by 249 cm.), c. 1770. **£12,000-15,000** *S*

A George III mahogany breakfront library bookcase, 7 ft. wide by 21 in. deep by 7 ft. 8 in. high. **£4,000-4,500** *PWC*

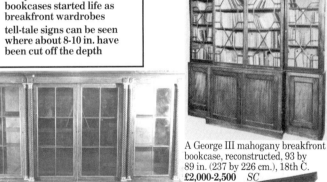

A George III mahogany breakfront bookcase, with brass mounts and brass panel rims, 12 ft. 6 in. wide by 8 ft. high. **£6,000-8,000** *GM*

A George III mahogany breakfront bookcase, reconstructed, 93 by 89 in. (237 by 226 cm.), 18th C. **£2,000-2,500** *SC*

A good Adam-style mahogany breakfront bookcase, inlaid with satinwood urns, acanthus leaf and swag decoration, 6 ft. 9 in. long by 8 ft. 5 in. high. **£3,500-4,000** *OL*

A George III mahogany breakfront library bookcase, 104 by 129 in. (264 by 328 cm.), third quarter of 18th C. **£12,500-15,000** *SC*

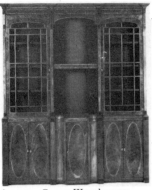

A narrow George III mahogany library bookcase, with boxwood-edged astragals, the whole crossbanded in tulipwood with boxwood stringing, 8 ft. 2 in. high by 7 ft. 2 in. wide (249 by 218.5 cm.), late 18th C. **£8,000-£10,000**   *S*

A George III-style library bookcase, in figured mahogany, 90 in. wide by 20 in. deep by 92 in. high, c. 1850. **£3,500-4,500**   *HAL*

A George III-style mahogany breakfront cabinet bookcase, the geometric astragal doors with bevelled glass, 8 ft. 8 in. high by 7 ft. 8 in. wide (264 by 234 cm.), c. 1890. **£3,500-4,000**   *SS*

A Georgian mahogany breakfront bookcase, 10 ft. long by 8 ft. tall. **£3,500-4,000**   *AGr*

A Georgian mahogany breakfront bookcase, 100 in. wide by 87 in. high. **£2,500-3,500**   *DA*

A large Georgian mahogany breakfront bookcase, 9 ft. by 8 ft. 6 in. high. **£6,000-8,000**   *AG*

A late Georgian mahogany breakfront bookcase. **£5,000-6,000**   *JF*

A Regency breakfront bookcase, with later broken triangular pediment centred by a reeded finial, the base with a fitted secretaire drawer, including maple-veneered short drawers, 79 in. wide by 101 in. high (201 by 256 cm.). **£6,000-7,000**   *C*

A Regency mahogany breakfront library bookcase, with stepped moulded cornice, 101 in. wide by 99 in. high (257 by 251 cm.). **£3,500-4,000**   *C*

A George IV mahogany breakfront bookcase, the base with a central secretaire drawer, 8 ft. 5 in. by 8 ft. 4 in. high. **£4,000-4,500**   *MMB*

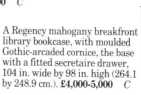

A Regency mahogany breakfront library bookcase, with moulded Gothic-arcaded cornice, the base with a fitted secretaire drawer, 104 in. wide by 98 in. high (264.1 by 248.9 cm.). **£4,000-5,000**   *C*

An early 19th C. mahogany breakfront bookcase, 73 by 99 in. high. **£4,000-4,500** *DWB*

A good parcel-gilt walnut breakfront bookcase, with arched glazed panels flanked by split spiral-twist pilasters, 7 ft. 2 in. high by 9 ft. 11 in. wide (219 by 302 cm.), c. 1840. **£3,000-3,500** *S*

A 19th C. mahogany bookcase, with dentil cornice, 72 in. wide. **£1,800-2,200** *BHW*

A Victorian mahogany breakfront library bookcase, 99 in. high by 100 in. wide. **£3,500-4,000** *Bea*

A large William IV mahogany breakfront bookcase, some damage, 15 ft. 3 in. by 2 ft. deep by 9 ft. 4 in. high. **£2,000-3,000** *PWC*

A 19th C. mahogany breakfront bookcase, 8 ft. by 6 ft. 7 in. wide. **£3,500-4,000** *AG*

A walnut-veneered bureau cabinet, the sloping fall front enclosing pigeonholes and short drawers, 74 in. high by 28½ in. wide. **£3,000-3,500** *Bea*

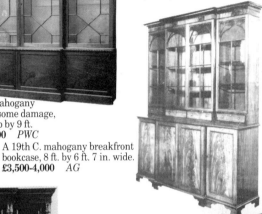

An Edwardian faded mahogany breakfront side cabinet, 4 ft. 2 in. wide by 6 ft. 6 in. high. **£1,600-£2,000** *Re*

A Victorian breakfront mahogany bookcase. **£2,000-2,500** *PLJ*

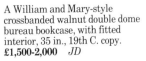

An Edwardian mahogany bookcase, 7 ft. wide by 4 ft. 6 in. high. **£400-600** *MIL*

A William and Mary-style crossbanded walnut double dome bureau bookcase, with fitted interior, 35 in., 19th C. copy. **£1,500-2,000** *JD*

A good William and Mary walnut double domed bureau cabinet, with arched bevelled edge mirror panels to the doors, enclosing adjustable shelves and pigeonholes, 2 candle slides below, the fall to the bureau with feather and crossbanding and a book rest, 39½ in. wide. **£10,000-£15,000** *PWC*

A Queen Anne oak bureau cabinet, the double domed cornice with a giltwood cartouche cresting, the fall-flap enclosing a finely fitted interior including a well, on later bracket feet, 40 in. wide (101.5 cm.). **£4,000-5,000** *C*

A small early 18th C.-style walnut double domed kneehole bookcase, 2 ft. 6 in. wide by 5 ft. 10 in. high, 20th C. **£600-900** *MMB*

A Queen Anne walnut bureau cabinet, the crossbanded doors with bevelled mirrors and enclosing shelves, drawers, pigeonholes and a pair of candle slides below, the lower part with a crossbanded flap enclosing a fitted interior, on later bracket feet, 3 ft. 5½ in. high by 3 ft. 6½ in. wide (104 by 107 cm.), c 1710. **£8,000-10,000** *S*

A small walnut-veneered bureau cabinet, 74 in. high by 28½ in. wide. **£3,000-3,500** *Bea*

A Queen Anne walnut bureau cabinet, with a broken arched cornice above a pair of doors with shaped tops and bevelled mirror panels, enclosing shelves, pigeonholes and drawers and with a pair of candle stands below, the lower part with a cross and chevron-banded flap enclosing a fitted interior, with restoration, 7 ft. 9 in. high by 3 ft. 6 in. wide (236 by 107 cm.), c. 1700. **£18,000-£22,000** *S*

A George I walnut bureau bookcase, with fully fitted interior, 3 ft. 3 in. **£5,000-7,000** *AMB*
This piece is a marriage.

A fine George I walnut bureau bookcase, the 2 dome shaped mirrored doors, one panel now missing, with candle slides beneath, the cross-grained and featherbanded sloping front enclosing a well fitted interior, 39 in. wide by 96 in. high by 23 in. deep. **£18,000-22,000** *B*

An early 18th C. walnut bureau cabinet, 39 in. **£8,000-10,000** *PWC*

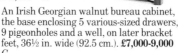

A small 'George II Chippendale' mahogany bureau cabinet, 36 in. wide by 89 in. high by 21½ in. deep, 19th C. copy. **£2,500-3,000** *B*

A yew wood bureau cabinet, the lower part with sloping flap enclosing a fitted interior including a well, 28 in. wide (71 cm.), 19th C. copy. **£2,500-3,000** *C*

An Irish Georgian walnut bureau cabinet, the base enclosing 5 various-sized drawers, 9 pigeonholes and a well, on later bracket feet, 36½ in. wide (92.5 cm.). **£7,000-9,000** *C*

A late George I walnut bureau bookcase, the fall-front enclosing a fitted interior and well, on later bracket feet, 85 by 44 in. (216 by 112 cm.), first quarter of 18th C. **£4,000-6,000** *SC*

A George III Chippendale mahogany bureau cabinet, with a fall-front enclosing a fitted interior of 2 rows of small drawers, interspaced by pigeonholes flanking a central cupboard door with internal drawer, 42 in. wide by 96 in. high by 23 in. deep. £3,000-3,500   B

A George II Virginian red walnut bureau cabinet bookcase, 3 ft. 6 in. overall. £4,000-5,000   WW

A late George II or early George III oak bureau cabinet, the lower part with a fall-front, interior lacking, 82 by 39½ in. (208 by 100 cm.), mid 18th C. £1,000-1,500   SC

A George II Cuban mahogany bureau cabinet bookcase, having an egg and dart floret carved moulded cornice, above an interior with 2 shelves and 8 small drawers, one a replacement, fitted with later mirrors, the flap enclosing a fitted interior, 3 ft. 8 in. overall. £2,500-3,000   WW

A George III mahogany bureau cabinet, the quarter-veneered flame-figured flap enclosing a fitted interior, Provincial, handles replaced, 7 ft. 9 in. high by 4 ft. 3 in. wide (236 by 130 cm.), c. 1770. £2,500-3,000   S

An early George III mahogany secretaire cabinet, 45 in. wide by 96 in. high (114 by 244 cm.). £3,500-4,000   C

A George III mahogany bureau bookcase, the fall revealing a fitted interior, 7 ft. 5 in. high by 3 ft. 10 in. wide (226 by 117 cm.), c. 1760. £1,800-2,400   SS

A George III mahogany bureau bookcase, the base with a sloping hinged writing surface, enclosing pigeonholes and drawers, 83½ by 39 in. (212 by 99 cm.), late 18th C. £1,500-2,000   SC

A mid-Georgian mahogany bureau cabinet, the sloping flap enclosing an interior fitted with 6 various-sized drawers and 2 slides, flanking a central cupboard door, on later bracket feet, 42 in. wide (107 cm.). £3,500-4,000   C

A George III mahogany bureau bookcase, the bureau with fitted interior, on ogee bracket feet, 42 by 80 in. high (107 by 204 cm.). £1,800-2,200   L

A red tortoiseshell-veneered bureau cabinet, the 6 ft. 6½ in. high by 3 ft. 7 in. wide (199 by 109 cm.), part late 18th C. £5,000-7,000   S

A George III mahogany bureau cabinet, with moulded dentilled cornice above a pair of glazed cupboard doors, enclosing shelves and 5 various-sized small drawers, the sloping flap enclosing a well-fitted interior, 45 in. wide (114.5 cm.). £6,000-7,000   C

A mahogany bureau bookcase, with inlaid interior, 37 in. wide, 19th C. copy. **£600-900**   *DA*

A George III mahogany bureau cabinet, with fitted interior. **£8,000-10,000**   *PLJ*

A George III fiddleback mahogany bureau cabinet, the solid cylinder enclosing a well-fitted interior, including a leather-lined reading flap, a pair of later silver-mounted inkwells and pen slides, 36 in. wide (91.5 cm.). **£8,000-£10,000**   *C*

A George III-style satinwood and tulipwood crossbanded bureau display cabinet, the fall revealing small drawers and pigeonholes, 5 ft. 9 in. high by 2 ft. 7½ in. wide (175 by 80 cm.). c. 1910. **£800-1,00** *SS*

A mahogany cylinder bookcase, the lower part with a fitted interior, including an inset baize writing slope, 99 by 45 in. (252 by 115 cm.), early 19th C. **£2,000-2,500**   *SC*
The top and bottom possibly not originally together.

A mahogany bureau bookcase, the slope front crossbanded in wide satinwood, box and ebony chequer border, with fitted interior, 41¾ in. wide. **£800-£1,200**   *WHL*

A mahogany bureau bookcase, the slope front crossbanded in wide satinwood, box and ebony chequer border, with fitted interior, 41¾ in. wide. **£800-£1,200**   *WHL*

A kingwood-banded satinwood bureau bookcase, 78 in. high. **£4,000-5,000**   *GSP*

A 19th C. twin pedestal cylinder front mahogany bureau bookcase 60 in. wide by 106 in. high. **£1,20 £1,500**   *PSH*

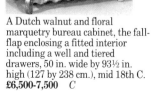

A Dutch walnut and floral marquetry bureau cabinet, the fall-flap enclosing a fitted interior including a well and tiered drawers, 50 in. wide by 93½ in. high (127 by 238 cm.), mid 18th C. **£6,500-7,500**   *C*

A Dutch walnut bureau bookcase, with panelled cupboard doors enclosing an unusually well-fitted interior with 19 various-sized drawers, 11 pigeonholes and 10 narrower pigeonholes, the sloping flap enclosing a further well-fitted interior, with various stepped drawers and pigeonholes and a well, 54 in. (137.5 cm.) wide, early 18th C. **£12,000-15,000**   *C*

A reproduction mahogany framed bureau bookcase, with slope front enclosing fitted interior. **£400-600** *WHL*

A Dutch walnut bureau cabinet, with a pair of shaped bevelled an glazed cupboard doors enclosing well-fitted interior of 11 drawers and 8 pigeonholes, above 2 candl slides, the base with a sloping fla enclosing a finely fitted interior including a well, 47 in. (120 cm.) wide, mid 18th C. **£7,000-8,000**

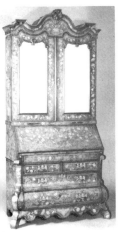

A Dutch walnut and floral marquetry bureau cabinet, the base with sloping flap enclosing a fitted interior with short drawers and a well, 48 in. wide by 99½ in. high (122 by 253 cm.). **£7,000-9,000**

A Dutch walnut and floral marquetry bureau cabinet, the base with sloping flap enclosing a fitted interior including a well, 67 in. wide, 93 in. high (160 by 236 cm.). **£6,000-7,000** *C*

A Dutch mahogany and floral marquetry bureau cabinet, with 2 panelled doors, inlaid with peacocks, enclosing 3 shelves and 3 drawers, the sloping flap enclosing an interior of 6 various-sized drawers and a well, 44½ in. (113 cm.) wide. **£6,000-7,000** *C*

South German walnut and burr-walnut bureau cabinet, the base with solid cylinder enclosing 10 various-sized shaped drawers, 9 in. (124.5 cm.) wide, mid 18th. **10,000-12,500** *C*

A South German walnut bureau cabinet, inlaid in fruitwood, the base enclosing a fitted interior, 43 in. wide by 77 in. high (109 by 196 cm.), mid 18th C. **£8,000-10,000** *C*

A South German walnut bureau cabinet, on stand, the inlaid bureau section with moulded fall-front enclosing a fitted interior, the later oak stand with hipped cabriole legs, 3 ft. 5½ in. high by 2 ft. 4 in. wide (106 by 71 cm.), c. 1740 **£1,500-2,000** *S*

A walnut and marquetry bureau cabinet, inlaid throughout with panels of foliate strapwork, the fall-front enclosing a stepped interior with short drawers, pigeonholes, a cupboard and a well, Low Countries, some alteration, 92 in. high by 40 in. wide, early 18th C. **£4,000-5,000** *Bea*

South German walnut and marquetry bureau cabinet, from the Mainz district, 55 by 112 in. high, 1760. **£90,000-110,000** *DWB*

An Italian walnut and giltwood bookcase bureau, of serpentine outline, decorated with applied, carved giltwood mounts in the rococo manner, fall-front revealing fitted drawers, and concealed well, 60 in. **£18,000-22,000** *LE*

A late Louis XVI ormolu-mounted mahogany bureau a cylindre, the top with a rectangular inset marble panel, the solid cylinder enclosing a fitted interior, one of the pair of deeper drawers fitted with a 'coffre fort', 43 in. (109 cm.) wide. **£2,500-£3,000** *C*

A George III mahogany breakfront secretaire library bookcase, 91 in. wide. **£4,000-5,000** *Re*

A George III mahogany breakfront secretaire bookcase, 7 ft. 8 in. high c. 1800. **£5,000-6,000** *SS*

A George III mahogany secretaire bookcase, the frieze with stringing and set with satinwood panels, the base with a secretaire drawer veneered with 2 oval panels, centred by a fan patera and enclosing an arrangement of drawers, 8 ft. 11½ in. high by 4 ft. 10½ in. wide (273 by 149 cm.), c. 1790. **£2,500-3,000** *S*

A small George III mahogany secretaire bookcase, the fitted secretaire drawer with a pair of panels above 3 long drawers, on bracket feet, containing a manuscript bill for beer, dated 1791, 7 ft. 2 in. high by 2 ft. 7 in. wide (219 by 79 cm.), c. 1790. **£6,000-8,000** *S*

A George III mahogany breakfront secretaire bookcase, 78 in. wide by 95 in. high. **£4,500-5,500** *GSP*

A George III mahogany secretaire bookcase, 8 ft. 11½ in. high by 4 ft. 10½ in. wide (273 by 149 cm.), c. 1790. **£2,500-3,000** *S*

MILLER'S *Antiques Price Guide builds up year by year to form the most comprehensive photo-reference system available. The first five volumes contain over 40,000 completely different photographs.*

A George III mahogany secretaire bookcase, the shaped cresting with 3 panels of satinwood fluting, with a fitted secretaire drawer, handles replaced, 7 ft. 7 in. high by 3 ft. 7 in. wide (231 by 109 cm.), c. 1780 **£2,000-2,500** *S*

A George III mahogany secretaire bookcase, the secretaire drawer panelled to resemble 2 drawers and enclosing a fitted interior with elmwood-veneered drawers, handles and urn replaced, 8 ft. 3½ in. high by 3 ft. 6 in. wide (253 by 107 cm.), c. 1775. **£4,000-4,500** *S*

A good Georgian mahogany secretaire bookcase, the lower section with a fluted canopy moulding over the secretaire drawer which encloses small drawers and pigeonholes, later brass drop handles, 29 in. wide. **£8,000-10,000** *PWC*

A George III mahogany secretaire bookcase, the moulded glazed doors enclosing adjustable shelves, the projecting moulded base with fitted secretaire drawer, 8 ft. 4 in. high by 3 ft. 9 in. wide (254 by 114 cm.), c. 1760. **£4,500-5,500** *S*

A secretaire bookcase, with neo-classical marquetry inlay the fall-flap secretaire drawer with drawers and pigeonhole 3 ft. 1 in. overall. **£3,000-3,50** *WW*

A large mahogany secretaire bookcase, the top with marquetry inlaid swan neck pediment, the fall-flap inlaid ribbon tie swags, with fitted interior cupboard, 5 ft. in. **£2,500-3,000**   *WW*

A George III mahogany secretaire bookcase, the fitted drawer below applied with beading and roundels, 89 in. high by 44 in. wide. **£3,500-£4,000**   *Bea*

A George III mahogany secretaire cabinet, outlined with ebonised and boxwood lines, the base with a well-fitted secretaire drawer, 47½ in. wide by 90 in. high (121 by 229 cm.). **£3,000-£3,500**   *C*

A George III mahogany secretaire bookcase, the secretaire fitting inlaid with musical instruments and floral sprays enclosing an interior of drawers and pigeonholes, 112 cm. wide, the inlay, late 19th C. **£1,500-2,000**   *Bon*

Georgian mahogany secretaire bookcase, having rosewood and boxwood inlaid roundel decoration, ft. 9 in. **£2,000-2,500**   *WSW*

A George III mahogany secretaire bookcase, the lower section with 2 long drawers forming a fitted secretaire, 7 ft. 11 in. high by 4 ft. 2 in. wide (241 by 127 cm.), c. 1790. **£2,000-2,500**   *S*

A George III mahogany secretaire bookcase, 7 ft. 10 in. high by 4 ft. 1 in. wide (239 by 125 cm.), c. 1790. **£2,500-3,000**   *SS*

A late George III mahogany secretaire bookcase, 99½ in. high by 53 in. wide. **£1,500-2,000**   *Bea*

George III mahogany secretaire bookcase, the later upper part with pair of glazed doors, the lower part with a moulded fall-front closing a fitted interior, on later bracket feet, 89 by 43 in. (226 by 9 cm.), the lower part early th C. **£1,500-2,000**   *SC*

A George III mahogany secretaire bookcase, the fitted writing drawer above 3 long graduated drawers, on shaped bracket feet, 7 ft. 1 in. high by 3 ft. 3½ in. wide (216 by 100 cm.), c. 1790. **£2,000-2,500**   *SS*

A late George III inlaid mahogany secretaire bookcase, 110 cm. wide. **£2,000-2,500** *HSS*

A Sheraton period mahogany secretaire bookcase, 88 in. high. **£3,000-3,500** *A*

A 19th C. mahogany secretaire bookcase, the pull-out secretaire drawer fitted with small drawers and pigeonholes, 47 in. wide. **£1,800-2,200** *PWC*

An early 19th C. mahogany secretaire bookcase, the base with partridge wood fittings, 42 by 93 in. high. **£2,400-2,800** *DWB*

An Edwardian 'Sheraton Revival' inlaid mahogany bureau bookcase, with satinwood crossbanding, slope fall-front enclosing well fitted satinwood interior, with pigeonholes and secret compartments, 65 in. wide by 85 in. high. **£1,500-1,800** *Re*

A fine Sheraton rosewood secretaire cabinet, with well fitted secretaire drawer, and 2 door cupboard below, inlaid with oval satinwood bands, with painted border simulating pearls, 33¾ in. wide by 76¾ in. high. **£12,000-£15,000** *GSP*

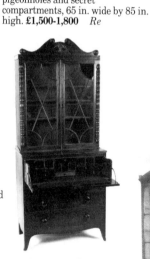

A Sheraton period pollard oak secretaire bookcase with ebony inlay, the secretaire drawer fitt with pigeonholes, drawers and marquetry inlaid central cupbo 3 ft. 5¾ in. wide. **£4,500-5,500** *GC*

A late Regency mahogany secretaire bookcase. **£1,800-£2,200** *JD*

A George IV mahogany secretaire bookcase, 43 in. wide. **£1,500-2,000** *Bea*

A Georgian mahogany secretai bookcase. **£1,000-1,200** *Wor*

A Regency mahogany secretaire bookcase, the projecting lower part with a panelled fitted secretaire drawer, 8 ft. high by 3 ft. 10½ in. wide (244 by 118 cm.), c. 1820. **£2,000-2,500** *S*

An early 19th C. mahogany secretaire bookcase, the lower section with secretaire drawer enclosing small drawers and pigeonholes, decorated with satinwood bands, string lines and gadrooned mouldings, 45 in. wide. **£1,800-2,200** *PWC*

BUREAUX

- Bureaux were not made in this counry until after the reign of Charles II
- this writing box on stand was initially produced in oak and then in walnut
- these were originally on turned or straight legs but cabriole legs became popular in the last decade of the 17th C.
- note the quality and proportion of the cabriole legs — good carving is another plus factor
- always more valuable if containing an *original* stepped interior and well
- also the more complex the interior — the more expensive
- from about 1680 most bureaux made from walnut, many with beautiful marquetry and inlay
- from about 1740 mahogany became the most favoured wood, although walnut was still used
- the 'key' size for a bureau is 3 ft. 2 in., as the width diminishes so the price increases dramatically
- original patination, colour and original brass handles are obviously important features for assessing any piece of furniture, but these are crucial when valuing bureaux and chests

satinwood
cretaire
binet, the
lid cylinder
closing a
ed
erior
cluding a
ize-lined
de, 33 in.
de
cm.), late
th C.
,000-3,500

A fine satinwood and marquetry secretaire bookcase, of small proportions, the lower part with a finely fitted drawer, inlaid throughout with swags, rosettes and flower filled vases, all within mahogany bandings, 79 by 28 in. (201 by 71 cm.), early 20th C. **£6,500-7,500** *SC*

A carved mahogany secretaire bookcase of Chippendale style, 2 ft. 2 in. wide by 4 ft. 9 in. high, late 19th C./early 20th C. **£700-900** *CDC*

early 18th C. walnut bureau,
top and fall-front feather and
ssbanded, the interior with
geonholes, cabinet, pillar drawers
d small drawers, 3 ft. wide.
,000-2,500   *PWC*

A walnut bureau, with fitted and stepped interior, 36¼ in., 20¼ in., 38¼ in., c. 1720. **£3,000-3,500**   *LA*

A Queen Anne walnut bureau, with sloping crossbanded flap, in need of restoration, 29½ in. wide (75 cm.). **£2,000-2,500**   *C*

Villiam and Mary walnut and
ssbanded bureau, decorated
h feather-banding, the fall
ealing a fitted and restored
erior with well, on later shaped
cket feet, restored, 3 ft. 3½ in.
h by 3 ft. wide (100 by 91.5 cm.),
700. **£1,600-2,000**   *SS*

*s price is affected by the
oration to this piece.*

A George I bureau, in straight-cut and pollard oak, the flap with cross and chevron-banding and enclosing a fitted interior, 3 ft. 1 in. wide (94 cm.), c. 1720. **£2,000-2,500**   *S*

A Queen Anne bureau, in finely figured walnut veneers, the herringbone-inlaid fall concealing a fitted interior with baize writing surface, small drawers, pigeonholes and a cupboard with early brasswork, 37½ in. wide by 20¾ in. deep by 40 in. high. **£4,500-5,000** *HAL*

A George I veneered walnut bureau, with stepped interior and well, 40 in. high by 36 in. wide by 20 in. deep, c. 1720. **£4,000-5,000** *AP*

A George I walnut and feather-banded bureau, the fall revealing a fitted interior, 3 ft. 6 in. high by 3 ft. 4 in. wide (107 by 102 cm.), c. 1720. **£2,800-3,500** *SS*

A George I crossbanded and herringbone inlaid veneered figured walnut bureau, 2 ft. 9 i wide. **£6,000-7,500** *LBP*

A George I walnut bureau, inlaid with boxwood stringing, the crossbanded fall revealing small drawers and pigeonholes, restored, stationery compartments altered, 2 ft. 9 in. wide (84 cm.), c. 1720. **£2,500-3,000** *SS*

A small George I walnut bureau, the front enclosing a cupboard, drawers, pigeonholes and a well, 2 ft. 6 in. wide. **£2,000-2,500** *T*

A George I walnut bureau, crossbanded and feather-banded. the fitted interior with a well, on later bracket feet, restored, 37 in (94 cm.). **£2,500-3,000** *L*

An 18th C. walnut bureau, with feather-banded fall-flap opening to a well fitted interior and well, feet and handles replaced, 3 ft. wide. **£2,500-3,000** *MMB*

A small George II mahogany bureau, the fall-front enclosing an interior, now depleted, 2 ft. 3 in. wide. **£2,500-3,000** *B*
This price due to the ideal size of this piece.

A walnut bureau, the fall-front enclosing a fitted interior and wel 41 by 36 in. (104 by 93 cm.), secon quarter 18th C. **£1,500-2,000** *S(*

A George II walnut bureau, with sloping crossbanded flap, enclosing a fitted interior with pigeonholes and short drawers, restorations, 37½ in. wide (95 cm.). **£2,000-2,500** *C*

A George I walnut bureau, the sloping front enclosing a well-fitted interior inlaid and crossbanded with arched, stepped and secret compartments, over a sliding well, 38 in. wide. **£2,500-3,000** *GM*

. mid Georgian walnut bureau,
he sloping flap enclosing a fitted
nterior, adapted, in need of
xtensive restoration, 36½ in.
1,000-1,500   *CSK*

A George II bureau, in walnut on
oak, the herringbone inlaid
crossbanded surface and fall
concealing stepped interior with
drawers, secret drawers,
pigeonholes, small cupboard and a
well, the brasswork original
throughout, replaced bracket feet,
36 in. wide by 20 in. deep by 40 in.
high, c. 1745. **£2,800-3,500**   *HAL*

A George II crossbanded walnut
bureau, some damage, 36 in.
£1,800-2,500   *JD*

A veneered walnut bureau with
stepped interior and serpentine
drawers, 3 ft. wide, c. 1740. **£1,800-
£2,500**   *PLJ*

George III mahogany bureau, the
tinwood crossbanded fall-front
closing a fitted interior of
pboard, drawers and pigeonholes,
in. wide. **£750-950**   *Re*

George III mahogany bureau, the
ossbanded fall-front enclosing a
ted interior with central
pboard door flanked by drawers
d pigeonholes, 36 in. wide,
1800. **£600-900**   *Re*

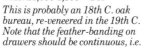

An early 19th C. inlaid and
crossbanded bureau, with fitted
inlaid stepped interior, old brass
handles and escutcheons, 36 in.
wide. **£1,000-1,500**   *DA*

*This is probably an 18th C. oak
bureau, re-veneered in the 19th C.
Note that the feather-banding on
drawers should be continuous, i.e.*

```
<<<<<<<<<<<<<<<<<<< ^
 v                 ^
 v                 ^
 v                 ^
 v                 ^
 v                 ^
 v>>>>>>>>>>>>>>>>>> ^
```

An early George II Cuban
mahogany bureau, the interior
with a central panelled cupboard
door, flanked by reeded secret
compartment pilaster, drawers and
pigeonholes, fitted with original
brass handles and escutcheons, 3 ft.
1 in. **£2,000-2,500**   *WW*

Georgian mahogany bureau, the
ted interior with secret
mpartments, 47½ in. **£800-1,200**

*is is a good bureau but the size
½ in. wide, is against it.*

A George III mahogany bureau, the fall-front
enclosing a simple fitted interior, 41 by 36 in.
(104 by 92 cm.), third quarter of 18th C. **£800-
£1,200**   *SC*

A Chippendale-period mahogany
bureau, with replacement handles,
39 in. wide by 22 in. deep by 43 in.
high, c. 1760. **£1,500-1,700**   *AP*

A George III mahogany bureau, decorated with crossbandings and inlaid stringings, having fitted interior, 3 ft. **£800-1,000**   *WSW*

A George III mahogany bureau, the fall-front revealing stepped fitted interior, 37¾ in. wide. **£1,000-1,500**   *BS*

A George III mahogany bureau, 36 in. high. **£1,000-1,500**   *DWB*

A Georgian mahogany bureau, with fitted interior, 3 ft. wide. **£800-1,200**   *WHL*

A 19th C. inlaid and crossbanded mahogany bureau, with fully fitted interior, 46 in. wide. **£800-1,200**   *DSH*

A Georgian mahogany bureau, the fall-front concealing smaller drawers, cupboard and secret compartments, 42 in. wide. **£800-£1,200**   *M*

An inlaid mahogany bureau, the fall-front enclosing well-fitted interior with shell marquetry inlays, 46 in. wide, early 19th C. **£800-1,200**   *Re*

This is a good bureau but its size 46 in. wide is against it.

An inlaid mahogany bureau, 30 in. wide, c. 1860. **£400-600**   *LRG*

A small Edwardian mahogany-veneered bureau, with shell inlay and crossbanding, the fall-front enclosing fitted interior, 31 in. wide by 16½ in. deep. **£300-500**   *BHW*

A George III inlaid and figured mahogany fall-front writing bureau, 47 in. wide. **£800-1,200**   *CBB*

A Dutch Colonial padouk wood miniature bureau, the fall revealing a fitted and serpentined interior with well, 1 ft. 11 in. high by 1 ft. 10 in. wide (58 by 56 cm.), c. 1760. **£4,000-6,000**   *SS*

Dutch East Indies solid padouk
ureau, the fall-front with a fitted
terior, 3 ft. 2 in. high by 3 ft.
in. wide (96 by 102 cm.), slightly
educed in height, third quarter of
8th C. **£3,500-4,500**   *S*

Dutch walnut bureau, of bombé
utlines, inset with floral
narquetry and chequered boxwood
nes, the sloping flap enclosing a
tted interior and well, 45½ in.,
ate 18th C. **£2,500-3,200**   *CSK*

Dutch marquetry bureau, the
linder front opening in
njunction with a pull-out writing
rface and enclosing a fitted
terior, 3 ft. 9 in. high by 3 ft.
in. wide (115 by 115 cm.), c. 1770.
,500-3,500   *S*

South German 18th C. walnut
rpentine fronted bureau, with
ssbandings and stringings, the
l-front with fitted interior of
wers and lockers including well,
in. wide. **£4,000-5,000**   *VV*

An 18th C. Dutch marquetry fall-
front bureau, the block serpentine
front with various designs, c. 1740.
£7,000-8,000   *Wor*

An early 18th C. marquetry walnut
bureau, having bombé shaped
front, the shaped interior fitted
with 8 short drawers, 4 pigeonholes
and sliding well. **£3,000-4,000**
WSW

NOTES ON DUTCH MARQUETRY BUREAUX

- beware badly split flaps and sides
- marquetry on walnut fetches more than marquetry on mahogany, which in turn fetches more than marquetry on oak
- cylinder bureaux as a general rule fetch less than fall front bureaux
- always look out for marquetry which includes bone and/or mother-of-pearl
- marquetry including birds and insects is slightly rarer than the usual floral marquetry

A Dutch mahogany cylinder
bureau, in 2 parts, the panel
cylinder opening in conjunction
with a slide above 3 drawers in the
bombé front, 3 ft. 8½ in. high by
4 ft. wide (113 by 122 cm.), c. 1775.
£1,500-2,000   *S*

*With a plain cylinder top this piece
has a lower price than a marquetry
equivalent.*

An early 19th C. Dutch marquetry
and walnut cylinder top bureau,
the pull-out writing slide activates
the cylinder front to reveal various
shaped front drawers, cupboard,
pigeonholes and secret
compartments, 4 ft. 8½ in. wide
(143.5 cm.). **£4,000-5,000**   *LBP*

A Dutch walnut and floral
marquetry bombé bureau, with
shaped fielded flap enclosing a
fitted interior, including a well, on
later bracket feet, 45 in. wide
(114 cm.). **£2,800-3,500**   *C*

An 18th C. Anglo-Dutch
marquetry bureau, the fall front
enclosing drawers, pigeonholes and
a well, later inlaid, 3 ft. 3½ in.
wide. **£1,600-2,200**   *GC*

A South German elm and walnut-veneered bureau on chest, the later veneered interior with pigeonholes, restored, 3 ft. 1 in. high by 3 ft. 2½ in. wide (94 by 98 cm.), c. 1720. **£3,500-4,500** *SS*

A North Italian marquetry bureau, inlaid with brass, ivory and mother-of-pearl, 2 ft. 7 in. wide, c. 1880. **£800-1,200** *MMB*

A Lombard walnut and marquetry secretaire chest, the crossbanded wire-hinged top and fall-front enclosing 10 similarly inlaid drawers, 37½ in. high by 59 in. wide, mid 18th C. **£3,000-3,500** *Bea*

A Louis XV small marquetry bureau, in quarter-veneered tulipwood, enclosed by quarter-veneered purple heart banding, with a fitted interior and a shelf, 3 ft. high by 1 ft. 11½ in. wide (92 by 60 cm.), c. 1750. **£2,000-3,000** *S*

A burr-walnut bureau on stand, in George I style, with a fitted interior above a drawer, 2 ft. 4 in. wide (71 cm.), c. 1920. **£800-1,200** *S*

A George I-style ladies walnut bureau, with oyster-veneered decoration and similar crossbanding to flap, 26 in., c. 1920. **£800-1,200** *JD*

A red walnut bureau on stand, the fall-front opening to reveal a fitted interior above a single drawer, 3 ft. 2 in. wide, partly 18th C. **£1,000-£1,500** *HyD*

A Dutch marquetry bureau on stand, the shaped fitted interior with a well, 37 in. (94 cm.), 19th C. **£1,400-1,800** *L*

A walnut bureau, on William and Mary-style turned legs and cross stretchers, 3 ft. 6 in. wide, early 20th C. **£500-700** *EG*

A Victorian writing desk, in rosewood, the enclosed interior with inkwell and 2 small drawers, 26 in. high. **£400-600** *BHW*

A rosewood bureau de dame, 26 in. wide, c. 1875. **£400-600** *WHL*

A rosewood bureau de dame, the shaped fall-front inlaid with a marquetry panel, the interior fitted with 3 drawers above a well, 3 ft. 1 in. high by 2 ft. 7 in. wide (94 by 79 cm.), c. 1870. **£1,200-1,500** *S*

A Louis XV kingwood marquetry
ecretaire en pente, with quarter-
eneered top, flap and sides inlaid
vith trailing flowers, the fitted
nterior including a well and 4
hort drawers, 2 ft. 10 in. wide
36.5 cm.), c. 1750, the plaques and
nounts added c. 1840. **£3,000-4,000**

An Edwardian ladies inlaid
mahogany bureau, by Maple & Co.,
29½ in. **£600-800** *JD*

An Edwardian painted satinwood
bureau, with a fitted interior, 3 ft.
8½ in. high by 2 ft. 7 in. wide (113
by 79 cm.), early 20th C. **£900-
£1,200** *S*

A Louis XV secretaire en pente, the
loping front enclosing a fitted
nterior with a well and with 2
rawers, now decorated in
mitation of scarlet-ground
)riental lacquer, with figures and
avilions and with gilt-bronze
)coco mounts, 3 ft. 1 in. high by
ft. 1 in. wide (94 by 94 cm.), mid
8th C. **£10,000-12,000** *S*

A French Louis XVI-style burr-
walnut veneered inlaid and
marquetry bureau de dame,
86.5 cm. wide, 19th C. **£5,000-6,000**
HSS

A French bombé bureau de dame,
in amboyna/thuya with kingwood
quarter-banding, the leather-lined
flap enclosing 3 shaped drawers,
3 ft. high by 2 ft. 5 in. wide (91 by
74 cm.), c. 1870. **£1,800-2,500** *S*

Louis Philippe ormolu and
rcelain-mounted tulipwood
reau de dame, the fall-flap
closing 6 shaped and tiered
awers and a well, 34 in. wide
5.5 cm.). **£3,000-4,000** *C*

An inlaid figured walnut bureau,
the flap enclosing a fitted interior
with a well, inlaid throughout with
scrollwork, 4 ft. 7 in. high by 2 ft.
9½ in. wide (140 by 85 cm.),
c. 1860. **£1,000-1,500** *S*

A kingwood and tulipwood
marquetry bureau de dame, the
concave serpentine fall-front and
the bombé sides and back inlaid,
the interior similarly inlaid and
with drawers and sliding wells,
2 ft. 9 in. wide (84 cm.), c. 1870.
£4,500-5,500 *S*

A William and Mary walnut
secretaire on chest, the cushion
frieze with a drawer and the
crossbanded flap with 2 chevron
bandings enclosing drawers,
removable pigeonholes and a
cupboard, on later bracket feet,
2 ft. 9½ in. high by 3 ft. 6 in. wide
(84 by 107 cm.), c. 1700. **£3,200-
£3,800** *S*

A William and Mary burr-walnut secretaire, 42 in. wide by 21½ in. deep by 73½ in. high, c. 1690. **£3,200-3,800** *LA*

A small Queen Anne oak fall-front secretaire, enclosing a well-fitted interior of small drawers, pigeonholes, surrounding a central compartment with door, 37 in. wide. **£800-1,200** *B*

A fine Queen Anne walnut and herringbone writing cabinet. **£12,000-15,000** *WM*

A Queen Anne walnut secretaire on chest, with moulded cornice and a convex frieze drawer above the quartered crossbanded fall-flap, framed by herringbone lines, enclosing a fitted interior with pigeonholes, drawers and a cupboard, 42½ in. wide (108 cm.). **£2,800-3,400** *C*

An early George III secretaire cabinet, the base with a secretaire drawer, fitted with 6 various-sized drawers and 8 elaborate pigeonholes, 43½ in. wide (111 cm.). **£1,800-2,400** *C*

A George III mahogany secretaire tallboy, 47 in. **£800-1,200** *CSK*

A George III mahogany secretaire linen press, with 5 sliding trays and a fitted secretaire drawer, 48 by 85 in. high (122 by 216 cm.). **£1,000-1,200** *L*

A 19th C. drop front figured mahogany secretaire, with fitted interior, 41 in. **£500-700** *GM*

A Biedermeier figured mahogany secretaire à abattant, the fall-front enclosing a well-fitted interior, crossbanded and inlaid, 3 ft. 6 in. wide by 5 ft. high. **£800-1,200** *CDC*

A Dutch marquetry and mahogany secretaire à abattant, with floral vase, bird and butterfly inlay and chevron banding, the fall revealing a stepped and fitted interior, 5 ft. 1½ in. high by 3 ft. 6½ in. wide (156 by 110 cm.), c. 1820. **£1,000-1,500** *SS*

A Dutch ormolu-mounted mahogany and marquetry secretaire à abattant, the fall-flap inlaid and enclosing a fitted interior, above 2 panelled cupboard doors enclosing 2 short drawers and a coffre fort, 38½ in. wide (98 cm.), early 19th C. **£2,000-2,500** *C*

A Continental mahogany secretaire à abattant of Biedermeier style, the fall-front enclosing a well-fitted interior, probably German, 42 by 64 in. (107 by 163 cm.) high, early 19th C. **£600-800** *L*

An Empire ormolu-mounted secretaire à abattant, with a fitted interior flanked by bronze and ormolu caryatids in the Egyptian style, 39 in. wide (99 cm.). **£2,500-£3,000** *C*

PRICES

The never-ending problem of fixing prices for antiques! A price can be affected by so many factors, for example:
- *condition*
- *desirability*
- *rarity*
- *size*
- *colour*
- *provenance*
- *restoration*
- *the sale of a prestigious collection*
- *collection label*
- *appearance of a new reference book*
- *new specialist sale at major auction house*
- *mentioned on television*
- *the fact that two people present at auction are determined to have the piece*
- *where you buy it*

One also has to contend with the fact that an antique is not only a 'thing of beauty' but a commodity. The price can again be affected by:—
- *supply and demand*
- *international finance — currency fluctuation*
- *fashion*
- *inflation*
- *the fact that a museum has vast sums of money to spend*

A Dutch burr-walnut side secretaire cabinet, the glazed cupboard doors enclosing a black and gold japanned interior, 53 in. wide (134.5 cm.). **£3,500-4,500** *C*

An amboyna and gilt metal secretaire de dame, in Louis XVI style, crossbanded, inlaid with stringing and with gilt metal borders, the interior containing small drawers and pigeonholes, 24 by 47 in. (61 by 120 cm.) high. **£1,500-2,000** *L*

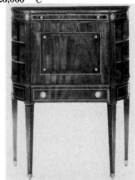

A small brass-mounted mahogany secretaire, in the manner of David Roentgen, the drawer below the panelled front flanked by a pair of spring-operated curved drawers, 4 ft. 1 in. high by 3 ft. 2 in. wide (125 by 96 cm.), c. 1780. **£3,500-£4,000** *S*

An early George III mahogany display cabinet, 7 ft. 7½ in. high by 3 ft. 7 in. wide (233 by 107 cm.), c. 1765. **£6,000-£8,000** *S*

A mid Georgian satinwood and yew wood display cabinet, 29½ in. wide by 59¾ in. high (75 by 152 cm.). **£1,000-1,500** *C*

A rare George III mahogany collector's cabinet, of breakfront architectural form, with a pierced oak gallery, the frieze inlaid with alternating cube and stepped parquetry banding in rosewood and satinwood, on a harewood ground, shaped tulipwood crossbanded on on square tapering legs, inlaid with husks and headed by stringing, 6 ft. high by 4 ft. 10 in. wide (183 by 147.5 cm.), c. 1780. **£1,800-2,400** *S*

A good George III-style mahogany breakfront display cabinet, crossbanded in satinwood and inlaid with boxwood lines throughout, bearing a Robson & Sons retailer's plaque, 83 by 50 in. (211 by 127 cm.), early 20th C. **£1,500-2,000** *SC*

An early 19th C. George III-style display cabinet, 48 in. wide. **£800-£1,200** *GM*

A Regency mahogany display cabinet, 8 ft. 2 in. high by 4 ft. wide (249 by 122 cm.), c. 1810. **£1,200-1,600** *S*

A 19th C. dentists' mahogany cabinet, the back fitted with 3 secret compartments, 110 cm. wide. **£800-1,200** *OT*

A 19th C. Chippendale-style inlaid mahogany display cabinet, 39 in. wide. **£350-420** *GM*

A late Victorian inlaid rosewood and marquetry side cabinet. **£600-£800** *JF*

A Victorian birds-eye maple and mahogany china display cabinet, 62 in. **£500-700** *A*

A 19th C. mahogany display cabinet on stand, the stand with single drawer with carved floral decoration, 34 in. wide. **£700-900** *WA*

A good 'Chinese Chippendale'-style mahogany display cabinet, 90 by 54 in. (230 by 137 cm.), late 19th C. **£1,500-2,000** *SC*

A Victorian ebony display cabinet, with gilt metal mounts, 88 in. **£2,000-2,500** *CSK*

A late 19th C. mahogany display cabinet, 42 in. **£350-450** *MN*

A good painted satinwood display cabinet on stand, of bowed breakfront form, 5 ft. 2 in. high by 4 ft. 3 in. wide (158 by 130 cm.), c. 1900. **£4,500-5,500** *S*

A satinwood and marquetry side cabinet by Maple & Co., inlaid throughout with marquetry flowers, scrolls, swags and masks, 8 ft. high by 5 ft. wide (244 by 152 cm.), c. 1900. **£5,000-6,000**

mahogany display cabinet, 3 in., c. 1900. **£300-400**   *TW*

A serpentine carved mahogany display cabinet, 6 ft. 8 in. high by 4 ft. 8 in. wide (203 by 142 cm.), c. 1910. **£1,800-2,500**   *S*

An inlaid mahogany display cabinet, in the French style, 26 in. wide by 5 ft. 4 in. high. **£600-800** *EG*

An Edwardian rosewood and satinwood inlaid corner what-not display cabinet, the doors inlaid with ribbon swags and fan medallion below a display shelf, 78 in. high by 33 in. wide. **£800-£1,200**   *CGC*

n inlaid Edwardian mahogany display cabinet. **£350-400**   *BA*

An Edwardian mahogany display cabinet, with mirror-lined back and 2 plate glass shelves enclosed by partly glazed doors, 41½ in. wide by 83 in. high. **£1,800-2,200**   *BM*

An Edwardian inlaid mahogany serpentine front china display cabinet, the top crossbanded in mahogany with burr-walnut rim and having floral marquetry decoration, 103.5 cm. wide. **£1,600-2,000** *HSS*

An Edwardian mahogany and inlaid display cabinet, 38½ in. **£400-500**   *MN*

Edwardian inlaid mahogany play cabinet, 54 in. wide. **£1,000-500**   *Re*

An Edwardian display cabinet, with bevelled glass fronted cupboards and display stands, with marquetry and bone inlay, 8 ft. 6 in. high by 5 ft. 6 in. wide. **£1,400-£1,800**   *Wor*

An Edwardian inlaid mahogany display cabinet, with satinwood ribbon and husk decoration, 41½ in. **£600-800**   *CKK*

An early 18th C. Dutch walnut and kingwood display cabinet on stand, 81 in. high by 64 by 24 in. **£2,000-£3,000**   *CGC*

A small Edwardian mahogany bow-fronted display cabinet and chest, 20 by 15 in. wide by 48 in. high. **£350-450**   *BHW*

An inlaid Edwardian glazed china cabinet. **£500-700** *PLJ*

A Dutch marquetry and walnut display cabinet on chest, fitted with electric light, 6 ft. 6 in. high by 2 ft. 11 in. wide (198 by 89 cm.), c. 1770. **£3,000-3,500** *SS*

A mahogany breakfront display cabinet, inlaid with foliage and stringing, 49 in. wide by 74 in. high. **£1,000-1,400** *GSP*

A Dutch walnut and marquetry display cabinet, inlaid with elaborate floral marquetry, 7 ft. 5 in. high by 6 ft. 1 in. wide (226 by 186 cm.), mid 18th C. **£6,000-8,000** *S*

Compared to the following display cabinet, this one has superior marquetry and 'stringing'. Also original velvet-lined interior.

A Dutch walnut and marquetry display cabinet on chest, 6 ft. 2 in. high by 3 ft. 1 in. wide (188 by 94 cm.), mid 18th C., marquetry 19th C. **£2,500-3,000** *S*

A Dutch walnut marquetry display cabinet, 67 in. wide by 92 in. high (170 by 234 cm.). **£3,500-4,500** *C*

A Dutch walnut and floral marquetry display cabinet, centred by a shell clasp above 2 geometrically-glazed cupboard doors, 80 in. wide by 95 in. high (203 by 241 cm.). **£4,000-6,000** *C*

These cabinets are still being reproduced by 'robbing' earlier pieces. Although the cost is high it under half that for an 18th C. article and little different from 19th C. cabinet here.

A Dutch walnut and marquetry display cabinet, 72 by 100 in. high (183 by 254 cm.). **£6,000-8,000** *L*

A late 18th C. Dutch oak corner cupboard, surmounted by floral motifs, 7 ft. 6 in. high. **£1,800-2,400** *AG*

An unusual 19th C. Dutch marquetry display cabinet, 37½ in. **£800-1,200** *MN*

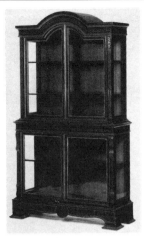

Cairene olivewood and parquetry splay cabinet, the overhanging chitectural cornice above a frieze th Arabic inscription, 6 ft. 4 in. gh by 3 ft. 3 in. wide (193 by cm.), 1900-20. **£2,000-2,500**   *S*

A German walnut display cabinet, with gilt bronze mounts, 5 ft. 2 in. high by 2 ft. 1 in. wide, c. 1880. **£1,200-1,500**   *S*

A Boulle display cabinet, 7 ft. 2 in. high by 4 ft. 1 in. wide, c. 1860. **£1,000-£1,500**   *S*

A grotesque baroque Italian display cabinet. **£800-1,200**   *Wor*

This interesting piece has started life as a cabinet on stand which has been raised by adding the base of a chair without back. The chair looks as if it may have been extremely interesting.

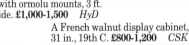

ilt bronze mounted mahogany splay cabinet, in Louis XVI style, t. 9 in. high by 2 ft. 6 in. wide by t. deep (206 by 78 by 30 cm.), 1880. **£1,800-2,200**   *S*

A late 19th C. French vitrine, in walnut with ormolu mounts, 3 ft. 11 in. wide. **£1,000-1,500**   *HyD*

A French walnut display cabinet, 31 in., 19th C. **£800-1,200**   *CSK*

An Empire-style mahogany vitrine, 27 in. **£800-1,200**   *CSK*

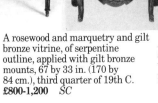

ingwood vitrine, with gilt nze mounts, 6 ft. 2 in. high by . 7 in. wide (188 by 109 cm.), 19th C. **£1,800-2,400**   *S*

A French brass-mounted mahogany bijouterie display cabinet, 32½ in. **£1,000-1,500** *GSP*

A rosewood and marquetry and gilt bronze vitrine, of serpentine outline, applied with gilt bronze mounts, 67 by 33 in. (170 by 84 cm.), third quarter of 19th C. **£800-1,200**   *SC*

A 19th C. walnut vitrine, with serpentine glazed front and sides with floral marquetry bouquets, in need of restoration. **£800-1,200** *WM*

A French gilt metal mounted kingwood and Vernis Martin vitrine, 31½, 69 in. high. **£1,000-£1,400** *GSP*

A carved and parcel-gilt and marquetry vitrine, with serpentine glazed front, 6 ft. 1 in. high by 3 ft. 7 in. wide (185.5 by 109 cm.), 1930's. **£1,400-1,800** *S*

A Louis XVI-style kingwood marquetry and parquetry vitrine with chased ormolu mounts, 6 ft. 3 in. high by 3 ft. 10 in. wide. **£2,200-2,800** *CDC*

A mahogany and gilt bronze and Vernis Martin vitrine, with 2 plate glass shelves, 67 by 25 in. diam. (170 by 64 cm.), 20th C. **£800-1,200** *SC*

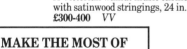

A walnut music cabinet, inlaid throughout with boxwood lines, 38½ by 23 in. (98 by 59 cm.), third quarter 19th C. **£350-450** *SC*

A Victorian walnut music cabinet, with satinwood stringings, 24 in. **£300-400** *VV*

An aesthetic influence mahogany music cabinet, 3 ft. 7 in. high by 2 ft. 1 in. wide (109 by 64 cm.), c. 1880. **£400-500** *S*

A William and Mary kingwood oyster cabinet, on later stand, 43 in. wide. **£1,400-1,800** *PWC*
Price low due to period cabinet bu later stand.

A William and Mary kingwood and rosewood and oyster walnut-veneered cupboard. **£3,000-3,500** *Wor*

A Charles II black-japanned cabinet on stand, the cabinet decorated in imitation Chinese lacquer, the interior with 10 drawers similarly decorated, the pierced silver gesso stand carved with flowers, leaves and cherubs, restored, overall height 5 ft. 1 in. by 3 ft. 3 in. wide (155 by 99 cm.), c. 1680. **£6,000-8,000** *S*

A Charles II walnut-veneered cabinet on stand, the pair of cross and chevron banded doors each inlaid with oval and curved spandrels and enclosing an arrangement of 11 drawers around a cupboard and with secret drawers, restored and legs replaced, 5 ft. 3½ in. high by 3 ft. 6 in. wide (161 by 107 cm.), c. 1670. **£1,500-2,000** *S*

A William and Mary oyster-veneered olivewood cabinet on stand, the doors enclosing an arrangement of 8 drawers and a central cupboard above a long drawer, restored, 4 ft. 7½ in. high by 2 ft. 11½ in. wide (141 by 98.5 cm.), c. 1700. **£5,500-6,500** *S*

A Queen Anne black and gold lacquer cabinet on stand, the doors highlighted in shades of gold and red mounted with brass lockplate and hinges enclosing 10 various-sized drawers, on later turned baluster legs, 42 in. wide (106 cm.). **£3,000-3,500** *C*

A William and Mary walnut chest on stand, the cushion frieze drawer above a crossbanded fall-front, stand restored, flap locked, 5 ft. 4 in. high by 3 ft. 7 in. wide (163 by 109 cm.), c. 1690. **£2,000-2,500** *S*

A burr-walnut and burr-ash cabinet on stand, the doors inlaid with an oval paterae and crossbanding inlaid with foliage, 5 ft. ¼ in. high by 2 ft. 6¼ in. wide (153 by 77 cm.), the top early 18th C., the base c. 1900. **£1,200-1,600** *S*

A Regency painted and penwork collector's cabinet, the doors enclosing an arrangement of short and long drawers, 76 in. high by 41 in. wide. **£2,500-3,000** *Bea*

A walnut and marquetry cabinet on stand, with a mirrored interior backed by marquetry inlaid drawer fronts, 113 cm. wide. **£3,000-4,000** *Bon*

A Flemish ormolo-mounted tortoiseshell, rosewood and ebony cabinet on stand, the interior panelled with mirrors surrounding central trompe d'oeil doorway inlaid with ivory and stained ivory with a cube pattern floor, 50½ in. wide (128.5 cm.), late 17th C. **£7,500-8,500** *C*

A Dutch marquetry and walnut cabinet on stand, with segmented veneers, the doors revealing star inlay to the reverse and an arrangement of drawers surrounding a cupboard, with mirror lined architectural interior, bearing painted and branded inventory numbers, stand restored, 5 ft. 5 in. high by 3 ft. 7½ in. wide (165 by 111 cm.), c. 1690. **£2,500-3,500** *SS*

A Dutch walnut cabinet on stand, the stand with one frieze drawer on spirally turned legs joined by an X-shaped stretcher and later oak ball feet, with ormolu carrying handles, 47½ in. wide (120.5 cm.), early 18th C. **£2,500-3,000** *C*

A Flemish painted table cabinet, with an arrangement of 10 drawers surrounding a cupboard with a mirrored interior, 1 ft. 10 in. high by 2 ft. 9 in. wide (56 by 84 cm.), mid 17th C., on a 19th C. ebonised stand with 4 spiral twist legs. **£2,000-3,000** *S*

A Goanese carved and inlaid hardwood chest on stand, 4 ft. 3 in. high by 2 ft. 10 in. wide (130 by 87 cm.), late 17th/early 18th C. **£4,500-5,500** *S*

A Florentine ebony cabinet, with ivory stringing and set with pietra dura panels, the doors opening to reveal an interior consisting of a central pediment flanked by 8 drawers, with rock crystal columns and gilt bronze mounts, c. 1700. **£3,200-4,000** *S*

A Japanese lacquer cabinet on stand, the cabinet with engraved brass mounts and handles, decorated in gilt with flowers and foliage on a black ground, 31½ in. high by 19½ in. wide. **£300-400** *Bea*

A fine ivory and ebony Vizigapatan cabinet on stand, the top intricately inlaid, the doors similarly decorated, the reverses inlaid with Indian figures enclosing 14 various sized drawers, with gilt metal carrying handles and chased hinges, the stand with foliate apron and rockwork cresting on cabriole legs, headed by C-scroll cartouches and scrolled feet, 36 in. (91.5 cm.) wide, mid 18th C. **£18,000-22,000** *C*

A Japanese black and gold lacquer dower chest, on carved scroll winged stand, 18th C. **£2,000-2,500** *Wor*

A pair of Oriental padoukwood collectors' cabinets on stands, the doors enclosing 8 drawers, the English mahogany stands with a blind fret frieze, 4 ft. 5 in. high by 1 ft. 8 in. wide (135 by 51 cm.), c. 1890. **£1,600-2,200** *SS*

A Portuguese rosewood cabinet or stand, contador, 30½ in. wide (77 cm.), 17th C. **£2,000-2,500** *C*

A Portuguese hardwood chest on stand, the drawers with rib-moulded decoration, 5 ft. 3½ in. high by 3 ft. 6½ in. wide (161 by 108 cm.), late 17th C. **£1,500-2,000** *S*

An Italian ebonised cabinet on stand, the reverse of the doors with grisaille roundels of Neptune and Venus, the later stand with a drawer, the cabinet 17th C., 23 in. wide (58 cm.). **£2,800-3,500** *C*

A small late 17th C. Chinese lacquered cabinet upon stand, the doors enclosing an interior of small drawers, the stand later, 27½ by 47½ in. **£1,400-2,000** *B*

A Spanish tortoiseshell cabinet of breakfront architectural form, with a fitted interior, 1 ft. 5 in. high by 3 ft. 6¾ in. wide (43 by 109 cm.), first half 17th C. **£700-900** *S*

A Portuguese rosewood chest on stand, 4 ft. 1 in. high by 2 ft. 7 in. wide (122 by 79 cm.), late 17th C. **1,500-2,000** *S*

An 18th C. Spanish papier peint table cabinet, chiefly in reds and green on a pale yellow ground, the front inscribed MANUEL LOPEZ, 1 ft. 11 in. by 2 ft. 11 in. wide. **£4,000-5,000** *T*

A Spanish tortoiseshell, ebony and rosewood table cabinet, with carrying handles, 41 in. wide (104 cm.), 17th C. **£700-900** *C*

A Spanish tortoiseshell, bone-inlaid and ebony cabinet on stand, 48 in. wide (122 cm.), the cabinet late 17th C. **£10,000-14,000** *C*

A fine Italian ivory, ebony and rosewood table cabinet, 13¾ in. wide (35 cm.), 17th C. **£1,000-1,500** *C*

A Spanish walnut table cabinet, 20½ by 33 in. (52 by 84 cm.), late 17th/early 18th C. **£500-700** *SC*

A Spanish ebonised, tortoiseshell and ivory cabinet on stand, 5 ft. 9 in. high by 3 ft. 7½ in. wide (175 by 110 cm.), mid 17th C. **£3,800-£4,400** *S*

A Spanish gilt metal mounted ivory, tortoiseshell and walnut cabinet on stand, inlaid top, 48 in. wide (122 cm.). **£4,500-5,500** *C*

A 19th C. North Italian rosewood and tortoiseshell cabinet. **£1,600-£2,000** *CW*

South German or Austrian miniature walnut cabinet, gallery damaged and incomplete, 2 ft. 4 in. high by 1 ft. 10½ in. wide (71 by 57 cm.), mid 18th C. **£800-1,200**

An Ulm marquetry cabinet, the rectangular hinged lid enclosing a well, above a pair of cupboard doors, enclosing a cupboard and 5 small drawers, 3 ft. high by 1 ft. 7 in. wide (91 by 48 cm.), c. 1600, on a later English stand with twist-turned legs. **£700-900** *S*

A Regency rosewood dwarf cabinet, with later bowed breakfront white marble top, lined with pleated cream silk on gilt metal paw feet, 57 in. wide (145 cm.). **£2,800-3,200** *C*

A seaweed marquetry table cabinet, in the manner of Gerrit Jensen, the doors enclosing 12 various-sized drawers with ivory knobs, on later turned ebonised feet, 16½ in. wide (42 cm.), late 17th C. **£1,500-2,000** *C*

A Regency satinwood dwarf cabinet, the D-shaped top crossbanded with rosewood and inlaid with chequered lines, 39 in. wide (99 cm.). **£4,000-4,500** *C*

A Regency maplewood side cabinet, with eared rectangular later hinged top, banded with rosewood, with an adapted interior, 36½ in. wide (93 cm.). **£3,000-4,000** *C*

A Regency rosewood chiffonier, with pierced brass gallery and column supports, with replacement panels, 36 in. wide (91.5 cm.). **£600-£800** *TW*

A late Regency rosewood chiffonier, later painted with musical trophies and scrolls and floral cornucopiae, stamped with the retailers — H. Mawer & Stephenson Ltd., 47½ in. high. **£1,500-2,000** *GSP*

REGENCY FURNITURE

- really an expression of the neo-classical taste which was evident all over Europe
- based on the French styles developed in the Consulate (1799-1804) and Empire (1804-15) periods
- one of the greatest English exponents was Thomas Hope
- mainly used mahogany and rosewood
- the decoration was based on many classical forms, Roman, Egyptian, Greek and Etruscan — often all used on one piece
- rosewood was often French polished and, when in short supply, was often simulated by painting on beech
- often noted for good brass inlay
- Regency furniture has not had an altogether happy time over the last year — with prices remaining relatively static if not falling back. This is probably something to do with the lack of Continental and American buyers but also the neo-classical as a style is quite dependent on fashion trends

A Regency rosewood chiffonier, 45¾ in. wide. **£700-900** *DSH*

A Regency ormolu-mounted rosewood dwarf bookcase, 61½ in. wide (156 cm.). **£3,000-3,500** *C*

A pair of Regency parcel gilt and simulated rosewood dwarf cabinets, with rectangular Carrara marble tops, 36 in. wide (91.5 cm.). **£3,000-£3,500** *C*

A Regency mahogany side cabinet 32 in. wide. **£1,500-2,000** *C*

A Regency mahogany chiffonier lacking feet, 36 in. **£1,000-1,500** *A*

A 19th C. satinwood cabinet, 31½ in. wide (80 cm.). **£1,000-1,500** *C*

A pair of rosewood side cabinets, of Regency design, with rectangular white marble tops, 29 in. wide (74 cm.). **£2,200-2,800** *C*

A pair of George IV rosewood small side cabinets, of bow-fronted breakfront form, now with applied parcel gilt decoration and yellow silk-lined doors, 2 ft. 11¾ in. high by 3 ft. 11¾ in. wide by 1 ft. 4¾ in. deep (91 by 121 by 42.5 cm.), c. 1830. **£6,000-8,000** *S*

A painted satinwood side cabinet, painted en grisaille with female classical figures, 32½ in. wide (82.5 cm.). **£1,500-2,000** *C*

A George IV rosewood, burr-walnut, calamander and mahogany side cabinet, 38 by 43 in. (97 by 110 cm.), second quarter of the 19th C. **£2,800-3,400** *SC*

A suite of George IV brass-inlaid mahogany side cabinets, comprising a breakfront cabinet, a pair of cabinets and a slightly smaller pair of alcove cabinets, the breakfront cabinet 3 ft. high by 6 ft. wide (92 by 183 cm.), the pair of cabinets 3 ft. high by 3 ft. wide (92 by 92 cm.), the smaller pair of cabinets 3 ft. high by 2 ft. 9 in. wide (92 by 84 cm.), c. 1820. **£18,000-£22,000** *S*

A pair of George IV rosewood-veneered side cabinets, each with a verde antico marble top, 3 ft. 1 in. high by 4 ft. wide (94 by 122 cm.), c. 1820-30. **£4,000-5,000** *S*

A pair of Victorian boulle cabinets, in brass and red tortoiseshell, the canted corners applied with ormolu mask mounts, 78 cm. wide, c. 1860. **£1,100-1,500** *Bon*

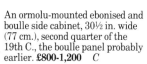

A George IV rosewood bookcase, the 2 pairs of distressed arched brass grille doors enclosing shelves, 3 ft. 2 in. high by 6 ft. 2 in. wide (97 by 188 cm.), c. 1825. **£800-1,200** *SS*

A William IV mahogany chiffonier, some veneer missing. **£250-350** *WHB*

An ormolu-mounted ebonised and boulle side cabinet, 30½ in. wide (77 cm.), second quarter of the 19th C., the boulle panel probably earlier. **£800-1,200** *C*

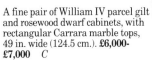

A fine pair of William IV parcel gilt and rosewood dwarf cabinets, with rectangular Carrara marble tops, 49 in. wide (124.5 cm.). **£6,000-£7,000** *C*

A pair of boulle small side cabinets, 5 ft. 4½ in. high by 2 ft. 8½ in. wide (103 by 82.5 cm.), c. 1860. **£1,800-£2,200**   *S*

A pair of fine Victorian walnut pier cabinets, with marquetry decoration, 30 in. **£800-1,200**   *JD*

An ormolu-mounted ebonised cabinet, with black-painted shaped and curved marble top, 42 in. wide (107 cm.). **£1,000-1,500**   *C*

A Louis XVI-style marquetry and parquetry side cabinet, with a grey marble top, 3 ft. 9 in. high. **£1,200-£1,600**   *AG*

A Victorian marquetry inlaid walnut display cabinet, 30 in. wide. **£300-400**   *BHW*

A pair of Victorian satinwood and ormolu-mounted bookcases, 3 ft. ½ in. high by 3 ft. wide (93 by 91.5 cm.), c. 1860. **£2,200-2,600**   *SS*

A French walnut meuble d'appui, 3 ft. 11½ in. high by 3 ft. 7 in. wide (121 by 109 cm.), c. 1900. **£800-£1,200**   *SS*

A pair of marble-topped maplewood breakfront side cabinets, each with a moulded eau Verona marble top, 3 ft. 6 in. high by 4 ft. 1½ in. wide (107 by 126 cm.), c. 1880. **£2,000-£2,500**   *S*

A dressing commode, by George Lock, 54½ in. high by 38 in. wide. **£800-1,000**   *Bea*

A Victorian walnut credenza. **£1,000-1,500**   *CW*

A mid 19th C. giltwood and gesso library cabinet, 39½ by 62 in. **£3,000-4,000**   *HyD*

An ormolu-mounted marquetry side cabinet, of breakfront form, 4 ft. high by 8 ft. ½ in. wide (122 by 245 cm.), c. 1870. **£1,600-2,200**   *S*

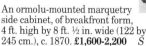

A Victorian walnut side cabinet 72 in. (183 cm.). **£800-1,000**   *L*

A pair of boulle side cabinets, the tops and sides inlaid with engraved brass Berainesque scenes on an ebony ground, 3 ft. 5 in. high by 3 ft. 1½ in. wide (104 by 95 cm.), mid 19th C. **£5,000-6,000**   *S*

A pair of ebonised boulle side cabinets, tops broken, 3 ft. 7½ in. high by 3 ft. 8½ in. wide (110 by 113 cm.), c. 1870. **£800-1,200**   *S*

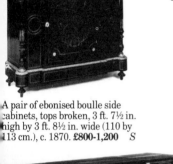

An ebony-veneered inverted breakfront side cabinet, 3 ft. 6½ in. high by 7 ft. wide (108 by 213 cm.), c. 1870. **£600-800**   *S*

A figured walnut side cabinet, with a moulded top and a mirrored door, crossbanded in tulipwood with gilt bronze mouldings and mounts, 3 ft. 5½ in. high by 4 ft. 2 in. wide (105 by 127 cm.), c. 1860. **£800-1,200**

A boulle side cabinet, in cut brass and pewter on a red tortoiseshell and ebonised ground, with black slate top, 3 ft. 6½ in. high by 4 ft. 3 in. wide (108 by 130 cm.), c. 1860. **£1,000-1,500**   *S*

A contre-partie boulle breakfront side cabinet, probably French, 3 ft. 7½ in. high by 6 ft. 7 in. wide (111 by 201 cm.), c. 1860. **£1,200-1,600**   *S*

Contre-partie refers to tortoiseshell inlaid on brass whereas the usual partie is the reverse.

A Napoleon III tulipwood veneered meuble d'appui, applied with gilt bronze pierced mounts, in the manner of Goutière, 4 ft. 1½ in. high by 4 ft. 3 in. wide (126 by 130 cm.), c. 1870. **£2,500-3,000**   *S*

A 19th C. ebonised and gilt metal mounted display cabinet, 48 in. wide. **£200-300**   *GM*

A late 19th C. walnut credenza, the top crossbanded in rosewood. **£1,500-2,000**   *Wor*

A Victorian walnut-veneered serpentine side cabinet, applied with gilt brass mounts and with kingwood crossbanding, 45½ in. high by 53 in. wide. **£800-1,000**   *Bea*

A Victorian ebonised and ormolu-mounted side cabinet, 140 cm. wide, c. 1860. **£700-900**   *Bon*

A kingwood meuble d'appui, with a white Carrara marble top, 3 ft. 9 in. high by 4 ft. 3 in. wide (114 by 129 cm.), 1840's. **£2,500-3,000**   *S*

A gilt bronze mounted kingwood side cabinet, in the style of Cressent, with a marble top, 3 ft. 11 in. high (119 cm.), late 19th C. **£2,500-3,000**   *S*

A mid Victorian carved and bleached walnut credenza, 68 in. wide. **£600-800** *DSH*

Low value due to marble top and painted, rather than inlaid, decoration. The painting is also a later addition.

A walnut credenza, 42 by 58½ in. (107 by 149 cm.), third quarter of 19th C. **£800-1,200** *SC*

Lower value than examples with gilt mounts and porcelain panels.

A mid Victorian inlaid burr-walnut breakfront credenza, with hand-painted 'Sèvres' panels, 5 ft. 6 in. wide (168 cm.). **£1,400-1,800** *LBP*

A Louis Philippe ormolu-mounted figured walnut credenza, 39 in. high. **£2,500-3,000** *GSP*

A mid Victorian walnut and inlaid credenza, decorated with boxwood stringing, ormolu mounts and floral porcelain panels, 67½ in. wide. **£1,400-1,800** *DSH*

A Victorian serpentine fronted ebonised and boulle credenza, 84 in. **£1,200-1,600** *JD*

A Victorian inlaid walnut serpentine front credenza, 72 in. **£1,600-2,000** *JD*

A Victorian walnut and marquetry side cabinet, with plate glass top, 38½ in. high by 50 in. wide. **£1,800-£2,500** *Bea*

A Louis XVI-style kingwood and porcelain-mounted side cabinet. **£800-1,000** *Bea*

A good burr-walnut and thuyawood side cabinet, with ebony and boxwood strapwork and foliage, 6 ft. 2 in. wide (188 cm.), late 1850's. **£2,800-3,400** *S*

A good walnut credenza, with tall mirror plate, 101 by 73 in. (257 by 186 cm.), mid 19th C. **£1,800-2,400** *SC*

A late Victorian inlaid maple and ebonised credenza, 74 in. **£800-£1,200** *JD*

A walnut side cabinet, with ormolu mounts and crossbanded in thuyawood, 3 ft. 8 in. high by 5 ft. 3 in. wide (112 by 161 cm.), mid 19th C. **£1,200-1,600** *S*

A Victorian walnut and marquetry credenza, the mirrored back above a shaped Carrara marble top, inlaid with boxwood lines and designs, 76 by 58 in. (193 by 148 cm.), mid 19th C. **£700-900** *SC*

An Empire rosewood side cabinet, with griotte marble top, 3 ft. high by 3 ft. 5½ in. wide (91 by 105.5 cm.), early 19th C. **£3,000-£3,500** *S*

A 19th C. rosewood and marquetry credenza. **£1,500-2,000** *DWB*

A Louis XVI gilt bronze mounted mahogany side cabinet, with white marble top, the back with interlaced double V mark, 2 ft. 11 in. high, 6 ft. ½ in. wide (89 by 184 cm.), c. 1785. **£10,000-12,000** *S*

A Louis XV Provincial carved walnut side cabinet, with restoration, 4 ft. 2 in. high by 4 ft. 5½ in. wide (127 by 136 cm.), c. 1770. **£1,000-1,500** *S*

A mid Victorian carved walnut chiffonier, with high arched mirror back, 61 in. wide by 92 in. high. **£700-900** *DSH*

FRENCH FURNITURE PERIODS

1610-1643	**Louis XIII**
1643-1715	**Louis XIV**
1715-1723	**Regence**
1723-1774	**Louis XV**
1774-1793	**Louis XVI**
	DIRECTOIRE
1793-1795	**Revolution**
1795-1799	**Directoire**
1799-1804	**Consulate**
1804-1815	**Empire**
	RESTORATION
1815-1824	**Restoration**
1824-1830	**Charles X**
	LOUIS-PHILIPPE
1830-1848	**Louis-Philippe**
1848-1852	**2nd Republic**
1852-1870	**Napoleon III**
1871-1940	**3rd Republic**

A good pair of Louis XVI mahogany side cabinets, with mottled grey marble tops, the friezes with ormolu bead and petal mouldings, 3 ft. 6 in. high by 2 ft. 9¼ in. wide (107 by 85 cm.), c. 1785, mirror panels later. **£4,000-£5,000** *S*

An Empire mahogany side cabinet, with Ste. Anne marble top, 2 ft. 11½ in. high by 4 ft. 3 in. wide (90 by 130 cm.), c. 1820. **£1,000-1,400** *S*

A rosewood side cabinet, the top with rectangular mirror plate, 6 ft. 6½ in. high by 5 ft. 8 in. wide (199 by 173 cm.), c. 1840. **£1,300-1,600** *S*

A good pair of Empire mahogany meubles d'appuis, each with a rectangular yellow- and white-veined black marble top, 3 ft. ½ in. high by 4 ft. 4 in. wide by 1 ft. 6¾ in. deep (92.5 by 132 by 47.5 cm.), c. 1815. **£7,500-8,500** *S*

An ormolu-mounted bois satine bibliotheque, with shaped rectangular breccia marble top, inlaid with end-cut kingwood foliage, stamped G. Durand, 30¾ in. wide (78 cm.). **£3,500-4,000** *C*

The firm of Durand, founded by Louis Durand in 1787 and taken over by his son Prosper-Guillaume in the mid 1830's, was one of the most successful of the period, supplying large quantities of furniture to Louis Philippe and the Royal family.

An Italian walnut side cabinet, 51½ in. wide (131 cm.), early 17th C. **£2,500-3,000**   *C*

A pair of Austrian walnut and fruitwood side cabinets, 33½ in. wide (85 cm.), early 19th C. **£1,800-£2,400**   *C*

A late 18th C. Dutch small mahogany and marquetry side cabinet, 30 in. wide. **£1,000-1,400** *PWC*

A mahogany cabinet, inlaid with radial boxwood lines, 39 in., late 18th C. **£1,000-1,400**   *CSK*

A George III mahogany linen press, the hanging compartment enclosed by a pair of beaded panel doors, 53 in. wide. **£1,000-1,500**   *O*

A German kingwood parquetry side cabinet, the top veneered with a basket weave pattern, the front outlined with gilt metal bead mouldings, 3 ft. 3 in. high by 4 ft. ½ in. wide (99 by 123 cm.), c. 1900. **£400-600**   *S*

A late 18th C. Austrian walnut cabinet on chest, 3 ft. 9 in. wide by 6 ft. 2 in. high. **£1,500-2,000** *CDC*

A Dutch walnut and floral marquetry armoire, 66 in. wide by 93 in. high (175.5 by 236 cm.). **£2,500-3,500**   *C*

A Dutch walnut marquetry armoire, early 18th C. **£6,000-£8,000**   *MMB*

A George III mahogany clothes press, John White, East Street, Chichester, 50 in. wide (127 cm.). **£1,200-1,500**   *C*

An Edwardian mahogany wardrobe, by Edwards and Roberts. **£1,600-2,000**   *DWB*

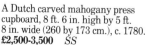

A William IV mahogany linen press. **£400-600**   *CoH*

A Dutch carved mahogany press cupboard, 8 ft. 6 in. high by 5 ft. 8 in. wide (260 by 173 cm.), c. 1780. **£2,500-3,500**   *SS*

A Dutch burr-walnut and floral marquetry armoire, 92 in. high. **£3,000-£4,000**   *C*

A George III mahogany canterbury, strung in ebony throughout, 21 by 21 in. (53 by 53 cm.), first quarter of the 19th C., the drawer later. £1,000-1,250 *SC*

A George III mahogany canterbury, the drawer lined in cedar, 19 by 18 by 12 in. (48 by 46 by 31 cm.), late 18th C. £700-900 *SC*

A good George III satinwood canterbury, 1 ft. 8½ in. high by 1 ft. 6 in. wide (51 by 46 cm.), c. 1790. £3,000-3,500 *S*

It is very rare to find a satinwood canterbury.

A mahogany canterbury, 20½ in. wide, early 19th C. £600-800 *EG*

A Regency mahogany canterbury, with brass feet with castors, 19 in. wide by 13 in. deep by 17 in. high, c. 1820. £900-1,100 *HAL*

An unusual Regency mahogany canterbury, 23½ in. wide (60 cm.). £1,800-2,400 *C*

A pair of George III-style mahogany magazine racks, 33 by 36 in. (84 by 92 cm.), 20th C. £800-1,200 *SC*

A Regency rosewood canterbury. £350-450 *M*

A Victorian rosewood music canterbury, 19 in. £400-500 *WB*

A late George III mahogany canterbury, 19 by 22 in. (48 by 56 cm.), first quarter of the 19th C. £350-450 *SC*

A William IV rosewood canterbury, 24 in. wide by 42 in. high. **£450-£550** *CLG*

An unusual Victorian Continental canterbury and oil lamp, in brass with rouge marble table top, glass shade not original, late 19th C. **£200-300** *WIL*

A Victorian walnut canterbury, 25 in. wide. **£500-700** *Re*

A late Regency rosewood canterbury and tiered stand, 1 ft. 1 in. wide by 4 ft. 4 in. high. **£600-£800** *MMB*

A Victorian walnut canterbury, with inlaid decoration to the top, 26½ by 18 in. **£500-600** *BHW*

A set of 6 late 17th C. walnut high back chairs, in the manner of Daniel Marot. **£4,000-5,000** *B*

A set of 4 Charles II walnut side chairs, restored, one stretcher replaced, third quarter of the 17th C. **£800-1,200** *SC*

A James II caned walnut chair, with crown and scroll top rail, c. 1685. **£200-250** *S*

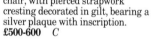

A pair of Edwardian walnut baronial armchairs. **£350-450** *M*

A James II black japanned side chair, with pierced strapwork cresting decorated in gilt, bearing a silver plaque with inscription. **£500-600** *C*

A 19th C. elm framed high back open armed Cromwellian chair, upholstered in contemporary tapestry. **£350-400** *CGC*

A heavily carved Charles I-style armchair, 19th C. **£200-250** *WP*

A set of 8 Charles II-style caned bleached beech dining chairs, including a pair of armchairs c. 1900. **£4,000-5,000** *S*

A set of 6 Victorian oak dining chairs. **£500-700** *V*

A set of 8 walnut dining chairs, including 2 armchairs in late Stuart style. **£600-700** *EG*

A set of 8 Jacobean-style Victorian oak dining chairs. **£800-1,000** *CoH*

A set of 10 Victorian carved oak dining chairs, in the Carolean style comprising: 2 carvers and 8 singles. **£1,800-2,400** *M*

A set of 9 19th C. Stuart-style dining chairs. **£1,000-1,400** *BHW*

A pair of George I red walnut chairs, with shaped splats. **£2,000-2,500** *DWB*

A fine pair of George I walnut side chairs, the arched backs with paper scroll top rails and solid vase-shaped splats, the plain seat rails centred by shells on cabriole legs headed by shells ending in claw-and-ball feet. **£12,000-14,000** *C*

A pair of Queen Anne walnut chairs, with needlework seats. **£1,600-2,000** *DWB*

A set of 6 walnut dining chairs, in Queen Anne style including an armchair, 1920's. **£1,400-1,600** *S*

1920's Queen Anne-style chairs have become very popular, particularly for the American market. Look out for the finely carved and 'long' sets.

A set of 6 George II walnut side chairs, restored. **£5,000-6,000** *L*

A rare George II red walnut armchair, the scroll moulded top rail carved with a crest in the form of an elephant and howdah standing on mantling, the open arms with finely carved lion mask terminals, second quarter of the 18th C. **£2,800-3,400** *SC*

The crest would appear to be that of CORBET, Baronets of Corbet, Salop.

A set of 16 Queen Anne-style stained walnut chairs, including a pair of armchairs, 1920's. **£4,000-£5,000** *S*

A set of 12 fine Queen Anne-style dining chairs, framed in mahogany with shell-carved and pierced vase splats. **£2,000-2,500** *MN*

A set of 6 inlaid mahogany Edwardian dining chairs. **£600-£700** *GBT*

329

A set of 7 19th C. mahogany framed dining chairs, in the Queen Anne style, comprising: 6 diners and a carver. **£500-600**   *WHL*

A set of 13 rush seat walnut dining chairs, including a pair of armchairs, c. 1900. **£700-800**   *S*

A set of 14 Queen Anne-style dining chairs, 1920's. **£3,000-3,500**   *WW*

A set of 8 Queen Anne-style walnut dining chairs. **£2,500-3,000**   *CW*

A fine pair of gilt gesso side chairs in the Queen Anne style, on cabriole legs headed by lion masks and foliate ribbon-tied swags, on paw feet, the upholstery of one stencilled C. Hindley & Sons, 134 Oxford St., the chairs numbered 08649. **£4,000-4,500**   *C*

A set of 8 walnut and marquetry dining chairs, including a pair of armchairs, and of Queen Anne style, with shaped top rails and shaped vase splats, inlaid throughout with delicate scrollwork and grotesque masks, c. 1910. **£7,000-8,000**   *S*

A set of 6 Queen Anne-style walnut dining chairs, including a pair of armchairs, 1920's. **£1,000-1,400**   *S*

A set of 6 George III mahogany chairs, the leaf carved cresting rails above pierced Gothic-style splats, restored, c. 1760. **£4,500-5,500**   *SS*

A set of 10 mahogany dining chairs, in George II style, including a pair of armchairs, the top rails carved with eagles' heads, c. 1900. **£6,000-7,000**   *S*

A set of 12 carved mahogany dining chairs, in George II style, including a pair of armchairs, c. 1920. **£8,000-12,000**   *S*

An important set of 12 Chippendale Gothic dining chairs, comprising 2 carvers and 10 singles, the triple cluster column back posts with crocketed pinnacles, c. 1765. **£85,000-100,000**   *B*

Exhibited: Georgian Furniture, Bethnal Green, 1890.

A set of 4 mid Georgian beechwood dining chairs. **£1,600-2,000**   *C*

A set of 4 George III fruitwood- framed dining chairs. **£400-600**   *Bea*

A fine early George III mahogany open armchair, with waved top rail and pierced interlaced splat carved with foliage sprays and headed by a C-scroll and rocaille cartouche, the plain seat rail on cabriole legs incised with trellis-and-dot and carved with acanthus clasps ending in foliate feet, the back rail replaced, 24 in. wide (62 cm.), the back 38 in. high (97 cm.). **£3,500-£4,000** *C*

The back of this chair corresponds almost exactly to a design included in Thomas Chippendale's, The Gentleman and Cabinet-Maker's Director, 1st edn., 1754, pl. No. XII.

A set of 6 mahogany dining chairs, in the Chippendale style, 19th C. **£1,800-2,400** *L*

A good set of 7 George III mahogany dining chairs, including a pair of armchairs, with cabriole legs headed by leaves, c. 1770. **£10,000-12,500** *S*

. set of 4 George III side chairs, the ell carved pierced splat backs ith flowers, leaf scrolls and oneysuckle. **£3,200-3,600** *WW*

A pair of Hepplewhite-style carved mahogany elbow chairs, late 19th C. **£450-500** *JD*

A mahogany open armchair, 19th C. **£200-300** *BHW*

A red japanned chinoiserie armchair, in late George II style, bearing the label Keeble Ltd, 10 Carlisle, W. c. 1920. **£600-700** *S*

. set of 14 Chippendale-style ahogany dining chairs, including armchairs, 19th C. **£3,000-4,000** *MB*

A fine set of 12 Chippendale-style mahogany dining chairs, including 2 carvers, 19th C. **£4,000-5,000** *MMB*

A set of 6 George III mahogany dining chairs, the serpentine cresting with pierced vase splats, c. 1770. **£1,600-2,000** *S*

A set of 8 single and 1 elbow Chippendale-style mahogany dining chairs, 19th C. **£2,000-2,500** *DWB*

A George II mahogany armchair, c. 1740. **£450-550** *SS*

A Chippendale design set of 7 dining chairs, including 1 carver late 19th C. **£700-900** *Wor*

A set of 6 Chippendale-style mahogany and fruitwood country made dining chairs, having pierced splat backs, some damage. **£1,600-£2,000** *GC*

A set of 16 Chippendale-period mahogany dining chairs, the backs with shaped and carved acanthus top rails, pierced and carved ribbon and floral splats, gadrooning to fronts, cabriole legs with acanthus knees, claw and ball feet comprising: pair carvers and 5 chairs with serpentine fronts and 9 chairs with straight fronts. **£18,000-22,000** *A*

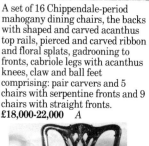

A pair of Georgian mahogany Chippendale-style chairs. **£80** **£1,200** *JD*

A set of 4 George I walnut chairs, including an armchair. **£3,000-£3,500** *T*

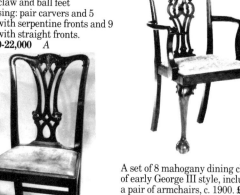

A set of 6 George III-style mahogany dining chairs, including 2 armchairs. **£500-700** *Bea*

A set of 12 mahogany Chippendale-style dining chairs, including 2 armchairs. **£3,200-3,600** *DWB*

A set of 8 mahogany dining chairs of early George III style, including a pair of armchairs, c. 1900. **£1,60** **£2,000** *S*

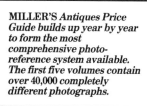

A set of 14 mahogany dining chairs, in George II style, including a pair of armchairs, early 20th C. **£4,500-5,500** *S*

A set of 6 mahogany Chippendale style dining chairs, some damage 19th C. **£500-700** *BHW*

A set of 14 early George III mahogany dining chairs, including a pair of armchairs, all re-railed, castors later, c. 1765. **£9,000-12,000** *S*

A set of 12 Edwardian Chippendale-design mahogany dining chairs, comprising 10 singles and 2 carvers. **£2,200-2,800** *M*

A mahogany elbow chair, c. 1760. **£400-500** *LA*

MAKE THE MOST OF MILLER'S

Every care has been taken to ensure the accuracy of descriptions and estimated valuations.

Where an attribution is made within inverted commas (e.g. 'Chippendale') or is followed by the word 'style' (e.g. early Georgian style) it is intended to convey that, in the opinion of the publishers, the piece concerned is a later — though probably still antique — reproduction of the style so designated.

Unless otherwise stated, any description which refers to 'a set', or 'a pair' includes a valuation for the entire set or the pair, even though the illustration may show only a single item.

A set of 8 George II-style mahogany dining chairs, including a pair of armchairs, the gadrooned carved seat rail on acanthus leaf-carved cabriole legs with claw and ball feet, c. 1900. **£1,800-2,400** *S*

A set of 5 Chippendale-style mahogany dining chairs, including an armchair. **£700-800** *Re*

A set of 8 mahogany dining chairs, including 2 armchairs, of late George II style. **£2,200-2,600** *JF*

A set of 8 Georgian mahogany single dining chairs, the backs with serpentine crestings, the splats of elaborately pierced and interlaced form. **£4,500-5,500** *HSS*

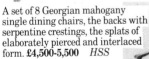

A set of 8 and 2 arm Chippendale-style mahogany dining chairs, 19th C. **£3,500-4,000** *AG*

A set of 6 George II red walnut chairs, c. 1750. **£6,000-7,000** *S*

A set of 8 George III-style mahogany chairs, including 2 armchairs, late 19th C. **£1,400-£1,800** *SC*

A set of 4 George II walnut dining chairs, the moulded backs with dish top rails, carved with drapery and a tassel, and with a tapered pierced splat, one back damaged, c. 1740. **£6,500-7,500** *S*

A set of 10 George III-style mahogany dining chairs, 19th C. £2,200-2,600 *Re*

A set of 13 mahogany dining chairs, the pierced splat backs with leaf carving in 'Chippendale' style, comprising: a pair of carver armchairs and 11 side chairs. £2,500-3,000 *WW*

A set of 6 George III mahogany dining chairs. £2,000-2,500 *C*

A walnut-carved chair, c. 1770. £400-500 *LA*

ENGLISH CHAIRS

- c. 1630 backs of chairs were like panelled sides from a coffer
- early 17th C. chairs very square and made of oak
- in Charles II period principal wood walnut — such chairs tend to break as walnut splits easily and is relatively soft
- chairs have carved top rails, often with a crown, the stretcher will then be similarly carved, the legs are either turned or plain and simple spirals — sometimes called barley sugar twists; the caning in the backs is usually rectangular — any chair with oval caning is highly desirable
- by the end of the 17th C. backs were covered in needlework, the cabriole leg made its appearance, now stretchers have subtle curves
- the beginning of the 18th C. — the Queen Anne spoon back chair — with upright shaped splat, plain cabriole front legs, pad feet
- George I — carved knees and ball-and-claw feet, solid splats were walnut or veneered, often in burr-walnut
- William Kent — introduced heavy carved mouldings — greatly influenced by Italian baroque
- from this time on chairs became lighter in design through the work mainly of Chippendale and Hepplewhite
- splats now pierced, legs square or tapered
- the square legs were also much cheaper than the cabriole legs, so they appealed to the large and growing middle class
- Hepplewhite, in particular, developed the chair with tapered legs, no stretchers and very plain splats
- during the 19th C. the taste was once again for heavier more substantial furniture

A set of 12 mahogany dining chairs, including 2 armchairs, of early George III design, the waved top rails carved with foliage above pierced splats, one bearing an ivory plaque inscribed 'Charles Winlowe, Cabinet Maker, Purfleet St, Kings Lynn'. £3,200-3,800 *C*

A set of 4 Chippendale-period mahogany dining chairs. £2,800 £3,400 *DWB*

A set of 6 late George III-style mahogany ladderback dining chairs, including 2 armchairs, 19th C. £1,000-1,250 *HSS*

A set of 4 George II mahogany dining chairs, with scroll crest rails, carved with leafage. £2,200-£2,600 *DWB*

A set of 6 19th C. Chippendale-design mahogany dining chairs. £600-800   M

A pair of George II walnut dining chairs, with paper scroll top rails, vase-shaped splats carved with tassels and flowerheads, and waved rails centred by shells on cabriole legs, headed by acanthus and claw and ball feet. £3,400-3,800   C

A set of 8 mahogany dining chairs, including a pair of armchairs, with the manufacturer's label of Cooper & Holt, c. 1900. £4,000-5,000   S

A set of 8 George III-style mahogany dining chairs, including 2 armchairs, 20th C. £1,600-2,200   SC

A set of 8 mahogany ladderback dining chairs, in Georgian style, including 2 armchairs. £1,800-£2,400   WW

A George III Chippendale-style mahogany ladderback chair, c. 1770. £250-300   LA

A set of 8 George III-style mahogany pierced ladderback chairs, including 2 armchairs, late 19th C. £1,600-2,200   SS

A set of 8 mahogany ladderback dining chairs, in George III style, including a pair of armchairs, 2 with later arms, second quarter 20th C. £1,000-1,400   S

A set of 7 early George III mahogany ladderback dining chairs, including an armchair, c. 1765. £1,000-1,500   S

Eight Chippendale-style dining chairs. £2,800-3,200   JD

A set of 8 George III-style mahogany dining chairs, including 2 open armchairs. £1,400-1,800   CSK

335

A set of 7 Edwardian mahogany dining chairs, of Hepplewhite design, including 2 armchairs. **£600-800** *M*

<hr>

CHAIRS

'A rule of thumb'

When assessing the value of single or sets of medium quality chairs, the following rule will give you a rough guide. Remember on sets of rare or early chairs these ratios will increase.

A Pair: *3 times single chair price*

Set of 4: *6 to 7 times single chair price*

Set of 6: *10 to 12 times single chair price*

Set of 8: *15 plus times single chair price*

A fine set of 7 Regency mahogany dining chairs, including an armchair, later blocks, and an armchair en suite of later date. **£4,500-5,500** *C*

A pair of George III mahogany armchairs, c. 1780. **£1,000-1,250** *S*

A set of 4 George III mahogany dining chairs, c. 1780. **£800-1,000** *S*

A Hepplewhite-style mahogany armchair, 19th C. **£180-220** *BHW*

A George III mahogany armchair the moulded arched top rail with slightly waisted sides, c. 1780. **£1,000-1,250** *S*

A set of 6 George III mahogany chairs, late 18th/early 19th C. **£3,200-3,600** *S*

A set of 8 George III dining chairs, including a pair of armchairs. **£5,500-£6,500** *C*

A set of 6 George III elbow chairs, restored. **£4,000-5,000** *CW*

An early George III mahogany chinoiserie armchair, with assymmetrical 'cockpen' trellis, c. 1760. **£2,500-3,000** *S*

A set of 8 George III cream-painted dining chairs, including a pair of armchairs. **£3,500-4,000** *C*

A set of 6 Hepplewhite-style mahogany dining chairs, including 2 armchairs, 19th C. **£1,000-1,400** *AG*

A set of 12 mahogany armchairs in George III style, c. 1900. **£4,000-£5,000** *S*

A set of 8 George III mahogany dining chairs, the moulded shield shaped backs with pierced interlaced splats headed by Prince of-Wales feathers, later blocks. **£6,000-6,500** *C*

A set of 8 Regency ebonised and gilt armchairs. **£2,500-3,000** *MMB*

A set of 3 Regency-style mahogany chairs, including an armchair, 1900. **£400-500** on

A fine pair of George III mahogany armchairs, the shield-shaped backs with conforming splat, pierced and carved with leaves and wheatears springing from a headed patera and fan quadrant, c. 1785. **£6,000-£7,000** *S*

A set of 12 George III-style mahogany dining chairs, including a pair of armchairs, c. 1890. **£1,700-£2,000** *S*

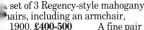

set of 8 George III-style mahogany cockpen open armchairs. **£3,000-3,500** *C*

A pair of caned bamboo armchairs, late 18th C. **£5,000-6,000** *S*

A set of 4 Regency japanned armchairs, the curved top rails painted with a flambeau above trellis crossbars, c. 1800. **£2,000-£2,500** *S*

A pair of George III 'bamboo' bergères in beech, c. 1800. **£2,500-£3,000** *S*

egency painted satinwood open chair, the top rail decorated h a grisaille panel. **£1,800-2,200**

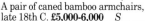

A set of 6 Regency armchairs, with painted beechwood simulated bamboo frames. **£1,500-1,800** *CSK*

A set of 10 Regency painted and parcel gilt chairs, including a pair of armchairs, decorated in gilt on a black ground, early 19th C. **£12,000-14,000** *S*

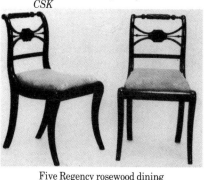

air of George III mahogany n armchairs. **£6,500-7,500** *C*

Five Regency rosewood dining chairs, the backs with brass star inlay, one chair with replacement mahogany splat. **£550-750** *O*

A set of 6 Regency ebonised and gilded open armchairs, later blocks. **£4,000-5,000** *C*

337

A set of 7 George III mahogany dining chairs, and an armchair en suite of later date. **£2,500-3,000** *C*

CHAIRS

- check seat rails are the same, with equal patination
- top rail should never overhang sides
- carving should not be flat
- if stretchers low, chair could have been cut down
- the height from floor to seat should be 1 ft. 6 in.

A set of 4 Regency rosewood and parcel-gilt open armchairs. **£7,000-£8,000** *C*

A pair of giltwood chairs, c. 1890. **£250-£300** *S*

A set of 6 Regency chairs, with painted beech frames. **£450-500**

An important set of 9 single and 2 carving Regency rosewood sabre leg dining chairs, with all-over ornate brass inlay. **£22,000-25,000** *MMB*

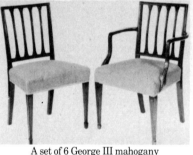

A set of 6 George III mahogany dining chairs, of Sheraton design, including 2 armchairs. **£800-900** *CSK*

A composed set of 6 mahogany dining chairs, including an armchair, late 18th C. **£600-800** *SC*

A set of 6 George III mahogany dining chairs, 5 stamped Ford, and a pair of Regency armchairs, similar. **£2,700-3,200** *C*

A set of 7 late 18th C. Sheraton-design dining chairs. **£900-1,100** *LE*

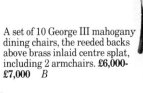

A set of 10 George III mahogany dining chairs, the reeded backs above brass inlaid centre splat, including 2 armchairs. **£6,000-£7,000** *B*

A set of 4 Regency ebonised and painted open armchairs. **£5,000-£6,000** *C*

A set of 7 mahogany and satinwood crossbanded dining chairs, including an armchair, 2 stamped Plested, c. 1880. **£1,000-1,300** *S*

A set of 4 Regency mahogany
dining chairs. **£500-700** *L*

A set of 8 mahogany dining chairs,
including 2 with arms, one arm and
4 single of the Regency period with
restorations, and 3 chairs later
replacements. **£2,000-2,500** *L*

A set of 6 late Regency mahogany
dining chairs. **£800-900** *L*

set of 6 William IV mahogany
dining chairs, restored. **£1,000-
1,200** *L*

A set of 8 mahogany dining
chairs,   including 2
armchairs, c. 1800. **£3,500-4,000**
HAL

A set of 8 George IV mahogany
dining chairs, including a pair of
armchairs, c. 1810. **£4,000-5,000**
S

set of 8 William IV mahogany
ow back dining chairs, including 2
rmchairs. **£900-1,000** *A*

A set of 6 Victorian mahogany bow
back dining chairs. **£700-800** *A*

A set of 6 Victorian mahogany
dining chairs. **£500-600** *GBT*

set of 6 Biedermeier mahogany
airs, the curved arched top rails
rved with lotus scrolls at each
d and with carved anthemion
ssbars, the padded seats on
uare sabre legs, Swedish or
nish, c. 1825. **£1,100-1,400** *S*

A set of 7 19th C. mahogany dining
chairs, including 2 armchairs.
£800-1,000 *DA*

A set of 7 late William IV
mahogany dining chairs, including
an armchair, second quarter
19th C. **£1,000-1,200** *SC*

A pair of mid 18th C. Portuguese padouk wood dining chairs. **£2,000-£2,500** *MIL*

A set of 4 Tuscan walnut chairs, late 16th C. **£2,500-3,000** *S*

A set of 10 South African Transitional tulbagh stinkwood dining chairs, c. 1820. **£3,500-4,000** *S*

A pair of Anglo-Dutch walnut chairs, early 18th C. **£600-700** *L*

A set of 6 Dutch walnut and marquetry side chairs, highlighted in mother-of-pearl and ivory, re-supported, early 18th C. **£7,000-£8,000** *C*

A set of restauration mahogan dining chairs, 2 modern, c. 182 **£2,100-2,500** *S*

A pair of 18th C. Portuguese hardwood side chairs. **£500-60C** *Bea*

A pair of Portuguese rosewood chairs, with deeply carved arched top rails above padded vase splats, mid 18th C. **£3,000-3,500** *S*

A set of 6 Baltic Biedermeier walnut chairs, c. 1840. **£3,000-£3,500** *S*

A Queen Anne walnut chair, c. 1710. **£600-700** *S*

A very fine pair of George II mahogany library chairs, the needlework made for the chairs in 1937. **£11,000-13,000** *T*

A pair of George II red walnut chairs. **£3,000-4,000** *CSK*

A set of 9 George III-style mahogany framed dining chairs. **£800-900** *GM*

An unusual pair of carved mahogany armchairs, in the French style, c. 1750. **£9,000-£11,000** *S*

A Victorian lady's mahogany amed chair. **£350-400** *M*

A set of 6 Victorian walnut salon chairs. **£900-1,100** *Bon*

A set of 14 William IV mahogany dining chairs, bearing a stamp J.J. Byrne & G. Henrys, Dublin. **£2,500-3,000** *GM*

A set of 4 parcel-gilt rosewood chairs, stamped Gillow and in Louis XVI style, c. 1870. **£500-600** *S*

pair of mid 19th C. rosewood utton-back scroll-arm library hairs. **£600-800** *RBB*

A set of 6 Victorian walnut salon dining chairs, on cabriole legs. **£800-1,000** *TL*

A set of 6 walnut and parcel-gilt side chairs, of George II design, 19th C. **£2,000-2,500** *C*

A set of 4 beechwood salon chairs, stained to resemble rosewood, French, 1840's. **£500-600** *S*

Victorian rosewood open arm asy chair. **£300-400** *JD*

A Victorian button-back chair. **£350-400** *CW*

A Victorian spoon back open armchair, in carved walnut frame. **£350-400** *BHW*

A Victorian walnut armchair. **£700-800** *Re*

A Victorian mahogany button-back lady's occasional chair. **£300-400** *Re*

Two Victorian rosewood buttoned-back armchairs. **£700-850** *MMB*

A button-back upholstered walnut armchair, late 19th C. **£300-350** *BA*

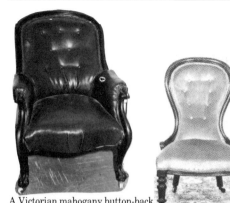

A Victorian mahogany button-back armchair. **£180-240**   *TM*

A Victorian lady's walnut framed chair. **£100-140**   *WSW*

A set of 4 painted and parcel-gilt corner armchairs, mid 19th C. **£1,600-2,000**   *S*

A George III mahogany caned tu shaped library bergère, the left a with a brass plate for reading equipment, with brass candle arr c. 1790. **£2,200-2,800**   *S*

A George II mahogany corner elbow chair. **£700-800**   *L*

A George III mahogany desk chair. **£3,000-3,500**   *C*

An 18th C. elm corner chair. **£350-£400**   *CW*

A George II mahogany bergère, the front legs carved with a cabochon at the knees, with leaf-scroll brackets and cabochon-carved pad feet, c. 1755. **£1,800-2,400**   *S*

A Regency mahogany writing chair, with U-shaped top rail and pierced arcaded back, framed by foliate scrolls and fitted with a hinged writing flap on brass runners. **£3,000-3,500**   *C*

A pair of George III mahogany tub armchairs. **£10,000-12,500**   *C*

A George II mahogany armchair, in the French style, the padded arms with handles and down-curve supports carved with rocaille decoration, c. 1755. **£2,000-2,500** *S*

A George III mahogany tub bergère. **£1,600-2,000**   *C*

A George III giltwood bergère. **£600-800**   *C*

A set of 3 Edwardian tub-shaped armchairs. **£300-400**   *BHW*

A Regency mahogany framed bergère. **£800-1,200** *Bon*

A pair of William IV mahogany bergères, castors replaced, c. 1830. **£2,400-2,800** *S*

A pair of 19th C. mahogany framed library chairs. **£4,000-4,500** *DWB*

An unusual George III mahogany leather-upholstered wing armchair. **£4,000-4,500** *C*

A George IV mahogany bergère, restored, second quarter of the 19th C. **£600-800** *SC*

A William IV chestnut hide chair, 40 in. high by 35 in. deep by 26 in. wide, c. 1830. **£800-950** *AP*

A George II walnut open armchair. **£2,000-2,500** *C*

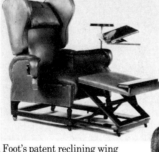

A pair of William IV mahogany bergère chairs. **£2,800-3,400** *L*

A Foot's patent reclining wing armchair, with adjustable back and seat, with a reading and wine table on brass supports, with Foot's Patent brass label, c. 1900. **£1,800-£2,400** *S*

A good pair of Charles II carved wing armchairs, one silvered, the other painted black, c. 1685. **£4,000-5,000** *S*

An 18th C. mahogany Gainsborough armchair. **£1,000-1,250** *A*

A 19th C. mahogany framed Gainsborough-style open armchair. **£350-450** *CGC*

The price indicates that the chair is a 19th C. copy.

A set of 4 mid 18th C. mahogany hall chairs. **£1,800-2,400** *DWB*

An Edwardian mahogany rocking chair, probably Flemish. **£300-350** *O*

343

A pair of William IV mahogany
hall chairs. **£180-250**   *Re*

A set of 4 Louis XIII walnut dining
chairs. **£3,000-3,500**   *C*

A pair of rare Georgian mahogan
'X' frame hall chairs, possibly Iri
£1,400-1,800   *JD*

A George I carved walnut and
upholstered wing armchair,
restored, c. 1720. **£1,800-2,400**
SS

A rare rosewood swivel chair, 30 in.
high (76 cm.), second quarter
19th C. **£300-350**   *SC*
Probably used as music stool.

A pair of mahogany hall
armchairs, in early George III
style, c. 1880. **£1,250-1,750**   *S*

A set of 6 Louis XV bleached
walnut chairs, mid 18th C. **£1,6(**
£2,000   *S*

A Georgian country hall porter's
chair, in ash and elm, with later
upholstery, 52 in. high (132 cm.).
£500-600   *L*

A pair of carved walnut French
bergères, 39 in. high, c. 1840.
£1,600-1,800   *AP*

A pair of late 19th C. oak ha
chairs. **£80-120**   *GBT*

A George III mahogany invalid's
chair. **£600-800**   *C*

A pair of late George II/early
George III elm hall chairs, c. 1760.
£400-450   *S*

An unusual 19th C. ship's
mahogany chair, the seat revolving
on a cast iron fluted column, fixed
to a circular mahogany base plate,
the cast iron support incised Archd.
Stewart and Co., Glasgow, No. 22.
£200-250   *PWC*

set of 6 Directoire stripped eechwood dining chairs, including pair of fauteuils. £2,000-2,500

A set of 12 Louis XV walnut and beechwood dining chairs, including a pair of fauteuils, probably Low Countries, 5 with replaced legs, some of the others with spliced and repaired legs. £5,000-6,000 C

A set of 7 Italian walnut dining chairs, 3 partly re-railed, 17th C., and another of later date. £3,200-£3,600 C

A set of 6 Baltic walnut chairs, probably Riga, c. 1840. £2,400-£2,800 S

A 19th C. salon armchair. £450-550 Re

set of 8 walnut dining chairs, rench, with restoration, late 7th C. £4,500-5,500 S

A set of 6 Lombard walnut and marquetry side chairs, late 18th/early 19th C. £1,600-2,200 Bea

A set of 3 walnut side chairs, with boxwood inlaid splats, Dutch, early 19th C. £400-450 SC

A pair of Empire ormolu-mounted mahogany curricle chairs. £1,400-£1,800 C

A Louis XV beechwood bergère, stamped I. Gourdin, c. 1760. £1,800-2,400 S

Jean-Baptiste Gourdin received Master 1748.

pair of Italian walnut side chairs, th restorations, 17th C. £1,000-,400 C

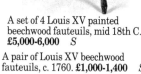

Louis XV-style beech framed rgère, late 19th C. £350-400 n

A Louis XIV walnut wing armchair, c. 1680. £1,500-2,000 S

A set of 4 Louis XV painted beechwood fauteuils, mid 18th C. £5,000-6,000 S

A pair of Louis XV beechwood fauteuils, c. 1760. £1,000-1,400 S

A Régence caned beechwood fauteuil, c. 1720. **£1,600-2,000** *S*

A set of 4 Louis XV carved giltwood fauteuils, c. 1755. **£3,200-3,800** *S*

A set of 3 early Louis XVI needlework-covered fauteuils, c. 1775. **£3,800-4,500** *S*

A Louis XVI caned mahogany fauteuil, stamped J.B.B. Dema c. 1785. **£1,800-2,400** *S*

A set of 4 Tuscan Renaissance walnut armchairs, each with 2 gilt finials of scrolling foliage, late 16th C. **£2,000-2,500** *S*

A set of 4 Louis XV Provincial walnut fauteuils, of small size, possibly Lyons, c. 1750. **£3,800-£4,500** *S*

A Louis XVI grey-painted fauteu stamped L.M. Pluvinet, c. 1780. **£1,000-1,250** *S*

A pair of Consulat mahogany armchairs, by Jacob Frères, made for the Tuileries Palace, branded T.H., TUIL and Pls. DES TUIL^ES, with 3 fleurs-de-lys within an oval, and with 2 partially defaced paper labels, 19th C. **£6,500-8,500** *S*

The partially indistinct stamp is almost certainly Jacob Frères rue Meslée, used from 1796 to 1803 by Georges II Jacob and Francois-Honoré-Georges Jacob, during which time they supplied much furniture for the Tuileries.

A good Flemish walnut armchair, late 17th C., back and seat with early 18th C. wool petit-point with added surround. **£900-1,100** *S*

A pair of Louis XV painted fauteuils, c. 1750. **£2,500-3,000** *S*

A set of 4 Louis XV white-painted and parcel-gilt fauteuils, one stamped P. Remy, some decoration added, mid 18th C. **£3,200-3,800** *S*

A Louis XV walnut bergère, stamped E.T. Nauroy, c. 1765. **£3,500-4,000** *S*

A pair of Empire mahogany armchairs, with ormolu mounts. **£1,500-1,800** *MMB*

A Louis XV walnut and beechw fauteuil, upholstered in contemporary petit-point floral needlework, stamped I.B. BOULARD. **£1,200-1,500** *C*

Spanish walnut armchair, 1700. **£2,000-2,500** *CAm*

A pair of carved oak and upholstered wing armchairs, probably German, c. 1860. **£450-£550** *SS*

A set of 6 French Empire mahogany armchairs, c. 1825. **£5,500-6,500** *AP*

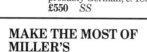

MAKE THE MOST OF MILLER'S

Miller's is completely different each year. Each edition contains completely NEW photographs. This is not an updated publication. We never repeat the same photograph.

A pair of North Italian giltwood armchairs, c. 1780. **£800-1,200** *S*

A pair of Dutch late 17th C.-style armchairs, in the style of Daniel Marot, 19th C. **£500-600** *CSK*

A pair of Tuscan walnut armchairs, the whole inlaid with geometric flowerheads and bandings, one heavily distressed, part late 16th C. **£1,200-1,800** *S*

A set of 4 Italian cream-painted and parcel-gilt fauteuils, and a pair of side chairs en suite, later blocks, one partially re-railed, late 18th C. **£2,200-2,600** *C*

fine Empire ormolu-mounted ahogany fauteuil, stamped ienne. **£3,500-4,000** *C*

A pair of beechwood fauteuils, perhaps Russian, early 19th C. **£3,500-4,000** *C*

A pair of Directoire cream-painted fauteuils, upholstered in contemporary floral tapestry, c. 1795. **£1,000-1,400** *S*

A good mid 19th C. beechwood and upholstered open arm elbow chair. **£700-800** *PWC*

pair of beechwood, walnut and arquetry armchairs, inlaid roughout with figures and rolling foliage, Dutch, second half the 19th C. **£600-700** *SC*

A pair of early Louis XV walnut fauteuils, upholstered in contemporary gros and petit-point needlework, minor differences. **£4,000-5,000** *C*

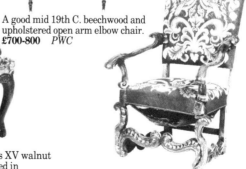

A Venetian walnut armchair, with restoration, late 17th C. **£1,400-£1,800** *S*

347

A suite of Russian brass-mounted mahogany furniture, comprising: a set of 5 chairs, including 2 armchairs and a sofa, lacking upholstery, 79 in. (201 cm.), early 19th C. £3,000-3,500   C

A George I red walnut 2-seater settee, 47 in. wide. £2,000-2,500 DSH

A Chippendale-period mahogany double chair back settee, the scrolling arms and backs with carved acanthus foliage, 52 in. £1,500-1,800   PWC

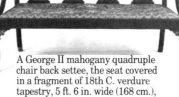

A George II mahogany quadruple chair back settee, the seat covered in a fragment of 18th C. verdure tapestry, 5 ft. 6 in. wide (168 cm.), c. 1750. £2,800-3,400   S

A late 18th C. pearlwood small settle, 114 cm. wide. £700-800 Bon

A 19th C. Dutch marquetry settee, 5 ft. wide. £700-800   AG

A mahogany framed George I-style settee, 56 in. wide, 19th C. £800-£1,200   WHL

An early 18th C. walnut and stained wood settee, 6 ft. 9 in. wide. £1,200-1,500   AG

A good George III mahogany sofa, the moulded frame with arched serpentine back, 5 ft. 5 in. wide (165 cm.), c. 1775. £10,000-12,500 S

A George III mahogany settee in the Hepplewhite style, 72 in. long. £2,500-3,000   GM

A small George III sofa, 48 in. wide (112 cm.). £1,200-1,500   C

A late George III giltwood sofa, 80 in. wide (203 cm.). £1,200-1,500 C

A Regency carved frame chaise longue, with scroll ends, on 4 sabre legs, with brass terminals and castors, upholstered in green and cream striped brocade. £500-700 EG

A Regency mahogany sofa, with a gadrooned crest to the shaped back 90 in. long. £600-700   BHW

A walnut chaise a meridienné, 70 in. wide (178 cm.), third quarter of the 19th C. **£450-550**   *SC*

A mahogany settee, 6 ft. 5 in. long (195 cm.), c. 1855. **£900-1,100**   *S*

A wood walnut double chairback settee, with outset moulded pierced leaf-carved arms to an upholstered seat, raised on carved cabriole legs, 5 ft. 9 in. (175 cm.), c. 1850. **£3,600-£4,200**   *S*

A Victorian carved rosewood and button upholstered settee, 5 ft. 6 in. wide (168 cm.), c. 1850. **£600-£700**   *SS*

A walnut suite, comprising: a chaise longue, an armchair, a low chair and 4 side chairs, mid 19th C. **£1,600-2,000**   *S*

A fine Louis XV walnut and beechwood chaise longue, possibly German, restorations, 87 in. wide (221 cm.). **£3,000-3,500**   *C*

A Victorian settee, with carved walnut frame, 74 in. wide. **£800-£1,000**   *HyD*

A beechwood salon suite, comprising: a settee, 5 ft. 6 in. wide (168 cm.); and an armchair and a low chair, en suite, possibly American, in the Anglo-French style, third quarter of the 19th C. **£900-1,200**   *S*

A Louis XVI painted duchesse, one end formed as a bergère, possibly German, 6 ft. 11 in. long (211 cm.), c. 1780. **£1,200-1,500**   *S*

A mahogany day bed, with gilt mounts, stamped JACOB, 6 ft. 6 in. long (198 cm.), part early 19th C. **£1,800-2,400**   *S*

A carved walnut suite, comprising: a sofa, an armchair, a low chair and 6 side chairs, mid 19th C. **£2,600-£3,200**   *S*

A marquetry suite, comprising: a sofa and 2 armchairs, the frames inlaid with Sheraton-style marquetry, late 19th C. **£450-550**   *S*

A caned mahogany settee, 6 ft. 10 in. wide (209 cm.), c. 1910. **£1,000-1,250**   *S*

A carved walnut confidante, in the French style, approximately 6 ft. 8 in. wide (203 cm.), c. 1850. **£2,500-3,000**   *S*

A Victorian walnut drawing room suite, comprising: a settee, 4 side chairs, an armchair and low chair, crossbanded in burr-walnut and with boxwood stringing, 5 ft. 5 in. wide (165 cm.), 1860's. **£1,500-1,800** S

A boardroom suite, comprising: a mahogany table of horseshoe form, and a matched set of 28 late Victorian walnut armchairs. **£3,500-4,000** *Bon*

A good carved walnut drawing room suite, comprising: a sofa, an armchair, a low chair and a set of 6 chairs, the sofa 6 ft. wide (193 cm.) c. 1870. **£1,400-1,800** S

A George II Irish mahogany chest on stand, 3 ft. 8 in. high by 4 ft. 3 in. wide (112 by 130 cm.), c. 1740. **£1,800-2,200** S

A mid Georgian mahogany chest on stand, Irish, 40 by 51 in. (102 by 130 cm.), mid 18th C. **£800-1,200** SC

An oak and elm ark or dough bin, Welsh, 4 ft. 7 in. wide (140 cm.), 1680-1700. **£500-600** S

A Tuscan parcel-gilt walnut cassone, 1 ft. 10 in. high by 4 ft. 5 in. wide (56 by 135 cm.), 16th C. **£1,200-1,500** S

A Tuscan walnut cassone, 1 ft. 7 in. high by 3 ft. 6½ in. wide (48 by 108 cm.), mid 16th C. **£2,500-3,000** S

MAKE THE MOST OF MILLER'S

Every care has been taken to ensure the accuracy of descriptions and estimated valuations.

Where an attribution is made within inverted commas (e.g. 'Chippendale') or is followed by the word 'style' (e.g. early Georgian style) it is intended to convey that, in the opinion of the publishers, the piece concerned is a later — though probably still antique — reproduction of the style so designated.

Unless otherwise stated, any description which refers to 'a set', or 'a pair' includes a valuation for the entire set or the pair, even though the illustration may show only a single item.

An Italian walnut cassone, with coffered lid, with restorations, 75 in. (190 cm.), 17th C. **£900-1,200** L

A cedar Adige coffer, the front poker-worked with fountains, on later ogee bracket feet, 31½ by 70 in. (80 by 178 cm.), late 17th C. **£600-800** SC

A Dutch East Indies brass-mounted rosewood blanket chest, 52½ in. wide (133 cm.), mid 18th C. **£1,200-£1,500** C

A Chinese black lacquer coffer, 62½ in. wide (159 cm.), early 18th C. **£1,800-2,200** C

A Dutch East Indies hardwood strong box, profusely mounted with brass, 32 in. wide. **£500-700** W

A fine 18th C. German walnut and inlaid domed top coffer, 44 in. wide. **£1,800-2,200** *PK*

A late 18th/early 19th C. Italian tortoiseshell coffer, on similar stand, 38½ in. **£2,500-3,000** *GSP*

A South German walnut and marquetry sarcophagus-shaped coffer, 26 in. wide (66 cm.), early 18th C. **£1,000-1,250** *C*

A late 18th C. Scandinavian dower chest, in pinewood, the exterior bound in studded ironwork and with faded floral decoration, 48 in. long by 23 in. deep by 27 in. high, c. 1800. **£500-600** *HAL*

A Queen Anne walnut marquetry chest of drawers, with rectangular crossbanded top, handles, back and feet replaced, 3 ft. 2½ in. square (98 cm.), c. 1700. **£1,800-2,200** *S*

A Tyrolean painted pine coffer, 2 ft. 8 in. high by 4 ft. 8¼ in. wide (81 by 143 cm.), c. 1620. **£1,800-2,400** *S*

A William and Mary walnut marquetry chest, feet replaced and with restorations, 2 ft. 11 in. high by 3 ft. 2¼ in. wide (89 by 97 cm.), c. 1700. **£2,500-3,000** *S*

A William and Mary walnut chest, the figured quartered surface geometrically inlaid with boxwood stringing, with early brasswork, now on shaped bracket feet, 35 in. wide by 21 in. deep by 31 in. high, c. 1700. **£2,500-3,000** *HAL*

A William and Mary walnut and marquetry chest, with later burr-veneered crossbanded top, with satinwood floral scroll on an ebonised ground, on later shaped bracket feet, restored, 3 ft. ½ in. by 3 ft. 3 in. wide (93 by 99 cm.), c. 1690. **£1,200-1,500** *SS*

The price reflects the restoration: plain veneered top and bracket feet.

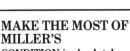

A good William and Mary laburnum oyster wood chest of drawers, 36 in. wide by 34 in. high. **£5,000-6,000** *B*

A Queen Anne walnut chest, with later brass drop handles and bracket feet, 3 ft. 2½ in. wide. **£600-£800** *EG*

A George III mahogany chest, the figured flamed surface with moulded edge above brushing slide and 4 cockbeaded drawers, with early replaced brasswork, the piece has replaced backboards, 34 in. wide by 20 in. deep by 32¼ in. high, c. 1800. **£1,200-1,500** *HAL*

MAKE THE MOST OF MILLER'S

CONDITION *is absolutely vital when assessing the value of an antique. Damaged pieces on the whole appreciate much less than perfect examples. However a rare desirable piece may command a high price even when damaged.*

A Queen Anne walnut chest, with chevron-banded drawers, and crossbanded top, with restoration, handles replaced, 3 ft. 1½ in. high by 3 ft. 3 in. wide (95 by 99 cm.), early 18th C. **£800-1,200** *S*

A walnut-veneered chest of drawers, with brass drop handles and crossbanding, 40 by 36 in. high. **£200-300** *WP*

The low price reflects the fact this was originally a chest on stand or 'highboy'. The ovolo cornice above 3 drawers is more generous than the foot. This is a common feature on chest-on-chest.

An early 18th C. walnut chest, the quarter-veneered top geometrically inlaid with boxwood lines, 33½ in. high by 36 in. wide. **£1,500-1,800** *Bea*

A small walnut bachelor's chest, the top unfolding to reveal a baize covered and fitted interior, 2 ft. 4½ in., early 18th C. **£6,000-£7,000** *MMB*

A George II chest, in figured walnut veneers of excellent fading and patina, the quartered herringbone-inlaid crossbanded surface with moulded edge above a brushing slide, 33 in. wide by 22 in. deep by 34½ in. high, c. 1740. **£3,500-4,000** *HAL*

A small George I walnut bachelor's chest, with hinged cross and featherbanded top, 2 ft. 6½ in. high by 2 ft. 4 in. wide (77 by 71 cm.), c. 1725. **£6,000-7,000** *S*

A George I yew wood chest, with a slide, 2 ft. 9½ in. high by 2 ft. 10 in. wide (85 by 86 cm.), c. 1720. **£3,200-£3,800** *SS*

A George II red walnut bachelor's chest, with moulded crossbanded hinged top, 2 ft. 8 in. high by 3 ft. wide (81 by 91 cm.), c. 1730. **£2,500-3,200** *S*

An early George II mahogany small chest of drawers, 2 ft. 10¾ in. wide (88.5 cm.), c. 1740. **£1,800-£2,400** *S*

An unusual 18th C. walnut bachelors chest, the crossbanded top inlaid with double herringbone opening to reveal a baize cover with secret compartment, 2 ft. 10 in. wide by 1 ft. deep by 2 ft. 5 in. high, early 18th C. **£8,000-£10,000** *MMB*

A George III yew wood chest, with a rectangular top on reduced ogee bracket feet, 31 by 34½ in. (79 by 88 cm.), third quarter 18th C. **£1,500-1,800** *SC*

A mahogany chest of 4 drawers.
350-400   *BHW*

An early George III mahogany
provincial bachelor's chest, top
right drawer replaced, 2 ft. 6½ in.
high by 3 ft. 1 in. wide by 1 ft.
5¾ in. deep (77.5 by 94 by 45 cm.),
c. 1760. **£4,000-4,500**   *S*

A small George III mahogany
chest, 2 ft. 7 in. wide (79 cm.),
c. 1760. **£1,400-1,800**   *S*

A George III mahogany chest,
handles later, 2 ft. 4¾ in. wide
(73 cm.), c. 1790. **£700-900**   *SS*

A George III mahogany serpentine
fronted chest, with later knob
handles, 41 in. **£1,600-2,000**   *CSK*

A Georgian inlaid mahogany
serpentine chest, 47 in. wide. **£400-
£600**   *GM*
*Possibly the base of a tallboy,
therefore with later inlaid top.*

An early George III mahogany
commode, with moulded serpentine
top above a slide, 2 short drawers,
the left one fitted with 4 inkwells, 2
lidded compartments and other
divisions, 38 in. wide (96.5 cm.).
£4,500-5,500   *C*

MILLER'S *Antiques Price
Guide builds up year by year
to form the most
comprehensive photo-
reference system available.
The first five volumes contain
over 40,000 completely
different photographs.*

An early George III mahogany
serpentine fronted chest, with a
brushing slide, 33 in. high by 43 in.
wide. **£7,000-9,000**   *Bea*

A gentleman's Georgian mahogany
serpentine front dressing chest,
fitted with a brushing slide, a
drawer with lined sliding surface,
adjustable mirror and numerous
fitted compartments, a few small
pieces of veneer missing, 3 ft.
9½ in. wide. **£3,500-4,000**   *GC*

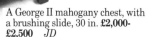

A George II mahogany chest, with
a brushing slide, 30 in. **£2,000-
£2,500**   *JD*

353

A George III serpentine fronted mahogany chest, 3 ft. 8 in. wide. **£1,600-2,000** *AGr*

A rare George III rosewood commode, the serpentine crossbanded top above a brushing slide, now on reduced feet, with restorations, 31 by 42 in. (79 by 107 cm.), third quarter 18th C. **£1,200-1,500** *SC*

A George III-style mahogany chest of serpentine outline, with cockbeaded drawers, 31 by 35 in. (79 by 81 cm.), reconstructed in the 19th C. **£700-900** *SC*

A Sheraton-style mahogany serpentine front chest, the top rosewood crossbanded, with ebony and boxwood stringing inset, 36 in. wide. **£2,500-3,000** *Fr*

CHESTS OF DRAWERS — GUIDE TO DATING

- early 17th C. drawers were nailed together
- up to c. 1660 drawers had bearers attached to the side which ran in deep grooves on the side
- after c. 1670 bottom runners, usually made of oak, appeared
- no 18th C. drawer completely fitted the space between front and back — a space was left for ventilation
- good quality drawers tend to have sides of oak, with rounded top edges
- the idea of veneering on flat surfaces came to England with the foreign influences of the Restoration
- c. 1680-90 walnut came to be used more and more along with the bracket foot
- in the mahogany period from c. 1740, the square shape gave way to the bow front, serpentine, etc.
- up to 1770 grain in bottom boards of drawers tended to run front to back, from 1770 the grain tended to run from side to side
- 18th C. cabinet makers made the bottom boards from 2 or 3 pieces of the same wood; the Victorians used one piece which was usually screwed
- satinwood appeared in chests c. 1780-90
- corner mouldings were a Sheraton innovation, hence give a date of after 1799
- if a chest has three short drawers one would suspect that it started life as the top of a tallboy
- 19th C. saw a gradual increase in size and decrease in quality as more and more chests were made to satisfy growing demand — many different woods, such as pine, mahogany, rosewood and walnut were used

A Georgian mahogany chest, the top crossbanded and inlaid, 35½ in. **£900-1,100** *JD*

An early George III mahogany chest, 34 in. (87 cm.) wide. **£1,600-£2,000** *C*

A George III serpentine fronted zebra wood-veneered chest, handles replaced, 2 ft. 11 in. high by 3 ft. 3 in. wide (89 by 99 cm.), c. 1790. **£2,600-3,200** *S*

A mid Georgian mahogany chest, 34 in. (86.5 cm.) wide. **£2,200-2,600** *C*

A George III mahogany serpentine chest, on later bracket feet, 40½ in. wide (103 cm.). **£3,200-3,800** *C*

A Regency rosewood-veneered serpentine chest, with boxwood line inlay, the top with a re-veneered section with Sheffield Plate ring and paterae handles, 4 ft. **£1,000-£1,250** *WW*

A Georgian mahogany chest of drawers, 37½ in. **£250-300** *BHW*

A Gillows mahogany chest of drawers, of bow front outline, stamped Gillows, Lancaster, 43 by 45 in. (109 by 114 cm.), early 19th C. **£400-500** *SC*

A George III mahogany serpentine secretaire chest, the top drawer fitted with pigeonholes and small drawers, some restoration, 40 in. high by 46 in. wide. **£2,000-2,500** *Bea*

A good George III satinwood-veneered serpentine fronted chest, with kingwood crossbanding and the top with a moulded edge, handles replaced, 2 ft. 9½ in. high by 2 ft. 9½ in. wide (85 by 85 cm.), c. 1775. **£4,800-5,500** *S*

An inlaid mahogany bow front chest, with satinwood crossbanded top, 39 in. high by 42 in. wide, early 19th C. **£800-1,200** *Bea*

A Georgian mahogany bow fronted chest, of a dark rich colouration with crossbanding and boxwood stringing, 40 in. wide. **£250-300** *BHW*

A walnut wellington chest, 21 in. wide. **£420-480** *BR*

An unusual Regency pollard oak and rosewood chest, with well-figured crossbanded leather-lined folding top, 31 in. wide (79 cm.). **£2,500-3,000** *C*

A late Georgian satinwood bow front chest, 3 ft. 10 in. by 3 ft. 6 in. high. **£3,200-3,800** *AG*

A George III mahogany dressing secretaire chest, the upper-most drawer containing sliding baize-covered writing surface and book rest with compartments beneath, 36 in. wide by 23 in. deep by 32 in. high, c. 1770. **£2,000-2,500** *HAL*

A Victorian mahogany wellington chest, 2 ft. wide by 1 ft. 6 in. deep by 51 in. high. **£450-550** *V*

An early Victorian mahogany wellington chest, 22 in. wide. **£450-£550** *MIL*

355

A Boulle-style secretaire semanier, ebonised and inlaid with red tortoiseshell, the secretaire compartment with false drawer fronts and 4 interior drawers, 4 drawers below, 27 in. **£800-1,000** *GSP*

A rosewood secretaire semanier, the top drawer above a secretaire section with 3 dummy drawers, enclosing a maple veneered fitted interior, French, 56 by 28 in. (142 by 71 cm.), third quarter 19th C. **£600-700** *SC*

A Victorian walnut secretaire wellington chest, 56 cm. wide. **£600-£800** *Bon*

A George III-style mahogany and crossbanded chest of drawers, 20½ by 32 in. **£350-400** *GM*

A Louis XV tulipwood semanier, indistinctly stamped, 20¾ in. wide (52.5 cm.). **£3,500-4,000** *C*

A mahogany secretaire wellington chest of 7 graduating drawers, 4 ft. 2 in. high by 1 ft. 10½ in. wide (127 by 57 cm.), c. 1870. **£650-750** *S*

A Louis XV-style chest, the moulded rouge marble surface above 4 drawers in crossbanded kingwood, 16½ in. wide by 12 in. deep by 37 in. high, c. 1870. **£700-£800** *HAL*

A pair of 19th C. French pedestal bombé chests, inlaid and crossbanded with ormolu mounts, handles and escutcheons, 20 in. wide by 40 in. high. **£1,000-1,400** *DA*

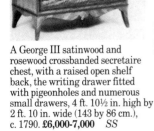

A George III satinwood and rosewood crossbanded secretaire chest, with a raised open shelf back, the writing drawer fitted with pigeonholes and numerous small drawers, 4 ft. 10½ in. high by 2 ft. 10 in. wide (143 by 86 cm.), c. 1790. **£6,000-7,000** *SS*

A George III mahogany secretaire, the leather-lined, panelled fall-flap enclosing a fitted interior, 25½ in. wide (65 cm.). **£3,000-3,500** *C*

An early 19th C. mahogany chest of drawers, 39 in. wide. **£500-600** *DA*

A Sheraton period mahogany secretaire, 49 in. wide. **£800-1,200** *GM*

A Regency mahogany secretaire and later bookcase, 6 ft. 7 in. overall. **£500-700** *CDC*

A small 18th C. oak Dutch bombé chest, with later brass drop handles, 36½ in. wide. **£700-900** *PWC*

A Victorian camphorwood secretaire military chest, 105 cm. wide. **£600-800** *Bon*

A small brass-mounted camphorwood campaign secretaire, in 2 parts, 3 ft. 3 in. high by 2 ft. 6 in. wide (99 by 76 cm.), c. 1870. **£1,000-1,200** *S*

A walnut-veneered Dutch chest, with quarter-cut serpentine moulded top, 2 ft. 7½ in. high by 2 ft. 8 in. wide (80 by 81 cm.), early 18th C. **£3,000-3,500** *S*

A camphorwood military secretaire chest, 3 ft. 6½ in. long. **£1,000-1,200** *OL*

A Dutch red walnut bombé chest, 43 in. (109 cm.), late 18th C. **£800-£1,000** *L*

A Dutch Colonial padouk-wood chest, probably Dutch West Indies, 33½ in. (85 cm.), 18th C. **£3,000-£3,500** *L*

A 19th C. Dutch mahogany bombé commode chest of drawers, 35 in. **£700-900** *JD*

An 18th C. Dutch flame faded mahogany-veneered bombé chest, 3 ft. 7 in. **£800-1,200** *WW*

A Continental mahogany bombé commode, possibly Scandinavian, 38 in. (97 cm.), late 18th C. **£2,000-£2,500** *L*

A Dutch walnut and floral marquetry serpentine fronted bombé commode, late 18th C. **£2,200-2,600** *JF*

A late 18th C. Dutch walnut and marquetry chest of bombé form, 98 cm. wide. **£1,800-2,400** *HSS*

A Dutch walnut floral marquetry commode, 3 ft., 18th C. **£1,800-£2,200** *MMB*

A Dutch marquetry bombé commode, inlaid with armorial devices, the armour-clad foot soldiers and flowers on a burr-walnut ground, later marquetry, 2 ft. 9 in. high by 3 ft. wide (84 by 91.5 cm.), mid 18th C. **£2,000-2,500** *S*

A Dutch walnut and floral marquetry bombé chest, 42 in. wide (109 cm.). **£3,400-3,800** *C*

An 18th C. Dutch marquetry chest inlaid with floral urns, birds and scrolls, 34½ in. **£1,400-1,800** *GSP*

A Dutch walnut and marquetry small bombé chest, 31 by 29 in. high (79 by 74 cm.). **£1,600-2,000** *L*

A marquetry commode in Transitional style, with a bow-fronted breakfront brocatelle marble top, the whole inlaid with flowers, birds and animals on a walnut ground, Dutch or German, 3 ft. 1 in. high by 2 ft. 8¾ in. wide (94 by 83 cm.), c. 1880. **£1,500-£2,000** *S*

An 18th C. walnut and ormolu mounted French commode of serpentine shape, the top and flanks having parquetry inlays, 4 ft. wide by 27 in. deep by 32 in. high. **£5,500-6,500** *V*

A small mid 18th C. Dutch marquetry chest, veneered in walnut, 3 ft. 4 in. **£1,800-2,400** *WW*

A Dutch marquetry chest, 32 in. **£1,400-1,800** *GSP*

A Dutch marquetry chest, inlaid with chequered lines and with gilt metal capitals, and folite scrolls and flowers on a mahogany ground, 36 by 39 in. high (91 by 99 cm.), early 19th C. **£1,000-1,400** *L*

A walnut commode, the top crossbanded with rosewood and basically early 18th C., partially reconstructed, 38 in. wide (97 cm.). **£3,200-3,600** *C*

A Regence walnut and rosewood commode, the chamfered rectangular top inlaid with a Maltese cross within geometric circles, German, 44 in. wide (114.5 cm.). **£7,000-8,000** *C*

A mid 18th C. French provincial chestnut bombé commode, 4 ft. 2 in. **£5,000-5,500** *WW*

A fine early Louis XV kingwood and tulipwood commode, with moulded breccia marble top, some of the mounts stamped C couronné poinçon, 56½ in. wide (144 cm.). **£8,000-10,000** *C*

A Louis XIV rosewood commode, of bombé shape, with parquetry decoration to all surfaces, 47 in. **£6,000-7,000** *A*

An 18th C. Flemish oak commode, 50 in. wide. **£2,000-2,500** *B*

An early Louis XV ormolu-mounted kingwood and floral marquetry tulipwood commode, the later moulded top inlaid a quatre faces, 52 in. wide (132 cm.). **£12,000-£15,000** *S*

A late 18th C. French rosewood parquetry commode chest, 37 in. **£3,600-4,200** *JD*

A small Louis XV kingwood commode, stamped Lardin JME, with a moulded mottled grey, white and beige marble top, the quarter-veneered tulipwood-veneered bombé front with 3 drawers, marble repaired, 2 ft. 9 in. high by 2 ft. 1½ in. wide (84 by 65 cm.), c. 1750. **£3,600-4,200** *S*

André-Antoine Lardin, 1724-90, received Master 1750.

A Louis XV gilt bronze mounted kingwood parquetry commode, stamped P. Roussel, of serpentine shape, with mottled grey and apricot marble top, 2 ft. 10 in. high by 3 ft. 9 in. wide (87 by 114 cm.), mid 18th C. **£7,500-8,500** *S*

Pierre Roussel, 1723-82, received Master 1745.

A Louis XV kingwood commode, stamped J. Lapie JME, with serpentine grey marble top, the rounded blind fluted corners with chevron veneered sides, 2 ft. 10 in. high by 4 ft. 3 in. wide (130 cm.), c. 1730. **£4,200-4,800** *S*

Jean Lapie, received Master 1762, probably repaired this piece.

A small Louis XVI French rosewood bombé commode, 36 in. wide. **£2,000-2,500** *B*

A Louis XV ormolu-mounted rosewood bombé commode, by L. Villedieu, 38 in. wide (96 cm.). **£4,500-5,500** *C*

Nicolay does not record this ébéniste.

A French kingwood breakfront commode. **£3,000-3,500** *DWB*

A Louis XV kingwood small commode, stamped Migeon JME, with brown-veined marble top, one mount stamped with the crowned C poinçon, 2 ft. 10 in. high by 1 ft. 11¼ in. wide (86.5 by 59 cm.), c. 1745. **£4,500-5,200** *S*

Pierre II Migeon 1701-57.

A Louis XV kingwood parquetry commode, stamped Lardin, with gilt bronze mounts, serpentine-shaped, mottled marble top, 2 ft. 10½ in. high by 4 ft. 2½ in. wide (87 by 128 cm.), mid 18th C. **£3,800-4,500** *S*

A Louis XV marquetry commode, with serpentine brescia marble top, 4 ft. 1½ in. wide (126 cm.), mid 18th C. **£3,200-3,800** *S*

A Louis XV kingwood serpentine small commode, the moulded mottled brown marble top above 3 long drawers, each with 2 crossbanded panels in stained holly, 2 ft. 8 in. high by 2 ft. 8 in. wide (81 by 81 cm.), mid 18th C. **£2,800-3,500** *S*

A Louis XVI mahogany commode, with ochre and white mottled marble top, stamped BVRB JME, marble replaced and restored, 3 ft. 10½ in. wide (118 cm.), c. 1780. **£4,000-4,600** *S*

A Louis XV-style kingwood serpentine commode. **£4,000-5,000** *DWB*

An Empire ormolu-mounted mahogany commode, with later rectangular grey marble top, stamped twice Chapius, 50 in. wide (127 cm.). **£1,000-1,200** *C*
Either Claude Chapius or the distinguished but shadowy Belgian ébéniste of the same name.

A Louis XVI Transitional-style tulipwood and purple heart serpentine commode, inlaid with foliate marquetry arabesques, boxwood lines and applied gilt metal mounts, 46 in. **£1,800-£2,400** *CSK*

A fine kingwood banded bombé commode, 55 in. wide by 29 in. deep by 36 in. high, 18th C. **£6,000-6,500** *B*

A pair of small Louis XV-style rosewood and mahogany veneered bombé commodes, with floral marquetry inlay, 27 in., 19th C. **£1,400-1,800** *WW*

A rosewood and marquetry bombé petite commode, French, 33 by 32 in. (84 by 81 cm.), third quarter of the 19th C. **£700-900** *SC*

A rosewood veneered petite commode, with brèche-violette moulded serpentine marble top, 2 ft. 9 in. high by 1 ft. 10 in. wide (84 by 56 cm.), c. 1900. **£800-1,000** *S*

A marquetry bombé commode, with a moulded mottled grey, beige and white marble top, 3 ft. 2½ in. high by 2 ft. 8½ in. wide (97 by 82 cm.), c. 1890. **£1,200-1,600** *S*

A kingwood commode, in Louis XV/XVI Transitional style, 3 ft. 1 in. high by 4 ft. 4½ in. wide (94 by 133.5 cm.), c. 1900. **£2,600-3,200** *S*

A small walnut and rosewood marquetry commode, in Transitional style, 2 ft. 4½ in. wide (72 cm.), c. 1920. **£1,000-1,250** *S*

A marquetry commode in Louis XVI style, inlaid with cube and chevron parquetry, 2 ft. 9 in. by 2 ft. 10½ in. (84 by 88 cm.), c. 1880. **£800-1,000** *S*

A Louis XVI-style kingwood, marquetry and parquetry commode, in the style of Riesener, 5 ft. 4 in. wide by 3 ft. 1 in. high, 19th C. **£1,800-2,400** *CDC*

A Louis XVI-style amaranth and parquetry inlaid serpentine commode, 32 in., 19th C. **£800-£1,000** *CSK*

A Louis Philippe kingwood commode, by Liebmann Freres, 2 ft. 10 in. high by 3 ft. 4¾ in. wide (87 by 103.5 cm.), 1840's. **£1,200-£1,500** *S*

A fine Louis Philippe maplewood commode, stencilled 'Maison Le Marchand H. Lemoine, Rue de Tournelles a Paris Ebeniste..', 51 in. wide (130 cm.). **£4,000-5,000** *C*

Louis-Edouard Lamarchand and Andre Lemoine were in partnership between 1846 and 1852, when Lemoine took over the business.

An ormolu-mounted rosewood marquetry commode, 48 in. wide (132 cm.), late 19th C. **£1,200-1,500** *C*

A kingwood commode, in Louis XVI style, with brèche-violette marble top, 2 ft. 10½ in. high by 3 ft. 3 in. wide (87.5 by 99 cm.), c. 1900. **£1,500-1,800** *S*

A boulle and ebony commode, with white marble top, constructed, c. 1870 using elements from earlier boulle furniture, 2 ft. 11½ in. high by 2 ft. 7½ in. wide (90 by 80 cm.). **£1,200-1,500** *S*

A French 19th C. commode, the drawers with kingwood herringbone veneers, 53 in. wide by 42 in. high. **£1,000-1,250** *BHW*

A late 17th C. walnut and marquetry chest, probably Austrian, 57½ in. wide. **£1,600-£2,200** *HyD*

A Continental burr-walnut commode, the bowed front with brushing slide, above 4 long drawers, supported on bun feet, late 19th C. **£500-700** *CDC*

An 18th C. South German walnut commode, 44 in. wide. **£4,000-4,600** *PWC*

A North Italian large walnut and marquetry commode, decorated with bone and boxwood inlay, 3 ft. 4 in. high by 5 ft. 2 in. wide (102 by 158 cm.), c. 1720. **£3,000-3,500** *SS*

A South German walnut, fruitwood and parquetry commode, 51½ in. wide (131 cm.), mid 18th C. **£5,000-£6,000** *C*

An Italian 18th C. walnut and marquetry inlaid serpentine front chest, the inlay in ivory and various woods, a few small pieces of veneer missing, 4 ft. 8 in. wide. **£3,200-3,600** *GC*

A Lombard walnut parquetry chest, 3 ft. 2½ in. high by 4 ft. 10 in. wide (98 by 147.5 cm.), mid 18th C. **£2,000-2,500** *S*

A pair of North Italian walnut and cedarwood small commodes, inlaid with bone, 2 ft. 10 in. high by 2 ft. 3 in. wide (86 by 69 cm.), c. 1720. **£2,500-3,000** *SS*

361

An Italian bombé small commode, in crossbanded and quarter-veneered kingwood, 2 ft. 8½ in. high by 1 ft. 9½ in. wide (83 by 55 cm.), c. 1750. **£2,800-3,400** *S*

A pair of Italian walnut, tulipwood and marquetry commodes, 54 in. wide by 33¾ in. high by 24 in. deep (137 by 85.5 by 61 cm.), late 18th C. **£7,000-8,000** *C*

A South Italian walnut and seaweed marquetry commode, on later turned oak feet, bearing a label inscribed Sigri Fratelli Barurioli PV a lierna n l, 55 in. wide (140 cm.), early 18th C. **£1,500-1,800** *C*

An Italian walnut and marquetry bombé commode, 33½ in. high by 36 in. wide. **£1,200-1,500** *Bea*

A Milanese walnut-veneered marquetry commode, the drawers and sides crossbanded in walnut and tulipwood, 2 ft. 10½ in. high by 4 ft. wide (87.5 by 122 cm.), c. 1780. **£3,000-3,500** *S*

A Milanese walnut commode, with quarter veneers and satinwood inlay, distressed, 2 ft. 10 in. high by 3 ft. 11 in. wide (86 by 120 cm.), c. 1780. **£2,000-2,500** *SS*

A Lombard marquetry commode, the top in quarter-veneered walnut, 2 ft. 9½ in. high by 4 ft. wide (85 by 122 cm.), c. 1790. **£1,800-2,200** *S*

A pair of Venetian cream and blue painted serpentine chests, 34 in. wide (86 cm.). **£1,200-1,600** *C*

A late 18th C. Milanese kingwood, walnut and marquetry commode, 35 in. high by 48 in. wide. **£4,000-£4,500** *Bea*

A Venetian painted commode, with flowers on a pale green ground, 2 ft. 11½ in. high by 4 ft. 5 in. wide (90 by 135 cm.). **£1,000-1,250** *S*

A Venetian painted commode of exaggerated baroque form, in mid 18th C. style, with a simulated verde-antico marble top, painted with flowers and chinoiserie on a yellow ground, with powder blue base, 3 ft. 1½ in. high by 2 ft. 6 in. wide by 1 ft. 9½ in. deep (95 by 76 by 55 cm.), c. 1900. **£800-1,200** *S*

A Spanish tortoiseshell-veneered chest, in 17th C. style, the kingwood-veneered top with bandings of ivory and ebony, and mother-of-pearl borders, 3 ft. 4½ in. high by 3 ft. 1½ in. wide (103 by 95 cm.), third quarter of the 19th C. **£3,600-4,200** *S*

USE THE INDEX!

Because certain items might fit easily into any of a number of categories, the quickest and surest method of locating any entry is by reference to the fully cross-referenced index at the back of the book. This is particularly true this year when certain sections, e.g. Worcester Porcelain and Oak Furniture have been featured in isolation.

An Iberian walnut inlaid commode, the crossbanded top with marquetry landscape inset, now without feet, 3 ft. high by 4 ft. 3 in. wide (91.5 by 130 cm.), c. 1770. **£900-1,200** *SS*

A Swedish walnut parquetry commode, of serpentine bombé form inlaid with diamonds within a crossbanding, mounts modern, 2 ft. 8½ in. high by 3 ft. wide (80 by 92 cm.), mid 18th C. **£1,800-2,400** *S*

A Swedish parquetry commode, the exterior with diamond laburnum-wood parquetry within broad crossbanding, with rococo gilt mounts, 2 ft. 6 in. high by 3 ft. 7 in. wide (76 by 107 cm.), c. 1770. **£3,200-3,800** *S*

A Swedish kingwood and burr-walnut serpentine commode, in mid 18th C. style, 3 ft. 2 in. wide (96.5 cm.), c. 1880. **£1,500-2,000** *S*

An ormolu-mounted amaranth and marquetry commode, after the model by J.-H. Riesener with eared splayed marble top, 55 in. wide (140 cm.). **£2,200-2,800** *C*

A 19th C. Swiss mahogany marquetry chest, 52 in. **£250-350** *O*

A sycamore mahogany and marquetry commode, the 2 long drawers veneered sans traverse with an urn filled reserve, Franco-Swedish, with restorations, 33 by 48½ in. (84 by 123 cm.), third quarter of 18th C. **£2,000-2,500** *SC*

A Continental straight front mahogany commode, 4 ft. 1 in., 18th C. **£3,000-4,000** *MMB*

A gilt metal-mounted mahogany commode, after the model by G. Beneman and J. Stockel, 70 in. wide by 38 in. high by 25½ in. deep (178 by 96.5 by 65 cm.). **£5,000-£6,000** *C*

The full history of the commode on which this is based is given in F. Watson, Louis XVI Furniture, 1960, fig. 45. It was one of 4 originally made by Stockel for the Comte de Provence which were purchased by the Garde Meuble in 1786. They then underwent extensive remodelling under the direction of Beneman — this and another companion (new) commode were placed firstly in the Queen's Bedchamber at Fontainbleau and were then moved to the Queen's Salon des Jeux in the same palace (necessitating further alterations to the already modified Stockel commode).

A Louis XVI walnut and parquetry cube inlaid commode chest, of 2 drawers, 3 ft. 4¼ in. wide. **£2,000-£2,500** *GC*

A marquetry commode, in George II style, made of panels of floral marquetry on a sycamore ground within tulipwood borders, 3 ft. 2 in. high by 5 ft. 1 in. wide (97 by 155 cm.), second quarter 20th C. **£1,500-2,000** *S*

A Maggiolini-style walnut and rosewood commode, with amaranth and ebonised banded borders inlaid with marquetry, stamped Gillows, Lancaster, 50½ in. **£1,400-1,800** *CSK*

A pair of George III-style plum mottled mahogany and sycamore crossbanded commodes, stamped 'Maple & Co. Ltd', one commode converted to a hi-fi cabinet with fittings, hinged top and additional metal feet and castors, 3 ft. 2 in. high by 3 ft. 1 in. (97 by 94 cm.), c. 1910. **£2,500-3,000** *SS*

A Dutch satinwood serving commode, the rising top crossbanded with figured mahogany, ebony and boxwood on a satinwood background, 42 in. wide, 18th C. **£800-1,100**   *B*

A mahogany commode, with chamfered serpentine top crossbanded with satinwood and 3 drawers in bowed centre, flanked by oval-inlaid concave cupboard doors, 60 in. wide (152.5 cm.). **£2,200-2,800**   *C*

A George III mahogany commode, in the manner of Gillows, the sides mounted with later foliate carrying handles, 28 in. wide (71 cm.). **£1,200-1,500**   *C*

An 18th C. walnut tallboy, the upper section with a cavetto moulded cornice, the drawers all feather-banded, 40 in. **£1,000-1,250**   *PWC*

WALNUT

- **the walnut period is generally accepted as running from c. 1670-1740, when mahogany took over as the major wood used**
- **walnut had many advantages: beautiful colour, suitable for veneer work, the burr and curl were particularly desirable, easy to carve**
- **it was, however, prone to worm**
- **cabinet makers replaced joiners as supreme craftsmen**
- **London became furniture making centre**
- **the first time one was able to distinguish between town and country pieces**
- **country chests were lined in pine**
- **Charles II reign heralded return of exiled aristocracy plus continental fashions in furniture**

Plus factors with walnut:—
- **patination and colour**
- **good choice of veneers**
- **with chests — a quartered top**
- **herringbone inlay**
- **crossbanding**
- **stringing**
- **marquetry**

A Queen Anne walnut chest on stand, legs replaced, 5 ft. high by 3 ft. 1 in. wide (153 by 94 cm.), c. 1710. **£1,500-2,000**   *S*

A Queen Anne walnut chest on chest, in well-figured burr-wood, with oak sides, 5 ft. 6½ in. high by 3 ft. 5 in. wide (169 by 104 cm.), c. 1710. **£3,000-3,500**   *S*

A Queen Anne walnut chest on stand, with herringbone crossbanding, with oak sides and on later cabriole legs, 39½ by 65½ in. high (100 by 166 cm.). **£1,400-1,800**   *L*

A William and Mary-style walnut chest on stand, 19th/20th C. **£500-£700**   *WSW*

An early 18th C. walnut chest on stand, 40 in. wide. **£1,400-1,800**   *A*

A Queen Anne walnut tallboy, on later bracket feet, 43½ in. wide (110.5 cm.). **£3,200-3,800**   *C*

A George III oak chest on stand, crossbanded in mahogany, 46 in. wide. **£600-700**   *Re*

An early 18th C. walnut tallboy, with cavetto cornice above fluted anted corners and feather-banded drawers, 39½ in. wide. **£1,200-1,500** *PWC*

n need of restoration.

A George I walnut secretaire tallboy, 43½ in. wide. **£2,000-2,500** *B*

A George I yew wood-veneered chest on chest, 5 ft. 7 in. high by 3 ft. 4½ in. wide (170 by 103 cm.). **£1,000-1,250** *S*

A George walnut tallboy, the base with a brushing slide and 3 drawers, the lowest with inlaid concave sunburst, with restoration, sunburst later, 5 ft. 8 in. high by 3 ft. 5½ in. wide (173 by 105 cm.), c. 1720. **£3,800-4,500** *S*

A George I walnut composite chest on chest, 39 in. wide. **£1,200-1,500** *LS*

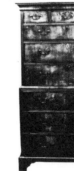

A George I walnut chest on chest, 3 ft. 4 in. wide by 5 ft. 5 in. high. **£1,400-1,800** *AMB*

A George I walnut composite chest on chest, 39 in. wide. **£1,200-1,500** *LS*

George I walnut chest on chest, 2 parts, 5 ft. 11 in. high by 3 ft. n. wide (181 by 102 cm.), c. 1725. **,500-5,500** *S*

A Georgian figured mahogany chest on chest, 45 in. wide. **£800-£1,000** *GBT*

A George I walnut chest on chest, 3 ft. 4½ in. wide, c. 1720. **£1,500-2,000** *S*

A George I walnut chest on chest, 3 ft. 7½ in. wide by 5 ft. ½ in. high (110 by 154 cm.). **£800-1,200** *S*

It is likely that the base has been reduced from 3 to 2 drawers.

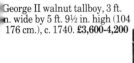

George II walnut tallboy, 3 ft. n. wide by 5 ft. 9½ in. high (104 176 cm.), c. 1740. **£3,600-4,200**

George I walnut chest on chest, e burr-veneered drawers with ahogany banding, 3 ft. 4½ in. de by 5 ft. 8 in. high (103 by 3 cm.), c. 1720. **£1,500-2,000** *S*

A George III mahogany tallboy, inset with satinwood panels, 42 by 72 in. high (107 by 183 cm.). **£800-£1,200** *L*

A George III mahogany tallboy, 6 ft. high by 3 ft. 6 in. wide (183 by 107 cm.), c. 1780. **£2,500-3,000**   *S*

A mid 19th C. mahogany wardrobe, Flemish, 60 in. wide. **£400-500** *Wlh*

An early 19th C. mahogany breakfront wardrobe cupboard, 8 ft. 1 in. wide by 24½ in. deep by 6 ft. 1 in. high. **£500-800**   *PWC*

Often purchased for conversion to breakfront bookcases.

A Regency wardrobe, the figured mahogany panels crossbanded and inlaid with brass and satinwood, 49 in. **£1,000-1,250**   *GM*

A large 19th C. Dutch mahogany wardrobe, 8 ft. 6 in. by 6 ft. 1 in. wide. **£500-700**   *AG*

An Henri III walnut cabinet, altered, 4 ft. 8 in. high by 2 ft. 11 in. wide (142 by 89 cm.), c. 1580. **£3,200-3,800**   *S*

A mahogany wardrobe, 85 in. wide. **£600-700**   *DA*

An Edwardian rosewood breakfront wardrobe, of architectural design, 7 ft. wide. **£600-800**   *Pea*

A walnut armoire, 80 by 63 in., partly mid 18th C. **£1,250-£1,500**   *SC*

A Dutch rosewood and marquetry armoire, 6 ft. 8 in. high, c. 1700, marquetry 19th C. **£2,800-£3,400**   *S*

A Dutch walnut and marquetry hanging wall cupboard, possibly inlaid in the 19th C., 37 by 41 in. (94 by 104 cm.), late 18th C. **£80 £1,200**   *SC*

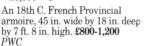

A Louis XV Provincial oak cabinet, 61½ in. wide (156 cm.). **£4,500-£5,500**   *C*

An 18th C. French Provincial armoire, 45 in. wide by 18 in. deep by 7 ft. 8 in. high. **£800-1,200** *PWC*

A Louis XV Provincial oak armoire, 80 by 60 in. **£800-1,200** *BHW*

A Dutch mahogany armoire, 75 66 in. (191 by 168 cm.), third quarter 18th C. **£500-600** *SC*

An ebony and marquetry breakfront bas d'armoire, the marquetry panels late 17th C., 85½ in. wide by 65 in. high (217 by 165 cm.). **£2,000-2,500** *C*

Danzig ebonized and walnut rmoire, 7 ft. 8½ in. high by 6 ft. ¾ in. wide (235 by 191 cm.), 1670. **£2,800-3,500** *S*

An Italian walnut cabinet, on later feet, 61 in. wide 17th C. **£4,500-5,500** *C*

A Louis XV kingwood parquetry small armoire, 4 ft. 6½ in. high, 3 ft. 3 in. wide (138 by 99 cm.), c. 1760. **£3,000-3,500** *S*

n Italian walnut (armadio) abinet, 36½ in. wide (93 cm.), asically 16th C. **£1,800-2,400** *C*

A pine and walnut armadio, on later claw feet, 28 in. wide (71 cm.), 16th C. **£1,200-1,600** *C*

A Tuscan walnut cupboard, 70 in. wide (178 cm.), basically late 16th C. **£4,500-5,500** *C*

A North Italian armoire, profusely inlaid and decorated with marquetry panels, with fitted interior enclosed by two moulded panel doors, 74 in. **£3,000-3,500** *LE*

Milanese ivory-inlaid ebony-eered and ebonised cabinet, the nt inlaid throughout with finely scrollwork and allegorical res in late 17th C. style, 6 ft. high by 4 ft. 2½ in. wide (193 28 cm.), c. 1870. **£1,500-2,000**

A Spanish walnut food cupboard, carved with geometric designs painted in red and green, framed by notched foliate borders, 25½ in. wide (65 cm.). **£2,000-2,500** *C*

A pair of Chinese Chippendale design fawn lacquered bow fronted standing corner cupboards, 50 by 92 in. high. **£1,200-£1,500** *GSP*

A George I black lacquer corner cupboard, 36½ in. high, c. 1715. **£800-1,000** *AP*

An early 18th C. black and gilt lacquered corner cabinet, 2 ft. 10 in. wide by 6 ft. 7 in. high. **£1,800-2,400** *GC*

George III bow fronted ahogany semi-circular side binet, probably the base of a nding mahogany corner cabinet. 00-900 *WM*

Right

A black and gold lacquered bow fronted corner cupboard, 22 in. wide by 36 in high, early 18th C. **£500-700** *Re*

An 18th C. mahogany panelled corner cupboard, 7 ft. 2 in. high by 3 ft. 11 in. wide. **£700-900**   *Fr*

A fine George III standing corner cabinet, in mahogany, 109 by 228 cm. high. **£2,000-2,500**   *OT*

A mahogany standing corner cupboard, the doors with satinwood fan-shaped spandrels, and strung throughout in satinwood, 93 by 51½ in. (236 by 131 cm.), early 19th C. **£2,400-2,800**   *SC*

A George III mahogany double corner cupboard, 78 in. high by 46 in. wide. **£1,400-1,800**   *B*

A George III mahogany standing corner display cabinet, 7 ft. 1 in. high (216 cm.), c. 1790. **£1,800-2,200**   *SS*

A George III mahogany bow fronted hanging corner cupboard. **£600-700**   *CDC*

A pair of Dutch walnut and marquetry corner cabinets, 35½ in. high by 32 in. wide. **£1,200-1,500**   *Bea*

CORNER CUPBOARDS

These cupboards were made right through the 18th century in various woods including walnut and mahogany, as well as oak. Examples in oak are usually 'country' versions of the more sophisticated pieces made in walnut or mahogany.

Corner cupboards with glazed doors, that are suitable for the display of porcelain or other objects, are the most sought after type. They are, however, far more difficult to find and are consequently more expensive.

Bow fronted examples are usually considered the most desirable, especially if they are fitted inside with two or three small drawers and the shelves are shaped.

These cupboards are usually constructed in two parts; 'marriages' do exist and whilst these may be acceptable, it should be reflected in a lower price. Check that the backboards of the two parts match and that the quality of timber and style of construction correspond.

An Edwardian mahogany inlaid standing corner cupboard, with pierced swan neck pediment, 3 ft. 1 in. by 7 ft. 10 in. high. **£1,800-2,200**   *MMB*

An Edwardian corner cupboard. **£1,000-1,250**   *PLJ*

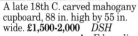

A large elm standing corner cupboard, 92 by 60 in. (234 by 153 cm.), the doors 18th C., reconstructed in the 19th C. **£700-£900**   *SC*

A late 18th C. carved mahogany cupboard, 88 in. high by 55 in. wide. **£1,500-2,000**   *DSH*

An Edwardian inlaid mahogany standing corner cupboard, 27 in. **£700-900**   *JD*

A George III mahogany standing corner cupboard, 95 by 45 in. (241 by 114 cm.), late 18th C. **£1,400-£1,800**   *SC*

A mahogany standing corner cupboard, 33 in. wide by 7 ft. 6 in. high, 19th C. **£600-800**   *EG*

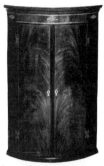

A George III mahogany bow front hanging wall cupboard, 46 by 31 in. (115 by 79 cm.), early 19th C. **£600-£700** *SC*

A 19th C. inlaid and crossbanded hanging corner cupboard. **£350-400** *GM*

A Georgian mahogany bow fronted hanging corner cupboard, 27 in. wide by 44 in. high. **£400-500** *PWC*

bow front mahogany and inlaid eorgian hanging corner cupboard, t. 3 in. high by 2 ft. wide (98 by cm.) **£250-350** *LRG*

For most examples of court cupboards, tridarns, etc., see the Oak and Country Furniture section.

A pair of ormolu-mounted and bois atine kingwood marquetry ncoignures, of Louis XV style, oth stamped twice G. Durand, 1½ in. (80 cm.). **£4,000-5,000** *C*

Edwardian inlaid and satinwood crossbanded veneered display cabinet, 3 ft. 3 in. high by 1 ft. 4 in. wide (98 by 40 cm.). **£250-£300** *LRG*

A Louis XV ormolu-mounted kingwood and tulipwood encoignure, 26 in. wide (66 cm.). **£3,200-3,600** *C*

An early 19th C. inlaid mahogany corner cupboard, 30 in. wide. **£400-£500** *DSH*

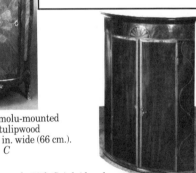

An unusual oak painted small side abinet, in mixed ococo, Elizabethan nd mediaeval styles, vith a pink and white eined marble top, 3 ft. igh by 1 ft. 11¾ in. vide (92 by 60 cm.), 1840. **£250-300** *S*

A pair of mahogany and marquetry encoignures, each with a moulded white Carrara marble top, 3 ft. 5 in. high by 2 ft. 7 in. wide (104 by 79 cm.), c. 1880. **£1,800-2,400** *S*

A pair of Louis XV tulipwood-veneered encoignures, 2 ft. 9 in. high by 2 ft. 2 in. wide (84 by 66 cm.), c. 1750. **£1,800-2,200** *S*

A serpentine boulle encoignure, with a white Carrara marble top, the whole inlaid with cut-brass foliage on a tortoiseshell ground, 3 ft. 6½ in. high by 2 ft. 4 in. wide (108 by 71 cm.), c. 1860. **£900-1,000** *S*

walnut press, on later turned t, 56 in. wide by 53 in. high (142 135 cm.), 17th C. **£1,200-1,500**

A rare walnut, pine and fruitwood hall cupboard, German, 73 by 61½ in. (186 by 156 cm.), mid 17th C. **£2,000-2,500** *SC*

A walnut and marquetry standing corner cupboard, the door early 18th C., possibly German, 42 in. wide (107 cm.). **£1,200-1,500** *C*

A Flemish side cabinet, the doors applied with painted and applied 'jewellery', divided by fluted balusters, carved with blind-fret strapwork, the plinth altered, now with block feet, 6 ft. 10 in. high by 3 ft. 8 in. wide (178 by 112 cm.), mid 17th C. **£1,200-1,500** *S*

DAVENPORTS

- The name derives from Gillow's cost book where an illustration of this piece of furniture appeared for the first time. Beside the illustration was written 'Captain Davenport — a desk'.
- first examples date from the late 1790's
- they were extremely popular during the Regency and well into Victoria's reign
- there are two quite distinct types of davenport — the quite severe Regency as opposed to the more generous and often highly carved Victorian
- they are bought by a quite different market — at the moment the walnut well carved Victorian can be said to be selling much better than the earlier Regency
- points to look out for: burr-walnut, satinwood, secret drawers or complex interior arrangement, good quality carving and cabriole legs, galleried top
- unless stated all davenports in this section are fitted with 4 real opposed by 4 dummy drawers.

A William IV rosewood davenport, the sliding rectangular boxed top with an inset leather-lined sloping flap, above a hinged side pen compartment, 24 in. **£800-1,000** *CSK*

A small Regency mahogany davenport, the swivelling top with leather-lined writing slope, 2 ft. 10½ in. high by 1 ft. 3½ in. wide (88 by 40 cm.), c. 1815. **£1,500-£1,800** *S*

A William IV rosewood veneered davenport, 21 in. **£800-1,000** *WW*

A George IV mahogany davenport, having sliding top with lined rising surface, 19¾ in. wide. **£800-1,000** *GC*

A Regency burr-elm swivel top davenport, of excellent colour, 32 in. high by 18½ in. wide by 20½ in. deep, c. 1815. **£1,800-2,200** *AP*

A Victorian walnut davenport. **£350-450** *CDC*

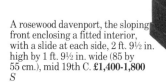

A rosewood davenport, the three-quarter gallery above a writing slope which slides forward over the knees, 1 ft. 8½ in. wide. (52 cm.), 1830's. **£1,000-1,250** *S*

A rosewood davenport, the sloping front enclosing a fitted interior, with a slide at each side, 2 ft. 9½ in. high by 1 ft. 9½ in. wide (85 by 55 cm.), mid 19th C. **£1,400-1,800** *S*

MILLER'S *Antiques Price Guide builds up year by year to form the most comprehensive photo-reference system available. The first five volumes contain over 40,000 completely different photographs.*

Victorian rosewood davenport,
e inset hinged writing slope
vealing small drawers, 2 ft. 9 in.
gh by 1 ft. 11½ in. wide (84 by
cm.), c. 1850. **£700-900**   *SS*

A figured walnut davenport, with
hinged stationery compartment
and sloping flap, 2 ft. 8 in. high by
1 ft. 9 in. wide (81 by 53 cm.),
c. 1850. **£700-900**   *S*

A William IV
rosewood
davenport, 20 in.
£800-1,200
WW

A rosewood veneered davenport,
with leather-lined sloping writing
surface and a three-quarters
wooden gallery, 3 ft. high by 2 ft.
11 in. wide (91 by 89 cm.), c. 1835.
£800-1,200   *S*

Victorian walnut serpentine
nted davenport, 22 in. **£800-
000**   *WAG*

A Victorian inlaid walnut
davenport, 21 in. **£700-900**   *JD*

A Victorian walnut
davenport, 21 in. wide.
£400-500   *BHW*

A Victorian burr-walnut
davenport. **£600-800**   *Fr*

osewood veneered davenport,
a shelf on a pierced scrollwork
ort, 3 ft. 5 in. high by 2 ft. wide
by 62 cm.), c. 1840. **£650-750**

A Victorian walnut and tulipwood
banded davenport, by Gillow,
stamped Gillow, 52 cm. wide.
£1,300-1,600   *Bon*

A Victorian burr-walnut
davenport. **£1,000-1,250**
DWB

A Victorian walnut davenport.
£1,000-1,200   *TL*

ictorian rosewood davenport,
n. wide. **£350-450**   *EG*

A Victorian inlaid burr-walnut
piano-fronted davenport, 24 in.
£700-900   *JD*

A walnut davenport, in well
figured wood and inlaid with small
burr-wood medallions, 3 ft. 2 in.
high by 1 ft. 9 in. wide (97 by
54 cm.), c. 1860. **£1,250-1,500**   *S*

An inlaid rosewood davenport by
Thomas Turner of Manchester,
22 in. wide. **£650-750**   *Re*

A William and Mary walnut marquetry desk, the crossbanded top folding open to reveal a fitted writing compartment, with a fall-down front, 37½ in. (95 cm.). **£4,000-4,500** *L*

An early 18th C. walnut and banded and herringbone inlaid kneehole desk. **£2,500-3,000** *DWB*

An early 18th C. kingwood oyster kneehole desk, the top crossbanded and inlaid in kingwood oysters, the front folds forward revealing a fitted cross-grained interior of small drawers and secret drawers, with later bracket feet, 41 in. wide. **£4,000-4,500** *B*

A kingwood oyster veneered kneehole desk, the crossbanded t inlaid with segmentally veneered roundels and strapwork, 93 cm. wide. **£1,250-1,500** *Bon*

Probably re-veneered.

A Queen Anne walnut kneehole desk, with crossbanded rectangular top, on later bracket feet, 31 in. wide (79 cm.). **£4,500-5,000** *C*

A Queen Anne walnut kneehole desk, with crossbanded and quartered moulded rectangular to 31½ in. wide by 16½ in. deep (80 b 42 cm.). **£4,500-5,000** *C*

A Queen Anne walnut kneehole desk, in well-figured wood, with feather- and crossbanded top, 2 ft. 6½ in. high by 2 ft. 7½ in. wide (77 by 80 cm.), c. 1710. **£3,200-3,600** *S*

KNEEHOLE DESKS

- kneehole desk is like a pedestal but with a recessed cupboard in between the pedestals
- it was most likely an 'upstairs' piece — hence being used as a dressing table/desk
- they were first made c. 1710 in walnut
- most then had 3 drawers across the top and 3 down each pedestal
- this piece of furniture has suffered from demand and there are many fakes and gross alterations
- many are made from chests of drawers (check the sides of the small drawers and if the desk has been made from a chest of drawers they will have a new side)
- it is unusual to have a brushing slide in a kneehole desk — this *could* point to a conversion.

A George I walnut kneehole des 35 in. wide (89 cm.). **£2,500-3,00** *C*

A George I walnut kneehole des with restoration, feet and handl replaced, 3 ft. wide (91 cm.), c. 1720. **£2,600-3,200** *S*

A George I walnut kneehole desk, 2 ft. 7 in. **£3,000-3,500** *AMB*

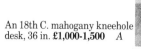

An 18th C. mahogany kneehole desk, 36 in. **£1,000-1,500** *A*

George II mahogany kneehole
sk, 2 ft. 7 in. **£1,600-2,000**
MB

A George III mahogany kneehole
desk, with slide. **£1,800-2,200**
Wor

A George II walnut kneehole
writing table, inlaid with
chequered stringing, 2 ft. 5½ in.
high by 2 ft. 7 in. wide (75.5 by
79 cm.), c. 1740. **£3,000-3,500**   *S*

late Georgian mahogany
eehole desk, 32 in. wide. **£3,000-
500**   *M*

A 19th C. mahogany serpentine
fronted kneehole dressing table,
47 in. wide. **£700-900**   *DSH*
*Possibly converted from a chest of
drawers.*

A George III 'plum pudding'
mahogany partners' desk, locks
and handles replaced, 2 ft. 9 in.
high by 5 ft. 5½ in. wide by 2 ft.
11½ in. deep (84 by 166.5 by
90 cm.), c. 1800. **£3,500-4,000**   *S*

Georgian mahogany partners'
sk, 58½ in. wide (148.5 cm.).
500-6,500**   *C*

A George III mahogany partners'
desk, on restored plinth base,
52 in. wide by 41 in. deep by
31½ in. high, c. 1790. **£3,500-4,000**
HAL

A mahogany roll-top desk, requires
restoration, 38½ in. high by
36½ in. wide (98 by 92.5 cm.),
c. 1800. **£1,500-1,800**   *TW*

Irish mahogany kneehole
rary table, bearing the trade
el of Turbitt of Coleraine &
wtown Limavady, handles later,
t. 9 in. high by 5 ft. 7 in. wide
by 170 cm.), early 19th C.
000-3,500**   *S*

A fine George III mahogany
partners' desk, 67½ in. wide
(171.5 cm.). **£12,000-14,000**   *C*

A George III mahogany cylinder
bureau on stand, stand reconstructed, 39½ in. high by 36 in.
wide. **£1,000-1,250**   *Bea*

A George III well-figured
satinwood cylinder bureau, in the
French style, with tulipwood
crossbanded top, above a cylinder
working in conjunction with a
leather-lined writing slide,
enclosing a fitted interior, 3 ft.
4½ in. high by 3 ft. 7 in. wide by
1 ft. 11½ in. deep (103 by 109 by
60 cm.), c. 1780. **£5,000-6,000**   *S*

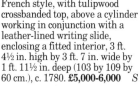

An unusual small George III
mahogany kneehole writing table,
the back with 2 real and 5 dummy
drawers matching the front, 3 ft.
4 in. wide (102 cm.), c. 1770.
£4,500-5,000   *S*

A George III-style mahogany and crossbanded Carlton House writing desk, inlaid with ebonised stringing, 3 ft. 3½ in. high by 4 ft. 5½ in. wide (100 by 136 cm.), c. 1910. **£1,000-1,500** *SS*

A decorated satinwood Carlton House writing table, 46 in. **£3,600-£4,200** *GSP*

An Edwardian rosewood kneehole pedestal desk, inlaid with marquetry panels, stamped Collinson & Lock, London, No: 8003, 50 in. **£1,500-1,800** *CSK*

A late 19th C. mahogany kneehole desk, 52 in. **£220-280** *WHL*

A late Victorian inlaid rosewood kneehole desk, 39 in. wide. **£500-£600** *M*

A George III-style mahogany kneehole pedestal desk, 54 in. **£1,500-2,000** *CSK*

A brass-mounted mahogany pedestal desk, in Empire style, 2 ft. 6 in. high by 4 ft. 10 in. wide (76 by 147 cm.), 19th C. **£2,500-3,000** *S*

A Victorian mahogany partners' desk, 72.5 in. wide (184 cm.). **£3,000-3,500** *C*

A George III mahogany Carlton House desk. **£1,800-2,200** *JF*
In need of some restoration.

A Chippendale-design mahogany pedestal desk, ivory label inscribed 'S. & H. Jewell, 26 Parker Street, London, W.C.2.', 5 ft. wide. **£900-£1,200** *PWC*

USE THE INDEX!

Because certain items might fit easily into any of a number of categories, the quickest and surest method of locating any entry is by reference to the fully cross-referenced index at the back of the book. This is particularly true this year when certain sections, e.g. Worcester Porcelain and Oak Furniture have been featured in isolation.

A Victorian walnut writing des with maker's plate of Ross & Co Dublin, 46 in. wide. **£800-1,200** *HyD*

A Carlton House writing table i satinwood, 42 in. wide. **£2,200-£2,600** *LT*

A walnut kneehole writing table, 2 ft. 6 in. high by 4 ft. 1 in. wide (7 by 125 cm.), c. 1870. **£1,800-2,200** *S*

An Edwardian mahogany pedest; desk, 48 by 28 in. **£700-800** *JD*

An ebonised kneehole writing table, inlaid with fruitwood stringing and arabesque foliage, 2 ft. 6½ in. high by 4 ft. wide (77 by 122 cm.), c. 1870. **£600-800** *S*

gilt metal mounted mahogany
mpire revival double-sided
artners' desk, 2 ft. 5½ in. high by
ft. 4½ in. wide (75 by 164 cm.),
1880. **£1,800-2,400**   *S*

An Edwardian writing desk, of
Carlton House design, veneered in
mahogany, with satinwood
crossbanding, with etched boxwood
and other marquetry inlay, 48 in.
£1,200-1,500   *MN*

An Edwardian mahogany kneehole
pedestal desk, inlaid with boxwood
geometric lines, 54 in. **£600-700**
CSK

Victorian mahogany writing
sk, 57 in. wide. **£600-700**   *Re*

A 19th C. mahogany secretaire
pedestal desk, 3 ft. 8 in. high by
4 ft. 11 in. wide (112 by 150 cm.),
c. 1880. **£700-900**   *S*

A late Victorian rosewood
serpentine fronted writing desk, by
Shoolbred & Co., London, 42 in.
high by 44 in. wide. **£800-1,200**
Bea

late 19th C. mahogany desk,
er mounted on castors, 99 by 40
39 in. **£1,200-1,600**   *WHL*

A Victorian mahogany pedestal
desk, 50 by 42 in. high. **£500-600**
WP

A Victorian inlaid mahogany
kidney-shaped writing desk, 48 in.
wide. **£800-1,000**   *M*

Victorian mahogany pedestal
k, the fitted writing drawer
h shaped fall front below a
izontal bank of 3 drawers, 4 ft.
1. wide. **£600-700**   *HyD*

A late 19th C. American made
walnut Wootton-type cylinder top
desk, 32 in. **£500-700**   *JD*

A Victorian pollard oak-veneered
kidney-shaped writing desk,
30 in. high by 54 in. wide. **£3,000-
£3,500**   *Bea*

A Wootton's walnut desk, the front
fitted with a lift-up frieze above a
fall front and fitted interior, with
label 'from Maple & Co. Ltd.,
London', 72 in. high, late 19th C.
£4,200-4,800   *L*

A Victorian mahogany cylinder top
pedestal desk, 4 ft. 11 in. wide by
4 ft. high. **£1,000-1,400**   *AGr*

375

A late 17th C. Dutch crossbanded walnut kneehole desk, 44 in. wide. **£1,800-2,200** *DSH*

An ebony burr-walnut and marquetry bureau mazarin, 45 in. wide (114 cm.). **£3,400-3800** *C*

An Edwardian Sheraton revival mahogany cylinder desk, with satinwood crossbands and boxwood and ebonised stringing, 48 in. wide c. 1905. **£1,500-1,800** *N*

An ormolu-mounted kingwood and tulipwood parquetry bureau à cylindre, of Louis XVI style, 52 in. wide (132 cm.). **£1,800-2,400** *C*

A Louis XV-style kingwood crossbanded bureau à cylindre, with ormolu mounts and satinwood stringing, 3 ft. 7½ in. high by 3 ft. 1 in. wide (110 by 94 cm.), c. 1900. **£2,000-2,500** *SS*

A fine ormolu-mounted amaranth and trellis parquetry bureau à cylindre, after J.-H. Riesener, stamped Henry Dasson 1886, 44½ in. wide (113 cm.). **£6,000-£7,000** *C*

This desk is a copy of bureau à cylindre supplied by Riesener for Marie-Antoinette's use at the Tuileries.

A Louis-Philippe ormolu-mounted kingwood and parquetry bureau, 49 in. wide (125 cm.). **£2,800-3,400** *C*

A Louis XV-style rosewood bureau à cylindre, inlaid with parquetry panels, 38 in. **£1,800-2,200** *CSK*

A Louis XVI-style mahogany kidney-shape veneered bureau de dame, 4 ft. 11 in. **£1,200-1,500** *WW*

An 18th C. French Provençal chestnut dresser, 62 in. **£2,000-£2,500** *A*

A Louis XVI-style mahogany bureau à cylindre, with ormolu mounts, with a fitted interior with sliding writing surface, 31 in. **£700-£900** *CSK*

FOR THE MAIN DRESSER SECTION SEE THE OAK AND COUNTRY FURNITURE SECTION.

An 18th C. elm dresser. **£800-1,200** *CW*

A kingwood bureau à gradin, with a timepiece flanked by 6 short drawers, the whole inlaid with a diamond parquetry trellis, 3 ft. 5 in. high by 3 ft. 5 in. wide (104 by 104 cm.), c. 1900. **£1,200-1,500**

DUMB WAITERS

- there is some controversy about when dumb waiters made an appearance
- they were certainly produced in the 1720's but are rare until the 1750's
- defined by Sheraton (Cabinet Dictionary 1803) as 'a useful piece of furniture, to serve in some respects the place of a waiter, whence it is so named'
- 18th C. dumb waiters *generally* consist of three tiers
- made usually from mahogany
- in Chippendale period supports often carved with foliage, acanthus leaves, broken scrolls, etc.
- Robert Adam's neo-classical style radically changed the design
- the pillars now tended to become plainly cylindrical with turned collars at top and bottom
- the late 18th C. and early 19th C. saw the introduction of pierced galleries often made of brass
- during the Regency period some dumb waiters made from rosewood
- marriages are around so beware
  - differing turning on 3 trays
  - two-tier examples (they can be right but are often 'naughty').

A George III mahogany dumb waiter, 40 in. high. **£500-700** *CSK*

A George III mahogany dumb waiter, 43½ in. high. **£700-900** *L*

A George III mahogany three-tier dumb waiter. **£700-900** *DWB*

A mahogany dumb waiter, 4 ft. 9 in. high, c. 1760. **£1,200-1,400** *S*

A George III mahogany dumb waiter, 24 in. **£800-1,000** *WW*

A Georgian mahogany dumb waiter, on triple baluster pillar and inverted arched tripod support, 47½ in. high (121 cm.). **£500-600** *LBP*

pair of early George III Smith's rary globe's, one terrestrial and e celestial, each incorporating a mpass, signed C. Smith & Son, 2 Strand, 3 ft. 7 in. high)9 cm.), early 19th C. **£9,000-2,000** *S*

A 12-inch Cary terrestrial globe, the sphere applied with coloured gores, English, 17 in. high (43 cm.), published 1821. **£700-900** *S*

A good pair of Cary's library globes, the terrestrial globe with adjustments and corrections to 1828 and the celestial globe dated 1799, 3 ft. 11 in. high by 2 ft. 3½ in. diam. (120 by 70 cm.), early 19th C. **£9,000-12,000** *S*

A fine Cary's new terrestrial globe, exhibiting the tracks and discoveries made by Captain Cook and others and dated London March 1, 1815, 32 in. wide by 47 in. high (81 by 119.5 cm.). **£5,500-6,500** *C*

A pair of 12-inch J. & W. Cary terrestrial and celestial globes, English, both globes and stands damaged, 18 in. high (46 cm.), published 1800 and 1812. **£1,200-£1,600** *S*

> **FOR TABLE AND MINIATURE GLOBES SEE THE SCIENTIFIC INSTRUMENT SECTION.**

A 12-inch Bate terrestrial globe on stand, the sphere applied with coloured gores and mounted in brass meridian, English, 19 in. high (48 cm.), published 1802. **£600-800** *S*

An 18-inch Malby's terrestrial globe on stand, published by H. G. Collins and supported by brass meridian, engraved with circle of degrees, English, the sphere cracked, 39 in. high (99 cm.), c. 1860. **£2,000-2,500** *S*

A pair of terrestrial and celestial globes, the celestial globe by Smith & Son, 63 Charing Cross, the terrestrial globe accurate to 1833, 3 ft. 6 in. high by 2 ft. diam. (107 by 61 cm.), first half 19th C. **£3,500-£4,000** *S*

A Regency brass mounted terrestrial globe, by Newton & So 66 Chancery Lane, and dated 184 26 in. wide (66 cm.). **£1,800-2,200** *C*

A mahogany terrestrial library globe, the Philips 18 in. Merchant Shipper's Globe on a stand bearing a maker's plaque inscribed 32 Fleet Street, London EC, 44 in. high (112 cm.), early 20th C. **£2,200-£2,600** *SC*

A William and Mary yew and burr-yew side table, with crossbanded moulded rectangular top inlaid with a compass-medallion, with later turned feet, 30¼ in. wide (77 cm.). **£4,000-4,500** *C*

A Queen Anne walnut table, 2 ft. 1½ in. high by 2 ft. 2 in. wide (64 by 66 cm.), c. 1710. **£300-500** *S*

A Queen Anne walnut side table, top re-veneered, 2 ft. 6 in. wide (76 cm.), c. 1710. **£1,500-1,800** *S*

A good Queen Anne walnut lowboy or side table, with crossbanded moulded top, 2 ft. 5 in. high by 2 ft. 5½ in. wide (74 by 75 cm.), c. 1710. **£3,200-3,600** *S*

A George I walnut lowboy, the quarter veneered top in burr-walnut crossgrained surround, 30 in. wide. **£1,800-2,400** *B*

A Queen Anne walnut side table, with rectangular cross- and feather-banded top, 2 ft. 6¼ in. wide (77 cm.), c. 1710. **£6,000-7,00** *S*

A George I crossbanded and herringbone inlaid walnut lowboy. **£3,000-3,500** *DWB*

A George I walnut lowboy. **£1,200-£1,600** *CDC*

A Queen Anne walnut lowboy, with moulded crossbanded top, 2 ft 3½ in. high by 2 ft. 6 in. wide (70 b 76 cm.), c. 1710. **£1,500-2,000** *S*

An 18th C. mahogany lowboy, 29½ in. **£600-800** *GSP*

A George II mahogany side table, 29½ in. wide (75 cm.). **£2,000-2,500** *C*

A George II walnut side table, the quartered bookmatched crossbanded surface with moulded edge, 32½ in. wide by 21 in. deep by 28 in. high, c. 1740. **£2,000-2,500** *HAL*

A George II walnut side table or lowboy, the crossbanded top with oak chevron stringing, 2 ft. 5½ in. high, 2 ft. 6½ in. wide (75 by 78 cm.), c. 1730. **£1,200-1,600** *S*

A Dutch walnut lowboy, in early 18th C. style, 2 ft. 6 in. high by 2 ft. 11½ in. wide (76 by 90 cm.), late 19th/early 20th C. **£600-800** *S*

A Georgian mahogany lowboy, 30 by 18 in. **£1,000-1,250** *JD*

An 18th C. Dutch marquetry lowboy, 29 in. **£1,500-1,800** *JD*

A William and Mary oyster veneered wall mirror, the plate re-silvered, 29 by 26 in. (74 by 66 cm.), late 17th/early 18th C. **£800-1,000** *SC*

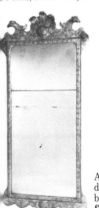

A George I giltwood mirror, with divided arched plate, 49½ in. high by 20 in. wide (126 by 51 cm.). **£3,000-3,500** *C*

A George II giltwood overmantel, the bevelled plate with shaped top corners below a boldly scrolled cresting carved and applied with acanthus, 3 ft. 9 in. high by 2 ft. 1 in. wide (114 by 63.5 cm.), c. 1740. **£2,800-3,400** *S*

A George I giltwood mirror, 65 by 2 in. **£3,500-4,000** *CSK*

A George I gilt-gesso mirror, with later bevelled rectangular plate, the eared and scrolled frame moulded with foliage on a punched ground, 49½ by 27 in. (126 by 68.5 cm.). **£1,200-1,600** *C*

A Queen Anne gilt-gesso and black lacquer pier glass, the cresting possibly later, 60 by 25 in. (152 by 63.5 cm.). **£2,500-3,000** *C*

A pair of George I looking glasses, 9 in. high by 22 in. wide. **£3,500-4,000** *Bea*

A George II gilded gesso and carved wood looking glass, 52 in. high, c. 1750. **£2,000-2,500** *AP*

A good George II giltwood pier glass, 62 by 21 in. **£2,000-£2,500** *SC*

An unusual George II giltwood wall mirror, the ribbon border and a wide border of yellow satinwood applied with cut-out prints, the border possibly originally with verre églomisé, 3 ft. 4 in. high by 2 ft. 7½ in. wide (102 by 80 cm.), c. 1750. **£1,500-2,000** *S*

A good George II carved pine frame, the scrolled flower-carved cresting supporting a pierced scallop-shell, with inverted breakfront sides and the apron carved with acanthus and flowerhead borders, now with a bevelled mirror plate, 4 ft. 6½ in. high by 3 ft. 2 in. wide (138 by 96 cm.), c. 1740. **£4,200-4,800** *S*

A late George II giltwood overmantel mirror, the divided mirror plate with a pierced pagoda cresting supported by C-scrolls, 5 ft. high by 2 ft. 6 in. wide (152 by 76 cm.), c. 1760. **£2,000-2,500** *S*

A George II rococo giltwood wall mirror, 5 ft. high by 2 ft. 11 in. wide (153 by 89 cm.), c. 1750. **£5,500-£6,500** *S*

A mid-Georgian walnut and parcel-gilt mirror, 30¼ by 16½ in. (77 by 42 cm.). **£1,500-2,000** *C*

A George III Carton Pierre mirror, 59 by 35 in. (150 by 89 cm.). **£1,200-£1,500** *C*

A fine early George III giltwood pier glass, attributed to Francis and John Booker of Dublin, the broken triangular pediment above a frieze with a pair of sphinxes flanked by fluting, 6 ft. high by 3 ft. 10 in. wide (183 by 117 cm.), c. 1765. **£10,000-12,500** *S*

A George II parcel-gilt red walnut wall mirror, 3 ft. 7 in. high by 2 ft. 9½ in. wide (109 by 85 cm.), c. 1735. **£1,400-1,800** *S*

A good early George III giltwood wall mirror, 5 ft. high by 2 ft. 1 in. wide (153 by 64 cm.), c. 1765. **£2,500-3,000** *S*

An early George III giltwood pier glass, the arched panels divided by a chain of flowers, the subsidiary panels enclosed by scrollwork with rocaille and hung with chains of flowers, 5 ft. 10 in. high by 2 ft. 10½ in. wide (178 by 88 cm.), c. 1760. **£3,400-3,800** *S*

A giltwood mirror, with oval plate in rockwork frame pierced and carved with C-scrolls and leafy branches rising to a cartouche cresting, 49 by 30½ in. (125 by 77 cm.). **£3,500-4,000** *C*

A mid 18th C. English carved and gilded pier glass, having the two original soft bevelled plates, 30 in. wide by 66 in. high, c. 1750. **£3,000-£3,500** *HAL*

A giltwood mirror, of Chippendale style, with bevelled rectangular plate, 75 by 39 in. (191 by 100 cm.). **£4,200-4,800** *C*

A Regency giltwood pier glass, with bevelled rectangular plate, 69 by 35½ in. (175 by 90 cm.). **£3,000-£3,500** *C*

A pair of Regency giltwood mirrors, 41 by 25¾ in. (104 by 65 cm.). **£2,400-£2,800** *C*

A pair of Regency giltwood small pier glasses, with white and gilt verre églomisé panels of windmills, 3 ft. 10½ in. high by 1 ft. 9½ in. wide (118 by 55 cm.), c. 1805. **£4,500-5,500** *S*

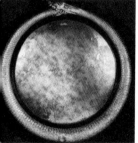

An unusual Regency convex mirror, with ebonised slip and scaly serpent frame, 27½ by 26 in. (70 by 66 cm.). **£2,000-2,500** *C*

A pair of George II-style giltwood oval wall mirrors, 3 ft. 8 in. high by 1 ft. 11 in. wide (112 by 59 cm.). **£3,000-3,500** *S*

A giltwood mirror of George II design, 60 by 30 in., late 19th C. **£1,200-1,600** *HyD*

A carved giltwood looking glass, 6 ft. high (183 cm.), 19th C. **£3,000-£3,500** *S*

Chippendale revival giltwood wall mirror, 5 ft. 7 in. high by 3 ft. in. wide (170 by 96 cm.), c. 1910. **£1,200-1,600** *S*

A giltwood overmantel in George II style, 4 ft. 7½ in. high by 5 ft. 10 in. (141 by 178 cm.), possibly c. 1840. **£1,600-2,000** *S*

A rococo asymmetrical giltwood mirror, in late George II style, 4 ft. 4½ in. high by 2 ft. 6 in. wide (133.5 by 76 cm.), c. 1900. **£800-£1,000** *S*

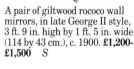

A pair of giltwood rococo wall mirrors, in late George II style, 3 ft. 9 in. high by 1 ft. 5 in. wide (114 by 43 cm.), c. 1900. **£1,200-£1,500** *S*

A carved giltwood and gesso looking glass, in George II style, 4 ft. 2 in. high by 4 ft. 6 in. wide (127 by 137 cm.), late 19th C. **£600-800** *S*

A parcel-gilt walnut looking glass in George II style, 4 ft. 7 in. high by 2 ft. 2½ in. wide (140 by 70 cm.), c. 1900. **£800-1,200** *S*

A pair of giltwood and gesso pier glasses, in Chippendale style, 6 ft. 11 in. high by 2 ft. wide (211 by 61 cm.), late 19th C. **£1,800-2,400** *S*

A carved giltwood frame, painted with badges, crests and the inscription Henricus IV Rex Angliae, originally larger, now with a rectangular mirror plate, 4 ft. high (122 cm.), 19th C. **£2,800-3,200** *S*

A George II-style giltwood and gesso wall mirror, 46 by 25 in. (117 by 64 cm.), late 19th C. **£350-450** *SC*

A George III-style red and gold lacquered pier mirror, 53 in. long by 30 in. wide. **£500-600** *Re*

MIRRORS
- mirror plate could not be made in large pieces until the late 18th C.
- William and Mary, Queen Anne and early Georgian mirrors were often made in 2 or 3 pieces — the joins were usually hidden by astragal bars
- if these have been removed, notches can be seen in the sides
- early mirrors were blown — hence the glass tended to be thinner at one end, which was always set at the top of the frame
- early glass is always generally thinner than its modern equivalent
- to measure the thickness of a piece of mirror glass — take a pointed object, place it on the mirror, note the distance between the point and its image
- old mirror glasses have a darker reflective quality
- often the backing has broken down in places, giving non-reflective spots.

A giltwood wall mirror, 60 by 29 in. (152 by 74 cm.), probably 18th C. **£450-550** *SC*

A pair of Queen Anne-style pier glasses, the replaced plates within giltwood frames, decorated by carved drapes and crested with carved cartouches, 18 in. wide by 55 in. high, c. 1840. **£1,200-1,600** *HAL*

A pair of carved giltwood and gesso looking glasses in George II style, 5 ft. 2 in. high by 2 ft. 9 in. wide (157 by 84 cm.), 20th C. **£1,200-1,500** *S*

A Dutch cream-painted mirror, 44 by 24½ in. (112 by 62 cm.), early 18th C. **£1,800-2,400** *C*

A Louis XV carved over door panel, with moulded frame centred at the top by a lion's mask, flanked by dragons, 4 ft. 9½ in. high by 5 ft. 8 in. wide (146 by 173 cm.), c. 1730. **£1,400-1,800** *S*

A pair of French provincial giltwood small looking glasses, 2 ft. 5 in. by 1 ft. 7 in. (74 by 48 cm.). **£800-1,200** *S*

A red boulle wall mirror, with bevelled plate within a canted border inlaid with scrollwork, 4 ft. 3 in. high by 2 ft. 5½ in. (129 by 75 cm.), third quarter of the 19th C. **£3,500-4,000** *S*

A carved giltwood and gesso girandole, in Regence style, 4 ft. 2 in. high by 2 ft. 10 in. wide (127 by 80 cm.), mid 19th C. **£300-350** S

A fine carved giltwood looking glass, surmounted by a Chinese bust and formed of flowers and leaf-carved scrolls, birds' heads and 3 Chinese heads, probably German, 6 ft. high (183 cm.), c. 1730. **£12,000-16,000** S

A pair of Italian giltwood mirrors, frames carved with acanthus leaves, 2 ft. 2 in. high by 1 ft. 2 in. wide (66 by 36 cm.), c. 1775. **£800-£1,000** S

A German engraved and painted glass looking glass, the arched cresting with an inner border and frieze panels, veneered in tortoiseshell, 1 ft. 8 in. high by 1 ft. 1½ in. wide (50 by 34 cm.), early 18th C. **£400-500** S

A large Roman giltwood frame, 6 ft. 4½ in. high by 5 ft. 6 in. wide (194 by 168 cm.), c. 1730. **£3,000-3,500** S

A fine pair of Danish parcel-gilt and mahogany mirrors, with rectangular bevelled plates, 44 by 24 in. (112 by 61 cm.), early 18th C. **£3,800-4,500** C

A pair of Scandinavian giltwood mirrors, 54 by 28 in. (137 by 71 cm.), partly 18th C. **£2,400-2,800** C

A giltwood girandole, German or Scandinavian, 34 by 18 in. (86 by 46 cm.), mid 18th C., and another similar of later date. **£900-1,000** C

A Swedish giltwood looking glass, 3 ft. 2 in. high by 2 ft. 8 in. wide (57.5 by 81.5 cm.), late 18th C. **£2,400-2,800** S

An early Georgian walnut frame bevelled toilet mirror, plate 19½ by 11½ in. **£300-350** JD

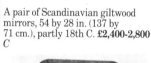

A George II swing frame mahogany toilet mirror, 9½ by 12 in. **£150-200** BHW

An early Georgian lacquered dressing and writing mirror, 17 by 38 in. (43 by 97 cm.). **£1,200-1,600**

A George I walnut and parcel-gilt toilet mirror, 19 in. wide (48 cm.). **£800-1,200** C

A mahogany boxwood strung serpentine front dressing table mirror. **£150-200** TM

A George II mahogany shield shaped cheval toilet mirror. **£220-£280** *DWB*

A George III mahogany crossbanded skeleton toilet mirror, 2 ft. 4 in. high by 1 ft. 10 in. wide (71 by 56 cm.), c. 1780. **£350-400** *S*

An Anglo-Indian ivory inlaid rosewood toilet mirror, 16 in. wide, 18th C. **£600-700** *C*

A 19th C. oval skeleton fram dressing table mirror, 11½ b 8½ in. **£60-90** *BHW*

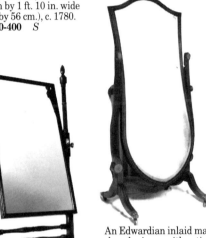

A Queen Anne-style walnut toilet mirror, 1 ft. 4 in. wide (46 cm.), c. 1920. **£250-300** *SS*

A 19th C. Dutch mahogany and marquetry cheval dressing mirr 49½ by 82 in. **£400-500** *DWB*

An Edwardian inlaid mahogany cheval mirror, with satinwood crossbandings, 62 in. high. **£400-£450** *Re*

A George III mahogany cheval glass, 33 in. wide by 24 in. deep by 69 in. high, c. 1800, plate probably later, shown without brass sconces. **£500-600** *HAL*

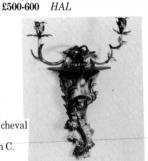

A carved wood and gilt-gesso w glass, overall height 167 cm., 19th C. **£1,200-1,600** *HSS*

A satinwood and tulipwood cheval mirror, 71 by 39 in. (180 by 99 cm.), second quarter 19th C. **£550-600** *SC*

A pair of Regency giltwood twin-branch wall lights, 27½ in. high (70 cm.). **£5,000-5,500** *C*

A pair of George III giltwood wall brackets, 22½ in. high by 15½ in. wide. **£4,500-5,500** *C*

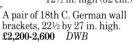

A pair of giltwood wall brackets, 12½ in. high (32 cm.) **£700-800** *C*

A pair of 18th C. German wall brackets, 22½ by 27 in. high. **£2,200-2,600** *DWB*

A pair of George III-style giltwood wall appliques, 43 in. (109 cm.), 20th C. **£400-600** *SC*

A pair of Regency rosewood and parcel-gilt polescreens, each with mirror-backed rounded rectangular banner, 50 in. high (127 cm.). **£600-£700** *C*

A painted 2-leaf leather screen, one side painted with a view of Hudson Bay and inscribed 'Hudson 1820', the other side with a promenading couple, probably American, each leaf 36 in. wide by 75 in. high (91.5 by 192 cm.), early 19th C. **£1,000-£1,250** *C*

The exotic birds perched amidst branches of trailing foliage and peonies suggest that the design was inspired by Chinese wallpaper. The screen may well have been commissioned to complement an existing chinoiserie interior.

An Anglo-Egyptian 2-fold screen, each hardwood frame enclosing a velvet worked panel, 76 by 48 in. (193 by 122 cm.), panels possibly 18th C., frame later. **£500-600** *SC*

A good 4-fold needlework screen, each walnut veneered fold enclosing 3 oval panels, each embroidered in coloured wool and silk, 6 ft. 4½ in. high, each fold 2 ft. 1 in. wide (194 by 63 cm.). **£3,000-3,500** *S*

An early 19th C. mahogany polescreen, inset with an 18th C. petit point picture, 1.42 m. high overall, 52 by 44 cm. embroidery. **£500-600** *P*

A rosewood fire screen, with a bright polychrome raised plush and wood worked panel, 44 by 23 in. (112 by 59 cm.), mid 19th C. **£300-£350** *SC*

A Sheraton-style mahogany 2-fold screen, 42 in. wide opened, 47 in. high. **£100-150** *Re*

A mahogany screen, with silk needlework panel, 'The Duke of Edinburgh's Wiltshire Regiment'. **£150-200** *GM*

A pair of polescreens, 61 in., the panels late 18th C., the stands later. **£1,000-£1,250** *SC*

A 4-fold nursery scrap screen, applied on each side with coloured lithographic scraps on a painted and varnished ground, 61¼ in. high (156 cm.), c. 1910. **£200-250** *S*

A Dutch painted and gilded 6-leaf screen, each leaf 20 in. wide by 84 in. high (51 by 213 cm.). **£4,500-£5,000** *C*

A fine giltwood 5-leaf screen, in the manner of Jean-Baptiste Pillement, the central panel with the coat of arms of the Duc d'Orleans, each leaf 22 in. wide by 73 in. high (56 by 185 cm.). **£10,000-12,500** *C*

A neo-classical-style satinwood screen and writing stand, painted and decorated with putti, in the style of Angelica Kauffmann, 17 in., 19th C. **£400-500** *CSK*

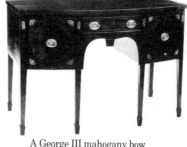

A Louis XV carved giltwood fire screen, with a rising panel covered on one side with a Beauvais tapestry panel after Jacques Neilson, woven with a ribbon-tied spray of flowers, on a scarlet damask ground, 3 ft. ½ in. high by 1 ft. 11½ in. wide (93 by 60 cm.), c. 1755. **£1,000-1,400** *S*

A small Sheraton period mahogany bow fronted sideboard, the top with rosewood crossband, inlaid with oval and quadrant floral panels. **£1,800-2,400** *PWC*

A George III mahogany bow fronted sideboard, crossbanded in rosewood, 54 in. wide. (138 cm.). **£3,000-3,500** *C*

A George III mahogany serpentine sideboard, with crossbanded top, the whole inlaid with satinwood quadrant and oval fan medallions, top repolished, 2 ft. 11 in. high by 4 ft. 5½ in. wide by 2 ft. 3 in. deep (89 by 136 by 68.5 cm.), c. 1775. **£3,800-4,200** *S*

A George III mahogany and crossbanded bow front sideboard, 3 ft. high by 5 ft. 10 in. wide (91.5 by 148 cm.), c. 1790. **£2,000-2,500** *SS*

A George III mahogany bow front sideboard, 5 ft. 5 in. wide. **£1,800-£2,200** *MMB*

A George III mahogany sideboard, of bowed breakfront form, the top, drawers and doors crossbanded in tulipwood, handles replaced, 3 ft. high by 5 ft. wide by 2 ft. 2¾ in. deep (91 by 152.5 by 68 cm.), c. 1780. **£2,800-3,400** *S*

A George III mahogany bow front sideboard, the figured surface crossbanded in satinwood above cellarets and a drawer with similar decoration and good quality replaced brasswork, 60 in. wide by 26 in. deep by 36 in. high, c. 1790. **£2,500-3,500** *HAL*

A George III mahogany bow front sideboard, with crossbanded top, the frieze drawer flanked on either side by a cellaret, 33½ by 48¼ in. (85 by 122.5 cm.), late 18th C. **£4,000-4,500** *SC*

A George III mahogany bow fronted sideboard, crossbanded in tulipwood, 4 ft. 6½ in. wide by 2 ft. 2 in. deep (138 by 66 cm.), c. 1775. **£1,200-1,600** *S*

An early 19th C. mahogany bow fronted sideboard, banded in satinwood and tulipwood, and with boxwood and ebony stringing, 48 by 26 in. deep. **£2,600-3,200** *DWB*

A George III bow fronted mahogany sideboard, with kingwood crossbanded top, 4 ft. 2½ in. wide by 3 ft. high (128 by 92 cm.), c. 1780. **£4,000-4,500** *S*

A fine Sheraton period mahogany breakfront sideboard, line inlaid, the top banded in satinwood with ornamentation of ribbon tie foliages and flowers in penwork, having a central drawer with recessed arch front drawer beneath, flanked by a cellaret, having a pot cupboard at one end, 6 ft. 10 in. **£3,000-3,500** *WW*

A George III mahogany sideboard, crossbanded in maple within boxwood lines, inlaid throughout with Tunbridge, 39¼ by 74 in. (99.5 by 188 cm.), first quarter 19th C. £2,400-2,800   *SC*

A late George III mahogany sideboard, 6 ft. 3¼ in. high (191 cm.), c. 1805. £3,500-4,000   *S*

A Hepplewhite period mahogany bow front sideboard, 5 ft. £2,400-£2,800   *WW*

A George III mahogany bow fronted sideboard, crossbanded with satinwood, with cellaret drawers inlaid with key-pattern lines, 65½ in. wide (166 cm.). £2,600-3,200   *C*

PATINATION

- means layers of polish, dirt, dust, grease, etc., which have accumulated over the years — really the whole depth of surface of a piece of antique timber
- the patination on different woods varies considerably but the same piece of wood will basically colour to the same extent (always allowing for bleaching by sunlight, etc.)
- walnut furniture often had an oil varnish applied to give it a good base to take the wax polish — this has led to the lovely mellow patina which is virtually impossible to fake
- dirt and grease from handling are important guides (especially under drawer handles, on chair arms, etc.) — these areas should have a darker colour — if they don't beware!
- pieces which have carving or crevices, dirt will have accumulated, giving dark patches
- colour and patination are probably the most important factors when valuing a piece of furniture
- by repolishing a piece of furniture and removing evidence of patination, a dealer can conceal replacement or conversion.

A George III mahogany sideboard, of bow front outline, inlaid throughout with broad satinwood bands, 37 by 67 in. (94 by 170 cm.), late 18th C. £2,000-2,500   *SC*

A George III mahogany serpentine fronted sideboard, with satinwood crossbanding, boxwood and fruitwood stringing, 38 in. high, by 66½ in. wide. £2,000-2,500   *Bea*

A George III satinwood and mahogany sideboard, with crossbanded serpentine top, with two cellaret drawers, 78 in. wide (198 cm.). £4,500-5,200   *C*

A George III mahogany bow fronted sideboard, crossbanded with satinwood, with cellaret drawers inlaid with key-pattern lines, 65½ in. wide (166 cm.). £2,600-3,200   *C*

A George III mahogany sideboard, the figured ebony inlaid surface with bow front above cellaret, cupboard and drawer, 75 in. long by 31 in. deep by 37 in. high, c. 1800. £2,500-3,200   *HAL*

A Georgian Sheraton-style bow fronted inlaid mahogany sideboard, 73 in. wide. £800-1,200   *GM*

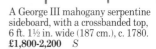

A George III mahogany sideboard, crossbanded in tulipwood, with a deep crossbanded drawer, the right hand one with a zinc-lined double drawer, 6 ft. 2 in. wide (188 cm.), c. 1780. £4,500-5,500   *S*

A George III mahogany serpentine sideboard, with a crossbanded top, 6 ft. 1½ in. wide (187 cm.), c. 1780. £1,800-2,200   *S*

A late George III mahogany sideboard, inlaid throughout with boxwood lines and chequer bands, 38 by 76 in. (97 by 193 cm.), largely early 19th C. **£400-500** *SC*

A George III inlaid mahogany sideboard, a sprung silver drawer released by a catch below, and 4 cupboard doors and inlaid with flowerheads, 6 ft. 1 in. wide by 2 ft. 6 in. deep. **£1,500-2,000** *T*

A Regency mahogany serpentine fronted sideboard, with satinwood crossbanding, boxwood and ebony stringing, 36 in. high by 63 in. wide. **£1,800-2,200** *Bea*

A pair of George IV faded mahogany bow front sidetables, with 2 deep and one shallow cockbeaded drawers, the proportions slightly differing, 104.5 and 109.6 cm. wide. **£4,500-5,500** *HSS*

A large Georgian mahogany bow front sideboard, 3 ft. 2 in. deep by 7 ft. 6 in. wide. **£1,400-1,800** *AG*

A George III mahogany and satinwood serpentine sideboard, with crossbanded top, formerly with brass rail, 76 in. wide (193 cm.). **£2,000-2,500** *C*

A Victorian mahogany pedestal sideboard, 64 in. wide. **£160-220** *BHW*

A George III mahogany sideboard, 72 in. wide (183 cm.). **£4,000-4,500** *C*

A George III mahogany and rosewood crossbanded large pedestal sideboard, inlaid with satinwood stringing, with 2 cutlery drawers, flanked by combined pedestals with an arrangement of drawers and cupboards, on a plinth base, now without the rear brass gallery, 7 ft. 8 in. wide (234 cm.), c. 1790. **£1,500-2,000** *S*

A mahogany sideboard, of bow front outline, carved in high relief with foliate swags and scrolls within bobbin and reel borders, centred by 2 Bacchanalian putti within an oval, 44½ by 82 in. (113 by 208 cm.). **£800-1,200** *SC*

A Regency mahogany sideboard, with a cupboard on the left and a cellaret drawer and cupboard on the right, 87 in. wide (221 cm.). **£2,800-3,400** *C*

A George IV mahogany 3-lobed bow front sideboard. **£400-600** *CDC*

A George IV mahogany sideboard. **£400-600** *CDC*

A George III mahogany sideboard, contained by tulipwood crossbandings, 51 by 96 in. (130 by 244 cm.), late 18th C., but inlaid throughout with boxwood sprays of flowers and bandings in the third quarter of 19th C. and fitted with a brass rail at that time. **£2,600-£3,200** *SC*

A Victorian sideboard, with walnut panels and crossbanding, with 3 oak-lined drawers, 102 in. wide by 107 in. high. **£600-700** *DA*

A Victorian 'George III' mahogany serpentine sideboard, with crossbanded top, flanked by quarter-veneered and oval inlaid cupboards, the whole inlaid with chequer stringing, 174 cm. wide. **£700-800** *Bon*

An Edwardian mahogany sideboard, in Sheraton style, the top and drawers crossbanded and string inlaid in satinwood, the legs with satinwood panels, ivory label inscribed J.S. Henry, London EC, 6 ft. wide. **£1,200-1,600** *PWC*

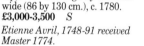

late 19th C. mahogany serpentine sideboard, of Sheraton esign, crossbanded, inlaid with atinwood and ebony stringing, 8 in. wide. **£600-700** *M*

A Louis XVI D-shaped mahogany console desserte, stamped E. Avril JME, with galleried white marble top, 2 ft. 10 in. high by 4 ft. 3 in. wide (86 by 130 cm.), c. 1780. **£3,000-3,500** *S*

Etienne Avril, 1748-91 received Master 1774.

A Dutch mahogany-veneered 'Klapbuffet', in Empire style, the hinged top opening to reveal 2 folding shelves and 2 hinged flaps, 120 cm. wide, 19th C. **£3,000-3,400** *CAM*

A Louis XVI kingwood and tulipwood marquetry console desserte, stamped J. Stockel JME, bow fronted and with a white marble top, the frieze inlaid with an interlaced geometric strapwork design and containing a central drawer, 2 ft. 11 in. high by 3 ft. 4 in. wide (89 by 102 cm.), c. 1775. **£3,000-3,500** *S*

Joseph Stockel, 1743-1802, received Master 1775.

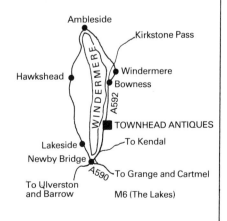

A mahogany sideboard, 19th C. **£200-250** *M*

The piece bears signs of restoration or conversion.

A Louis XVI mahogany console desserte, with white marble top, 2 ft. 11 in. high (89 cm.), c. 1780. **£6,500-7,500** *S*

A 19th C. German walnut sideboard, 84 in. wide. **£1,000-1,400**
WAY

A George II mahogany rectangular occasional table. **£2,000-2,500**
DWB

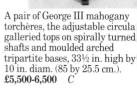

A pair of George III mahogany torchères, the adjustable circular galleried tops on spirally turned shafts and moulded arched tripartite bases, 33½ in. high by 10 in. diam. (85 by 25.5 cm.). **£5,500-6,500**   *C*

A pair of George III mahogany tripod torchères, 3 ft. 5 in. high b 1 ft. wide (104 by 31 cm.), c. 176 **£3,500-4,500**   *S*

A William and Mary occasional table, in elm and oak, the octagonal surface on barley-twist stem and shaped carved feet, 2 of which are inscribed with an 'F', 13 in. wide by 12 in. deep by 31½ in. high, c. 1690. **£600-700**   *HAL*

A Queen Anne gilt-gesso stand, with later inset square verde antico marble top, on cabriole legs headed by shells and foliage moulded with bellflowers and edged with C scrolls, ending in foliate scrolled feet; and another, en suite, of later date, 14 in. square, 28½ in. high (35.5 by 72 cm.). **£4,000-4,500**   *C*

A 'Moorish' walnut sideboard, the pierced Isnik cornice, above a mirror-plate flanked by Mishrabiya, the frieze with 3 drawers carved with Islamic caligraphy, inlaid with ivory and mother-of-pearl geometric devices, probably English, 6 ft. 11 in. high by 4 ft. 7 in. wide (211 by 140 cm.), c. 1880. **£3,200-3,600**   *S*

A fine pair of Regency giltwood tripod stands, in the manner of Thomas Hope, each with later mahogany top, 14½ in. diam. b 32½ in. high (37 by 82.5 cm.). **£7,500-8,500**   *C*

A pair of George III giltwood torchères, in the manner of Adam, each circular fluted platform set with paterae and raised on 3 slender legs faced with coin pattern, headed by ram's heads, ending in ram's hooves, 4 ft. 9 in. high (145 cm.). **£3,000-3,500**   *S*

A Louis XVI marble gilt bronze and tortoiseshell base, for an organ clock, 19 in. wide (48 cm.), late 18th C. **£1,200-1,500**   *S*

A George III mahogany urn stand, with concealed slide. **£300-400**
DWB

A pair of 19th C. mahogany tables, each with pierced fret galleries, blind fret friezes, by Edwards and Roberts, 14½ by 27½ in. high. **£1,200-1,500**   *DWB*

A French 19th C. boulle jardinière with pierced ormolu gallery, 32 in. wide. **£200-250**   *DSH*

A rosewood square tapering pedestal, veneer slightly chipped on top, 46¾ in. high. **£240-£300** *WHL*

A fine pair of Italian neo-classical ebony, mahogany and parcel-gilt torchères, with circular Carrara marble tops, 19 in. wide by 54½ in. high (48.5 by 138 cm.), early 19th C. **£4,200-4,600** *C*

A pair of carved giltwood and gesso stands, tops now with mirror panels, 3 ft. 2½ in. high (98 cm.), 19th C. **£600-800** *S*

An ormolu-mounted and rosewood etagère, bearing the label of Paul Sormani, 101 Charles Street, 30 in. wide (76 cm.), late 19th C. **£3,000-£3,500** *C*

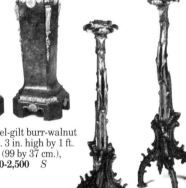

A pair of parcel-gilt burr-walnut pedestals, 3 ft. 3 in. high by 1 ft. 2½ in. square (99 by 37 cm.), c. 1910. **£2,000-2,500** *S*

A pair of carved giltwood torchères, 3 ft. 6 in. high (107 cm.), mid 18th C. **£1,800-2,200** *S*

A pair of Venetian blackamoor torchères, the turbaned blackamoors each holding a shaped breche-violette marble tray carved with tassels, wearing a green and cream doublet, scarlet breeches and clogs, 56 in. high and 55 in. high (142.5 and 140 cm.), early 18th C. **£6,500-7,500** *C*

A Louis XV-style kingwood and tulipwood plant stand, 49 in. **£1,500-£1,800** *CSK*

A pair of Franco-Flemish giltwood torchères, 5 ft. 2 in. high (185 cm.), figures late 17th C., tops and bases 19th C. **£3,200-3,800** *S*

A pair of Venetian painted blackamoor stands, each with a figure in polychrome feather skirt, on rockwork base, one with an arm damaged, 3 ft. 8 in. high by 2 ft. 2 in. diam. (112 by 66 cm.), 18th/19th C. **£6,000-7,000** *S*

A pair of painted and gilded blackamoor torchères, fitted for electricity, 86½ in. (220 cm.) high, second quarter 19th C. **£6,000-7,000** *C*

A polychrome blackamoor stand, 38½ in. high. **£1,000-£1,250** *Bea*

A rare pair of Peruvian stuffed leather pedestal tables, dressed in mid 17th C. cavalier costumes with maroon jackets and red capes, 3 ft. 2 in. high by 1 ft. 4 in. wide (97 by 41 cm.), 20th C. **£700-900** *S*

A George III mahogany tripod music stand, with a ratchet adjustable top on an adjustable column stem and downswept supports, 53 in. high (135 cm.), third quarter of the 18th C. **£700-£900** *SC*

A Victorian walnutwood reading stand, adjustable for height, 1 ft. 4 in. wide. **£300-400** *CDC*

STOOLS

- until the middle of the 17th C. stools were virtually the only form of seat for one person
- many 17th C. 'joint' or 'joyned' stools have been reproduced
- look for good patination, colour and carving on oak examples. Yew-wood examples with good turning are highly desirable
- by the end of the 17th C. the chair was taking over and the oak stool became less popular, walnut stealing the show from about 1670
- stools now tend to follow the style of chairs of the period, they also tend to be upholstered

- many Queen Anne stools have stretchers
- these have usually disappeared by George I
- when mahogany was introduced from 1730-40, stools became simpler, the cabriole leg being replaced with the straight leg, often with stretchers
- mid 18th C. the 'drop-in' seat became fashionable
- some stools made from chairs (this can increase the value of the chair 20 times)
- check for hessian under the seat — never used until 1840 (often conceals some alterations)

A papier-mâché music or reading stand, 4 ft. 4 in. high approx. (132 cm.), c. 1840. **£1,200-1,500** *S*

A pair of George III mahogany window seats, the ends with arched rails on reeded foliate supports, headed by flowerheads and tapering legs, joined by stretchers, 45 in. wide (114 cm.). **£3,600-4,200** *C*

A late George II mahogany stool, on cabriole legs carved at the knees with addorsed C scrolls and acanthus, on claw and ball feet, 1 ft. 8 in. wide (51 cm.), c. 1750. **£2,000-2,500** *S*

A Regency rosewood stool, recaned seat, stamped SM, and H. **£900-£1,100** *T*

A pair of George IV mahogany foot stools, 18 by 21 in. (46 by 53 cm.), second quarter of the 19th C. **£700-£800** *SC*

An Anglo-Chinese padouk stool, top upholstered with a small yellow-ground Chinese rug with 5 blue dragons, 1 ft. 7 in. high by 1 ft. 11 in. wide (48 by 59 cm.), second quarter 19th C. **£1,000-1,250** *S*

A George II-style walnut stool, 18 by 25 in. (46 by 64 cm.), 19th C. **£400-500** *SC*

A pair of carved giltwood stools, covered in Louis XVI Aubusson floral tapestry on an ivory ground, 1 ft. 8½ in. diam. (52 cm.), 19th C. **£1,500-1,800** *S*

MAKE THE MOST OF MILLER'S

Price ranges in this book reflect what one should expect to pay for a similar example. When selling one can obviously expect a figure below. This will fluctuate according to a dealer's stock, saleability at a particular time, etc. It is always advisable to approach a reputable specialist dealer or an auction house which has specialist sales.

A good 'rope' stool, in the manner of Fournier, 1 ft. 3½ in. high by 1 ft. 9 in. diam. (39 by 53 cm.), mid 19th C. **£1,800-2,200** *S*

A George III artists mahogany chest, 27 in. **£600-800**   *DWB*

A George II mahogany architect's pedestal desk, with cockbeaded mouldings and gilt brass loop handles, the baize-lined top adjusting on double ratchets, the fall-front enclosing an interior fitted with 5 narrow drawers, above a baize-lined sliding writing surface, with a central well flanked by 6 lidded compartments inlaid A-Z in oval boxwood panels, 49½ in. wide by 38 in. high, c. 1760. **£4,500-5,500**   *N*

A Georgian mahogany architect's table, with dropside slats, the front extending on 2 legs to reveal a compartment. **£1,800-2,200**   *JF*

A Georgian mahogany architect's table, with double adjustable rising hinged top, the front with pull-out drawer with interior compartments, restored, 36 in. (92 cm.). **£1,500-1,800**   *L*

A George II mahogany architect's desk, the rectangular ratchet adjustable top formerly with an inset surface, in need of restoration, 36 by 50 in., early 19th C. **£1,000-£1,250**   *SC*

A George IV oak architect's or writing table, the mahogany-veneered double-hinged top crossbanded in rosewood, 2 ft. 4½ in. high by 4 ft. wide (72 by 122 cm.), c. 1815. **£2,500-3,000**   *S*

A Regency mahogany draughtsman's table, the top raised on ratchet swivel candle shelves, 39 in. wide. **£500-600**   *WHB*

A mahogany slope top clerk's desk, y Gillows of Lancaster, with pen-nd-ink compartment and slide to ach end, with reeded mouldings hroughout, stamped 'Gillows, ancaster', 37 in. wide, c. 1835. **1,300-1,600**   *N*

A George IV mahogany architect's or draughtsman's combined table and cabinet, stamped Gillow, the panelled body with a pair of doors lined in pleated silk and enclosing adjustable shelves, 2 ft. 8½ in. high by 3 ft. 5½ in. wide (83 by 105 cm.), c. 1820. **£3,000-3,500**   *S*

A George III-style mahogany combined folio stand and writing table, inlaid with satinwood medallions and chevron stringing, made-up, 1 ft. 11 in. wide when closed (57 cm.), c. 1900. **£700-900**   *SS*

A George I mahogany card table, the folding top revealing a playing surface with guinea scoops and candlestands, the 4 cabriole legs finely carved with scrollwork and ball and claw feet, one with gate action, 34 in. wide by 32¼ in. deep by 25½ in. high, c. 1720. **£2,000-£2,500**   *HAL*

A George I walnut, card table, with concertina action, 34 in. **£5,500-6,000**   *DWB*

An early Georgian walnut D-shaped tea and card table, 31 in. wide. **£700-800** *CSK*

A mid Georgian mahogany double fold-over tea and gaming table, with trays and candlestands, 36 in. wide. **£1,400-1,800** *M*

An early Georgian mahogany card table, the fold-over top revealing 4 counter wells and candlestands, with concertina rear action. **£1,200 £1,500** *V*

A George II mahogany card table, the projecting top and the interior with candlestands and candlewells, 2 ft. 9½ in. wide (85 cm.), c. 1740. **£2,600-3,200** *S*

A George II mahogany card table, the polished interior with candlestands and money wells and with a drawer in the frieze, the interior formerly baize-lined, 2 ft. 4½ in. high by 3 ft. 1 in. wide (72 by 94 cm.), c. 1740. **£1,800-2,200** *S*

A late George II mahogany serpentine-fronted card table, the top with egg and dart molding, 2 ft. 11½ in. wide (90 cm.), c. 1750. **£3,000-3,500** *S*

A late George II mahogany card table, 2 ft. 5 in. high by 3 ft. wide (74 by 92 cm.), c. 1755. **£2,400-£2,800** *S*

A George II mahogany games table, the rectangular fold-over top, baize lacking, 28½ by 35½ in. **£1,800-2,200** *SC*

A George II red walnut card table, the top enclosing a baize-lined interior with candlestands and counter wells above one frieze drawer, 35 in. wide (89 cm.). **£4,000-5,000** *C*

A George II 'concertina' action mahogany card table, the top baize lined, 2 ft. 5½ in. high by 3 ft. wide (75 by 91 cm.), c. 1750. **£5,000-£6,000** *S*

A George III mahogany card table, in the French taste, with crossbanded leather-lined top inlaid with lines, 33 in. wide (84 cm.). **£900-1,100** *C*

An early George III mahogany card table, the fold-over baized-lined top with squared eared corners, 36 in. (91 cm.). **£1,600-2,000** *L*

A George III mahogany serpentine tea or games table, in the French style, 2 ft. 8½ in. wide (83 cm.), c. 1770. **£3,000-3,500** *S*

An early George III mahogany card table, with baize-lined folding top, 36 in. wide (91.5 cm.). **£1,600-2,000** *C*

A George III mahogany serpentine card table, in the French style, with moulded top, the interior with 4 panelled candle wells, 3 ft. 1 in. (94 cm.), c. 1770. **£2,500-3,000**   *S*

A fine pair of George III card tables, with baize-lined moulded serpentine tops, 36½ in. wide '92.5 cm.). **£5,000-5,500**   *C*

A George III mahogany serpentine card table, with concertina-action frame, 2 ft. 5 in. high by 3 ft. wide (74 by 91 cm.), c. 1770. **£1,800-£2,200**   *S*

A pair of George III rosewood and satinwood crossbanded card tables, 36 in. wide. **£7,500-8,500**   *Re*

A pair of George III mahogany card tables, the baize-lined crossbanded breakfront tops on square tapering legs, 37½ in. wide (95.5 cm.). **£5,000-6,000**   *C*

A pair of Georgian mahogany card tables, the chamfered baize-lined tops inlaid with geometric designs, adapted, 36 in. wide (91.5 cm.). **£8,000-10,000**   *C*

The well figured wood and the presence of 6 legs rather than 4 makes these tables unusual and thus more desirable.

A Sheraton-period mahogany fold-over top card table, the top with a broad satinwood crossband, 35 in. wide. **£700-900**   *PWC*

A pair of Georgian crossbanded mahogany tea and card tables, 38 in. wide and 29 in. wide by 38 in. open, c. 1810. **£2,000-2,800**   *AP*

A Sheraton-design mahogany-veneered 'D' shape card table, the flame-veneered top crossbanded in satinwood with a kingwood border, with baize-lined interior, 3 ft., 19th C. **£800-1,200**   *WW*

A Sheraton-period satinwood fold-over top card table, all over painted with neo-classical designs at a later date, and inlaid with string lines, 3 ft. wide. **£1,500-2,000**   *PWC*

A Sheraton figured satinwood card table, the hinged folding crossbanded surface above ebony decorated apron on slim turned legs, bears signature and date T. Darwen, Lancaster, 1805, 36 in. wide by 17 in. deep by 28 in. high. **£2,000-2,500**   *HAL*

A George III mahogany card table, the top crossbanded in purpleheart, on square tapered legs headed by inlaid shell paterae, 91 cm. wide. **£800-1,200**   *Bon*

A George III satinwood card table, painted with a bat's wing motif and a wide band of chrysanthemums on a rosewood ground, enclosing a circular blue velvet panel, 32½ in. wide (82.5 cm.). **£2,000-2,500**   *C*

A George III mahogany and satinwood crossbanded card table, 37¼ in. wide. **£700-800** *DSH*

A pair of late Georgian plum mahogany and satinwood games tables, each with a fold-over top, 29¼ by 36 in. (74 by 91.5 cm.), early 19th C. **£1,500-2,000** *SC*

A George III serpentine mahogany card table, crossbanded in coromandel-wood, 3 ft. wide (92 cm.), c. 1780. **£1,200-1,500** *S*

An early 19th C. mahogany half round card table, the top rosewood crossbanded and baize lines. **£600-£700** *WIL*

A George III sycamore and rosewood card table, in the manner of John Linnell, the baize-lined semi-circular top inlaid with swags of flowerheads and trellis, 32 in. wide (81 cm.). **£6,000-7,000** *C*

Similar trellis marquetry, presumably inspired by contemporary Parisian examples, appears on a pair of side tables supplied by Linnell to the Duke of Argyll for Inverary Castle, c. 1780, (H. Hayward and P. Kirkman, William and John Linnell, 1980, figs. 307-311).

A pair of George III mahogany card tables, with semi-circular baize-lined folding tops crossbanded with rosewood and satinwood, 36 in. wide (91.5 cm.). **£3,500-4,000** *C*

An 18th C. Sheraton-style half round fold-over card table, with inlaid crossbanded top. **£350-400** *Fr*

A George III mahogany demi lune card table, with tulipwood crossbanded top and frieze, 96 cm. wide. **£800-1,000** *Bon*

A George III mahogany demi lune card table, the crossbanded top inlaid with an urn, foliate scrolls and husk chains, 92 cm. wide, the inlay late 19th C. **£600-800** *Bon*

A Regency rosewood card table, the swivelling D-shaped top now leather lined, the whole inlaid with brass stringing and foliage, 3 ft. wide (91.5 cm.), c. 1820. **£900-1,100** *S*

A Regency rosewood 'D' shaped card table, with yew-wood banding, the fold-over top revealing a green baize lining, 3 ft. wide (91.5 cm.), c. 1810. **£800-900** *SS*

A fine pair of Regency calamander and satinwood card tables, the baize-lined top with scrolled satinwood banding and swivelling to reveal compartments, with concave-sided quadripartite bases and ormolu paw sabots, 36 in. wide (91.5 cm.). **£9,000-10,000** *C*

A Regency rosewood, crossbanded and brass inlaid 'D' shaped card table, 35 in. **£600-700** *DWB*

A pair of Regency mahogany folding rectangular card tables, 36 in. wide. **£1,400-1,800**   *WHB*

A pair of Regency rosewood card tables, inlaid with cut brass and stringing, each with a rectangular fold-over top, in need of restoration, 2 ft. 11¾ in. wide (91 cm.), c. 1810. **£3,000-4,000**   *SS*

A Regency rosewood card table, with crossbanded 'D' shaped top, 27¾ in. high by 36 in. wide. **£600-£700**   *Bea*

A Regency rosewood brass inlaid card table, with folding rectangular top, with ormolu mounts to the frieze and base, 3 ft. **£1,200-1,600**   *MMB*

A pair of Regency brass-inlaid rosewood card tables, each with folding baize-lined top, 36 in. wide (91.5 cm.). **£3,000-4,000**   *C*

A Regency rosewood-veneered swivel top card table, baize lined, 3 ft. **£800-900**   *WW*

A serpentine card table, the burr-elm top with a giant parquetry diamond with an inner elaborate geometric design, with original green baize interior, hinges broken, 2 ft. 5½ in. high by 2 ft. 11 in. wide (75 by 89 cm.), c. 1840. **£700-900**   *S*

A fine pair of Regency ormolu-mounted calamanderwood card tables, tops inlaid with burr-maple bands and ormolu beading, on scrolled quadripartite bases inlaid with rosettes, 36 in. wide (91.5 cm.). **£6,000-7,000**   *C*

A George III-style satinwood games table, 38½ by 36 in. open (98 by 91.5 cm.), last quarter of the 19th C. **£1,500-1,800**   *SC*

A Victorian rosewood fold-over top card table, 37 in. wide. **£450-550**   *PWC*

A William IV rosewood card table, with baize-lined, beaded, rounded rectangular top, 37 in. wide (94 cm.). **£1,000-1,250**   *C*

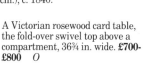

A pair of rosewood serpentine card tables, each moulded hinged top with a circular baize-lined well, on a jewelled columnar support with acanthus carved downswept legs, 3 ft. wide (91.5 cm.), c. 1840. **£1,600-2,200**   *S*

A Victorian rosewood card table, the fold-over swivel top above a compartment, 36¾ in. wide. **£700-£800**   *O*

A walnut and marquetry serpentine card table, the swivelling top inlaid with flowers and rococo scrolls, 3 ft. wide (91 cm.), c. 1850. **£1,000-1,250** *S*

A pair of Victorian rosewood folding top card tables, c. 1860. **£1,000-1,250** *WHL*

A Victorian burr-walnut fold-over card table, of serpentine outline, 34 in. wide. **£500-600** *M*

An early Victorian rosewood card table, the fold-over top with baize interior, 34½ in. wide. **£600-700** *GM*

A Victorian rosewood card table, 2 ft. 11¾ in. wide (91 cm.), c. 1840. **£300-400** *SS*

A rosewood tea or games table, 29½ by 24 in. (75 by 61 cm.), mid 19th C. **£400-500** *SC*

A late Victorian rosewood envelope card table. **£600-700** *CW*

A mahogany and cut brass envelope card table, 30½ by 21½ in. (77 by 55 cm.), late 19th C. **£550-£600** *SC*

Small tables are increasingly popular, especially those of dual purpose and expanding.

A marquetry card table, in the French style, the slightly breakfront swivelling top veneered in harewood, and inlaid with foliate scrolls, 2 ft. 6 in. high by 2 ft. 10 in. wide (76 by 87 cm.), c. 1870. **£900-£1,100** *S*

An early Victorian walnut card table. **£500-600** *CDC*

A Victorian walnut and marquetry games table, the top inlaid with a chessboard flanked by clusters of musical instruments, the frieze fitted with a small drawer, 97 cm. wide, c. 1860. **£900-1,100** *Bon*

A Victorian walnut games table, the fold-over serpentine top above a conforming frieze carved with flowering foliage, 30½ by 34½ in. (77 by 87 cm.), third quarter of 19th C. **£450-550** *SC*

A chess table, in penwork and ivory-inlaid ebony, 2 ft. 5½ in. high by 1 ft. 11 in. square (75 by 58.5 cm.), c. 1850. **£900-1,100** *S*

A George III-style mahogany and satinwood games table, baize lacking, 30 by 36 in. (76 by 92 cm.), late 19th/early 20th C. **£600-700** *SC*

A Dutch walnut and floral marquetry card table, early 19th C. **£800-1,200** *JF*

A Dutch card table, inlaid with foliate marquetry and geometric boxwood lines, 31½ in., 19th C. £700-900   *CSK*

A rare cherrywood games table, with hinged rectangular top and frieze drawer at each end, French or Flemish, with restoration, 2 ft. 4½ in. high by 2 ft. 10 in. wide (73 by 86 cm.), c. 1700. £2,500-3,000   *S*

A marquetry games table, the quarter-veneered rosewood top with a ribbon border and a central oval of an arch, the polished interior lined in leather and with 4 wells, Spanish or Portuguese, 3 ft. 3 in. wide (99 cm.), c. 1790. £1,500-£1,800   *S*

A late 17th C. walnut and marquetry games table, some restoration and renewals, 31 by 31¼ in. closed. £7,000-8,000   *WB*

A Louis XVI brass-mounted mahogany games table, with double hinged semi-circular top, 3 ft. 7 in. wide (109 cm.), c. 1785. £2,000-2,400   *S*

A purpleheart parquetry card table, in Louis XVI style, the baize-lined interior swivelling to reveal a fitted well on stop-fluted tapering circular legs, headed by gilt brass paterae and with gilt bronze laurel leaf sabots, 2 ft. 6 in. high by 3 ft. ¼ in. wide (76 by 92 cm.), c. 1870. £2,000-2,500   *S*

A French boulle and ebonised card table, with ormolu mounts, the fold-over serpentined top revealing green baize lining, 2 ft. 11½ in. wide (90 cm.), c. 1860. £600-800   *S*

A George III rosewood lady's occasional table, the octagonal lifting surface crossbanded in holly and other woods, 17 in. wide by 13 in. deep by 28 in. high, c. 1800. £1,000-1,300   *HAL*

An unusual George III satinwood work table, the top crossbanded with rosewood, fitted with a single flap, with concealed catch forming a door on square tapering legs, 15 in. wide (38 cm.). £1,200-£1,500   *C*

A pair of mahogany and fruitwood work tables, with oval inlaid rounded rectangular tops crossbanded with tulipwood, 18 in. wide (46 cm.). £1,500-1,800   *C*

George III satinwood and rosewood-crossbanded work table, the top inlaid with geometric ebony and boxwood stringing, formerly with a work bag, 2 ft. 4½ in. high by 1 ft. 8 in. wide (72 by 51 cm.), c. 1800. £3,000-3,500   *S*

A George III satinwood needlework table, 19 in. wide by 15 in. deep by 29 in. high, c. 1800. £1,000-£1,300   *HAL*

A Charles X maplewood card table, by Jacob, with rectangular baize-lined folding top, the plain frieze with expanding action, inlaid in rosewood with anthemions and rosettes, stamped Jacob., 34 in. wide (86 cm.). £1,400-1,700   *C*

A George III harewood work table, the domed hinged crossbanded lid inlaid with a zig-zag line punctuated with leaves, the interior lined with silk, the frieze drawer fitted with an inkwell and divisions above a sliding work bag. 3 ft. high by 1 ft. 6 in. wide (91 by 46 cm.), c. 1795. **£1,500-1,800** *S*

A George III mahogany and rosewood work table, the burr-walnut veneered top with broad rosewood crossbanding, 27½ by 16 by 13 in. (70 by 41 by 33 cm.), early 19th C. **£400-500** *SC*

A late Sheraton mahogany work box, inlaid with rosewood and ebony stringing. **£800-1,000** *Fr*

A late George III rosewood sewing writing and games table, the divided top with baize-lined interior incorporating a small sunken panel concealing writing fitments, with a drawer in the frieze and a sewing bag below, 2 ft 6 in. high by 1 ft. 10 in. wide (76 b 56 cm.), c. 1800. **£1,800-2,200** *S*

A George III mahogany sewing table, the drawers fitted with compartments above sewing bag drawer, now altered, 20½ in. **£250-£350** *O*

A Regency mahogany work table, inlaid with rosewood bands, 19½ in. **£300-350** *CSK*

An early 19th C. mahogany work table, 22 by 30 in. extended. **£150-£200** *BHW*

A George III mahogany and rosewood banded and boxwood lin inlaid work table, 20 in. **£550-650** *DWB*

A Regency-period rosewood-veneered cheveret, brass line inlaid, 20 in. **£1,500-2,000** *WW*

A Regency mahogany work table the top framed by ebonised lines, with a frieze drawer and a work basket, 21 in. wide (53.5 cm.). **£2,200-2,600** *C*

A late Regency mahogany drop-leaf work table, 17½ by 19½ in. **£600-£700** *JD*

A Regency needlework table, with upper part in fine rosewood veneers, the folding surface inlaid with satinwood stringing, the upper drawer containing baize-covered writing surface and compartments for inkwells, pens, etc., the lyre-form supports in ebony with brass strings, 32 in. wide by 20 in. deep by 39 in. high, c. 1820. **£2,000-2,300** *HAL*

A Regency coromandel rectangular work table, distressed, 2 ft. wide (61 cm.), c. 1810. **£800-1,000** *SS*

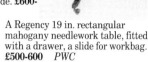

A Regency rosewood work table, 30 in. high by 33½ in. wide. **£600-£700** *Bea*

A Regency rosewood work table, the top inset with a cream-lacquered panel decorated with leaves, enclosing a fitted interior, 15 in. wide (38 cm.). **£800-1,000** *C*

Provenance:
By tradition Queen Charlotte and inscribed on an ivory plaque 'Painted by Her Majesty Queen Charlotte, 1787'.

A Regency 19 in. rectangular mahogany needlework table, fitted with a drawer, a slide for workbag. **£500-600** *PWC*

A Regency rosewood and brass-inlaid combined games, reading and work table, the top painted in gouache with a spray of flowers, above a shallow drawer inlaid for backgammon and with a slide inlaid for chess, above a fitted writing drawer with a work bag below incorporating a fitted tray, inlaid throughout with brass stringing and foliage, 2 ft. 5½ in. high by 2 ft. 3 in. wide (75 by 68.5 cm.), c. 1815. **£3,600-4,200** *S*

An early Victorian oak work table, by Holland & Sons, with baize-lined folding rectangular top, crossbanded with pollard oak above a concave frieze drawer, 21¼ in. wide (54 cm.). **£500-600** *C*

A Victorian birch combination writing and work table, with rising slope, 21 in. wide. **£700-800** *A*

Victorian figured mahogany work table, with fully fitted interior. **£400-500** *M*

A Victorian mahogany work and games table, 19 in. (48 cm.). **£500-£600** *L*

A walnut combined games and work table, the fold-over top enclosing cribbage, chess and backgammon boards, inlaid throughout with boxwood lines, 28½ by 24 in. (72 by 61 cm.), mid 19th C. **£650-800** *SC*

Victorian burr-walnut work table, with fitted drawer. **£300-350** *M*

A smart Victorian walnut combined games and work table, the fold-over top inlaid in boxwood and ebony, above a frieze drawer fitted with velvet-lined compartments, above a sliding workbag, 27¼ by 27 in. (69 by 68.5 cm.), third quarter 19th C. **£800-900** *SC*

A Victorian walnut work table, with fitted interior, c. 1850-60. **£275-325** *JT*

An early 19th C. rosewood work table, with frieze drawer, 28½ in. wide. **£150-200** *GM*

An early Victorian mahogany work table, the interior fitted in rosewood. **£320-380**   *M*

A pair of Louis Philippe ormolu-mounted tulipwood work tables, each with crossbanded quartered hinged top, 12½ in. wide (32 cm.). **£2,000-2,500**   *C*

An unusual rosewood 2-tier table, 30 by 17 in. (76 by 43 cm.), mid 19th C. **£450-550**   *SC*

A satinwood 'kettle-drum' work table, the hinged top inlaid with a giant patera, with velvet covered drum-shaped bag, 2 ft. 5½ in. high by 1 ft. 4 in. diam. (75 by 41 cm.), c. 1900. **£1,250-1,500**   *S*

A brass-inlaid mahogany writing and work table, the frieze with a baize-lined slide and 2 drawers, the wider one fitted for needlework and the narrow one for writing equipment, Russian or German, 1 ft. 7¼ in. wide (49 cm.), c. 1800. **£1,000-1,250**   *S*

A Biedermeier mahogany work table, with crossbanded chamfered lid, enclosing a divided and lidded interior, 22¼ in. wide (56 cm.). **£500-700**   *C*

A Queen Anne gilt-gesso centre table, in the manner of Moore and Gumley, re-gilded, 3 ft. 3 in. wide by 2 ft. 1¼ in. deep (99 by 64 cm.), c. 1700. **£2,200-2,600**   *S*

A George III kidney-shaped mahogany table, the baize-lined top above a frieze drawer, 2 ft. 5 in. high by 2 ft. 3 in. wide (74 by 69 cm.), c. 1790. **£1,000-1,250**   *S*

A pair of George III mahogany tables, the crossbanded tops segmentally-veneered, tops distressed, 2 ft. 4½ in. high by 1 ft. 8½ in. wide, c. 1800. **£3,000-3,500**   *S*

A Regency mahogany centre table, with octagonal marble top inlaid with chess squares in various specimen marbles, 29½ in. wide (79 cm.). **£1,000-1,250**   *C*

A Regency brass-mounted calamanderwood-veneered table, 2 ft. 3 in. high by 1 ft. 8 in. square (69 by 51 cm.), c. 1805. **£1,200-£1,500**   *S*

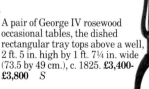

A Regency rosewood centre table, the top inlaid in cut brass, some damage, 28½ in. high by 38 in. wide. **£4,200-4,800**   *Bea*

A pair of George IV rosewood occasional tables, the dished rectangular tray tops above a well, 2 ft. 5 in. high by 1 ft. 7¼ in. wide (73.5 by 49 cm.), c. 1825. **£3,400-£3,800**   *S*

A fine Regency rosewood centre table, the top inset with Italian specimen marbles and a central roundel, 29 in. diam. (73.5 cm.). **£1,800-2,200**   *C*

A pair of Regency rosewood and coromandel crossbanded centre tables, 3 ft. 2 in. wide (97 cm.), c. 1810. **£2,200-2,800**   *SS*

A fine Regency satinwood centre table, the top inset with 6 pietra dura panels decorated with figures and buildings, 42½ in. wide (108 cm.), the pietra dura 17th/18th C. **£5,800-6,500**   *C*

A rosewood occasional table, 24 in. long by 17 in. deep by 29 in. high, c. 1820. **£1,100-1,300**   *HAL*

George IV carved mahogany centre table, 3 ft. 5 in. wide (104 cm.), c. 1825. **£900-1,100**   *SS*

A brass-inlaid rosewood and parcel-gilt centre table, the top inlaid with geometric pattern borders, 76 in. diam. (193 cm.). **£9,000-11,000**   *C*

A Regency rosewood centre table, with moulded circular tip-up top on turned splayed shaft, 53½ in. diam. (136 cm.). **£1,500-2,000**   *C*

fine maplewood and mahogany entre table, above pierced quatrefoil frieze, the top inlaid with various neo-classical motifs, probably Irish, 44 in. diam. (112 cm.), c. 1830. **£4,200-4,800**   *C*

A William IV rosewood table, the leather-lined crossbanded top with a gilt bronze acanthus border, the tip top raised on 3 boldly scrolling legs, 4 ft. 4 in. diam. (137 cm.), 1830's. **£4,500-5,500**   *S*

A marquetry centre table, inlaid with bands and sprays of flowers and butterflies on a walnut, rosewood and ebony ground, 3 ft. 3½ in. diam. (100 cm.), c. 1840. **£1,800-2,200**   *S*

n Anglo-Indian satinwood, ebony nd parcel-gilt centre table, 2 ft. in. high by 3 ft. 10 in. diam. (69 117 cm.), c. 1830. **£1,200-1,500**

A walnut and marquetry centre table, the top inlaid with a broad banding of etched ivory, applied with gilt metal mounts and bead mouldings throughout, 29 by 36 by 21 in. (74 by 92 by 53 cm.), third quarter of the 19th C. **£1,250-1,500**   *SC*

A fine William IV colonial ebony centre table, the top inlaid in various woods, including satinwood, sadicu, calamander, stinkwood and rosewood, bordered by herringbone, ivory and ebony bandings, Goanese or Cape, the top faded and in need of some restoration, 28½ by 45½ in. (72.5 by 115 cm.), second quarter of the 19th C. **£2,000-2,500**   *SC*

A Victorian rosewood occasional table, the top inlaid with flowers and foliage, 38½ by 19 in. **£350-400**   *BHW*

A fine Victorian ormolu-mounted walnut, mahogany, tulipwood and marquetry table, bearing the trade label of 'GP Holmes and Co., House Furnishers, Old Town Street, Plymouth', 54 in. wide (137 cm.), mid 19th C. **£2,600-3,200** *C*

A specimen marble centre table, the circular top inlaid with a collection of early specimen marbles, 2 ft. 8½ in. high by 2 ft. 11½ in. wide (82.5 by 90 cm.), c. 1860. **£2,600-3,200** *S*

A hardstone marquetry occasional table, probably Ashburton, 2 ft. ½ in. diam. (61 cm.), c. 1850. **£1,000-1,250** *S*

The hardstones used include green onyx, white agate, lapis and amber

A satinwood-veneered centre table, the top inlaid with a concave diamond of ribbon-tied husks and with a partridgewood crossbanding, 2 ft. 5½ in. high by 3 ft. 4½ in. wide (75 by 103 cm.), c. 1890. **£3,000-£3,500** *S*

A Victorian rosewood wine table, 22 in. **£380-440** *O*

A pair of beechwood tables, 2 ft. 8½ in. high by 5 ft. 6 in. wide by 3 ft. deep (83 by 168 by 92 cm.), c. 1880. **£800-1,000** *S*

A George I-style walnut centre table, the verde antico marble slab above a plain shaped frieze, 134 cm. wide, 19th C. **£1,000-1,250** *Bon*

A small mid Victorian walnut occasional table. **£250-300** *Co*

A painted satinwood centre table, the centre with a roundel of Marie Antoinette, 2 ft. 4 in. high by 2 ft. diam. (71 by 61 cm.), c. 1900. **£900-£1,100** *S*

A satinwood and marquetry circular table, the top inlaid with a ribbon-tied trophy within a swagged border, 2 ft. 5½ in. high by 1 ft. 10 in. wide (75 by 57 cm.), c. 1900. **£800-1,200** *S*

An Edwardian 'Sheraton' painted satinwood occasional table, 69 cm. wide. **£500-600** *Bon*

A Flemish ivory-inlaid kingwood veneered centre table, 2 ft. 5 in. high by 4 ft. 1 in. wide (74 by 125 cm.), late 17th C., with 19th restoration. **£1,400-1,800** *S*

A Dutch oval mahogany centre table, inlaid with chequer stringing, 101 cm. wide, late 18th C. **£600-£700** *Bon*

A Dutch tulipwood and marquetry table, the top inlaid with oyster veneers and a band of scrolling foliage, 37½ in. wide (95 cm.), late 18th C. **£2,400-2,800** *C*

Regency-style giltwood and gesso ntre table, the Sienna marble top a moulded frieze, 33 by 58 by in. (84 by 148 by 89 cm.), 20th C. ,800-3,400   *SC*

A Louis XV centre table, the hinged leather inset opening to reveal a simple veneered interior, the exterior now lacquered and with rococo gilt bronze mounts, 2 ft. 6 in. wide (76 cm.), mid 18th C. **£2,800-3,400**   *S*

A Louis XV marquetry table en chiffonier, in quarter-veneered kingwood, the hinged top inlaid with scrolls, with a mirror-lined interior, 2 ft. 5 in. high by 1 ft. 6 in. wide (74 by 46 cm.), c. 1755. **£3,000-£3,500**   *S*

A Louis XVI kingwood table en chiffonier, stamped C. Topino JME, with an oval white Carrara marble top, 2 ft. 5½ in. high by 1 ft. 3 in. wide (75 by 38 cm.), c. 1770. **£5,500-£6,500**   *S*

Charles Topino, received Master 1773.

n early Louis XVI kingwood and lipwood table en chiffonier, amped I.P. Dusautoy, JME, 2 ft. ½ in. high by 1 ft. 7 in. wide (75 by .5 cm.), c. 1780. **£3,000-3,500**   *S*

ean-Pierre Dusautoy, 1719-1800, ceived Master 1779.

An ormolu-mounted parquetry gueridon, in the manner of RVLC, the galleried top inlaid with trelliswork and cut flowerheads, above one frieze drawer, 19½ in. wide (49.5 cm.). **£3,000-3,500**   *C*

A Directoire bronze gueridon, 3 ft. 2½ in. high by 1 ft. 7½ in. diam. (70 by 50 cm.), c. 1790. **£2,200-2,600** *S*

A walnut and marquetry small centre table, the burr-walnut top with a broad ebonised surround, inlaid with strapwork and roses, 2 ft. 5½ in. high by 2 ft. 6 in. diam. (75 by 76 cm.), c. 1850. **£1,800-£2,200**   *S*

Transitional fruitwood gueridon, y Hache, the plain frieze with 2 rawers crossbanded with sewood, stamped Hache Fils a renoble, 22½ in. wide (57 cm.). ,800-3,200   *C*

A Louis XVI brass-mounted bouillotte table, the galleried rust marble top with strong grey and white mottling, 2 ft. 3 in. high by 1 ft. 10 in. diam. (68 by 55 cm.), c. 1780. **£2,800-3,200**   *S*

An Empire brass- and bronze-mounted circular centre table, the quarter-veneered top with engine-turned border and central white marble panel, painted with an antique classical bearded head, 2 ft. 4 in. high by 2 ft. 6 in. diam. (71 by 76 cm.), c. 1810. **£5,500-6,000**   *S*

A gilt bronze porcelain-mounted centre table, with a circular Sèvres-style plaque, plaque signed Houbrite and with interlaced 'L's' in underglaze blue, 2 ft. 4 in. high by 1 ft. 8½ in. diam. (71 by 52 cm.), c. 1880. **£2,000-2,400**   *S*

A small quarter-veneered kingwood table, stamped G. Durand, 2 ft. 4½ in. high by 1 ft. 2 in. wide (72 by 35 cm.), c. 1860. **£1,200-1,500**   *S*

G. Durand 1838-62.

A Louis XV kingwood bureau plat, with gilt tooled lined surface, 2 ft. 8 in. by 4 ft. 3 in. **£1,000-1,250** *GC*

405

A walnut centre table, in the French style, the tulipwood crossbanded top inlaid with geometric stringing, on an amboyna ground, one side badly faded, 4 ft. 2 in. wide (127 cm.), 1850's. **£700-900**   *S*

An ormolu-mounted and walnut centre table, 2 ft. 6 in. high by 4 ft. 4½ in. wide (76 by 133 cm.), mid 19th C. **£1,000-1,250**   *S*

A Louis XV-style kingwood and marquetry centre table, with plate glass top, 31 in. high by 56 in. wide, 19th C. **£1,800-2,200**   *Bea*

A porcelain-mounted giltwood centre table, one roundel cracked, one repaired, 2 ft. 5 in. high by 1 ft. 9½ in. diam. (74 by 54.5 cm.), late 19th C. **£3,000-3,400**   *S*

A gilt bronze-mounted kingwood centre table, with a brèche-violette top, 4 ft. 2 in. wide (132 cm.), c. 1910. **£1,200-1,500**   *S*

A walnut and marquetry serpentine centre table, the quarter-veneered top inlaid with a spray of flowers, within a brass-bound tulipwood crossbanding, 2 ft 5 in. high by 2 ft. 8½ in. long (73 by 83 cm.), c. 1860. **£500-600**   *S*

A tulipwood, ebony, sycamore and olivewood marquetry and parquetry centre table, 45 in. diam. top by 30 in. (76 cm.) high, 20th C. **£2,800-3,400**   *SC*

A giltwood centre table, with moulded rectangular breccia marble top, 76½ in. wide (194 cm.). **£10,000-12,000**   *C*

A rosewood and gilt bronze bureau plat de dame, enclosing a distressed inset silk surface, French or German, 29½ in. by 26 in. (75 by 66 cm.), third quarter of 19th C. **£700-800**   *SC*

A giltwood centre table, with green and white marble top, the frieze carved with strapwork and foliage, centred by a female mask, 2 ft. 6 in. high by 5 ft. 5 in. wide by 2 ft. 8½ in. deep (76 by 165 by 82.5 cm.), 1880-1900. **£3,600-4,200**   *S*

A Bois de Citron parquetry gilt bronze mounted occasional table, 2 ft. 5 in. high by 2 ft. 3 in. wide (74 by 68.5 cm.), c. 1900. **£1,200-£1,500**   *S*

A Tuscan walnut table, the baluster-shaped trestle supports faced with bosses, 2 ft. 6½ in. high by 3 ft. wide (77 by 91 cm.), mid 16th C. **£1,500-1,800**   *S*

A decorated occasional table, with green ground and red ochre floral painting, with marble top, 2 ft. 11 in. high by 2 ft. 11 in. wide, c. 1870. **£500-600**   *LRG*

A Tuscan walnut table, on 4 flat eaf-carved S scroll legs, with lion aw feet, 2 ft. 8½ in. high by 4 ft. ide (83 by 122 cm.). **£2,400-2,800**

A pair of Italian giltwood centre tables, each with massive black-bordered verde antico marble top, 53 in. wide (115 cm.), c. 1830. **£3,800-4,500**   *C*

A carved wood centre table, in the form of 3 winged monopodia, the top veneered in malachite and Sienna marble, 3 ft. 10 in. diam. (117 cm.), 19th C. **£9,000-11,000** *S*

A 19th C. Italian walnut centre table, 27 in. diam. **£700-900**   *PWC*

A 19th C. Italian specimen table, the top inset with 119 specimen marbles and semi-precious stones, 36½ by 21¾ in. **£1,000-1,250**   *MN*

19th C. Italian parquetry and arquetry centre table, 30 in. high ⅞ 29½ in. diam. **£400-600**   *Bea*

An Italian walnut and parquetry oval occasional table, with restorations, 57 cm. wide, late 18th C. **£1,000-1,250**   *Bon*

Swiss walnut table, the top laid with panels of marquetry, t. 6¾ in. high by 3 ft. 4½ in. wide 8 by 103 cm.), mid 17th C. ,400-1,800   *S*

An Edwardian satinwood and marquetry oval occasional table, the quarter-veneered top with an oval fan inlay, inlaid in etched boxwood, rosewood and olivewood, 29 by 19 in. (74 by 48 cm.), early 20th C. **£650-750**   *SC*

An Italian ivory-inlaid ebony and rosewood centre table, 41 in. wide (104 cm.). **£1,400-1,700**   *C*

A fine Tyrolean walnut and oak centre table, 38 in. wide (97 cm.), basically 17th C. **£2,400-2,800**   *C*

George III mahogany breakfast ble, banded in satinwood and sewood, the down-curved legs laid with paler wood stringing, amped 'JAs. Shoolbred & Co. 47', 4 ft. 2 in. long (127 cm.), 1800. **£3,500-4,000**   *S*

A Swiss walnut centre table, carved with geometric designs and flowerheads, on bobbin turned legs, 36½ in. wide (93 cm.), 17th C. **£1,000-1,250**   *C*

A George III mahogany octagonal tip-up breakfast table, 42½ in. **£1,000-1,250**   *DWB*

407

A George III partridgewood and rosewood breakfast table, with crossbanded tip-up top, 54¼ in. wide (138 cm.). **£2,400-2,800** *C*

A George III mahogany breakfast table, the top crossbanded and inlaid with boxwood and ebony stringing, the base inlaid with ebony lines, bearers replaced, 2 ft. 4 in. high by 4 ft. 1½ in. diam. (71 by 126 cm.), c. 1790. **£5,000-5,500** *S*

A George III mahogany breakfast or dining table, 5 ft. 1 in. by 3 ft. 10 in. (155 by 118 cm.), c. 1805. **£3,600-4,200** *S*

A good Regency tulipwood breakfast table, the rectangular snap-top crossbanded in satinwood and bordered in ebony and boxwood stringing, 149 by 116 cm. **£6,000-£7,000** *P*

A Georgian mahogany breakfast or dining table, 5 ft. 1 in. by 3 ft. 11½ in. **£1,000-1,250** *PWC*

A George III mahogany breakfast table, the figured folding surface with moulded edge, 53½ in. wide by 39 in. deep by 39 in. high, c. 1800. **£1,800-2,200** *HAL*

A George III mahogany breakfast table, with well-figured oval tip-up top, crossbanded with satinwood, 56 in. wide (142 cm.). **£3,000-3,500** *C*

A George III mahogany breakfast table, 28½ by 59 by 40 in. (72 by 150 by 101 cm.), first quarter of the 19th C. **£1,800-2,200** *SC*

A Regency mahogany breakfast table, inlaid with ebony panels, 4 ft. 10½ in. by 3 ft. 5 in. **£1,600-£2,000** *PWC*

A late Georgian mahogany breakfast table, the oval 'plum pudding' top with a wide crossbanding, repairs, 44 by 40 in. (112 by 102 cm.). **£800-1,200** *L*

A Regency rosewood breakfast table, (142 cm.). **£3,200-3,600** *C*

A Regency mahogany breakfast table, the hinged surface with a broad crossband, with original brass feet and castors, 66 in. long by 42 in. deep by 28 in. high, c. 1825. **£2,800-3,200** *HAL*

A George III mahogany breakfast table, the top banded in rosewood, 2 ft. 5 in. high by 5 ft. wide (74 by 153 cm.), c. 1800. **£2,800-3,400** *S*

A George III plum pudding mahogany breakfast table, the tip-up top crossbanded with satinwood and faded rosewood, 52½ in. wide (133 cm.). **£7,500-8,500** *C*

A Regency mahogany breakfast table, the tip-up top inlaid with ebonised lines, 64 in. wide (163 cm.). **£1,000-1,250** *C*

A Regency breakfast table, the mahogany veneer crossbanded in rosewood, 4 ft. 10 in. by 3 ft. 10 in. **£2,000-2,500** *AGr*

Where can you find the largest selection of Victorian, Edwardian and shipping furniture in London?

at Phelps. Where else!

- ★ Large quantity of Victorian, Edwardian and 20s furniture of all types and quality.
- ★ Single items to containers shipped worldwide.
- ★ Extensive showrooms and warehouse.
- ★ Restoration and upholstery services.
- ★ Competitive prices.
- ★ Illustrated brochure on request.

Write to
Robert Phelps, Phelps Ltd.,
129-135 St. Margarets Road,
East Twickenham TW1 1RG, London, England

or telephone us on: 01-892 1778 & 7129. Telex: 261541

PHELPS *Limited*
ESTABLISHED 1870

Members of the L.A.P.A.D.A.

A Regency mahogany and rosewood crossbanded breakfast table, 44 in. wide by 58 in. long, c. 1810. **£2,800-3,200**   *AP*

A rosewood breakfast table, the top crossbanded with satinwood, 47½ in. wide (121 cm.). **£1,600-£2,000**   *C*

A rosewood-veneered breakfast or dining table, 4 ft. 10 in. diam. (148 cm.), c. 1840. **£1,000-1,250**   *S*

A Regency rosewood dining table, 50 in. diam. **£800-1,200**   *PWC*

A Regency mahogany breakfast table, the top crossbanded in rosewood, 47 in. diam. **£800-1,200**   *CSK*

A Regency rosewood breakfast table, the tip-up top crossbanded with satinwood framed by ebonised and boxwood lines, 60½ in. wide by 42½ in. deep (154 by 108 cm.). **£5,000-5,500**   *C*

A Regency mahogany breakfast table, with oval tip-up top, 59½ in. wide (151 cm.). **£3,600-4,200**   *C*

A Regency rosewood breakfast table, the oval top contained by a broad amboyna banding and cast gilt bronze border, 29 by 56 by 44 in. (74 by 142 by 112 cm.), second quarter of the 19th C. **£2,000-2,500**   *SC*

A George IV rosewood breakfast table, the well-figured hinged top and bead-moulded edge, 4 ft. 2 in. diam. (127 cm.), c. 1825. **£1,000-£1,250**   *S*

A Regency oval rosewood breakfast table, the tip top with brass beading, gilt mounts to the supports, 50 in. long. **£1,000-1,250**   *TW*

A Regency-period brass inlaid rosewood dining table, 51 in. across, c. 1810. **£3,800-4,400**   *AP*

A Regency rosewood centre table, with well-figured crossbanded top, on octagonal shaft and concave-sided splayed quadripartite base ending in acanthus feet, 42½ in. wide (121 cm.). **£1,000-1,250**   *C*

A Regency brass-inlaid rosewood breakfast or dining table, the top with a broad crossbanding, inlaid with anthemion, with a grained lotus carved pillar, caned and reeded sabre legs with brass castors, underframe replaced, 3 ft. 9 in. long (114 cm.), c. 1820. **£3,000-£3,500**   *S*

An early Regency figured mahogany breakfast table, in the manner of George Smith, having a moulded brass edge and beaded frieze, 3 ft. 10 in. diam. **£5,800-£6,400**   *WW*

A William IV mahogany breakfast table, the crossbanded and segmented flamed-veneered top with gadrooned borders, 54 in. £1,200-1,500   *CSK*

A Victorian walnut and marquetry breakfast table, made for the Great Exhibition of 1851, 52 in. £2,200-£2,800   *Re*

An early Victorian rosewood dining table, by C. Hindley & Sons, with a circular tip-up top, 28¾ in. high by 52½ in. diam. £800-1,200   *Bea*

An early Victorian mahogany dining table, the circular tip top inlaid with rings of satinwood, 46 in. diam. £400-600   *BHW*

A marquetry circular table, the hinged burr-elm top with an inlaid rosewood medallion, 2 ft. 6 in. high by 4 ft. 3 in. diam. (76 by 130 cm.), 1850. £1,500-2,000   *S*

A Victorian rosewood and amboyna dining table, 49 in. £2,200-2,600   *JD*

A mid Victorian burr-walnut loo table. £500-700   *Fr*

A walnut breakfast table, the tilt-top inlaid with bands of foliate marquetry with boxwood line borders, 51 in. £800-1,000   *CSK*

The price would indicate a later veneered top.

An inlaid centre table, the hinged moulded top quarter-veneered in rosewood, with flower panels in walnut and other woods, 4 ft. 8½ in. diam. (144 cm.), c. 1850. £2,200-£2,800   *S*

A Victorian walnut loo table. £800-£1,000   *EEW*

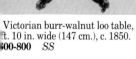

A Victorian burr-walnut loo table, 4 ft. 10 in. wide (147 cm.), c. 1850. £500-800   *SS*

A Victorian walnut oval breakfast table, the quarter-veneered snap top on a turned pillar, 29 by 58 in. (74 by 147 cm.), third quarter of 19th C. £600-800   *SC*

An early Victorian mahogany breakfast table, 30 in. high (76 cm.) by 54 in. diam. top, mid 19th C. £800-1,000   *SC*

A rare yew wood loo table, 5 ft. wide (152.5 cm.), c. 1850. £600-800   *S*

A Victorian walnut oval table, with inlaid central panel and borders with boxwood stringing, 53 in. wide. £400-600   *WHB*

mid Victorian walnut loo table. £500-700   *BHW*

A Victorian walnut breakfast table, 3 ft. 6 in. diam. £400-600   *V*

411

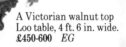

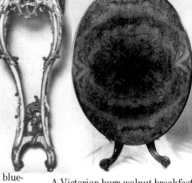

A William IV rosewood console table, with Sienna marble top, 34 by 42 in. (87 by 107 cm.), second quarter of 19th C. **£500-600**   *SC*

A pair of corner console tables, 3 ft. 1½ in. high by 1 ft. 10 in. wide (95 by 56 cm.), from a side table of c. 1840. **£1,000-1,250**   *S*

A Victorian walnut top Loo table, 4 ft. 6 in. wide. **£450-600**   *EG*

A pair of French cream and blue-painted petites consoles, with Sicilian jasper tops, 12¼ in. wide by 32 in. high by 10½ in. deep (31 by 81 by 27 cm.), one mid 18th C., one probably of later date. **£1,600-2,000**   *C*

A Victorian burr-walnut breakfast table, complete with protective cover, 56 by 45 in., c. 1860. **£600-£700**   *TW*

A Louis XV carved giltwood console table, with serpentine mottled rust-coloured marble top, 2 ft. 10½ in. high by 4 ft. 5 in. wide (87 by 135 cm.), c. 1735. **£3,000-£3,500**   *S*

A Louis XIV giltwood side table, with mottled green and white marble top, with restoration, 2 ft. 8½ in. high by 3 ft. 5½ in. wide (82 by 106 cm.), c. 1700. **£5,000-6,000**   *S*

A pair of George IV parcel-gilt rosewood side tables, 2 ft. 11½ in. high by 2 ft. 10½ in. wide (90 by 87.5 cm.), c. 1820. **£3,000-3,400**   *S*

A pair of Roman giltwood pedestal tables, with a serpentine grey marble top, marbles modern, 3 ft. 1½ in. high by 1 ft. 9¾ in. wide (93 by 55 cm.), early 18th C. **£1,000-£1,250**   *S*

A giltwood and gesso pier table, with a serpentine moulded green and red marble top, 36 by 62 in. by 158 cm.), mid 19th C. **£1,000-£1,250**   *SC*

A small pair of ebonised and parcel-gilt side tables, with canted eared moulded Carrara marble tops, joined by 2 platforms, both marbles damaged and repaired, 22½ in. wide (57 cm.). **£1,400-1,800**   *C*

A George III mahogany dining table. **£1,200-1,600**   *JF*

A large oak sectional gateleg dining table, 5 by 14 ft., probably 19th C. **£2,000-3,000**   *WW*

A 19th C. Georgian-design dining table, composite piece, 7 ft. 5 in. (226 cm.) fully extended. **£800-£1,000**   *LBP*

A Roman parcel-gilt side table, with moulded mottled simulated marble top, probably originally with marble top, 2 ft. 8½ in. high by 4 ft. 7 in. wide (82 by 140 cm.), late 17th/early 18th C. **£2,400-£2,800**   *S*

A mahogany 4-pedestal dining table, 4 ft. 6 in. wide by 9 ft. 6 in. long fully extended (137 by 290 cm.). **£14,000-16,000** *S*

A George III mahogany dining table, 60 by 53½ in. (152.5 by 136 cm.). **£1,500-1,800** *C*

A George III Cumberland action mahogany dining table, 4 ft. 5 in. wide (135 cm.), c. 1800. **£1,500-£1,800** *SS*

A Hepplewhite-period mahogany extending sectional dining table, ft. 11 in. wide by 8 ft. (extended). **£1,200-1,600** *WW*

A George III mahogany 3-part dining table. **£1,000-1,500** *CDC*

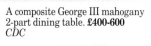

A composite George III mahogany 2-part dining table. **£400-600** *CDC*

A mahogany 3-pillar dining table, with one extra leaf, 4 ft. wide by 9 ft. 8½ in. fully extended (122 by 296 cm.), c. 1780, but top and bottom associated. **£6,500-7,500** *S*

George III mahogany dining table, complete with an additional af, 149 cm. wide extended. **£1,000-1,250** *HSS*

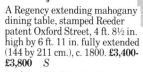

A Regency extending mahogany dining table, stamped Reeder patent Oxford Street, 4 ft. 8½ in. high by 6 ft. 11 in. fully extended (144 by 211 cm.), c. 1800. **£3,400-£3,800** *S*

Ambrose Heal London Furniture Makers 1680-1840 records John Reeder, Upholder at No. 392 Oxford Street, London 1783-1803.

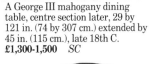

A George III mahogany dining table, centre section later, 29 by 121 in. (74 by 307 cm.) extended by 45 in. (115 cm.), late 18th C. **£1,300-1,500** *SC*

late George III mahogany twin llar dining table, originally with flaps, 80 in. long by 56 in. wide. **£1,800-2,200** *HyD*

A George III mahogany dining table, to seat up to 10, 112 in. long by 45 in. wide by 28 in. high, c. 1800. **£2,800-3,200** *HAL*

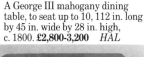

George III-style mahogany ardroom table, 120½ by 80½ in. **£700-900** *CSK*

A Regency mahogany patent dining table, extending to fit 3 extra leaves, 45 by 110 in. (115 by 280 cm.), fully extended. **£5,500-£6,500** *C*

A Georgian mahogany dining table, with 2 spare leaves, 52 in. wide by 76 in. long opening to 110 in. **£1,200-1,600** *DA*

413

A Regency mahogany dining or boardroom table, inlaid with a line of ebony stringing and crossbanding, 164 in. long, maximum by 60 in. wide by 28 in. high, c. 1830. **£3,200-3,800**   *HAL*

A Regency mahogany metamorphic dining table, of patent design, extending from a side table, 26 by 60 in., to a banqueting table, 156 by 60 in., with the addition of 5 leaves on a concertina action. **£3,500-4,200**   *HyD*

A Regency mahogany extending dining table, 5 ft. by 12 ft. 4 in. fully extended (153 by 376 cm.), c. 1810. **£4,500-5,500**   *SS*

An early Victorian mahogany extending dining table, 5 ft. 3 in. diameter, extending with 3 extra leaves to 10 ft. 10 in., maximum extension approximately 18 ft. **£1,200-1,600**   *CDC*

A Regency mahogany 2-pillar dining table, 2 extra leaves, top and base associated, 28 in. high by 46 in. wide by 97 in. long. **£1,800-2,200**   *Bea*

A Regency mahogany dining table, 47 by 125 in. long (119.5 by 338 cm.). **£3,000-3,500**   *C*

A Regency mahogany dining table, with restoration, some legs replaced, 50 by 130 in. **£1,000-1,400**   *DSH*

A William IV mahogany extending dining table, on 14 ringed and gadrooned tapering legs with brass castors, with 2 contemporary leaves, 4 ft. 1 in. wide by 10 ft. 3½ in. fully extended (122 by 313 cm.), c. 1830. **£2,400-2,800**   *S*

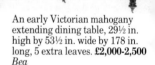

A mahogany extending dining table, 2 ft. 4½ in. high by 11 ft. 3½ in. long (73 by 344 cm.), c. 1850 **£800-1,200**   *S*

A late William IV mahogany 3-pillar dining table, 29 by 110 in. (74 by 279 cm.), second quarter of the 19th C. **£4,200-4,800**   *SC*

An early Victorian oak extending dining table, 4 ft. 3 in. by 6 ft. 6 in. extended. **£400-600**   *WW*

An early Victorian mahogany extending dining table, 29½ in. high by 53½ in. wide by 178 in. long, 5 extra leaves. **£2,000-2,500**   *Bea*

A George IV mahogany 3-pedestal dining table, with 2 extra leaves, 3 ft. 11 in. wide by 9 ft. 9 in. fully extended (120 by 297 cm.), c. 1825. **£3,000-3,500**   *S*

A William IV mahogany extending dining table, 29 by 154 in. including 4 leaves, by 55¼ in., second quarter of the 19th C. **£2,000-2,500**   *SC*

A fine William IV mahogany extending dining table, by Robert Jupe, the circular top opening to admit 8 further leaves, stamped Johnstone Jupe & Co. New Bond St. London no. 11382, 55 in. closed (140 cm.) by 71 in. extended (181 cm.). **£8,000-12,000**   *C*

Jupe took out a patent for an expanding circular dining table in 1835. The firm of Jupe, Johnstone & Co. is recorded by Heal at 67 New Bond Street between 1835 and 1839.

A George III-style mahogany
3-pillar dining table, 29 by 150 in.
(74 by 381 cm.) extended, including
2 leaves, by 47 in. (120 cm.), early
20th C. **£2,500-3,000**   *SC*

A mahogany 2-pillar dining table,
30 by 82 in. (76 by 209 cm.)
extended, including a leaf, by
42½ in. (108 cm.), the pillars partly
18th C. **£800-1,000**   *SC*

A mahogany extending dining
table, the extension leaves missing,
60 in. diam. (153 cm.), 19th C.
£1,200-1,500   *L*

An early 19th C. mahogany
3-pillar dining table, 48 by 101 in.
£7,500-8,500   *DWB*

A walnut gateleg table, 44 in. wide,
open (112 cm.), 17th C. **£1,500-
£1,800**   *C*

A mid Georgian mahogany gateleg
table, 46¼ in. wide, open (117 cm.).
£450-550   *C*

A cherrywood oval gateleg table,
possibly American, 3 ft. 6 in. by
3 ft. 9¾ in. open (107 by 116 cm.),
early 18th C. **£1,200-1,500**   *S*

GATELEG TABLES
FACTORS INFLUENCING PRICE
- Oak tables are most
  common; therefore walnut
  and fruitwood tables
  command higher
  comparative prices
- Double action gateleg
  tables are very sought after
- Beware of replacement
  leaves

A George I red walnut oval drop
leaf dining table. **£1,000-1,250**
DWB

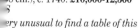

A George II large mahogany oval
drop leaf table, 6 ft. 8 in. by 6 ft.
9 in. fully extended (203 by
208 cm.), c. 1740. **£10,000-12,500**
S

*Very unusual to find a table of this
size.*

**For more gateleg tables, see
the Oak and Country
Furniture section**

A George III yew wood drop leaf
table, 3 ft. 6 in. wide (107 cm.),
c. 1770. **£500-700**   *SS*

A late Regency rosewood
Sutherland table, 43 in. wide
(109 cm.). **£800-1,000**   *C*

A George III mahogany Pembroke
table, inlaid with double stringing
lines, 34 by 39½ in. (86 by 100 cm.)
extended. **£800-1,000**   *L*

A late George III mahogany
Pembroke table, with a tulipwood
crossbanded edge, the drawer
opening half way open with a
further lockable 'secret'
compartment, the square tapering
legs edged in boxwood on brass
castors, 3 ft. ½ in. open (92 cm.),
c. 1790. **£1,400-1,600**   *S*

A 19th C. spider-leg, drop leaf
table, 2 ft. 9 in. high by 2 ft. 6 in.
wide (82 by 75 cm.). **£300-350**
LRG

415

PEMBROKE TABLES

- became popular in the mid to late 18th C., possibly designed and ordered by Henry Herbert, the Earl of Pembroke (1693-1751)
- on early examples the legs were square which are by far the most desirable
- later tables had turned legs
- the turned and reeded legs are much less popular
- those with oval or serpentine tops more desirable
- flaps should have three hinges

- rounded flaps and marquetry again increase desirability
- satinwood was greatly favoured, particularly with much crossbanding and inlay
- the Edwardians made many fine Pembroke tables which have been known to appear wrongly catalogued at auction
- many 18th C. Pembroke tables have chamfering on the insides of the legs

A George III serpentine Pembroke table, the top veneered in kingwood and quarter-banded in tulipwood, 2 ft. 3½ in. high by 2 ft. 11 in. open (70 by 89 cm.), c. 1780. **£4,000-£4,500** *S*

A Regency mahogany Pembroke table by Gillows, Lancaster, 36 in. wide, open (91.5 cm.). **£2,500-3,000** *C*

An unusual George III mahogany 'harlequin' Pembroke writing table, the oval top with a sliding centre section, revealing a baize-lined writing surface, 2 ft. 6 in. long by 3 ft. 7 in. wide, open (81 by 109 cm.), c. 1775. **£1,200-1,500** *S*

A George III mahogany Pembroke table, with twin-flap top, crossbanded with satinwood and framed by boxwood lines, 39½ in. wide, open (100 cm.). **£2,000-2,500** *C*

A George III mahogany Pembroke table, with serpentine twin-flap top, crossbanded with rosewood, 38¼ in. wide, open (97 cm.). **£2,400-2,800** *C*

A George III mahogany Pembroke table, the top inlaid with a satinwood patera, 36¼ in. (92 cm.) wide, open. **£3,800-4,200** *C*

(l.) A Sheraton-period mahogany Pembroke table, the well-figured top with satinwood crossbands, with string inlaid square taper legs, 38 by 28½ in. **£1,200-1,500**

(r.) A Sheraton-period mahogany Pembroke table, the top satinwood banded, 31 in. wide. **£600-800** *PWC*

A Sheraton mahogany Pembroke table, the top with a broad satinwood band inlaid with a strand of flowers and foliage, with a rosewood outer band, the square taper legs with inlaid string lines, 42 by 31½ in. with flaps up. **£4,800-5,400** *PWC*

A Sheraton mahogany Pembroke table, the top with a broad satinwood band. **£500-700** *PWC*

A George III mahogany Pembroke table, the oval folding crossbanded surface above ebony inlaid drawers, drawer pulls replaced, 45 in. wide by 34 in. deep by 28 in. high, c. 1800. **£800-1,000** *HAL*

A George III mahogany and tulipwood crossbanded Pembroke table, 29 by 36½ in. **£1,500-1,800** *DWB*

A George III mahogany Pembroke table, the top inlaid with parquetry, 41½ in. wide (105.5 cm.). **£2,000-2,500** *C*

A George III satinwood and harewood Pembroke table, 44 in. wide (112 cm.). **£4,000-4,500** *C*

A George III mahogany Pembroke table, the folding surface inlaid and crossbanded with satinwood, above cockbeaded drawers, 38 in. wide by 33 in. deep by 28 in. high, c. 1790. **£1,800-2,200** *HAL*

A George III mahogany Pembroke table, the crossbanded folding top inlaid with satinwood and amaranth bands, with boxwood borders, 33 in. **£2,000-2,500** *CSK*

A George III satinwood Pembroke table, with tulipwood crossbanding and edged with stringing, 29½ by 37 in. extended (75 by 94 cm.). **£1,600-2,000** *L*

A Georgian inlaid mahogany Pembroke table. **£2,400-2,800** *AMB*

A George III burr-yew Pembroke table, 43 in. wide. **£4,400-£4,800** *C*

A George III satinwood Pembroke table, the top with rosewood crossbanding and edged with ebony stringing, the top split, 31 by 42 in. extended (79 by 107 cm.). **£1,400-£1,800** *L*

A Regency fiddleback mahogany Pembroke table, the top crossbanded in rosewood, 41 in. wide, open (104 cm.). **£2,000-2,500** *C*

A Georgian-style inlaid mahogany Pembroke table, 28 by 14 in., late 19th/20th C. **£400-500** *JD*

A mahogany drop-leaf table, 54 by 37 in., 19th C. **£150-200** *BHW*

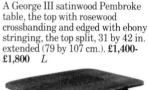

A Regency rosewood Pembroke table, 42½ in. wide, open (108 cm.). **£800-1,000** *C*

A George III mahogany sofa table, crossbanded in satinwood and kingwood, 57 in. extended. **£1,000-£1,250** *HyD*

A late George III mahogany sofa table, inlaid with simple bandings, 2 ft. 3½ in. high by 4 ft. 10 in. wide (70 by 147 cm.), c. 1815. **£1,400-£1,800** *S*

A Dutch marquetry table, inlaid overall with shell, floral and leaf designs on a mahogany ground, 25 by 43 in. (63 by 109 cm.) extended, 19th C. **£600-800** *L*

A George IV mahogany sofa table, the top inlaid with ebonised stringing, 5 ft. 4 in. wide, open (163 cm.), c. 1820. **£900-1,100** *S*

A George III mahogany sofa table, 28 by 56 in. (71 by 142 cm.), late 18th C. **£1,400-1,800** *SC*

A George III mahogany crossbanded sofa table, with boxwood and ebony stringing, 36½ in. wide. **£800-1,000** *WHB*

A Regency mahogany sofa table, with kingwood crossbanding and inlaid with boxwood lines, 28 in. high by 36 in. deep by 52 in. wide. **£1,200-1,500** *Bea*

A Georgian mahogany sofa table, 65 in. full extent, c. 1800. **£3,000-£3,500** *AP*

A mahogany and rosewood Regency-style sofa table. **£500-£600** *Fr*

A Regency mahogany sofa table, 39 by 62 in. extended (99 by 158 cm.). **£900-1,100** *L*

A fine calamanderwood, pollard oak and rosewood sofa table, 54 in. (137 cm.) wide. **£4,200-4,800** *C*

SOFA TABLES

- an elegant feminine writing table, usually with two shallow drawers
- genuine ones are rarer than it might appear
- either had two vertical supports or a central pillar
- many fine examples made in mahogany with satinwood or rosewood stringing and crossbanding
- rosewood examples can be of exceptional quality
- examples with stretchers tend to be later
- lyre end supports, particularly with a brass strip, are likely to increase value
- many sofa tables have been made from old cheval mirrors
- if the stretcher rail is turned and has a square block in the centre — it could be from a converted cheval mirror
- many good sofa tables have been carved with Egyptian heads in the manner of Thomas Hope
- long drawers are undesirable but many have been cut down

A Regency mahogany, inlaid and crossbanded sofa table, cracked top, in need of restoration, 60 in. wide. **£1,000-1,250** *DSH*

A George III satinwood sofa table, the top inlaid with ebony lines and crossbanded in rosewood, restored, 29 by 60 by 26 in. (74 by 153 by 66 cm.), late 18th C. **£14,000-£17,000** *SC*

A Regency mahogany sofa table, the top crossbanded with rosewood, 62 in. (157.5 cm.) wide, open. **£4,500-5,500** *C*

A Regency mahogany sofa table, twin-flap top with a velvet-lined easel, one drawer fitted with a narrow pen drawer, 60½ in. (154 cm.) wide, open. **£3,500-4,000** *C*

A Regency inlaid mahogany sofa table, 35 in. wide. **£4,000-4,500** *GM*

A Regency mahogany sofa table, the top banded in rosewood, 3 ft. 4 in. closed 5 ft. 1 in. open. **£1,400-1,600** *T*

A rare George IV burr-yew wood sofa table, with crossbanded top, 4 ft. 11 in. (150 cm.) wide, open, c. 1825. **£1,000-1,250** *S*

A Regency satinwood sofa table, inlaid with ebonised stringing, 3 ft. 1 in. (94 cm.) wide when closed, c. 1810. **£2,400-2,800** *SS*

A Regency oak and rosewood sofa table, the top inlaid with a broad band, 57¼ in. (145.5 cm.) wide, open. **£3,500-4,000**   *C*

An Anglo-Indian solid teak sofa table, 4 ft. 4 in. (132 cm.) wide, open, c. 1830. **£800-1,000**   *S*

A George IV partridgewood sofa table, the top crossbanded in calamander, 2 ft. 4½ in. high by 4 ft. wide (72.5 by 122 cm.), c. 1820. **£1,800-2,200**   *S*

A fine Regency pollard oak sofa table, with rounded rectangular 2-flap top on spindle-filled trestle ends, the frieze edged with entrelac, 63 in. (160 cm.) wide, open. **£4,500-5,500**   *C*

A late Regency rosewood-veneered sofa table, with crossbanded top, on elegant trestle supports, each with a U on a pair of C scrolls and gilt paw feet, 2 ft. 4 in. high by 5 ft. 2 in. open (71 by 157 cm.), c. 1815. **£5,500-6,000**   *S*

A Regency rosewood sofa table, 5 ft. ½ in. (153.3 cm.) wide, open, c. 1815. **£2,000-2,500**   *S*

A Regency brass-mounted rosewood-veneered sofa table, attributed to John McLean, the top with satinwood crossbanding and with a pair of cedar-lined drawers, the trestle supports and sabre legs inset with ribbed panels of brass, with restoration, 5 ft. 1½ in. (156 cm.) open, c. 1810. **£10,000-£12,500**   *S*

A late Regency rosewood sofa table, 48 in. **£600-800**   *CSK*

A rosewood sofa table, the top with fruitwood stringings, 59 in. (150 cm.) wide. **£800-1,000**   *C*

A Regency rosewood sofa table, the top crossbanded in satinwood and strung in ebony, the 2 drawers with brass inlay and beading. **£10,000-£12,500**   *Wor*

A fine Regency rosewood-veneered sofa and games table, the top crossbanded in burr-yew, the central panel sliding and reversing to form a chess and cribbage board and enclosing a backgammon well, 4 ft. 11 in. (150 cm.) open, c. 1805. **£15,000-18,000**   *S*

A Regency mahogany and rosewood sofa table, 62 in. (157 cm.) wide. **£1,600-2,000**   *C*

A Regency rosewood games and sofa table, inlaid throughout with brass lines and anthemions, the crossbanded top with a central sliding reversible section inlaid with a chessboard and revealing a tooled leather backgammon surface, 28 in. high by 53 in. wide. **£6,000-7,000**   *Bea*

A Regency rosewood sofa table, with crossbanded top, 63 by 27 in. **£800-1,200**   *HyD*

A late Regency mahogany sofa table, 36 in. **£1,000-1,250**   *PWC*

A Regency rosewood and cut brass sofa table, 28 by 57 in. (71 by 145 cm.), extended by 28 in. (71 cm.). **£1,500-1,800**   *SC*

A Regency rosewood sofa table, the top with a wide pollard oak banding, 4 ft. 11 in. (150 cm.) open, c. 1820. **£1,500-1,800**   *S*

A rosewood sofa table, inlaid with brass stringing and with brass mounts, 34 in. wide, 19th C. **£1,000-1,250**   *EG*

A Regency rosewood sofa table, with chamfered rectangular twin-flap top framed by a satinwood band, on solid lyre-shaped supports, inlaid with compass-medallions and splayed legs, 58¾ in. (149 cm.) wide, open. **£1,250-1,500**   *C*

An ormolu-mounted parcel-gilt and rosewood sofa table, 55¼ in. (140.5 cm.) wide, open. **£2,400-£2,800**   *C*

A Regency rosewood sofa table, 59 by 27 in. **£2,500-3,000**   *A*

A Regency rosewood pedestal sofa table, inlaid with cut brass and stringing, distressed, 2 ft. 11½ in. (90 cm.) wide when closed, c. 1810. **£1,200-1,500**   *SS*

A Regency rosewood sofa table, heavily inlaid with brass, with crossbanded top and folding flaps, 4 ft. 9 in. by 2 ft. 4 in. **£6,500-7,500**   *MMB*

A Regency rosewood and cut brass inlaid sofa table, 3 ft. (91.5 cm.) wide, c. 1810. **£1,800-2,200**   *SS*

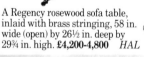

A Regency rosewood sofa table, inlaid with brass stringing, 58 in. wide (open) by 26½ in. deep by 29¾ in. high. **£4,200-4,800**   *HAL*

A George III-style small yew-wood sofa table, 2 ft. (61 cm.) wide when closed, c. 1930. **£350-400**   *SS*

A George I walnut rectangular writing table, the original brass ring handles to real and dummy drawer fronts. **£3,200-3,600**   *DWB*

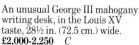

A late Georgian mahogany occasional table, inlaid with ebony stringing, 39 by 33 in. **£300-350**   *M*

An unusual George III mahogany writing desk, in the Louis XV taste, 28½ in. (72.5 cm.) wide. **£2,000-2,250**   *C*

A Charles X satinwood sofa table, inlaid with scrolled lines, stamped Deman, 54 in. (137 cm.) wide open. **£1,500-1,800**   *C*

An unusual George III rectangular mahogany writing table, 56 by 25½ in. **£500-600** *PWC*

Left

A George III painted satinwood lady's writing table, the hinged top banded in mahogany, enclosing a leather-lined flap and compartments, 2 ft. 6 in. high by 4 ft. 8 in. wide (76 by 51 cm.), c. 1775. **£500-600** *S*

An unusual George III mahogany and satinwood draw-leaf writing table, the crossbanded rectangular top with a slide, 49 in. (125 cm.) wide, open. **£1,800-£2,200** *C*

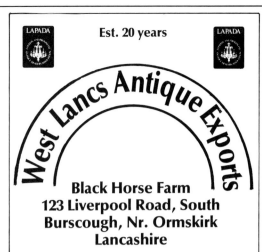

An unusual Regency mahogany writing table, with leather-lined U-shaped top, the frieze with 5 drawers, 91 in. wide by 58 in. deep (230 by 147 cm.). **£12,000-15,000** *C*

A George III mahogany writing table, in the French taste, the crossbanded serpentine top fitted with a baize-lined slide and a drawer on the right, formerly with a rising screen, 26¾ in. wide by 31½ in. high (68 by 80 cm.). **£3,000-£3,500** *C*

A George III rosewood lady's writing table, to a design by Thomas Sheraton, with hinged leather panel enclosed on 3 sides by a low gallery, each side containing a hinged drawer released by a push button, the back with an arched spring-operated fire-screen similarly operated, 3 ft. high by 2 ft. 6 in. wide (92 by 76 cm.), c. 1795. **£3,500-4,200** *S*

A George III oval mahogany lady's writing table, the top crossbanded in satinwood and with a rising fire-screen panel at the back, the frieze with a baize-lined slide and a drawer, 2 ft. 3 in. wide (68 cm.), c. 1785. **£1,500-1,800** *S*

A mahogany writing table, with quarter-veneered top, legs replaced, 2 ft. 6½ in. high by 3 ft. 5 in. wide (77 by 104 cm.), c. 1765. **£4,800-5,500** *S*

Thomas Chippendale's Director illustrates a design for a table of identical form but with slight variations of decoration and handles as plate L1.

A late George III mahogany reading and writing table, 2 ft. 5 in. high by 2 ft. 8 in. wide (74 by 81 cm.), c. 1800. **£1,500-1,800** *S*

A lady's early 19th C. inlaid satinwood and lacewood grained writing table, incorporating a pull-up fire-screen, 22 in. wide. **£2,500-3,000**   *LBP*

A Regency rosewood and brass line inlaid library writing table, in need of restoration, 3 ft. 9 in. wide. **£4,000-4,500**   *GC*

A Sheraton-style mahogany writing table, in the manner of Duncan Phyfe, the hinged top with a later leather inset, with ebony string lines, 23 in. wide, 19th C. **£800-1,200**   *PWC*

A 19th C. French-style walnut-veneered bureau plat, by Edwards and Roberts, banded in kingwood and line inlaid, 4 ft. 4 in. **£1,500-£1,800**   *WW*

A late Regency Irish mahogany writing table, 54 by 27 in. **£2,000-£2,500**   *DWB*

A Regency rosewood double-sided writing table, restored support and replaced leather top, 43½ in. wide. **£1,500-1,800**   *DSH*

A William IV mahogany writing table, with later base, 4 ft. 8 in. by 2 ft. 6 in. **£600-700**   *CDC*

A William IV ebony and maple writing table, 48 in. wide (122 cm.). **£1,600-2,000**   *C*

A Victorian kingwood and marquetry writing table, by Gillow, 106 cm. wide. **£1,000-1,250**   *Bon*

An early 19th C. English walnut-veneered marquetry serpentine writing table, in the French manner, one leg with old worm, 3 ft. **£800-1,000**   *WW*

A Regency rosewood writing table, the top with a hinged flap enclosing inkwells and a pen tray, stamped I. Young, 22¾ in. wide (60.5 cm.). **£2,800-3,200**   *C*

A Gillows mahogany small writing table, with a leather writing surface above a drawer, stamped Gillows Lancaster, 2 ft. 4 in. high (71 cm.), c. 1830. **£900-1,100**   *S*

A mahogany writing table, stamped Gillows Lancaster, the top with unusual 'fiddle' figuring, 5 ft. 2 in. open (157 cm.), c. 1840. **£1,600-2,000**   *S*

An ebonised satinwood-veneered writing table, in the manner of Holland, 3 ft. 6 in. wide (107 cm.), c. 1850. **£1,000-1,250**   *S*

A Victorian inlaid walnut ladies writing desk, with ormolu mount, 42 by 18 by 35 in. high. **£600-700**   *CEC*

A George III-style mahogany library writing table, 33 by 60 by 31 in. (84 by 153 by 79 cm.), early 20th C. **£500-600** *SC*

A Louis XV bois satine bureau plat, with gilt bronze mounts, 2 ft. 6 in. high by 4 ft. 10 in. wide (76 by 147 cm.), mid 18th C. **£4,500-5,000** *S*

An Empire ormolu-mounted mahogany bureau plat, 57 in. wide (144 cm.). **£2,000-2,500** *C*

An Edwardian mahogany surprise writing cabinet, inlaid with satinwood bands and boxwood lines, the top enclosing a leather-lined writing panel and elevating stationery compartment, marked Asprey, London, 26¼ in. **£700-800** *CSK*

A Louis Philippe ormolu-mounted tulipwood bureau plat, 55 in. long (140 cm.). **£1,800-2,200** *C*

An ebonised writing table, the inlaid leather top edged with ormolu beading, mid 19th C. **£250-£300** *BA*

A late Victorian mahogany kneehole writing table, inlaid with satinwood bands and boxwood lines, 48 in. **£450-550** *CSK*

A George III-style mahogany desk, 42 in. **£900-1,100** *CSK*

A fine ormolu-mounted writing table, the crossbanded rectangular top with gadrooned ebonised border, inset with a panel of 17th C. floral marquetry in the style of A. C. Boulle, 53½ in. wide by 29 in. high (136 by 74 cm.), c. 1830. **£5,000-5,500** *C*

A satinwood writing desk, with a leather-lined writing surface and a drawer in the frieze, probably Scottish, 4 ft. high by 2 ft. 11½ in. wide (122 by 90 cm.), c. 1840. **£900-£1,100** *S*

A late 19th C. mahogany writing table, 3 ft. 4 in. by 2 ft. **£700-800** *CoH*

A Louis XV kingwood writing table, stamped Schmitz JME, in quarter-veneered wood, 2 ft. 3½ in. high by 1 ft. 4 in. wide (70 by 41 cm.), c. 1765. **£4,500-5,000**   *S*
Joseph Schmitz, received Master 1761.

An Edwardian satinwood writing table, having inlaid decoration, 48 in. wide. **£1,500-1,800** *A*

A Louis-Philippe kingwood and tulipwood bureau plat, with crossbanded serpentine leather-lined top, with ormolu border and shell angle clasps, 54 in. wide (137 cm.). **£3,200-3,600** *C*

423

A gilt bronze-mounted painted bureau plat, in Louis XV style, 2 ft. 6 in. high by 4 ft. 10 in. wide (76 by 147 cm.), 19th C. **£2,200-2,600** *S*

A Louis-Philippe satinwood and gilt metal bureau plat, crossbanded with harewood, and with gilt metal shaped mounts to the rim, 132 cm. wide. **£1,800-2,200** *HSS*

A mid 19th C. ormolu-mounted marquetry library table, on a walnut ground, with ivory flowers and etched mother-of-pearl butterflies, 47 in. **£1,000-1,250** *GSP*

A Louis XV-style kingwood and tulipwood bureau plat, 89 cm. wide, mid 19th C. **£600-700** *Bon*

A Louis-Philippe serpentine bureau plat, in the Louis XV manner, veneered in kingwood with tulipwood crossbanding, 36¼ in. wide. **£1,000-1,250** *GC*

A gilt bronze-mounted ebonised bureau plat, in Louis XV style, 4 ft. 2 in. wide (127 cm.), late 19th C. **£2,000-2,500** *S*

A gilt metal-mounted mahogany bureau plat, attributed to Henry Dasson, with 2 short drawers on the left and a deep drawer with removable compartment and coffre fort on the right, 2 ft. 5 in. high by 5 ft. 7 in. long (74 by 170 cm.), c. 1880. **£4,500-5,000** *S*

An ormolu-mounted mahogany and kingwood bureau plat, 52 in. wide (132 cm.). **£1,600-2,000** *C*

An ormolu-mounted mahogany bureau plat, in the manner of J. H. Riesener, stamped twice and signed once Henry Dasson 1878, 45½ in. wide (115 cm.). **£7,500-8,500** *C*

A large 18th C. Sheraton mahogany and satinwood oval library table, 72 in. long by 46 in. wide. **£20,000-22,500** *BS*

A Swedish walnut and parquetry bureau plat and serres papiers, inlaid throughout with a parquetry trellis on a rosewood ground, 3 ft. 11 in. high by 4 ft. 2½ in. wide by 2 ft. 3¼ in. deep (119 by 128 by 69 cm.), c. 1790. **£1,500-1,800** *S*

An unusual George III mahogany extending library table, the rectangular cleated top divided into 2 panels outlined with stringing, and with draw leaves, castors missing, 2 ft. 3½ in. high by 3 ft. 4 in. wide, closed (70 by 102 cm.), c. 1790. **£1,500-1,800** *S*

A mahogany drum top table, with 41½ in. diam. top, with restorations, 30 in. high (76 cm.), second quarter of the 19th C. **£800-1,000** *SC*

A Regency mahogany library table, 41 in. wide by 39 in. deep by 29 in. high, c. 1820. **£3,800-4,200** *HAL*

A George III mahogany library table, 43 in. wide (109 cm.). **£2,600-£3,000** *C*

A late Regency burr-oak and parcel-gilt library drum table, in the Grecian taste, 53 in. diam. **£2,000-2,500**   *B*

A George IV mahogany library table, 72 in. diam. (183 cm.). **£3,000-3,500**   *C*

A Regency mahogany library table, the circular revolving surface fitted with an embossed hide, above cockbeaded drawers and dummy drawers, 41 in. diam. by 31 in. high, c. 1820. **£1,700-1,900**   *HAL*

A late Regency rosewood library table. **£800-1,000**   *JD*

An important Regency mahogany library table, the top inset with gilt-tooled green leather, with 4 drawers at the front and back, the drawers and sides faced with bronze anthemion appliques and pairs of metal knob handles, 2 ft. 5 in. high by 6 ft. long by 4 ft. 6 in. deep (75 by 198 by 137 cm.), c. 1820. **£40,000-50,000**   *S*

A fine Regency rosewood library table, with crossbanded top heavily inlaid with a leafy brass border. **£8,000-12,000**   *MMB*

A faded rosewood library table, by Holland & Sons, 4 ft. wide (122 cm.), c. 1835. **£1,800-2,200**   *S*

A small Regency rosewood library table, inlaid with brass stringing and tulipwood crossbanding, 3 ft. wide (91.5 cm.), c. 1810. **£2,000-£2,500**   *S*

A William IV rosewood library table, 4 ft. 6 in. wide (137 cm.), c. 1830. **£900-1,100**   *SS*

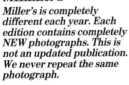

A William IV rosewood library table, 54 by 28 in. **£600-700**   *JD*

A George II gesso side table, with Carrara marble top, and an egg and dart moulding above a frieze, carved with stylised Greek key pattern, 2 ft. 9½ in. high by 5 ft. 1 in. wide (85 by 155 cm.), c. 1740. **£25,000-30,000**   *S*

A William and Mary walnut side table, 40½ in. wide. **£600-700**   *Re*

A Georgian mahogany Irish tray top table, 2 ft. 4 in. long (71 cm.). **£2,200-2,600**   *LBP*

A George II walnut side table, with later top, 54 in. wide (137 cm.). **£2,600-3,000**   *C*

A rosewood library table, with an inset top, leather lacking, 29½ by 57 by 28 in. (75 by 145 by 71 cm.), mid 19th C. **£800-1,000**   *SC*

A George II mahogany side table, the top possibly a late replacement, probably Irish, 50 in. (127 cm.). **£3,000-3,500** *L*

A walnut side table, with crossbanded moulded rectangular top, 28 in. wide (71 cm.). **£1,000-£1,250** *C*

A George II carved mahogany side table, 2 ft. 11½ in. wide (90 cm.), c. 1750. **£1,000-1,250** *SS*

A George II mahogany side table, the top with tin-glazed tiles, later handles, the tiles largely distressed, 28 by 35 in. (71 by 89 cm.), second quarter of the 18th C. **£500-600** *SC*

A pair of George III mahogany and painted elliptical side tables, each with mahogany top, painted decoration renewed, 2 ft. 11 in. high by 4 ft. wide (89 by 122 cm.), c. 1775. **£6,000-7,000** *S*

An 18th C. mahogany side table, 30 in. **£350-450** *O*

A satinwood pier table, 48½ in. wide (123 cm.). **£3,000-3,500** *C*

A George III pier table, with radiating harewood panels from an inlaid satinwood medallion, 54 by 35½ in. high. **£2,800-3,400** *GSP*

An unusual pair of late George III painted coromandel-veneered demi-lune side tables, the tops with penwork scenes from the Iliad, the veneered frieze applied with carved boxwood urns, joined with laurel swags, 2 ft. 10 in. high by 3 ft. ¼ in. wide by 1 ft. 5½ in. deep (86 by 92 by 44.5 cm.), bases c. 1775, tops early 19th C. **£3,200-3,800** *S*

An early George III mahogany small serpentine side table, 3 ft. wide (92 cm.). **£6,000-6,500** *S*

A George III satinwood side table, the top crossbanded with rosewood, the adapted frieze banded with stained fruitwood, 56 in. wide (143.5 cm.). **£3,000-3,500** *C*

A George III satinwood semi-elliptical side table, crossbanded in tulipwood. **£3,800-4,200** *DWB*

A George III satinwood-veneered D-shaped side table, crossbanded in kingwood, the legs joined by a veneered shelf, 2 ft. 8 in. high by 1 ft. 8 in. wide (81 by 51 cm.), c. 1790. **£3,800-4,200** *S*

A pair of George III painted satinwood and giltwood side tables, the white and gilt frieze with a band of paterae-filled roundels, tops distressed, 2 ft. 6½ in. high by 3 ft. 9 in. wide (78 by 114 cm.), c. 1770. **£12,000-15,000** *S*

A George III giltwood side table, with a rectangular verde antico marble top, formerly with feet, marble top later, 2 ft. 11½ in. high by 5 ft. 5 in. wide (90 by 166 cm.), c. 1785. **£2,000-2,500**   *S*

A George III mahogany serving table, with crossbanded top, the drawers outlined in boxwood and ebony, 74 in. wide. **£1,500-1,800** *HyD*

A George III mahogany silver table, 36½ in. wide (93 cm.). **£2,400-2,800**   *C*

A Regency mahogany breakfront serving table, 9 ft. wide. **£1,000-£1,400**   *Re*

A George III inlaid mahogany jardinière or lamp table, 22 in. wide. **£150-200**   *GM*

A George III mahogany side table, 58½ in. wide (148.5 cm.). **£3,800-£4,200**   *C*

A papier-mâché side table, 2 ft. 4½ in. high by 2 ft. 10 in. wide (72.5 by 86.5 cm.), c. 1840. **£450-550**   *S*

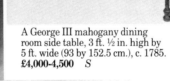

A George III mahogany dining room side table, 3 ft. ½ in. high by 5 ft. wide (93 by 152.5 cm.), c. 1785. **£4,000-4,500**   *S*

An Irish Regency mahogany side table, with Italian specimen marble top, the frieze carved and pierced with various false books, 38 in. wide (96.5 cm.). **£4,500-5,000** *C*

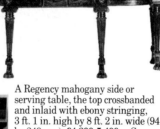

A Dutch marquetry side table, the whole now inlaid with marquetry flowers, 2 ft. 4 in. wide (71 cm.), mid 18th C. **£2,000-2,400**   *S*

A Regency mahogany side or serving table, the top crossbanded and inlaid with ebony stringing, 3 ft. 1 in. high by 8 ft. 2 in. wide (94 by 249 cm.). **£4,800-5,400**   *S*

A William IV mahogany serving table, the bowed centre with concealed drawer, 96½ in. wide by 34 in. deep. **£400-500**   *BHW*

A Moorish walnut side table, 2 ft. 8 in. high by 3 ft. 3 in. wide (81 by 99 cm.), c. 1880. **£900-1,100**   *S*

Moorish Moresque furniture became popular from the 1872 International Exhibition. These pieces are very similar in style to pieces imported from Cairo by Rottman, Strome & Co., c. 1886.

A Dutch walnut, rosewood and floral marquetry side table, 29½ in. wide (79 cm.), early 18th C. **£1,800-£2,200** *C*

A serpentine mahogany dining room side table, probably Scottish, 6 ft. 1 in. wide (185 cm.), late 18th C. **£2,800-3,400** *S*

A Louis XVI tulipwood and fruitwood side table, 21½ in. wide (55 cm.). **£1,200-1,600** *C*

A small Louis XVI D-shaped kingwood-veneered side table, with mottled grey marble top, 2 ft. 9½ in. high by 2 ft. 1 in. wide (85 by 63 cm.), c. 1780. **£800-£1,200** *S*

A William & Mary walnut side table, the surface with unusual crossed leafy inlay, on later turned feet, 31 in. wide by 21 in. deep by 30 in. high, c. 1690. **£2,800-3,200** *HAL*

A French walnut side table, 45 in. wide at rear by 22 in. deep overall, 19th C./20th C. **£500-600** *BHW*

A Victorian rosewood tea table, 37 in. **£700-900** *DWB*

A Victorian rosewood fold-over top tea table, 3 ft. wide. **£450-£550** *PWC*

A Regency rosewood pedestal tea table. **£500-600** *CDC*

A Piedmontese kingwood-veneered side table, with a quarter-veneered quarter-banded top, 2 ft. 8½ in. high by 3 ft. 4½ in. wide (85 by 103 cm.), c. 1760. **£1,500-1,800** *S*

A George III mahogany tea table, with a fold-over top, 29 in. high by 35 in. wide. **£400-500** *Bea*

A Regency mahogany fold-over tea table, 36 in. wide. **£500-600** *M*

An early George II mahogany tea table, the flaps above a well, 30 in. **£300-400** *WW*

A 19th C. mahogany tea table, 28 in. diam. **£350-450** *M*

A William IV rosewood serpentine tea table, 3 ft. **£450-550** *WW*

An early 19th C. mahogany fold-over top tea table, 35 in. **£350-450** *PWC*

A Victorian burr-walnut folding tea table. **£200-250** *GBT*

A Regency mahogany fold-over tea table, crossbanded in rosewood, 34 in. wide. **£1,200-1,500** *GM*

A George III mahogany tea table, inlaid with ebony stringing, 35 in. **£350-450** *GM*

A Regency mahogany fold-over tea table, 37 in. wide. **£600-700** *GM*

A Chippendale-period mahogany tea table, the fold-over top with moulded edging, 35 in. **£800-1,000** *M*

A George III mahogany tea table, some restoration, 28½ in. high by 35 in. wide. **£1,000-1,250** *Bea*

A George III mahogany tea table, with satinwood-veneered frieze, restored, 30 by 40 in. (76 by 102 cm.), third quarter of 18th C. **£450-550** *SC*

A Georgian mahogany half-moon folding-top tea table, 27 in. **£800-€1,000** *JD*

A Sheraton-period mahogany and satinwood crossbanded dressing table, the 2 flap folding-top enclosing a fitted interior, with folding mirror and small compartments, 24¼ in. wide. **£650-£750** *LS*

A George III mahogany tea table, with well-figured semi-elliptical folding top, 39 in. wide (99 cm.). **£1,400-1,600** *C*

The difference between a tea and card table is simply that the flap of the latter is baize or leather inlaid.

A mahogany dressing table, 4 ft. 9½ in. high by 4 ft. wide (146 by 122 cm.), c. 1840. **£900-1,100** *S*

An Irish carved mahogany serpentine tea table, the fold-over top with brass stringing, 3 ft. 1 in. wide (94 cm.), c. 1750. **£2,000-2,500** *SS*

A 19th C. French ebonised brass-mounted curio cabinet, 29 in. high. **£350-450** *GM*

A mahogany kneehole pedestal dressing table, inlaid with geometric boxwood lines, enclosing a fitted interior with bevelled folding triple mirrors, swivel wing trays and glazed panels, labelled Mappin & Webb Ltd., 158,162 Oxford Street, W., 40 in. **£900-1,100** *CSK*

A Dutch walnut and beechwood kneehole poudreuse, inlaid with marquetry and geometric boxwood lines, the top enclosing compartments and a hinged mirror plate, late 18th C. **£600-800** *CSK*

A late Victorian harewood and satinwood banded display table, 76 cm. wide. **£500-600** *Bon*

An inlaid satinwood display table, 2 ft. 7½ in. high by 3 ft. 4 in. wide (79 by 102 cm.), c. 1900. **£1,200-£1,400** *S*

A mahogany specimen cabinet, with gilt metal borders and mounts, late 19th C. **£250-300** *TW*

A 19th C. Empire-style ormolu-mounted mahogany circular specimen table, 21 in. diam., c. 1880. **£850-950** *N*

A satinwood and ebonised display table, stamped Edwards & Roberts, inlaid with stringing and joined by a waved X-stretcher, Irish, 2 ft. 8 in. high by 3 ft. 2 in. wide by 1 ft. 10 in. deep (81 by 97 by 57 cm.), second quarter 19th C. **£700-900** *S*

It is unlikely that this table was made by Edwards & Roberts in London, but was most probably retailed by them at which time the stamp would have been added.

A walnut and floral marquetry tripod table, the tip-up top crossbanded with yew wood, inlaid with a vase of flowers on an ebony ground, 40 in. wide (102 cm.), early 18th C. **£1,500-1,800** *C*

A most unusual bijoutiere, in 17th C. Flemish manner, the framework cover in 18th C. needlework with studding, 25 in. wide by 14 in. deep by 28½ in. high, probably c. 1800. **£450-500** *HAL*

A George III tripod table, the top veneered and crossbanded in partridgewood with a bamboo banding, 2 ft. 4½ in. high by 1 ft. 10 in. wide (72 by 56 cm.), c. 1795. **£1,000-1,250** *S*

A George II mahogany tripod table, the circular top with 'pie-crust' edge and 'bird-cage' support, 2 ft. 4 in. high by 2 ft. 2 in. diam. (70 by 66 cm.), c. 1750. **£3,500-4,000** *S*

A George III mahogany tripod table, damaged and pieces missing, 29 in. diam. (74 cm.). **£600-700** *L*

A small George II mahogany tripod table, the shaped circular dished top on a delicate spirally fluted stem and spirally reeded knop, 1 ft. 9½ in. high by 1 ft. diam. (54 by 30 cm.), c. 1740. **£3,500-4,000** *S*

A George III-style mahogany tripod table, veneered with satinwood reserves, 31 in. (79 cm.), third quarter 19th C. **£350-400** *SC*

A George III mahogany bird-cage snap top table, top diam. 70 cm. **£400-500** *OT*

A mahogany tripod table, with tip-up pie-crust top, open bird-cage, spreading fluted shaft and cabriole base carved with acanthus foliage, 29½ in. diam. (75 cm.). **£1,400-£1,700** *C*

A Georgian mahogany wine table. **£140-180** *TM*

A Georgian mahogany tip-up table, 27½ in. diam. **£250-300** *BHW*

A George III mahogany tripod table, the rectangular tip-up top with waved gallery on fluted shaft, 26 in. wide (66 cm.). **£3,500-4,000** *C*

A mahogany tray top table, on bird-cage support, 27 in. diam., 19th C. **£250-300** *BHW*

A George II mahogany tripod table, the waved circular hinged top now carved and pierced with acanthus and shells, 2 ft. 5½ in. diam. (75 cm.), the table c. 1755, the carving c. 1870. **£350-400** *S*

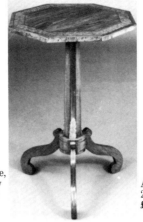

A mahogany tripod table, 2 ft. 7½ in. high, c. 1740. **£800-1,000** *S*

egency black lacquer lamp e, 19¾ in. wide (50 cm.). 00-1,600 *C*

Two japanned and papier-mâché tripod tables, tops cut from Regency trays, 2 ft. 5 in. high. **£800-1,000** *S*

A pair of ormolu-mounted rosewood and pollard oak occasional tables, 19½ in. wide (49 cm.). **£2,000-2,400** *C*

A mahogany tripod wine table, 2 ft. 1¼ in. high, c. 1755. **£2,000-2,500** *S*

A pair of rosewood tables, 3¾ in. wide, c. 1820. 1,400-1,600 *HAL*

A mid-Georgian mahogany tripod table, 28 by 31 in. (71 by 79 cm.), mid 18th C. **£500-700** *SC*

A mid-Georgian walnut tripod table, 26 in. wide. **£1,800-2,000** *C*

A Georgian crossbanded mahogany snap-top occasional table, 27 in. **£2,200-2,500** *JD*

n unusual skull and cross-bones ruitwood tripod table, with etachable top supported on a rame of carved wooden bones, entred by wooden skull inscribed Auri Sacra Fames! Das Florestas e Laurenco Marques J Gomes 6.3.18', 2 ft. 5 in. high by 1 ft. 1½ in. wide (74 by 60 cm.), dated 918. **£850-950** *S*

A rosewood, tulipwood and gilt bronze centre table, the top inlaid with scrolling strap work contained by a gilt border, French, 30 by 25½ in. (76 by 65 cm.), late 19th C. **£250-300** *SC*

A nest of 4 Regency rosewood and satinwood quartetto tables, with crossbanded rectangular tops, 12¼ in., 14¼ in., 16 in., 18 in. wide (31 cm., 36 cm., 41 cm., 46 cm.). **£2,500-3,000** *C*

An unusual set of Regency satinwood and rosewood quartetto tables, the tops differently inlaid with amboyna, rosewood, birds' eye maple and chess squares, the smallest with trough base, from 23 in. to 16¼ in. (60 to 41 cm.). **£4,200-4,600** *C*

A quartetto of tables, the largest 30 by 21¼ in. (76 by 54 cm.), early 19th C. **£750-850** *SC*

A nest of 3 early 19th C. rosewood tables, the largest 21 in. wide. **£450-500** *Re*

A nest of 4 Edwardian satinwood quartetto tables, each with a narrow rosewood band edged with stringing, the largest 19 in. (48 cm.). **£800-1,000** *L*

A set of 4 Victorian black lacquered and papier-mâché occasional tables, decorated with gilt foliate scrolls in mother-of-pearl inlaid borders, 25 in. **£1,000-1,250** *CSK*

A George III mahogany crossbanded and boxwood line inlaid toilet chest, 24 in. **£600-700** *DWB*

A mahogany quartet of tables, 28½ by 19½ in. (72.5 by 49.5 cm.), early 20th C. **£650-750** *SC*

A nest of Regency style mahogany quartetto tables, 1 ft. 9 in. high. **£250-300** *CDC*

A set of 3 George III-style mahogany quartetto tables, 21 in., 19th C. **£180-220** *CSK*

A George III mahogany dressing table, the hinged crossbanded and divided top with a well fitted interior, including a mirror and lidded wells, with a baize-lined brushing slide, 2 ft. 9 in. high by 1 ft. 10 in. wide (84 by 56 cm.), c. 1780. **£2,000-2,400** *S*

A George III mahogany tray top commode, 21¾ in. wide, c. 1790. **£400-500** *WHB*

A pair of satinwood bedside cupboards, with marble tops, 34 in., c. 1840. **£1,400-1,700** *AP*

A Regency mahogany kneehole dressing table, 3 ft. 3½ in. wide (100 cm.), c. 1810. **£1,200-1,500** *SS*

A George III satinwood, fruitwood and faded rosewood dressing table, the divided rectangular top crossbanded with bat's-wing spandrels, enclosing a fitted interior including a mirror slide, 4 lidded compartments, 23½ in. wide (60 cm.). **£1,800-2,200** *C*

A pair of George III mahogany bedside cabinets, each with inlaid surface above single cockbeaded door, 13½ in. wide by 13½ in. deep by 30 in. high, c. 1800. **£1,400-1,800** *HAL*

A pair of rosewood and parquetry bedside cupboards, of Louis XVI style, inlaid with trellis-and-rosette pattern parquetry, 21½ in. wide (55 cm.). **£2,200-2,600** *C*

A Louis XV kingwood, tulipwood and floral marquetry table de toilette, the central flap mirror-backed, the outer 2 enclosing lidded compartments fitted with 6 drawers below a leather-lined slide, 33 in. wide (84 cm.). **£2,200-2,600** *C*

A lady's mahogany dressing table, inlaid with ebony stringing, the lift-up top inset with a bevelled mirror and revealing a silver and blue enamelled toilet service, a swing drawer to each side fitted with matching needlework and manicure set, in all 25 pieces, 34 in. wide, c. 1920. **£1,500-1,800** *M*

A small Louis Philippe ebonised dressing table, the hinged top inlaid in coloured woods, within a banded burr-walnut border, the open rosewood interior with a rectangular mirror, 50 cm. wide. **£250-300** *HSS*

An Edwardian mahogany inlaid 3-piece bedroom suite, comprising: a wardrobe, a dressing table, 47 in. wide, and a bedside cupbord, 15½ in. **£500-600** *DA*

A late George III mahogany serving table, the frieze crossbanded with rosewood, fitted with a tablet-centred drawer, 69 in. wide (175 cm.). **£4,500-5,000** *C*

A 19th C. Continental walnut bedroom suite, comprising: a large double bed, a marble topped chest of drawers, c. 1850. **£1,000-1,500** *WAY*

USE THE INDEX!

Because certain items might fit easily into any of a number of categories, the quickest and surest method of locating any entry is by reference to the fully cross-referenced index at the back of the book. This is particularly true this year when certain sections, e.g. Worcester Porcelain and Oak Furniture have been featured in isolation.

A Victorian oak and cast iron reading bracket and circular table. **£100-120** *BHW*

A pair of ormolu-mounted mahogany tricoteuses, of Louis XVI style, one stamped twice Henry Dasson 1877, 26 in. wide (66 cm.). **£5,000-5,500** *C*

A pair of Louis XV circular tulipwood veneered bedside cupboards, stamped Cosson JME, in quarter veneered wood with green-stained Greek key border, restored, 2 ft. 5½ in. high by 1 ft. 2½ in. wide (75 by 37 cm.), c. 1770. **£10,000-12,000** *S*

Jacques-Laurent Cosson, received Master 1765.

A coffee table, inlaid with oyster veneer, with scalloped tray top, 45 by 27 in. **£250-300** *BHW*

A mahogany specimen table, applied with brass galleries throughout, 48 by 24 in. (122 by 61 cm.), early 20th C. **£380-440** *SC*

A mahogany hunt table, 5 ft. 11½ in. wide (182 cm.), c. 1840. **£1,400-1,800** *S*

A rare rosewood lap table, the rectangular top hinged about a cylinder on a finely moulded column support, 30 by 34 in. extended (76 by 86 cm.), second quarter of the 19th C. **£750-850** *SC*

The unusual hinging about a cylinder has almost doubled the table's value.

A Regency mahogany drinking table, the moulded top with central detachable panel, 76 in. **£1,000-£1,250** *CSK*

An Orme & Son full size billiards table No. 3304, having an oak frame round a 5-piece thick slate bed, with a G.R.P. billiard table shade fitted for electricity, a cotton table cover with embroidered border, a smoothing iron and table brush. **£3,500-4,000** *WIL*

An Orme & Son, Manchester oak billiard marker board, containing an ivory set of billiard and snooker balls. **£280-340** *WIL*

An 8-seater mahogany dining/billiards table, complete with cue stand, cues, balls and scoreboard, 3 ft. high by 9 ft. long by 4 ft. 6 in. wide (90 by 270 by 135 cm.), early 20th C. **£1,500-1,800** *LRG*

A William IV mahogany cue stand. **£550-650** *AMB*

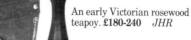

An early Victorian rosewood teapoy. **£180-240** *JHR*

Regency rosewood teapoy, the over with satinwood marquetry, nclosing a fitted interior with four inged caddies and a contemporary ut glass mixing bowl, 17 in. wide y 29 in. high. **£1,500-1,800** *Re*

A Regency mahogany combined cellaret and teapoy, the lid crossbanded in rosewood, the body with ebonised stringing and bosses and containing 6 original stoppered cut-glass bottles, 2 lidded canisters and 2 zinc waste bins, 2 ft. 9 in. high by 1 ft. 6½ in. wide (84 by 47 cm.), c. 1810. **£1,800-2,200** *S*

A George III mahogany teapoy, the crossbanded lifting surface with fitted interior, which still has original tin tea containers and kettle rack with brass handles, 16 in. wide by 11 in. deep by 24½ in. high, c. 1790. **£1,000-1,200** *HAL*

A George II-style mahogany washstand, with a blue printed Wedgwood jug and basin, 36 in. overall (92 cm.), late 19th/early 20th C. **£300-350** *SC*

A mid-Georgian mahogany washstand, with original wash bowl and stopper, 24 in. wide. **£120-160** *GM*

Regency rosewood teapoy. **£200-250** *M*

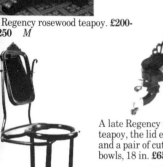

A late Regency rosewood pedestal teapoy, the lid enclosing 4 canisters and a pair of cut-glass mixing bowls, 18 in. **£650-750** *CSK*

An unusual Victorian bentwood ashstand, with swing toilet irror. **£120-150** *Re*

A late George III mahogany whatnot, 5 ft. high by 1 ft. 7 in. wide (153 by 48 cm.), c. 1805. **£3,000-3,400** *S*

An Empire ormolu-mounted burr-maple washstand, fitted for electricity, the moulded Carrara marble top with a frieze drawer, fitted with leather-lined slide, 32½ in. wide (82.5 cm.). **£5,500-6,000** *C*

A late George III mahogany whatnot, 47 by 20½ in. (120 by 52 cm.), early 19th C. **£700-800** *SC*

A Georgian mahogany whatnot, 18 in. **£500-550** *JD*

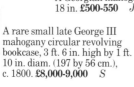

A rare small late George III mahogany circular revolving bookcase, 3 ft. 6 in. high by 1 ft. 10 in. diam. (197 by 56 cm.), c. 1800. **£8,000-9,000** *S*

A late Regency rosewood small 2-tiered stand, 2 ft. 6 in. wide. **£300-350** *MMB*

A 'Georgian' gilt corner hanging whatnot, 5 ft. tall by 27 in. wide. **£420-460** *GR*

A mahogany whatnot, 49 by 20 in. (125 by 51 cm.), second quarter of 19th C. **£380-440** *SC*

A brass inlaid Regency rosewood reading stand, 45 in. high, c. 1810. **£1,400-1,600** *AP*

A Victorian mahogany whatnot, 20 in. **£450-£550** *JD*

A Victorian walnut inlaid corner whatnot, 56 in. high **£300-400** *J?*

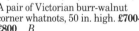

A Victorian rosewood whatnot, stamped 'Charles & Edward', 19 in. wide. **£380-440** *EG*

A pair of Victorian burr-walnut corner whatnots, 50 in. high. **£700-£800** *B*

A Victorian rosewood bow-fron whatnot, 26 in. wide. **£360-400** *EG*

A Victorian walnut music canterbury, inlaid with banding and satinwood stringing, 2 ft. 1 in. wide (64 cm.), c. 1850. **£600-700** *SS*

A Victorian burr-walnut 3-ti whatnot, 31 in. wide. **£250-3(** *TW*

A chinoiserie japanned table, 2 ft. 7½ in. high, 1920's. **£600-700** *S*

MAKE THE MOST OF MILLER'S

CONDITION *is absolutely vital when assessing the value of an antique. Damaged pieces on the whole appreciate much less than perfect examples. However a rare desirable piece may command a high price even when damaged.*

A late 19th C. French rosewood etagère, 16 by 12 in. **£150-200** *BHW*

A 3-tier lacquered whatnot, 33 by 20 in. **£70-100** *WP*

A set of early George III mahogany hanging bookshelves, 3 ft. 2 in. high by 2 ft. 2¼ in. wide (96 by 66.5 cm.), c. 1760. **£1,400-1,600** *S*

An ormolu and calamanderwood 3-tier etagère, 13 in. diam. (33 cm.), 19th C. **£1,500-1,800** *C*

A pair of Charles X mahoga 3-tier etagères, each with ve antico marble top, 23¾ in. w (60 cm.). **£3,800-4,200** *C*

pair of George III sycamore and arquetry hanging shelves, tlined with satinwood and ebony, ½ in. wide by 38½ in. high (62 by cm.). **£3,500-3,800**   *C*

A set of late Georgian style standing mahogany shelves, 27½ by 20½ in. (70 by 52 cm.), second quarter of the 19th C. **£600-700** *SC*

A fine pair of ormolu-mounted bois satine hanging corner shelves, 30 in. high (76 cm.). **£2,200-2,600**   *C*

A pair of 18th C. wine coolers, 70 in. high. **£3,500-4,000** *LT*

A pair of George III mahogany dining room pedestals and urns, each pedestal with a tap with ivory handle, and a door applied with a crossbanded oval, 5 ft. high (153 cm.), c. 1775. **£1,800-2,400** *S*

A George III mahogany cellaret, with a fitted interior, 25 by 21¼ in. (63.5 by 54 cm.), first quarter of the 19th C. **£800-1,000** *SC*

. George III mahogany brass-bound ellaret, the reframed stand on noulded square legs, 26 in. wide 6 cm.). **£2,200-2,600** *C*

A George III mahogany wine cooler, crossbanded in satinwood, 2 ft. 1 in. high by 1 ft. 5½ in. wide (64 by 44 cm.), c. 1775. **£900-1,100** *S*

A George III mahogany octagonal wine cooler, liner lacking, 2 ft. 3 in. high by 1 ft. 9 in. wide (69 by 53.5 cm.), c. 1775. **£1,000-1,250** *S*

George III mahogany brass-bound ine cooler, on later stand, 24 in. ide (61 cm.). **£1,150-1,300** *C*

A William IV mahogany wine cooler, inlaid with ebonised arcading, 1 ft. 4½ in. high by 3 ft. 2 in. wide (42 by 97 cm.), c. 1830. **£3,500-3,800** *S*

A late Georgian mahogany wine cooler, 27½ in. **£700-900** *CSK*

George III mahogany and brass-ound wine cooler, the hinged cover ow with a baize lining and ssociated tray, the tapered square gs with later carved angle rackets, 1 ft. 6 in. wide (46 cm.), 1790. **£800-1,000** *SS*

A George III mahogany campana-shaped wine cooler, 26 in. diam. **£5,000-5,500** *DWB*

A George III oval mahogany cellaret, the stand with outset square legs, with leather castors, 2 ft. 4 in. high by 2 ft. 2 in. wide (71 by 66 cm.), c. 1770. **£2,000-2,400** *S*

An early 19th C. mahogany wine cooler, lid damaged, 27 by 19 in. **£400-500**   *JD*

A George III mahogany wine cooler, the interior with alterations, 2 ft. 3 in. high, 1 ft. 7 in. wide (68.5 by 48 cm.), c. 1770. **£1,000-1,250** *S*

A Regency mahogany and inlaid wine cooler, 31 in. wide. **£800-1,000** *DSH*

A late Regency mahogany sarcophagus wine cooler, outlined in ebony, 31 in. (79 cm.). **£700-900** *L*

A Georgian mahogany cellaret, interior divisions missing, first half 19th C. **£600-700**   *WIL*

A George III mahogany cellaret, slightly raised top crossbanded an enclosing a later galvanised liner 14 by 19 in. (36 by 48 cm.), early 19th C. **£340-380**   *SC*

A mahogany wine cooler, of sarcophagus form, with a crossbanded hinged cover, 19 by 29 in. (48 by 74 cm.), second quarter 19th C. **£700-900**   *SC*

A George IV mahogany cellaret, 2 ft. 1½ in. high by 2 ft. 6 in. wide (65 by 76 cm.), c. 1820. **£550-650** *S*

A Georgian brass-bound mahogany wine cooler, 18 in. **£500-700**   *JD*

A mahogany wine cooler, in George III style, after a design by Robert Adam, 2 ft. 5 in. high by 1 ft. 7½ in. wide (74 by 49.5 cm.), c. 1880. **£1,200-1,500**   *S*

A George III Irish mahogany peat bucket, 21 in. high by 18 in. diam. **£1,300-1,500**   *HyD*

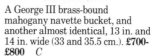

A George III brass-bound mahogany navette bucket, and another almost identical, 13 in. and 14 in. wide (33 and 35.5 cm.). **£700-£800**   *C*

A George III brass-bound mahogany peat bucket, 14 in. h by 13½ in. wide. **£500-600**   *Be*

A George III brass-bound mahogany peat bucket, 15½ in. wide (39 cm.). **£700-800** *C*

A George III mahogany oval peat bucket, with brass liner, 12 in. **£650-750** *DWB*

A George III mahogany peat bucket, 13¾ by 15¼ in. (35 by 38.5 cm.), late 18th C. **£550-650** *SC*

A George III mahogany plate bucket, 13½ by 14¾ in. (34 by 37.5 cm.), late 18th C. **£550-650** *SC*

A pair of George III mahogany plate buckets, 16¼ in. (42 cm.). **£4,000-4,500** *S (WJS)*

A George III mahogany plate bucket, 13 in. high. **£1,400-1,600** *AG*

A pair of George III brass-bound mahogany plate buckets, with lift-out copper liners and brass handles, 12 in. wide (30.5 cm.). **£1,800-2,200** *C*

A pair of leather fire buckets, painted with the Arms of England, against a red ground, swing handles, one with a hole in the bottom, the other stamped L. on base, 11½ in. high (29.2 cm.), 19th C. **£800-1,000** *S*

A leather-covered sedan chair, with hinged top, 5 ft. 3 in. high (160 cm.), late 18th C. **£1,400-£1,700** *S*

A Louis XVI sedan chair, the leather top with brass nails. **£1,500-2,000** *WW*

A late Georgian inlaid mahogany step commode, with liner, 26½ by 17 in. high. **£120-160** *WP*

A late George III mahogany metamorphic library armchair, in the manner of Morgan and Saunders, the chairback released by a brass catch opening to form a set of 4-tread library steps, Irish, 1810. **£2,200-2,600** *S*

A George III mahogany library steps table, 34 in. wide (86 cm.). **£2,200-2,500** *C*

A set of Regency mahogany bedside steps, with leather lined treads, the upper fitted as a commode, 19¼ in. wide (50 cm.). **£2,800-3,400** *C*

A set of late George III mahogany bedside steps, the top tread with a tambour cupboard, the second tread pulling forward to reveal a pot cupboard, 2 ft. 6 in. high by 2 ft. 5 in. wide (76 by 74 cm.), c. 1810. **£1,800-2,200** *S*

A Regency mahogany metamorphic library chair/steps, in the manner of Morgan and Saunders, c. 1820. **£1,800-2,200** *S*

A set of late George III mahogany bedside steps, 1 ft. 11 in. high by 2 ft. long (58.5 by 61 cm.), c. 1800 **£2,200-2,600** *S*

A rare mid-Georgian mahogany pole step ladder, with a typical hinged action, 83 in. (211 cm.), mid 18th C. **£500-600** *SC*

An inlaid rosewood coal purdonium, late 19th C. **£160-200** *BA*

A very rare George II solid walnut baby walker, 18 by 21 in. (46 by 53 cm.), second quarter 18th C. **£3,200-3,600** *SC*

A George I oak pipe-rack, 15½ in. wide by 43 in. high (39 by 109 cm.), dated 1726. **£550-650** *C*

An unusual mahogany library ladder, when closed of tube form, and dividing and opening to form an 8-rung ladder, 107½ by 9½ in. circumference (273 by 24 cm.), early 19th C. **£600-700** *L*

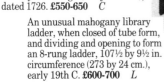

A pair of George III-style yew wood library steps, 45½ in. (115 cm.), 20th C. **£450-500** *SC*

A papier-mâché coal cabinet, inlaid with mother-of-pearl and painted with flowers, the lid painted with a view of Chepstow Castle, 22½ in. high, 20 in. wide, mid 19th C. **£450** **£500** *Bea*

A George I walnut and oak linen press, 31¾ by 73 in. high. **£3,200-£3,600** *DWB*

A jockey scale, English, 46 in. wide (117 cm.), c. 1880. **£350-400** *S*

A Victorian walnut cot, with slatted body, 3 ft. 8 in. long. **£420-£460** *T*

A 19th C. music or reading stand, the fully adjustable stand with candle holder, 11 in. wide by 11 in. deep by 53 in. high, c. 1870. **£350-£400** *HAL*

A South German walnut prie-dieu with a pull-out hinged kneeling section with hinged lid and dummy drawer front, chevron banded throughout and inlaid with scrolls, 3 ft. 1½ in. high by 2 ft. 2 in. wide (95 by 66 cm.), mid 18th C. **£1,400-£1,700** *S*

A parcel-gilt and painted sled, possibly German, 84 in. long (214 cm.). **£900-1,100** *C*

A pair of Venetian painted wood cylindrical cupboards, 31½ in. high. **£300-400** *Re*

A George III mahogany and ivory bird cage, the cornice set with urns, divided by ivory balls above swags, with drapes divided by neo-classical columns and with a spring-loaded panelled front door, the plinth inset with a sliding zinc-lined tray, 2 ft. 5 in. high, the base 1 ft. 4 in. square (74 by 41 cm.), c. 1790. **£8,000-£9,000** *S*

A pair of beechwood urns, on pedestals, 6 ft. 1 in. high, c. 1940. **£700-800** *S*

A pair of Venetian painted figures of monkey footmen, raised on octagonal marbled plinths, 4 ft. 6 in. high (137 cm.), mid 19th C. **£2,800-3,400** *S*

A mahogany dummy board, 18½ in. (123 cm.), last quarter 19th C. **£400-500** *SC*

A Victorian mahogany pot cupboard. **£120-150** *TW*

A rare ebony-veneered, ivory-inlaid fireplace, by Owen Jones, made for Fonthill by Jackson & Graham, 11 ft. high, 6 ft. 8 in. wide (335 by 203 cm.), c. 1867-70. **£15,000-£18,000** *S*

Provenance:
Fonthill House, Wiltshire, by way of Barton Hill House to where it was moved in the latter part of the 19th C. Made for the collector Alfred Morrison (1821-97), heir to Lord Elgin. Morrison added a room to Fonthill to house his fine collection of Chinese porcelain. Owen Jones (1809-74) was one of the earliest designers using Moorish decoration.

An oak fireplace, the overmantel with a coat-of-arms, 7 ft. 11 in. high by 5 ft. 9 in. wide (241 by 175 cm.), the overmantel panel early 17th C., the remainder 19th C. **£2,800-3,400** *S*

A dummy board, 44 in. high (114 cm.), last quarter 19th C. **£500-600** *SC*

A set of 3 gilt chinoiserie decorated, black lacquered papier-mâché tea trays, 18 in.-30¼ in. (45.5 cm.-77 cm.), early 19th C. **£1,400-1,700** *LBP*

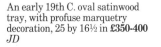

An early 19th C. oval satinwood tray, with profuse marquetry decoration, 25 by 16½ in **£350-400** *JD*

A parcel-gilt bronze and cast-iron Gothic revival fireplace, possibly by E. W. Pugin, 3 ft. 9 in. high by 4 ft. 1 in. wide (114.5 by 155 cm.), c. 1840. **£1,200-1,500** *S*

441

TREEN

The term 'Treen' is used to describe any small wooden object associated with domestic, professional, trade or agricultural life and is a word not usually associated with any object larger than a spinning wheel. More usually treen objects are lathe-turned and are not those made by the cabinet-maker or joiner. Decoration may take a number of forms, carving, poker-work, inlay and, in the case of some Scandinavian objects, painting. Treen collectors fall into two groups. The antique dealers who have always appreciated these small pieces as a complement to their stock and who have enjoyed them for their colour, interest value and as light relief from cabinet furniture. The second group is a small but dedicated band of collectors, many of whom have furnished their homes and have quenched their thirst for collecting with what, until recently, were reasonably cheap objects with an interesting history and background.

In common with other subjects Treen has its well-known collectors, perhaps the best known is the late E. H. Pinto who, with his wife, assembled one of the largest and most comprehensive collections ever made. His enthusiastic researches into Treen and illustrations from his collection formed the basis of what remains the standard work on the subject, 'Treen and Other Wooden Bygones'. The majority of his collection was purchased by the Birmingham City Art Gallery and is on display there. Owen Evan-Thomas, although a dealer, did much the same on a smaller scale with his fascinating book 'Domestic Utensils in Wood'. Bert Isher, a West Country dealer, made a collection of treen which, when sold during the '70's, set new record prices. More recently, the W. J. Shepherd Collection of over 1,600 items was sold by Sotheby's in December 1983 and realised over £200,000. The interest in the Shepherd sale was such that the well-illustrated catalogue sold out before the sale actually took place. However, many of the illustrations from that sale form the sections on Treen in this book.

For the beginner, Treen collecting offers a reasonably inexpensive subject with many areas to choose from in which to specialise. At the lower end of the market, sewing and needle-work-related items as well as Tunbridgeware and Souvenirware are worth following. Specialist dealers in Treen do exist but they will normally stock only the rare and expensive: general antique shops can often prove a good hunting ground for Treen. Specialised auction sales devoted to Treen rarely take place but furniture sales may have a few pieces tucked away and the house sale will always have the odd cardboard box of bits that must be inspected.

The already devoted collector will be all too well aware of the frustrating scarcity and expense of fine examples with the early pieces as well as smoking- and drinking-related objects already well into four figures. For the dedicated collector research into the subject will always be very much a part of the enjoyment and most collectors will want to compile a catalogue of their collection with notes of similar pieces in reference books and museums. Many pieces from the established collections retain the catalogue labels, often printed with the owner's name as a refinement. These labels will always create confidence as well as value and interest to the devotees.

by Graham Child, Sotheby's.

A 19th C. brass and mahogany pill board, with graduated scale from 6 to 24, with shaped handle, 33 cm. long. **£120-150** *S (WJS)*

These boards were used by apothecaries for the manufacture of tablets on a small scale.

An 18th C. lignum vitae searce, the turned moulded circular body with removable threaded turned foot, the centre of the bowl fitted with a fine brass mesh, 12 cm. diam., early 18th C. **£100-130** *S (WJS)*

A searce is a sieve used by apothecaries for sieving powder used in pill-making, after the crystals have been crushed by pestle and mortar.

A lignum vitae pestle and mortar, mortar 23 cm. high, pestle 41 cm. long, c. 1680. **£400-450** *S (WJS)*

A 19th C. mahogany stethoscope, lathe-turned and inscribed with the initials RIE RMH GCT, 17 cm. **£150-180** *S (WJS)*

A 19th C. turned mahogany salve container, of acorn form, with tapered lid and turned finial, 10 cm. high. **£65-75** *S (WJS)*

A beechwood and iron body massager, with turned wood handle, the iron work embossed ROLEO and fitted with 14 turned beechwood rollers, 14 cm. long. **£120-150** *S (WJS)*

An early 18th C. elmwood mortar and pestle, mortar 17 cm. high, pestle 24 cm. long, c. 1700. **£150-£200** *S (WJS)*

A 19th C. turned beechwood dentist's drill tip holder, 14 cm. high, c. 1890. **£100-130** *S (WJS)*

There is a tremendous interest amongst dentists for any piece of treen associated with their profession.

A lignum vitae pestle and mortar, the mortar carved with a band of guilloche and a wide band of acanthus leaves, divided by a band of moulding, dated 1660, mortar 24 cm. high, pestle 36 cm. long, mortar late 17th C., carved at a later date. **£500-550** *S (WJS)*

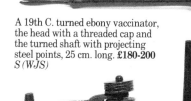

A 19th C. turned ebony vaccinator, the head with a threaded cap and the turned shaft with projecting steel points, 25 cm. long. **£180-200** *S (WJS)*

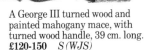

A mid 19th C. boxwood pill silverer, with threaded lid and turned foot, 9 cm. high. **£100-120** *S (WJS)*

c.f. Pinto, Treen, plate 8, figure H. After the pills had been formed and had dried, they were moistened with mucilage of accia and mixed with silver leaf. The container was shaken in a rotary motion until the pills were evenly coated with silver.

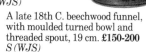

A turned rosewood body massager, with turned shaft, fitted with 3 ring turned massaging wheels, 16 cm. **£120-150** *S (WJS)*

A late 18th C. beechwood funnel, with moulded turned bowl and threaded spout, 19 cm. **£150-200** *S (WJS)*

With the Owen Evan-Thomas collection number 886. c.f. Owen Evan-Thomas, Domestic Utensils of Wood of the XVI-XIX Century, plate 61.

A mid 19th C. brass and mahogany travelling scale set, with turned brass weighing bowls, contained within a moulded mahogany box with a fitted drawer, drawer 24 cm. wide, c. 1840. **£65-70** *S (WJS)*

A boxwood and lignum vitae sand glass, with circular turned moulded ends, 8 cm. high. **£35-45** *S (WJS)*

A pair of 19th C. mahogany coaching dials, 31 cm. diam. **£650-£700** *S (WJS)*

Coaching dials, usually in pairs, to indicate the times of departure of the passenger and mail coaches. Similar example c.f. Pinto, Treen, pl. 295.

A boxwood eyesight tester, with graduated scale and brass disc, the end fitted with a turned eye-piece and lens, 31 cm. **£120-160** *S (WJS)*

A 19th C. ceremonial axe, of the Gardeners Friendly Society, the blade painted with crossed shovel, fork and rake, 60 cm. **£260-300** *S (WJS)*

A George III turned wood and painted mahogany mace, with turned wood handle, 39 cm. long. **£120-150** *S (WJS)*

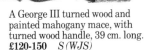

A pair of George III beechwood maces, with turned handles and painted rectangular panels, 64 cm. long. **£140-180** *S (WJS)*

A late 19th C. oak mason's presentation tamper, made from part of the Long Chamber and carved with a coat-of-arms, 18 cm. **£45-55** *S (WJS)*

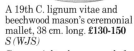

A Victorian turned painted beechwood policeman's truncheon, 43 cm. long. **£100-130** *S (WJS)*

n 18th C. mahogany apothecary's avelling chest, by Louttit of ondon, with 4 glass jars with oxwood lids, a pair of scales, a wter pestle, weights, with 14 ass jars with ground stoppers, 38 25 cm. **£1,000-1,200** *S (WJS)*

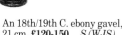

An 18th/19th C. ebony gavel, 21 cm. **£120-150** *S (WJS)*

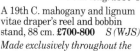

A 19th C. lignum vitae and beechwood mason's ceremonial mallet, 38 cm. long. **£130-150** *S (WJS)*

Ceremonial tools were made for presentation to nobilities invited to lay foundation stones of buildings and vary in use and decoration.

An ebony and silver-mounted presentation gavel, the head with an engraved silver mount, dated 25 March 1776, 21 cm. **£200-250** *S (WJS)*

A 17th/18th C. yew wood gavel, with spirally-turned handle and chip carved head, possibly Welsh, 23 cm. long. **£350-400** *S (WJS)*

An early 19th C. walnut ballot box, the lid with hinged section and screw locking device, 26 cm. long. **£130-160** *S (WJS)*

A 19th C. mahogany and lignum vitae draper's reel and bobbin stand, 88 cm. **£700-800** *S (WJS)*

Made exclusively throughout the 19th C. for use in homes and shops. Known as bobbin trees in Yorkshire.

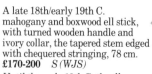

A late 18th/early 19th C. mahogany and boxwood ell stick, with turned wooden handle and ivory collar, the tapered stem edged with chequered stringing, 78 cm. **£170-200** *S (WJS)*

Until the early 19th C. the ell was a common measure for cloth on the Continent; in England it was officially 1¼ yds.; in Scotland 37.2 in.

An early 19th C. beechwood tally stick, 59 cm. long. **£140-160** *S (WJS)*

This tally stick was reputedly saved from the furnace by Webb and given to his nephew.
The burning of these tally sticks started the fire that caused the destruction of The Houses of Parliament in 1834. Tally sticks were used in most European countries as a simple method of recording transactions. Until 1824, tallies were officially used in England in The Courts of The Exchequer for making receipts of monies paid to and by officials.

A 19th C. oak and brass half meter measure, dated 1820 and stamped JRD, 62 cm. long. **£40-50** *S (WJS)*

A pair of 19th C. beechwood draper's yardsticks, painted with leaves, flowers and fans and with turned handles, 104 cm. long. **£200-£250** *S (WJS)*

An 18th C. oak ballot box, 18 cm. high by 20 cm. wide. **£200-250** *S (WJS)*

An early 19th C. travelling compass, inscribed December 19th 1817, 6 cm. diam. **£180-200** *S (WJS)*

A late 17th/18th C. numismatist's scales, in etched beechwood box, possibly Dutch, 9 cm. long. **£60-80** *S (WJS)*

A 19th C. half pint measure, branded E. R. 4. LCC, 8 cm. **£45-55** *S (WJS)*

A late 18th/early 19th C. ash boat tiller, 79 cm. long. **£160-200** *S (WJS)*

(*l.*) A set of late 18th C. brass sovereign scales, in mahogany case, by A. Wilkinson of Ormskirk, late of Kirby (near Liverpool), 14 cm. **£90-110** *S (WJS)*

During the second half of the 17th C. and during the 18th C. gold coins were worth more than their face value, so the exchange rate against silver coins was decided by weight. Similar examples c.f. Owen Evan-Thomas, 'Domestic Utensils of Wood', plate 67, figs. H, I and J.

(*r.*) An early 18th C. travelling sundial, in boxwood case, dated 1751, 6 cm. long. **£180-220** *S (WJS)*

A 19th C. dual ship's watch glass, contained in a pollard ash frame, 25 cm. high. **£400-500** *S (WJS)*

A late 18th C. mahogany fid, with carved Turk's head handle and pointed shaft, 54 cm. long. **£400-£450** *S (WJS)*

Fids were used to open the strands of a rope for splicing; when made in metal they are called marlin spikes.

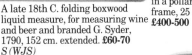

A late 18th C. folding boxwood liquid measure, for measuring wine and beer and branded G. Syder, 1790, 152 cm. extended. **£60-70** *S (WJS)*

An 18th/19th C. pearwood double measure of turned cup form with waist moulding, 9 cm. high. **£55-65** *S (WJS)*

An 18th/19th C. articulated artist's lay model, 97 cm. high. **£2,000-2,200** *S (WJS)*

An 18th/19th C. walnut measure, of plain turned cylindrical form, with copper bands inscribed County of Southampton, 19 cm. **£150-175** *S (WJS)*

Often found in sets; used by Weights and Measures Department of Borough Councils.

An 18th C. boxwood shoemaker's measure, the upstand carved as a buckled boot, 39 cm. **£210-250** *S (WJS)*

A 19th C. ash double measure of turned cylindrical form, with ringed decoration, the exterior branded, 19 cm. high. **£75-85** *S (WJS)*

An early 19th C. mahogany waywiser, by J. Bennett, London, the silvered dial calibrated for yards, poles, miles and furlongs, and with a turned pole handle, 129 cm. long. **£500-600** *S (WJS)*

Waywisers were used for measuring distances and were essentially the work of a cabinet-maker and a clock or mathematical instrument maker, the latter's name engraved on the dial which is arranged upside down so the person pushing could read the distance in yards, or links, poles, chains, furlongs and miles.

An 18th C. oak and metal bound brickmaker's mould, 32 by 14 cm. **£20-30** *S (WJS)*

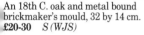

A pair of beechwood hop shoes, with leather straps and ridged soles, 31 cm. long. **£50-70** *S (WJS)*

A mid 19th C. mahogany miniature tripod table, 19 cm. high, 24 cm. diam., c. 1840. **£210-250** *S (WJS)*

A 19th C. steel and boxwood ceremonial sickle, chip-carved handle incised 1881, formerly with bells in a leather collar to the handle, 64 cm. **£70-80** *S (WJS)*

A 19th C. beechwood rattle for bird scaring, with turned wooden handle, 26 cm. long. **£50-70** *S (WJS)*

Rattles were used for bird scaring, often the task of a child, as a fire alarm, or in the case of an emergency.

A 19th C. beechwood and pine berrypicker, 26 cm. long. **£65-75** *S (WJS)*

An 18th/19th C. ashwood sheep or goat's collar, of bentwood form, with locking piece and gouge-carved decoration, 17 cm. **£60-70** *S (WJS)*

An 18th/19th C. yew wood wimbel, 41 cm. long. **£300-350** *S (WJS)*

Wimbels, also known as wimbrels, twisters, thraacrooks, throwhooks, were used for twisting ropes out of straw, used for binding corn stooks, making haystacks or for thatching.

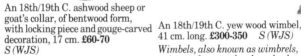

A 19th C. beechwood honing stone carrier, of pencil form, 26 cm. long. **£30-35** *S (WJS)*

Similar examples Pinto, pl. 85, figs. F. G. and H. described as Swiss.

A 19th C. mahogany whip and boot jack, 100 cm. **£120-150** *S (WJS)*

An early 19th C. mahogany boot jack, 85 cm. high. **£260-300** *S (WJS)*

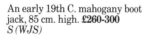

A 17th C. Welsh hawthorn basting stick handle, the bowl carved E. Hanna Thornton, November 26, 1667, 72 cm. long. **£600-700** *S (WJS)*

An 18th C. beechwood Negus strainer, 21 cm. long. **£200-250** *S (WJS)*

With the Owen Evan-Thomas collection label number 642.

An 18th C. ladle, with pewter bowl and turned wood handle, 31 cm. long. **£70-80** *S (WJS)*

A 16th/17th C. elm double sided platter, of square form with a salt sinking to each side and with shaped pierced handle, 24 cm. long. **£500-550** *S (WJS)*

c.f. Pinto, Treen, pl. 84 for similar example.

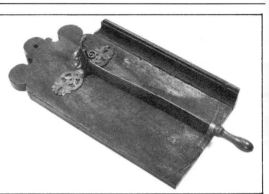

A 17th C. French walnut saladier, the steel cutter with an iron fixing plate and turned handle, 81 cm. long. **£400-500** *S (WJS)*

With the Owen Evan-Thomas collection number 926.
A saladier, used in most Western European countries in apothecaries shops for cutting roots into manageable sizes, prior to grinding and in the kitchen for preparing vegetables.
c.f. Pinto, Treen, illustrates a similar example, pl 134, figure b.

A 19th C. brass and ebonised pastry marker, the cruciform head with rotating wheel, 21 cm. long. **£50-60** *S (WJS)*

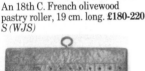

An 18th C. mahogany rolling pin, with pewter handles, 46 cm. long. **£200-250** *S (WJS)*

An 18th C. yew wood citrus fruit squeezer, with arrow head and turned threaded handle, 15 cm. long. **£120-140** *S (WJS)*

An 18th C. French olivewood pastry roller, 19 cm. long. **£180-220** *S (WJS)*

A 19th C. steel and beechwood meat cleaver, 28 cm. long. **£55-65** *S (WJS)*

An 18th C. beechwood basting spoon, 34 cm. long. **£30-40** *S (WJS)*

A 17th C. leather covered oak laundry tally board, pierced with holes within squares and with a list of articles to be laundered, 23 by 20 cm. **£500-550** *S (WJS)*

A 17th C. oak and brass laundry tally, the face with 10 dials engraved with the articles to be laundered and revolving discs numbered 1-12. **£1,000-1,200** *S (WJS)*

Formerly in the collection of the Rev. C. J. Sharp.
c.f. Pinto, Treen, illustrated plate 310.

A 19th C. Scandinavian beechwood washing bat, with shade-shaped blade, chip carved with initials and dated 1842, 38 cm. **£280-340** *S (WJS)*

A 17th/18th C. Scandinavian beechwood washing bat, 31 cm. long. **£200-250** *S (WJS)*

Washing bats were originally used for washing clothes in streams; the items of clothing were placed on stones or rocks and beaten with a bat.

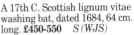

A 17th C. Scottish lignum vitae washing bat, dated 1684, 64 cm. long. **£450-550** *S (WJS)*

A 17th C. English oak mangling board, the front chip carved with roundels, within a zig-zag border, with a cartouche carved with berries and supported by dolphins, dated 1673 and with initials, 64 cm. **£500-600** *S (WJS)*

Mangling boards were made in Europe and particularly in Scandinavia and Friesland. Wet clothes were placed around a roller which was moved backwards and forwards on a flat surface using downwards pressure.

An early 19th C. Scandinavian painted and carved boxwood mangling board, the handle in the form of a horse, dated 1814, 69 cm. **£500-600** *S (WJS)*

Scandinavian mangling boards were made during the long winter months as a home industry. They were richly carved and often painted and hung up inside, when not in use, as a decoration; displayed outside as an indication that the washing was all in.

An 18th/19th C. beechwood washing bat, 54 cm. long. **£500-600** *S (WJS)*

The elaborate carving with the use of a heart might indicate that this was given as a love token.

446

A late 17th/early 18th C. oak and silver-mounted pencil case, German, 16 cm. long **£220-300** S (WJS)

Owen Evan-Thomas, Domestic Utensils of Wood, illustrated plate V, and Owen Evan-Thomas catalogue, figure V, plate 68.

An early 19th C. magnifying glass, with turned mahogany handle contained within a case inlaid with ebony stringing and with split turned tapered handle, 20 cm. long. **£320-400** S (WJS)

An 18th C. small oak box mangle, the mangle boards fitted with 2 lidded compartments for stones and with turning handle, 61 cm. high, 55 cm. wide. **£1,400-1,600** S (WJS)

Full size box mangles were considerably larger, often some 7 ft. or 8 ft. in length, and when the compartments were filled with stones, had a weight of nearly a ton. This small example might have been made for a child, or as a device for small items of clothing.

An 18th C. lignum vitae pounce pot, the circular dished threaded lid pierced with rows of concentric piercing, 11 by 9 cm. diam. **£220-£300** S (WJS)

Pounce was originally used to scour and degrease skins, i.e. vellum or parchment, before writing and was made from powdered cuttle fish or pumice, mixed with Sandarach resin. Later used to dry the ink and when mixed with magnesia mica to give a frosted effect.

A 19th C. beechwood and ebonised desk ink set, 19 cm. long. **£70-90** S (WJS)

A 19th C. lignum vitae inkwell, carved in the form of a boxer dog, the hinged head containing a pottery ink reservoir, 13 cm. high. **£750-850** S (WJS)

An early 19th C. burr yew wood quill stand, the top with 3 apertures and a turned body, 9 cm. **£80-100** S (WJS)

An 18th C. applewood pounce pot, with turned dished threaded lid, 9 cm. high, 7 cm. diam. **£100-150** S (WJS)

A George III mahogany house letter box, 18 cm. wide. **£140-180** S (WJS)

Formerly in the possession of Sir George Airy, Astronomer Royal, who lived at Playford House, Suffolk.
Letter boxes of openwork form were made in order that the staff may see if mail is to be collected without opening the box.

A late 17th C. lignum vitae pounce pot, 4 cm. high by 7 cm. diam. **£250-£300** S (WJS)

A 19th C. lignum vitae paper weight, 14 cm. **£270-300** S (WJS)

An early 19th C. mahogany paper weight, carved in the form of a clenched fist, 14 cm. **£130-160** S (WJS)

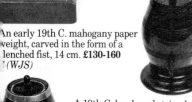

A 19th C. hardwood string box, 13 cm. high. **£70-90** S (WJS)

A 19th C. hardwood string box, 11 cm. **£120-140** S (WJS)

An early 19th C. rosewood letter rack, 13 by 23 cm. **£180-220** S (WJS)

A 19th C. lignum vitae double string box, with finial fitted with a blade, 29 cm. high. **£250-300** S (WJS)

447

A 19th C. lignum vitae string box, 13 cm. high. **£65-85** *S (WJS)*

A 19th C. lignum vitae string box, 18 cm. high. **£200-250** *S (WJS)*

A rosewood jewellery box, 18 cm. wide. **£90-110** *S (WJS)*

A late 17th C. walnut door letter box, 25 cm. wide. **£260-300** *S (WJS)*

A 19th C. lignum vitae string box, 10 cm. high. **£80-90** *S (WJS)*

A rosewood stationery casket of wedge form, with 4 interior divisions, the whole with 'Berlin woolwork' border, 17 cm. wide. **£110-150** *S (WJS)*

c.f. Edward H. and Eva R. Pinto, Tunbridge, plate 12.

A rosewood games box, with a fitted interior containing a cribbage board and cards, the top and cavetto sides banded with 'Berlin woolwork', 27 cm. wide. **£180-220** *S (WJS)*

An ebony inkstand, inlaid throughout with floral mosaic, the top with 3 lidded compartments, fitted with ivory handles, 28 cm. wide. **£250-300** *S (WJS)*

Pinto collection label MT 28.

An early 19th C. Regency work basket and cover, with a maplewood banding, the sides with a Vandyke border, 21 cm. wide. **£220-260** *S (WJS)*

A rosewood visiting card tray, the everted rim 'Berlin woolwork' and mosaic border, the central panel inlaid in cube parquetry, 27 cm. wide. **£200-250** *S (WJS)*

A Regency period book trough, veneered in pollarded oak, with a maple band inlaid pollarded oak tulips, ebony line inlay, 12 in. **£600-650** *WW*

A rosewood writing slope, with sloping double lidded top, the interior fitted with compartments and inkwells, 31 cm. wide. **£250-£300** *S (WJS)*

c.f. Edward H. and Eva R. Pinto, Tunbridge and Scottish Souvenir Woodwork, plate 26.

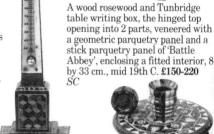

A wood rosewood and Tunbridge table writing box, the hinged top opening into 2 parts, veneered with a geometric parquetry panel and a stick parquetry panel of 'Battle Abbey', enclosing a fitted interior, 8 by 33 cm., mid 19th C. **£150-220** *SC*

A thermometer stand, by H. Hollanby, with ivory gauge, the rosewood and mosaic plinth on bun feet, 12 cm. high. **£110-130** *S (WJS)*

A rosewood book tray, 38 cm. wide. **£280-320** *S (WJS)*

A Cleopatra's Needle thermometer stand, with cube pattern and mosaic inlay throughout, the thermometer mounted on an ivory calibrated tablet, 20 cm. high. **£110-130** *S (WJS)*

c.f. Edward M. and Eva R. Pinto, Tunbridge, plate 12.

A miniature chamber candlestick, the mahogany base inlaid with an end grain mosaic panel, 5 cm. high. **£70-90** *S (WJS)*

stickware and mosaic ring stand,
m. **£95-105** *S (WJS)*

1 18th C. oak offertory box,
ssibly Scottish, 25 cm. long.
5-60 *S (WJS)*

*1166, Henry II ordered that
unks should be placed in all
rish churches to collect offerings
· the relief of the Holy Land. In
rly Christian times, the boxes
·re opened on Christmas Day and
e contents, known as the 'dole of
e Christmas box', were distributed
· the priest on Boxing Day.*

1 18th C. turned oak offertory
ay, 30 cm. diam. **£95-105**
(WJS)

1 18th C. mahogany offertory
ay, 20 cm. wide. **£250-300**
(WJS)

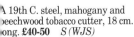

An early 19th C. mahogany and
rass shepherd's crook, 127 cm.
550-650 *S (WJS)*

*Possible alternative use by a butler
o pull down a chandelier to
xtinguish the candles.*

1 19th C. steel, mahogany and
beechwood tobacco cutter, 18 cm.
ong. **£40-50** *S (WJS)*

*Tobacco was imported in cake or
plug form to be cut into saleable
quantities by the retailer.*

An 18th C. 12-sided offertory plate,
30 cm. wide. **£150-180** *S (WJS)*

*Reputedly from a Bristol church
distressed during the Second World
War.*

A 17th C. oak offertory tray, of
turned circular form, formerly with
a metal liner, 31 cm. diam. **£80-120**
S (WJS)

An 18th C. beechwood inlaid
offertory box, 20 cm. long. **£65-85**
S (WJS)

A 19th C. olivewood scroll pointer,
with carved ivory hand-turned
shaft centred by a ball, 26 cm. long.
£250-300 *S (WJS)*

*Pointers of this type are used by a
Rabbi or Synagogue official to
follow the lines when reading from
the Holy Scrolls.*

An 18th/19th C. mahogany choir
master's pitch pipe, 32 cm. long.
£150-180 *S (WJS)*

*Pitch pipes were used in churches
that had no organ.*

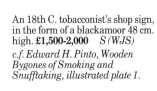

A 19th C. brass, steel and
beechwood tobacco cutter, 36 cm.
£30-40 *S (WJS)*

A mahogany and rosewood watch
stand, the hoop supported on
baluster pillars with stickware
collars, 17 cm. high. **£85-105**
S (WJS)

A 17th/18th C. pine, beech and
ashwood sermon glass, the sand
filled double bowl within chip
carved uprights, 24 cm. high. **£550-
£650** *S (WJS)*

An 18th C. oak prayer bookcase, in
the form of a book carved with
scrolls and strapwork, the side with
wooden pin locking mechanism,
dated 1773, with sliding lid, 11 cm.
long. **£200-250** *S (WJS)*

An 18th C. tobacconist's shop sign,
in the form of a blackamoor 48 cm.
high. **£1,500-2,000** *S (WJS)*

*c.f. Edward H. Pinto, Wooden
Bygones of Smoking and
Snufftaking, illustrated plate 1.*

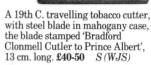

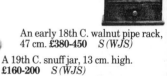

An 18th/19th C. Dutch tobacco box, of coopered construction, in ebony, walnut and boxwood, with brass bands, 12 cm. high. **£220-260** *S (WJS)*

A late 18th C. mahogany church warden's pipe rack, with 2 divisions, 68 cm. long. **£550-650** *S (WJS)*

c.f. Pinto, plate 363.

A 19th C. travelling tobacco cutter, with steel blade in mahogany case, the blade stamped 'Bradford Clonmell Cutler to Prince Albert', 13 cm. long. **£40-50** *S (WJS)*

An early 18th C. walnut pipe rack, 47 cm. **£380-450** *S (WJS)*

A 19th C. snuff jar, 13 cm. high. **£160-200** *S (WJS)*

An early 19th C. mahogany and ebonised tobacco jar, the interior lead-lined and with lead weighted lid, 15 cm. high. **£180-240** *S (WJS)*

An early 18th C. silver-mounted yew wood snuff jar, 15 cm. high. **£500-600** *S (WJS)*

A 19th C. olivewood tobacco barrel, 11 cm. high. **£130-170** *S (WJS)*

An 18th/19th C. lignum vitae tobacco jar, 14 cm. high. **£180-220** *S (WJS)*

An early 19th C. yew wood tobacco jar, 12 cm. high. **£280-320** *S (WJS)*

An 18th/19th C. mahogany church warden's pipe rack, inlaid with satin birch lozenges and with brass mounted tray and ball feet, 44 cm. high. **£170-220** *S (WJS)*

An 18th C. oak tobacco jar, the interior fitted with a pottery liner, 28 cm. high. **£220-300** *S (WJS)*

A 19th C. rosewood and mahogany tobacco jar, 16 cm. high. **£400-450** *S (WJS)*

An 18th C. lignum vitae tobacco jar, 32 cm. high. **£600-700** *S (WJS)*

An 18th C. oak tobacco jar, the interior tin-lined, 19 cm. high. **£250-300** *S (WJS)*

An early 19th C. lignum vitae tobacconist's counter snuff urn on stand, 55 cm. high. **£700-800** *S (WJS)*

An early 19th C. rosewood tobacco jar, the lid with dished snuff container, 20 cm. high. **£450-500** *S (WJS)*

An early 19th C. mahogany tobacco jar, the lid fitted with a snuff container, the interior lined with foil, 26 cm. high. **£300-350** *S (WJS)*

An 18th/19th C. lignum vitae tobacco jar, the interior fitted with a conforming weight, 26 cm. high. **£400-450** *S (WJS)*

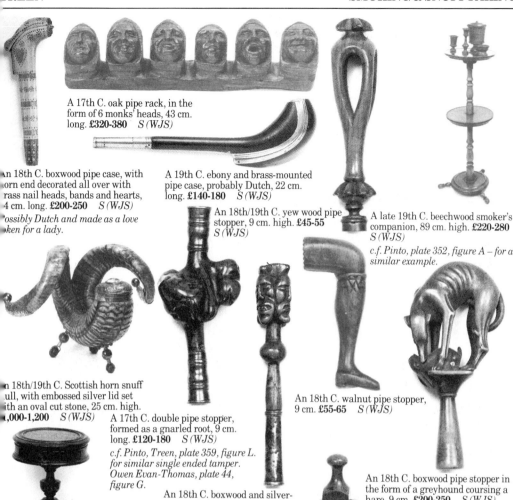

A 17th C. oak pipe rack, in the form of 6 monks' heads, 43 cm. long. **£320-380** *S (WJS)*

An 18th C. boxwood pipe case, with horn end decorated all over with brass nail heads, bands and hearts, 24 cm. long. **£200-250** *S (WJS)*

Possibly Dutch and made as a love token for a lady.

A 19th C. ebony and brass-mounted pipe case, probably Dutch, 22 cm. long. **£140-180** *S (WJS)*

An 18th/19th C. yew wood pipe stopper, 9 cm. high. **£45-55** *S (WJS)*

A late 19th C. beechwood smoker's companion, 89 cm. high. **£220-280** *S (WJS)*

c.f. Pinto, plate 352, figure A – for a similar example.

An 18th/19th C. Scottish horn snuff mull, with embossed silver lid set with an oval cut stone, 25 cm. high. **£1,000-1,200** *S (WJS)*

A 17th C. double pipe stopper, formed as a gnarled root, 9 cm. long. **£120-180** *S (WJS)*

c.f. Pinto, Treen, plate 359, figure L. for similar single ended tamper. Owen Evan-Thomas, plate 44, figure G.

An 18th C. boxwood and silver-mounted pipe stopper, 9 cm. **£220-£300** *S (WJS)*

An 18th C. walnut pipe stopper, 9 cm. **£55-65** *S (WJS)*

An 18th C. boxwood pipe stopper in the form of a greyhound coursing a hare, 9 cm. **£200-250** *S (WJS)*

c.f. Pinto, Treen, plate 258, figs. H. & J. for similar examples.

A 19th C. mahogany tobacconist's tobacco press, 20 cm. high. **£50-60** *S (WJS)*

19th C. tobacconist's counter snuff box, the turned moulded lid inlaid with the initials M Mc C on a satinwood ground, 16 cm. high. **£130-150** *S (WJS)*

An 18th C. yew wood tobacconist's counter snuff box, 9 cm. diam. **£110-130** *S (WJS)*

An 18th C. walnut tobacconist's counter snuff box, 13 cm. diam. **£120-160** *S (WJS)*

17th C. Italian walnut and ivory inlaid snuff rasp case, the sides inlaid with bands of ivory and the front and back inlaid with ivory, boxwood and ebony and with brass lidded snuff spoon to one end, containing the rasp, 9 cm. **£400-500** *(WJS)*

An early 19th C. French burr maple snuff box, signed Montagny F., the interior tortoiseshell-lined, 9 cm. diam. **£300-350** *S (WJS)*

During the first quarter of the 19th C. French snuff box makers developed a method of impressing a design on to burr timbers, usually maple. The impression, made with a die stamp, was improved by hand carving, and the interior lined with ivory or tortoiseshell.

An 18th C. French boxwood snuff rasp case, of flat tapered form, carved with the order of St. Espirit (a star, the sun, the moon, fleur de lys) and the date 1740, 20 cm. long. **£250-300** *S (WJS)*

An 18th C. horn and silver-mounted snuff mull, the lid set with a silver-mounted onyx panel and fitted with 3 silver and 1 boxwood snuff tools, 12 cm. long. **£500-600** *S (WJS)*

An 18th C. French walnut snuff rasp case, 18 cm. long. **£160-200** *S (WJS)*

An early 19th C. French burr maple snuff box, the lid impressed with the busts of Voltaire and Rousseau, 9 cm. diam. **£130-180** *S (WJS)*

(1) An early 19th C. walnut parquetry and piquet work boot snuff box, 10 cm. long. **£125-145**

(2) An early 19th C. mahogany snuff box, 11 cm. **£110-140**

(3) A 19th C. yew wood snuff box, 13 cm. long. **£130-150**

(4) An early 19th C. mahogany ebonised snuff box, in the form of a three-buttoned boot, with piquet worked lid, 9 cm. **£280-320**

(5) A late 18th C. boxwood snuff box, with silver buckle, the hinged lid with a silver thumbpiece and plaque engraved J.W., 11 cm. **£270-£310** *S (WJS)*

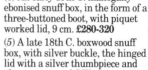

An 18th C. burr walnut snuff box, lined with tortoiseshell, the lid inlaid with an oval ebony panel, 13 cm. long. **£160-200**   *S (WJS)*

c.f. Pinto, Treen, plate 366, figure H, for similar example.

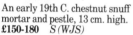

An early 19th C. coquilla nut snuff box, 9 cm. **£70-90**   *S (WJS)*

A coquilla nut snuff box, 8 cm. long. **£55-65**   *S (WJS)*

A 19th C. burr wood snuff box, lined with tortoiseshell, 16 cm. long. **£90-110**   *S (WJS)*

An early 19th C. chestnut snuff mortar and pestle, 13 cm. high. **£150-180**   *S (WJS)*

An early 19th C. trick snuff box, in the form of an engine-turned decorated ball, 6 cm. diam. **£55-65** *S (WJS)*

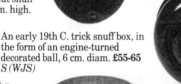

A 19th C. ebony screw top snuff box, with ivory centre stud, 8 cm. diam. **£70-80**   *S (WJS)*

An 18th/19th C. Scandinavian burr wood snuff box, with copper spout and brass ring and leather loop, 8 cm. diam. **£180-220**   *S (WJS)*

A 19th C. snuff box, inlaid in various woods and with reeded sides, 11 cm. long. **£55-65** *S (WJS)*

A 17th/18th C. burr maple wood brass-mounted snuff flask, with turned spout and threaded pipe tamper stopper, Scandinavian, 12 cm. diam. **£350-400**   *S (WJS)*

c.f. Owen Evan-Thomas, Domestic Utensils of Wood, plate 62.

A wood and bone snuff box, with the initials RB and the date 1704 and the motto It is a friend to whom I lend, 10 cm. long. **£1,200-£1,300**   *S (WJS)*

c.f. Owen Evan-Thomas, Domestic Utensils of Wood, plate 38, for similar examples.

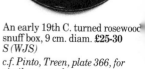

A 19th C. burr wood snuff box, 10 cm. long. **£160-190**   *S (WJS)*

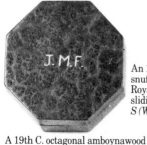
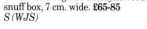

A 19th C. beechwood snuff box, 8 cm. diam. **£85-95**   *S (WJS)*

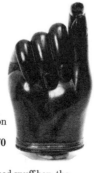

An 18th C. oak bellows-shaped snuff box, with nailed decoration Royal George Sunk 1782, with sliding back, 13 cm. long. **£60-70** *S (WJS)*

A 19th C. octagonal amboynawood snuff box, 7 cm. wide. **£65-85** *S (WJS)*

An 18th C. yew wood snuff box, the silver-mounted hinged lid inscribed Queen Mary's Yew, 12 cm. **£650-£750**   *S (WJS)*

An early 19th C. turned rosewood snuff box, 9 cm. diam. **£25-30** *S (WJS)*

c.f. Pinto, Treen, plate 366, for similar examples.

A 17th/18th C. green stained burr wood tobacco box, 14 cm. diam. **£380-440** *S (WJS)*

A 19th C. beechwood snuff box, the finger and thumb holding a pinch of snuff, 9 cm. high. **£350-450** *S (WJS)*

c.f. Pinto, Treen, plate 367, figures Q and R, for similar examples.

A 19th C. snuff box, formed from naturalistic burr maple, 14 cm. long. **£250-300** *S (WJS)*

An early 19th C. coquilla nut snuff box, possibly Dutch or German, 9 cm. **£55-65** *S (WJS)*

c.f. Pinto, Treen, plate 368, for similar examples.

An early 19th C. coquilla nut snuff box, possibly Dutch or German, 10 cm. high. **£250-300** *S (WJS)*

Coquillas are the nuts of the Attelea Funifera, a palm known in Brazil as the Piassaba. The trees thrive in the swampy ground on the eastern side of South America.
B. Seeman, in his Popular History of Palms and their Allies, published in 1856 records 'The nuts of the Pissaba are an article of commerce, long brought to England under the name of Coquillas'.

An early 19th C. coquilla nut snuff box, in the form of a standing priest, possibly Dutch or German, 9 cm. high. **£450-500** *S (WJS)*

An early 19th C. coquilla nut snuff box, in the form of a seated baboon, possibly Dutch or German, 9 cm. **£130-160** *S (WJS)*

A French cigar humidor dispenser, with kingwood veneered doors and brass mounts, 25 cm. high, c. 1880. **£90-110** *S (WJS)*

An early 19th C. coquilla nut snuff box, in the form of a dwarf, possibly Dutch or German, 8 cm. **£100-120** *S (WJS)*

An early 19th C. coquilla nut snuff box, in the form of a hunchback, possibly Dutch or German, 9 cm. **£200-250** *S (WJS)*

A 19th C. rosewood cigar humidor and dispenser, with turned finial which activates the opening mechanism to display cigars in brass holders, 25 cm. high. **£250-£300** *S (WJS)*

(t.l. and r.) A pair of late 19th C. turned yew wood standing cups, 19 cm. high. **£220-280**

(t.c.) An 18th C. lignum vitae spice cup, with turned threaded lid and acorn finial, 19 cm. high. **£220-280**

(b.l.) A late 17th C. lignum vitae goblet, with engine-turned body, ring-turned stem and engine-turned foot, 14 cm. high. **£80-120**

Retaining the Owen Evan-Thomas label, catalogue number 488.

(b.r.) A 19th C. yew wood goblet, 14 cm. high. **£150-180** *S (WJS)*

A 17th C. pearwood goblet, the turned bowl decorated with pokerwork peacocks, divided by scrolled hearts and within bands of linking scrolls, 20 cm. high. **£3,000-£4,000** *S (WJS)*

An 18th C. coconut tumbler, carved with laurel bordered ovals, with a crest and the initials JSC, 10 cm. high. **£130-160** *S (WJS)*

A pair of 17th/18th C. macassar ebony wine goblets, 11 cm. high. **£350-400** *S (WJS)*

An 18th C. coconut tumbler, 10 cm. high. **£35-45** *S (WJS)*

An 18th C. coconut christening flask, carved with flowers and an urn, and the name DI LETSOME PEERS, BORN AUGUST 19th 1755, 11 cm. long. **£95-105** *S (WJS)*

An 18th C. nut goblet, with moulded shaped silver rim, on baluster-turned lignum vitae stem and turned silver-mounted foot, 16 cm. high. **£450-550** *S (WJS)*

An 18th C. pearwood goblet, the tapered bowl with ring-turned decoration and shaped silver mount decoration, 17 cm. high. **£450-550** *S (WJS)*

A coconut cup and cover, 19 cm., early 19th C. **£65-75** *SC*

An 18th C. pearwood goblet, the base branded W.R., 20 cm. high. **£300-400** *S (WJS)*

A 17th C. Scandinavian horse-head kasa, in painted birch, bearing indistinct date, 38 cm. wide. **£1,600-1,900** *S (WJS)*

The 'horse-head' kasa has its origins in the pre-historic ritual of the Sacrificial Horse cult. Most extant dated examples are 18th C. being hollowed out from a solid block of birch. The much larger honed variety of kasa evolved from peasant drinking festivals when it was contested who could empty the vessel at the fewest draughts. c.f. Pinto, Treen, plate 47.

An 18th C. mulberry wood goblet, 16 cm. high. **£500-£600** *S (WJS)*

A horse-head kasa, in painted birch and with the name Knud Johannessen Leiken 1862, 36 cm. wide. **£950-1,050** *S (WJS)*

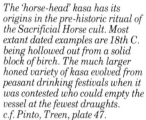

(*l.*) A Norwegian polychrome burr wood kasa, the outside of the bowl painted in blue, the rim with inscription, the inside painted red with a foliate design in yellow, white and black, 32 cm. across, c. 1831. **£750-850**

(*c.*) A Norwegian birchwood kasa, 32.4 cm. wide overall, 19th C. **£650-£750**

(*r.*) A Norwegian polychrome wood kasa, in the form of a dragon, brightly painted with flowers in red, yellow, green, black and white against a dark blue ground, 40.6 cm. wide overall, second half 19th C. **£300-400** *S*

A 17th C. yew wood octagonal lidded tankard, possibly Scottish, 19 cm. high. **£600-700** *S (WJS)*

A 17th C. lamhog in willow, the handle in the form of a canine creature with long tail, 19 cm. high. **£260-300** *S (WJS)*

In contrast to metters, lamhogs or piggins are circular and taper to a flared base. They were shaped and hollowed from a single block of wood varying enormously in size and capacity. Their decoration normally consisted of two incised horizontal bands but sometimes they were engraved with the Gaelic 'Céad mile fáilte' meaning 'A hundred thousand welcomes'.

A Norwegian polychrome wood kasa, the exterior painted with a running band of S-decoration in cream, red and black, possibly Hardanger, slightly distressed condition, 40.6 cm. over handles, 18th C. **£700-900** *S*

A 17th C. Irish lamhog, in willow, 18 cm. high. **£350-400** *S (WJS)*

Retaining Evan-Thomas collection label ref. 915.

An 18th C. Scandinavian birchwood peg tankard, 20 cm. high. **£600-700**   *S (WJS)*

An 18th C. burr birch Scandinavian peg tankard, 23 cm. high. **£500-600** *S (WJS)*

An 18th C. Scottish cog, of coopered construction, in walnut and beechwood, with 10 willow bands, 8 cm. wide. **£250-300**   *S (WJS)*

A 17th C. lignum vitae small wassail bowl or loving cup, 17 cm. high, 15 cm. diam. **£450-500** *S (WJS)*

The words 'waes-hael', 'was-haile' or 'wass-heil' have all passed into our language as 'wassail'. Wassailing is a term used to describe community drinking, usually associated with festive occasions.
Recipes vary according to local customs. Good ale, or in some cases, wine were the basis to which sugar, cloves and cardamoms were added, together with a small roasted apple for each drinker. Egg white was also added to produce a froth, giving rise to the name 'lamb's-wool'.

(1) A Norwegian polychrome stavework pitcher, painted with flowers in yellow, white, green and blue against a red ground, probably Hallingdal, 37.5 cm. high, 19th C. **£300-400**

See Hauglid, Native Art of Norway, p. 101, for another very similar.

(2) A Norwegian polychrome stavework pitcher, painted dark greenish black and red, 37 cm. high, late 18th/early 19th C. **£400-£500**

(3) A Norwegian stavework pitcher, 43.2 cm. high, early 19th C. **£480-560**

(4) A Norwegian stavework pitcher, painted a dark greenish black, with geometric punched decoration, 37.5 cm. high, early 19th C. **£380-460**   *S*

A 17th/18th C. lignum vitae two-handled quaich, with silver-mounted handles and willow banding, 14 cm. wide. **£200-250** *S (WJS)*

A late 17th C. lignum vitae wassail bowl, 9¼ in. high. **£500-600**   *Bea*

A 17th C. lignum vitae wassail bowl, 31 cm. high. **£1,600-2,000** *S (WJS)*

A mid 17th C. lignum vitae wassail bowl of 4¾ gallon capacity, 34 cm. high, 34 cm. diam. **£4,500-5,500**   *S (WJS)*

With the Owen Evan-Thomas collection label no. 464.

An 18th C. Scandinavian peg tankard, in birchwood, the cover centred by raised and gilded decoration, 27 cm. high. **£2,100-£2,600**   *S (WJS)*

Mediaeval tankards were capacious by today's standards, often holding as much as two quarts. Drunkenness was an obvious effect of such large drinking vessels and in order to resolve this problem King Edgar introduced the peg or pin tankard. It was decreed that cups set with pins or pegs at certain levels should be provided and that anyone drinking past the level of one peg at a single draught was liable to forfeit one penny, half of which would be retained by the accuser, the other half being given to the town in which the offence was committed. The aforementioned practice has made its mark on the English language for the expression 'have a peg' is in common use today.

An 18th C. bicker, of coopered construction, with extended stave handles, 13 cm. wide. **£120-150** *S (WJS)*

A 17th C. lignum vitae wassail bowl or loving cup, 18 cm. high, 14 cm. diam. **£380-480**   *S (WJS)*

A late 17th C. lignum vitae monteith, 25 cm. high, 31 cm. diam. **£4,500-5,500** *S (WJS)*

Monteith bowl was a communal cooler for drinking glasses, allowing the drinking vessels to hang in cool water by the foot, the term monteith is reputed to have come from a fantastical Scot, Monsieur Monteigh who wore the bottom of his cloak or coat notched. The majority of monteith bowls were made in silver and it is rare to find such a piece in wood. Pinto suggests that 'try-outs' were made in wood before being attempted in silver or earthenware.

A George III mahogany coaster, 48 by 20 cm. **£950-1,050** *S (WJS)*

A George III mahogany beer barrel coaster, with brass bound coopered barrel and tap, 47 cm. high by 58 cm. wide. **£1,600-2,000** *S (WJS)*

An 18th C. sycamore punch ladle, the triple twist stem terminating in the form of a dog's head, 38 cm. long. **£400-450** *S (WJS)*

Owen Evan-Thomas collection number 286.

A 17th C. lignum vitae wassail bowl and cover, the engine-turned moulded lid with turned finial and spice well, the interior fitted with a set of 3 graduated lignum vitae dippers similarly turned, 24 cm. high. **£4,200-5,000** *S (WJS)*

A pair of 19th C. mahogany brass-bound travelling flasks, of coopered construction, 14 cm. long. **£280-360** *S (WJS)*

A 19th C. pilgrim bottle, inscribed FREDERICK CARLSSON Obverse: LIFE IS A PAIN THE POET SAYS BUT THAT I DENY — CAN SORROW FROM THE GOBLET FLOW OF PAIN FROM BEAUTY'S EYES. DRAW THE CORK AND FILL YOUR GLASS MAKE YOURSELF WELCOME WHILE IT LASTS. FRANCIS FOSTER, dated 1821, 43 cm. high. **£480-560** *S (WJS)*

A 17th/18th C. lignum vitae coffee mill, the finial with later cap for nutmeg and the base containing the handle, 21 cm. high. **£250-300** *S (WJS)*

An early 18th C. lignum vitae coffee mill, 24 cm. high. **£500-600** *S (WJS)*

Two 18th C. oak costrel, with iron bands and iron loop handle, one branded JA, 18 cm. long. **£85-95** *S (WJS)*

Probably of Welsh origin.

An 18th/19th C. light and dark oak coopered costrel, bound with osier hoops and with a cork bung, 15 cm. long. **£35-45** *S (WJS)*

A pair of 18th C. beer coasters, the shaped pine bases within inscribed brass galleries, 51 cm. long. **£4,800-£5,500** *S (WJS)*

Beer coasters of this type for use in servants' halls and taverns were designed for use on dining tables and normally follow a figure of 8 pattern. The larger end would have accommodated the bombard and the smaller end a series of blackjacks, tankards or mugs.

A George III mahogany table bottle coaster, together with 4 contemporary bottles bearing original labels, SHERRY, BITTERS, WHISKY, CLOVE, 48 cm. wide. **£2,200-2,500** *S (WJS)*

An 18th C. beechwood ladle, with quadruple twist stem carved in the shape of a fish grasping a scrolling leaf as the bowl rest, 33 cm. long. **£200-260** *S (WJS)*

MAKE THE MOST OF MILLER'S

When a large specialist well-publicised collection comes on the market, it tends to increase prices. Immediately after this, prices can fall slightly due to the main buyers having large stocks and the market being 'flooded'. This is usually temporary and does not affect very high quality items.

An early 19th C. coffee mill, in brass and mahogany, on bun feet, 32 cm. high. **£250-300** *S (WJS)*

An 18th C. mahogany bottle crane, 56 cm. high. **£300-400** *S (WJS)* *c.f. Pinto, Treen, plate 49K.*

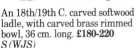

An 18th/19th C. carved softwood ladle, with carved brass rimmed bowl, 36 cm. long. **£180-220** *S (WJS)*

An 18th/19th C. yew wood nutcracker, 15 cm. long. **£250-300** *S (WJS)*

An 18th/19th C. walnut nutcracker, 19 cm. **£120-160** *S (WJS)*

A 17th/18th C. boxwood nutcracker, 15 cm. long. **£280-360** *S (WJS)*

An 18th C. French fruitwood nutcracker of lever form, 21 cm. long. **£450-500** *S (WJS)*

A late 18th C. wood figure of a sailor, his mouth operating as a nutcracker, painted in polychrome, on wood base, 9½ in. high. **£65-75** *WHL*

A 19th C. walnut nutcracker of screw type, 21 cm. **£95-105** *S (WJS)*

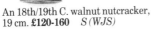

An 18th C. oak stay busk, carved with a heart and the date AD 1751 beneath the initials MH and RW on reverse. **£280-360** *S (WJS)*

The verb 'to busk' means to dress or to attire. A busk is a wood or bone stiffener for inserting in the corset or corsage. Highly carved and decorated stay busks were made as love tokens and worn or carried in little pockets in the fronts of bodices.

An 18th C. yew wood double love spoon, 23 cm. long. **£400-500** *S (WJS)*

An 18th/19th C. beechwood love spoon, 25 cm. long. **£520-600** *S (WJS)*

An 18th/19th C. love spoon, 25 cm. long. **£250-300** *S (WJS)*

An 18th C. sycamore love spoon, 28 cm. **£180-220** *S (WJS)*

An 18th C. walnut stay busk, chip carved with the initials AR 1779. **£150-190** *S (WJS)*

An 18th/19th C. Carnaervon boxwood love spoon, 19 cm. **£120-£150** *S (WJS)*

An 18th C. beechwood stay busk, 29 cm. long. **£130-180** *S (WJS)*

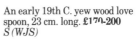

An early 19th C. yew wood love spoon, 23 cm. long. **£170-200** *S (WJS)*

A 19th C. oak double love spoon, dated 1876, 13 cm. long. **£160-190** *S (WJS)*

An early 16th C. double-sided boxwood comb, 17 by 12 cm., c. 1500. **£1,200-1,500**   *S (WJS)*

c.f. Pinto, Treen or Small Woodware Through the Ages, plate 2, and Treen and Other Wooden Bygones, plate 382, illustrates a similar example.

A 19th C. rosewood and boxwood egg cup stand, in boxwood and rosewood, and centred by a turned boxwood and rosewood spire handle with ivory finial, 24 cm. **£850-950** *S (WJS)*

A mahogany two division sliding cheese coaster, on brass castors, 17½ in., c. 1800. **£350-400**   *GM*

(*l.*) A pair of Georgian mahogany and brass wheel bellows, 31 in. **£180-220**

(*r.*) A pair of Georgian mahogany and brass wheel bellows, 22 in. **£130-180**   *PWC*

A 19th C. mahogany egg cup stand, 19 cm. high. **£450-500**   *S (WJS)*

An 18th/19th C. mahogany cat, with 6 turned spindles and revolving turned centre, 36 cm. high. **£75-95**   *S (WJS)*

c.f. Macquoid, Dictionary of English Furniture, revised edition, page 220, figures 1 and 2.
A cat, a tripod rest of turned wood or metal, used to support plates or a dish to be warmed by the fireplace. Pinto describes them as work basket stands. The term cat may derive from the position next to the fire or the way in which it falls on its feet.

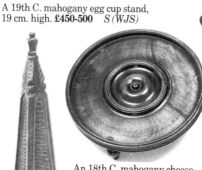

An 18th C. mahogany cheese board, 21 cm. diam. **£160-200** *S (WJS)*

A late 18th C. mahogany cheese coaster, 43 cm. long. **£600-700** *S (WJS)*

An early 19th C. mahogany cheese board, raised on 3 brass and leather castors, 25 cm. diam. **£280-320** *S (WJS)*

A 17th/18th C. French walnut nutmeg grater, 23 cm. high. **£800-£900**   *S (WJS)*

With the Owen Evan-Thomas collection label no. 141.
Inscribed in ink 'From the Bragge Collection'.
c.f. Evan-Thomas, Domestic Utensils of Wood, illustrated page 91, plate 35, fig. A.

An 18th C. mahogany cheese board, 23 cm. diam. **£210-270** *S (WJS)*

An 18th C. boxwood cheese scoop, 13 cm. **£60-£80**   *S (WJS)*

An early 18th C. boxwood cheese scoop, dated 1710, with the initials W.P., 13 cm. long. **£280-320** *S (WJS)*

Cheese scoops, also called spitters or scuppits, were used for eating apples as well as cheese.

A mid 18th C. boxwood cheese scoop, with turned knop and pierced handle fitted with 2 balls and dated 1754, with plain tapered scoop, 18 cm. **£160-200**   *S (WJS)*

A boxwood and bone cheese scoop, dated 1772, 14 cm. **£170-200** *S (WJS)*

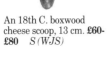

An 18th C. cheese scoop, with rosewood turned handle and tapered scoop, 13 cm. **£75-85** *S (WJS)*

A late 17th C. walnut spice box, the rectangular stepped lid moulded and fitted with a spoon drawer, the sliding front parquetry veneered and crossbanded, enclosing an arrangement of 8 small crossbanded drawers with brass handles, 23 cm. high by 23 cm. wide. **£600-650** *S (WJS)*

A pair of 18th C. beechwood spice jars, possibly Scottish, 14 cm. **£500-£600** *S (WJS)*

An 18th C. spice box, the interior with 4 divisions, 13 cm. high. **£160-£190** *S (WJS)*

An early 19th C. rosewood pepper mill, with turned acorn finial, 20 cm. **£150-180** *S (WJS)*

Similar example, Owen Evan-Thomas, Domestic Utensils of Wood, plate 31 and 33.

An early 18th C. brass and chestnut pepper mill, with cylindrical brass top, 18 cm. high. **£450-500** *S (WJS)*

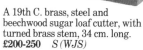

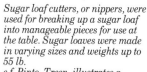

A 19th C. brass, steel and beechwood sugar loaf cutter, with turned brass stem, 34 cm. long. **£200-250** *S (WJS)*

Sugar loaf cutters, or nippers, were used for breaking up a sugar loaf into manageable pieces for use at the table. Sugar loaves were made in varying sizes and weights up to 55 lb.
c.f. Pinto, Treen, illustrates a similar example, plate 139, figure 9.

An early 19th C. octagonal mahogany spice box, decorated with basketwork and mouldings, 22 cm. wide. **£380-460** *S (WJS)*

A pair of late 18th C. oak and silver salt shakers, 18 cm. **£220-280** *S (WJS)*

An early 16th C. sycamore spice grinder, the top bowl fitted with a pierced sieve, with polychrome decoration. **£2,200-2,600** *S (WJS)*

Similar examples were recovered from the Mary Rose.

An 18th/19th C. mahogany salt, 7 cm. **£80-90** *S (WJS)*

A pair of 18th/19th C. fruitwood salts. **£70-90** *S (WJS)*

An 18th/19th C. beechwood pepper pot, 15 cm. **£110-150** *S (WJS)*

An early 19th C. coquilla nut nutmeg grater, in 2 sections, 15 cm. **£190-240** *S (WJS)*

An early 17th C. hardwood and ivory castor, 15 cm. high. **£370-430** *S (WJS)*

A 19th C. mahogany brass and marble menu holder, with steel and brass spring jaws, on octagonal marble and mahogany base, 24 cm. high. **£35-45** *S (WJS)*

A late 18th C. mahogany urn and cover, with acorn finial, ovoid body, probably a duck egg cup, 15 cm. high. **£140-180** *S (WJS)*

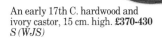

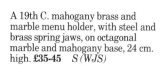

An 18th/19th C. beechwood pap boat, with leaf carved body and scrolling moulded handle, possibly Scandinavian, 12 cm. **£250-300** *S (WJS)*

Pap boats were used for artificial feeding of invalids and babies, examples are also found in horn and silver.

Two 18th C. burr ash spice flasks, both 24 cm. high. **£950-1,050** *S (WJS)*

A pair of 18th C. mahogany dish slopes, 19 cm. **£400-450** *S (WJS)*

Slopes were used for tilting a plate for the diner to enjoy the gravy from a plate that had no well.
Pinto, Treen, illustrates similar examples, plate 62, figures N, O and P.
Also Treen and Other Wooden Bygones by Jane Toller, plate 7.

An 18th C. walnut double ended spoon box, 19 cm. long. **£95-105**
S (WJS)

An early 18th C. walnut baby walker, with iron bandings and fastening with ball-turned supports to a flat stretcher, raised on brass castors, 70 cm. wide. **£900-1,000**
S (WJS)

A number of devices were made to contain the toddler; this type encouraged walking.

An early 19th C. mahogany watch stand, 24 cm. wide. **£70-100**
S (WJS)

An 18th C. squirrel cage, for use in conjunction with a spit, the cage inlaid with lozenges, boxwood and ebony stringing, to the left a double cage divided by a drawer with a further drawer beneath, and to the right a circular tread mill above a drawer, 58 cm. high by 48 cm. wide. **£250-350** *S (WJS)*

A set of 12 early 17th C. sycamore roundels, contained within a turned beechwood box, each roundel centred by a verse, the box 18 cm. diam. **£2,600-3,000**
S (WJS)

Roundels were placed before each guest at the end of a banquet with the plain side upwards and were used for cheese and confections. After Grace the roundels were reversed and each verse sung or recited by the guests in turn as roundelays to the accompaniment of a lute.

c.f. Pinto, Treen, plate 77 illustrates similar examples.

An 18th C. Dutch oak foot warmer, 28 cm. wide. **£180-220** *S (WJS)*

Foot warmers, which were made in metal as well as wood, date from the 18th to 19th C. Most of the earliest surviving examples are Dutch or Scandinavian and appear in oval, circular or square form. Foot warmers were often intricately carved and mounted with brass carrying handles which enabled them to be hung up as household ornaments when not in use. The heat source was provided by either a charcoal pan or hot water container inserted into the warmer itself. Their portable nature enabled them to be used in churches and carriages as well as the home.
c.f. Pinto, Treen, plate 126.

An 18th C. mahogany salt box, 26 cm. wide. **£320-400** *S (WJS)*

A George III mahogany tripod stand, terminating in a clenched fist grasping a turned pole, 85 cm. high. **£1,400-1,800** *S (WJS)*

Possibly used for the display of cravats.

An 18th C. mahogany adjustable knee rest, with turned adjustable collar, the tripod base fitted with a screw thread and turned handle, 34 cm. **£260-300** *S (WJS)*

Possibly used as a chin support to secure the head for eye inspection or testing.

A pair of 19th C. chestnut and yew wood dressing table candlestands, 23 cm. wide. **£260-300** *S (WJS)*

A 19th C. fruitwood lacemaker's lamp, with shaded glass bowl, 19 cm. high. **£150-200** *S (WJS)*

When the glass bulb was filled with water it acted as a simple lens for the candlelight.

A 19th C. mahogany lacemaker's
lamp stand, 18 cm. high. **£65-75**
S (WJS)

A 19th C. Scandinavian oak and
beechwood taper box, 32 cm. long.
£700-800   *S (WJS)*

An 18th C. flintlock tinder lighter,
with a mahogany grip, 22 cm. long.
£280-360   *S (WJS)*

An 18th C. amboyna turned spill
vase, 13 cm. high, and a 19th C.
mahogany ring turned spill vase,
13 cm. high. **£320-380**   *S (WJS)*

A pair of 19th C. rosewood
adjustable candlestands. **£500-600**
DWB

A pair of early 19th C. mahogany
night light sconces, 26 cm. high.
£220-300   *S (WJS)*

A pair of 18th C. pearwood
candlesticks, 13 cm. high. **£220-**
£280   *S (WJS)*

A pair of early 19th C. rosewood
table candlesticks, 23 cm. high.
£450-500   *S (WJS)*

A pair of George III mahogany
candlesticks, with brass classical
urn-shaped sconces, 37 cm. high.
£500-600   *S (WJS)*

An early 18th C. wrought iron rush
light nip, on a turned stepped yew
wood base, 24 cm. high, together
with an 18th C. oak rush light nip,
14 cm. high. **£300-350**   *S (WJS)*

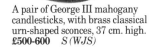

A pair of macassar ebony
candlesticks, 14 cm. high. **£55-65**
S (WJS)

A mid 17th C. wrought iron rush
light, mounted on a sycamore half-
cone base, 17 cm. high. **£65-75**
S (WJS)

An 18th C. rush light nip, on a
turned fruitwood baluster, 19 cm.
high, with a wrought iron rush
light nip, on a stained walnut base,
26 cm. high. **£170-200**   *S (WJS)*

*Rushes were gathered during late
summer and autumn, soaked in
water and sun dried. Children and
the elderly peeled the outer layer
leaving the pith which, when dipped
in kitchen fat several times,
produced a simple candle. Gilbert
White's Natural History of
Selbourne records that a good rush,
2 ft. 4 in. long, would burn for 57
minutes.*

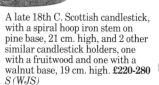

A late 18th C. Scottish candlestick,
with a spiral hoop iron stem on
pine base, 21 cm. high, and 2 other
similar candlestick holders, one
with a fruitwood and one with a
walnut base, 19 cm. high. **£220-280**
S (WJS)

461

A pair of late 18th C. fruitwood adjustable wig stands, the mushroom caps above baluster turned stems, with ivory screws, 26 cm. high. **£250-300** S (WJS)

Although wigs were known to have been worn as far back as Egyptian and Roman times it was not until the early 16th C. that the French were attributed with creating a fashion for wigs. Queen Elizabeth I set the trend amongst her court by wearing dyed wigs to compliment her costume and it was not until 1660 that they attracted widespread popularity in England.
It is interesting to note that the expression 'to pull the wool over one's eyes' stems from the

highwayman's practice of approaching his victim from the rear and pushing the wig over his eyes while relieving him of his money.
Wigs suffered a temporary relapse in popularity between 1665 and 1680 due to the Great Plague when it was considered that plague ridden hair might be used for their manufacture. The art of wig making reached its zenith at around 1765 and finally by 1795 when a tax of a guinea per head was levied on powdered hair, the fashion declined rapidly until it was exclusive to the legal profession alone.

Two similar late 17th C. yew wood rush light holders, with brass and copper handles, 8 cm. diam. **£190-£220** S (WJS)

A 19th C. boxwood glove powdering flask, 13 cm. high. **£55-65** S (WJS)

The majority of existent glove powdering flasks date from Queen Victoria's reign when long tight gloves were the fashion. Powder was used both domestically and in shops so that tight gloves could be eased over ladies' hands without effort. c.f. Pinto, Treen, plate 388.

An 18th C. lignum vitae head scratcher, the handle with Turkish knot collar and knop, 41 cm. long. **£195-205** S (WJS)

An 18th C. lignum vitae wig powdering 'carrot', 12 cm. long. **£90-110** S (WJS)

The stalk end of the 'carrot' would have originally incorporated some form of squeeze bulb, probably made of soft leather.

A 19th C. Scottish carved boxwood 'fiddle stock' knitting sheath, 21.5 cm. long. **£70-90** S (WJS)

A mid 19th C. japanned and parcel gilt 'face et Nuque' mirror by Heals, 46 cm. high retracted. **£280-£360** S (WJS)

Several versions of the 'face et Nuque' mirror are illustrated in Heals 1856-57 catalogue but few examples have survived intact. The design employed an ingenious arrangement of 2 adjustable mirrors, the pivoted face mirror is surmounted by a telescopic overhead mirror adjustable to any angle enabling the lady to view the front, top, back and sides of her head. c.f. Pinto, Treen, plate 391.

A late 18th C. mahogany and walnut collar box, with a segmented veneered lid, the interior containing a tray, 17 cm. diam. **£140-170** S (WJS)

Although references to the invention of knitting (claimed to be originated by the Scots) are traceable to the 15th C. the earliest existent knitting sheaths date only to the 17th C. The knitting sheath was employed to release the fingers of the right hand for 'throwing' the worsted, and also to support the weight of the knitted material. When not in use the sheath was tucked under the right armpit.
Knitting sheaths were pierced to a depth of about 2 inches to hold the bow-shaped needles then in use. A belt called a 'cowband' which the sheaths were fastened to, incorporated a hook called a 'clue-holder' (clue was the name for a ball of yarn) that supported the long end of a piece of knitting to prevent it hanging down.
Similarly to love spoons, knitting sheaths were often presented to sweethearts as love tokens. Some were elaborately carved for this purpose and encased appropriate messages.

A 19th C. cedarwood 'goose wing' knitting sheath, 29 cm. long. **£19-£25** S (WJS)

A 19th C. mahogany knitting sheath, 18 cm. long. **£70-80** S (WJS)

An 18th/19th C. North Country cedarwood knitting sheath, inlaid with a heart, lozenge and a roundel, the tip with a brass cap, 12.5 cm. long. **£65-75** S (WJS)

A 19th C. Welsh mahogany 'chain' knitting sheath, one end with the message 'Remember me when this you see and bear me in your mind W. Nelson; Nov. 9th 1831', 42 cm. long. **£100-130** S (WJS)

An 18th C. Welsh boxwood and silver-mounted knitting sheath the 'lantern' handle containing 2 balls, 25.5 cm. long. **£130-150** S (WJS)

A 19th C. fruitwood knitting sheath, 10 cm. long. **£90-100** S (WJS)

An early 19th C. oak and rosewood reel stand, 33 cm. high. **£300-350** *S (WJS)*

An early 19th C. rosewood two-tier reel stand, 26 cm. high. **£320-380** *S (WJS)*

A 19th C. beechwood wool winder, 112 cm. high. **£50-70** *S (WJS)*

An early 19th C. mahogany and ebony reel stand, surmounted by a silk winder, the plinth base containing a drawer, 29 cm. high. **£320-380** *S (WJS)*

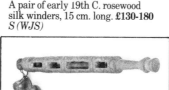

A pair of early 19th C. rosewood silk winders, 15 cm. long. **£130-180** *S (WJS)*

A 19th C. cedar and oak spinning wheel, inlaid with chevron bandings, 60 by 67 cm. wide. **£900-1,000** *S (WJS)*

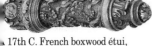

A 17th C. French boxwood étui, 21 cm. long. **£250-300** *S (WJS)*

During ancient times needles were made from wood, thorn, ivory, and even animal bones. Prior to the 17th C. needles came in a variety of metals including bronze, iron and gold. It was not until the late 17th C. that the English steel hand sewing needle industry became sufficiently important to warrant a prohibition of imports.

Needles continued to be a costly product until the mechanisation of the industry in the 19th C. It was thus as treasured objects that needles were kept in ornate cases of the finest workmanship. These étuis were often made of boxwood and carved from the solid with tight fitting caps to prevent rust.

Thirty-two bone bobbins, English, mid 19th C. **£120-160** *S*

A collection of 18th C. turned and carved lace bobbins, the majority with coloured glass spangles. **£130-£180** *S (WJS)*

The art of lace-making is thought to have originated in Venice or Flanders and later spread to England. In this country lace-making established its reputation most prominently in Bedfordshire, Devonshire and Buckinghamshire. Needlepoint and pillow lace-making date at least to the mid 16th C.

The materials employed in the manufacture of bobbins include bone, ivory and wood. In addition bobbins were often decorated with carving (sometimes including inscriptions) and also pewter which was an effective embellishment to intricate turning.

The coloured Venetian glass spangles attached to many examples enabled the lace-maker to distinguish between the numerous bobbins in simultaneous use. c.f. Pinto, Treen, plate 331.

A collection of 23 turned softwood bobbins, dating from 1840, contained in carved wood cigar cabinet, 24 cm. high by 32 cm. wide. **£120-150** *S*

An early 19th C. elm and mahogany lace bobbin winder, 31 cm. **£40-60** *S (WJS)*

An 18th C. Scandinavian fruitwood miniature shoe, 10 cm. long. **£320-£380** *S (WJS)*

c.f. Pinto, Treen, plate 429.

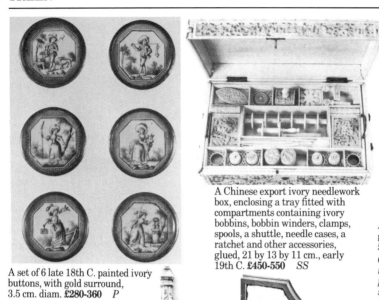

A set of 6 late 18th C. painted ivory buttons, with gold surround, 3.5 cm. diam. **£280-360** *P*

A Chinese export ivory needlework box, enclosing a tray fitted with compartments containing ivory bobbins, bobbin winders, clamps, spools, a shuttle, needle cases, a ratchet and other accessories, glued, 21 by 13 by 11 cm., early 19th C. **£450-550** *SS*

A late 18th C. oak and mahogany goffering stack, 40 cm. high. **£600-£700** *S (WJS)*

Goffering stacks were used during the 17th, 18th and 19th Centuries for pleating fabrics. The damp starched cambric was woven between the wooden 'quills' which were held tight by wedges driven into the uprights.
c.f. Pinto, Treen, plate 156.

A Victorian silver gilt scissors case, with foliate engraving by George Unite, Birmingham, probably 1870. **£60-80** *HyD*

A silver and enamel étui, of angular form, the interior with engraved and cast silver-topped knife and awl, enamel restored, in ambrotype case with cut velvet and silk lining, 9 cm., mid 17th C. **£300-£350** *S*

A musical necessaire, with sewing accoutrements and small cylinder musical movement playing 2 airs, French, 30 cm. long, c. 1840. **£600-£700** *S*

A European sewing machine, by The Coventry Machinists Co. Ltd., with raised arm, removable wood platform, gilt decoration and ornamental treadle, with hand wheel for bobbin winding. **£1,000-£1,200** *CSK*

Two early 20th C. lignum vitae diabolo, one 14 cm. long, the other 10 cm. long. **£80-100** *S (WJS)*

The game Diabolo was popular in England early this century but was originally an 18th C. French game. The aim was to balance the diabolo on a thin cord supported by 2 sticks held in each hand.
c.f. Pinto, plate 241, fig. J.

A 'Palais Royal' gilt metal and mother-of-pearl sewing box, the lid mirror-lined, the ribbonwork and velvet tray almost complete with carved mother-of-pearl implements, Paris, very slight damage, 17 cm., early 19th C. **£400-500** *S*

An 18th/19th C. mahogany puzzle, 13 cm. wide. **£90-110** *S (WJS)*

A 19th C. sycamore alphabet board, 38 cm. high. **£250-300** *S (WJS)*

A 19th C. mahogany and inlaid book card case, with concealed drawer, 16 cm. high. **£90-110** *S (WJS)*

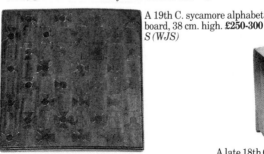

An 18th C. beechwood and mahogany chessboard, 33 cm. wide. **£85-95** *S (WJS)*

A late 18th C. burr walnut-veneered money box, in the form of a bow front chest, 15 cm. high. **£140-180** *S (WJS)*

A 19th C. Indian padduk chuck rum board, of rectangular form, with circular depressions, the handle in the form of a pierced scroll cresting, 31 cm. wide. **£250-300** *S (WJS)*

Chuck rums, once the currency in South India, were small silver coins. They were counted by shaking over a board with a recorded number of depressions into which the coinage fell. c.f. Pinto, Treen, plate 296.

A 19th C. sycamore bilboquet, 29 cm. high. **£60-80** *S (WJS)*

*During 16th C. France, Henry III popularised the game of bilboquet, which had hitherto only been played by children.
It also became in vogue amongst the Stuart Court and since then has gained a more widespread popularity. The game consists of a turned stick surmounted by a shallow cup. A ball is attached to the stick by a cord. The aim of the game is simply that of tossing the ball in the air and capturing it in the cup.*

A 19th C. lignum vitae bilboquet, 22 cm. high. **£55-65** *S (WJS)*

An 18th C. fruitwood owl lure, 13 cm. long. **£90-110** *S (WJS)*

An early 19th C. mahogany and brass cartridge case extractor, 23 cm. long. **£65-75** *S (WJS)*

An early 19th C. lignum vitae powder flask, with silver emblem, 15 cm. long. **£70-90** *S (WJS)*

An 18th/19th C. beechwood lark lure, the top set with faceted mirrors and on a revolving brass collar, 52 cm. high. **£85-105** *S (WJS)*

*Larks are attracted to anything that glitters. The stake would be driven in the ground and the arched mirrored top rotated to attract the larks.
c.f. Pinto, Treen, plate 248, for a similar example.*

An 18th C. horn and brass-mounted powder horn, with threaded mahogany plug and spring-loaded powder dispenser, 76 cm. long. **£180-200** *S (WJS)*

A 19th C. coquilla nut bilboquet, 17 cm. high. **£60-70** *S (WJS)*

A 19th C. oak and beechwood jay lure, with ratchet mechanism, 9 cm. long. **£70-90** *S (WJS)*

A.T. collection label no. 195.

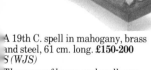

A 19th C. spell in mahogany, brass and steel, 61 cm. long. **£150-200** *S (WJS)*

*The game of knurr and spell was confined to the North of England and was a game played by 2 players whose aim is to drive the knurr (ball made of ivory, lignum vitae or boxwood) the greatest distance. The mechanism is triggered by a pummel kibble or striking stick.
c.f. Pinto, Treen, figure 234, figs. f and g.*

A late 18th C. yew wood and ivory cribbage board, 18 cm. long. **£250-£300** *S (WJS)*

A 19th C. rosewood playing card press, the lid inset with petit-point needlework, 21 cm. long. **£160-200** *S (WJS)*

A 19th C. rosewood and mother-of-pearl inlaid cribbage board, 25 cm. long. **£35-45** *(WJS)*

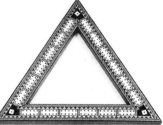

A 19th C. mahogany triangular cribbage board, inlaid with ivory, boxwood and rosewood, 29 cm. long. **£160-200** *S (WJS)*

An 18th C. boxwood cribbage board, inlaid with brass, ebony and ivory, inscribed 'Nathanial Charles, 1731', 33 cm. long. **£200-£250** *S (WJS)*

CLOCKS – MARKET TRENDS

In a generally buoyant antiques market clocks have seen an appreciable escalation in prices. This is particularly noticeable with longcase clocks, which suffered from a very flat period for several years.

Over the past 12 months prices have increased by approximately 40%. Items such as late 17th Century marquetry longcases are now making £6,000 where they would have struggled to make £4,000 a year ago. This has also led to an interesting increase in the auctions of longcases with high level of restoration. This is another indication of a strong market as clocks are being restored (an expensive process) prior to being entered for auction. Two to three years ago there were many unrestored examples.

The carriage clock market still seems rather stagnant although prime examples are gradually increasing in price.

This is a general comment, not only for clocks but across the board — the quality items are pulling ahead of the ordinary more than ever.

Value Points for Clocks
- prime example
- original condition
- unusual features
- good maker
- rarity
- the intricacy of the movement
- complexity

An early 18th C. longcase clock, red lacquer, by Isaac Lowndes of London, 7 ft. 9 in. high. **£1,000-1,200** *CDC*
This type of lunarwork would normally greatly increase the value of a clock — due to the price band one can only assume the case was poor.

A mahogany longcase clock, the 8-day movement rack striking, the 14 in. circular brass dial signed P. Hunter, Edinburgh, the case with moulded plinth, the waist with shallow rectangular pilasters, 7 ft. 1 in. **£500-600** *L*
Circular dials on longcase clocks are the least commercial, hence apparent low price.

A 19th C. Scottish longcase clock, by H. Rutherford of Jedburgh, the circular painted dial in a mahogany case with turned pillars flanking central doors. **£300-350** *WHL*

A good George III crossbanded mahogany longcase clock, the 14 in. brass dial signed Finney, Liverpool, the movement with anchor escapement and striking on a bell, 98 in. (249 cm.), late 18th C. **£2,800-3,200** *SC*
Brass dials with painted 'moon roller' discs in the arch have been increasingly sought after during the past year.

A large George III mahogany longcase clock, pagoda top, fluted quarter columns to trunk with break-arch waist door, the 12 in. engraved brass break-arch dial with subsidiary seconds dial and calendar aperture, inscribed 'Robert Wood, London', the 5-pillar 8-day 3-train movement with rack, quarter hour carillon of 8 bells (including pendulum and weights), 101 in. (257 cm.) high. **£2,000-2,500** *SS*

A late Regency mahogany longcase clock, the white painted circular dial in case with carved scroll border, on tapered support and rectangular plinth, 8-day movement, by James Andrew Kelley, Glasgow, 77 in. high. **£400-500** *WHB*
Typical Scottish circular white dial clock, very uncommercial.

A mahogany longcase clock, the 12 in. brass break-arch dial with silvered chapter ring, subsidiary seconds dial and calendar aperture, name disc in arch inscribed 'William Robertson, Wooller', 89 in. (226 cm.) high, 18th C. **£2,500-3,000** *SS*

Left

A mahogany longcase clock, by Thomas Butterfield of London, 91 in. high, c. 1780. **£1,800-2,400** *AP*

George III mahogany ongcase clock, the 12 in. ktensively engraved lvered dial with bsidiary seconds dial gned 'William Ferguson, inwick', the 8-day ovement with centre heel anchor escapement, ntre seconds hand, in. (236 cm.) high. ,200-1,400 *SS*

A George III mahogany longcase clock by David Davis of London, with 8-day movement, silver chapter ring, date aperture, silent and strike and second hand, 7 ft. 5 in. **£4,000-4,200** *MMB*

USE THE INDEX!

Because certain items might fit easily into any of a number of categories, the quickest and surest method of locating any entry is by reference to the fully cross-referenced index at the back of the book. This is particularly true this year when certain sections, e.g. Worcester Porcelain and Oak Furniture have been featured in isolation.

A George III mahogany longcase clock, the 12 in. dial signed J. Wainwright, Northampton, and with engraved centre, seconds and calendar dials and a moon disc in the arch, in a solid mahogany case with a concave-sided cresting, stop-fluted columns flanking the dial. **£1,700-£2,100** *S*

Left

A George III mahogany longcase clock, with panelled plinth, flame-veneered arched trunk door, arched hood, engraved silvered dial signed Edwd Dunn, London, with subsidiary seconds and calendar aperture, strike/silent in the arch, 4-pillar movement with rack strike and anchor escapement, 7 ft. 11 in. (240 cm.) high. **£1,500-£1,700** *C*

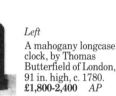

A George III mahogany longcase clock by James Smith of London, with 8-day movement, brass chapter ring and spandrels, date aperture, 7 ft. high. **£1,600-1,800** *MMB*
Plinth reduced.

A George III 8-day longcase clock, with 12 in. arched brass dial, signed 'Frans Reavill/London', seconds dial, calendar aperture, strike/silent dial in the arch, in mahogany case, 89 in. high. **£1,200-£1,400** *Bea*

A George III mahogany longcase clock, the arched hood with fretted pediment, free standing columns at the corners, the arched brass dial with silvered disc in the arch inscribed John Berry, London, bell striking, 8-day movement, 7 ft. 2 in. **£700-900** *PWC*

A George III 8-day longcase clock, with 13 in. arched brass dial, silvered chapter ring with inner calendar ring, the arch with sidereal time and phase of the moon, signed 'Thompson, Whitehaven', in walnut case. **£1,800-£2,000** *Bea*

An unusual mahogany longcase regulator, signed W. Page Gt. Portland St. London/Regulator, the movement with cut out arched plates, deadbeat escapement, maintaining power, 6 ft. 1¼ in. (186 cm.) high. **£3,800-4,200** *C*

A late 18th C. mahogany 8-day striking longcase clock, the movement with an engraved silvered dial the arch pierced with a painted plate of men o' war at anchor and a rocking man o' war in front, signed Edward Bo[...] Chichester, the hood with pagoda surmount, dentil cornice above a glazed door with brass corinthia[...] capped reeded columns. **£1,000-1,200** *WW*

An 8-day mahogany automaton longcase clock, the 12 in. brass dial signed Samuel Raworth, Plymouth on the silvered chapter ring and also around the arch, subsidiary seconds and date aperture in the florally engraved centre, the arch containing a seesaw automaton, 8 ft. (244 cm.) high. **£1,100-£1,300** *Bon*

Architectural pediment not original.

A mid 18th C. mahogany longcase clock, the arched brass dial with silvered centre second hand and date aperture, silvered silent/strike ornate gilt metal spandrels, signed Eardley Norton, London — No. 1102, 84 in. high. **£1,800-2,400** *WAG*

An early George III mahogany longcase clock, the 12 in. brass dial signed Thomas Stansbury, Hereford, on a boss in the arch, the movement with anchor escapement, the case with ogee stepped pediment centred by a vase finial, blind fretted frieze, 106 in. (269 cm.), third quarter of 18th C. **£2,300-2,500** *SC*

An 8-day George I walnu[...] longcase clock, by Thoma[...] Martin, London, with crossbanded plinth and waist door, 12 in. arched brass dial with penny moon in the arch, ringed winding holes, the silvered chapter signed, 5 ringed pillars and insid[...] countwheel strike, 88 in. high, c. 1730. **£1,200-1,4[...]** *Re*

An inlaid satinwood longcase clock, the 12 in. dial signed Samuel Aris Leicester Fields London, the movement with 5 pillars, the case inlaid with ebony stringing and with a shaped cresting and 5 urn finials, the waist door inlaid with 2 maidens in an oval panel, the plinth with a wreath of olive, 7 ft. 4 in. (224 cm.) high. **£4,000-5,000** *S*

A George III mahogany longcase clock, by Nathaniel Brown, Manchester, arched brass and silvered dial with moon phase, in figured mahogany case having swan neck pediment, dentillated and with carved rose terminals, additional plinth, 8 ft. high, c. 1780. **£2,200-£2,400** *CDC*

Added plinth (as stated), otherwise a good clock.

A mahogany longcase clock, the 8-day 5 pillar repeating movement rack striking, the 12 in. arched brass dial with silvered chapter ring with inner calendar circle, the matted centre with silvered oval plaque signed Saml. Fish, London, the arch with central strike/silent dial, flanked by applied plinth, 8 ft. 4 in. **£2,400-2,700** *L*

This is a good clean example of a London clock, c. 1785.

A late Georgian mahogany longcase clock, the case with panel to plinth, the hood with waved cresting and brass bezel to circular painted dial with seconds and date rings, signed Hughes Frith St. Soho, 6 ft. 10 in. (209 cm.) high. **£1,200-1,400** *C*

An 8-day longcase clock, a mahogany case with brass and steel fretted arch dial, by Reid & Sons, Newcastle, having Whittington and Westminster chimes. **£1,300-1,500** *JD*

A mahogany chiming longcase clock, the 13 in. brass dial signed Russell's Ltd., 10 Exchange Street, Manchester, chime/silent and Whittington/Westminster subsidiary dials in the arch, the massive movement with deadbeat escapement, 3 trains, striking on a series of 9 tubular gongs, with a mercury pendulum, 100 in. (254 cm.), early 20th C. **£3,500-4,000** *SC*

Left
An early 19th C. French mahogany month regulator, the 8¾ in. silvered dial signed R. Revel, the movement with plain pillars, 5 wheel train with maintaining power on the barrel and outside deadbeat escapement, with cylindrical pallets 6 ft. 5 in. (196 cm.) high. **£2,200-3,000** *S*

An Edwardian 8-day longcase clock, silvered chapter ring, chime/silent and Whittington/Westminster chimes dial in the arch, the movement with deadbeat escapement, chiming on 8 tubular bells and striking on one gong, 102 in. high. **£1,600-1,900** *Bea*

469

A mahogany and marquetry longcase clock, the arched brass dial with chime/silent ring, silvered chapter ring, seconds ring, panel inscribed W.R. Turk, Deal, 3 train movement quarter chiming on tubular gongs, the case inlaid with urns, scrolling foliage, ribbon bows, wreaths, satinwood bands and string lines, 7 ft. 11 in. high. **£1,400-£1,500** *PWC*

A fine late Victorian longcase clock, striking and chiming movement, Westminster/Whittington chimes, on 8 tubular gongs, painted moon phases dial in the arch, contained in carved oak case with bevelled glazed panel doors, 7 ft. 10 in. **£2,000-2,200** *EH*

An inlaid mahogany longcase clock, the 13½ in. dial signed Andw. Robertson Glasgow, in a case with a dentil-carved swan neck cresting and fluted columns flanking the dial, 7 ft. 3 in. (221 cm.) high. **£1,200-1,400** *S*

An Edwardian longcase clock, by J. Smith & Sons Clerkenwell, 3 train quarter striking movement chiming on 9 tubular bells, Westminster/Whittington strike/silent, in mahogany case with glazed panel door, fluted side columns terminating lions paws and with lions mask surmount, 7 ft. **£1,800-£2,500** *EH*

Miller's is a price GUIDE Not a price LIST

The price ranges given reflect the average price a purchaser should pay for similar items. Condition, rarity of design or pattern, size, colour, pedigree, restoration and many other factors must be taken into account when assessing values.

A mahogany longcase clock, with quarter striking on 5 tubular gongs, the dial with Roman numerals and subsidiary seconds and chime/silent dials, the central panel inlaid with foliage, the case with a glazed waist panel and crossbanded with satinwood, 99 in. (250 cm.) high, c. 1910. **£1,100-1,300** *S*

An Edwardian mahogany longcase clock, inlaid in engraved and coloured woods with flowerheads, 8-day movement, striking on 8 bells, chime/silent and seconds dials, inscribed S. Meredith, Penryn. **£1,000-1,200** *N*

A mahogany longcase clock, with arched hood, turned and fluted columns at the corners, the trunk with fluted canted corners and bar glazed inspection door, the 3 train movement with Westminster/Whittington and St. Michael chimes, 7 ft. 1 in. **£900-1,100** *PWC*

Left
An Edwardian inlaid quarter chiming longcase clock, the 3 train 8-day movement rack striking, deadbeat escapement, beat adjustment, Harrison's maintaining power, and Westminster chiming on tubular gongs, the case inlaid with scrolls and an urn and with outline stringing and bevel glazed door, 7 ft. 9 in. **£1,400-1,600** *L*

An oak longcase clock, with quarter striking on 8 bells and 5 gongs, the hood flanked by buttresses and surmounted by crocketted finials, the case with an arched glazed door applied with a plaque dated 1901, 99 in. (238 cm.) high, late 19th C. **£1,200-1,300** *S*

A musical mahogany longcase clock, the 3 train movement with a 7½ in. barrel driving 9 hammers striking on a piano soundboard, stamped Elliot's patent, the case with a glazed waist flanked by columns, 91 in. (231 cm.) high, c. 1880. **£1,500-1,700** *S*

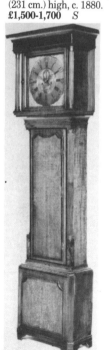

Right

An oak longcase clock, the 14 in. brass dial with a silvered chapter ring and moon work, signed Major Sholfield, Manchester, on later ogee bracket feet, 90 in. (229 cm.), late 18th C. **£1,000-1,200** *SC*

Left

An oak 30-hour longcase clock, the 10 in. brass dial signed Wolley, Codnor, date aperture and pierced brass spandrels, the plain case with a glass bull's-eye in the rectangular trunk door, 75½ in. (192 cm.) high, last quarter of the 17th C. **£550-750** *SC*

Plinth reduced, hood altered.

18th C. oak longcase clock, by Chris Johnson of Knaresborough, brass dial with scrolled spandrels, square hood, dentil cornice, 30-hour movement striking on a bell, c. 1780. **£700-800**

An oak longcase clock, the 13 in. brass dial signed T. Richardson, Weverham, with a seconds subsidiary and calendar aperture, quadrants flanking the crossbanded waist door, 81 in. (206 cm.), late 18th/early 19th C. **£950-1,050** *SC*

A mid 18th C. mahogany longcase clock, with silvered dial and 8-day movement, by John Hunter of Bristol, 7 ft. 3 in. high. **£700-1,000** *T*
The flat silvered dial detracts from this otherwise pleasant clock.

Left

An 18th C. mahogany longcase clock, by Alexander Miller, Edinburgh, the crossbanded case with boxwood stringing, the trunk with inlaid pilasters, 12 in. break arch brass dial incorporating subsidiary seconds and date pointer, 8-day rack striking movement with anchor escapement, 84 in. high. **£1,100-1,300** *Re*

An 8-day mahogany automaton longcase clock, 12 in. brass dial signed in the matted centre William Mason, London, the chapter ring with arcaded minutes, an automaton figure of 'Father Time', the case flanked by Corinthian pilasters, shell pattern inlays and medallion corners, 7 ft. 2½ in. (220 cm.) high. **£1,200-1,400** *Bon*

A mahogany longcase clock, crossbanded throughout, the 12 in. brass dial signed in the arch Henry Pye, Falmouth, the movement with anchor escapement and rack striking on a bell, 89 in. (228 cm.), late 18th C. **£650-750** *SC*

An early 19th C. mahogany inlaid and crossbanded 8-day longcase clock, by Fisher, Bath, 12½ in. painted break arch dial with subsidiary seconds and date crescent, 90 in. high overall, c. 1800. **£550-650** *Re*

An 8-day oak and mahogany automaton longcase clock, with 13 in. brass dial, signed on the chapter ring W. Young, Edinburgh, the arch containing an automaton 'Father Time', mahogany crossbanding, 7 ft. 4 in. (224 cm.) high including finial. **£1,100-1,200** *Bon*

Right

A black lacquered month going longcase clock, 5 pillar movement with latched plates, chapter ring signed John Blake, Croydon, the hood with glazed side panels, plain pilasters and domed crestings, case heavily restored, 7 ft. 7 in. **£1,200-£1,400** *L*
John Blake, Croydon, 1767-84.

A late 18th C. 8-day longcase clock, by David Collier, Gatley, case of oak with crossbanding to plinth and trunk, 13 in. brass dial with subsidiary seconds and date, engraved centre, rolling moon dial in the arch, 89½ in. high. **£900-1,100** *Re*

472

A George II mahogany longcase clock, by John Lea, London, the trunk canted and reeded, 8-day movement with 5 ringed pillars, one missing, inside countwheel, anchor escapement, 12 in. dial, signed on a cartouche in the arch, 94 in. overall. **£1,200-1,400** *Re*

An 18th C. longcase clock, oak case crossbanded in walnut, the hood with free standing pillars, 12 in. brass dial, signed on a cartouche to the centre of the dial, John Allen, Macclesfield, 4 pillar 8-day movement with inside countwheel, 79 in. high. **£800-900** *Re*

A mid 18th C. longcase clock, the brass arched dial with silvered chapter ring, seconds and date aperture, the 8-day movement with silent/strike, maker James Scholefield of London, 94 in. high. **£2,000-2,200** *VAG*

A mahogany longcase clock, the 12 in. brass dial signed Thomas Dugless, Stody, strike/silent in the arch, the movement with anchor escapement and rack striking, in a good mahogany case, with arched pediment, fluted columns flanking the dial above an arched door with a good feather-figured panel, with 2 weights and a pendulum, 93 in. (236 cm.), late 18th C. **£1,800-2,200** *SC*

An early 18th C. oak longcase clock, by Jonathan Rigg of Guisborough, the brass dial with chased spandrels and set with a George I medallion, square hood with moulded cornice. **£800-900** *M*

This clock has an interesting shallow arch.

A George III black lacquered 8-day longcase clock, the movement with arched dial having chinoiserie engraved spandrels, strike/silent, subsidiary seconds and date aperture, signed John Johnstone, London, pagoda hood, the waist with an arched top door decorated with figures in a summer palace and horseman, 8 ft. 3 in. overall. **£1,050-1,200** *WW*

A Georgian lacquer longcase clock. **£900-1,000** *RBB*

A George II black japanned longcase clock, the 12 in. dial signed Saml. Guy London in the arch, engraved borders, the movement with 5 ringed pillars and rack striking, the case decorated with well-drawn chinoiserie landscapes in shades of red and gold, 6 ft. 11 in. (211 cm.) high. **£950-1,050** *S*

An early 18th C. 8-day longcase clock, in a black japanned case, brass dial with silvered chapter ring and cherub spandrels, with subsidiary seconds and date aperture, inscribed William Kipling, London and Tempus Fugit, 223 cm. high overall. **£1,400-1,600** *HSS*

473

A George II green lacquer 8-day longcase clock, the hood and case decorated with chinoiserie panels of figures and pavilions in gardens, within borders of flowers, arched brass and silvered face with flowering urn spandrels, strike/silent dial, inscribed George Halifax, Doncaster. **£2,000-2,200** *N*

A George III 8-day longcase clock, with 12 in. arched brass dial, strike/non-strike lever, gilt brass spandrels representing the Seasons, signed in the arch 'Robt. Bertrand/London', in lacquer case with gilt chinoiserie decoration, 99 in. high. **£2,600-3,000** *Bea*

A late 18th C. black lacquered longcase clock, the brass dial with silvered chapter ring, with engraved foliate designs surmounted by a boss engraved Thos. Pearson, Newcastle, the 8-day movement with anchor escapement, 6 ft. 8 in. high. **£900-1,100** *AG*

A very small and rare japanned longcase clock, the 8¼ in. dial signed Chr. Gould London, with narrow seconds ring, cherub spandrels divided by engraved leaves, the movement with 5 ringed pillars and outside countwheel, the waist door and plinth decorated with chinoiserie buildings, ships and birds on a dark green ground, 5 ft. 10 in. (188 cm.) high, c. 1690. **£9,000-11,000** *S*

A 19th C. carved oak longcase clock, with broken-arch pediment to square hood, the 11 in. square brass dial signed 'Walter Prestidge, Towcester', the 8-day movement with rack striking on a bell, 82½ in. (210 cm.) high. **£350-450** *SS*

An 8-day longcase clock, in carved oak base, having swan neck pediment, the trunk with shaped door, the brass dial with silvered sun surmount, striking movement by Kingsnorth, London, 88 in. high. **£700-800** *VV*

An oak longcase clock, the 12 in. brass dial inscribed 'Made by Geoe. Carter, Seaham, for Henry Wall Smith, 1839', the movement with anchor escapement and rack striking on a bell, the case with columns flanking the dial, later carved with foliage, 83 in. (211 cm.), early 19th C. **£400-500** *SC*

A black lacquer longcase clock, the 8-day 5 pillar movement rack striking, the 12 in. arched brass dial with subsidiary seconds dial, date aperture, signed Alexr. Glass, London, the arch with strike/silent dial, the case with shortened moulded plinth, decorated overall with gilt chinoiseries, 6 ft. 10 in. **£1,100-1,300** *L*

A George III mahogany longcase clock, with 14 in. painted dial with lunar arch, painted with figures in the spandrels, the movement with anchor escapement and rack striking on a bell, swan neck pediment above a 'verre eglomisé' inset frieze, fluted columns flanking the dial and quadrants flanking the shaped waist door, 88 in. (224 cm.), late 18th C. **£900-1,000**   *SC*

A mahogany automaton longcase clock, 8-day movement, 12 in. arched brass dial, the silvered centre engraved with sailing ship, fort, setting sun and further building, the arch with rocking ship against a seascape background, signed Richard Pinn, Sidmouth, 7 ft. 3 in. c. 1786. **£1,400-£1,600**   *L*

Right

A mahogany longcase clock, with painted 14 in. dial with subsidiary seconds and calendar dials, with a lunar dial in the arch, the trunk with a Gothic arched door flanked by ring-turned pillars, 91 in. (230 cm.). **£600-700**   *SC*

An oak longcase clock, the 12 in. arched brass dial signed William Kipling, London, calendar aperture and seconds subsidiary, signed Tempus Fugit, on a boss in the arch, the case with break-arch pediment, the door carved with a shell moulded recess and genre scene below, 94½ in. (240 cm.), 19th C. **£700-£800**   *SC*

Heavily carved cases uncommercial at present hence price.

> ## USE THE INDEX!
> *Because certain items might fit easily into any of a number of categories, the quickest and surest method of locating any entry is by reference to the fully cross-referenced index at the back of the book. This is particularly true this year when certain sections, e.g. Worcester Porcelain and Oak Furniture have been featured in isolation.*

A good 18th C. 8-day longcase clock, with 13 in. arched brass dial, signed Barvise, Cockermouth, concentric calendar ring, seconds dial, phase of the moon arch, in oak and walnut crossbanded case, 95 in. **£700-900**   *Bea*

An early 19th C. mahogany longcase clock, by J. & O. Buchann, Ashton, 13½ in. painted dial, signed, incorporating centre date sweep, rolling moon in the arch, with centre sweep seconds, deadbeat escapement, 89 in. high overall. **£800-£900**   *Re*

Left

An oak and mahogany longcase clock, the 13 in. white enamel dial with a lunar dial in the arch, the case with a swan-neck pediment and 'verre eglomisé' panelled frieze, and quadrants flanking the shaped waist door, 90 in. (229 cm.), early 19th C. **£800-900**   *SC*

A mahogany longcase clock, by Abraham of Frome, with 8-day striking movement, the 12 in. painted face with calendar and rolling moon, a swan-neck pediment, 90 in. high, c. 1820. **£600-700**   *V*

A Charles II oyster-veneered walnut longcase clock, the 10 in. square dial with script signature Thomas Tompion Londini Fecit, single screwed winged cherub spandrels, narrow silvered chapter ring and subsidiary seconds in the matted centre, the movement with latches to the dial feet and 6 ringed pillars, inside countwheel strike and bolt-and-shutter maintaining power to anchor escapement with back cock, restorations, 6 ft. 6 in. (199 cm.) high. **£19,000-21,000**   *C*

Literature: R. W. Symonds, Thomas Tompion, 1951, p. 34, fig. 12, p. 77, fig. 52. P. C. Dawson, C. B. Drover & D. W. Parkes, Early English Clocks, 1982, p. 254, pl. 341/2.

An oak longcase clock, the 8-day movement rack striking, 12 in. painted dial, the spandrels painted with shells, signed Jn. Hancock, Yeovil, the arch with automaton scene of a painting auction, the auctioneer's gavel moving with the swing of the pendulum, 7 ft. **£600-700** *L*

The automaton scene in the arch should add considerably to the price.

A mahogany longcase clock, the 14 in. painted dial signed J. Tipping, Liverpool, with lunar dial in the arch, the movement with anchor escapement and rack striking on a bell, the case with a swan-neck pediment, outset columns flanking the dial and reeded corners flanking the shaped waist door, 89 in. (226 cm.), early 19th C. **£500-700** *SC*

This clock suffers from being too wide.

A 1¼ second pendulum longcase clock movement, with latches to the dial feet and 5 ringed slender pillars, inside countwheel strike and bolt-and-shutter maintaining power to the anchor escapement with long pendulum, the 10 in. square dial signed William Clement Fecit, in a walnut and marquetry case with some ebonised mouldings, with repousse brass frieze, 6 ft. 5¼ in. (196.2 cm.) high. **£7,500-£9,500**   *C*

An 18th C. 8-day longcase clock, by William Kipling, London. **£2,500-2,700** *Bea*

This clock had altered works and a restored case but was desirable enough to make a good price.

A Dutch walnut longcase clock, the 12 in. brass dial signed on the silvered chapter ring Thomas Loor, Amsterdam, the 4 pillar movement with Dutch striking, in a case with stringing and shell pattern inlays, break-arch hood, 7 ft. 6 in. (229 cm.) high, c. 1740. **£2,400-3,000** *Bon*

A late 18th C. Dutch marquetry longcase clock by Jan B. Vryhoff, Amsterdam, with 8-day movement, striking on a single bell, 7 ft. 9 in. high **£3,200-4,000**   *AG*

A Charles II walnut quarter striking calendar longcase clock, with convex moulded case, the 10⅛ in. square dial signed in script Tho: Tompion Londini Fecit, with apertures for weekday with planet, month and date and central alarm disc, the 2 train movement with latches to the dial feet and 6 ringed pillars, separate alarm train to right side, ting-tang quarter strike via single large outside countwheel and pump action for either of 2 bells and with bolt-and-shutter maintaining power and anchor escapement, with restorations, 6 ft. 10¼ in. (209 cm.) high. **£17,000-£18,000**   *C*

Literature:
The Clock and Watch Collector, August 1952, p. 527.
P. G. Dawson, The Design of English Domestic Clocks 1660-1700, in A.H. Soc. Supplement No. 1, 1956, p. 14 and fig. 24.
Ernest L. Edwards, Weight Clocks at Chester, in A.H., September 1964, p. 248.

A Georgian walnut longcase clock, the dial signed John Watts Canterbury, the movement with 4 ringed pillars, inside countwheel strike and anchor escapement, 7 ft. (214 cm. high. **£750-950**   *C*

Left
A mid 18th C. walnut and marquetry longcase clock, by Symon Van Leeuwen, Amsterdam, the 12 in. arched brass dial with silvered chapter ring, the twin train movement with 5 ringed latched pillars, Dutch striking on 2 bells with anchor escapement, the case with a silver presentation plaque, 7 ft. 6 in. (2.70 m.) high. **£3,000-4,000**   *P*

A Georgian walnut and chevron pattern line inlaid longcase clock, the 8-day striking movement with anchor escapement, having brass dial with silvered chapter ring, inscribed William Avenall, Gravesend, 7 ft. 3½ in. high. **£2,000-2,500** *GC*

A walnut and marquetry longcase clock, the flat-top hood formerly rising but now pulling forward, now containing a movement with 4 ringed pillars, inside countwheel and anchor escapement, the 11 in. square dial signed John Davis Windsor, 6 ft. 10 in. (207 cm.) high. **£2,000-3,000**   *C*

Left
A fine marquetry longcase clock, partly green stained, 11 in. square dial signed Chr: Gould Londini Fecit on the silvered chapter ring with every minute numbered, the movement with 5 ringed pillars, outside countwheel strike and anchor escapement, 6 ft. 9 in. (205 cm.) high. **£8,000-9,000**   *C*

A Queen Anne walnut longcase clock, the 11 in. brass dial inscribed at the base Jo. Knibb Oxon, the movement with 4 ringed pillars, anchor escapement and internal countwheel strike on bell, 6 ft. 7 in. (201 cm.) high. **£4,500-5,000**   *C*

Left

A late 17th C. walnut and seaweed marquetry longcase clock, with glazed side frets and tea caddy top to hood, with 11 in. square brass dial, the chapter ring signed Luke Wise, Reading, the 8-day movement with inside countwheel striking on a bell, 84 in. (213 cm.) high. **£3,500-4,000** *SS*

An unusual and early walnut and marquetry musical longcase clock, with glazed side doors to hood, the 12 in. square brass dial plate with silvered chapter ring inscribed John Watts, Stamford, the 8-day movement with 3 trains, the musical train playing one of two tunes on 8 bells with 15 numbered hammers, released every 4 hours by a pin on the outside countwheel, the seconds pendulum with an unusual form of beat adjustment, 90 in. (229 cm.) high. **£6,000-£7,000** *SS*

An early 18th C. walnut longcase clock, with glazed side panels, pendulum sight glass in waist door, the 11 in. square brass dial with name plaque inscribed John Tickell, Crediton, the 30-hour chain-driven lantern posted movement with outside countwheel striking on a bell, 85½ in. (217 cm.) high. **£750-850** *SS*

A George III ebonised bracket clock, the dial painted with a rustic scene and inscribed 'Robert Kelvey, Gainsboro', the movement converted from verge to anchor escapement, repeat work missing, and striking on a bell, in a bell-top case, 21 in. high (53 cm.). **£850-950** *SS*

A fine 18th C. walnut endive marquetry longcase clock, the 11 in. brass dial plate with silvered chapter ring inscribed J.V. Brussel, Amsterdam, the 8-day 5 latched pillar movement with inside barrel latchplate Dutch striking on 2 bells (hour strike on large bell, half-hour repeat on small bell), 80½ in. (205 cm.) high. **£3,500-£4,500** *SS*

A walnut and marquetry longcase clock, the 11 in. square brass dial signed Isaac Lowndes in ye Pall Mall, the movement with anchor escapement and outside countwheel, in need of some restoration, 79 in. (201 cm.), late 17th C. **£8,000-9,000** *SC*

A green lacquer bracket clock, 5 pillar movement with verge escapement, signed Dan De St. Leu, Watchmaker to Her Majesty, London, the 7 in. broken arched brass dial with silvered chapter ring, the matted centre with date and false pendulum apertures, and repeat signature on a silvered insert, contained in bell-top case, decorated overall with gilt chinoiseries, 21 in. (53.5 cm.). **£2,000-2,500** *L*

Daniel De Saint Leu, London, 1753-97, watchmaker to the Queen in 1766, made a very fine bracket clock in silver case for the Spanish Court.

A Victorian ebonised chiming bracket clock, with silvered chapter ring inscribed J.C. Jennens & Son, Great Sutton Street, London, with subsidiary chime/silent, fast/slow and Westminster chimes/8 bells/ 10 bells, dials, the triple fusee movement with similarly inscribed backplate, in a bell-top case applied with foliate mounts, together with matching bracket plinth, 31 in. high overall (79 cm.). **£1,100-1,300** *SS*

A George III mahogany repeating bracket clock, with silvered dial inscribed Tho⁵. Simson, Hertford, with subsidiary strike/ silent and fast/slow dials, twin fusee movement, the back plate engraved with a basket of flowers and foliage, in a break-arch case with scale pierced brass side frets, 18½ in. (47 cm.). **£1,100-1,300** *SS*

A George III Irish mahogany repeating bracket clock, with false pendulum aperture and signed in the arch 'Gordon, Dublin', the twin fusee movement with verge escapement, backplate signed Alex^R. Gordon, Dublin, in a break-arch bell-top case, 18 in. (46 cm.). **£750-900** *SS*

A Victorian mahogany chiming mantel clock, chime/silent, fast/ slow and chime on 8 bells/ Westminster chime dials in the arch, the triple fusee movement chiming on bells and gongs, case flanked by pillars and applied with gilt foliate mounts and finials, 27 in. (69 cm.). **£800-900** *SS*

An 18th C. walnut bracket clock, female caryatid figures to each side, arched silvered dial, signed Henry Jenkins, London, having subsidiaries for rise and fall regulation and strike/silent within the arch, the twin fusee verge movement with engraved backplate, 1 ft. 10 in. high (56 cm.). **£1,600-1,800** *P*

A mid 18th C. ebonised quarter-repeating bracket clock, with silvered chapter ring, calendar and false pendulum apertures, subsidiary strike/silent dial and inscribed in the arch William Scafe, London, the twin fusee movement converted to anchor escapement, the similarly inscribed backplate engraved with scrolling foliage, in an inverted bell-top case, 23 in. (58 cm.). **£1,200-1,800** *SS*

HINTS TO DATING BRACKET CLOCKS

DIALS

Square dial	to c. 1770	pre-George III
Broken arch dial	from c. 1720	George I or later
Round/painted/silvered	from c. 1760	George III or later

CASE FINISH

Ebony veneer	from c. 1660 to c. 1850	Carolean to mid-Victorian
Walnut	from c. 1670 to c. 1795	Carolean to mid-Georgian
Marquetry	from c. 1680 to c. 1740	Carolean to early Georgian
Rosewood	from c. 1790	from mid-Georgian
Lacquered	from c. 1700 to c. 1760	Queen Anne to early Georgian
Mahogany	from c. 1730	from early Georgian

A rare late 17th C. bracket clock, signed Francis Still, London, mock pendulum, date aperture, in a basket top walnut case decorated with scroll marquetry. **£4,000-£5,000** *WL*

A George III mahogany musical repeating bracket clock, the dial with subsidiary chime/silent and 6 tune selector, the triple fusee movement with verge escapement, playing on 13 bells at the hour and with pull repeat, the backplate with engraved borders, inscribed And^{w.} Bateman, London, movement restored, 26½ in. high (67 cm.). **£2,200-2,500** *SS*

A good George III bracket clock, the arched brass dial with silver chapter ring and 2 dials above, one strike/silent, the other up/down, the dial signed Wm. Sterck, London, well engraved scroll backplate, fusee movement in an ebonised case with carrying handle, 18 in. high. **£1,400-1,600** *WL*

A small ebonised bracket clock, the silvered dial with subsidiary strike/silent dial inscribed Barwise, London, the similarly inscribed shaped backplate with twin fusee movement, in a break-arch bell-top case, with scale pierced side frets, 14 in. (36 cm.). **£2,000-3,000** *SS*

A George III mahogany repeating bracket clock, the silvered dial inscribed Robt. Wood, London, with subsidiary seconds and strike/silent dial in the arch, verge escapement, and similarly inscribed backplate with stylised foliate engraved borders, in a bell-top case with foliate carved and pierced side panels, restored, 21 in. (53 cm.). **£900-1,000** *SS*

A Victorian mahogany chiming mantel clock, the silvered chapter ring inscribed Richard Evans, Liverpool, chime/silent, slow/fast and chime on 8 bells/Westminster dials in the arch, the movement in a bell-top case surmounted by finials, with pierced side frets, with foliate mounts, 28 in. (71 cm.). **£1,100-1,500** *SS*

An early 18th C. ebonised bracket clock, by Andrew Dunlop, London, the 7½ in. (19 cm.) arched brass dial with signed silvered chapter ring, mock pendulum aperture, the arch containing a silvered and engraved alarm dial, the fusee movement with pull quarter repeat striking on 6 bells, the backplate engraved, the alarm train missing, 1 ft. 7 in. high (48 cm.). **£1,700-£2,000** *P*

A good Regency mahogany bracket clock, by Robert Newman, London, with break arch top, 8-day, 5 pillar movement, rack striking on a gong, with shaped plates and strike/silent mechanism, 16 in. high. **£600-700** *Re*

A George III bracket clock, with arched brass dial and silver chapter ring and strike/silent dial above, signed James Gale, London, in a walnut case with engraved brass grills and carrying handles to sides, engraved brass backplate, 26 in. high. **£2,000-2,500** *WL*

A George III ebonised quarter-striking bracket clock, bell-top case, the dial signed Thos. Brett, London on a silvered sector in the matted centre with concentric date ring to the silvered chapter ring, moon-phase in the arch, the movement with triple fusees, quarter-strike on 6 bells, verge escapement, with restorations, 21 in. high (53 cm.). **£1,500-2,000** *C*

A mahogany bracket clock, by Benjamin Nicholson, Plymouth, the break arch pediment surmounted by brass carrying handle, the silvered dial, signed, with seconds subsidiary and strike/silent in the arch, the twin train movement with anchor escapement, 1 ft. 7 in. (48 cm.). **£900-1,100** *P*

BRACKET CLOCKS			
Case Finish			
Ebony veneer	from c. 1660 to c. 1850	Mahogany	from c. 1730
Walnut	from c. 1670 to c. 1795	**Dials**	
Marquetry	from c. 1680 to c. 1740	Square dial	to c. 1770
Rosewood	from c. 1790	Broken arch dial	from c. 1720
Lacquered	from c. 1700 to c. 1760	Round/painted silvered	from c. 1760

A George III satinwood bracket clock, the 8-day movement with double fusee, pull repeat, the backplate with engraved border, by S. & C. Joyce, London, white enamel dial, ebony stringing, painted stylised borders, on brass ogee bracket feet, 13½ in. high. **£1,400-1,600** *O*

A Regency mahogany chiming bracket clock, the 8 in. painted dial signed Yonge & Son Strand London, and with pierced hands and strike/silent at XII, the 3 train movement chiming on 8 bells, anchor escapement and engraved borders to the backplate, 20 in. high (51 cm.). **£1,300-1,500** *S*

An 18th C. ebonised bracket clock, by Benjamin Stennett, London, flanked by fluted canted angles, the silvered chapter ring with subsidiary seconds, the subsidiary strike/silent and date dials mounted below, the rise and fall regulator marked above the XII, the twin train movement having an ebony rod pendulum, 2 ft. high (61 cm.). **£1,300-1,500** *P*

A double basket-top bracket clock, the 7 in. dial signed Geo. Tyler London in the pendulum aperture, mask spandrels and moon disc and calendar in the arch between strike/silent and pendulum adjustment dials, the movement with 6 ringed pillars and altered verge escapement, the case veneered in walnut, basket composed of latticework panels divided by gadrooning, with restoration, repeating work removed, 21 in. high (53 cm.), c. 1730. **£1,700-2,000** *S*

An 18th C. ebonised musical bracket clock, by John Grantham, London, the sides with caryatids, the 6½ in. arched brass dial with enamel centre, and 2 subsidiary dials in the arch for chime/silent and 6 tune indicator, the 3 train movement with a carillon of 14 bells, engraved backplate with anchor escapement, 1 ft. 8 in. (50 cm.). **£1,800-£2,400** *P*

A marquetry bracket clock, the 7 in. dial with leaf-engraved centre, and cherub spandrels, the movement with verge escapement, outside numbered countwheel, the case inlaid with sprays of leaves and flowers on an ebonised ground and with a gilt-metal basket, with restoration, repeating work removed, 14 in. high (35.5 cm.), c. 1700. **£1,900-£2,200** *S*

A George III mahogany musical bracket clock, the 8 in. dial signed John Taylor London, between chime/not chime and strike/silent dials, with centre calendar hand, seconds dial and rococo spandrels, the 3 train movement with 8 bells and a pin-drum mounted at right angles to the plates, the backplate engraved with foliate scrolls and flowerheads, 21½ in. high (54.5 cm.). **£3,100-3,500** *S*

This clock may be dated c. 1770-80. The escapement was probably converted in the first quarter of the 19th C.

A very small ebonised chiming alarum bracket clock, the 4 in. dial signed J. Bushman London, the upper corners with regulation and alarum dials, flanking a pierced calendar dial in the arch, the 3 train movement chiming the quarters on 6 bells and with verge escapement and pull alarum, in a moulded bell-top case with a pierced dome, with restoration, 11½ in. high (29 cm.), c. 1720. **£4,000-5,000** *S*

John Bushman was Free of the Clockmakers' Company from 1692 to 1725.
Note the 'nose to tail' placing of the fusees and the unusual position of the going barrel.

An ebonised bracket clock, the dial signed Jonathan Lowndes in Pall Mall London, cherub spandrels and strike/silent aperture, the movement with 5 ringed pillars, verge escapement, the similarly signed backplate engraved with scrolling leaves and flowers, in a case with a basket top composed of cherubs masks, leaves and flowers, with restoration, repeating work removed, 13 in. high (33 cm.), c. 1685. **£1,800-2,000** *S*

A late 19th C. ebonised 3 train quarter-chiming fusee bracket clock. **£800-1,000** *MMB*

An 18th C. hour repeating bracket clock, with 7 in. dial inscribed John Waldron, Cornhill, London, with calendar aperture and strike/silent lever, engraved backplate in mahogany case, with inverted bell-top, 16 in. high. **£1,100-1,400** *GSP*

An ebonised striking bracket clock, by Haley & Milner, London, signed in the arch, strike/silent lever, in a bell-top case, movement by Thwaites, 19 in. high. **£1,200-1,400** *Re*

An ebonised double basket top bracket clock, the 4 pillar movement with partly latched plates, later anchor escapement, lacking repeat work, the backplate engraved with scrolls, and signed Brounker Watts, London, the matted centre with engraved calendar and false pendulum apertures, the case with a dome composed of masks, cornucopiae, scrollwork and flowers, repousse gilt metal mounts framing the dial, sides and back, 18¼ in. (46.3 cm.). **£2,400-2,600** *L*

Brounker Watts was apprenticed to Joseph Knibb, 1684, and was free in 1693.

An 18th C. English bracket clock, the brass and silvered arched dial signed ANd. DUNLOP, LONDON, 3 fusees striking and chiming on 6 bells, strike/silent to arch, date and pendulum aperture, engraved backplate, in ebonised basket top case, 19 in. **£1,800-2,000** *A*

An oak bracket clock, the movement quarter-striking on 8 bells, the silvered dial signed J W Benson, 25 Old Bond Street, London, the case flanked by fluted columns and surmounted by a moulded top centred by a finial, conforming bracket, 26½ in. high (67 cm.), c. 1870. **£450-650** *S*

A mahogany striking bracket clock, by Chas. Howse, London, brass dial with circular signed silvered centre, arch with strike/silent, break arch case with padded top, 17 in. high. **£2,000-3,000** *MMB*

A late 18th C. mahogany bracket clock, the dial signed Hartman, Bridge, the arch with strike/silent, 15½ in. **£750-1,000** *MMB*

An early 19th C. bracket clock, by Barwise, London, with white enamel dial and twin subsidiaries above for strike/silent and rise/fall, in an arched rosewood case, 13 in. high. **£1,600-1,800** *DWB*

A walnut quarter repeating bracket clock, the 5 pillar movement with verge escapement, pull quarter repeat on 6 bells, the backplate engraved with scrolls, and signed Jacob Massy, London, the square brass dial with wheatear border, winged cherub head spandrels, matted centre with calendar and false pendulum apertures, contained in an inverted bell-top case, some restorations, 17 in. (43 cm.). **£1,500-1,800** *L*

Jacob Massy, Leicester Fields, London, was free in 1715 and is recorded as working until 1725.

HINTS TO DATING BRACKET CLOCKS

DIALS

Square dial	to c. 1770
Broken arch dial	from c. 1720
Round/painted/silvered	from c. 1760

CASE FINISH

Ebony veneer	from c. 1660 to c. 1850
Walnut	from c. 1670 to c. 1795
Marquetry	from c. 1680 to c. 1740
Rosewood	from c. 1790
Lacquered	from c. 1700 to c. 1760
Mahogany	from c. 1730

An ebonised bracket clock, by Winterhalder & Hoffmeier, the movement stamped W & H Sch. with quarter-striking on 2 gongs subsidiary slow/fast and chime/silent in a broken arched case surmounted with a figure of Mercury, 22½ in. high (57 cm.), c. 1890. **£350-450** *S*

A mahogany bracket clock, the movement with half-hour striking and chain fusees, the dial signed Maple & Co. London, in a broken arched case with pierced brass fretwork sides, with pendulum, 21½ in. high, c. 1900. **£500-600** *S*

An early 19th C. bracket clock, with 3½ in. square dial signed Desbois. London, the movement with anchor escapement, in mahogany case with fluted moulded pediment, lacks handle, 9 in. high. **£600-700** *Bea*

A George III repeating bracket clock, with arched brass dial, signed William Threlkeld, London, pendulum and calendar aperture, seconds dial and pierced gilt brass spandrels, the movement with anchor escapement and pull repeat, chiming on 6 bells and with engraved backplate, in ebonised case with inverted bell-top, movement requires attention, 19¾ in. high. **£1,000-1,200** *Bea*

A mahogany alarum bracket timepiece, signed on the silvered dial Thos. Hunter Jnr., Royal Exchange, London, concentric alarum setting disc, in inverted bell-top case, 13½ in. high. **£800-£1,000** *Bea*

A late 18th C. ebony-veneered bracket clock, with strike/silent and seconds dials, signed John Wickes, London, fretted gilt brass side panels, the repeating movement with backplate inscribed John Wickes London, 21 in. high. **£1,000-£1,200** *PWC*

A mahogany striking bracket clock, arched dial with strike/silent regulator, date aperture, central plate engraved with a landscape with sailing vessels off, signed Joseph Green, London, foliate and scroll spandrels, the backplate foliate engraved, ogee brass bracket feet, 21½ in. high. **£700-£900** *WHL*

A George III musical bracket clock, arched brass dial with matt centre, silvered chapter ring, calendar aperture, signed in the arch Frans Wells/London and with strike/silent dial and dial to select one of four tunes, 'A Minuet, March, Tumpaty Tump, Aria', movement with fusee going, striking and chiming trains, with pull repeat mechanism chiming with 15 hammers on 10 bells, engraved backplate, in ebonised case with fret side panels, gilt metal mounts and moulded bell-top with carrying handle, slight damage to case, 21¼ in. high. **£2,000-2,500** *Bea*

George I ebonised striking bracket clock, signed Sam Vick, London, regulation ring in the arch, the twin fusee movement with rise-and-fall, verge escapement, backplate engraved with birds amidst scrolls, pull quarter-repeat removed, the case slightly distressed, 17½ in. overall height (44.5 cm.). **£1,100-1,400** *C*

A George III repeating bracket clock, with 6¾ in. arched silvered dial, signed Jno. Davidge, London, strike/silent dial in the arch and with engraved floral spandrels and calendar aperture, the movement with fusee going and striking trains, with pull repeat, with anchor escapement and with engraved backplate, in mahogany case with gilt brass mounts, moulded bell-top, 20½ in. high. **£600-700** *Bea*

A George II ebonised striking bracket clock, the dial signed 'Rich. Grigg London', with false pendulum, blocked, and calendar aperture, mask-and-scroll spandrels and strike/silent in the arch, now converted to anchor escapement, with pull quarter repeat, 19 in. high (48 cm.). £1,100-£1,300 *C*

(*l.*) A Regency mantel clock, with white painted dial, inscribed Bennett Greenwich, in brass inlaid rosewood case, 18 in. high. £350-£450

(*r.*) A late 18th C. mahogany bracket clock, with painted dial, the backplate engraved with basket of flowers, fish scale grilles and bracket feet, 15½ in. £700-800 *GSP*

A George I walnut striking bracket clock, signed 'C. Goode London', false pendulum and calendar aperture in the matted centre and with mask-and-scroll spandrels and strike/silent in the arch, movement with quarter-strike and verge escapement, with restorations, 15 in. high (38 cm.). £2,100-2,600 *C*

MAKE THE MOST OF MILLER'S
- *Look for the code letters in italic type following each caption.*
- *Check these against the list of contributors at the front of the book to identify the source of any illustration.*
- *Remember — valuations may vary according to locality; use of the codes can allow this to be taken into account.*

A late Stuart marquetry bracket clock, 7 in. square dial signed 'Gretton London', on the silvered chapter-ring enclosing false pendulum and calendar aperture, movement with ringed pillars, converted to anchor escapement and signed Charles Gretton London, 14½ in. high (37 cm.). £5,500-7,500 *C*

A small ebony quarter-repeating basket-top bracket clock, strike/silent aperture at XII, the movement with 7 ringed pillars, pull quarter repeat on 3 bells, inside rack striking, later anchor escapement, signed 'Benjamin Be London', 13½ in. high (34.5 cm.), c. 1680. £2,100-2,300 *S*

A George III mahogany bracket clock, the 7 in. dial signed 'Yeldrae Notron London' above a painted moon disc in the arch and with calendar aperture, strike/silent at III and rococo spandrels, the repeating movement with verge escapement and bob pendulum, 18 in. high (46 cm.). £1,300-£1,600 *S*

An ebony-veneered quarter-repeating bracket clock, the dial signed 'Windmills London' below a calendar dial in the arch and with pendulum aperture, strike/silent aperture at III, the 5 pillar with pull quarter-repeat on 6 bells and later anchor escapement, 18½ in. high (47 cm.), c. 1720. £1,600-£2,000 *S*

A late Regency satinwood lancet bracket clock, with ebony inlay, brass lion handles and Gothic tracery frets to the sides on ball feet, 8 in. circular silvered dial, 18½ in. high (47 cm.). £500-600 *C*

An early George III ebonised bracket clock, the 7 in. dial signed 'Jno. Harrison Newcastle', scroll spandrels and a landscape in the arch with a windmill, the sails turning with the strike, the repeating movement with verge escapement, 18 in. high (46 cm.). £1,000-1,500 *S*

A Regency mahogany bracket clock, with double fusee movement, by 'Wright of London'. **£550-650** *JD*

A mahogany and cut brass bracket timepiece, the movement signed 'Barraud & Lund, Cornhill, London, no. 1823', contained in a rectangular case surmounted by a pineapple finial, 13 in. (33 cm.), the bracket 5 in. (13 cm.), early 19th C. **£600-700** *SC*

A South German bracket clock, the dial with false pendulum aperture in the engraved gilt centre within arcaded silvered chapter ring, with subsidiary repeat/silent, strike/silent and weekday rings in the arch, the triple going-barrel movement with verge escapement and quarter striking and repeat, 20½ in. high (57 cm.). **£1,600-1,900** *C*

A George III red lacquer striking bracket clock, the dial signed 'Willm. Creak London' in sectors in the matted centre with calendar aperture, scroll spandrels and strike/silent in the arch, verge escapement and engraved backplate, 19 in. high (48 cm.). **£5,500-6,500** *C*

Lacquer bracket clocks now always expensive. Bought more as furnishing pieces than as horological items.

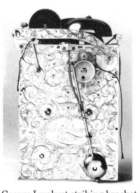

A George I walnut striking bracket clock with alarm, by Dan. Quare, London, 138, the dial signed and numbered, with concentric alarm disc and false pendulum aperture, the movement with verge escapement with rise-and-fall regulation, pull quarter-repeat and pull wind alarm, 16½ in. high (42 cm.). **£23,000-26,000** *C*

A late Stuart ebonised striking bracket clock, with gilt metal repoussé 'double' basket top, signed 'J. Windmills London', with ringed winding holes and calendar aperture, strike/silent above XII, the movement converted to anchor escapement and a pull quarter-repeat train removed, 15½ in. high (39 cm.). **£4,000-5,000** *C*

A George III tortoiseshell striking bracket clock, for the Turkish market, signed 'Geo. Clarke London', with false pendulum and Turkish numbered calendar apertures and silvered chapter-ring, movement with chain fusees, silk-suspended verge escapement, pull quarter-repeat on 6 bells, 17 in. high (43 cm.). **£2,300-2,600** *C*

A George II ebonised striking bracket clock, signed 'William Webster, Exchange Alley, London', the dial with false pendulum aperture, intersecting subsidiary rings for regulation and strike/silent, subsidiary date ring in arch, the movement with twin fusees, pull quarter repeat, repaired, on 6 bells, 17 in. high (43 cm.). **£3,000-4,000** *CNY*

A late Victorian bracket clock, by Charles Frodsham, in mahogany case, with ormolu caryatids and mounts. **£550-650** *JD*

A George III mahogany striking bracket clock, the silvered engraved dial signed 'George Jeffreys Chatham', with calendar aperture and strike/silent in the arch, fusee movement converted to anchor escapement, 21¼ in. high (54 cm.). **£1,700-2,000** *C*

A George II ebonised striking bracket clock, signed 'Thos. Gardner London', a rocking figure in the arch with the motto 'This World's a Farce and all Things show it', 18 in. high (47 cm.). **£2,000-2,500** *C*

A George II ebonised striking bracket clock, signed 'Richard Peckover London 513', with false pendulum aperture, silvered chapter ring, mask-and-scroll spandrels and strike/silent disc in the arch, 17½ in. high (44.5 cm.). **£1,000-1,200** *C*

A fine and small gilt metal automaton quarter-striking and musical bracket clock, for the Chinese market, the front with 3 paste-set roundels below and a rotating similar roundel above the enamel dial with centre seconds, movement with 3 chain fusees towards the centre, striking work on the front plate, the 6 quarter bells to the base, 9 in. high (23 cm.), c. 1800. **£3,500-4,000** *C*

A George III mahogany striking bracket clock, signed 'William Story London', the silvered chapter ring with scroll spandrels and strike/silent in the arch, fusee movement, knife-edge verge escapement, and backplate profusely engraved with foliate scrolls, 18 in. high (46 cm.). **£1,800-£2,100** *C*

A Louis XIV period bracket clock, by Mynuel a Paris, the boulle with dark brown tortoiseshell interspersed with brass inlay and ormolu mounts, the pediment with a figure of Father Time with scythe, the 8-day spring driven striking movement with 5 tapered pillars, original verge escapement, with original shaped bracket, c. 1700. **£3,500-4,500** *Re*

A boulle bracket clock, the dial signed 'Martinot à Paris', the arched case inlaid with brass strapwork and foliage, 27½ in. high (70 cm.), mid 19th C. **£900-£1,000** *S*

A Louis XV boulle bracket timepiece, the gilt dial centred with a musical trophy, the 4 pillar movement stamped 'Dubois à Paris', 28½ in. (73 cm.), with matching bracket 12 in. (30 cm.). **£1,200-1,800** *SS*

A good ebony bracket clock, by John Berry, London, with 5 in. brass dial, with a pendulum aperture and calendar aperture, striking on 3 bells, the case applied with fluted corner pilasters and finely cut and engraved brass side and spandrel grilles, on brass bracket feet, 15 in. (38 cm.), second quarter of the 18th C. **£7,500-£8,500** *SC*

An unusual gilt bronze bracket clock and bracket, signed 'Myniiel à Paris', 31 in. high (79 cm.), part 18th C. **£4,000-5,000** *S*

An early Louis XV boulle bracket clock, the dial and movement signed 'Lenoir à Lyons', the associated Louis XVI boulle base mounted with masks and a portrait medallion of Henri IV, 16½ in. high (41 cm.), 18th C. **£6,200-7,000** *S*

A gilt metal bottom-wind striking carriage clock, the movement with lever platform, strike and repeat on gong, stamped Le Roy & Fils, 6 in. high (15 cm.). **£750-850**   *C*

A brass carriage clock, by T. Hyde, Sleaford, one glass panel cracked to side. **£150-200**   *BHW*

A French gilt brass carriage clock, the twin train lever movement with push repeat and alarm, 8½ in. high (21 cm.). **£800-900**   *P*

A brass grande sonnerie carriage clock, stamped L.F. Paris, for Louis Fernier et Frere, 6¼ in. high (15.5 cm.). **£850-1,000**   *C*

An engraved gorge grande sonnerie alarum carriage clock, the movement with lever platform, striking and repeating on 2 gongs, signed for Hunt & Roskell, London, No. 5631, 6 in. high (15 cm.). **£2,000-2,500**   *Bon*

A miniature porcelain-mounted carriage timepiece, numbered 867, 3 in. high (7.5 cm.). **£600-£700**   *Bon*

A porcelain-mounted carriage clock, the repeating movement numbered 5889, lever platform, 5.5 in. high (14 cm.). **£450-550**   *Bon*

A French mid 19th C. gilt brass carriage clock, by Bolviller A Paris, twin train movement, with countwheel strike on a bell, 6 in. high (15 cm.). **£700-800**   *P*

A French gilt brass and white metal grande sonnerie alarum carriage clock, the movement with lever escapement, compensated balance, gong striking, repeating at will, and with selection lever in the base for 'Hours and Quarters', 'Silent', and 'Quarters Only', with leather case, 7½ in. (19 cm.). **£750-850**   *L*

A French brass carriage clock, the twin train lever movement stamped Drocourt, with gong strike, 6¾ in. high (17 cm.). **£450-£550**   *P*

A French brass carriage clock, the 2 train movement with lever escapement, compensated balance, blued steel spiral spring, bell striking, numbered 3001, bearing the trade stamp of Francois Arsene Margaine, in a Corniche type case, 6½ in. (16.5 cm.). **£400-500**   *L*

An enamel-mounted carriage timepiece, the single train movement with lever escapement, compensated balance and blued steel spiral spring, with carrying case, 15.5 cm. **£250-300**   *L*

A rosewood mantel or travelling clock, the 3½ in. dial signed Frodsham, Gracechurch Street, London, repeating movement with chain fusees, maintaining power, underslung lever escapement with monometallic balance and gong striking with provision for adjusting the hammer, 10 in. high (25.5 cm.). **£2,500-3,000** *S*

A late Victorian repeating carriage clock, the 8-day movement with platform lever escapement and with repeat mechanism striking on one gong, 6¾ in. high. **£800-900** *Bea*

A French brass carriage clock, the 2 train movement with lever escapement, compensated balance and blued steel spiral spring, striking the hours and half hours on a bell, and stamped Japy Freres & Cie, Exposition 1855, Grand Med d'Honneur, 6¾ in. (17.2 cm.). **£350-£400** *L*

An ebonised travelling or mantel timepiece, the 3 in. silvered dial signed De La Salle & Christie Cannon St. London, the movement with chain fusee, the underslung lever escapement with monometallic balance, 7 in. high (18 cm.). **£700-900** *S*

A French engraved repeater carriage clock, 6½ in., c. 1870. **£450-480** *CCL*

A chronometer carriage clock, signed M.F. Dent 33, Cockspur Street London, the repeating movement with spotted plates, chain fusees, maintaining power and half-hour gong striking, spring detent escapement, circular weights, timing nuts and 2 small weight screws, 8½ in. high (21.5 cm.). **£7,500-8,500** *S*

A carriage clock, the repeating lever movement with gong striking, 5¼ in. high (13.5 cm.), and a moulded gilt metal stand, 1¾ in. high (4.5 cm.). **£600-700** *S*

An ebonised striking carriage clock, by Arnold & Dent London, the twin chain fusee movement with compensated balance, chipped hair cracks, 8⅛ in. high (20.5 cm.). **£2,500-3,000** *C*

An enamelled brass striking carriage clock, 6½ in. high (16.5 cm.). **£2,500-3,000** *C*

A gilt brass repeating alarum carriage clock, lever escapement striking on a gong, in an engraved oval case, 7 in. (18 cm.), late 19th C. **£700-800**   *SC*

A grande sonnerie silver cased carriage clock, with split compensated balance to lever platform stamped J.S. No.1012, signed No. 10545 Leroy & Fils 15 & 16 Palais Royal Paris, the Anglaise case of silver with some gilt metal mouldings, 7¼ in. high (18.5 cm.). **£1,900-2,200**   *C*

A French carriage timepiece, 5¼ in. high. **£350-400**   *PWC*

A Leroy & Co. petite sonnerie carriage clock with alarm, the restored silvered dial inscribed 'L. LeRoy et Co., 7 Bd. de la Madelaine, Paris', the lever movement numbered 18300, striking on gongs and with alarm dial, 7½ in. high (19 cm.), fitted leather carrying case. **£700-800**   *SS*

A repeater carriage clock, inscribed London & Ryder, 17 New Bond Street, 7 in. high, with morocco covered travelling case. **£1,100-£1,400**   *PWC*

A repeating carriage clock, with lever escapement and gong strike, 8 in. high (20 cm.). **£600-800**   *SS*

A Victorian carriage timepiece, inscribed 'Simmons, London', the chain and fusee movement with maintaining power, the lever escapement with compensation balance, 8 in. (20 cm.). **£1,100-£1,300**   *SS*

A 19th C. French brass and champlevé enamel lever carriage timepiece, 6 in. high (15 cm.). **£250-£300**   *P*

A Richard & Co. petite sonnerie repeating carriage clock, the movement with lever escapement ting-tang striking on gongs with maker's mark 'R. & Co.', 7½ in. high (19 cm.). **£550-650**   *SS*

A brass inlaid rosewood night timepiece, the watch type movement with verge escapement, signed Robt. Groves, London. **£150-£200** *L*

A good and small travelling clock, the arched dial signed Vulliamy London, the movement with chain fusees, maintaining power, plain monometallic balance of square section with compensation curb and gong striking, 7½ in. high (19 cm.), with the original mahogany travelling case. **£6,000-£7,000** *S*

The lack of a carrying handle is unusual in a Vulliamy clock with a balance and not a pendulum.

An English gilt metal carriage clock, the chain fusee timepiece movement signed Barwise London 6 in. high (15 cm.). **£650-800** *C*

An unusual brass-inlaid mahogany travelling or mantel clock, with the repainted signature James McCabe, 9½ in. high (24 cm.), c. 1835, with a mahogany travelling case. **£2,500-3,000** *S*

A Richard & Co. oval 4-glass mantel clock, 14 in. (36 cm.). **£500-£600** *SS*

A rosewood mantel clock, signed J.L. Japple, London, the 2 train fusee movement repeating on a gong, anchor escapement, 11 in. high (28 cm.). **£850-1,050** *Bon*

A rare 18th C. elephant mantel clock, the movement with typical adjustment work and anchor escapement, the backplate signed Vulliamy London No. 281, the case proabably French, 19½ in. high (50 cm.). **£1,800-2,500** *S*

A 19th C. mahogany and brass inlaid mantel timepiece, inscribed Jackson, Brompton, 1 ft. 3½ in. high (39 cm.). **£400-500** *P*

An 8-day drum fusee free-sprung lever timepiece, Charles Frodsham, No. 2173, the escapement with spring banking, with original carrying case. **£1,600-2,000** *SS*

A fine early 19th C. gilded metal mantel clock, by Bevan, Birkenhead. **£400-500** *JD*

A Georgian mahogany double fusee bracket clock, by Kettlewell, Leeds. **£450-500** *JD*

A George III gilt metal and marble clock, signed Lewis Panten London, the timepiece fusee movement with short pendulum, 14¼ in. high (36 cm.). **£800-900** *C*

An early 19th C. ormolu-mounted bronze mantel timepiece, the chain fusee movement with anchor escapement and a plaque signed Geo. Yonge London, probably English, 12 in. high (30.5 cm.). **£700-800** *S*

A mahogany 8-day mantel chronometer, the movement with massive pillars, chain fusee and spring detent escapement, 8 in. high (20.5 cm.). **£1,800-2,200** *S*

A Regency rosewood English double fusee clock, 12 in., c. 1820. **£650-680** *CCL*

A French Empire mantel clock, with visible anchor escapement, the movement stamped S. Marti, Paris, 19 in. **£300-350** *GSP*

A Regency mantel clock, in the manner of Weeks, 8 in. wide (20 cm.). **£1,200-1,500** *C*

A French green lacquer chinoiserie mantel clock, 9½ in., c. 1890. **£125-£165** *CCL*

A 19th C. cartouche shape cast gilt brass case 8-day mantel clock, inscribed C. Brandt, London, 12 in. **£200-250** *WW*

A gilt metal mantel clock, signed Grimalde & Johnson, Strand London, with anchor escapement, 10 in. high (25.5 cm.). **£600-800** *S*

Recorded working between 1809 and 1825.

A walnut Westminster bracket clock, 13 in., c. 1930. **£120-140** *CCL*

A miniature marquetry long case clock, the timepiece movement with platform lever escapement, inscribed Exd. by J. Sewell, 30 Cornhill, London, 18 in. (45.7 cm.). **£200-250** *L*

A Eureka oak case mantel clock, No. 4394, 14½ in., c. 1906. **£450-£480** *CCL*

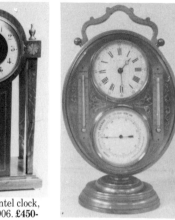

A brass cased clock, by Hamilton, with barometer and thermometers. **£150-180** *GBT*

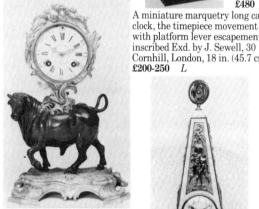

A Louis XV bronze and gilt bronze bull mantel clock, signed Causard à Paris, 17 in. high (44 cm.), mid 18th C. **£3,500-4,000** *S*

A Louis XVI marble and gilt bronze obelisk mantel clock, 28 in. high (71 cm.), c. 1780. **£2,000-2,500** *S*

A Louis XV gilt bronze mantel clock, the later enamel dial and movement signed Balthazard à Paris, 20 in. high (51 cm.), c. 1760. **£1,800-2,200** *S*

A Louis XV gilt bronze mantel timepiece, signed Fluteau À Montargis, now with an English fusee movement, 26½ in. high (67.5 cm.), c. 1735. **£4,500-5,500** *S*

A small Louis XV/XVI Transitional bronze and gilt bronze mantel clock, with a chipped enamel dial signed Chles. du Tertre à Paris, movement with outside countwheel, hands, bezel and pendulum lacking, 12 in. high (30.5 cm.), c. 1775. **£3,500-4,000** *S*

An inlaid Edwardian mantel clock, 6¼ in., c. 1910. **£40-50** *CCL*

An Empire gilt bronze mantel clock, the movement with outside countwheel, signed Paris, 20 in. high (51 cm.). **£1,400-1,600** *S*

A French 8-day mantel clock, 19th C. **£450-550** *WIL*

A small Louis XVI white marble and gilt bronze mantel clock, the dial signed Rogue à Paris, the similarly signed movement numbered 735 and with silk suspension and outside countwheel, 15 in. high (38 cm.), c. 1785. **£1,300-1,500** *S*

A Georgian satinwood mantel clock, Grant, Fleet St., London, the twin train fusee movement signed within an engraved floral swag, Grant, London, No. 318, the pendulum with rise/fall adjustment, 1 ft. 1 in. high (33 cm.). **£3,500-£4,500** *P*

A rosewood 4-glass mantel timepiece, signed 'Vulliamy London', the movement with chain fusee, half-deadbeat escapement steel rod pendulum, 7½ in. high (19 cm.), 19th C. **£3,500-4,000** *C*

A Victorian silver-mounted boudoir clock, C.E., London 1887, 8¼ in., in fitted case. **£500-600** *CSK*

A gilt bronze timepiece, 7½ in. (19 cm.), in a leather covered travelling case bearing a Benson's retailer's stamp, third quarter 19th C. **£500-600** *SC*

An English silver boudoir clock, 4¼ in., c. 1890. **£320-340** *CCL*

A small clock, with Westminster chimes on gongs, in the shape of a bracket clock, 10½ in., c. 1900. **£120-140** *CCL*

A late Victorian oak and ormolu-mounted chiming bracket clock, the 3 train chain and fusee movement chiming on 8 bells and 5 gongs, 29 in. high. **£1,200-1,400** *CSK*

An Edwardian balloon clock, with French movement, 7½ in. **£60-80** *CCL*

An Edwardian timepiece, in the shape of a bracket clock, with mother-of-pearl and brass inlay, 11 in. **£80-95** *CCL*

A Louis XVI gilt bronze and white marble mantel clock, the enamel dial signed Hoguet à Paris, the movement with silk suspension and outside countwheel, 13½ in. high (34.5 cm.), c. 1785. **£2,500-£3,000** *S*

Probably Toussaint-François Hoguet, who was Master in 1779.

A Louis XVI white marble and gilt bronze lyre clock, the movement with visible motion work, pin-wheel escapement and outside countwheel, 21½ in. high (54.5 cm.), c. 1785. **£3,500-4,000** *S*

A late 18th C. gilt brass, grand sonnerie striking calendar Pendule D'Officier, by Courvoisier & Co., the circular brass movement No. 10910, with visible steel striking work, 9½ in. high (24 cm.). **£2,000-£2,500** *P*

A Directoire gilt bronze mantel clock, with a chipped enamel dial signed Folin à Paris, the movement with silk suspension and outside countwheel, 18½ in. high (47 cm.), c. 1795. **£900-1,200** *S*

An Empire ormolu mantel clock, 10 in. wide (25.5 cm.). **£650-750** *C*

A Restauration gilt bronze chariot clock, the movement with silk suspension and circular plates, 17½ in. high (44.5 cm.), c. 1820. **£1,400-1,600** *S*

A Palais Royal ormolu and glass mantel clock, signed Raingo Fres, Paris, 11 in. high (28 cm.), c. 1830. **£500-550** *C*

A gilt bronze porcelain and champleve enamel mantel clock, 1 ft. 3 in. (38 cm.). **£1,500-2,000** *S*

An Empire gilt bronze mantel clock, the movement with circular plates and outside countwheel, 19½ in. high (49.5 cm.), early 19th C. **£1,100-1,500** *S*

A French white marble and ormolu lyre-shaped mantel clock, with 2 train movement, 1 ft. 2 in. high (35 cm.). **£900-1,000** *Bon*

A French early 19th C. marble and ormolu-mounted mantel clock, dial inscribed Piolaire À Paris, the twin train movement with anchor escapement 1 ft. 8 in. high (51 cm.). **£850-950** *P*

A good gilt bronze and porcelain calendar mantel clock, by J. B. Delettrez, 17 in. high (43 cm.). **£2,500-3,000** *S*

An early 19th C. serpentine marble and ormolu mantel clock, the movement stamped 'Bourdin à Paris, 1821', with silk suspension, outside countwheel and bell strike, 23½ in. high (60 cm.). **£550-650** *SS*

An early 19th C. Viennese grande sonnerie automaton mantel clock, the dial with a chipped enamel chapter ring, the 3 train movement with anchor escapement and gong striking, some mounts replaced, 26½ in. high (67.5 cm.). **£850-1,150** *S*

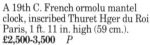

A 19th C. French ormolu mantel clock, inscribed Thuret Hger du Roi Paris, 1 ft. 11 in. high (59 cm.). **£2,500-3,500** *P*

An early 19th C. Viennese grande sonnerie automaton mantel clock, the 3 train movement with anchor escapement and gong striking, some mounts restored, 26 in. high (66 cm.). **£850-1,050** *S*

A gilt bronze mantel clock, in Louis XV style, dial signed Monbro Fils Aine à Paris, 19½ in. high (49 cm.), mid 19th C. **£1,100-1,400** *S*

19th C. marble and French ormolu mantel clock, by Robin à Paris, 1 ft. 4 in. high (41 cm.). **£2,000-2,500** *P*

An early 19th C. French mantel clock. **£550-650** *DWB*

A mid 19th C. French rococo-style gilt mantel clock, the movement with outside countwheel striking on a bell, 20 in. high (51 cm.). **£750-£950** *SS*

PRICE

Prices vary from auction to auction — from dealer to dealer. The price paid in a dealer's shop will depend on
1) *what he paid for the item*
2) *what he thinks he can get for it*
3) *the extent of his knowledge*
4) *awareness of market trends.*
It is a mistake to think that you will automatically pay more in a specialist dealer's shop. He is more likely to know the 'right' price for a piece. A general dealer may undercharge but he could also overcharge.

A French ormolu mantel clock of Louis XVI design, the dial signed Frodsham and Co, the French movement striking on a gong, 16 in. high. **£1,200-1,400** *CSK*

A 19th C. French mantel clock, with dial signed Aubanel & Rochat, 8-day movement, No. 284 striking on one bell, 22 in. wide, 16½ in. high. **£350-400** *Bea*

A French gilt, bronze and marble mantel clock, 24½ in. high, early 19th C. **£300-400** *MMB*

A French ormolu and marble mantel clock, 21 in. high, 19th C. **£170-200** *MMB*

A French gilt metal and porcelain-mounted mantel clock, wood base and glass dome, 14½ in. high, 19th C. **£450-550** *MMB*

A 19th C. French bronze and ormolu mantel clock, the bell striking movement with outside countwheel, inscribed Moser, Paris, 22½ in. wide by 31 in. high. **£550-£650** *PWC*

A gilt bronze mantel clock, in Louis XVI style, the dial signed J.A. Lepaute à Paris, 19½ in. high (49.5 cm.), mid 19th C. **£1,300-£1,800** *S*

A gilt and patinated bronze mantel clock, by Deniere a Paris, 21½ in. high (55 cm.), c. 1860. **£650-750** *S*

A French ormolu clock, by Henri Marc of Paris, 9½ in., c. 1840-60. **£380-420** *CCL*

A porcelain-mounted ormolu mantel clock, with perpetual calendar, the circular movement with strike on bell and visible Brocot escapement, French, 17 in. high (43 cm.), second half 19th C. **£2,500-3,000** *C*

A gilt bronze and porcelain mantel clock, the movement stamped Raingo Freres Paris, the dial with roman numerals, the waisted case cast with foliage and applied with trailing stems, with porcelain flowers, on a fitted conforming base, with pendulum, 14½ in. high (37 cm.), c. 1860. **£500-600** *S*

A wooden French carriage clock, striking on a bell, with marquetry case, 9 in., . 1860. **£260-280** *CCL*

A French Regency champlevé enamel mantel clock, by Maple & Co., Paris. **£550-600** *JD*

A 19th C. French mantel clock, signed Stanley A Paris, the twin rain movement with anchor scapement, 1 ft. 5 in. (43 cm.). **750-850** *P*

A 19th C. French ormolu mantel clock. **£350-450** *JD*

A gilt bronze and porcelain mantel clock, 18¼ in. high (46.5 cm.), c. 1880. **£500-700** *S*

A gilt bronze and porcelain mantel clock, 16 in. high (41 cm.), c. 1870, with giltwood plinth. **£700-800** *S*

gilt bronze and porcelain mantel ck, the movement with outside untwheel, signed Lenoir a Paris, t. 2 in. (36 cm.), c. 1870. **£900-,200** *S*

An alabaster 'swinging cherub' clock, 9¼ in., c. 1880. **£220-240** *CCL*

A gilt and patinated bronze and white marble mantel timepiece, the movement with platform lever escapement, 2 ft. 1½ in. c. 1880. **£2,000-2,500** *S*

Left
A good and large gilt bronze and porcelain mantel clock, the movement stamped Bourdin a Paris, 1 ft. 10½ in. (57 cm.), c. 1870. **£3,000-3,500** *S*

A gilt bronze and champlevé enamel mantel clock, the movement stamped J Marti Paris and Maple & Co. Limited Paris, the dial signed Maple & Co. Paris, 1 ft. 3 in. (38 cm.), c. 1880. **£800-1,000** *S*

A French porcelain-mounted gilt bronze mantel clock, the movement with Brocot type suspension, bell striking, and bearing the trade stamp of Japy Freres, 16¾ in. (42.5 cm.). **£400-450** *L*

A large brass-cased mantel clock, in the Baroque style, the 8-day movement striking on gongs, French, 55.5 cm. high, c. 1880. **£280-320** *TKN*

A mantel clock, in the Louis XIV style, the 8-day striking movement stamped with the maker's name and 'MOUV.FIN.', French, 50 cm. high, c. 1870. **£200-250** *TKN*

According to Tardy, this firm worked at the Rue Neuve St. Francois, 1850-60 and Rue Debelleyme, 1870.

A porcelain and gilt bronze mantel clock, by Japy-Freres, 1 ft. (30 cm.), c. 1880. **£1,300-1,500** *S*

A French gilt bronze mantel clock, the 2 train movement with Brocot type suspension, bearing the trade stamp of S. Marti, 19 in. (48 cm.). **£450-500** *L*

A French gilt bronze mantel clock, the later 2 train movement with Brocot type suspension, signed Jn. Leroy a Paris, 12½ in. (31.7 cm.). **£400-450** *L*

A French clock, striking on a gong, with blue cloisonné and Chinese numerals and brass dogs of Fo, 14¾ in., c. 1890. **£950-1,100** *CCL*

A French gilt brass and enamel mantel clock, the 2 train movement with Brocot type suspension and gong striking, signed Leroy & Fils, Paris, 14.5 in. (37 cm.). **£400-500** *L*

A gilt bronze and porcelain mantel clock, the movement striking on a bell, French, 15 in. (38 cm.), third quarter of 19th C. **£300-350** *SC*

498

A gilt bronze glass and white marble mantel clock, the movement stamped Samuel Marti, the dial signed Galibert, Le Havre, 15¾ in. high (40 cm.), c. 1900. **£900-1,000** *S*

A green lacquer striking mantel clock, 16 in., c. 1900. **£220-240** *CCL*

A French silver metal and shagreen cased timepiece, the movement with lever escapement, 3¾ in. high (9½ cm.). **£150-200** *P*

A French balloon clock, with mother-of-pearl inlay, on brass feet, 11½ in., c. 1910. **£90-110** *CCL*

A spelter 'swinging elephant' clock, with Junhans movement, 11 in., c. 1900. **£150-180** *CCL*

A German timepiece, in the form of a miniature grandfather clock, 10½ in., c. 1880. **£60-80** *CCL*

A Bulle electric clock, the mechanism mounted behind the dial, 1 ft. 2½ in. high (41 cm.). **£120-150** *P*

A French Bulle clock, in mahogany case, 13½ in., c. 1920. **£140-160** *CCL*

An Austro-Hungarian gilt silver-coloured metal and enamel mantel timepiece, in the form of an eastern temple, 11 in. high (28 cm.). **£400-£500** *SS*

A James McCabe mahogany wall clock, the 12 in. white painted dial inscribed 'James McCabe, London', the chain-driven twin fusee movement with bell strike, 23 in. high (58 cm.). **£500-650** *SS*

An American striking gingerbread clock, by Newhaven Clock Co., 25 in., c. 1870. **£80-90** *CCL*
Original dial — many repainted.

An 18th C. German silver clock, the later lever movement contained in a broken arch case, 5¾ in. high (14.5 cm.). **£1,800-2,400** *C*

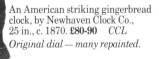

An 18th C. brass lantern clock for the Turkish market, having a posted frame surmounted by a bell and with a crescent finial above, the brass dial signed 'Geo. Clarke, Leaden Hall Street, London, no. 5399', the 2 train movement with countwheel strike and verge escapement, 11 in. high (28 cm.). **£800-900** *P*

A brass lantern clock, the dial engraved with flowerheads, signed 'Tho. Power Weallingborow', silvered chapter ring, posted frame movement with internal short bob, verge escapement and countwheel strike on bell, pierced frets, 15¼ in. high (39 cm.). **£1,600-2,000** *C*

A brass lantern clock, the movement with verge escapement, bob pendulum and outside countwheel, inscribed later Henry Jones in ye Temple, 15½ in. (39 cm.), early 18th C. **£1,000-1,200** *SC*

A lantern clock, the later brass dial with moon phase and well engraved with stars and allegories of the wind below a foliate pierced and engraved fret, the posted weight drive movement, probably French, converted to anchor escapement, 9½ in. (24 cm.), c. 1700. **£800-900** *SS*

A rare alarum lantern clock, the 6¼ in. dial signed 'Robert Cosbey at the dyall in Rood lane London', with narrow chapter ring and silvered alarum disc, the movement with reconverted balance wheel, the alarum work at the back, 15 in. high (38 cm.). **£2,500-3,000** *S*

A small alarum lantern timepiece, the dial signed 'Jno. Rolyat London', and with alarum disc and later minute hand, the movement with verge escapement and bob pendulum, 8¾ in. high (22 cm.). **£1,000-1,500** *S*

An 18th C. lantern clock, by N. Barwell, Bristol, the posted frame with pierced frets and surmounted by a bell, the movement with verge escapement and countwheel strike, 1 ft. 2 in. (36 cm.). **£1,200-1,500** *P*

A brass lantern clock, signed 'J. Davis Windsor' on the chapter ring and formerly with central alarm disc, 30-hour posted frame movement with verge escapement and countwheel strike on bell above, with alterations, 15 in. high (38 cm.). **£1,200-1,500** *C*

A rare quarter-striking lantern clock, the dial signed 'Marcos Peres London', the 3 train movement with verge escapement, bob pendulum and two bells, the central quarters train with countwheel mounted on the great wheel, the striking train with outside countwheel, 18 in. high (46 cm.). **£3,500-4,000** *S*

A wing alarum lantern clock, the 7½ in. dial with alarum disc and broad chapter ring, verge escapement, the pendulum between the 2 trains, and outside alarum work, in a posted frame with urn finials and foliate cresting pieces, 15 in. high (38 cm.). **£2,000-£2,500** *S*

A late Stuart brass miniature lantern clock, of typical form the florally engraved dial signed 'Thomas Knifton at the (Crossed Keys) in Lothbury Londini', with single pierced hand and narrow chapter ring, anchor escapement, countwheel strike on bell above, suspension loop and steady spikes, 8¾ in. high (23 cm.). **£2,500-3,000** C

A skeleton clock, the silvered chapter ring inscribed 'Ganthony Cheapside, London', the movement with deadbeat escapement and maintaining power, on a rosewood and cut brass base, striking on an overhead bell, 14½ in. (37 cm.), second quarter of the 19th C. **£1,500-2,000** SC

A 19th C. skeleton timepiece, based on the Scott monument, the single fusee movement with lever escapement and fast/slow adjustment, the brass frame pierced with Gothic tracery above a gilt figure of Scott and a dog, 18½ in. (47 cm.). **£600-800** SS

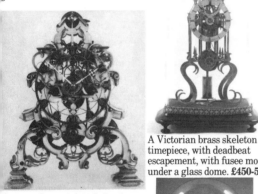

A very substantial 19th C. gilt brass chiming skeleton clock, the pierced chapter ring with blue enamelled numerals, the triple fusee movement with anchor escapement chiming on 8 bells, with mercury pendulum, in a massive scroll pierced frame with matted decoration inscribed 'Bennett, Cheapside, London', marble base missing, 23 in. high (59 cm.). **£8,000-9,000** SS

This is a superb example.

A Victorian brass skeleton timepiece, with deadbeat escapement, with fusee movement under a glass dome. **£450-500** JD

A Victorian brass skeleton timepiece, with fusee movement, under a glass dome. **£350-400** JD

A Victorian brass skeleton timepiece, with fusee movement, under glass dome, with one-at-the-hour strike. **£350-400** JD

An early Victorian brass striking skeleton clock, of Lichfield Cathedral type, annular chapter ring above the signature 'G. Rossi Norwich', the movement with chain fusees, 6 spoked wheels, deadbeat escapement, micrometer regulated pendulum, stepped base on oval wood stand with mother-of-pearl inlay, 16½ in. high (42 cm.). **£650-850** C

An unusual skeleton timepiece, with annular chapter ring signed 'Wm. Smith Musselburgh Maker & Inventor', the movement driven by a spiral spring and with chain fusee, the chain running under a pulley holding the spring, 6 slender columns framing the spring, on a circular oak base, 16 in. high (41 cm.). **£1,200-1,400** S

A skeleton clock of York Minster type, the movement with chain fusees and anchor escapement, the half hours struck on a bell and the hours on a gong, in a typical pierced frame supported on a bow-ended grey veined white marble base, 23 in. high (58.5 cm.). **£1,400-1,600** S

Left
A 19th C. French brass skeleton clock, with unusual 3 wheel train movement, under glass dome. **£600-700** JD

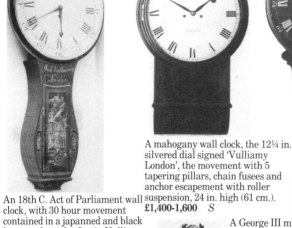

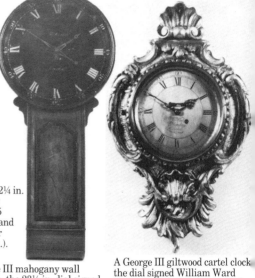

An 18th C. Act of Parliament wall clock, with 30 hour movement contained in a japanned and black lacquered case by Justin Vulliamy of London, 4 ft. 1 in. high, c. 1750. **£4,000-4,500** *AG*

A mahogany wall clock, the 12¼ in. silvered dial signed 'Vulliamy London', the movement with 5 tapering pillars, chain fusees and anchor escapement with roller suspension, 24 in. high (61 cm.). **£1,400-1,600** *S*

A George III mahogany wall timepiece, the 23½ in. dial signed W. Thomas Lincoln, the movement with tapering plates, anchor escapement, 4 ft. 11 in. high (150 cm.). **£1,300-1,500** *S*

A George III giltwood cartel clock the dial signed William Ward Bloomsbury London, 21 in. high (58 cm.). **£1,100-1,500** *C*

A George III giltwood cartel clock, signed Grayham London, 29 in. high (74 cm.). **£2,300-2,600** *C*

An Empire bronze and gilt bronze wall clock, the dial signed Mme. Gentilhomme, Palais Royal à Paris, 3 ft. high (91.5 cm.), early 19th C. **£2,600-3,000** *S*

An English 10 in. convex double fusee wall clock, 10 in., c. 1880. **£430-450** *CCL*

An 8-day wall clock. **£120-150** *GBT*

An English fusee dial clock, signed by Oetzmann & Co., 16 in., c. 1900. **£110-120** *CCL*

A German gilt metal clock, the backplate signed Johann Michael Brugel fecit in Wurtzburg, distressed, now lacking the countwheel, crownwheel and front swinging pendulum, 15 in. high (38 cm.), basically 17th C. **£5,000-£6,000** *C*

A gilt bronze wall clock, the movement stamped Bernard, Lyov à Paris, signed Devie La Rochelle, 16 in. high (41 cm.), c. 1880. **£500-£600** *S*

An 18th C. Friezland painted tin wall clock, with alarm, 12 in. (30 cm.). **£1,100-1,500** *SS*

A late 19th C. French gilt brass wall clock, the movement with be strike, 32 in. high (81 cm.). **£500-£600** *SS*

A gilt bronze and porcelain clock garniture, the dial signed Howell & James Paris, 1 ft. 2 in. (36 cm.), with pendulum, flanked by a pair of candelabra, 1 ft. 10½ in. (57 cm.), 2 glass domes, 3 gilt bases, c. 1870. **£1,700-1,900** *S*

A gilt bronze and porcelain clock garniture, 22½ in. high (57 cm.), and a pair of candelabra, 18½ in. high (47 cm.), c. 1880. **£900-1,200** *S*

A Japanese striking pillar clock, the striking mechanism forming the weight within the trunk, length overall 47 cm., 19th C. **£950-£1,050** *S*

A gilt bronze and white marble clock garniture, the dial signed Gille l'Aine à Paris, 15 in. high (38 cm.), and a pair of candelabra, 13¼ in. high (34 cm.), c. 1890. **£550-750** *S*

A composed second Empire parcel gilt bronze clock garniture, 1 ft. 4 in. (41 cm.), and a pair of candelabra, each with 3 candle nozzles, 1 ft. 2 in. (36 cm.), c. 1850. **£1,400-1,600** *S*

A gilt bronze and blue ceramic clock garniture, 1 ft. 10½ in. (57 cm.), with a pair of candelabra, 1 ft. 11 in. (58 cm.), c. 1890. **£1,700-2,000** *S*

A composed gilt bronze and white marble clock garniture, 1 ft. 8½ in. (52 cm.), and a pair of candelabra, 1 ft. 5¼ in. (44 cm.), c. 1880. **£3,000-£3,500** *S*

A mid 19th C. French clock garniture, inscribed 'Regnant À. Paris', with striking German movement, flanked by two 7-light candelabra with vase supports, 23½ by 27 in. high. **£500-600** *WHL*

A 19th C. French gilt metal and porcelain clock garniture, the clock with 8-day movement striking on one bell, 15¼ in. high, and with a pair of urns, 12 in. high. **£400-£500** *Bea*

A Victorian marble clock set, surmounted by bronze figures. **£350-400** *JD*

A large gilt spelter and red marble clock garniture, 3 ft. 3 in. (96 cm.), flanked by a pair of candelabra, with restorations, 3 ft. 4 in. (102 cm.), c. 1890. **£1,200-1,400** *S*

A square gilt metal verge table clock, with alarum by Franz Kreittmayr of Prague, 11 cm. square, early 18th C. **£2,800-3,400** *S*

A square gilt metal striking table clock, the going side with detached fusee gut, verge escapement, later brass balance and spring, 10.8 cm. square, c. 1640. **£2,500-3,000**   *S*

A square German gilt metal striking table clock, with alarum, the iron and brass frame with iron trains throughout, iron fusee with gut for the going, standing barrel for the striking, and sounding on a bell between the plates, later plain balance with spring contained within the circle of the countwheel, on 4 later bun feet, 120 mm. square, second half of the 16th C. **£5,000-6,000**   *S*

A gilt brass timepiece table compendium, the movement with defective lever escapement and plain steel 3-arm balance, in original leather covered case bearing the trade label of John Cockburn, 28 George St., Richmond, base 9 in. wide (23 cm.). **£3,000-4,000**   *L*

This fine quality English movement strongly resembles the work of Thomas Cole, the one slight variation being the pivots of the barrel arbor, which though finely finished, vary slightly in size.

A German gilt metal standing table clock, by Samuel Haug, Augsburg, the movement with brass trains, fusee and chain for the going train, verge escapement, converted to pendulum, alarum train lacking, 460 mm. high overall, early 17th C. **£10,000-£12,000**   *S*

An unusual early 19th C. mantel timepiece, the skeletonised 3½ in. dial pierced with compass and dividers, the movement with circular plates, pinwheel escapement and half seconds pendulum, the base mounted with Masonic symbols, 15 in. high (38 cm.), with a glass dome. **£1,300-£1,500**   *S*

A South German gilt metal table clock, the movement signed Georg Schmidt August, engraved resting barrels for the countwheel strike and for the going with later bridge cock, lacking balance, 12¼ in. high (31 cm.), substantially c. 1625. **£5,000-6,000**   *C*

A German gilt metal hexagonal table clock, now with 19th C. striking movement, the original frame pillars remaining, 430 mm high, early 17th C. **£4,000-5,000**   *S*

A small oak regulator, with minute bell, signed Earnshaw, London, the movement with a train of 3 wheels, Huygens' winding, deadbeat escapement with wood pendulum rod and provision for striking one at the minute, door lacking, swelling trunk and rectangular plinth, 5 ft. 6 in. high (168 cm.). **£2,500-3,000**   *S*

Such clocks are sometimes termed journeyman's clocks. The bell may be used at will for rating and regulating purposes in the workshop.

A 19th C. French table clock, by Vittoz, Paris. **£650-750**   *DWB*

A German gilt metal tabernacle table clock, the movement with brass top and base plates, the cornerposts and trains basically of iron but with brass fusees, countwheel and contrate wheel for the later verge escapement, now lacking the side-swinging pendulum, distressed, with alterations, 13 in. high (33 cm.), c. 1600. **£4,500-5,000**   *C*

A brass lighthouse clock, with a revolving glass drum-cased clock face, with brass pointer and small figure of a sailor, English, 21 in. high (53.5 cm.), mid 19th C. **£200-£300**   *S*

A mahogany longcase regulator, the 8-day movement with deadbeat escapement, Harrison's maintaining power, shouldered heavy plates, signed P.G. Wilson, Inverness, 6 ft. 7½ in. **£750-850**   *L*

A Scottish mahogany regulator, the 10¼ in. dial signed Alexander Ferguson Cupar Fife, the 6 pillar movement with maintaining power and 4 wheel train, with anchor escapement and seconds pendulum with wood rod, 4 ft. 1 in. high (124.5 cm.). **£3,200-4,000**   *S*
Recorded working in 1780.

An unusual ormolu-mounted mahogany month regulator, the enamel dial signed Lepaute A Paris and also Dubuisson, the striking movement with 3 plates and 5 wheels in each train, the weight-driven going train between the front 2 plates and with delicately cut wheels and deadbeat escapement, the anchor with a long shaft and the pendulum with beat adjustment and black-painted metal rod, the striking train between the back 2 plates and with outside countwheel, 7 ft. high (214 cm.). **£5,500-6,500**   *S*

A rare late Louis XVI mahogany month regulator, signed Antide Janvier in gilt and Coteau in red script, the movement with shaped plates, offset winding squares, 4 wheel trains and pin-wheel escapement, the pendulum suspended from the backboard and with beat adjustment, 9-bar compensation rod, enamel temperature indication and lenticular bob, 6 ft. 10 in. high (208 cm.). **£17,000-19,000**   *S*

A gilt metal strut clock, by Thos. Cole, No. 1058, retailed by London & Ryder, 17 New Bond Street, London, the signed going barrel movement with plain steel balance to lever escapement and attached key wind, 5¾ in. high (14.5 cm.). **£700-900**   *C*

A 19th C. turret clock, by W. Benson, Ludgate Hill, London, with going and striking train on iron frame with weights and pendulum, frame 40 by 20 in. **£550-£650**   *WHL*

An 18th C. brass-framed sand clock, with half and full hour glasses, 4½ in. high (11.4 cm.). **£600-700**   *P*

A silver pair cased verge watch, No. 338 by William Kipling of London, the movement with pierced Egyptian pillars and winged masked balance cock with broad pierced foot, 5.8 cm. diam., c. 1710. **£800-1,000**   *S*

A silver pair cased alarum verge watch, signed Autram, London, No. 431, 5.8 cm. diam. **£2,000-2,500**   *Bon*

Joseph Autram, a. 1697, cc. 1706, died 1723.
Watchmaker and clockmaker to George I.

A silver pair cased verge watch, signed on the backplate T. Tompion E. Banger London, the inner case lacking the winding shutter and with the number 3330, 5.5 cm. diam., early 18th C. **£1,300-1,600**   *S*

A good gold pair cased centre seconds Duplex watch, by John Henderson of Dumferline, dated AD 1806, both cases hallmarked 1804, 5.5 cm. diam., and with short gold chain and key. **£1,100-1,300** S

A gold quarter-repeating Duplex watch, No. 6530, by Barwise of London, the full plate movement with plain 3-armed balance, hallmarked 1815, 5.4 cm. diam. **£1,000-1,300** S

An 18 ct. gold open faced keywound lever watch, the fusee movement No. 1618 and signed J. & W. Howden & Co., Southbridge, Edinburgh, hallmarked London 1820, 5.3 cm. **£400-500** SC

A gold quarter-repeating musical watch, 6 cm. diam., c. 1820. **£2,500-£3,000** S

A good gold Massey crank roller lever watch, No. 8535, by S. I. Tobias & Co. of Liverpool, the movement with plain gold balance and Liverpool jewelling, regulator with compensation curb, 5.1 cm. diam., c. 1820. **£600-750** S

A silver pair cased centre seconds verge watch, by Thos. Brown, Birmingham, No. 6521, hallmarked London 1821, 5.5 cm. **£180-220** SC

An 18 ct. yellow gold cased open faced pocket watch, the gilt fusee lever movement with maintaining power, signed John Kidder, London No. 557, hallmarked London 1821. **£300-400** SS

A good gold lever watch, No. 1844, by Charles Spears of Liverpool, the half-plate movement with plain gold balance, hallmarked Chester 1832, 5 cm. diam. **£800-900** S

An 18 ct. yellow gold hunting cased stop seconds pocket watch, the gilt three-quarter plate lever movement with compensation balance, signed 'Reid & Sons, Newcastle on Tyne', with subsidiary seconds and 60-minute recorder dial, No. 16677, gold cuvette. **£300-350** SS

An 18 ct. gold open faced keywound lever watch, by Litherland Davies & Co., Liverpool, No. 21621, with a three-quarter plate movement, bi-metallic compensated balance, hallmarked Chester, 1842, 5 cm. **£250-300** SC

A gold pair cased quarter repeating lever watch, signed Eardley Norton, London, 5.7 cm. diam. **£900-1,000** P

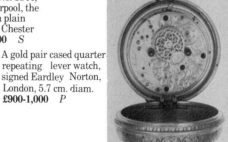

A heavy gold hunting cased keyless lever watch, movement inscribed E. Howard & Co. Boston, 205649 and with the letter N, 5.7 cm. diam., c. 1875. **£1,400-1,600**   *S*

A gold hunter cased lever watch, the nickel plated bar movement signed Jules Jurgensen Copenhagen No. 8849 on the barrel bridge, with large compensated balance, 5.6 cm. diam. **£2,200-2,500** *C*

A gold repousse pair cased verge watch, the movement signed 'Cha⁵. Clay London 959', repainted enamel dial, London –?–, 4.7 cm. diam. **£1,000-1,200**   *C*

An 18 ct. gold lighter watch, by Dunhill, 4 by 3.7 cm., import mark London 1928. **£600-800**   *S*

A gold open faced fusee keyless lever watch, No. 2945 by Arnold & Lewis Late Simmons, 7 St. Anns Square, Manchester, the half-plate movement with compensation balance, hallmarked 1931, 5.1 cm. diam. **£600-700**   *S*

A gold hunter cased Tourbillon watch, the movement signed 'Cha⁵. Frodsham 27 South Molton Street London, AD FMsz No. 09790', with one minute tourbillon carriage, lever escapement, overcoiled free sprung blued spring, 2-arm bi-metallic compensated balance, keyless wound fusee and chain, the case London 1918, maker's mark H.M.F., 6.1 cm. diam. **£28,000-£32,000**   *C*

A rare silver 'Purse' lighter watch by Dunhill, 4.3 by 4.7 cm., import mark London 1927. **£500-600**   *S*

A mid 18th C. gold single cased repeating pocket watch, the verge movement inscribed 'Isaac and Jacques Rey, Freres'. **£800-900** *PWC*

A Louis XVI gold and enamelled case watch, the keywind movement with verge escapement, inscribed 'Vauchez, à Paris, No. 13845'. **£1,000-1,200**   *GC*

Daniel Vaucher, or Vauchez, an eminent maker, is recorded 1767-86; his son, Jean Henri Vaucher, 1779-89; and Louis Theodore Vaucher was born in 1775 and died in 1806.

A gold hunter cased minute-repeating keyless lever chronograph, the movement signed 'Chas. Frodsham London AD Fmsz No. 09764', London 1903, 4.9 cm. diam., leather case. **£3,000-3,500** *C*

A repousse gold pair cased quarter-repeating verge watch, No. 7902, by Williamson of London, in original fishskin outer protecting case, 5.5 cm. diam., mid 18th C. **£3,000-3,500**   *S*

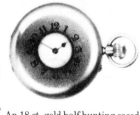

An 18 ct. gold half hunting cased keyless lever watch, the three-quarter plate movement No. 275316, hallmarked London 1914, 4.9 cm. diam. **£350-450**   *SC*

A silver verge oignon, No. 7 by Etienne Dominice, 5.8 cm. diam., early 18th C. **£1,300-1,500**   *S*

A Louis XVI gold case watch, maker's mark H.D., the keywind verge escapement inscribed 'Gudin à Paris'. **£800-1,000** *GC*

A gold and split pearl centre seconds Duplex watch, for the Chinese market by Bovet of Fleurier, with glazed polished steel movement, 5.6 cm. diam., early 19th C. **£4,000-5,000** *S*

A late 18th C. French gold cased open-faced verge fusee pocket watch, signed 'Ch^{les.} Bertrand à Paris, No. 8379'. **£300-400** *SS*

A silver verge alarum watch, No. 3756 by Charles Oudin of the Palais Royal, 5.7 cm. diam., c. 1820. **£400-500** *S*

A gilt metal and tortoiseshell quarter-repeating verge watch, for the Turkish market by JN. leRoy à Paris, No. 15210, hands lacking and chipped, 6 cm. **£300-400** *SC*

A French gold quarter-repeating cylinder watch, the movement with plain balance, gilt cuvette signed Robert O. Courvoisier, stamped K 18 24870 PHMI 1785, 6.0 cm. diam. **£1,600-2,000** *C*

A French gold verge watch, the bridge cock movement signed Jn. LeRoy À Paris, 4.7 cm. diam. **£900-£1,000** *C*

A French gold quarter-repeating cylinder watch, the Lepine calibre movement with plain steel balance, the gilt cuvette signed Baullier à Paris, 5.4 cm. diam. **£900-1,000** *C*

A small gold cylinder watch, No. 12461 by Charles Oudin et Fils of Palais Royal No. 52, 2.1 cm. diam., 19th C. **£400-500** *S*

A French gold quarter-repeating cylinder watch, the Lepine calibre movement with overcoiled blued spring, plain balance, hanging barrel, repeating via 2 hammers on gongs, gilt cuvette signed L. Epine à Paris No. 7875, 6.1 cm. diam. **£1,200-1,400** *C*

A Swiss gold open face watch, with single hand, signed American Watch Case Co., No. 88467, 4.3 cm. diam. **£300-£400** *CNY*

A good slim gold and champleve enamel cylinder watch, No. 10737 by Edward Robert Theurer, of Chaux-de-Fonds, 4.5 cm. diam., c. 1850. **£1,900-2,200** *S*

A Swiss 14 ct. gold hunter-cased calendar chronograph, the split plate movement with overcoiled blued spring, 5.5 cm. diam. **£1,700-£2,000** *C*

A Swiss gold hunting cased keyless pocket chronometer, No. 9989, the damescened nickel movement with wolf's tooth winding, pivoted detent escapement, compensation balance, 5.3 cm. diam., c. 1870. **£900-1,200** *S*

An American parti-coloured gold hunting cased watch, the keyless lever movement with compensation balance, signed 'Elgin National Watch Co., Elgin'. **£250-300** *SS*

A Swiss gold and enamel verge watch, the bridge-cock movement signed Ph^e. Terrot Geneve 15706, 5.7 cm. diam. **£900-1,100** *C*

A silver gilt satchel, containing a Swiss cylinder movement, dated 1876, pendent from a short chain and loop, 2.8 cm. long. **£450-550** *S*

An 18 ct. gold Swiss hunter-cased keyless lever minute repeating chronograph, 5.8 cm., c. 1900. **£2,300-3,000** *Re*

A Swiss 19th C. full hunting cased gentleman's pocket watch, the jewelled keyless lever movement with compensation balance, dated 1884. **£500-600** *SS*

An American triple-colour gold hunting cased keyless lever pocket watch, the nickel bar movement with countersunk jewelling, compensation balance, signed Time King, Illinois Watch Co., No. 3744871'. **£500-600** *SS*

A silver and silver gilt Continental verge watch, signed Johann Geo Braun Augustae, 5.9 cm. long. **£1,300-1,600** *P*

An American gold keyless lever watch, the nickel plated three-quarter plate movement signed Am. Watch Co. Waltham Mass. Safety Pinion, 1805515, gold cuvette signed J.E. Caldwell & Co. Philadelphia, hair cracks, case plain, inscribed cover interior, 5.2 cm. diam. **£500-600** *C*

A gold automatic oyster wristwatch, by Rolex, 3.3 cm., c. 1950. **£700-800** *S*

An 18 ct. gold automatic perpetual calendar moonphase wristwatch, by Patek Philippe, Model No. 27460 Q, Movement No. 1119298, 3.7 cm., with a fitted 18 ct. gold strap with box and instructions, import mark London 1973. **£7,000-£8,000** *S*

An 18 ct. gold wristwatch, by Patek Philippe, the movement signed and No. 952275, 3.5 cm., stamped .750, with a strap, c. 1940. **£400-600** *S*

An 18 ct. gold wristwatch, by Patek Philippe, No. 631425, 2 by 4.2 cm., with a 9 ct. gold strap, import mark London 1949. **£900-1,000** *S*

A gold automatic oyster wristwatch, by Rolex, 3.4 cm., with a flexible strap, c. 1955. **£350-500** *S*

A gold automatic oyster wristwatch, by Rolex, 3.4 cm., with a gold strap. **£800-1,000** *S*

An 18 ct. gold Vacheron-Constantin watch, on a lizard skin strap. **£1,000-1,200** *HGA*

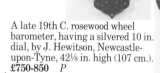

A late 19th C. rosewood wheel barometer, having a silvered 10 in. dial, by J. Hewitson, Newcastle-upon-Tyne, 42⅛ in. high (107 cm.). **£750-850** *P*

An 18 ct. gold Vacheron et Constantin wristwatch. **£550-650** *SC*

A gold and diamond wristwatch, by Vacheron & Constantin, c. 1975. **£1,000-1,300** *S*

A mid 19th C. wheel barometer, by F. Belloni, of Shaftesbury, in figured mahogany case. **£500-600** *LBP*

An 18th ct. gold Prince wristwatch, by Rolex, No. 74997, 2 by 4 cm., import mark Glasgow 1930. **£1,100-1,300** *S*

A rosewood and mother-of-pearl combined barometer and timepiece, the timepiece dial inscribed 'Gabriele, 61 Cornhill, London', 48 in. (122 cm.), mid 19th C. **£400-500** *SC*

A banjo barometer, by G. Kalabergo of Banbury, in mahogany case with boxwood stringing, 3 ft. 2 in. high (97 cm.), c. 1820. **£300-400** *SS*

An 18 ct. gold wristwatch, by Vacheron & Constantin, No. 448846, stamped .750, 3.1 cm., c. 1950. **£600-700** *S*

An 18 ct. white gold diamond and sapphire wristwatch, by Rolex, 1.5 by 2.9 cm., import mark Glasgow 1924. **£600-700** *S*

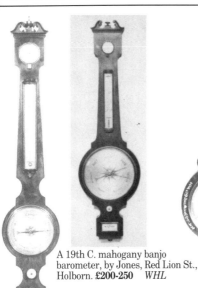

A 19th C. mahogany banjo barometer, by Jones, Red Lion St., Holborn. **£200-250** *WHL*

A mahogany and ebony lined banjo barometer, signed 'Dollond, London', 36½ in., early 19th C. **£900-1,000** *CSK*

A rosewood and mother-of-pearl wheel barometer, the 9½ in. silvered dial signed 'Pozzai, Liverpool', restored, 40 in. overall (102 cm.), mid 19th C. **£250-300** *SC*

A 19th C. inlaid barometer, by F. Postorelli London, 3 ft. 6 in. high. **£100-150** *GM*

A Georgian mahogany and boxwood lined clock/banjo barometer, the timepiece watch movement signed W.G. Shaw, London 825, the spirit level signed John Bond, Warranted Coton, 34½ in. high. **£650-750** *CSK*

A 19th C. rosewood stick barometer, the ivory plates engraved 'Jones, Optician, 201 Strand, London', 38 in. high (96.5 cm.). **£350-450** *P*

A George III mahogany stick barometer, by Dolland, London. **£1,500-1,800** *DWB*

A 19th C. mahogany banjo barometer, by Stebbing, Southampton 39 in. high. **£160-200** *CLG*

A mid Georgian walnut stick barometer, the calibrated gauges signed 'M. Ash, Birmm', the base inlaid with ivory with a Tonbridgeware lozenge, 37 in. high (94 cm). **£2,000-2,500** *C*

A late 18th C. mahogany stick barometer, signed 'M. Berge', London', 37 in. high (94 cm.). **£600- £700** *P*

A 19th C. mahogany bow-front ship's barometer, engraved 'Bradford, Minories, London, Improved Marine', 36½ in. high (92.7 cm.). **£750-850** *P*

A Bennett mahogany marine stick barometer, signed 'T. Bennett, Cork', behind door, now lacking mercury thermometer, with brass suspension ring, lacking gimbal mount, Irish, 38 in. high (96.5 cm.), second quarter 19th C. **£500-600** *S*

A Victorian walnut stick barometer, the ivory plates engraved 'Gargony, 41 Bull Street, Birmingham', 42¾ in. high (108.6 cm.). **£220-280** *P*

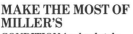

A 19th C. Admiral Fitzroy's storm barometer, by Negretti & Zambra, London. **£300-350** *WHL*

511

An early 19th C. figure mahogany stick barometer, with satinwood stringing, inscribed 'Molliner Fecit'. **£650-750** *LBP*

A 19th C. walnut stick barometer, the ivory plates inscribed 'L. Casella, Maker to the Admiralty, London, 37½ in. high (95.2 cm.). **£350-450** *P*

A Nugent Wells mahogany marine stick barometer, ivory 27 to 31 scale, divided into tenths together with vernier, English, 37 in. high (94 cm.), second quarter of the 19th C. **£500-600** *S*

A fine late Georgian mahogany bow fronted stick barometer, signed 'Verthington and Allan London', 39 in. high (99 cm.). **£1,300-1,500** *C*

A late Georgian mahogany bow-fronted stick barometer, silvered scale signed 'Ramsden London', with vernier, 39 in. high (99 cm.). **£1,700-2,000** *C*

A good mahogany stick barometer, the ivory register inscribed 'Steel & Son, Dukes Place, Wapping, Liverpool', 40½ in. (103 cm.), mid 19th C. **£900-1,000** *SC*

A rosewood ship's barometer, the ivory register inscribed 'I. & A. Walker, Liverpool', 39 in. (99 cm.), second quarter of the 19th C. **£1,000-1,200** *SC*

A William IV mahogany pillar barometer, 38 in. **£700-800** *CSK*

A Georgian bow front 'flame' mahogany stick barometer, the silvered dial signed 'Vassali, Scarborough', the reverse applied with a trade label from A. Rizzi, 40⅛ in. high (102 cm.). **£800-900** *P*

A marine stick barometer, mounted with mercury thermometer and sympiesometer, English, 36½ in. high (93 cm.), third quarter of the 19th C. **£800-£900** *S*

A W. J. Salmon mahogany marine stick barometer, mahogany body inlaid with mother-of-pearl decoration and applied with mercury thermometer, English, 37½ in. high (95 cm.), mid 19th C. **£700-800** *S*

A stick barometer, inscribed 'Standard No. 663', above a japanned trunk, 46 in. (107 cm.), late 19th/early 20th C. **£250-350** *SC*

A George III mahogany stick barometer, the silvered register signed 'J. B. Daneer, Manchester', and with dual verniers including Yesterday Noon, inlaid throughout with ebony lines, 38 in. (96 cm.), early 19th C. **£850-950** *SC*

The less usual features increasing the value of this barometer include facilities for more information such as dual verniers and the construction of the case, i.e. the bow front trunk.

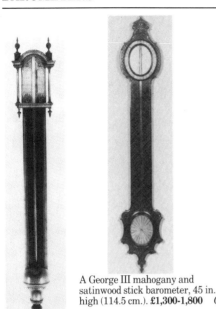

A George III mahogany and satinwood stick barometer, 45 in. high (114.5 cm.). **£1,300-1,800** *C*

An unusual early walnut wall barometer, top finial lacking, 40 in. high (102 cm.). **£2,000-2,500** *S*

See Nicholas Goodison, English Barometers 1680-1860, plate 8, for a reproduction of John Patrick's second advertisement, datable to c. 1710, wherein a very similar barometer is illustrated.

A George III mahogany stick barometer, 39 in. high (99 cm.). **£650-950** *SS*

A rare George III inlaid mahogany stick barometer, with a free-standing hygrometer, supported by brass scrolls and with provision for adjustment, 40 in. high (102 cm.). **£1,000-1,400** *S*

A brass marine stick barometer, English, 36 in. high (92 cm.), 20th C. **£400-500** *S*

A 2-day marine chronometer, by John Bruce & Sons, 7¼ in. wide. **£700-900** *Bea*

A small 2-day marine chronometer, by Brockbank & Atkins, No. 1239, with Earnshaw spring detent escapement, compensated balance wheel, diam. of bezel 4 in. **£950-£1,050** *Bea*

A small 2-day marine chronometer, by Brockbank & Atkins, No. 1124, Earnshaw spring detent escapement, compensation balance, diam. of bezel 100 mm. **£1,200-£1,500** *S*

A rare early 19th C. Continental mountain altitude barometer, the brass nameplate signed 'Rordorf, Toledo N.286 à Naples, and further engraved 'Honble Henry R. Westenrà', 50 in. high standing (127 cm.). **£650-750** *P*

An 8-day marine chronometer, signed 'French, Royal Exchange, London, No. 7474', the movement with Earnshaw spring detent escapement, with trade label in the lid of John Walden, 5 York Street, Jersey, diam. of bezel 130 mm. **£3,000-3,500** *S*

A 2-day marine chronometer, the spotted movement signed 'Charles Frodsham, London', Earnshaw spring detent escapement, compensation balance, diam. of bezel 125 mm. **£1,300-1,500** *S*

A very rare 'Paul Ditisheim' 2-day marine chronometer, the Earnshaw escapement with spring steel detent secured to side of gilded banking block, cut bi-metallic balance with compensation screws, contained in brass bowl and gimbals in 3-tier mahogany brass-bound box, with ivory plaques inscribed 'Paul Ditisheim 144 La Chaux de Fonds', 100 mm. diam. **£4,500-5,500** *C*

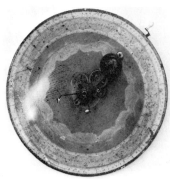

An Aide and Wedderburn brass and steel Universal equatorial dial, hinged chapter ring engraved on two faces, gnomon and folding latitude quadrant, in mahogany case, Scottish, 5½ in. wide (140 mm.), mid 19th C. **£500-600** *S*

A Newton & Co. table orrery, applied with print of a calendar, compass points and zodiac constellations, lacking 3 turned wood feet, and spheres representing the sun, earth and moon, English, 17 in. (435 mm.), early 19th C. **£1,500-1,800** *S*

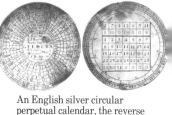

A rare German brass astrolabe, signed GE HART, dated 1524. **£15,000-18,000** *CNY*

An important gilt metal compendium dial, by Erasmus Habermel, signed on the obverse, the reverse with zodiacal scale, the movable pointer possibly adapted and dial for Horae Generales, a plumb to one side, gilding worn and with later strut stand, 117 by 107 mm., c. 1580. **£9,000-11,000** *C*

An English silver circular perpetual calendar, the reverse engraved with the names of the months and number of days, Saints' Days, Dominical Letter, starting with 1689, Epacts, golden numbers, etc., 2⅞ in. (73 mm.), 1689. **£1,100-1,500** *S*

Sold with the lot is an explanation from the Science Museum on the workings of the instrument.

A German ivory diptych dial, the cover with wind compass, the interior with vertical and horizontal dials and inset compass, signed and dated Nicholaus Miller 1651, stamped with his device, a crown, 90 mm. closed. **£1,300-1,600** *C*

A French ivory and pewter diptych dial, of Dieppe type, the cover with equatorial dial, the interior with volvelle for lunar and year calendar and azimuth dial, signed Charles Bloud le Jeune A Dieppe, 81 mm. closed, c. 1700. **£1,100-£1,400** *C*

A Gabriel Bloud ivory diptych dial, the upper outer dial engraved with pin gnomon dial and floral decoration, signed Fait apr Gabriel Bloud a Dieppen, French, 3¼ in. by 2¾ in. by ½ in. when closed (8.3 by 7 by 1.3 cm.), c. 1660. **£1,400-1,700** *S*

From the construction of the compass rose it is apparent that there originally would have been an elliptical scale adjusted by the disc inset in the base; this scale is now missing. For illustrations of similar dials see F. A. B. Ward, European Scientific Instruments, No. 112.

A Charles Bloud ivory diptych dial, the upper outer face engraved with equinoctial pin-gnomon dial on 0-12-0 scale, pin housed in compartment at side, now missing, the inner lower face inset with magnetic compass with rose engraved with four cardinal points, French, when closed 6 by 22¾ by 27½ in. (155 by 576 by 695 mm.), c. 1660. **£1,900-2,200** *S*

A German gilt metal pocket dial, for latitudes 48°/49°, signed Johann Willebrand in Augsburg 48, fitted tooled leather case, 48 mm. square. **£2,200-2,400** *C*

A John Bird brass sundial, mounted with shaped gnomon for latitude 54°50, English, third quarter of the 18th C. **£280-340** *S*

An early French sundial and compass. **£1,000-1,300** *HGA*

A German gilt metal octagonal pocket dial, by Johan Martin Augsburg, the folding plumb bob bracket with latitude adjustment for the string gnomon, gnomon fixing bar broken, leather case, 67 mm., early 18th C. **£1,700-2,000** *C*

A Francis Wollaston moveable planisphere, published by J. Cary, English, published 1829. **£250-300** *S*

A wood armillary sphere, by Georg Edelamare of Paris, with printed paper covered ecliptic, the centre with terrestrial globe, French, 20½ in. high (52 cm.), 18th C. **£700-£1,000** *S*

A brass Butterfield dial, signed Butterfield a Paris, the octagonal dial with inset magnetic compass, spring-loaded bird gnomon and engraved with four hour scales for latitudes 43°, 46°, 49° and 52°, in original leather base, French, 3 in. long (7.5 cm.), c. 1700. **£650-750** *S*

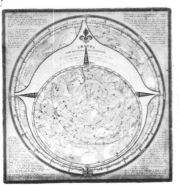

A Smith's new moveable planisphere, to ascertain the position of the stars at any time, with revolving cardboard disc printed with the heavens, English, published 1850, 15½ in. square (394 mm.). **£200-250** *S*

A Chapotot brass Butterfield dial, the octagonal dial with 3 hour scales, spring loaded folding gnomon, French, 2⅜ in. wide (6 cm.), early 18th C. **£600-700** *S*

A Chinese ivory combined sundial and compass, by Jiang Huiynan of Fengshan, the sundial adjusted by a folding strut, hinged brass gnomon, the fixed compass engraved with the cardinal points and inscribed with 12 Terrestrial branches (signs of the Zodiac), 19th C. **£650-750** *S*

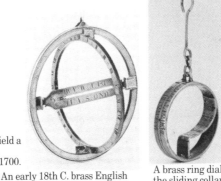

A Butterfield silver dial, the octagonal plate signed Butterfield a Paris, in original leather case, French, 2 in. long (50 mm.), c. 1700. **£800-1,000** *S*

An early 18th C. brass English Universal equinoctial ring dial, unsigned, the meridian ring engraved on one side in two quadrants and on the other with a 0-90° scale for determining the sun's meridian altitude, 8 in. diam. (20.3 cm.). **£1,400-1,800** *P*

A brass ring dial, the sliding collar having a single pin hole, with outer, inner and supplementary scales, the inner bar stamped P.S. (Proctor, Sheffield?), 1⁹⁄₁₆ in. diam. (4 cm.). **£280-340** *P*

A Dutch brass Universal ring dial, signed H. Sneewins Fecit, 130 mm. diam. of meridian ring. **£1,800-£2,200** *CNY*

Henricus Sneewins was part of a family of instrument makers active in the mid 17th C.

A brass Universal ring dial, with sliding suspension to meridian ring engraved with latitude scale for northern and southern hemispheres, and with 0° to 90° altitude scale on reverse, 95 mm. diam. of meridian ring, 18th C. **£800-1,000** *CNY*

A 19th C. brass equinoctial dial by Walter Busnell, Calcutta. **£400-500** *P*

A rare Aegidius quinniet brass combined Universal equinoctial dial and nocturnal, lettered around the base, Horologium Universale factore Aegidio Quingnet Antuerp, Antwerp, 2 in. diam. (50.8 mm.), c. 1560. **£9,000-11,000** *S*

A Universal equinoctial dial by this maker in the Brussels Royal Museum of Art and History is signed Egidius Quingnet and dated 1557.

A George Adams brass walker's meridianal compass, signed Invented by R. Walker Made by Geo. Adams, and small condenser sliding over a calendar scale, in mahogany case on later stand, English, late 18th C. **£4,000-5,000** *S*

This unusual compass was presented by Ralph Walker of Jamaica in 1793 as a means of finding longitude at sea by the magnetic variation. The sundial mounted above the compass indicates true north when adjusted for solar time and the difference between this reading and the compass heading was deemed to be the variation.

A rare W. Hooper overhead of 'tell-tale' compass, the 5 inch diam. printed compass card suspended in brass drum case, English, 9 in. wide (23 cm.), early 19th C. **£650-£750** *S*

A turned ivory compass, the 4 inch. diam. printed compass card by Lerebours, pivoted under glass cover, French, 5½ in. diam. (14 cm.), late 19th C. **£400-450** *S*

A boxwood and brass combined clinometer and compass, fitted with two levels and fore and aft sights, by T. Cooke & Sons Ltd. **£100-140** *P*

A rare 3 inch pocket globe by Charles Price, early 18th C. **£1,600-£2,000** *S*

This globe is in remarkably good condition. Charles Price was, by apprenticeship, a clockmaker, but worked as an instrument maker, globe maker and cartographer.

An early 19th C. pocket globe, labelled Newton's new and improved Terrestrial Globe, and bearing the information of Captain Cook and other navigators' transoceanic journeys, 2⅞ in. diam. (7.5 cm.). **£600-700** *P*

An early 19th C. mahogany travelling globe, contained in a turned mahogany case. **£500-600** *S (WJS)*

A 2¾ inch Nathaniel Hill pocket globe, the sphere applied with hand-coloured gores and printed A New Terrestrial Globe by Nath Hill 1754, English, published 1754. **£800-1,000** *S*

A 2¾ inch Dollond pocket globe, the sphere applied with hand-coloured gores, tropics, equinoctial line poles and other details with cartouche overlaid with plate printed Dollond London 1809, English, early 19th C. **£700-800** *S*

A 3 inch Cary pocket globe, the sphere applied with hand-coloured gauze and label printed 'Cary's Pocket Globe Agreeable to the Latest Discoveries', English, first quarter of the 19th C. **£700-800** *S*

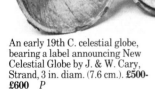

An early 19th C. celestial globe, bearing a label announcing New Celestial Globe by J. & W. Cary, Strand, 3 in. diam. (7.6 cm.). **£500-£600** *P*

A Nugent Wells brass octant, with vernier, magnifier, tangent and clamping screws, coloured filters and mahogany handle, in case with two telescopes, Welsh, 7½ in. radius (19 cm.), mid 19th C. **£500-£600** *S*

A McGregor ebony octant, the brass index arm with clamping and tangent screws and vernier scale and filters, in mahogany case, Scottish, 9½ in. radius (24 cm.), first half of the 19th C. **£350-400** *S*

SEXTANTS

- invented by Hadley in 1731
- double frame sextant introduced in c. 1780
- early examples in wood and metal
- after 1800 generally all of brass construction
- addition of fine decoration, ivory and silver adds to value
- makers of note: Cary, Troughton, Berge, Bardon.

An unusual Crichton ebony sextant, with 0°-135° ivory scale, brass index arm with vernier and clamping and tangent screws, in oak case with telescope, filter and trade label, 9 in. radius (23 cm.), mid 19th C. **£500-600**   *S*

A 19th C. brass 'lightweight' sextant, the frame mounted with a telescope attachment, signed Potter, Poultry & Tower Hill, London, in a mahogany case with sighting tubes, 7 in. (17.8 cm.). **£350-400**   *P*

A Breithaupt & Sohn brass alidade, in original case, German, 23¼ in. long (59 cm.), late 19th C. **£700-800**   *S*

A Cary ebony octant, with clamping screw and vernier, peep-hole eye piece and filters, in oak case, English, 9½ in. radius (24 cm.), early 19th C. **£400-450**   *S*

An early 19th C. brass sextant, the frame signed Berge London, late Ramsden, with telescope attachment, the vernier mounted with a magnifier attachment adjusted by worm screw, in a mahogany case, the handle, telescope, magnifier and one leg lacking. **£650-750**   *P*

A rare Berge pocket sextant, in original leather covered box, English, 2½ in. (6.5 cm.), 1800-1808. **£1,600-2,000**   *S*

A W. & S. Jones brass box sextant, with vernier and magnifier, telescope and two coloured filters, in brass drum case, English, 2¾ in. diam. (70 mm.), early 19th C., in mahogany case. **£350-400**   *S*

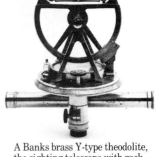

A Banks brass Y-type theodolite, the sighting telescope with rack and pinion focusing to the eyepiece and spirit level mounted in parallel, English, in mahogany case with trade label, with further telescope 10 in. high (255 mm.), early 19th C. **£1,200-1,500**   *S*

An Elliott Bros. brass box sextant, index arm with vernier, in brass drum case with lid and leather carrying case, English, 3 in. (77 mm.) diam., c. 1900. **£250-300**   *S*

A brass sextant, with vernier, tangent and clamping screws, filters and boxwood handle, in mahogany case, with four telescopes, English, 6½ in. radius (16.5 cm.), late 19th C. **£400-500**   *S*

An unusual Troughton & Simms brass transit theodolite, English, 9 in. high (23 cm.), late 19th C. **£900-1,000**   *S*

An early 19th C. brass English theodolite, the base plate signed Webb, 408 Oxford Str., LONDON, in a mahogany case, 14 in. wide (35.6 cm.). **£600-700**   *P*

An anodised brass Hall's pocket theodolite and level. **£160-200**   *P*

A brass theodolite, in original oak case with brass plumb-bob and carrying handle, English, length of telescope 8 in. (200 mm.), c. 1800. **£850-950**   *S*

A Troughton & Simms brass Y-type theodolite, in fitted mahogany case with plumb-bob, and with tripod, 27 cm. high, mid 19th C. **£700-800**   *TKN*

A W. & S. Jones brass Y-level, the telescope with rack and pinion focusing, signed W. & S. Jones, 30 Holborn London, on staff head, English, in mahogany case, 19¼ in. long (48 cm.), c. 1800. **£250-300** *S*

A French brass graphometer, signed Vincard a la Boussolle, 9.5 cm. radius, c. 1725. **£800-1,000** *CNY*

Two late 18th C. brass protractors, one signed Jardin a Paris. **£60-80** *P*

A late 18th C. French brass sector, signed Jardin, Paris, and engraved with various scales, Solides, Metaux, Plans, Poligones and Co. **£150-200** *P*

(l.) A brass sector rule, the hinge engraved with an heraldic rose, 165 mm. long closed, late 17th C. **£800-1,000**
(r.) A fine pair of brass proportional dividers, reduction circle, unsigned, with iron points and trefoil fixing nut, South German, possibly Augsburg, 249 mm. long, c. 1600. **£1,800-2,200** *C*

A Walkers 'Cherub' III taffrail ship log, in original box, containing brass shoe, log register, two rotators, small tin of Walkers solidified oil, spare log register glass. **£150-200** *SS*

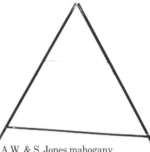

A W. & S. Jones mahogany Denton's canal level, English, when open 50½ in. high (128 cm.), early 19th C. **£250-300** *S*

A rare brass architectonic sector, engraved on both faces of the arc with various architectural scales, English, radius 12 in. (30.5 cm.), third quarter 18th C. **£3,500-4,000** *S*

A brass sector, probably Italian, 17th C. **£1,200-1,500** *CNY*

A set of Butterfield brass drawing instruments, including protractor, sector, set square, compass and dividers, in red leather-covered case, French, 7½ in. high (190 mm.), early 18th C. **£1,500-£2,000** *S*

A Lorieux Lepetit brass reflecting circle, the wheel frame with 0°-180°-0° silvered scale, telescope, filters and hinged handle, French, 10½ in. diam. (26.5 cm.), c. 1900, in fitted mahogany case with accessories. **£900-1,100** *S*

A French brass circumferentor, signed Charot a Paris, c. 1775. **£800-1,000** *CNY*

A canivet brass graphometer, the pivoted alidade with open wire sights, French, 10 in. wide (25.5 cm.), c. 1761. **£800-900** *S*

An 18th C. brass folding sector and rule, signed Butterfield A Paris. **£200-250** *P*

A large pair of Gilbert brass gunner's calipers, English, 22 in. radius (55.8 cm.), second half 18th C. **£750-850** *S*

An E. J. Dent's patent brass dipleidoscope, the platform with screw adjustment mounted with compass needle and 0°-30° scale, bubble level and prism, English, in fitted mahogany case, 4¼ in. wide (11 cm.), mid 19th C. **£900-1,100** *S*

The dipleidoscope determines the apparent time of noon using two mirrors and a plane glass arranged as a prism. By reflection of the sun's rays two images reach the eye, merging into one when the sun's centre is on the meridian.

A 19th C. brass Miner's Dial, the silvered brass compass rose engraved with leaves and signed J. Casartelli, Manchester, and fitted with an edge-bar needle, 13.5 in. wide (33.7 cm.), in mahogany case. **£250-300** *P*

A 19th C. lacquered brass adjustable cross-head, by G. & E. Davis, Leeds, 6 in. wide (15.2 cm.), in a mahogany case. **£280-340** *P*

An 18th C. 3-draw telescope, unsigned, the draw tube made of oiled card stained pale green, mounted in ivory with a brass eyepiece and the outer tube covered with rayskin, lens lacking, 68.8 cm. long extended. **£400-500** *P*

A 19th C. brass Gregorian telescope, signed John Cuthbert, London, the body tube 7 cm. (2¾ in.) diam. and 30.2 cm. (11⅞ in.) long. **£600-700** *P*

A collection of Dring & Fage patents, catalogues and other documents, including a Dring & Fage catalogue and price list with line drawings, in painted tin case. **£900-1,000** *S*

A 2½ in. James Short brass Gregorian reflecting telescope, signed around the eyepiece aperture 'James Short, Edinburgh, 1735.27.65', in fitted mahogany case, length of tube 13 in. (33 cm.), together with 2 solar filters, 2 end caps and 2 eyepieces. **£4,000-5,000** *SS*

A ¾ in. Leonardo Semetecolo leather and horn refracting telescope, Italian, extended length 31 in. (790 mm.), late 18th C. **£220-£280** *S*

A 3 in. brass Gregorian reflecting telescope on stand, the leather covered tube with open sights, long shank and screw focusing to the secondary mirror, English, length of tube 25 in. long (635 mm.), c. 1740. **£650-750** *S*

A Troughton 3 in. brass refracting telescope on stand, the tube 107 cm. long, in mahogany case with accessories, late 18th C. **£700-£800** *TKN*

A good 2½ in. Tuther brass Gregorian reflecting telescope on stand, with focusing to the primary mirror by knurled knob and screw, English, length of tube 9 in. 229 mm.), in original mahogany case, first quarter of the 19th C. **£800-900** *S*

(l.) A 2½ in. Ramsden brass refracting telescope on stand, together with supporting strut with ivory-handled securing nut, English, length of tube 26 in. (660 mm.), late 18th C. **£750-850** (r.) A brass Gregorian refracting telescope on stand, with long lever-and-screw focusing to the secondary mirror, English, length of tube 14 in. (355 mm.), early 19th C. **£500-600** *S*

An early Victorian astronomer's brass telescope on brass tripod, by Ross of London, having 8 interchangeable lenses, in original box. **£800-900** *JD*

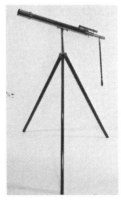

A 19th C. brass refracting telescope, unsigned, bearing a 6.4 cm. (2½ in.) lens and 94 cm. (37 in.) long. **£250-300** *P*

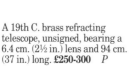

A 2½ in. Broadhurst Clarkson & Co. brass refracting telescope, focusing to the eyepiece by rack and pinion, length of tube 30½ in. (77.5 cm.). **£300-350** *SS*

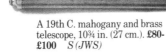

A 19th C. mahogany and brass telescope, 10¾ in. (27 cm.). **£80-£100** *S (JWS)*

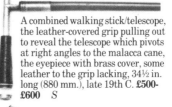

A combined walking stick/telescope, the leather-covered grip pulling out to reveal the telescope which pivots at right angles to the malacca cane, the eyepiece with brass cover, some leather to the grip lacking, 34½ in. long (880 mm.), late 19th C. **£500-£600** *S*

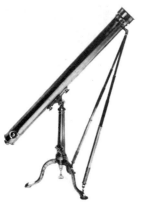

A 3¼ in. brass refracting telescope on stand, the tube with sighting telescope mounted in parallel and with 3 telescopic supporting struts, signed Primavesi Bros. Bournemouth, English, in mahogany case with accessories, late 19th C. **£1,200-1,400** *S*

An 18th C. brass screw barrel microscope, signed E. Culpeper Fecit, 4⅝ in. wide (11.7 cm.), complete with 5 objectives, ivory handle, forceps, a case of slides and other accessories. **£2,200-2,800** *P*

A late 18th C. brass aquatic or botanical microscope, signed Cary, London, in fitted mahogany case, 9.5 cm. (3¾ in.) wide, containing accessories. **£180-240** *P*

A gilt brass reflecting telescope, by P. Dollond, Strand, London, with side view finder and threaded direction adjustment, barrel 26½ by 4¼ in. diam., in mahogany case. **£2,600-3,200** *HyD*

Peter Dollond was working near Exeter Exchange, Strand, London, between 1752-1763.

An unusual wooden solar microscope, the mirror mounted in brass trunnion and window mount with 4 brass securing screws, probably Continental, 20 in. long (51 cm.), 18th C. **£4,000-5,000** *S*

A Shuttleworth brass Culpeper-type microscope, English, late 18th C. **£1,000-1,500** *S*

A rare W. & S. Jones opaque solar microscope, in mahogany case with reflecting box for opaque objects, two lens slides and a slide with six lenses, racked focusing defective, English, length of case 14 in. (35.5 cm.) wide, late 18th C. **£3,200-£3,600** *S*

A good pair of nickel plated brass Target Shooting Range binoculars, unsigned, but posibly by J. H. Steward, in a fitted mahogany case, 41.6 cm. (16⅜ in.) wide. **£320-400** *P*

A Dollond brass monocular microscope, in its mahogany case with accessories, 17½ in. high (44.5 cm.), together with the original printed directions and cloth illustration. **£1,600-2,000** *SS*

An 18th C. brass pillar microscope, with spring stage, one objective, rack focusing and sub-stage mirror on mahogany base, 10½ in. high, in mahogany case. **£500-600** *CSK*

An 18th C. brass screw barrel microscope, unsigned, in a fishskin covered case, 15.6 cm. (6⅛ in.) wide, with a numbered set of 6 objectives, a slide holder, 6 ivory slides, a live box, a supplementary stage, forceps and glass slides. **£750-850** *P*

A Wilson screw barrel, brass simple microscope, complete, English, 2 in. high (50 mm.), in case with 3 numbered lenses and 3 bone-mounted slides, case 3½ in. wide (89 mm.), last quarter of the 18th C. **£500-600** *S*

A Swift & Son brass binocular microscope with rack and pinion focusing, fully mechanical circular stage with sub-stage and plano/concave mirror below, 16 in. high (41 cm.), in mahogany case with accessories, c. 1895. **£700-800** *S*

A large format brass monocular microscope, 21 in. high (53 cm.), the separate plain stage and plano concave mirror supported by a telescopic stand, 12 in. high (30.5 cm.), in fitted mahogany case together with accessories. **£1,000-£1,300** *SS*

A good 19th C. lacquered brass Martin-type drum microscope, unsigned, in fitted mahogany case, 11 in. wide. (28 cm.), with a numbered set of 6 objectives, forceps, bull's-eye condenser, slides and other accessories. **£200-250** *P*

A Collins brass binocular microscope, with focusing by rack and pinion, 16 in. high (41 cm.), in mahogany case, damaged, with 4 oculars, 4 objectives, analyser and polariser and other accessories, English, c. 1880. **£450-550** *S*

A reflecting microscope, signed John Cuthbert, London, 1828, lacks reflecting objectives. **£1,500-2,000** *CSK*

A late 19th C. brass compound binocular microscope, by R. & J. Beck, 31 Cornhill, London, No. 6905, in a fitted mahogany case, 17⅛ in. high (43.5 cm.), with accessories. **£450-500** *P*

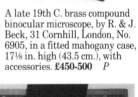

A Powell & Lealand brass binocular microscope, English, 18 in. high (46 cm.), c. 1870. **£600-£800** *S*

A Charriere amputation set, comprising of two Liston-type knives, a tourniquet and bone saw, in walnut case, 16 by 9½ in. (40.5 by 24 cm.), French, mid 19th C. **£650-750** *S*

A 19th C. lacquered brass syringe, signed F. Walters & Co., in a mahogany case, 10⅞ in. wide (27.6 cm.), with accessories. **£100-£150** *P*

A hypodermic syringe, 2 needles and a bottle for solution contained in a plated case, 3 in. high (7.6 cm.). **£350-400** *P*

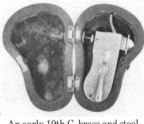

A rare steel scarificator, the spring blade with trigger release and small compartment for storing the single blade, probably Continental, 4¼ in. high (10.8 cm.), early 18th C. **£500-600** *S*

A set of 4 lancets, by English & Son, Brighton & Lewes, with tortoiseshell guards and contained in a silver case, 2½ in. high (6.3 cm.), c. 1847. **£220-260** *P*

An early 19th C. brass and steel single bladed scarificator, stamped Brace, Salisbury, 4 in. long (10.2 cm.). **£250-300** *P*

521

A Place & Co. amputation set, the mahogany case containing saws, 3 Liston-type knives, bone cutters, forceps, retractors and tourniquet, 17 in. wide (43.2 cm.), English, mid 19th C. **£550-650** *S*

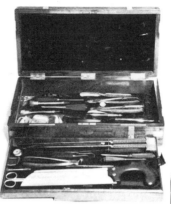

An Arnold & Sons general-purpose surgeon's instrument set, the mahogany case containing two layers of instruments for amputation, trepanning and tooth extraction, 16¾ in. wide (42.5 cm.), English, late 19th C. **£500-600** *S*

A set of Weedon amputation instruments, in fitted mahogany case, 16½ in. wide (41.9 cm.), English, mid 19th C. **£200-250** *S*

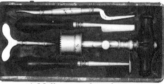

A Melbye cased trephine set, comprising a trepanning perforator and screw, an elevator and 2 lenticulars, in leather case, lid lining now missing, 9½ in. wide (24 cm.), c. 1780. **£950-1,050** *S*

An early 19th C. set of steel, brass and ebony trepanning instruments, by Evans, including 2 trephines and associated instruments, in a mahogany case, 8⅟₁₆ in. wide (20.5 cm.). **£600-700** *P*

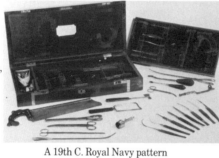

A 19th C. Royal Navy pattern surgeon's general operation kit, by W. & H. Hutchinson, Sheffield, in fitted brass bound mahogany case, 19 in. wide (48.2 cm.). **£750-850** *P*
The condition of the contents of this case, although rusty, may be considered restorable.

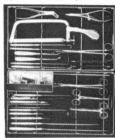

A J. Pohl general purpose surgical instrument set, the mahogany case with lift-out frame of Liston knives, scalpels and lithotomy instruments, the frame below with saw and other surgical instruments, 15¾ in. wide (40 cm.), Continental, 20th C. **£200-300** *S*

An 18th C. steel French amputating saw, by Noel, Paris, 18¾ in. long (47.6 cm.), c. 1750. **£550-650** *P*

A medicine chest, the walnut case with recessed brass carrying handle, 12 in. wide (30.5 cm.), English, c. 1840. **£450-500** *S*

A mahogany medicine chest, when closed 8¾ in. wide (22 cm.), English, second quarter 19th C. **£500-550** *S*

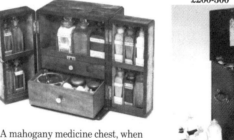

A George III mahogany apothecary's cabinet, 11 in., c. 1800. **£750-850** *WW*

A George III mahogany medicine chest, 11 in. high (28 cm.). **£350-£400** *SS*

A mahogany medicine chest, with racks of medicine bottles, the top with further drawer for scales and ointment tins, when closed 11½ in. wide (29 cm.), English, c. 1820. **£700-800** *S*

A mahogany and ebony strung domestic medicine chest, the rear of the chest fitted with a five-bottle poison compartment, the chest 13 in. wide by 17¾ in. high (33 by 45.1 cm.). **£800-900** *P*

A Georgian mahogany domestic medicine chest, 9½ in. wide (24.1 cm.). **£800-900** *P*

A late 19th C. mahogany domestic homoeopathic box, by Leath & Ross, 9 Vere Street, Oxford St., W, 8¾ in. wide (22.2 cm.). **£300-350** *P*

A pair of iron delivery forceps, 17½ in. long (45 cm.), and a steel perforator, 10½ in. long (26.5 cm.), early 19th C. **£220-260** *S*

A Georgian mahogany and boxwood strung domestic medicine chest, 6¾ in. high (17.1 cm.). **£250-£300** *P*

An electro-magnetic medical machine, 10½ in. long (26.5 cm.), English, third quarter of 19th C. **£180-240** *S*

A combined stethoscope and pleximeter, in turned fruitwood with ivory connecting ring, English, 8¼ in. high (210 mm.), late 19th C. **£170-200** *S*

A speaking tube or hearing aid, with turned ivory trumpets, English, 60 in. long (153 cm.). late 19th C. **£150-200** *S*

An Imari barber-surgeon's bowl, Japanese, 10¼ in. diam. (25.5 cm.), 17th C. **£400-450** *S*

A portable leech jar, the bulbous ceramic body with pierced pewter screw-on lid and handle, French, 6 in. high (15 cm.), late 19th C. **£600-700** *S*

A steel-framed orthopaedic corset, waist measurement 26 in. (66 cm.), late 18th or early 19th C. **£400-600** *S*

A pair of glass carboys, English, 42½ in. high (1,080 mm.), late 19th C. **£400-500** *S*

An English earthenware leeches jar and cover, glazed in green with gilt scrollwork and lettering, some damage, 14 in. high (36.2 cm.), c. 1840. **£550-650** *P*

A pair of apothecary's carboys, of yellow glass, with cork stoppers, English, 15 in. high (380 mm.), late 18th C. **£150-200** *S*

A set of 7 pharmaceutical drug jars, English, 10 in. high (25.5 cm.), mid 19th C. **£200-250** *S*

A phrenology head pen stand, stamped by F. Bridges Phrenologist, the ceramic head applied with transfer of the various human characteristics, English, 5½ in. high (140 mm.), mid 19th C. **£350-£400** *S*

(l.) A late 18th C. medical knife by Savigny, with a silver metal ferrule. **£200-250**
(l.c.) A good 19th C. phrenological bust of small size, the cranium outlined with the regions of the Moral Sentiments. **£250-300**
(r.c.) A set of 19th C. burnished steel and ivory handled dental scaling instruments, 6 in. wide (15.2 cm.) **£300-350**
(r.) An unusual 19th C. folding horn medicine spoon. **£90-110** *P*

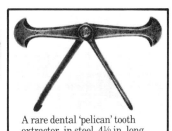

A rare dental 'pelican' tooth extractor, in steel, 4½ in. long (11 cm.), 18th C. **£1,000-1,200** *S*

There is tremendous interest in these rare early dental instruments. This year has seen some extremely high prices, not always foreseen by the auction houses. This item was estimated at £60-80.

523

A dentist's iron treadle drill. **£180-220** *SS*

A dental 'pelican' tooth extractor, with turned ebony knob operating an endless screw to accommodate any size of tooth, 5½ in. long (14 cm.), late 18th C. **£1,500-2,000** *S*

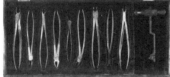

A set of dental instruments, in leather roll within metal case applied with label Teeth Extraction Instruments. **£300-350** *S*

(l.) An anatomical model of the human dentition, with porcelain teeth, c. 1900. **£200-250** *S*
(r). A set of dental prosthesis, with porcelain teeth mounted on silver plates and with clasp for existing teeth, English, c. 1800. **£200-250** *S*

A George III silver pocket dental kit, in an embossed leather case, 5⅛ in. long (13 cm.). **£450-500** *P*

MEDICAL INSTRUMENTS

Of all medical instruments, the most sought after are the cased sets, and the earlier the better. 18th and early 19th Century instruments tend to have ivory handles and the bleeding knives have tortoiseshell cases. During the middle of the 19th Century they were changed to plain ebony handles which were then chequered (like a gun stock) to stop the surgeon's hand from slipping.

Instruments for post-mortem operations are not as sought after since the interest is on instruments for operating on the living, not the dead. Early para-medical accessories such as ear-trumpets, artificial limbs and false teeth, early stethoscopes, medicine spoons, pap boats — in silver, plate, pewter, brass, porcelain, wood, ivory, etc., etc., are also collected.

Professor Lister's pronouncement in 1872, that all instruments should be sterilised before operating, spelled the end of decorative ivory or wood handles, since these cannot be properly sterilised, and from that time on they were made with chrome-plated handles. These are nowadays greeted with stifled yawns by collectors, but almost anything else which is pre-1870 is of interest.

For further information read 'Antique Medical Instruments' by Elizabeth Bennion, Sotheby Parke-Bernet Publications.

An early 19th C. dental scaling kit, a simulated leather covered case, 2½ in. wide (6.3 cm.). **£280-340** *P*

A Carl Zeiss refractometer, No. 869, for measuring the refracted index of transparent materials, supported on column above tripod base, fitted wooden carrying case with set of instructions, German, 15 in. high (38 cm.), c. 1897. **£500-600** *S*

Five male catheters, 3 of silver, one of steel with ivory handle and one other, mid 19th C. **£100-150** *S*

A collection of dental instruments, including a tooth-key with a straight steel shank, a tortoiseshell-cased fleam, an ebony-handled mirror and 6 other steel extractors, mid 19th C. **£500-600** *S*

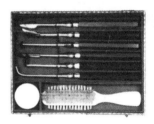

A set of 6 dental hygiene instruments, in fitted leather case, English, 6 in. wide (150 mm.), late 19th C. **£500-600** *S*

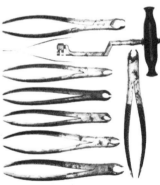

A set of cased dental extraction instruments, the case 18 in. wide (460 mm.), English, mid 19th C. **£500-600** *S*

A Cuthbertson-pattern electrostatic friction generator, in pine case with accessories, English, 18½ in. high (47 cm.), c. 1810. **£900-1,000** *S*

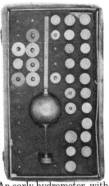

An early 19th C. lacquered brass pocket flea glass, in a silk-lined fishskin covered case, 3¼ in. wide (8.2 cm.), also a brass protractor. **£150-200**   *P*

A W. R. Dell & Son brass chronometer, the brass and steel beam with divisions in Imperial and metric. **£200-300**   *SS*

An early hydrometer, with float and 30 brass weights, in original leather-covered wooden case, English, 7½ in. long (19 cm.), 1750-80. **£180-240**   *S*

A Thomas Harris mahogany waywiser, the 7 inch diam. dial engraved with scales for miles, furlongs and poles, English, 54 in. high (137 cm.), early 19th C. **£400-£500**   *S*

A 19th C. lacquered brass mounted specimen viewer, 3½ in. high (8.9 cm.). **£120-150**   *P*

A brass Helio chronometer, by Pilkington & Gibbs Ltd, Preston, c. 1910. **£180-220**   *P*

A brass rounding up tool, with an almost complete set of accessories, length of base 250 mm., late 19th C. **£450-500**   *S*

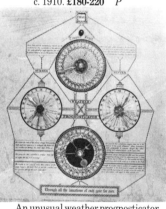

A Short & Mason solar chronometer with 4 inch diam. glass sphere focusing the sun's rays on to two cardboard hour charts, English, 20th C. **£500-550**   *S*

A Negretti & Zambra sunshine recorder Mk IIIC, 10 in. high (25.5 cm.), and an accompanying Negretti & Zambra clinometer, English, 6½ in. high (16.5 cm.), c. 1920. **£500-550**   *S*

An unusual weather prognosticator, published by C. Upham, Bookseller, Exeter, in gilt frame, English, 17¼ by 15¼ in. (438 by 388 mm.), c. 1831. **£400-500**   *S*

A late 19th C. elementary geological collection of approximately 200 specimens contained in a mahogany cabinet, numbered and cross-referred with descriptions in an accompanying notebook, 15⅛ in. wide (38.4 cm.). **£350-400**   *P*

fine quality lacquered brass ...roscope, unsigned, with ...cessories and instruction book, ...⅝ in. high (24.4 cm.). **£320-400**   *P*

A rare Newton & Co. brass gyroscope, in mahogany case complete with two weights and steel needles, English, 7½ in. high (190 mm.), last quarter of the 19th C. **£500-600**   *S*

A Cary brass chronometer, in its fitted mahogany case with instructions for use in the lid, 5½ in. high (14 cm.). **£150-200**   *SS*

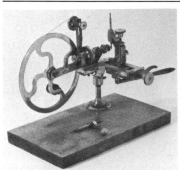

A 19th C. brass and steel wheel topping tool, 13¹⁵⁄₁₆ in. wide (33.8 cm.). **£250-300** *P*

A 19th C. anodised brass dipleidoscope, the hour arc engraved E. I. Dent, Patentee, London, 4¼ in. square (10.8 cm.), with levelling screw and rectangular compass box, the scale divided 0-60°. **£450-500** *P*

A 19th C. lacquered brass spectroscope accessory, signed John Browning, London, having a short telescope fitted to a 360° scale with vernier attachment, in a fitted mahogany box, 6³⁄₁₆ in. wide (15.7 cm.). **£250-300** *P*

A 19th C. lacquered brass Lord Kelvin's patent voltmeter, the silvered 7¾ in. (19.7 cm.) diam. dial engraved with a scale 0-300v, in a mahogany case, 15 in. high (38.1 cm.). **£100-150** *P*

A Messer air pump, on mahogany base, lacking operating handle, English, 15 in. (38 cm.), late 18th C. **£200-250** *S*

An air pump, complete with double-action pump operated by a handle, English, 18 in. long (46 cm.), late 18th C. **£250-300** *S*

A quarter-plate Stereoscopic Compy.'s sliding-box wet-plate camera, and a printing frame. **£600-700** *CSK*

A French half-plate walnut sliding-box wet-plate camera, with Petzval-type brass-bound portrait with rack focusing. **£450-500** *CSK*

A fine 5 x 4 Gandolfi's tailboard camera, with Schneider Symmar 150 mm. f/5.6 lens in Compur 1 shutter, extension tubes, focusing magnifier, rising-and-cross front, tilting-back and 3 matching d.d.s **£500-600** *CSK*

A rare 4.5 cm. by 6 cm. Korelle-P miniature plate camera, with Tessar 7.5 cm. f/2.8 lens in rim set Compur shutter, in leather carrying-case. **£350-400** *CSK*

A whole-plate Rouch's-Patent portable camera, with Ross Rapid Symmetrical lens with one Waterhouse stop, sliding lens panel and hinged base board, folding to cover rear focusing screen. **£120-£160** *CSK*

A W. Watson Alpha hand-and-stand camera, 3¼ by 4¼ in. with Wray 5½ in. f/8 lens, rack-and-pinion focusing, English, c. 1895. **£200-250** *S*

A Sanderson tropical hand-and-stand camera, 3¼ by 4¼ in. with Tessar 13.5 cm. f/4.5 lens, English, c. 1920. **£350-400** *S*

A rare quarter-plate Dallmeyer's Naturalist long-focus reflex camera, with Jamin brass-bound combinable lens with rack focusing, focal-plane shutter, top sliding focusing eye-piece and rear focusing screen. **£450-500** *CSK*

A half-plate Shew-type mahogany folding strut camera, with brass-bound Petzval-type lens with rack focusing. **£200-250** *CSK*

A Horne & Thornthwaite sliding-box dry-plate camera, 4¾ by 7¼ in., the lens, signed, with Waterhouse stops, focused by brass worm-screw, English, 1880's. **£450-550** *S*

A quarter-plate Parks-style hand-and-stand camera. **£280-360** *CSK*

A fine early mahogany and brass stereoscopic camera, by G. Hare of London, body in original condition, with slight damage, and alteration to fit d.d.s., with original lens board, with later Thornton-Pickard stereoscopic shutter fitted, with 4 d.d.s. **£300-350** *P*

A massive Hunter Penrose Ltd. copy camera, 14½ by 18 in., with Ross 13 in. f/10 Aro Process Xpres lens, on base 46 in. (1,168 mm.) long, English, c. 1920. **£150-250** *S*

A 5 by 4 Rouch's-Patent Eureka hand camera, with Rouch's Anastigmat f/6.8 lens, string-cocked T.-P. roller-blind front shutter, integral T.-P. focal-plane shutter. **£350-400** *CSK*

A half-plate tropical Thornton-Pickard Ruby Reflex camera, with Goerz Celor Dopp. Anastigmat 180 mm. f/4.8 lens, brown leather bellows and focusing hood and one d.d.s. **£750-850** *CSK*

A 4¼ by 6¼ mahogany stereoscopic tailboard camera, by W. I. Chadwick, Manchester, with Chadwick 3 in. stereo lenses, each with wheel stops, T.-P. stereo roller-blind shutter with pneumatic control valve, 4 d.d.s. **£300-400** *CSK*

A rare Birtac 17.5 mm. cinematograph camera/projector, No. 69 by Bert Acres, The Northern Photographic Works Ltd., Barnet, with accessories. **£1,700-2,000** *CSK*

A 3¼ by 6½ stereoscopic mahogany folding strut camera, probably by Shew, pneumatically-controlled guillotine shutter and rack focusing. **£550-650** *CSK*

A rare Mollier's Le Cent Vues 35 mm. camera, taking 100 18 mm. by 24 mm. exposures on 35 mm. cassette-loaded perforated film, with Hermagis Anastigmat 40 mm. f/3.5 lens. **£400-600** *CSK*

A rare V. P. Thornton-Pickard
Limit focal-plane miniature plate
camera, with Cooke Series II f/6.5
lens, folding viewfinder and
focusing screen. **£750-850**   *CSK*

A Carl P. Stirn Waistcoat camera,
with conical lens and plate
revolving knob marked 1 to 6, 6 in.
(153 mm.) diameter, in original
cardboard box with 6 plates and
advertising ephemera, c. 1886.
£500-600   *S*

A Photoret Magazine Snap-Shot
Watch camera, by The Magic
Introduction Co., New York. **£50-
£100**   *CSK*

*The first wholly American
manufactured novelty watch
camera design by W. K. L. Dickson
and patented in July and November
1893 by Herman Casler.*

A Compass miniature camera, 24
by 36 mm. with Kern CCL 35 mm.
f/3.5 lens, shutter speeds 4.5 to
1/500 sec., Swiss, c. 1937. **£500-550**
S

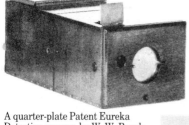

A quarter-plate Patent Eureka
Detective camera, by W. W. Rouch
& Co. Ltd., London, with brass-
bound R.R. lens with Waterhouse
stop, internal clockwork roller-
blind shutter with key, sliding-box
focusing and integral changing
back. **£300-350**   *CSK*

A replica Voigtlander all-brass
daguerreotype camera, with lens
with rack focusing and cap and
circular focusing screen, with
conical housing and focusing
magnifier. **£1,100-1,300**   *CSK*

*See Gernsheim: The History of
Photography, 1955 pl. 63, for an
illustration of the original camera.*

A Nettel Camerawerke Argus
Monocular Detective camera,
retailed by Watson Ltd., 45 by
60 mm. with Holos f/6 lens, in
leather case, with 12 plate holders,
c. 1912. **£500-600**   *S*

A British Ferrotype Co. 'The
Telephot' button camera, c. 1911.
£500-550   *S*

A Telephot button camera, by the
British Ferrotype Co., Blackpool,
No. 2246. **£250-300**   *P*

A Polyrama Panoptique,
French, mid 19th C. **£400-
£500**   *S*

A 4.5 cm. by 6 cm.
Ernemann Ermanox focal-
plane camera, No.
1253800. **£400-500**   *CSK*

A Lewis Machine Gun camera, by
Thornton-Pickard, for 120 roll film,
96 cm. long. **£300-400**   *P*

A good Polyrama Panoptique, with 12 day-or-night tissue slides, in original cardboard box, 6¼ in. 158 mm.) wide, French, dated 1851. **£450-500** *S*

A Riley Brothers biunial lantern 'The Monarch', replaced illuminant and one condenser and lens combination missing, 26 in. (660 mm.) high, English, late 19th C. **£250-300** *S*

A J. Robinson the 'Luzo' box camera, 6 by 6 cm., on roll film Aplant 70 mm. f/11 lens, in leather case, English, c. 1889. **£700-800** *S*

A rare prototype 2¼ by 3¼ roll-film twin-lens reflex camera, by Newman & Guardia, with Dallmeyer Anastigmat f/6 lens. **£750-850** *CSK*

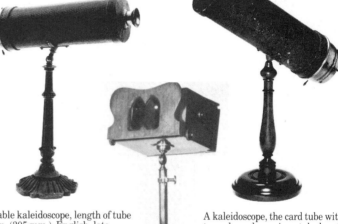

A table kaleidoscope, length of tube 12 in. (305 mm.), English, late 19th C. **£450-550** *S*

A kaleidoscope, the card tube with turned wood eye-piece, tube length 13 in. (330 mm.), English, late 19th C. **£250-350** *S*

A walnut Improved Cosmorama pedestal table stereoscope, by Burfield & Rouch..., Registered Septr. 15, 1854, 15½ in. high. **£250-£300** *CSK*

A late 18th C. mahogany zograscope, 26 in. (66 cm.) high. **£350-400** *S (WJS)*

The zograscope is thought to have been invented during the middle of the 18th C. Initially the device was used by short-sighted people who, due to contemporary convention, would not be seen wearing glasses in public. In fact this optical aid was designed for viewing prints, etc., in a magnified form. Hand-coloured engravings with titles running from right to left were printed specifically for use with zograscopes. c.f. Pinto, Treen, plate 296.

A British Mutoscope & Bio-graph Co. Ltd. 'Kinora' viewer, 18 in. 458 mm.) high, together with 10 reels of still photographs, in cardboard cases, English, c. 1905. **750-850** *S*

A Negretti & Zambra 'Magic Stereoscope No. 213', 16½ in. (420 mm.) high, English, 1856-60. **£400-500** *S*

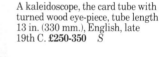

n S. W. Fores phenakistiscope, complete with 12 hand-coloured discs, the largest disc 9¾ in. 25 cm.) diam., English, published 833. **£500-600** *S*

A zoetrope, the tinplate painted drum with original paper label stuck to drum base, raised on, replaced, turned wooden base, 14 in. (36 cm.) high, with 6 coloured paper strips, English, c. 1880. **£250-£300** *S*

ENGLISH GLASS PRICE TRENDS 1983-84

Glass collecting is still a relatively small, specialist, field in the whole range of collecting. The majority of collectors of English glass are British, although there is overseas interest, particularly in coloured glass, and there are some fine collections outside Great Britain.

The predominance of British collectors has tended to keep prices within reason and, except for one or two specialised sections, English glass prices have beaten inflation over the past 30 years.

Particular sections that have appreciated above the average include Beilby enamelled glass, good colour twists and glass with fine and unusual engraving. Glass has appreciated fast in the London salerooms over the past 18 months, but can be obtained more cheaply outside the Capital. Even so, fine examples, particularly those that can be confidently given an Irish attribution, are becoming very expensive for the ordinary collector. The recent growth of the 'Furnishing Antiques' section of the market has had a marked effect on table and display glass.

Good quality 18th and 19th century English coloured glass continues to appreciate. This is helped by the large overseas demand and there is a genuine scarcity of the better examples.

The last two years has seen a dearth of English glass and prices that slipped back about 18 months to two years ago have recovered and even improved for the better examples. It is a reasonable assumption that, whilst the present temporary scarcity continues, competition for good quality items will result in an acceleration in prices.

It is not that a large amount of glass has disappeared from the market for ever; although collections are lost into Museums (the Peter Lazarus collection being a good example). In the late 60's and early 70's there was not the interest in English glass (or any glass for that matter) that there is today, and the number of collectors and dealers were far fewer. Moreover, some fine collections came on to the market to be bought either by collectors or dealers (and museums) to add to or form new collections due to increasing interest in glass. This is a cyclical occurrence and, in time, the older and some of the more recently

formed collections will come on to the market to be dispersed again.

The major London salerooms were able to mount regular monthly sales, whereas today they can manage only about three a year. (This discounts the large amount of mediocre glass that is transferred to their minor salerooms where it can be sold more quickly, and without the same high overheads of their main salerooms.)

Recently a large collection of Jacobite engraved glass was sold in London and, in spite of the unusually large number of examples, these made good prices, with demand apparently still unsated.

It would be encouraging to think that this is the start of a new cycle.

by **R. G. Thomas**

A Bohemian enamelled ruby glass casket, decorated in white, orange and gilding with musical trophies and scrolling foliate borders, gilt metal mounts, key, 15.1 cm., c. 1850. **£350-450** *S*

a pair of ruby glass lustre vases, each painted in colours with garlands of flowers and stylised designs, hung with a double row of prism drops, complete with glass domes and wood stands, 37 cm., late 19th C. **£200-250** *Bea*

A Bohemian green glass vase of campana form, decorated in silver with floral sprays and raised on star-cut base, 13 cm., c. 1860. **£80-£120** *SS*

A Bohemian goblet in deep ruby glass, cut with wide flutes, enamelled in colours and gold with scrollwork and flower sprigs, 20 cm. **£250-300** *P*

A silvered and gilt dark green glass beaker, cut with 4 rows of printies, each containing flowers or scrolls, some gilding rubbed, 11.7 cm., c. 1840. **£200-250** *S*

ruby glass beaker, enamelled with polychrome floral sprays and gilt enriched foliage, 14 cm. high. **50-70** *TKN*

A Bohemian green goblet, the flared faceted sides painted in gold and foliage, surmounted by baskets of fruit below a wide gilt rim, 13 cm. **£350-450** *P*

A Bohemian cut glass goblet, flashed with ruby glass and decorated with tangerine gilt-enriched floral scrollwork, 15 cm. high. **£150-200** *TKN*

A silvered and gilt 'Annagrün' beaker of thistle shape, the octagonal body decorated with heart-shaped designs of flowers and foliage, cut base, 11.1 cm., c. 1840. **£400-500** *S*

An overlay spa glass, the translucent blue overlay carved with panels, small chips to foot, 13 cm., c. 1840. **£100-150** S

A ruby-stained spa beaker, one inscribed 'S. Lewinski', gilt rim, 11.5 cm., c. 1850. **£250-300** S

A gilt spa glass, the glass clear on the exterior and translucent green on the interior, studs chipped, 11.8 cm., c. 1840. **£180-240** S

An engraved amethyst-stained spa beaker, 12.2 cm., c. 1840. **£300-350** S

A Bohemian Hyalith engraved goblet, inscribed 'Fürstenbad, Oürtlerbad, Fürstliche u. Bitzchumsche saus zu Teplitz', with a richly gilt interior, 14 cm. high, c. 1840. **£800-900** C

A Bohemian engraved beaker, decorated with the Last Supper after Leonardo da Vinci, probably engraved by Anton Simm, Gablonz, 13 cm., c. 1830. **£2,100-2,500** S

A 'Perlbecher', chips to rim, 10.5 cm., c. 1830. **£200-250** S

A large Bohemian amber-flash 'Souvenir' goblet, engraved with 3 named views of Wiesbaden, 23.5 cm. high, c. 1860. **£220-300** C

A central European flared tumbler, enamelled in colours, 12 cm., mid 18th C. **£500-£600** C

A Baccarat enamelled armorial tumbler, decorated in colours, 9.5 cm., c. 1835. **£2,500-3,000** C

A central European dated butcher's beaker, the reverse inscribed 'VIVAT das metzger handwerck, 1733' above a foliage spray, 10.5 cm., 1733. **£900-1,000** C

A central European flared beaker, enamelled in blue and white, the reverse enriched in iron-red and yellow, 9 cm., mid 18th C. **£350-£400** C

A dated marriage beaker, the reverse with an inscription and the date 1746 above a stylised flower spray, Thuringia, 13 cm. **£300-350** C

A Silesian engraved bell-shaped beaker, 10 cm., c. 1745. **£300-400** *C*

An early Bohemian engraved beaker, inscribed above 'Ich Liebe Dies Wert Sind', 11 cm., c. 1700. **£400-450** *S*

A family humpen, enamelled in colours with 5 gentlemen of the 'Auer' family, shallow kick-in base, Central Germany, dated 1654 and perhaps 17th C., 23.5 cm. **£3,500-£4,000** *C*

An early wine bottle, with remains of cork, 19 cm., c. 1670. **£550-600** *S*

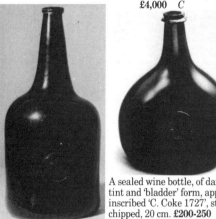

(l.) A wine bottle, with seal 'P. Gregory Biddeford 1771', 24 cm. high. **£250-270**

(r.) A large Ricketts wine bottle, of Imperial pint size, with seal containing a crown, griffin and 'K' below, 29 cm. high, c. 1840. **£90-£110** *Som*

A sealed wine bottle, of dark green tint and 'bladder' form, applied seal inscribed 'C. Coke 1727', string-rim chipped, 20 cm. **£200-250** *S*

A butter dish, cover and stand, with cut diamond decoration and notch cut edges, cut ball finial, 14 cm. diam., c. 1820. **£130-140** *Som*

A tappit-hen sealed and dated wine bottle, the applied seal inscribed 'Dr. Blair 1771', with a kick-in base, 31 cm. **£350-400** *C*

'Tappit-hen' bottles contain 3 normal bottles (2.25 litres), and are said to be of Scottish origin used for the storage of Port.

A central European 'Milchglas' bowl, enamelled in tones of russet, blue, yellow and green, 16.5 cm., mid 18th C. **£250-300** *S*

An unusual marbled bowl, the body formed of 'schmelzglas' in tones of white, blue, yellow and rust-red, small everted circular base, probably German, 9 cm. diam., 17th C. **£550-650** *S*

As with so many techniques which originated with Venice, this type of glass was also made in the German lands.

A cut-glass turnover fruit-bowl, on knopped stem and high foot cut with facets and flutes, Irish, 27 cm. diam., c. 1810. **£550-650** *C*

A Venetian standing bowl, with red, white and blue enamel dots between white-dash borders, 29 cm. diam., 16th C. **£2,200-3,000** *C*

A pair of bowls, the bodies diamond and prism cut, with fan cut rims, plain feet star cut underneath, 10.3 cm. high, c. 1825. **£220-250** *Som*

An Irish round fruit bowl, the body cut with hexagonal facets on rim, the radially moulded bowl with a band of scale cutting, 24 cm. diam., 20 cm. high, c. 1790. **£530-590** *Som*

An early Venetian gilt and enamelled bowl, with a dark blue trail, decorated with gilt scale pattern with superimposed blue, green, white and red enamel dots, 26.8 cm. diam., 15.5 cm. high, early 16th C. **£5,500-6,500** *S*

An Irish canoe-shaped bowl, the body with diamond, star and split cutting, crenellated rim, on a stem with moulded, domed 'lemon squeezer' foot, 31 cm. wide, c. 1790. **£400-450** *Som*

An Irish cut oval butter dish and cover, diamond cut and with crenellated rim, 15 cm. high, c. 1810. **£220-240** *Som*

(*l.*) A Bristol or South Staffordshire opaque white glass candlestick, 25 cm. high, c. 1770. **£180-200**

(*r.*) A Bristol or South Staffordshire cornucopia in opaque white glass, 18 cm. high, c. 1770. **£120-160** *Som*

A pair of Victorian cut candlesticks, with domed and scalloped cut feet, 23 cm. high, c. 1860. **£80-90** *Som*

A pair of cut-glass ormolu-mounted 2-light candelabra, with all-over diamond cutting, with ormolu foliage-scroll and eagle's head branches supporting rectangular wax-pans, 35.5 cm. high, c. 1820. **£2,100-2,500** *C*

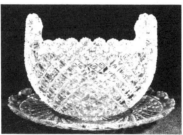

A heavy butter dish, with fan handles, cut overall with cross cut diamonds, with fan cut rim, stand of lighter metal with similar decoration, plate 19.2 cm. diam., c. 1830. **£110-120** *Som*

(*l.*) A wine glass cooler, with broad flute cut base, with monogram for Louis Phillipe, 9.5 cm. high, c. 1830. **£45-50**

(*r.*) A wine glass cooler, with comb flute cut base, and star engraved decoration, 11.4 cm. high, c. 1810. **£45-50** *Som*

Two similar wine glass coolers, with flute cut bases and a band of egg and tulip engraving, 10.8 and 11.7 cm. high, c. 1810. **£35-45** each *Som*

A sugar bowl, with diamond cut body and fan cut rim, on a knopped stem, the plain foot star cut underneath, 12.5 cm. high, c. 1825. **£65-75** *Som*

A candlestick, the ribbed socket on a stem with an annular knop and double series opaque twist, domed conical foot, 19.5 cm. high, c. 1760. **£700-800** *Som*

A George III moulded and cut glass table candelabrum, 23 in. (59 cm.) high. **£500-600** *L*

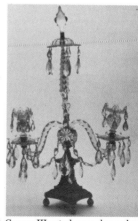

A George III cut glass and ormolu table candelabrum, 25 in. (63 cm.) high. **£600-700** *L*

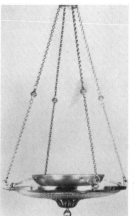

A pair of candelabra, each with 3 scrolling sliced branches terminating in metal nozzles with cut drip pans bearing pendant 'icicle' drops, some drops missing, 45 cm. high, c. 1830. **£200-300** *S*

A pair of Regency ormolu-mounted cut-glass hanging dish-lights, 19 in. (48 cm.) wide. **£3,500-4,000** *C*

A Regency ormolu-mounted cut-glass hanging dish-light, the circular dish with diamond cut decoration and a foliate knop, 30 in. (76 cm.) wide, and another similar, 27 in. (68.5 cm.) wide, both fitted for electricity. **£3,400-4,000** *C*

A fine cut-glass and Wedgwood jasper ware 5-light chandelier, with tapering diamond-pattern baluster body, one plaque missing, 51 in. (129.5 cm.) high. **£2,500-3,500** *C*

A cut-glass 5-light chandelier, the stem with 3 faceted knops headed by a star-shaped domed corona, fitted for electricity, the glass mainly early 19th C., 26 in. (66 cm.) high. **£1,200-1,500** *C*

Three unusual opaline carafes (*l.*) Light green opaline, 21 cm. high, c. 1840. **£160-180**
(*c.*) Lavender-blue opaline with traces of 'Rum' in gilt, 22 cm. high, c. 1840. **£160-180**
(*r.*) Opaque-white, 20 cm. high, c. 1840. **£120-140** *Som*

A cut-glass 5-light chandelier, with baluster and knopped stem headed by a faceted domed corona suspending pendant drops, fitted for electricity, the glass mainly early 19th C., 31 in. (79 cm.) high. **£1,700-2,000** *C*

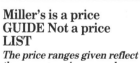

A 'Bitters' bottle, the shouldered body, cut with printies and flutes, c. 1840, 18.3 cm. high. **£75-85** *Som*

A set of 3 green decanters and stoppers for BRANDY, HOLLANDS and RUM, named in gilt, the reverses with a foliage-spray very slight chips to stoppers, c. 1800, 23 cm. high. **£600-700** *C*

A globe and shaft serving bottle and stopper, 28 cm., early 18th C. **£400-450** *S*

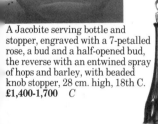

A Jacobite serving bottle and stopper, engraved with a 7-petalled rose, a bud and a half-opened bud, the reverse with an entwined spray of hops and barley, with beaded knob stopper, 28 cm. high, 18th C. **£1,400-1,700** *C*

Miller's is a price GUIDE Not a price LIST

The price ranges given reflect the average price a purchaser should pay for similar items. Condition, rarity of design or pattern, size, colour, pedigree, restoration and many other factors must be taken into account when assessing values.

A set of 3 emerald-green wine bottles with thumb cut bodies and fluted necks, plated metal/cork toppers for 'Brandy', 'Rum' and 'Whiskey', in plated frame, c. 1850, 27.5 cm. high. **£270-290** *Som*

A good pair of rib moulded amethyst bottles with neck collars and plated metal corks, c. 1845, 30 cm. **£260-280** *Som*

A ruby glass spirit flagon, with pewter mount and pewter/cork stopper, c. 1870. **£90-110** *Som*

A garniture of Bristol blue glass decanters and stoppers, with gilt wine label cartouches, gilding rubbed, late 18th C., 9 in. high. **£250-300** *WW*

A pair of green ovoid decanters, the bodies with gilt simulated wine labels with gilt lozenge stoppers with initials, c. 1790, 25 cm. **£300-340** *Som*

A Bristol blue spirit bottle with canted corners, pouring neck and cut ball stopper, the body with gilt simulated wine label, c. 1800, 16.3 cm. high. **£180-200** *Som*

A pair of Bristol blue decanters, the club-shaped bodies with gilt simulated wine labels, with lozenge stoppers with gilt initials, c. 1790, 19 cm. **£300-330** *Som*

A Bristol blue barrel-shaped spirit decanter with gilt wine label for 'Hollands', with ball stopper, c. 1800, 16.5 cm. high. **£140-160** *Som*

A good pair of Bristol blue ovoid decanters, the bodies with gilt simulated wine labels, gilt stoppers 'R' and 'H', c. 1790, 192 mm. high. **£320-340** *Som*

A set of 3 green hexagonal cut spirit decanters with gilt wine labels, with ball stoppers, ('Hollands' neck cracked), 17.4 cm. high. **£280-320** *Som*

A pair of tapered decanters, the bases and necks flute cut, moulded star cut bases, lozenge stoppers, probably French, 22 cm. high, c. 1800. **£270-290** *Som*

A very rare 3 bottle port madeira trolley, in black papier mâché with brass fittings, fitted with 3 ovoid decanters, with flute cut bodies and cut neck rings, cut mushroom stoppers, 43 cm. long, c. 1810. **£1,000-1,200** *Som*

Two decanter trolleys are rare, 3 decanter trolleys are extremely rare.

A marked Irish decanter and stopper, marked 'Waterloo Cork', the shoulders engraved with star floral festoons and the initials 'WR', with moulded bulls-eye stopper, 27 cm. high, c. 1820. **£450-500** *S*

An Irish spirit decanter, the base flute moulded below an engraved ship, 3 feathered neck rings and moulded target stopper, the underneath faintly marked 'Waterloo Glass Co., Cork', 200 mm. high, c. 1810. **£350-400** *Som*

MAKE THE MOST OF MILLER'S

- *Look for the code letters in italic type following each caption.*
- *Check these against the list of contributors at the front of the book to identify the source of any illustration.*
- *Remember — valuations may vary according to locality; use of the codes can allow this to be taken into account.*

A good pair of ovoid Irish decanters, with base moulding and two triangular neck rings, moulded target stoppers, the bodies engraved with initials 'WMW', looped floral and hatched rose decoration, 23.2 cm. high, c. 1800. £550-600 Som

(l.) A tapered plain decanter, with lozenge stopper, 23.5 cm. high, c. 1790. £120-130

(c.) A tapered plain decanter, with a band of star and printy engraving, 25.5 cm. high, c. 1800. £120-130

(r.) A tapered plain decanter, 24.5 cm. high, c. 1800. £120-130 Som

A pair of Irish cut decanters, with geometric cut design, with 3 annulated neck rings and hollow cut mushroom stoppers, 22.5 cm. high, c. 1840. £300-340 Som

A pair of heavy Irish cut decanters, with flute cutting at base and neck, band of diamond panels, and 3 annulated neck rings, cut mushroom stoppers, 20 cm. high, c. 1825. £330-360 Som

A Sheffield plated stand containing 3 spirit bottles, with flute and strawberry diamond cutting, cut neck rings, cut hollow mushroom stoppers, 22.3 cm. high, c. 1825. £300-340 Som

A pair of heavy cut decanters, with flute cut bases, band of cut diamonds and prism cut necks, unusually tall cut mushroom stoppers, 21 cm. high, c. 1825. £320-340 Som

Three octagonal spirit bottles, cut with bands of diamonds and flutes, cut ball stoppers, plated metal frame, bottles 16.6 cm. high, c. 1810. £270-290 Som

A pair of Victorian ships decanters, with 2 neck rings and ball stoppers with air tears, 17 cm. high, c. 1860. £140-160 Som

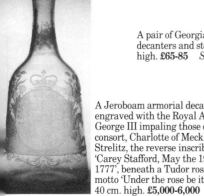

A pair of Georgian cut-glass decanters and stoppers, 21 cm. high. £65-85 SS

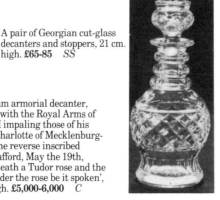

A Jeroboam armorial decanter, engraved with the Royal Arms of George III impaling those of his consort, Charlotte of Mecklenburg-Strelitz, the reverse inscribed 'Carey Stafford, May the 19th, 1777', beneath a Tudor rose and the motto 'Under the rose be it spoken', 40 cm. high. £5,000-6,000 C

A cut-glass decanter and stopper, engraved with the Prince of Wales feathers above the motto 'Ich Dien', chip to rim and foot rim, 35.5 cm. high, and a port glass en suite, 13.5 cm. high, c. 1810-15. £1,200-£1,500 C

From an extensive table service made to the order of the Prince Regent, a large part of which remains at Windsor Castle.

A baluster goblet, with pointed double-ogee bowl, on an angular knop and basal swelling enclosing an extended air bead, 21 cm. high, c. 1700. **£1,800-2,000** *S*

A baluster wine glass, the flared bowl set on a collar over annulations, bead knop and teared true baluster, basal knop, 18.4 cm. high, c. 1720. **£160-200** *S*

A baluster wine glass, with funnel bowl, with an inverted baluster hollow knop stem, 5¼ in. (13.3 cm.), c. 1720. **£170-200** *SC*

A baluster wine glass, with bell bowl, over annulated knop, true baluster and basal cyst, 16.5 cm. high, c. 1720. **£150-180** *S*

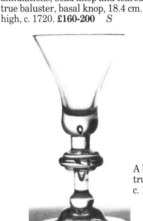

A baluster wine glass, the funnel bowl with flared rim, the stem composed of opposing balusters flanking a flattened knop, 14.5 cm. high, c. 1720. **£200-250** *S*

A baluster goblet, with bell bowl, knop enclosing a tear between 2 plain sections above a base knob, 18 cm. high, c. 1725. **£400-500** *C*

A balustroid wine glass, of drawn-trumpet shape, 16 cm. high, c. 1725. **£140-180** *C*

An engraved balustroid wine glass, the drawn-trumpet bowl with a border of fruiting vine, 17 cm. high, c. 1730. **£180-220** *C*

A baluster goblet, with flared funnel bowl, 17.5 cm. high, c. 1730. **£180-220** *C*

A balustroid wine glass, with a bell bowl, the stem with a triple annulated knop above an inverted baluster knop, 16 cm. high, c. 1730. **£210-250** *C*

A balustroid wine glass, the bell bowl supported on a plain stem above an inverted baluster knop enclosing a tear, 17 cm. high, c. 1730. **£130-160** *C*

A balustroid wine glass, with bell bowl, the stem with a shoulder knop above a double-drop knop and base knob enclosing a tear, very minor chip to rim, 16 cm. high, c. 1730. **£150-190** *C*

Right

A Newcastle wine glass, the bell bowl with clasped hands below a crown and floral surround, the reverse 'De Vrindschipp', on a shoulder air beaded knop, 19.5 cm. high, c. 1750. **£700-800** *Som*

A composite-stemmed wine glass, with a round funnel waisted bowl, 16 cm. high, c. 1750. **£110-150** *C*

Right

A balustroid wine glass, the bell bowl on a composite stem with central air beaded knop, 120 mm. high, c. 1745. **£280-300** *Som*

An unusual bell goblet, with opposing everted funnels, one with clapper, joined by a moulded pedestal section flanked by collars, probably Central German, 18.7 cm. high, c. 1730. **£450-500** *S*

A Newcastle engraved goblet, the stem with a beaded dumb-bell knop above an inverted baluster section and base knob, 17 cm. high, c. 1750. **£300-350** *C*

A Newcastle Dutch engraved armorial goblet, the funnel bowl engraved with the arms of the City of Groningen, on a multi-knopped stem, 18.5 cm. high, c. 1750. **£550-£650** *C*

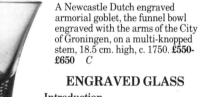

A composite-stemmed wine glass, the stem filled with airtwist spirals, set into a beaded inverted baluster section enclosing a tear above a base knob, 16 cm. high, c. 1750. **£150-200** *C*

Left

A Newcastle engraved wine glass, on a multi-knopped stem enclosing an elongated tear, 18 cm. high, c. 1745. **£400-500** *C*

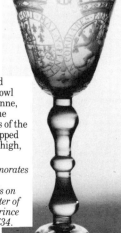

Right

A Newcastle Dutch engraved Alliance goblet, the funnel bowl engraved with the arms of Anne, daughter of George II, and the arms of the United Provinces of the Netherlands, on a multi-knopped stem and domed foot, 21 cm. high, c. 1745. **£1,300-1,600** *C*

This goblet probably commemorates the alliance formed between England and the Netherlands on the marriage of Anne, daughter of George II, and William IV, Prince of Orange, on 25th March, 1734.

Newcastle airtwist wine glass, the slender stem filled with spiral threads, 16 cm. high, c. 1755. **£160-190** *C*

ENGRAVED GLASS

Introduction

Engraving on glass is an ancient craft dating back to Egyptian times and was accomplished in various ways.

This short note cannot possibly hope to cover the whole field of English glass and glasses in any detail; the period 1690-1840 has been chosen and is mostly concerned with drinking glasses.

Methods of Engraving

(a) *Diamond Point* Where the required design was produced by a diamond or graver.

(b) *Wheel Engraving* Where the design was effected with copper wheels, varying in size from a pinhead upwards; the wheels being fed with a mixture of either oil or water and sand. This engraving could be highlighted by polishing part of the engraving. Also, the depth of engraving could be varied to produce high and low relief effects, combined with polishing.

(c) *Stipple Engraving* Here the required design was effected by the use of a diamond needle and hammer to produce a series of dots or short scratched lines. The closeness of the dots and their intensity produced a shading effect.

(d) *Acid Etching* This required the surface of the glass or vessel to be covered with a varnish or resin, and the design then scratched through with a needle or other sharp tool. The surface was then exposed to hydrofluoric acid fumes to etch through the scratched design.

The above methods have continued in use up to the present time.

English Engraved Glass

Decoration on glass during the period under review fell into two categories; either to make the glass or vessel more attractive, or to indicate a use; to record a sentiment, event, toast, or to support a current cause.

During the early part of the period under review, there was little attempt to emulate the Dutch and German engravers whose work was invariably of high artistic merit and quality, and whose chosen subjects were diverse. On English glass, it was expressed quite crudely in flowers and foliage, birds and insects. In the earlier wheel engraving there was a predominance of floral designs, hence in the early 1740's and onwards, these glasses were referred to as 'flowered glasses'. Crude attempts at portraiture were also made.

It was not until the third quarter of the 18th century onwards, with some notable exceptions, that the skill of the engravers had progressed to a state where attempts at high and low relief carving and polishing were attempted.

The soft English lead glass was particularly suitable for engraving and was used by a number of Dutchmen for some fine work.

Application of the Various Techniques to English Glass

(a) *Diamond Point* Although outside the period under review mention must be made of a small group of soda lime glasses attributed to the London glass house of Jacob Verzelini in the late 16th century, and thought to have been engraved by an Anthony Lysle or Lisley. These and one or two other glasses are notable for this type of engraving, but very few glasses were engraved with the diamond point between 1690 and 1840. Some early 18th century heavy balusters and some Newcastles were decorated and, where the decoration is contemporary with the glass, it is important and rare. There is also a small group of Jacobite glasses, the 'Amen' glasses, which show various cyphers and a varying number of verses of the Jacobite anthem or hymn, ending in 'Amen'. These are unsigned and are thought to have been engraved in either Scotland or the North of England, possibly by one unknown engraver, and after the defeat of Prince Charles Edward Stuart at Culloden Moor in April 1746.

(b) **Wheel Engraving**

(i) This was the preferred method of engraving during the 18th and early 19th century, but there is little evidence of it having been used before about 1740, and, as remarked earlier, it usually took the form of floral sprays, meanders and borders. Some of the earliest glasses of this type had baroque scrolling and meanders, attributed to the influence of immigrant German engravers, following the accession of George I in 1715.

(ii) Particular mention must be made of the Jacobite glasses which were engraved some 15 to 20 years later and which have commanded such attention and popularity up to the present time. The dating and the significance of the various motifs on these glasses is still the subject of debate and disagreement, but considered opinion is that few of these glasses can be dated to before Culloden in 1746. Jacobite engraved glasses continued to be produced through the various stem formations (plain, air-twist, opaque and faceted) until the death of Prince Charles Edward

A pair of Jacobite airtwist wine glasses, the funnel bowls engraved with a 6-petalled rose and a bud, the reverses with a butterfly, c. 1750, 15.5 cm. high. **£350-450** C

Stuart in 1788. Countless numbers of old glasses have been later engraved. There were also the counter Jacobite glasses supporting the Loyalists but these are considerably fewer in number.

(iii) The fruiting vine and hops and barley motifs were used extensively on wine and ale glasses respectively. In the former case, unless there is some special feature about the engraving, they command very little attention. The engraved ale glasses more so. Much rarer are the glasses engraved with either, or both, apples and the word 'CYDER'.

(iv) Further on in the 18th century, about 1760, the hatched type of decoration, and bands of stylised tulips and small polished ovals appeared, particularly on the facet stem glasses, although this type of decoration will be found on earlier glasses.

(v) Rummers were a popular glass for decoration in the late 18th and early 19th centuries, when more ambitious attempts at pictorial decoration and landscapes were undertaken.

(vi) The list of political and historical subjects, etc., is too long to be covered in this short note but, glass with any engraving other than that covered in the previous paragraphs is rare, the numbers of each subject attempted is not large and they are highly regarded by collectors. Barrington Haynes' 'Glass Through the Ages' lists in detail the specialised subjects used by the glass engravers in this period.

(vii) Many English glasses, mostly the Newcastle and facet stem types, were engraved in Holland. These are mostly unsigned. However, the workshop of Jacob Sang carried out fine work — A number are signed, but are rare.

(viii) Decanters were also engraved from about 1750. A few shaft and globe were Jacobite decorated, but examples are rare. Later in the century (about 1760), shouldered and tapered decanters were engraved, with bands of floral decoration, husks and swags. The egg and tulip design was often used. A certain number of these decanters were engraved with the name of a wine, this usually being in a floral cartouche. In the early 19th century, Irish decanters were engraved with decoration of social, political and patriotic significance, but these are rare. Also, patterns such as bands of laurel leaves, chains, stars and the vesica pattern were often combined with cutting; the star, slice and facet being a favourite combination.

(c) **Stipple Engraving** This type of engraving was carried out on a limited number of English glasses of high quality, particularly Newcastle and facet stem types. This was only seriously attempted by the Dutch, notably Frans Greenwood and David Woolf. Some of these examples were signed, a larger number have been attributed to these artists. A few glasses were engraved in the early 19th century by 'L. Adams', and there are a number of others with late facet stems, but these should not be confused with the delicacy of the 18th century stippled examples.

(d) *Acid Etching* Research and experimentation into acid etching of glass was undertaken on the Continent in the 18th century but it was not until the second quarter of the 19th century that any serious attempt was made to employ this method in England. Apsley Pellat, in his book 'Curiosities of Glassmaking' in 1830, refers to the difficulties encountered with this method of decoration. (An account of the development of the Acid Etching technique is contained in the publication 'The Glass Circle' vol. 3 1979.)

Dating Engraved Glass

(a) It has often been remarked by the early writers on English Glass that it is extremely difficult, if not impossible, to date the engraving on any antique glass with any certainty.

(b) New engraving has a rough chalky appearance. Age and wear shades down this harshness so that any glass that has been engraved for a century or more will exhibit a grey shading if a white cloth is placed behind clean engraving. More importantly wear will cause a smooth satin sheen on any flat exposed part of the engraving.

(c) On the simpler engraved glasses the quality of engraving is not necessarily an indication of age as ability varied from one engraver to another. (In Vol. 3 of 'The Glass Circle' is a very interesting paper on an attempt to classify the different engravers of the Jacobite glasses.)

(d) If a particular glass hasn't any known ownership or provenance, then it is really a matter of judgment as to whether the engraving is contemporary with the glass and its known period of execution.

by **R. G. Thomas**

Four balustroid wine glasses,
(*l.*) Bell bowl, base knopped stem
and folded conical foot, 13.5 cm.
high, c. 1750. **£90-100**

(*l.c.*) Round funnel bowl, centre and
base knopped stem, folded conical
foot, 16.2 cm. high, c. 1750. **£110-
£120**

(*r.c.*) Round funnel bowl, shoulder
knopped stem, plain conical foot,
15.2 cm. high, c. 1750. **£90-100**

(*r.*) Round funnel bowl, shoulder
knopped stem, folded conical foot,
15.4 cm. high, c. 1745. **£90-100**
Som

A cordial, the small round funnel
bowl on a plain stem with long air
tear, 17 cm. high, c. 1750. **£190-
£210** *Som*

Four plain stem wine glasses, with
ogee bowls and folded conical feet.
(*l.*) Engraved fruiting vine,
13.3 cm. high. **£80-85**

(*l.c.*) Engraved fruiting vine,
14.8 cm. high. **£55-60**

(*r.c.*) Bowl rib moulded and
engraved with band of roses,
14.5 cm. high. **£120-130**

(*r.*) Engraved with band of
hatching, 12 cm. high. **£65-70**
Som

A rare small cordial glass,
the bell bowl on a stem
with multi-spiral airtwist,
plain conical foot, 13.2 cm.
high, c. 1740. **£240-270**
Som

A rare composite stem airtwist
wine glass, the trumpet bowl on a
drawn multi-spiral airtwist, with
base teared knop, 15 cm. high,
c. 1740. **£180-200** *Som*

A Jacobite wine glass, the funnel
bowl engraved with the Jacobite
rose and one bud, with a double-
knopped multi-spiral airtwist stem,
16 cm. high, c. 1750. **£300-350** *S*

A good Jacobite Fiat
cordial, the small
trumpet bowl
engraved with a
Jacobite rose and 2
buds, 'Fiat' on the
reverse, on a drawn
stem with multiple
spiral airtwist,
15.5 cm. high,
c. 1748. **£500-600**
Som

A fine airtwist wine glass, the
bucket bowl engraved with tulips
and floral/sprig decoration, single
series cable airtwist stem, 18.5 cm.
high, c. 1740. **£330-370** *Som*

An engraved airtwist
goblet, of Jacobite
significance, the stem
filled with airtwist spirals
and applied with a
vermicular collar, 19.5 cm.
high, c. 1750. **£500-600**

A Jacobite airtwist wine glass, the
funnel bowl engraved with a
6-petalled rose, a half-opened bud
and a closed bud, the reverse
inscribed 'Fiat', 16 cm. high,
c. 1750. **£500-600** *C*

An engraved airtwist wine glass, of
Jacobite significance, 15 cm. high,
c. 1750. **£120-160** *C*

A Jacobite airtwist wine glass,
16 cm. high, c. 1750. **£150-200** *C*

Four airtwist wine glasses:
(*l.*) A trumpet bowl, mercury corkscrew twist, plain conical foot, 16.3 cm. high, c. 1745. **£110-130**

(*l.c.*) A moulded trumpet bowl, shoulder knopped multiple spiral airtwist, plain conical foot, 17 cm. high, c. 1750. **£120-140**

(*r.c.*) A bell bowl, double knopped multiple spiral airtwist stem, plain conical foot, 15.7 cm. high, c. 1750. **£210-230**

(*r.*) A bell bowl, multiple spiral airtwist stem with vermicular collar, plain conical foot, 16.5 cm. high, c. 1750. **£210-230**   *Som*

A Beilby enamelled goblet, on a plain stem, conical foot, 17.8 cm. high, c. 1770. **£1,500-1,800**   *S*

An engraved airtwist wine glass, the bell bowl engraved and polished with a trailing branch of fruiting vine, 16.5 cm. high, c. 1750. **£170-200**   *C*

A Beilby wine glass, the ogee bowl enamelled in white with fruiting vine, double series opaque twist stem, plain conical foot, 15 cm. high, c. 1760. **£950-1,000**   *Som*

A Beilby opaque twist wine glass, the funnel bowl enamelled in white with 2 goats, on a double series opaque twist stem, 15 cm. high, c. 1765-70. **£2,400-2,800**   *C*

A wine glass, the rounded funnel bowl hammer-moulded round the lower half, set on a multi-spiral airtwist stem with shoulder knop, 16.8 cm. high, c. 1755. **£150-180**   *S*

A Beilby wine glass, the ogee bowl enamelled in white with floral scrolls, double series opaque twist stem, probably by Mary Beilby, 15 cm. high, c. 1765. **£900-1,100**   *Som*

An engraved airtwist wine glass, for 'Capillaire', of drawn-trumpet shape, 14 cm. high, c. 1750. **£140-£170**   *C*

The cordial 'Capillaire' was syrup apparently made from maidenhair fern (Capillaris herba) and flavoured with orange water.

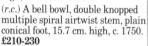

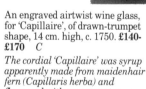

A rare wine glass, the wrythen moulded deceptive bowl on a double series opaque twist stem, plain conical foot, 14.3 cm. high, c. 1760. **£220-£260**   *Som*

A Jacobite airtwist cordial glass, of drawn-trumpet shape, on a conical foot, 13.5 cm. high, c. 1750. **£350-£400**   *C*

A pair of Lynn wine glasses, the ribbed round funnel bowls on stems with double series opaque twist stems, 15.5 cm. high, c. 1760. **£520-£580**   *Som*

A Jacobite wine glass, engraved with Jacobite rose, 2 buds, oak leaf, star and the motto 'Fiat', 15.5 cm. high, c. 1760. **£400-500**   *S*

(*l.*) A cordial glass, with pantop bowl, on a double series opaque twist stem, and rare folded foot, 14.5 cm. high, c. 1760. **£220-240**

(*c.*) A wine glass, with pantop bowl, on a multi-spiral centre knopped airtwist stem, plain conical foot, 14.5 cm. high, c. 1750. **£200-220**

(*r.*) A wine glass, with pantop bowl, engraved with fruiting vine, on a plain stem and folded conical foot, 15.3 cm. high, c. 1750. **£160-190**
Som

An opaque twist wine glass, the flared ogee bowl on a stem with tapes around a triple corkscrew, 14.5 cm. high, 18th C. **£50-60**
Bon

Four ale glasses, with the deep found funnel bowls engraved with hops and barley, on stems with double series opaque twists, and plain conical feet,
(*l.*) 18.5 cm. high, c. 1760. **£200-220**
(*l.c.*) 19 cm. high, c. 1760. **£210-230**
(*r.c.*) 19 cm. high, c. 1760. **£200-220**
(*r.*) 16.8 cm. high, c. 1760. **£180-200**
Som

A colour twist wine glass, the stem with a translucent dark blue corkscrew spiral edged in opaque-white within an opaque 5-ply spiral, 14.5 cm. high, c. 1770. **£550-£650** *C*

An engraved tartan twist wine glass, the stem with red, white and green twisted central core within 4 opaque spiral threads, 14 cm. high, c. 1770. **£500-600** *C*

A dram glass, inscribed 'THE FRIENDLY HUNT', 8.9 cm., c. 1750. **£130-180** *S*

A tartan twist wine glass, with a slender bell bowl, the stem with an opaque corkscrew core edged in brick red within pale translucent green and a pair of opaque spiral threads, 17 cm. high, c. 1770. **£550-650** *C*

An opaque twist ratafia glass, the slender funnel bowl with hammered flutes to the lower part, the stem with a laminated corkscrew core within 2 spiral threads, 20 cm. high, c. 1765. **£250-£300** *C*

A Jacobite firing glass, the bell bowl engraved with a rose spray, 10 cm. high, mid 18th C. **£400-450** *C*

A pair of rare green rummers, the ovoid bowls panel moulded, on collared tapered stems, plain conical feet, 12.3 cm. high, c. 1830. **£300-350** pair   *Som*

An unusual set of 3 small lime-green ribbed flutes, with base collars and ribbed conical feet, 11 cm. high, c. 1820. **£85-95**   *Som*

A rare pair of amethyst wine glasses, the ribbed double ogee bowls with hollow bases, collared knopped stems, plain conical feet, 12 cm. high, c. 1825. **£140-160** *Som*

A green tinted wine glass, the double ogee bowl, 15 cm. high, c. 1770. **£300-350** *C*

A green wine glass, with a double ogee bowl, 15 cm. high, c. 1760. **£750-850** *C*

A stipple-engraved facet stemmed wine glass, attributed to David Wolff, the stem cut with diamond facets and on a plain foot, 15.5 cm. high, c. 1790. **£4,000-5,000** *C*

A 'Façon de Venise' serpent stem goblet, the stem enclosing corkscrew white and red threads, flanked by pincered turquoise blue trails, Lowlands, 18.6 cm., c. 1650. **£950-1,050** *S*

A stipple-engraved facet stemmed wine glass, attributed to David Wolff, with stippled rounded bowl, the stem cut with hexagonal facets, 15.5 cm. high, c. 1790. **£4,000-£5,000** *C*

A 'Façon de Venise' engraved serpent stem goblet, the rounded funnel bowl decorated in diamond point with exotic birds perched on floral sprays interspersed with insects, the bowl supported on a collar over ribbed hollow knops and incised-twist coiled stem, Lowlands, 23.2 cm., c. 1650-70. **£4,000-4,500** *S*

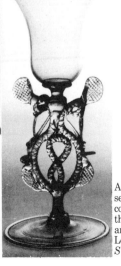

A Low Countries engraved opaque twist goblet, the rounded bowl engraved in diamond point and stippled with a Bacchanalian putto, the stem with an opaque gauze core, within spiral threads, 17.5 cm. high, c. 1790. **£900-1,000** *C*

A 'Façon de Venise' 'verre a serpent', set on an elaborately coiled stem, enclosing white threads with outer pincered trails and serpent heads, probably Lowlands, 20 cm., 17th C. **£750-850** *S*

A 'Façon de Venise' serpent stem goblet, the bell-shaped bowl set on a coiled stem, enclosing white threads with pincered outer trails, Lowlands, 23 cm., 17th C. **£500-600** *S*

A Potsdam engraved goblet, on a baluster stem, base knop and conical foot, embellished with stiff leaves, glass crizzeled, 22 cm., c. 1710. **£250-300** *S*

A Lauenstein marriage goblet, inscribed 'A LA DOUCE VIOLENCE AUX PLAISIRS DE L'HYMEN IEAN DANS LA CAVE', the reverse with initials AG and LW and the date 24, April 1776, on a facet-cut knopped stem, lion rampant mark, 24.5 cm. high, third quarter of the 18th C. **£900-£1,000** *C*

Three engraved Lauenstein goblets, the bowls inscribed 'Bouvons Aimons Baisons, Plus Etre Que Paroitre' (sic) and 'Aux Belles Qui Ne Sont Pas Fieres', 18 cm. high, last quarter of the 18th C. **£1,100-1,300** *C*

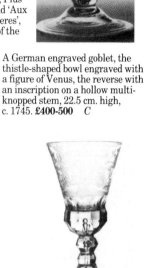

A German engraved goblet, the thistle-shaped bowl engraved with a figure of Venus, the reverse with an inscription on a hollow multi-knopped stem, 22.5 cm. high, c. 1745. **£400-500** *C*

A Dutch goblet, the thistle-shaped bowl with facet-cut lower part engraved with the arms of William IV of Orange, 19.5 cm. high, c. 1750. **£350-400** *C*

A Dutch engraved armorial baluster goblet, the funnel bowl engraved with the arms of the United Provinces of the Netherlands, on a folded conical foot engraved with a floral and berried foliage band, the glass c. 1700, the engraving mid 18th C., 21 cm. high. **£1,300-1,500** *C*

A pair of Thuringian armorial goblets, the funnel bowls with the arms of George II above the motto Dieu et Mon Droit and the arms of Louis XV, the conical feet with folded rims engraved with a foliate band, 22.5 cm. high, c. 1760. **£1,100-1,300** *C*

A Dutch engraved armorial goblet, the thistle-shaped bowl with facet-cut lower part engraved with the arms of the Seven Provinces, 20 cm. high, c. 1750. **£350-450** *C*

A Dutch engraved composite-stemmed goblet, the reverse inscribed 'Het Welvaaren van de Cram Vrouw En Jongeboren', set of a swelling section filled with airtwist spirals, above a beaded facet-cut inverted baluster stem, 20.5 cm. high, c. 1765. **£900-1,000** *C*

A German armorial roemer, the wide shallow cup-shaped bowl engraved with a coat-of-arms, the hollow cylindrical stem decorated with applied prunts and milled trail, 20.5 cm., 17th/18th C. **£1,200-1,500** *S*

A Royal armorial goblet, decorated with the Royal Arms of Great Britain, the reverse with the arms of Saxonby, probably Central German, 21 cm., 18th/19th C. **£200-£250** *S*

A German wine glass, the funnel bowl engraved with inscription, supported on an inverted pear-shape hollow knop stem, 8¾ in. (22.3 cm.), second quarter of the 18th C. **£180-220** *SC*

A pair of Bohemian goblets, finely engraved and signed by H. J. Boam, with a tiger and a wild boar, 6½ in. (16.5 cm.), 19th C. **£450-550** *SC*

An amethyst wine glass of roemer type, the cup bowl on a hollow raspberry prunted stem, trailed conical foot, 11.5 cm. high, c. 1825. **£130-160**   *Som*

A Potsdam/Zechlin engraved and gilt Royal goblet, with cut knopped stem, domed foot cut with flutes, the details picked out in gilt, 22 cm., c. 1730. **£1,400-1,600**   *S*

A Bohemian zwischengold armorial goblet, for the Dutch market, on a fluted inverted baluster stem, the conical foot cut with ovals, 17.5 cm. high, c. 1740. **£1,600-1,800**   *C*

(*l.*) A sweetmeat, the double ogee bowl with everted rim, on a Silesian moulded stem, 15.3 cm. high, c. 1755. **£130-160**

(*r.*) A sweetmeat, the ogee bowl with flared rim, on a short stem, with air beaded knop, terraced domed foot, 10.5 cm. high, c. 1720. **£300-340**   *Som*

A good sweetmeat or champagne glass, the ovoid body with everted rim, on a bobbin knopped stem, 12.7 cm. high, c. 1720. **£320-340**   *Som*

A finely painted opaque flask, South Staffordshire, 15 cm. high, 1755-60. **£850-1,000**   *C*

A rare opaque twist sweetmeat, the double ogee radially moulded bowl with everted rim, on a stem with multi-spiral opaque twist, 13.5 cm., c. 1760. **£330-360**   *Som*

A German armorial rectangular flask, with pewter mount and screw cover, enamelled in colours, 19.5 cm. high, second quarter of the 18th C. **£1,000-1,200**   *C*

A dark brown bottle glass pitcher, probably Nailsea, 21.5 cm., c. 1810. **£230-260**   *Som*

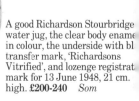

A rare jelly glass, with trumpet-shaped bowl, cushion knop and domed foot reticulate moulded, 113 mm. high, c. 1720. **£180-200** *Som*

A Nailsea flagon, the crown glass body with marvered opaque-white inclusions, applied loop handle, 17.8 cm., c. 1810. **£230-260**   *Som*

A good Richardson Stourbridge water jug, the clear body enamel in colour, the underside with bl transfer mark, 'Richardsons Vitrified', and lozenge registrat mark for 13 June 1948, 21 cm. high. **£200-240**   *Som*

A good Irish jug, 13.5 cm., mid 18th C. **£60-80**   *Bon*

A Nailsea bottle glass cream jug, with marvered white splashes, 11.5 cm. high, c. 1800. **£170-190** *Som*

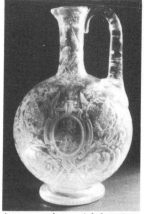

A very rare ruby-flashed engraved claret jug, decorated on both sides with hunting scenes silver replacement foot marked for 1920, probably engraved by Franz Tieze, glass probably Pugh Glass House, Dublin, 33 cm., c. 1880. **£800-1,000** *S*

The hunting scenes depicted were probably taken from popular prints.

An engraved armorial claret jug, probably Webb, 27 cm., c. 1870-80. **£500-600** *S*

A fine documentary engraved claret decanter, 24 cm., and a goblet en suite, 18 cm., probably Molineaux Webb, 1860's. **£650-750** *S*

A Baccarat dated scattered millefiori weight, including a cane with 'B1847', on a ground of short lengths of latticinio cable, entwined with coloured ribbon, 8 cm. diam. **£700-800** *C*

A Baccarat concentric millefiori mushroom weight, in shades of white, pink, red, blue and green set within a torsade of opaque gauze, entwined by cobalt-blue threads between mercury bands, 7.8 cm. diam. **£1,000-1,200** *C*

A Silesian 'Zwischenglas' claret jug, of flattened form, decorated in gilding, with amatory trophies on one side, 10⅜ in. (26.3 cm.), 19th C. **£150-200** *SC*

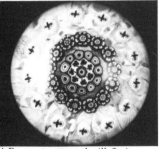

A rare Baccarat upright bouquet weight, in blue, white, green, red, set within a torsade of opaque gauze, entwined by blue threads between mercury bands, 7 cm. diam. **£1,300-1,500** *C*

A Baccarat patterned millefiori weight, 7.6 cm. diam. **£1,000-1,200** *S*

A Baccarat garlanded butterfly weight, with purple, blue, green, red, cobalt-blue, orange and white, star-cut base, 7.3 cm. diam. **£800-£900** *S*

A Baccarat primrose and garland paperweight, in red, white, blue, 6.5 cm. diam. **£650-750** *P*

A Baccarat miniature buttercup weight, in peach, white, yellow, green, 4.5 cm. diam. **£1,100-1,400** *C*

A Baccarat tulip bud weight, with 6 turquoise buds, 4 small green leaves, 7.8 cm. diam. **£800-900** *C*

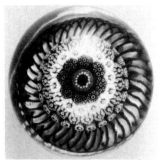

A St. Louis mushroom weight, in green, salmon-pink, white and royal blue, 8.5 cm. diam. **£1,000-£1,200**   *S*

A Clichy signed close millefiori weight, 8 cm. diam. **£1,300-1,500**   *C*

A signed St. Louis patterned millefiori weight, the central large pastry mould cane within a 7-pointed star arrangement of canes in pink and white, framed with tubular lime-green staves with turquoise centres, cane marked 'SL', 7.7 cm. diam. **£2,700-£2,900**   *S*

A St. Louis crown weight, with red and blue twisted ribbon, alternating with entwined latticinio thread, 7.2 cm. diam. **£1,000-1,200**   *C*

A St. Louis dahlia weight, in pink, yellow, green stalk, 8.3 cm. diam. **£650-750**   *S*

A St. Louis fuchsia weight, in green, pale mauve and white latticino thread, 6.9 cm. diam. **£2,000-2,500**   *C*

A St. Louis upright-bouquet weight, in red and blue and green, 7.1 cm. **£650-700**   *S*

A rare St. Louis 3 dimensional salamander weight, the translucent green glass moulded in relief with the serpent finely gilt, 8.6 cm. **£6,000-7,000**   *S*

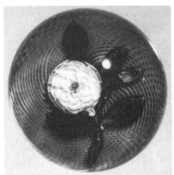

A St. Louis pompon weight, in white, pale yellow and green, on a salmon-pink ground of swirling latticinio thread, 7.3 cm. diam. **£750-950**   *C*

A New England apple weight, realistically moulded in shades of red, amber to greenish-yellow, 7.3 cm. **£500-700**   *S*

A Gillinder faceted concentric mushroom weight, predominantly white in colour with a central red and white set-up, 8.3 cm. **£450-550**   *S*

A St. Louis faceted pink clematis weight, the clear glass set with 14 striated overlapping pink petals, with a lime-green centre, set on a mound of white latticinio, 7 cm. **£400-500**   *S*

An unusual set of 6 sweetmeat glasses, in neo-Baroque style, probably Steinschönau, possibly for Lobmeyr, 11 cm., late 19th C. **£1,800-2,000**   *S*

A St. Louis scent bottle and stopper, with royal blue double ogee container, set on a paperweight base, 15.1 cm. **£800-900** *S*

An engraved claret jug and 2 goblets, on fluted shoulder knopped stems, London or Stourbridge, the jug 26 cm. high, c. 1880. **£900-1,000** *C*

A New England scent bottle with stopper, with a concentric millefiori weight in green, cobalt-blue, white and red, 21.6 cm. **£350-400** *S*

A pair of Bohemian engraved amber-tinted scent bottles, 7¼ in. high, 19th C. **£250-300**   *GC*

A suite of Venetian table glass, the pale blue glass with polychrome painted medallions, comprising: a flower bowl, a pair of candlesticks, 6 finger bowls and stands, 6 champagne glasses, 18 wine glasses in sizes, and a pair of sweetmeat dishes. **£800-900**   *HyD*

A Bohemian 'Zwischengold' scent bottle, minor rim chip, 9 cm. high, c. 1735. **£450-550**   *C*

A Bohemian scent bottle and stopper, the opalescent pale green body cased in clear glass and painted in white and gold, 21 cm. **£250-300**   *P*

A set of 3 miniature chinoiserie opaque square scent bottles, with metal-gilt mounts and opaque stoppers, the glass London or South Staffordshire, one bottle repaired, the case 5.5 cm. high, 1760-65. **£400-450**   *C*

MILLER'S *Antiques Price Guide builds up year by year to form the most comprehensive photo-reference system available. The first five volumes contain over 40,000 completely different photographs.*

A glass scent casket, with rope pattern and beaded metal mounts and handles, containing 6 square scent bottles and stoppers, French, 15.5 cm., 19th C. **£400-500**   *L*

A silver filigree-cased necessaire, with 2 opaque glass silver-mounted miniature bottles and stoppers painted and gilt, with a silver ear-spoon, a bodkin, a pair of tweezers and a pencil, the glass London or South Staffordshire, the case 5 cm. high, c. 1765. **£600-700**   *C*

A Bristol blue scent bottle, diamond facet cut and decorated in gilt, London decorated gold wrythen cap, 8 cm. high, c. 1760. **£750-850**   *Som*

A fine large oval diamond cut scent bottle, with cut ribbed edge, silver screw cap, 16.5 cm. long, c. 1800. **£140-160** *Som*

An extremely rare large Bristol blue scent/toilet water bottle, the body diamond facet cut, with gilt floral decoration, flute cut and gilt foot, cut and gilt ball stopper, probably London decorated, 18.5 cm. high, c. 1770. **£600-700** *Som*

A large cameo glass scent bottle, in pale blue and white, hinged silver-gilt cap, 26.5 cm., 1880's. **£500-600** *S*

A ruby glass scent bottle, the hinged silver cap marked Birmingham, 24.5 cm., 1880's. **£800-900** *S*

A cut-glass sulphide scent bottle and stopper, set with a profile portrait of George IV, Apsley Pellatt, 12 cm. high, c. 1820. **£500-£600** *C*

A large heavy cut scent bottle of dark 'metal', the body cog-wheel cut, with a band of small cut diamonds on top surface, similarly cut mushroom stopper, probably Irish, 10.5 cm. high, less stopper, c. 1830. **£170-190** *Som*

A miniature yellow and white cameo glass scent bottle, screw cap, 4.5 cm., 1880's. **£250-300** *S*

A ruby and white scent bottle, the white overlay carved with a flower spray, 6 cm., 1880's. **£300-350** *S*

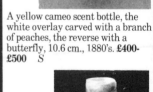

A cameo glass swan's head scent bottle, in yellow and white, the silver hinged cap marked Chester, 1884, 22 cm. **£1,300-1,500** *S*

A yellow cameo scent bottle, the white overlay carved with a branch of peaches, the reverse with a butterfly, 10.6 cm., 1880's. **£400-£500** *S*

A yellow cameo glass scent bottle, the white overlay carved with trailing plumbago and fuchsia, the silver screw cap by Sampson Mordan & Co., London, 1883, minute chip, 14 cm. **£500-600** *S*

A ruby scent bottle, the white overlay carved with a flower spray, the hinged silver cap marked London, 1884, 14.7 cm. **£450-550** *S*

A Webb ivory cameo scent bottle, the tinted opaque-cream glass acid-etched and engraved in Japanese style, silver screw cap, marked London 1902, marked 'THOS. WEBB & SONS, 1902'. **£400-500** *S*

An ivory cameo scent bottle, the opaque-white glass stained to simulate ivory, 5.7 cm., late 19th C. **£110-140** *S*

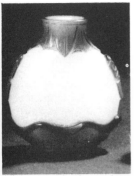

A cameo scent bottle, simulating the Chinese, in white glass overlaid in blue, by Daniel and Lionel Pearce at Thomas Webb & Sons, 5.7 cm., late 19th C. **£350-400** *S*

A rare cameo scent bottle, in green and blue glass, by Daniel and Lionel Pearce at Thomas Webb & Sons, 6 cm., late 19th C. **£400-500** *S*

A Central European 'milchglas' tankard, enamelled in typical colours, 10.3 cm., mid 18th C. **£350-£400** *S*

A rare 18th C. painted Bohemian opaline 'milchglas' tankard, decorated with figures, slightly damaged. **£350-400** *JD*

A Farrier's Guild dated cylindrical tankard (Zunfthumpen), enamelled in colours, Central Germany, dated 1762, 18.5 cm. high. **£2,400-2,600** *C*

A Central European tankard, with hinged pewter cover, enamelled in colours, the cover with ball thumbpiece, 15 cm. high, 18th C. **£1,000-1,200** *C*

A single-handled cut-glass mug, with blue overlay, 10.5 cm. **£60-70** *TKN*

A Bohemian amber-flashed mug, engraved with the hotel 'Belle Vue at Aix la Chapelle', 12 cm., 19th C. **£80-100** *Bon*

An engraved tankard, engraved with a view entitled 'Die Landecker Bäder', trimmed rim, 11 cm., c. 1830. **£200-250** *S*

A Bohemian 'Tiefschnitt' tankard and silver-mounted porcelain cover, attributed to F. Zach, the silver thumbpiece set with a green gemstone attached to the applied scroll handle, 16 cm. high, c. 1855-60. **£500-600** *C*

A 'Façon de Venise' tazza, Venetian or Lowlands, 14.5 cm., 16th/17th C. **£1,200-1,400** *S*

These tazze were reproduced in Victorian times.

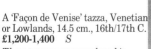

A pink-stained engraved spa tankard and cover, stained in pink and engraved with named views, 18.2 cm., c. 1850. **£700-800** *S*

A pair of small opaque baluster vases, painted in the 'famille rose' palette, South Staffordshire, 1755-60, 11.5 cm. high. **£500-600** *C*

A pair of chinoiserie opaque-opaline vases, South Staffordshire, 1755-60, one with restoration to foot rim, 15 cm. high. **£400-500** *C*

A small chinoiserie opaque vase, painted in a bright palette, South Staffordshire, 1755-60, 12.5 cm. high. **£700-800** *C*

A celery vase, the trumpet body with band of diamonds, prism and slant blaze cutting, notched rim on a knopped stem, plain foot star cut underneath, 21.5 cm. high, c. 1810. **£100-120** *Som*

An opaque beaker-vase, painted in a 'famille rose' palette, South Staffordshire, 1755-60, hair crack to foot, 17.5 cm. high. **£500-£600** *C*

A Burmese glass vase, in pink and yellow with frilled rim, 9 cm. high, c. 1890. **£50-60** *S*
As these vases have been reproduced recently in large quantities — a mark improves saleability.

A good Irish pickle jar, of unusual shape, cut with blazes, diamonds and bridge fluting, on a plain stem and conical foot, 17.5 cm. high, c. 1800. **£170-190** *Som*

A marked Webbs Burmese vase, in flesh tones shading to yellow, marked on the base 'Thos. Webb & Sons, Queens Burmese Ware, Patented', 20.8 cm. high, late 19th C. **£140-160** *S*

A cameo vase, the pale yellow ground overlaid in opaque-white, and with white line rim and foot rim, Stourbridge, 30.5 cm. high, c. 1890. **£900-1,200** *C*

A cameo double overlay oviform vase, the bright yellow ground overlaid in white on pink, Stourbridge, very slight chip to rim, 9 cm. high, c. 1880. **£650-850** *C*

A cut celery vase, the bucket bowl, flute and prism cut, with a band of diamonds, star cut plain conical foot, 20.5 cm. high, c. 1825. **£110-£130** *Som*

A large English cameo vase, the amethyst ground overlaid in white, 29.5 cm. high. **£900-1,100** *P*

A cameo glass vase, in blue overlaid in white, 15 cm. high, c. 1880. **£350-450** *S*

A cameo glass vase, by 'Thomas Webb & Sons', with crimson ground, moulded mark to base, 7¼ in. high. **£850-950** *A*

A 'Façon-de-Venise' filigree waisted vase, applied with vertical lattimo threads, Low Countries, 9.5 cm. high, 16th/17th C. **£250-300** *C*

An English cameo vase, the deep turquoise ground overlaid in white, 20.2 cm. high. **£850-1,050** *P*

A 'Façon de Venise' filigree vase, the body decorated with widely-spaced alternate plain and filigree opaque-white threads, 8.5 cm. high, c. 1600. **£400-500** *S*

A pair of large French opaque-opaline baluster vases, painted by 'Jean-François Robert' in a bright palette, 51 cm. high, c. 1850. **£2,100-2,300** *C*

A 'Façon de Venise' kuttrolf (Angster), Lowlands or Germany, 29 cm. high, 17th C. **£2,000-2,500** *S*

A vase, the rim and neck with spiral green and red twist, 17.4 cm. high, c. 1850. **£150-200** *S*

A French opaline vase, decorated in colours by 'Jean-Baptiste Desvignes' 15 cm. high, c. 1825. **£3,000-3,500** *C*

A 'Façon de Venise' filigree salt, with blue and white 'a retorti' decoration, Low Countries and perhaps Antwerp, 6.5 cm. diam., 17th/18th C. **£500-600** *C*

A pearl satin glass vase, the body in brown on opaque-white decorated with 'federzeichnung' and vermicular gilding, 15.2 cm. high, second half 19th C. **£300-350** *S*

A massive opaline glass vase, with blue strapwork design to the neck and foot, trimmed in gilt, 59 cm. high. **£650-850** *Bon*

(*l.*) A Swiss stained glass armorial panel, painted with the coat of arms of the 'Tschudi' family, 12½ by 9 in. (32 by 23 cm.), c. 1602. **£700-800**

(*r.*) A good Swiss stained glass armorial panel, 'circle of Lukas Zeiner', the shield slightly later, a few panes cracked, 14 by 11 in. (36 by 28 cm.), early 16th C. **£1,200-£1,400** *S*

A good Swiss stained glass armorial panel, against a gold coloured background, the whole framed by tree-like columns supporting a canopy of Gothic scrolling foliage, minute fragments of one pane missing, 14 by 11 in. (36 by 28 cm.), early 16th C. **£1,800-2,000** *S*

A late 19th or early 20th C. English stained glass panel, of the Virgin and Child, in the style of 'Burne Jones', oak frame, 113 by 39 cm. **£300-400** *C*

A Nailsea crown glass snuff jar, with turned over rim and graphite pontil mark, 29 cm. high, c. 1790-1810. **£100-120** *Som*

A pair of 'Bristol' blue glass bells, with diamond moulding and clear baluster handles, 29 cm. high, c. 1860. **£180-200** *Som*

A 'Thomas Webb & Son' cameo glass plaque, 'The Flower Girl', by 'T & G Woodall', signed, 32.5 cm. diam. **£15,000-17,000** *P*

An unusual beaded glass rectangular panel, worked in cloisonné technique, probably North Italian, 114 by 69 cm., early 19th C. **£350-400** *Bon*

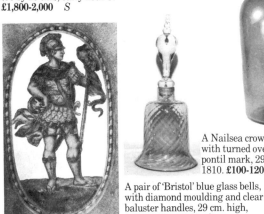

A group of 45 Tassie glass paste medallions, impressed in white paste, pale green or pink or white on coloured glass, some with inscriptions, the majority in original gilded rolled paper frames, numbered, 1-1¾ in. (2.5-4.5 cm.), early 19th C. **£250-300** *S*

It is most unusual to find these cameos in the original paper frames and it is to be presumed the numbers refer to one of the Tassie, Leicester Square catalogues as they do not tally with Raspe's large catalogue of 1791.

A rare set of four opaque-white glass cruets, with turned wooden caps, 14.5-16 cm., c. 1760. **£500-£600** *S*

An opaque cruet bottle, with silver cover and plated mount to rim, 21 cm. high, c. 1755-60. **£500-600** *C*

An unusual set of 3 green bells, of top hat shape, clear baluster handles, 28 to 30 cm. high, c. 1870. **£260-280** *Som*

A 'Bristol' blue glass spittoon, 22.5 cm. diam., c. 1870. **£75-85** *Som*

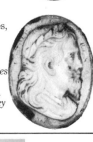

ART NOUVEAU INTRODUCTION

During the second half of the nineteenth century, European artists and intellectuals were growing increasingly discontented with the accepted principle that the greatest of man's artistic achievements were rooted in the classical past.

Sources of Inspiration

Nature, not classical precedent, was felt to be the true wellspring of honest creative endeavour, and it was the craftsman, not the effete designer remote from his materials, whom nature would inspire to create objects of 'honest' beauty. Morris' philosophy, which was founded on a romantic view of mediaevalism as expressed in the Arthurian legend, saw the machine was entirely inimical to this ideal. Nevertheless, he and others like him were breaching the walls of tradition and paving the way for a new art; an art which would have nothing to do with privilege and wealth, or with museums and galleries; an art which would touch every aspect of life through its expression in everyday objects.

The return to nature as a source of inspiration had been largely a consequence of the introduction to the western world of Japanese art, notably at the World Exhibition held in London in 1862. In France the influence was no less strong, though it arrived a few years later. Western artists were fascinated by the abstraction of natural forms, and by the expression of the unity of all nature which this allowed. The theme of the woman-flower was one that, more than any other, would later be universally regarded as the hallmark of the new art.

Two Schools

Although the new gospel spread throughout Western Europe and America, the interpretation of its message was by no means uniform. Each artist or group of artists sought individual means of expression, and a wide variety of styles emerged. Although there are many 'grey areas', it is possible to divide Art Nouveau into two broad categories: the ascetic school, as typified by Rennie Mackintosh, and the sensuous school of which Gallé was one of the chief exponents.

Looked at in a historical context, it becomes evident that the direction taken by the French designers was a dead end. Although their creations were, in the main, beautifully made — and have since provided inspiration for a few modern designers — the First World War rendered them irrelevant and the movement ceased abruptly there and then. The other branch, however, continued to bear fruit, paving the way for the modernist school, the Bauhaus and much that is best in architecture and design of the present day.

Since the 1960's, Art Nouveau has found increasing favour with collectors — and prices have risen accordingly. Nevertheless, there is a wealth of material on the market, much of which is well within the pocket of even the quite modest collector. Of course, signed original pieces by the great names of the movement are rarely seen outside museums and the most important collections, but, even today, local auction houses turn up good quality furniture, glass, ceramics, metalware and jewellery at prices which are comparatively modest and still represent good value for money.

Prices

The pieces illustrated have been selected to represent a broad cross section of the products of the Art Nouveau movement which are likely to be found on the market today.

It cannot be too strongly stressed that condition is of the utmost importance in the consideration of any price. This is particularly so in the case of Art Nouveau. Because the Art Nouveau period was relatively recent — it may reasonably be said to have ended by 1918, though a number of manufacturers continued to produce the more popular lines after that date — a great many pieces are to be found in absolutely perfect condition. Many, too, were produced in considerable quantity, and it would be unreasonable to expect a piece bearing even slight damage to realise as much as an identical, but perfect specimen.

An Art Nouveau mahogany clock, fashioned in the manner of Majorelle, the dial set with mother-of-pearl numerals, with shaped brass hands, 32 cm. high. **£550-650**

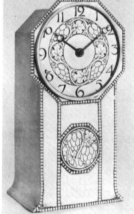

A silver cased mantel timepiece, by Liberty and Co., the French movement with platform lever escapement, and stamped with the lion trademark of Duverdrey and Bloquel, the case engraved with a presentation inscription, Birmingham 1910 by Liberty and Co., 21.7 cm. high. **£750-850**   *L*

A Goldscheider pottery clock, the case with stylised mistletoe decoration inscribed 'Amicitia Vincit Horas', 20 in. high. **£300-350** *Re*

An unusual gilt bronze and glass panelled clock, with internal bronze panels pierced with grasses revealing green-marbled glass beneath, with French movement, one panel signed with a C.F.S. monogram, the glass possibly made by Tiffany, 41.50 cm. high. **£700-£800** *P*

An unusual Moorcroft 'Claremont' timepiece, signed W. Moorcroft, Rd. No. 420081, 14 cm. high. **£600-700** *P*

A Liberty and Co. pewter and enamel clock, stamped English Pewter Made by Liberty and Co., c. 1905. £250-350 S

A Gallé fire polished cameo glass bowl, the cloudy grey ground overlaid in cherry red, cameo mark 'Gallé', 8½ in. diam. £450-600 CSK

GALLÉ, Emile
(1846-1904)

If not the father, certainly one of the foremost figures of the French Art Nouveau movement, Emile Gallé was the founder of the Nancy school. After a liberal education, he began his working life as apprentice to his father, a studio glassmaker. The development of his unique Art Nouveau style is considered to have dated from about 1884, and within six years he was running a factory supplying large quantities of studio glass to, among others, the Parisian shop of Sebastian Bing, the international entrepreneur. The shop was called l'Art Nouveau.

Gallé was widely imitated by other glass workers, but few, if any, could match his technical skill or artistic feeling. In 1880 he began to produce Art Nouveau furniture of extremely high quality, often embellishing his products with inlays — notably mother of pearl — and characteristically delicate marquetry designs.

Following his death in 1904, articles produced by his factories continued to be signed 'Gallé', but all were marked with a star from that time onward.

A Liberty and Co. pewter clock, designed by Archibald Knox, with wing-like flanges either side set with abalone, unmarked as base plate is missing, 38 cm. high. £1,300-1,600 P

A large Art Nouveau clock, with enamelled dial, by Liberty & Co. £350-450 ASA

A Gallé cameo landscape vase, grey glass tinted with yellow, overlaid in brown, cameo mark 'Gallé', c. 1900. £250-300 S

A Gallé cameo glass landscape bowl, in grey/yellow glass, overlaid in brown, cameo mark 'Gallé', c. 1900. £400-500 S

Landscape decoration especially on larger pieces tends to prove more popular than floral decoration; preference is mirrored in price.

A Gallé cameo glass landscape vase, in grey and yellow glass overlaid in blue and brown, intaglio mark 'Gallé', 18.75 cm., c. 1900. £600-800 S

'MOULD BLOWN' OR 'BLOW OUT'

Pieces produced by this method are popular with collectors as they incorporate both moulded and cameo carved (or acid-etched) detailing, the detail being in higher relief than straightforward cameo and of much more 'rounded' appearance.

A Gallé green glass and enamelled covered vase, streaked internally with pink and yellow, heightened with gilding, enamelled in colours, Nancy depose, signed on base 'E. Gallé', damage to base and handle, 26 cm. high. £350-400 P
Perfect £500-700

A good Gallé cameo glass centrepiece, the amber-tinted body overlaid with two tones of ruby glass acid-etched with primula, signed in cameo 'Gallé', 46 cm. long. £2,400-2,600 P

A large overlay baluster-shaped vase, by Emile Gallé, minor chip to base, signed E. Gallé on a leaf, 42.5 cm. high, c. 1900. **£550-650** *CAm*

CAMEO GLASS

The body is overlaid with a 'skin' of coloured glass, sometimes in several layers and reduced by various methods to produce a relief image. The processes for this reduction are acid-etching, the most general form, using bitumen of Judea as an acid-resistant agent, or carving with a wheel or both processes together.

Sometimes a piece may be painted or stencilled with coloured decoration which superficially may resemble cameo decoration.

An overlay glass vase, by Emile Gallé, the yellow and white ground overlaid in mauve, signed Gallé in the overlay, 49.5 cm. high. **£500-£700** *CAm*

A Gallé clear glass jug, enamelled in colours (base enamelled Emile Gallé depose), 9½ in. high. **£300-£400** *CSK*

Gallé enamelled glass of this type although early, c. 1880, tends to be restrictive in price as a result of both shape and decoration following more conventional tastes.

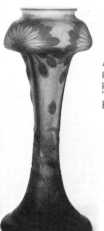

A Gallé cameo glass vase, the greyish body overlaid with pale green and brown, signed in cameo 'Gallé' with star preceding, 34 cm. high. **£350-450** *P*

A triple overlay glass vase, by Emile Gallé, the matt clear ground overlaid in white, ochre and green, signed Gallé in the overlay, 42 cm. high, c. 1900. **£600-700** *CAm*

An Art Nouveau marbled frosted glass vase, signed Gallé, and with red and green cameo cut vine, fruit and leaf decoration, 10 in. high. **£550-650** *DSH*

(l.) A Gallé bottle vase, cameo signature, 23.5 cm., c. 1900. **£450-£550**

(l.c.) A Gallé bottle vase, with purple wisteria on yellow ground, cameo signature, 15 cm., c. 1900. **£300-400**

(r.c.) A Gallé cameo glass vase, acid etched through violet overlay, cameo signature, 11.5 cm., c. 1900. **£400-500**

(r.) A Gallé bottle vase, yellow metal cased in lavender blue, cameo signature, 24 cm., c. 1900. **£400-500** *SS*

A Gallé cameo glass vase, the amber-tinted body overlaid with pale blue and amethyst acid-etched, signed in cameo 'Gallé', 25.25 cm. high. **£600-650** *P*

Although not mentioned in the description this piece had an original retail paper label 'Gallé Nancy' on base — an added feature of interest to a collector.

A tall Gallé cameo glass vase, the greyish body tinted amber in places, overlaid with amethyst glass, signed in cameo 'Gallé' with star preceding, 40 cm. high. **£650-£800** *P*

The star preceding the signature was included after Gallé's death in 1903 as a tribute to him and was used for a short time after. Traditionally unpopular with collectors this star does not necessarily indicate inferior quality.

A large Gallé cameo glass vase, cameo mark 'Gallé', 45.25 cm., c. 1900. **£900-1,100** *S*

A Gallé cameo glass oviform vase, the greyish body overlaid with two tones of ruby glass, signed in cameo 'Gallé', 25.50 cm. high. **£850-950** *P*

A Gallé cameo glass vase, of pale yellow metal cased in deep blue and carved with bleeding hearts, cameo signature and retailer's label, 14.5 cm., c. 1900. **£400-450** *SS*

A Gallé cameo glass vase, in grey glass with blood red on the interior of the neck and upper body, overlaid in purple etched with sprays of flowering anemones, cameo mark 'Gallé', 37.25 cm., c. 1900. **£1,000-1,200** *S*

A Gallé cameo glass vase, yellow tinted grey glass body overlaid in shades of sealing wax red, cameo mark 'Gallé', 23 cm., c. 1900. **£650-£850** *S*

A pair of pewter-mounted iridescent glass vases, attributed to Loetz, the undersides marked 'Juventa Prima Metal', 31 cm., c. 1900. **£350-450** *S*

A Loetz iridescent glass vase, decorated with bands of peacock blue and golden iridescence, contained within a bronze mount, signed on base of glass 'Loetz of Austria', 18 cm. high. **£250-300** *P*

The bronze foliate mount on this piece is an added decorative feature and the glass is signed 'Loetz Austria', not all pieces signed thus are genuine — beware!

A Gallé marine cameo glass vase, the lemon-tinted body having inky blue striations and overlaid with orange glass acid-etched with seaweeds and a snail, signed in cameo 'Gallé', 24.50 cm. high. **£1,100-1,300** *P*

A Loetz iridescent glass vase, exhibiting a green-golden iridescence and internally decorated with horizontally meandering banding, 32 cm. high. **£250-350** *P*

Although a good shape 'green' iridescent glass is not considered 'popular' presently.

A Loetz overlaid iridescent glass vase, in amber glass decorated with dappled splashed peacock lustre, overlaid in silver, 22.75 cm., c. 1900. **£600-700** *S*

The silver overlay is achieved using an electrolysis technique whereby the silver gradually builds up to a required thickness; some examples may be found stamped with the word 'Deposit'.

The same technique was used by the New York porcelain makers 'Lennox'.

A Loetz 'Phenomena' iridescent glass vase, the glass of rose pink tone decorated with blue feathered horizontal banding and splashes of gold iridescence, 26 cm. high. **£700-£850** *P*

A pair of iridescent glass vases, attributed to Loetz, in salmon pink glass with deep blue on the bowl with regular patches of peacock/gold iridescence, 16 cm., c. 1900. **£650-800** *S*

An iridescent glass vase, attributed to Loetz, covered with an all-over pulled thread design in a silvery yellow and blue iridescence, 7¼ in. high. **£350-400** *CSK*

A Loetz iridescent glass bowl, designed by Michael Powolny, of ruby tone with internal crackled silver iridescence, having a pale green rim and supported on three black glass ball feet, 26.50 cm. diam. **£250-300**

The popularity of Viennese designers made this piece more popular than had it not been attributable to a particular designer.

A Loetz glass vase, the shape designed by Josef Hoffmann, the red glass vessel having a black glass rim, 22.25 cm. high. **£250-350** *P*

The designer 'Josef Hoffmann' reflecting the current interest in Viennese works of art was responsible for the popularity of this piece.

An iridescent glass vase, attributed to Loetz, in deep blue glass decorated with splashed peacock lustre, 26 cm., c. 1900. **£250-300** *S*

A Loetz iridescent glass vase, the deep ruby glass decorated with vivid peacock blue iridescent threaded and meandering bands, 17 cm. high. **£350-450** *P*

An iridescent glass vase, attributed to Loetz, white glass decorated at the base with dappled pink/peacock lustre and pots of bright green with tiny metallic inclusions, the neck in dappled gold lustre, underside with faintly enamelled mark '2/219n787', 42.5 cm. **£200-250** *S*

As only attributable to 'Loetz' this piece of lower value. Definite attribution constitutes a higher price.

A Loetz iridescent glass vase, decorated with fine blue meandering bands and having random pale peacock blue/violet splashes overall, 21.50 cm. high. **£250-350** *P*

A Loetz cameo glass vase, the pale lemon body overlaid with pale brown, apple green and red, signed in cameo 'Loetz', 15.50 cm. high. **£400-500** *P*

Loetz is normally thought of as iridescent glass and therefore when cameo pieces such as this appear they prove popular.

An unmarked Loetz iridescent glass shell vase, the shell splashed with a gold-green lustre, mottled surface, 23 cm. **£200-250** *Bon*

A Tiffany Favrile vase, in green on a shaded iridescent gold and silver ground, engraved on the foot-rim 2375K L. C. Tiffany — Favrile, and with engraved numerals on the pontil, 33.5 cm. **£1,500-2,000** *L*

A small Tiffany Favrile 'paperweight' vase, decorated with green glass lily pads and white 'cane' florets against a pale golden iridescent ground shading to violet at the base, unmarked, probably had paper retail label, 6 cm. high. **£600-700** *P*

A Loetz iridescent glass vase, the aubergine glass decorated with iridescent feather-design, signed Loetz Austria, 14 cm. high, c. 1900. **£450-550** *CAm*

559

DAUM BROTHERS, Auguste (1853-1909), Antonin (1864-1930)

Makers of decorative domestic glassware, the Daum Brothers turned to art glass production following the Paris Exhibition in 1889. Since they worked in Nancy, it is not unnatural that they should have been greatly influenced by Gallé — with whom they are invariably unfavourably compared. Inevitable as such comparison is, it is unfortunate, because their work is highly competent and frequently displays a high standard of artistic merit.

A French painted glass spray scent bottle, in imitation of cameo glass, late 19th C. **£60-80** *BA*

Although unmarked this piece is probably 'Daum', the gilt marks on base are prone to wear and often disappear.

A Daum glass vase, internally decorated with pink florets having orange centres, against a streaked pink brown, orange and blood-red ground, signed around the base 'Daum Nancy', 43.50 cm. high. **£350-550** *P*

A Daum cameo glass plafonnier, the amber-tinted body overlaid with two tones of ruby glass, with gilded attachments embellished with ivy leaves, signed in cameo 'Daum Nancy France', 41 cm. diam. **£1,000-1,500** *P*

A Daum cameo glass vase, the greyish yellow ground merging through orange to green at the base, overlaid in orange and green, cameo mark Daum Nancy, 19¼ in. high. **£900-1,000** *CSK*

A D'Argental cameo glass vase, in amber glass overlaid in shades of russet brown, cameo mark 'D'Argental', 30 cm., c. 1900. **£300-£350** *S*

A Daum cameo glass vase, in amber glass shading to deep red, overlaid in rich rust brown, cameo mark 'Daum Nancy', 54.5 cm., c. 1900. **£600-800** *S*

A Muller Frères cameo glass vase, the dark grey-blue glass acid etched with trees and a lake beneath a pink sky, etched signature 'Muller Fres. Luneville', 6½ in. (16.5 cm.), c. 1906. **£250-350** *SC*

ART NOUVEAU FURNITURE

Perhaps in no other area than furniture is the divergence of paths taken by Art Nouveau designers so evident. Prior to the late nineteenth century, furniture design had been closely related to architectural design, often employing the lines, proportions and decorative devices of the great buildings of the Greek and Roman empires. Exponents of the new art, turning their backs on classical precedent, introduced an entirely new sculptural element into their furniture.

While all Art Nouveau is based upon themes drawn from nature, the French and Southern European designers tended to accentuate the swirls and sensuous curves which are the external, visible characteristics of natural growth, while the Scottish and other Northern European schools sought a more abstract, and usually austere, form of expression, suggesting rather than describing their theme. The latter groups often worked in oak, while the opulence of the more flamboyant Continental styles was generally captured in more decorative — and sometimes quite exotic — timbers. Not uncommonly, metals, ceramics, leather and even parchment were used for decorative embellishment in addition to the more traditional inlays of ivory and contrasting wood veneers.

Not all furniture is representative of the 'high' Art Nouveau styles, and much that is totally in keeping with today's taste, can be bought at prices which are not unreasonable considering the consistently high standards of workmanship and materials which characterise them.

An Arts and Crafts style walnut armchair, probably Belgian, 132 cm. high. **£1,000-1,300** *C*

An E. W. Pugin oak 'Granville' chair, stamped P.O.D.R., mark for 1870, 83 cm. **£900-1,000**   *S*

MAJORELLE, Louis (1859-1926)

Following his father's death in 1879, Majorelle took over the family furniture business in Nancy, making reproductions of eighteenth century designs. Some ten years later, recognising the commercial possibilities of the Art Nouveau style, he began to reorganise his workshops and catalogues and, by 1900, he had become France's leading manufacturer of Art Nouveau furniture.

Although the spirit of Art Nouveau was opposed to machine made products, Majorelle mechanised his workshops, enabling him to produce highly fashionable furniture at prices which brought it within the reach of a reasonably wide market.

A tub armchair, 70.5 cm. high by 68.5 cm. max. wide, 1890's. **£80-120** *S*

A pair of J. & J. Kohn 'Fledermaus' side chairs, designed by Josef Hoffmann, J. & J. Kohn label beneath upholstery, 80 cm. high, c. 1907. **£400-500**   *S*

An oak dining suite, designed by C. F. A. Voysey, with 6 chairs, table 300 cm. approx. max. length, chairs 90 cm., c. 1898/1900. **£2,000-£3,000**   *S*

A mahogany marquetry etagère, by Louis Majorelle, 124.5 cm. high. **£1,000-1,300**   *C*

A set of 2 elbow and 5 single Edwardian mahogany dining chairs. **£600-700**   *DSH*

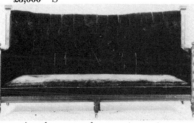

A mahogany and marquetry centre couch, in the manner of William Morris & Co., inlaid with stylised foliage in boxwood and stained sycamores, 7 ft. 8 in. wide (234 cm.), 1890's. **£1,500-1,800**   *S*

Made for Highfield Hall, Leek, for Sir Anthony Nicholson, J.P., family of silk manufacturers. It was made for a visit of Prince George in 1900.

A Morris & Co. mahogany 'Saville' armchair, designed by George Jack. **£650-700**   *P*

An Edwardian mahogany 7-piece suite comprising: 2-seat settee, 2 armchairs and 4 single chairs. **£650-750**   *DA*

An Art Nouveau mahogany settle, 129 by 127.5 cm. **£350-400**   *P*

A pair of J. & J. Kohn 'Fledermaus' armchairs, designed by Josef Hoffmann, J. & J. Kohn labels, 80 cm., c. 1907. **£900-1,000**   *S*

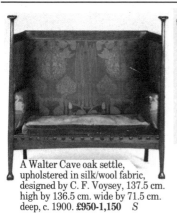

A Walter Cave oak settle, upholstered in silk/wool fabric, designed by C. F. Voysey, 137.5 cm. high by 136.5 cm. wide by 71.5 cm. deep, c. 1900. **£950-1,150**   *S*

An English walnut side cabinet, with a grey slate top, and 4 cupboard doors, inlaid with slate panels, 3 ft. 1 in. high by 4 ft. 10½ in. wide (94 by 149 cm.), 1900-20. **£300-400**   *S*
The small plate panels are replacements, presumably instead of the original pietra dura panels.

An Art Nouveau mahogany cabinet. **£150-200**   *MN*

A mahogany buffet, 246 cm. high by 115 cm. wide by 50.5 cm. deep, 1880's. **£2,000-2,500**   *S*

An Art Nouveau mahogany display cabinet, inlaid with stylised flowers and coloured leaded lights, pilasters to sides. **£250-300**   *BA*

An Art Nouveau oak desk with copper hinges and handles, 122 by 115.5 cm. **£550-650**   *P*

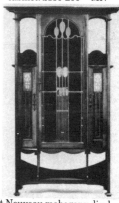

An Art Nouveau mahogany display cabinet, 5 ft. 9 in. high by 3 ft. 8 in. wide (175 by 112 cm.), c. 1910. **£700-800**   *SS*

A large oak sideboard, in the style of C. F. A. Voysey, 84 in. wide by 85½ in. high. **£450-500**   *WHB*

A white-painted and inlaid desk and chair, inlaid in wood, abelone and mother-of-pearl and white synthetic laminate, 101 cm. high by 99.5 cm. wide by 51.5 cm. deep, c. 1905. **£1,200-1,400**   *S*

A Gallé 2-tier marquetry table, inlaid in various woods, inlaid signature, 87 cm. high, c. 1910. **£400-500**   *S*

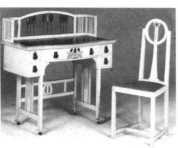

A Bechstein Arts & Crafts period upright grand piano, in mahogany case, the iron frame numbered 63626, 61 in. wide. **£1,100-1,300**   *Re*

An Arts and Crafts Manxman piano, by Baillie Scott. **£26,000-£28,000**   *CW*

LAMPS

It was during the closing years of the nineteenth century that electricity began to be used for domestic lighting, and it is hardly surprising that its cause was rapidly espoused by workers in metal and glass. Far and away the most popular and fashionable designer of lamps for the new electric lights was Louis Comfort Tiffany (1848-1933) an American aesthete with a highly developed talent for marketing. His workshops produced a wide range of lamps characterised by the use of stained glass window techniques employing iridescent coloured glass to create the effect of beauty at all times, whether illuminated from within by the lamp, or not.

The French glassmaker, René Lalique, also developed the technique of building electric lights into bases on which he placed glass sculptures.

An Aesthetic Movement brass and glass hexagonal hall lantern, 2 ft. 10 in. high by 1 ft. 2 in. wide (86 by 36 cm.), c. 1880. **£1,800-2,000**   *S*

late 19th/early 20th C. alabaster lamp, 36 in. high (92 cm.). **£450- £500**   *SS*

A Gallé cameo 'magnolia' table lamp, the amber-tinted body overlaid with two tones of rich ruby glass acid-etched with branches of magnolia, signed in cameo on base and shade 'Gallé', 58 cm. high. **£6,500-7,500**   *P*

A good Müller Frères cameo glass table lamp, the glass of yellow tone streaked with colours, overlaid with red and brown glass acid-etched with anemones, signed in cameo 'Muller Freres, Luneville', 73 cm. high. **£6,000-7,000**   *P*

A tall and good Daum cameo glass table lamp, the predominantly yellow body shading to amethyst at the edges and overlaid with streaked red, greyish white and deep blue, signed in cameo on shade and base, 'Daum, Nancy' and monogram respectively, 66 cm. high. **£7,500-9,000**   *P*

A leaded glass lampshade, unmarked but attributed to Tiffany, 30.5 cm. diam. **£450-550**   *P*

JEWELLERY

The fluid stylisation of form which characterises the Art Nouveau movement lends itself admirably to jewellery design, as does the preoccupation of artists of the period with flowers and insects.

Broadly speaking, Art Nouveau jewellery falls into one of two categories: the very highly priced, 'decadent' pieces which were individually designed for the wealthiest leaders of Parisian fashion, and the more modest, sometimes mass-produced, accessories which found greater favour with the British market. Particularly attractive to today's buyers are the silver and bright enamel pieces which were included in Liberty's range.

An unusual silver, gold and enamel pendant necklace, 5 cm., c. 1910. **£300-350**   *S*

An Austrian silver and plique-à-jour enamel brooch, 3.9 cm. wide, stamped '800 Silver', c. 1905, and a silver and plique-à-jour enamel bar brooch, in the form of a scarab, turquoise enamel and plique-à-jour enamel details, 5 cm., maker's mark 'G.K.', stamped 'Real Silver', c. 1910. **£250-300**   *S*

A Liberty & Co. gold enamel and mother-of-pearl pendant necklace, maker's mark, stamped 15 ct, 7 cm. overall length, c. 1910. **£350-£400**   *S*

A Liberty & Co. 'Cymric' silver and enamel waist clasp, designed by Archibald Knox, stamped maker's mark, Birmingham 1905. **£250-300** *CSK*

A George Hunt cruciform pendant, marked on back with 'G.H.' in shield, 9.50 cm. long, on chain. **£180-220** *P*

A Liberty & Co. 'Arts and Crafts' necklace, on chain 6 cm. **£60-80** *P*

An Art Nouveau pendant, unmarked but in the German style, probably by Murrle Bennett. **£50-£60** *P*

A German Art Nouveau brooch, pierced and set with a plaque of amethyst flanked by two ovals of mother-of-pearl with a faceted amethyst drop, silver-coloured metal stamped '900', depose and with monogram for Carl Hermann of Pforzheim, 4 cm. across. **£160-200** *P*

A Liberty & Co. enamelled pendant, of flower form, enamelled in blue and green with wirework stamens and mother-of-pearl centre, 3.25 cm. **£120-160** *P*

An unusual Perry & Co. brass 'posy' brooch, fashioned as a butterfly, stamped with design lozenge for 1868 and 'Perry & Co. London', 5 cm. across. **£80-120** *P*

This piece may have been designed by Christopher Dresser for Perry & Co. having married into the family in 1854 with his marriage to Thirza Perry, a lecturer at South Kensington.

A gold, turquoise and pearl necklace, stamped 'Reg 422909' on one cage, 40.50 cm. **£100-120** *P*

(1.) An Arts and Crafts gold and lapis lazuli ring, showing affinities to the work of John Paul Cooper or Henry Wilson. **£150-200**

(2.) An Arts and Crafts ring, characteristic of the Birmingham School work under the influence of Gaskin. **£90-120**

(3.) A Theodor Fahrner opal ring, stamped '925', 'FAHRNER' and 'TF' monogram. **£180-240**

(4.) A George Hunt ring, marked 'GH' in shield. **£70-90**

(5.) An Arts and Crafts ring, with central oval cabochon of lapis lazuli, stamped 'Sterling'. **£70-90** *P*

An Arts and Crafts pendant, set with 2 almandine garnet cabochons and further garnet drop, 3.50 cm. **£80-120** *P*

The leaf motifs show the characteristics of the work of Sybil Dunlop.

An Arts and Crafts pendant, with a turquoise cabochon, with vine and turquoise drop below, 4.50 cm. **£80-£120** *P*

A good Arts and Crafts gold, silver, plique-à-jour and opal hair ornament, attributed to Henry Wilson on stylistic grounds, 17 cm. long. **£1,400-1,700** *P*

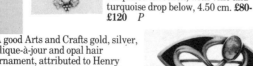

A Charles Horner silver opal and turquoise enamel brooch, maker's mark, Chester, 1907, 3.25 cm. **£70-£90** *S*

(t.) An Arts and Crafts pendant, with an oval plaque of lapis lazuli, set with a blister pearl and having a freshwater pearl drop, on chain, 4 cm. across. **£70-90**

(t.c.) An Arts and Crafts necklace, characteristic of the work of the Birmingham School under the influence of Gaskin, length of pendant 5 cm. **£180-220**

(b.c.) A Liberty & Co. gold, amethyst and pearl necklace, designed by Archibald Knox, 39 cm. long. **£450-500**

(b.) A Liberty & Co. 'Arts & Crafts' necklace, 41 cm. long. **£140-170** *P*

A silver and copper tea caddy and cover, by Albert Edward Jones, stamped maker's initials Birmingham, 1913, 5 in. high. **£80-£120** *CSK*

A Connell's silver dressing table set, designed by Kate Harris, marked 'W.G.C.' and London hallmarks for 1899/1901/1902, width of tray 30 cm. **£550-750** *P*

Although this set has Connell's marks one normally finds this design made up by William Hutton and Sons.

An Art Nouveau pendant brooch, with central circular plaque of mother-of-pearl flanked by enamelled leaves of shaded blue and white, 5 cm. across, sold with Liberty & Co. fabric covered oval box and cover. **£260-320** *P*

An unusual Arts and Crafts necklace, set with 3 plaques of Tiffany iridescent 'cypriote' glass, flanking a rose-cut diamond, with glass drop below and suspended on chains spaced with further mounted segments of Tiffany glass, the catch also set with glass, 44 cm. long. **£800-900** *P*

An unusual John Paul Cooper silver cup and cover, stamped with beetle mark and dated 1903, 16.50 cm. high. **£160-200** *P*

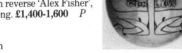

An Alexander Fisher silver and enamelled presentation trowel, signed on reverse 'Alex Fisher', 20 cm. long. **£1,400-1,600** *P*

A Keswick School of Industrial Arts silver buckle, in Art Nouveau style, 3 in. each half stamped KSIA in an oval, in original case. **£200-£250** *DWB*

SILVER

If there was any material in which English Art Nouveau craftsmen can be said to have achieved supremacy over those of other nationalities, it was silver. The emergence of the Arts and Crafts movement stimulated a vigorous revival of interest in all kinds of metalwork, but most notably silver and pewter, and the patronage of Arthur Lazenby Liberty ensured a good outlet for high quality work. Styles reflected the mood of romantic mediaevalism which was a major source of inspiration to British exponents of Art Nouveau and is best typified by Liberty's 'Cymric' range of silver goods.

Liberty and Company, founded by Arthur Lazenby Liberty in 1875, began their commercial production of silver in 1899. The old Celtic word 'Cymric' was chosen as a trade name for the silver as an acknowledgement of the influence of ancient Celtic illuminated manuscripts on the designs. The 'Cymric' range of silver was mass-produced by W. H. Haseler of Birmingham.

The essential synthesis of material and form which represents one of the guiding principles of Art Nouveau is achieved as surely in the best of English silver of the period as it was by Gallé in glass. The use of strongly coloured enamels and semi-precious stones to enliven smooth areas of polished metal or emphasise sinuous line decoration served greatly to heighten the effect of restrained opulence, so important in silver-ware of tasteful distinction.

A Liberty & Co. 'Cymric' silver spoon, designed by Archibald Knox, maker's mark, 'Cymric' mark, Birmingham, 1901, 20.25 cm. **£500-600** *S*

KESWICK SCHOOL OF INDUSTRIAL ART

Founded as an evening institute in 1884 by Canon and Mrs. Rawnsley. Expanded to include daytime classes in 1898. Harold Stabler and Herbert J. Maryon, the metalworker and jeweller, were full-time directors and designers at the school. The metalwork and jewellery was sold through The Home Arts and Industries Association.

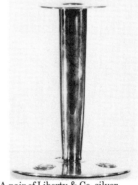

A pair of Liberty & Co. silver candlesticks, the circular bases with 3 blue-green enamelled entrelac bosses, stamped maker's mark, Birmingham 1905, 5¾ in. high. **£400-500** *CSK*

A Gold and Silversmiths Company silver box, maker's marks for London, 1901, 10.50 cm. high, 22 oz. **£350-400**   *P*

An Edwardian Art Nouveau rose bowl, makers Hamilton and Inches, Edinburgh 1902, 38 oz., 9 in. diam. by 6½ in. high. **£450-500**   *CDC*

An Edwardian Art Nouveau claret jug, Birmingham 1905, 10½ in. high. **£500-600**   *CDC*

An English silver tea set, marked GD.DF, London 1901, total weight 35.5 oz., height of teapot 14 cm. **£260-340**   *P*

An unusual Hukin & Heath plated metal and glass biscuit barrel, marked 'H & H' and No. '1894', 13.50 cm. across. **£130-180**   *P*

The inventive nature of this piece could indicate the strong influence of Christopher Dresser in its design.

A Hukin & Heath plated toast rack, designed by Christopher Dresser, H & H mark, lozenge registration mark for 9th October 1878, 'Designed by Dr. C. Dresser' and No. '1987', 13.50 cm. high. **£1,100-1,400**   *P*

A 5-piece electroplated metal tea service, set on green ball feet on stepped bases, 60.5 cm. max. width, 1930's. **£450-500**   *S*

A plate 'aesthetic movement' kettle, the design attributed to Christopher Dresser, maker's marks for R. & R. Hodd & Sons, and a design lozenge for 16th May 1878, 18.50 cm. high. **£180-240**   *P*

This piece shows the same aspect of design as the kettles fashioned in copper by Benham and Froud.

A Hukin & Heath plated sweetmeat bowl, designed by Christopher Dresser, stamped 'H & H No. 2047' and 'Designed by Dr. C. Dresser', 17 cm. across. **£550-£650**   *P*

An unusual Dixon and Sons plated teapot, designed by Christopher Dresser, maker's marks, facsimile signature and No. '2277', 13 cm. high. **£4,500-5,000**   *P*

A William Hutton and Sons Ltd. electroplated cruet, inspired by a design by Christopher Dresser, maker's mark, 16.75 cm. high, c. 1900. **£65-95**   *S*

A Hukin & Heath plated sweetmeat dish, designed by Christopher Dresser, stamped 'H & H' and No. 2593, 17 cm. across. **£65-95**   *P*

A Heath & Middleton silver pepper pot, the design attributed to Christopher Dresser, maker's marks JTH. JHM, Birmingham 1892, 8.50 cm. high, 1.50 oz. **£600-£700** *P*

A Russian Art Nouveau rectangular pen tray, by O. Korlyukov, Moscow 1899-1908, 26 cm. wide. **£700-800** *C*

An unusual Arts and Crafts metal and enamelled triptych, by Nelson and Edith Dawson, all panels signed with 'D' and 2 dated '1901', 27 cm. high. **£1,200-1,400** *P*

PEWTER

Pewter is an alloy, consisting mainly of tin, which has been used in Britain since Roman times. When no lead is used in the alloy, pewter tends to remain bright and almost like silver; the higher the proportion of lead, the darker the colour.

Largely ousted during the nineteenth century, pewter was revived as a material by exponents of the Arts and Crafts movement, and their contemporaries and successors, followers of the Art Nouveau.

In Britain and German particularly, Art Nouveau pewter work achieved great popularity and high standards of craftsmanship. Liberty's 'Tudric' range of pewter-wares, decorated with motifs taken from the Celtic, included tea and coffee services as well as clocks, tableware, bowls and vases. The chief German exponent was Engelbert Kayser (1840-1911), whose range was as extensive as Liberty's, but fashioned in the 'high' Art Nouveau style.

A French enamelled cigarette case, after a design by Eugene Grasset, silver coloured metal, maker's mark 'MZ', French poincons, 8 cm. wide. c. 1900. **£350-400** *S*

A William Hutton & Sons silver faced photograph frame, inset with blue and green enamelled panels, stamped maker's mark London 1903, 8 in. high. **£650-750** *CSK*

A polished pewter photograph frame, the design attributed to Archibald Knox, with oak back, 7 in. high. **£400-500** *CSK*

An electroplated pewter Jugenstil mirror frame, probably Kayserzinn, 46 cm., c. 1900. **£400-500** *S*

'An Art Nouveau WMF white metal mirror, stamped marks, 14½ in. high. **£200-250** *CSK*

An Art Nouveau silver faced rectangular mirror, stamped maker's mark W.N. Chester 1903, 12 in. high. **£150-200** *CSK*

An Art Nouveau WMF white metal mirror, stamped marks, 20 in. high. **£500-600** *CSK*

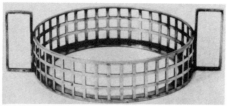

A Wiener Werkstatte dish mount, designed by Josef Hoffmann, silver-coloured metal, 2 Wiener Werkstatte monograms, maker's and designer's monograms, Austrian poincons, 13.25 cm. wide, c. 1905. **£650-750** *S*

A Hutton and Sons silver and enamelled picture frame, heightened with blue and green enamelling, maker's marks and hallmarks for London 1904, 21 cm. high. **£800-900** *P*

An Art Nouveau electroplated dressing table mirror, stamped V.S., 19½ in. high. **£300-350** *CSK*

An Arts and Crafts wrought iron and copper hearth set, possibly made by the Birmingham Guild of Handicrafts, poker 65.5 cm., shovel 67.5, tongs 67 cm. **£160-220** *P*

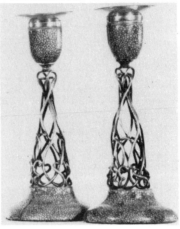

A pair of Leuchare silver and shagreen candlesticks, stamped maker's mark WL and Leuchare, London and Paris, London 1887, 8 in. high. **£300-350** *CSK*

A brass, wood and glass punch set, comprising: 12 brass cups with glass liners, 9.5 cm. high, and a large circular twin-handled tray, 51 cm. diam., stamped with crossed swords and C.D.E. in shield, 76.5 cm. high overall. **£400-450** *P*

An Art Nouveau silver on pewter bowl, 1 ft. 4½ in. high by 1 ft. 11 in. wide. **£250-300** *CDC*

An Art Nouveau WMF electroplated and glass jardinière, stamped marks, 18 in. wide. **£200-£250** *CSK*

A large spun brass mounted glass punch bowl and ladle, glass ladle with brass tipped glass stem, 37 cm., c. 1910. **£250-300** *S*

An Art Nouveau pewter and glass claret jug, the green tinted glass jug mounted on a pewter pedestal foot and overlaid with trailing leaves and flowers, 12¼ in. high. **£100-150** *CSK*

A pair of WMF electroplated pewter 2-branch candlesticks, 10½ in. **£1,000-1,400** *DWB*

An Art Nouveau claret jug, by WMF, the green glass with pewter mounts, stamped W.M.F. EP 1/10 and small 'as', 16½ in. **£300-350** *WHL*

'Au Guartier Latin' by Alphonse Mucha, in colours on wove paper, with margins, framed, 15⅜ by 11⅜ in. (39 by 29 cm.). **£800-900** *CG*

'L'Automne' by Alphonse Mucha, lithograph in colours on poster paper, with margins framed, 31⅛ by 13 in. (79 by 33 cm.). **£550-650** *CG*

A set of 3 Art Nouveau pewter wallsconces. **£250-300** *AG*

Paillettes d'Or, by Paul Jouve, lithograph in colours on poster paper, with margins, small tear and creases, framed, 52 by 23.5 cm. (20½ by 8⅞ in.). **£600-650** *CG*

Zdenka Cerná, Tournée Européenne de la Violencelliste (M.H. p. 115, ill. 68; B. A63), by Alphonse Maria Mucha, lithograph printed in colours, 1913, on thin wove paper, printed by V. Neubert, Prague, with margins, some very slight creasing, linen backed, unframed, L. 103 by 103.7 cm. **£700-800** *C*

An Art Nouveau trinket box, Birmingham, 1905. **£80-100 HGA**

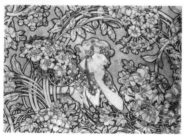

'Les Femmes Parmi Les Fleurs', panneau decoratif, by Alphonse Mucha, printed on velvet, shades of pink, maroon and green, signed in the block 'Mucha', 75.5 by 54 cm. approx., c. 1900. **£500-600** *S*

A March Brothers pewter and enamel box and cover, 12.5 cm. high. **£110-150** *P*

'L'Hiver', by Alphonse Mucha, lithograph in colours on poster paper, with margins, some stains in the lower margin, framed, 30¾ by 12⅝ in. (78 by 32 cm.). **£550-650** *CG*

An Art Nouveau bronze dish,
8¼ in. wide. **£400-450** *CSK*

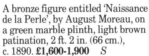

Aristide Bruant dans son Cabaret
(L.D. 348; A.15; A.W. 14), by Henri
de Toulouse-Lautrec, lithograph
printed in colours, 1893, first state
(of 2) before letters, with the
address of the printer Verneau,
with foldmarks, part split in places,
with various repaired tears and
some losses at the edges, unframed,
140.5 by 99.5 cm. **£800-900** *C*

'Grafton Gallery 1983' by Eugene
Grasset, chromolithographic panel,
signed with 'E.G.' monogram,
printed by Verdoux Ducourtioux &
Huillard, Sc. framed and glazed, 71
by 49 cm. **£350-400** *P*

A Gurschner bronze Art Nouveau
tray, modelled as the head of an
Ophelia-like maiden, wearing a
gold band with green-stained
chalcedony cabochon, signed
'Gurschner Vienne' and 'deposé',
21 cm. **£550-650** *P*

An Art Nouveau bronze figure, by
R. D. Fabricius, signed, of good
patination, 2 ft. 6 in. high overall.
£1,000-1,200 *WHL*

A bronze figure entitled 'Naissance
de la Perle', by August Moreau, on
a green marble plinth, light brown
patination, 2 ft. 2 in. (66 cm.),
c. 1890. **£1,600-1,900** *S*

An Art Nouveau bronze bust of a
young girl, on waisted, veined
marble socle, 17¼ in. high. **£400-
£450** *CSK*

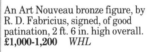

A tall Art Nouveau metal figure,
by Flora, with plaque inscribed
'Reverie d'Été par Flora', signed on
base 'Flora', 76 cm. high. **£350-400**
P

A gilt bronze figure, 'Muse des
Bois', cast from a model by Edouard
Drouot, on a rockwork mound on
circular antico marble base,
inscribed E. Drouot, 13 in. high.
£300-350 *CSK*

A Gennarelli bronze figure, signed
'A. Gennarelli', 43 cm. high. **£600-
£700** *P*

A bronze figure entitled 'Le Reveil',
by Hippolite Moreau, rich red/
brown patination with a marble
socle, 2 ft. 4 in. (71 cm.), c. 1890.
£1,300-1,500 *S*

A good bronze group of a young
woman, by Mathurin Moreau,
green weathered patination, 3 ft.
4 in. (103 cm.), c. 1880. **£3,000-
£3,500** *S*

A bronze seated figure of a young
woman, cast from a model by
Maurice Bouval, greenish brown
patina, inscribed 'Bouval 22LB',
20 cm. high. **£300-350** *C*

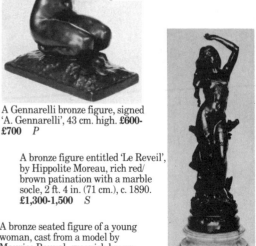

A Barrias allegorical bronze figure, the straps of her costume set with turquoise studs, on square green onyx base, signed 'E. Barrias' and founder's marks for Susse Freres, Paris, 85 cm. high. **£600-700**   *P*

A good Bertram Mackennal bronze figure, 'Truth', signed 'Mackennal' and 'London, June 12, 1894', 67 cm. high. **£17,000-19,000**   *P*

'Salome', by Sir Edgar Bertram Mackennal, bronze with rich brown patination, signed and inscribed London, Hohwiller Fondeur Paris, Salome, on a marble socle, 11½ in. (29 cm.), overall, c. 1897. **£6,500-£7,000**   *S*

A gilt bronze figure of a girl reading a book, cast from a model by Charles Korschann, inscribed 'Ch. Korschann, Paris', small damages to bronze base, 36.5 cm. high. **£450-500**   *C*

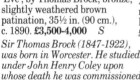

'Eve', by Thomas Brock, bronze, slightly weathered brown patination, 35½ in. (90 cm.), c. 1890. **£3,500-4,000**   *S*

Sir Thomas Brock (1847-1922), was born in Worcester. He studied under John Henry Coley upon whose death he was commissioned to complete any unfinished works. He was knighted in 1911, and received many honours from the art world as a whole. His work includes the Victoria Memorial outside Buckingham Palace.

A French or Italian gilt bronze and marble bust of Laura, 50 cm. high, late 19th/early 20th C. **£1,000-£1,200**   *C*

A figure of a nymph, by Joseph Crossland McClure, bronze with rich brown patination, 27½ in. (70 cm.), c. 1900. **£1,000-1,200**   *S*

A bronze allegorical figure of Summer, by Paul Rafael Montford, rich green/dark brown patination, 2 ft. 4¼ in. (72 cm.), c. 1910. **£900-£1,100**   *S*

A bronze and ivory group of Diana on horseback, by Celestin Anatole Calmels, rich gilt, light brown and dark brown patination, 1 ft. 8½ in. (52 cm.), c. 1880. **£3,200-3,500**   *S*

A William Morris 'Hammersmith' hand-tufted carpet, the streaked indigo field with an all-over 'Persian' design, in vivid red, blues, green and salmon, enclosed by a main rust red tulip and foliate meandering border, 380 by 286 cm. **£6,000-7,000**   *P*

An Arts and Crafts hand-tufted woollen carpet, with pale red and pink tudor roses on pale blue stems, with green leaves, all against a beige field, 390 by 340 cm. **£4,000-4,500**   *P*

A large Arts and Crafts hand-tufted woollen carpet, probably woven at Donegal, in beige, ochre and indigo, 480 by 477 cm. **£1,000-1,500**   *P*

A large hand-woven Arts and Crafts carpet, showing affinities to the designs of Archibald Knox and probably retailed through Liberty & Co., 540 by 335 cm. **£8,000-9,000** *P*

A Gallé faience cat, its blue glazed body painted with sprays in pinks, mauves and yellow, with a grey lace bonnet and wearing a gilt chain necklet with dog medallion, the applied green glass eyes with black pupils, painted mark on base, E. Gallé Nancy, 13¼ in. high. **£1,600-1,800** *CSK*

An amusing Louis Wain model of a pig, with green and lemon body, facsimile signature and 'Made in England', 12 cm. high. **£100-150** *P*

A Burmanstofts faience Art Nouveau jardinière and stand, decorated in relief in blue, blue/grey, yellow and turquoise, impressed marks and numbered '2273/4', 99.5 cm. high. **£250-300** *P*

A Brannam/Barnstaple vase, picked out in dark coloured glazes, incised signature and date 1916, 20 in. (50.8 cm.). **£170-200** *SC*

(l.) A Mintons art pottery jardinière, 9½ in. high, c. 1890. **£120-180**
(r.) A Mintons Secessionist pottery jardinière, 10 in. high, c. 1900-1908. **£150-200** *CDC*

A Louis Wain pottery figure of 'The Lucky Haw-Haw Cat', painted green and blue, with an aperture in the back, possibly for a vase, black painted signature Louis Wain, 5 in. high. **£130-160** *CSK*

(l.) A Linthorpe pottery plate, designed by Christopher Dresser, with a speckled jade green glaze, impressed 'Linthorpe' HT monogram for Henry Tooth and facsimile Dresser signature, 29 cm. diam. **£150-180**

(c.) A Della Robbia vase and cover, decorated in sgraffito technique and coloured slips, against a shaded turquoise ground, Galleon mark, JS initials for George Seddon and painted by Liz Wilkins, numbered 74A/74B, 29 cm. high. **£150-180**

(r.) A Pilkington Lancastrian circular wall plate, by William Salter Mycock, painted in ruby, orange and silver lustres, impressed Bees mark but later signed with WSM monogram dated 1919, 33 cm. diam. **£80-120** *P*

A Ruskin high-fired vase, glazed in a shaded turquoise and lavender speckled and streaked in green, impressed oval mark and dated 1907, 21.1 cm. **£180-220** *S*

A Wedgwood vase, decorated by Alfred Powell, the body painted in shades of blue, green, brick-red and bronze-lustred mauve, impressed Wedgwood, incised P.21, painted monogram, 89, 38 cm., c. 1910. **£400-500** *S*

A Royal Copenhagen erotic group, of a man tethered to a rock embraced by a woman rising from the waves, all coloured in typical soft tones, wave mark and 'ØF' in underglaze blue, incised '1132A.W.', incised artist's monogram 'T.L.' and date 1897, 47 cm. **£550-650** *SS*

A pair of Royal Dux porcelain figural vases, modelled with scrolling golden leaves and pink tinged flowers, raised pink triangle mark, 16½ in. high. **£250-£300** *CSK*

A Rozenburg twin-handled pottery vase, by Jan Van Der Vet, decorated in colours against inky blue ground, printed crown and stork mark, artist's monogram, dated code for 1902, 35.75 cm. high. **£250-300** *P*

A small Rozenburg 'egg-shell' vase, painted in greens, yellow, purple, black and orange, painted factory marks, numbered 1588 and date code for 1900, 12.5 cm. **£250-300** *P*

A Villeroy and Boch 'Mettlach' Art Nouveau wall plaque, in pale pink, matt red and petrol blue, with a gilded rim, impressed factory marks and number '2549', 46 cm. diam. **£250-300** *P*

A large Rozenburg dish, the dark blue ground painted with a Chinese dragon and the border with yellow geometrical pattern, marked Rozenburg Den Haag 758 NKx, 1896, 3 minor chips repaired, 44 cm. diam. **£300-400** *CAm*

A matched pair of Royal Dux figures, 30.5 cm. **£180-240** *Bea*

ROZENBURG

The Rozenburg workshops in The Hague undoubtedly produced the finest of all Art Nouveau ceramics. The products of this workshop were much more delicate than those of other Art Nouveau potters, since most Rozenburg wares were made of wafer thin porcelain as opposed to the 'thicker', 'heavier' pottery wares produced by most other Art Nouveau potters.

A Royal Dux figure of a boy, picked out in pale colours and gilding, applied triangle mark and impressed 1810, 20¾ in. (52.5 cm.), c. 1900. **£160-200** *SC*

A Royal Dux bowl, painted in typical muted enamel colours and gold, 28.2 cm. **£250-300** *Bea*

A Doulton stoneware butter dish, decorated by Florence Barlow, impressed and incised marks for Florence Barlow and Bessie Newberry, dated 1887. **£250-350** *DWB*

A Royal Dux porcelain figure of female nude, with pink drape, seated on green rocky base, marked P. Aichele, No. 1379, 18½ in. high. **£400-500** *DSH*

A pair of Royal Dux porcelain figural vases, modelled with scrolling golden leaves and pink tinged flowers, raised pink triangle mark, 16½ in. high. **£250-300** *CSK*

CERAMICS

In general, the Art Nouveau movement unleashed a flood of studio pottery of mediocre quality. There were, nevertheless, a number of studios and individual craftsmen who produced outstanding work and made great technical advances in order to give substance to their artistic vision. Notable among these was Ernest Chaplet (1835-1909) who developed a succession of unique coloured glazes, the secrets of which he burned before his death. Of the English potters, William Howson Taylor earned international acclaim for the oriental-inspired wares from his Ruskin Pottery at Smethwick.

A Doulton Lambeth lamp, by Florence E. Barlow, decorated with 3 oval pâte-sur-pâte panels, the removable reservoir incised with fan-shaped leaves, r.m., dated 1884, 'F.E.B.' monogram numbered 571, with 'R.B.' assistant's monogram, 63.5 cm. high. **£450-500** *P*

A Doulton Lambeth stoneware 3-handled loving cup, by Florence E. Barlow, decorated in pâte-sur-pâte, in green and white against a buff ground, with blue, green and white beaded borders, with silver rim, r.m. & e., 'F.E.B.' monogram, 16 cm. high. **£300-350** *P*

A pair of Royal Doulton vases, incised by Hannah Barlow and Florence Roberts, glazed in brown, olive and blue, minor restoration to one rim, impressed lion, crown and circle, incised artists' monograms and numerals, date code for 1903, 28.1 cm. **£500-600** *S*

A pottery baluster vase, painted pâte-sur-pâte, on a pale blue ground, by Florence Barlow, impressed Royal Doulton, 12 in. high. **£300-350** *CSK*

Florence more frequently painted in slip and also worked on Doulton other than stoneware.

A pair of Doulton vases, decorated by Hannah Barlow and Florence Roberts, detailed in brown glaze against a stippled buff ground between tube-lined floral borders glazed in brown, pale-green and blue, one cracked, impressed Lambeth mark, incised artists' monograms, 78 and assistant's initials of Bessie Newbery, 32 cm., 1890's. **£450-500** *S*

DOULTON WARES

Doulton marks — abbreviations

o.u.m.	— oval undated mark
o.m.	— oval mark, dated
c.m.	— circular mark
r.m.	— rosette mark
r.m. & e.	— rosette mark and England
d.l.e.	— Doulton Lambeth England
d.s.l.	— Doulton Silicon Lambeth
d.s.p.	— Doulton & Slaters Patent
c.m.l. & c.	— circle mark, lion & crown
c.m. & l.	— circle mark and lion
r.d.e.	— Royal Doulton England
s.c.m.	— slip-cast mark
i.c.f.m.	— impressed circular faience mark
r.d.f.	— Royal Doulton Flambé
b.r.m. & c.	— Burslem rosette mark & crown

An oviform vase, incised and painted in grey-blue between band of dark green leaves, outlined in white on a green ground, by Hannah Barlow, impressed Royal Doulton England, 11½ in. high. **£280-340** *CSK*

A pair of Doulton stoneware vases, by Hannah Barlow, 7 in., dated 1888. **£400-500** *DWB*

A Doulton ewer, incised by Hannah Barlow and Eliza Simmance, glazed in shades of green, brown and mauve, impressed Lambeth mark, incised artists' initials, 653 and 1000, dated 1877, minor chip to foot, 35.3 cm. **£350-400** *S*

A jug, incised with a cat and 4 kittens, in pale blue on a stoneware ground and a blue and green foliage neck and handle, by Hannah Barlow, impressed Doulton Lambeth 1880, 9 in. high. **£600-700** *CSK*

This is an interesting subject — which adds considerably to the value.

A Lambeth Doulton teapot and cover, by Hannah Barlow, incised with goats. **£250-350** *WHB*

A pair of Doulton stoneware vases, incised by Hannah Barlow, picked out in brown and green coloured glazes, incised artist's mark, impressed factory marks, 11 in. (28 cm.), late 19th C. **£600-700** *SC*

A large Royal Doulton ovoid vase, incise decorated by Hannah Barlow, incised artist's and assistant's monogram for Florence E. Roberts, lion, crown and circle mark, scallop repair at base, 54 cm **£300-500** *Bon*

A large Royal Doulton ovoid stoneware vase, incise decorated by Hannah Barlow, with monogram for Florence E. Roberts, impressed lion, crown and circle mark, 49 cm. **£400-600** *Bon*

An unusual Doulton Lambeth longcase clock by Frank Butler, on caramel ground with stylised acanthus leaves and applied with a single stylised floret, heightened in varying tones of blue, incised 'Doulton Lambeth 1884' and with artist's monogram, chip to hood, 31 cm. **£650-750** *Bon*

A large Doulton Lambeth stoneware vase, incised by Hannah Barlow, heightened with brown against a buff ground, and bordered by green and blue incised leaves and florets by Frank Butler, both artists' monograms, assistant's mark for Emma Martin, 38 cm. high, dated 1876. **£500-600** *P*

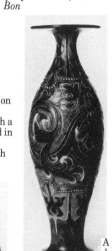

A pair of Doulton stoneware vases, decorated by Frank Butler, 17¾ in. 19th C. **£800-900** *SC*

A Royal Doulton stoneware vase, by Frank A. Butler, in greens, amber, blues and white, c.m.l. & c. and 'F.A.B.' monogram, numbered '347' and Bessie Newbery as assistant, 41 cm. high. **£200-250** *P*

A pair of Doulton vases, tube-lined and beaded by Frank Butler, glazed in blue and brown against a mottled olive ground, impressed Lambeth mark, incised artist's and assistant's initials, 3439, 28.6 cm., c. 1900. **£200-280** *S*

A Royal Doulton stoneware vase, by Mark V. Marshall, with a crushed strawberry ground decorated in lilac and pale green, c.m.l. & c., artist's initials, numbered '96' and 'M.H.' possibly for Marion Holbrook and date letter for 1902, 31 cm. high. **£700-£800** *P*

A Doulton vase, tube-lined by Frank Butler, glazed in blue and brown against an olive ground, impressed Lambeth mark, incised artist's and assistant's monograms, 58, 33.8 cm., c. 1900. **£250-300** *S*

A Royal Doulton vase, tube-lined by Frank Butler, glazed in brown and palest pink against a mottled green ground, impressed lion, crown and circle, incised artist's initials, 647, impressed date code for 1902, 44.8 cm. **£300-350** *S*

A jug, with a blue rim, the body moulded with blue and brown foliage within a white border, by Mark V. Marshall, impressed Doulton Lambeth England, 9¾ in. high. **£65-80**   *CSK*

A Royal Doulton 'Sung' vase, glazed in ruby shading through inky-blue to mottled apple green, c.m.l. & c., 'Sung', 'Noke' and 'F.M.' monogram for Fred Moore, 13 cm. high. **£120-180**   *P*

A pair of Royal Doulton vases, decorated by Frank Butler, glazed in ochre, lavender and sage-green against a panelled mottled blue and stippled buff ground, impressed lion, crown and circle, incised artist's monogram, 991, assistant's initials of Jane Hurst, date code for 1906, 47.2 cm. **£500-£600**   *S*

A good Royal Doulton stoneware oviform vase, by Francis C. Pope, with white flowers in relief and pale brown scrolling foliage against a muted purple ground, c.m.l. & c., signed 'F.C.P.', No. '537' and date code for 1916, 41 cm. high. **£1,000-£1,200**   *P*

A Royal Doulton 'Chang' snuff bottle, with a crackled thick white glaze streaked in red, amber and blue, brown and green, C.M., 'Chang', 'Noke', 'HN' monogram for Harry Nixon and dated code for 1925, 6 cm. high. **£280-320**   *P*

A pair of Doulton Lambeth stoneware oviform vases, by Harry Simeon, painted in blue, brown and mustard, impressed Lambeth faience mark with 'Faience' cancelled, signed 'HS' and numbered '369', 32.50 cm. high. **£500-600**   *P*

A pair of Royal Doulton vases, incised by Francis C. Pope, glazed in green and blue against a tan ground, impressed lion, crown and circle, incised artist's and assistant's initials, 98, impressed date code for 1904, 38.2 cm. **£500-£600**   *S*

A Doulton vase, incised by Mark V Marshall, glazed in shades of green and blue, impressed Lambeth mark, incised artist's and assistant's initials, 990, 27.1 cm., dated 1883. **£180-220**   *S*

A Doulton Lambeth faience vase, probably decorated by Margaret E. Thompson, in shades of green, blue, pink and yellow, impressed and printed marks, numbered L7782, 26.5 cm., c. 1910. **£350-400**   *S*

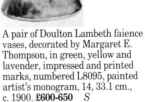

A Doulton Lambeth stoneware timepiece, by George Tinworth, modelled as a small theatre, incised 'H. Doulton & Co., Lambeth', artist's 'G.T.' monogram, and 'L.B.' and 'P.K.' assistants' initials, 21 cm. high. **£950-1,050**   *P*

A pair of Doulton Lambeth faience vases, decorated by Margaret E. Thompson, in green, yellow and lavender, impressed and printed marks, numbered L8095, painted artist's monogram, 14, 33.1 cm., c. 1900. **£600-650**   *S*

An unusual and early Doulton stoneware jug, by George Tinworth, in blue and brown, o.u.m., 'GT' monogram, 'S.G.' monogram, for Sarah Gathercole impressed 'B' and incised on inner neck 'B', 22 cm. high. **£250-300**   *P*

A Doulton stoneware mouse group 'Waits', by George Tinworth, in shades of blue and ochre, impressed Lambeth mark, 14 cm., c. 1880. **£400-500** *S*

A Doulton 'gunpowder plot' menu-holder, modelled by George Tinworth, incised monogram, the base titled 'I See No Reason Why Gunpowder Treason Should Ever Be Forgot', glazed in shades of olive and ochre, impressed Lambeth mark, menu-holder repaired, 10.8 cm., 1880's. **£400-450** *S*

A large Doulton vase, painted by Geo. White, signed, with the legend of Orpheus and Eurydice in Hades, incised shape number 1210 and date code for 1911, one handle repaired, 16¼ in. **£900-1,000** *S*

The theme of Orpheus and Eurydice was also used by George White in conjunction with F. J. Hancock on the 'Diana' vase exhibited at the Paris Exhibition of 1900.

A Doulton Lambeth spill vase, 'Homeless', by George Tinworth, in green, brown and blue, r.m., 'G.T.' monogram, assistant's initials for Emma Shute, inscribed title, restored, 10.25 cm. high. **£120-150** *P*

A large Doulton Burslem vase and cover, painted by G. White, signed, the neck and foot with green and gilt borders, printed mark, cover chipped and repaired, 20¾ in., c. 1910, and a mahogany pedestal. **£600-700**

A pair of Royal Doulton vases, each printed and painted with Arabs on camels, in green, yellow and orange, printed and painted marks, 24 cm. high, 20th C. **£250-300** *SS*

A Doulton Lambeth musical mice group, 'Harpy Violincello', by George Tinworth, glazed in blue, brown and green, r.m., traces of monogram due to damage, inscribed title, 13 cm. high. **£200-£250** *P*

A 3-handled mug, commemorating the 'Hoisting of the Flag at Pretoria', in green and blue glazes, impressed Doulton Lambeth England, 10½ in. high. **£500-600** *CSK*

MAKE THE MOST OF MILLER'S

Miller's is completely different each year. Each edition contains completely NEW photographs. This is not an updated publication. We never repeat the same photograph.

(l. & r.) A pair of Royal Doulton 'blue children' oviform vases, the bases marked 'Royal Doulton Flambe', 29 cm. high. **£280-360** *P*
(c.) A Royal Doulton 'blue children' globular vase, c.m.l. & c. and date code for 1931, 17 cm. **£130-180** *P*

A rare Doulton jug, incised by Edgar Wilson, glazed in shades of blue and green, impressed Lambeth mark, incised artist's monogram, 270, 24 cm., dated 1882. **£250-300** *S*

A Doulton Slaters patent vase, the body decorated with chine-gilt panels of charcoal-grey and royal blue, separated by pink bands, r.m., d.s.p., painted 'M.L.', X1974, 25.95 cm. high. **£80-100**   *P*

(l.) A Doulton Lambeth salt-glazed figure of a Boer War soldier, designed by John Broad, green and caramel base, impressed marks, 30.5 cm. **£350-400**

(c.) A Doulton Burslem urn, painted by D. Dewsberry, on an ivory ground, bordered by gilt friezes, printed mark, 36 cm. **£180-£220**

(r.) A Royal Doulton 'Chinese jade' vase, covered with a green streaked glaze, printed mark, 15 cm. **£450-£500**   *Bon*

A jug, with brown glazed borders, the body printed in black with the Handyman, a sailor from H.M.S Powerful, flanked by bust portraits of Capt. H. Lambton and P. M. Scott, impressed Doulton Lambeth England, 8½ in. high. **£150-200** *CSK*

MARTIN BROTHERS (Robert, Charles, Walter and Edwin)

Robert Wallace Martin was the first born of the Martin brothers, and it seems to have been he who directed the energies of his brothers into producing the kind of grotesque, neo-Gothic stoneware that made their name. The Fulham studio that he set up in 1873 proving too small, the brothers moved to larger premises in Southall four years later. Although they made many similar pieces, no two are identical. The studio ceased production in 1914.

'The Studio Southall Pottery', an autotype photograph on wood, depicting Walter Frazer, Robert Wallace and Edwin Martin, and signed by each, taken in 1912, this one dating between 1913-15, the later date being the year of Edwin's death. **£100-150**   *P*

A Royal Doulton 'Chang' vase, glazed in shades of crimson, blue and green and over-painted with brightly coloured butterflies, faintly impressed Doulton and numerals, painted Doulton, 24.5 cm., c. 1925. **£1,000-1,200**   *S*

A Martin Brothers stoneware bird, with detachable head, glazed in blues, greens and browns, with large metallic brown beak, head inscribed Martin Bros. London & Southall 3-1895, base inscribed Martin Bros. London, 11¾ in. high. **£1,500-2,000**   *CSK*

A Martin Brothers fantastic animal, incised Martin Bros., London & Southall, 10 1895, body with crack, head with firing cracks and chip, 10¾ in., on wood plinth. **£4,000-4,500**   *DWB*

A Martin Brothers fantastic animal, inscribed Martin Bros. London and Southall, 10 1895, firing cracks to the body, 11¼ in., on wood plinth. **£3,500-4,000** *DWB*

A Martin ware figure of a grotesque bird, the head incised R.W. Martin Bros. London & Southall, 30 cm., mounted on a wood base. **£2,500-3,000**   *L*

A Royal Doulton Sung vase, with a mauve, amber and crimson ground, a mottled brown glaze pouring down, printed lion, crown and circle, Flambé, impressed Doulton and numerals, painted Sung script mark, No. 2653 E, dated 3-24, 19.4 cm. **£400-500**   *S*

A Martin Brothers face jug, incised R. W. Martin and Brothers, London and Southall, 20 12 1898, 8½ in. **£1,100-1,400**   *DWB*

A Martin ware triple bird group, each creature having a removable head, signed on heads and base 'R. W. Martin & Bros. Southall' and 'B-37', 17 cm. high. **£1,000-1,200**   *P*

This piece is an example of the work produced by Clement Martin in collaboration with Captain H. Butterfield.

A Martin Brothers stoneware model of a grotesque bird, the removable head with a long beak, all glazed in tones of browns, olive-green and pale blue, signed 'R.W. Martin & Bros. London & Southall' on base and head and dated '5-1884', 33 cm. high overall. **£3,500-4,000**   *P*

A Martin Brothers face jug, each side well-modelled with a smiling face, the eyes picked out in black and white against the buff glaze, incised marks and dated 8-(18)98, spout chipped, 19.5 cm. **£400-500**   *SS*

A large Martin Brothers stoneware vase, incised and glazed in shades of blue, on a pitted brown and biscuit ground, incised R. W. Martin & Bros. London & Southall 2:1892, 17½ in. high. **£300-350**   *CSK*

Floral Martin ware is less sought after than that incised with or modelled as grotesque fish, birds, monsters, etc.

A Robert Wallace Martin & Brothers stoneware face jug, the 2 impish grinning faces covered in a matt ochre glaze, incised R.W. Martin & Bros. London & Southall, 1-1-1903, 6 in. high. **£300-400**   *CSK*

A Martin Brothers oviform pottery vase, heightened and coloured in shades of brown and white against a buff ground, incised 'R. W. Martin & Bros. London & Southall, 4-1887', 20 cm. high. **£450-500**   *P*

A pair of stoneware slender baluster vases, by the Martin Brothers, incised and painted in shades of brown and green with exotic birds, incised Martin Bros. London & Southall, 6-1897, 26.2 cm. high. **£500-600**   *C*

Right

A Martin Brothers pottery vase, incised 'Martin Bros. London & Southall, 10-1901', 18 cm. high. **£250-300**   *P*

A Martin Brothers stoneware face jug, covered in a bright ochre glaze, incised R.W. Martin & Brothers, London & Southall 3-1-1903, 8¾ in. high. **£1,100-1,300**   *CSK*

Two Martin Brothers ovoid vases, incised with fish and sea creatures beneath the waves, incised Martin Brothers London and Southall 12 1905, 9¾ in. **£1,600-1,800**   *DWB*

A Martin Brothers pottery vase, coloured in shades of brown against a buff ground, incised 'Martin Brothers London and Southall, 4-1890', 13.25 cm. high. **£300-350**   *P*

A Martin Brothers vase, in green, blue and brown against a speckled buff ground, incised mark and dated 8-1885, minor chip to handle, 19 cm. **£250-300**   *S*

A pair of Martin Brother's vases, with honey coloured glaze, incised marks and dated 6-1904, 26.4 cm. **£750-850**   *S*

A Martin Brothers 'Gourd' vase, glazed in mottled shades of green and brown, incised mark and dated 9-1899, 22 cm. **£450-500**   *S*

An unusual Martin Brothers clock-case, glazed in shades of blue and brown, incised marks, No. 23, dated 3-1875, 30.6 cm. **£550-650**   *S*

A Martin Brothers jardinière, glazed in blue, green and brown, incised mark and dated 9-79, 23 cm. **£250-350**   *S*

A De Morgan lustre dish, decorated in ruby and salmon-pink lustre, impressed 17, painted EK initials, late Fulham period, 36 cm., 1898-1907. **£500-600**   *S*

A De Morgan lustre dish, in ruby and salmon-pink, impressed numerals 17, late Fulham period, 36.8 cm., 1898-1907. **£300-350**   *S*

A Martin Brothers bowl, glazed in brown against a washed blue and green ground, incised mark and dated 7-1911, 23.7 cm. **£350-400**   *S*

A Robert Wallace Martin and Brothers stoneware jug, on an ochre ground, incised R.W. Martin & Bros, London & Southall 2-1887, 8¼ in. high. **£350-400**   *CSK*

A De Morgan lustre dish, decorated in ruby, salmon-pink and buff, impressed numerals 24, late Fulham period, 36.4 cm., 1898-1907. **£400-450**   *S*

An early Martin Brothers clock-case, applied with trails of ivy, glazed in shades of green, brown and blue, incised R. W. Martin Fulham, 6, one wing restored, one wing-tip with minor restoration, 28.2 cm., c. 1874. **£350-450**   *S*

Two De Morgan lustre dishes, one decorated in ruby lustre with a griffin, the other with an infant, the latter with painted ad infinitum mark, late Fulham period, 30 and 30.5 cm., 1898-1907. **£350-400**   *S*

An unusual Martin ware tile picture, depicting grotesque fish, painted in muted enamel colours, each tile inscribed 'Martin Brothers London', some damage, 37 by 44.2 cm. **£500-600**   *Bea*

A De Morgan lustre dish, decorated in ruby and salmon-pink, late Fulham period, cracked, 35.8 cm., 1898-1907. **£150-200**   *S*

A William De Morgan circular dish, painted by Frederick Passenger, in ruby lustres against white, signed with initials 'F.P.', 37 cm. diam. **£200-250** *P*

A Pilkington Royal Lancastrian lustre pottery vase, by W. S. Mycock, painted with golden galleons on a crimson lustre ground, impressed mark, painted artists monogram, 9¼ in. high. **£180-240** *CSK*

Mycock frequently appears as an artist on Lancastrian wares and is thus less sought after than others such as Forsyth, Rogers.

An early Pilkingtons double gourd lustre vase, by William S. Mycock, painted in crimson and silver lustres, on a blue and green ground, base with impressed bees mark and dated 1906, painted with galleon, cyprus trees and artists monogram within a shield. **£500-£600** *CSK*

A Bernard Moore flambé model of a monkey, signed 'B.M.' internally, 9 cm. high. **£120-150** *P*

A lustre pottery vase, attributed to William De Morgan, painted by Frederick Passenger, in pink and ruby lustres on a white ground, blue painted initials FP. on base, 7¼ in. high. **£160-190** *CSK*

A Moorcroft Macintyre vase, coloured in shades of green, blue and yellow, printed Macintyre mark, painted signature in green, 18 cm., c. 1900. **£300-350** *S*

Two Bernard Moore lustre vases, the globular and slender ovoid bodies painted with scrolling foliage beneath the glaze, 6 and 8¼ in. high. **£80-100 each** *CDC*

A large earthenware bottle vase, painted after Christopher Dresser, on a green washed ground, facsimile signature, 75 cm. **£400-£450** *SS*

A Moorcroft Macintyre Florian ware beaker, printed Florian mark, incised WM des., 5¼ in. high. **£120-160** *CSK*

A Moorcroft Spanish pattern oviform vase, in reds, butterscotch and pale brown against a shaded beige-blue ground, signed W. Moorcroft and part of Liberty retail label, 27 cm. high. **£350-450** *P*

A pair of Moorcroft Macintyre pottery vases, painted with blue and yellow cornflowers and green foliage on a blue and white ground, printed Macintyre mark, signed in green W. Moorcroft, 11¾ in. high. **£600-700** *CSK*

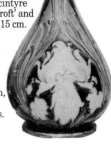

An unusual Moorcroft Macintyre vase, heightened with ruby lustre against deep blue in panels, an olive-green ground, Macintyre mark, signed 'W. Moorcroft' and 'M2980', repaired neck, 15 cm. high. **£120-180** *P*

A Moorcroft vase, in shades of deep rose, ochre and olive against a mottled blue-green ground, impressed Moorcroft Burslem, painted signature in green, minor chips, 31.6 cm., c. 1910. **£200-300** *S*

A Moorcroft vase, tube lined in white, coloured in shades of green, blue and yellow, printed Rd. No. 326689, painted W. Moorcroft des. in green, 25.1 cm., c. 1910. **£250-£350** *S*

A Macintyre-Moorcroft vase, trailed and picked out in bright translucent glazes with a design of pansies, printed Macintyre mark in sepia, full signature in green with the date 1912, 12 in. (30.5 cm.). **£300-350** *SC*

A Moorcroft pottery bowl, painted with the pomegranate pattern, red and purple fruit and green leaves on a pale green and blue-green ground, signed in green W. Moorcroft, 10 in. diam. **£250-£300** *CSK*

A Moorcroft fish vase, with ivory and grey coloured fish, against a grey-pale brown ground, impressed 'Moorcroft — Made in England' and signed 'WM', 17.5 cm. high. **£200-£250** *P*

A Moorcroft vase, tube lined in white coloured in shades of green and blue, printed Liberty mark, painted W. Moorcroft des. in green, 25.7 cm., c. 1910. **£400-450** *S*

A Macintyre-Moorcroft vase, printed Macintyre mark in sepia, full signature in green and the date 1912, 11 in. (28 cm.). **£250-300** *SC*

A pair of Moorcroft vases, slip-trailed with the pomegranate design coloured in deep rose, green and mauve against a blue ground, minor chip and flake to foot, impressed Moorcroft, Burslem, England, painted signature in green, 23.9 cm., c. 1915. **£400-450** *S*

A pottery vase, by William Moorcroft, in shades of purple, pink and white on a merging green and turquoise ground, incised, impressed and painted marks, 14½ in. **£160-200** *WHL*

A tall and unusual Moorcroft hazeldene vase, decorated in moonlit-blue, impressed 'Moorcroft — Made in England', signed W. Moorcroft 'Garfield Set? Vase', and dated 1920, 46.5 cm. high. **£450-550** *P*

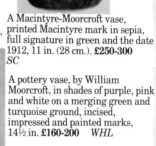

A Moorcroft vase, painted with the pomegranate pattern, orange and red fruits with ochre foliage on a cinnamon and blue ground, impressed Burslem mark, signed W. Moorcroft in green, 8½ in. high. **£180-220** *CSK*

USE THE INDEX!

Because certain items might fit easily into any of a number of categories, the quickest and surest method of locating any entry is by reference to the fully cross-referenced index at the back of the book. This is particularly true this year when certain sections, e.g. Worcester Porcelain and Oak Furniture have been featured in isolation.

(*l.*) A Moorcroft vase, decorated with band of pink and green flowers on inky-blue ground, impressed mark, painted signature and label, 3¼ in. high, c. 1940. **£45-£55**

(*r.*) A Moorcroft vase, in red-brown toning to dark blue, label covering impressed and painted marks, 3¼ in. high, c. 1940. **£60-70** *TW*

ART DECO INTRODUCTION

The horrors of the 1914-18 War must have done much to destroy the innocent belief that truth is to be found in beauty, for the Art Nouveau movement was not only killed outright during that period, but immediately afterwards, its memory was ridiculed and its products derided. Life was short. Security was a myth. Beauty was transient.

The term Art Deco is one that is applied, not to a single thematic style, but to all products which embody the escapist characteristics of the inter-war period. The influences are many and the range virtually limitless. Throughout, however, the emphasis is on the decorative aspect, for the term is simply a contract of part of the title of 'L'Exposition Internationale des Arts Decoratifs et Industriels Modernes', and was coined for the Minneapolis Exhibition, The World of Art Deco, as recently as 1966. The scope that this gives is both a blessing and a curse. For the collector, it offers a wealth of material from the beautiful to the bizarre, from high art to the frankly kitsch; but to the archivist it affords no clear guidelines beyond his own intuitive feeling for the period.

ANYTHING GOES

This was the jazz age; the age of the flapper; when to be up-to-date was to be outrageous, and to be outrageous was to be up-to-date. (Is it mere chance that punk fashion and renewal of interest in Art Deco coincide? Or that flower power should have heralded the rediscovery of Art Nouveau?) If the various elements which went to make up the Art Deco movement had a single, unifying function, it was to stimulate rather than to sedate; therefore the most obvious characteristics of mainstream Art Deco are extreme stylisation of natural forms, geometric shapes and patterns, and striking (sometimes strident) colour combinations. Some designers were strongly influenced by Egyptian motifs unearthed in the tombs of the Pharaohs during the first quarter of the century, while others reflect the Cubist movement, which was flourishing contemporaneously.

The work of serious and committed designers and artists was widely adapted — and frequently debased — for a mass market which seemed insatiable in its demand for 'modern' everything. Accordingly, the most mundane of objects began to find themselves produced in modish shapes and daubed with geometric designs in the ubiquitous orange and black symbols of 1920's and 30's modernity.

A Lalique glass-cased timepiece, moulded with dense interwoven branches of prunus blossom, with a French 'A.T.O.' movement, moulded 'Lalique', 11.5 cm. high. **£400-600**   *P*

A Lalique opalescent glass timepiece, 'Naiades', the square surround moulded with 6 mermaids, heightened with green staining, moulded 'R. Lalique', engraved 'France', 11 cm. square. **£700-800**   *P*

A Lalique opalescent glass timepiece, 'Inseparables', heightened with blue staining, moulded 'R. Lalique, France', having an easel back, 11 by 11 cm. **£300-500**   *P*

Often found with painted dials depicting subject matter in keeping with the glass decoration, add 25%.

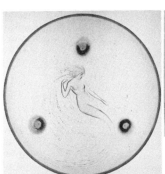

A Lalique opalescent glass dish, 'Trépied Sirène', moulded 'R. Lalique', etched 'France, No. 376', 36.5 cm. diam. **£700-900**   *P*

Mermaids appeal to Japanese buyers.

A brass mantle clock, by W. Penaat, with starfish-shaped bronze face, 25 cm. high, 1920. **£450-550**   *CAM*

A Lalique vase, 'Bellecour', catalogue no. 933, 28.5 cm. **£500-£700**   *L*

A large Lalique dish, 'Phallenes', of deep blue metal, engraved signature, 39 cm., 1930's. **£800-£1,000**   *SS*

Colour is important. Should this same dish appear for sale in opalescent form the value would be reduced to 50% of the above. The use of stain should not be mistaken as colour.

A Lalique opalescent inkwell and cover, 'Quatre Sirènes', engraved 'R. Lalique, France', moulded 'Lalique', 16 cm. diam. **£300-500**   *P*

A Lalique glass vase, engraved signature, 20 cm., 1930's. **£200-250** *SS*

A Lalique globular glass vase, 'Sauterelles', moulded with green-stained grasshoppers on a matt blue stained ground, engraved in block letters 'R. Lalique', 27.5 cm. high. **£1,000-1,200** *P*

A Lalique car mascot, 'Victoire', moulded signature, minor chips, 25.6 cm., 1930's. **£1,000-1,500** *SS*

Also known more popularly as 'Spirit of the Wind'. Often have rotating coloured filters in chromed base, which bathe the piece in colours whilst vehicle travels along.

A Lalique frosted glass vase, 'Languedoc', heightened with traces of blue staining, etched script mark R. Lalique France No. 102, 8¾ in. high. **£900-1,000** *CSK*

A Lalique frosted glass ram's head, impressed 'R. Lalique France', 9.5 cm., 1930's. **£1,400-1,600** *S*

For other car mascots by Lalique see the Transport section.

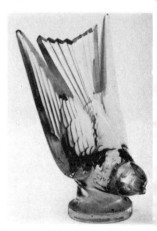

A Lalique pink tinted glass swallow mascot, moulded mark 'R. Lalique', 15.25 cm., 1930's. **£500-600** *S*

A Lalique eagle head mascot, in original chromed metal Rolls Royce base, moulded mark 'R. Lalique France', 10 cm. height of mascot, 1920's. **£800-900** *S*

GLASS LALIQUE, René (1860-1945)

Lalique began life as a jeweller and, after an inauspicious start, had progressed to world renown by the turn of the century. Following a commission to design scent flasks for the Coty perfume manufacturers, he founded his first glass works, Verrerie de Combs-la-Ville in 1908, at which time his work was squarely in the Art Nouveau style. Some 10 years later, he had again emerged as a world leader in his new field of manufacturer of mass-produced art glass, and it is estimated that by the 1930's, he had produced over 10,000,000 pieces. In addition to scent flasks and glass jewellery, Lalique produced vases and bowls, car mascots and glass sculptures, all to an extremely high standard and all eminently collectable. Almost all Lalique glass is marked

Apart from Lalique, other moulded glass manufacturers of note included Degues, Etling, Genet et Michon, Hunebelle and Verlux.

A frosted and clear glass figure, 'Suzanne', moulded R. Lalique, 22 cm. high (8¾ in.). **£1,400-1,600** *CG*

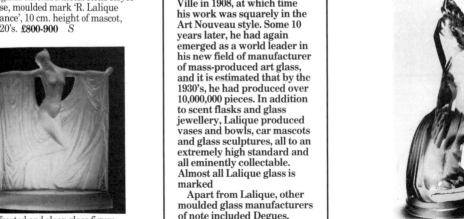

A Lalique glass cockerel mascot engraved 'R. Lalique France', 20 cm., 1920's. **£600-800** *S*

GLASS

Although there has been relatively little outright faking of art glass, wrong signatures are sometimes added and, in the case of lamps and scent flasks with stoppers particularly, false marriages are made. Virtually every piece made by the important artists is illustrated in various reference works. When in doubt, seek documentary evidence of the genuineness of the piece in question. As a general rule, glass is valued according to the technical skill involved in its manufacture. At the top end of the scale are the signed 'one-off' pieces of the masters; at the other are the run-of-the-mill pieces for everyday use — water jugs, drinking glasses, vases and so on. Between the two extremes lie the great majority of collectable glass; the mass-produced replicas of masterful originals.

A Lalique vase, 'Aigrettes', engraved mark and No. 488, base chipped, 25 cm. **£400-600** *SS*

A Lalique blue opalescent glass bowl, moulded with a frieze of budgerigars, heightened with blue staining, etched 'R. Lalique France', 9¼ in. diam. **£600-700** *CSK*

A Lalique opalescent glass vase, 'Bacchantes', engraved signature, 25 cm. high, c. 1930. **£2,500-3,000** *SS*

A Lalique satin glass vase, 'Bacchantes', moulded in high relief, etched script mark R. Lalique, France, 9½ in. high. **£600-800** *CSK*

This piece in opalescent glass would be more popular and in coloured glass even more desirable.

A Lalique glass oviform vase, 'Yvelines', heightened with pale brown staining, signed 'R. Lalique, France' and 'No. 975', 20 cm. high. **£400-500** *P*

A Lalique green glass globular vase, 'Druides', signed 'R. Lalique France' and 'No. 937', 18 cm. high. **£650-800** *P*

A pair of misty grey opaque vases, with high relief of birds of paradise, inscribed in italics 'R. Lalique, France, No. 988', 10 in. tall. **£1,200-£1,400** *BA*

A set of 4 Lalique glass menu holders, in blue, green, amber and frosted glass, moulded 'Lalique' and hallmarks for Birmingham, 1924, 5 cm. high. **£400-450** *P*

A Lalique glass bowl and cover,
heightened with pink-brown
staining, engraved mark
'R. Lalique France No. 614',
15.5 cm., 1920's. **£400-500** *S*

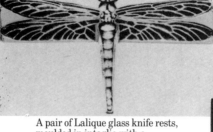

A pair of Lalique glass knife rests,
moulded in intaglio with a
dragonfly, heightened with deep
blue staining, each engraved
'R. Lalique', 10 cm. wide, 1920's.
£250-300 *S*

Three Lalique glass perfume
bottles, one for 'Jasmine' by Coty,
green staining, 14 cm.; one
moulded as large open dahlia,
green enamel details and staining,
14 cm., stencilled 'R. Lalique
France'; third moulded with beaded
swags, 14 cm., moulded
'R. Lalique', 1920's. **£250-350** *S*

A Lalique black glass perfume
bottle, moulded 'R. Lalique',
9.25 cm., 1920's. **£350-450** *S*

Two Lalique glass perfume bottles,
one of lozenge section, heightened
with blue staining, the other
swollen cylindrical, also
heightened with blue, engraved
'R. Lalique' and 'R. Lalique No.
478', 12.5 and 10.25 cm., 1920's.
£250-350 *S*

Three Lalique perfume bottles, for
Worth, one deep blue, one similar
form, clear glass, third spherical,
moulded with stars, moulded
marks 'R. Lalique', 13.25, 8 and
10.5 cm., 1930's. **£200-300** *S*

Six Lalique sherry glasses, 3¼ in.
high. **£60-80** *CSK*

A large Lalique glass fish, 'Gros
Poisson Algues', on a bronze base,
enclosing a lamp fitment, moulded
'R. Lalique' and 'France', 39 cm.
total height. **£1,400-1,600** *P*

A Lalique frosted glass hanging
light shade, heightened with amber
staining, with silk hanging cords,
etched R. Lalique France, 18¼ in.
diam. **£450-500** *CSK*

A modern 'Cristal Lalique' glass
vase, signed 'Lalique, France' and
with paper retail label, 24 cm. high.
£300-400 *P*

Three Lalique glass perfume
bottles, one squat with fluted
flanges, one moulded as an open
water lily, third an atomiser, green
staining, engraved 'R. Lalique
France No. 516' and '522', atomiser
moulded 'R. Lalique', 6.5, 7.5 and
12 cm., 1920's/1930's. **£200-300** *S*

A modern 'Cristal Lalique' glass
model of a swan, designed by Marc
Lalique, signed 'Lalique, France'
and with paper retail label, 36 cm.
long. **£350-500** *P*

*Although modern this piece is large,
imposing and good quality,
although second-hand effectively.*

A modern 'Cristal Lalique' glass bowl, 'Serpent', designed by Marie-Claude Lalique, signed 'Lalique, France' and paper retail label, 22.5 cm. diam. **£200-300** *P*

Although 'Modern' this piece is well conceived and a good buy at this price at auction, as this type of Lalique is a break with tradition but a 'classic' in its own right.

A Daum etched glass vase, pale blue glass etched with horizontal bands, against a frosted ground, faint stencilled mark on the underside 'Daum Nancy', 22 cm., c. 1930. **£120-160** *S*

An Orrefors large presentation glass vase, Simon Gate and E. Wejdljch, 'To The Right Honourable The Lord Mayor of London And The Lady Mayoress In Memory Of Their Visit To The Stockholm Exhibition 1930', inscribed Orrefors 1928. S. Gate, E. Wejdljch, No. 333, 11¼ in. high. **£1,200-1,500** *CSK*

The high price of this piece must reflect the interest in its's presentation and commemorative value as well as its high quality.

A Daum green tinted etched glass vase, acid etched with stippled horizontal banding, incised 'Daum Nancy France', 32 cm., 1930's. **£260-320** *S*

An Orrefors 'Graal' vase, by Edward Hald, internally decorated in dark green with fish swimming, signed 'Orrefors-Graal No. 602A Edw. Hald', 12.5 cm. high. **£200-£300** *P*

An Etling opalescent glass figure, moulded 'Etling France 141', 33.5 cm. high. **£280-340** *P*

This example has some damage to base, perfect one could have expected **£350-450**

An Orrefors 'Graal' glass vase, by Edward Hald, etched marks, 5½ in. high. **£180-240** *CSK*

(*l.*) & (*r.*) A pair of green Art glass cylindrical vases, signed Daum, Nancy, 11 in. high. **£250-300**

(*c.l.*) A green Art glass conical shaped vase signed Daum, Nancy, 8½ in. wide. **£75-95**

(*c.r.*) A green Art glass 3 tier shaped vase, signed Daum, Nancy, 13 in. high. **£80-100** *DSH*

Green tinted acid engraved Daum tends to prove less popular than examples in smoked grey.

PRICES

The never-ending problem of fixing prices for antiques! A price can be affected by so many factors, for example:

- *condition*
- *desirability*
- *rarity*
- *size*
- *colour*
- *provenance*
- *restoration*
- *the sale of a prestigious collection*
- *collection label*
- *appearance of a new reference book*
- *international finance — currency fluctuation*
- *fashion*
- *inflation*
- *the fact that a museum has vast sums of money to spend*

An Orrefors engraved glass vase, engraved 'Orrefors L 2903 B9P', original Orrefors paper label, 24.25 cm., 1940's. **£100-150** *S*

A large Orrefors engraved glass vase, designed by Simon Gate, engraved mark 'Orrefors Gate 2566 B9 . .', 35 cm., 1940's. **£350-450** *S*

A bordeau-coloured pumpkin-shaped glass vase, by Andries Copier, signed Leerdam Unica AD Copier, 13 cm. high, 1927. **£200-300** *CAm*

A C. Chauvel Art Deco satin glass bowl, base stamped RENE GORO, France, 1 ft. 7 in. wide. **£40-60** *CDC*

A glass punchbowl and cover, the design attributed to Otto Prutscher on stylistic grounds and probably made by Meyr's Neffe, flashed in amber, 31 cm. high, and with glass ladle. **£100-150**   *P*

A rounded cubic grey glass vase, by Andries Copier, with air bubble inclusions, surrounded by blue circles, signed Leerdam Unica M 348 AD Copier, 19.5 cm. high, 1931-32. **£250-350**   *CAm*

A triple gourd iridescent glass vase, by Ferdinand von Poschinger the deep blue ground decorated with triple red feather motif, unsigned, 15 cm. high. **£650-700** *CAm*

A large Sabino opalescent glass vase, engraved mark 'Sabino France', 38.5 cm., c. 1930. **£300-400** *S*

An oviform glass vase, by Andries Copier, with air bubble inclusions, on a crackled oxidized ground, the interior neck with a bordeau red band, signed Keerdam Unica AA 128 AD Copier, 16.5 cm. high, 1949. **£250-300**   *CAm*

An oviform glass vase, by Andries Copier, with air bubble inclusions on an irregular blue ground, signed Leerdam Unica W 44 AD Copier, 22 cm. high, 1944. **£450-500** *CAm*

A massive green tinted glass vase, engraved mark 'Andre Thuret', 17 cm., 1920's. **£200-300**   *S*

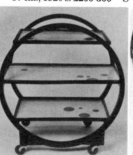

An Almeric Walter pâte-de-verre tray, of greyish tone, shading to green at its edges, the moth with muted brick-red and blue tone shading through olive-green to mauve, signed 'A. Walter Nancy', and 'H. Berge Sc.', 16 cm. **£800-£1,000**   *P*

An Art Deco tea trolley, 80 cm. high. **£250-300**   *P*

Five Vedar glass goblets, each painted with a panel of naked female figures and peacocks, with trailing tail feathers of blue, pink and green, 3 signed Vedar, 8 in. high. **£200-300**   *CSK*

An Andre Thuret 'freeform' glass vase, edged with green and speckled with golden particles, signed on base, 'Andre Thuret', 30 cm. high. **£1,200-1,400**   *P*

A William Burges painted wood and pietra dura marble furniture surmount, the red painted structure of stepped shape incorporating marble panels inlaid with coloured marbles with bands and foliate motifs, signed 'Willielmus . Burges . Me . Fieri . Fecit . Anno . Domini . MDCCCLXXIII .', 105 by 52.5 cm. **£7,000-8,000**   *P*

Use the Index!
Because certain items might fit easily into any of a number of categories, the quickest and surest method of locating any entry is by reference to the index at the back of the book. This has been fully cross-referenced for absolute simplicity.

Two white painted plywood 'Isokon' nesting tables, designed by Marcel Breuer, 61 by 46 by 35.5 cm. and 61 by 42 by 34 cm., c. 1935. **£350-400** *S*

A 'Barcelona' chair and stool, designed by Mies Van der Rohe, designed 1929, 73 cm. high. **£700-£800** *S*

A pair of cantilever Modernist armchairs, 77 cm. high, 1930's. **£600-700** *S*

A Modernist chrome and glass coffee table, 61.5 cm. diam. by 50.5 cm. high, 1930's. **£200-300** *S*

A Modernist chromed tubular steel sofa, 161 cm. wide by 82 cm. high, 1930's. **£500-600** *S*

A pair of French Art Deco armchairs, 64 cm. high by 73 cm. wide, late 1920's. **£500-600** *S*

A 1930's coffee table in pale burr-wood, 101 cm. wide by 62 cm. high. **£200-300** *S*

A Bauhaus bedroom suite, comprising small cabinet, small dressing table, chair, 2 bedside tables and 2 single bed-ends, 58.5 cm. high bedside table, 1930's. **£500-600** *S*

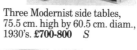

An Art Deco Macassar ebony-veneered dressing table, 120.5 cm. wide by 153.3 cm. high, 1930's. **£600-700** *S*

An Art Deco grand lit en lac d'or, 179 cm. wide. **£1,000-1,300** *C*

Three Modernist side tables, 75.5 cm. high by 60.5 cm. diam., 1930's. **£700-800** *S*

A Leleu Macassar ebony and mirror glass dressing table, affixed plaque signed 'J. Leleu', 76 cm. high by 100 cm. wide by 48 cm. deep, 1930's. **£800-900** *S*

A Finmar Ltd. plywood armchair, designed by Alvar Aalto. Finmar label, 60.75 cm. high, 1930's. **£100-£140** *S*

A set of 6 Finmar Ltd. plywood dining chairs, designed by Alvar Aalto, Finmar labels, stamped 'Alto Design Made In Finland', 80 cm. high, 1930's. **£400-500** *S*

An Ambrose Heal 1925 fully fitted 2 storey oak and chrome finished kitchen cabinet, 8 ft. high by 4 ft. 8 in. wide (240 by 140 cm.). **£500-£600**   *LRG*

An oak secretaire, 96 cm. wide by 145 cm. high. **£600-700**   *Bon*

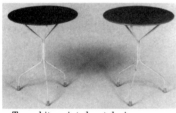

Two white-painted metal wire tables, designed by Ernest Race, 55 cm. high by 50.5 cm. diam. of top, designed, c. 1951. **£100-150**   *S*

A Gordon Russell 'fifties' mahogany sideboard, with maker's plaque 'Gordon Russell Ltd, Broadway, Worcs.', 121.5 cm. **£250-£300**   *P*

A large oak wall bookcase, mouse in relief, 31.3 cm. wide by 182 cm. high. **£1,200-1,400**   *Bon*

A pair of 'Mouseman' oak single beds by Robert Thompson of Kilburn, carved with a mouse, 114.5 cm. high, bed-head, 76.5 cm. high bed-end, 1930's. **£250-350**   *S*

A 'Mouseman' oak wardrobe, by Robert Thompson of Kilburn, carved with a mouse, 167.5 cm. high by 106.75 cm. wide, 1930's. **£650-750**   *S*

A chromed steel framed chair, designed by Gio Ponti, 107 cm. high, 1950's. **£400-500**   *S*

A 'tulip' table and 4 chairs, designed by Eero Saarinen, 81 cm. height of chairs, 106.5 cm. diam. table, designed 1956. **£100-150**   *S*

A Gimson oak bureau cabinet, 114 cm. wide by 167 cm. high, 1950. Suggest **£2,500-3,000**   *P*

A Betty Joel oak dining table, label marked 'Token Handmade Furniture designed by Betty Joel made by E. Kerhe at Token Works Portsmouth July 1934', 137 cm. wide by 76 cm. high. **£120-200**   *S*

A white-painted metal wire-work rocking chair, designed by Ernest Race, 76.5 cm. high, c. 1951. **£60-80**   *S*

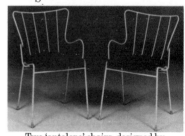

Two 'antelope' chairs, designed by Ernest Race for the South Bank, Festival of Britain, 78.5 cm. high, designed 1950-51. **£500-600**   *S*

A large CVP smoked glass coffee table, curved board 'U'-shaped, 53 cm. high by 134 cm. wide by 66 cm. deep, 1970's. **£130-200** *S*

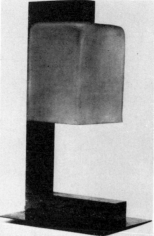

A Modernist bronze and nickel-plated table lamp, possibly Desny, 31 cm., c. 1930. **£300-350** *S*

A metal and glass lamp by Rene Lalique, the shades engraved R. Lalique, 78 cm. high, c. 1925. **£500-600** *CAm*

A pâte-de-verre oval pendant, with a beetle having brick-red shell-like wings, greyish legs and antennae against an olive-green ground streaked with yellow, marked with 'A.W.' initials for Almeric Walter, with cord, 7 cm. long. **£350-500** *P*

A Lalique amber glass hanging lampshade, moulded 'R. Lalique, France', hooks for suspension, 38 cm. diam. **£250-350** *P*

An Art Deco alabaster electric lamp, the girl wearing a jewelled bikini top, holding the acorn shaped shade on her head, 36 in. high. **£350-400** *AG*

An Almeric Walter pâte-de-verre pendant, having a blue-green scaly body resting on a green leafy branch laden with berries against a greyish ground streaked with blue, signed with 'AW' and 'N' for Nancy and 'B' mark for Henri Berge as modeller, with cord, 6.5 cm. **£600-£650** *P*

A Lalique blue glass oval pendant, moulded with the confronting bodies of wasps, signed 'R. Lalique', 5.5 cm. long. **£400-500** *P*

An Argy Rousseau pâte-de-cristal pendant, detailed in blue, green and purple, with original silk hanging cord and tassel in matching colours, moulded 'G.A.R.', 6.5 cm., 1920's. **£300-400** *S*

Pâte-de-verre and pâte-de-cristal are both made of powdered glass which has been beaten so that it fuses.

An Almeric Walter pâte-de-verre circular pendant, moulded with a pink, blue and yellow orchid against a speckled pink and blue ground of muted tones, marked 'AWN' for Walter of Nancy, 'B' for Henri Berge and 'France' on reverse, with cord, 4.75 cm. diam. **£200-300** *P*

A Lalique 'serpent' glass brooch, in gilt metal with reflective backing and green staining, stamped with 'RL' and 'Lalique' on mount, 4 cm. diam. **£750-850** *P*

An Omar Ramsden silver cruet set, each engraved 'Omar Ramsden me Fecit', maker's marks, London 1921, 9 cm. height of mustard pot. **£800-900** *S*

An Art Deco 'Egyptianesque' bracelet, with scarab beetles, with sapphire bodies and wings in red enamel, marcasite and pale green and mauve plique-à-jour enamels, silver-coloured metal, unmarked, 19.5 cm. long. **£900-1,000** *P*

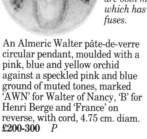

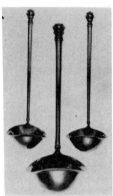

A set of 3 Omar Ramsden silver ladles, in original silk and velvet-lined wood box, maker's marks, London 1923, 20.75 and 17 cm. long. **£700-800**   *S*

A large Sibyl Dunlop silver punchbowl, maker's mark, London, 1938, 16.5 cm. **£1,700-1,900**   *S*

A heavy 3-piece tea service, in the Art Deco style, 1932 by Wakley and Wheeler, 15.4 cm. height of tea pot. **£500-600**   *L*

A 4-piece matching tea set in Art Deco style, 1911/35/6, and an oblong tray, incurved at the angles, end handles, 22 in. long (56 cm.), 1934, all Emile Viner, Sheffield, 77 oz. 8 dwt. (2,407 gm.) all in. **£800-900**   *S*

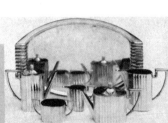

A Viennese tea/coffee service, tea pot, coffee pot, hot water jug, sugar basin, cream jug and tray, silver coloured metal, various marks, 19 cm. height of coffee pot, c. 1930. **£1,400-1,600**   *S*

A French Art Deco enamelled box and cover, stamped with French poincons and maker's lozenge for 'S.A.M. with palette mark', 13.25 by 11.25 cm. **£250-300**   *P*

A Cartier silver cigarette box, stamped 'Cartier London', maker's mark, London 1954, 10.25 cm. **£350-400**   *S*

A George Jensen silver coffee set, designed by Sigvard Bernadotte in 1952, stamped 'Sigvard' and maker's marks with London import marks for 1956, height of pot 23.5 cm., 50.5 oz. **£1,000-1,200**   *P*

An Edgar Brandt wrought iron and bronze decorative panel, 'Lè Cigognes D'Alsace', embellished in gilt bronze, 193 by 126 cm. **£7,500-£8,500**   *P*

Replicas of Brandt's original 1922 panels were installed in the interiors of the lifts at Selfridges in London, this being one of them.

An electro-plated cocktail shaker, in the form of a champagne bottle, 13½ in. high. **£250-300**   *Re*

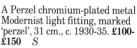

A Perzel chromium-plated metal Modernist light fitting, marked 'perzel', 31 cm., c. 1930-35. **£100-£150**   *S*

An unusual silver and glass hookah, maker's mark 'BBS', London 1954, 41 cm. high. **£450-£500**   *P*

A bronze figure cast from a model by Charles Sykes of a winged female, in an angled reclining posture, inscribed Chas. Sykes, 14¼ in. high. **£650-700** *CSK*

A large William Reid-Dick green-patinated bronze figure, 'Boy with Frog', signed 'Reid Dick 1931', 68 cm. high. **£3,000-4,000** *P*

There is a similar figure to this, situated in the Queen's Garden, Regent's Park, resulting from a visit by Queen Mary to the previous owners garden in the 30's and admiring the piece on offer. The owner, instead of giving the figure as a present to the Queen, as was often the case when a piece was admired, gave her instead the name and address of the sculptor.

A French Art Deco polychrome bronze statuette, of a woman dancer, cast from a model by A. Gory, surface rubbed in areas, on octagonal mottled marble base, 51 cm. high. **£600-700** *C*

A green painted bronze figure, cast from a model by Fayral, on buff stone base, inscribed Fayral, 20½ in. high. **£450-500** *CSK*

A pair of early 20th C. cast bronze book-ends, inscribed 'Raoul Benard', 9½ in. high (24 cm.). **£170-£200** *LBP*

A gilt bronze figure, 'Juggler', cast from a model by Claire J. R. Colinet, on buff onyx base, inscribed Cl. J.R. Colinet, 7 in. high. **£200-250** *CSK*

A Duverand cold-painted bronze figure, gold cold-painted, the flowers and bowl in painted plastic, mottled stepped brown marble base, base with lightly engraved mark 'Duverand', 30.5 cm., 1930's. **£400-450** *S*

A patinated bronze figure of a naked dancer, with hoop, by A. Bouraine on variegated marble socle, 18 in. **£500-600** *EH*

A Colinet bronze group of 2 dancing Bacchantes, marble engraved 'Cl. J. R. Colinet', 56.5 cm., 1930's. **£1,500-1,600** *S*

A large Art Deco bronze figure, by Lorenzl, c. 1920. **£400-500** *ASA*

A bronze nude figure, 'The Message of Love', cast from a model by Pierre Le Faguays, on tapering veined black marble pedestal on octagonal base, inscribed Le Faguays, 30½ in. high. **£1,600-£1,800** *CSK*

A bronze and ivory figure, with coloured enamel decoration, by Gerdago, c. 1920. **£2,000-2,500** *ASA*

A cold painted bronze figure, in the manner of Frederick Preiss, on an Algerian onyx plinth, 9½ in. (24 cm.), c. 1920. **£220-280** *SC*

A bronze figure of a girl, by Bruno Zach, 1 ft. 1½ in. (34.3 cm.), on a marble column 4½ in. (11 cm.), rich light brown patination, c. 1910. **£1,200-1,400** *S*

An Art Deco electro-plated figure, by G. H. Gantchell, on black marble hexagonal base, 11¼ in. high. **£50-60** *CDC*

A bronze figure, cast from a model by Lorenzl, on hexagonal green onyx pedestal with hexagonal base, inscribed Lorenzl, 19¼ in. high. **£600-700** *CSK*

A Chiparus cold-painted metal figure of a kneeling huntress, 59.5 cm., 1930's. **£900-1,000** *S*

A bronze bust of a man's head, 'Energie', signed 'Kelety' and stamped bronze '255', on rectangular marble base with presentation plaque, rich rubbed green patination, 14½ in. high (37 cm.), second quarter 20th C. **£500-600** *SS*

A 1930's bronzed group of 3 racing greyhounds, on black marble base, signed Limousin, 27½ in. long overall. **£180-220** *DSH*

A bronze and ivory figure, 'Oriental Water Carrier', from a model by Dominique Alonzo, inscribed D. Alonzo, Etling Paris, 13½ in. high. **£650-750** *CSK*

A bronze and ivory figure, of a young concertina player, signed D.H. Chiparus, 10 in. (26 cm.), early 20th C. **£500-550** *SC*

Care should be taken in considering the value of any ivory/part ivory pieces as plastic reproductions abound.

A Colinet bronze group of a woman and 2 greyhounds, signed in the maquette 'Cl. J. R. Colinet', 45 cm., 1920's. **£1,100-1,500** *S*

An Art Deco gilded bronze and ivory group of 2 children, as flower and fruit sellers, by Joseph D'Aste signed, 9 in. high. **£500-600** *M*

A Preiss cold painted bronze and ivory figure, 'Lighter than Air', bubble missing, 34 cm. high, 1920's. **£1,600-1,900** *SS*

A Chiparus bronze and ivory figure, 'Innocence', 14½ in. **£1,200-1,400** *Bea*

ART DECO BRONZE AND IVORY FIGURES

- produced in large quantities in the 1920's and 1930's
- many made in Vienna and Paris
- bronze frequently cold-painted; ivory mainly hand-carved and hence no two figures absolutely identical
- figures in other cheaper materials such as spelter and plaster were mass-produced and many of these are of poor quality
- F. Preiss works are highly collectable, especially his fine ivory carving of children and classical nudes
- D. Chiparus and C. Colinet were both known for their nudes but also for highly theatrical figures
- Bruno Zach has become associated with figures of a decidedly erotic nature: girls with whips and tight-fitting garments
- many fakes have appeared on the market — watch crudely carved ivory faces and hands; the bronze is often cast in original moulds but fakers find the join to the ivory difficult to make smooth and flowing
- discolouration and cracks on the ivory can detract seriously from value, particularly on the face

A Preiss bronze and ivory figure, 'The Archer', unmarked, base chipped, ivory feet replaced, 22 cm., 1930's. **£2,000-2,500** *SS*

A Preiss ivory figure, on onyx base, signed, 18 cm. **£260-300** *SS*

A Chiparus bronze and ivory figure, 'Le Coup De Vent', signed on base 'D.H. Chiparus', 31.25 cm. high. **£1,800-2,200** *P*

A Lorenzl painted bronze and ivory figure, on green onyx base, signed on reverse 'Lorenzl', 33 cm. high. **£750-850** *P*

A Gilbert bronze and ivory figure, of a pierrette, signed on the maquette 'A. Gilbert', 22.75 cm., 1920's. **£400-500** *S*

.) A Preiss painted bronze and ivory figure, 'Aphrodite with Tazza 'Fruit', signed on bronze 'F. Preiss', 21.5 cm. high. **£1,000-1,200**

.) A Preiss painted bronze and ivory figure, 'Aphrodite', signed on bronze 'F. Preiss', 22 cm. high. **£1,000-1,200** *P*

A painted bronze and ivory figure, 'Girl on Wall', cast and carved from a model by Ferdinand Preiss, inscribed F. Preiss, 9 in. high. **£800-900** *CSK*

PREISS, Johann Philipp Ferdinand

Perhaps the best known of those sculptors who chose bronze and ivory as their medium, Preiss, a German, worked in Berlin. Comparison of his figures with many of those made by the Paris-based artists highlights the then German ideal of the master race. Instead of the sensuousness and sometimes frank eroticism of the French school, many of the Preiss figures display a fresh air healthiness of spirit as they earnestly pursue their sporting activities. The sheer numbers of Preiss figures in circulation preclude his having made each one individually. It is generally accepted that he designed all the figures himself, employing a number of sculptors to work, almost on a production line basis, on their various component parts, which he would then assemble.

A cold painted ivory and bronze figure, on stepped onyx base, signed 'M. Munk, Vienna', 35 cm., c. 1900. **£450-500** *SS*

A Bizarre batchelor tea set, by Clarice Cliff, painted in greens, orange and yellow, printed marks. **£200-250** *CSK*

A Clarice Cliff Bizarre lotus vase, painted with the 'Honolulu' pattern, striped green and black trees with orange, red and yellow foliage, printed marks, 11½ in. high. **£1,100-1,300** *CSK*

MAKE THE MOST OF MILLER'S

CONDITION *is absolutely vital when assessing the value of an antique. Damaged pieces on the whole appreciate much less than perfect examples. However a rare desirable piece may command a high price even when damaged.*

A Clarice Cliff 'Applique' Bizarre lotus vase, painted in the 'Lucerne' design, in orange, yellow, green and black, with a deep blue sky above, printed and painted marks, impressed, Isis, 9¾ in. high. **£1,300-£1,500** *CSK*

A Clarice Cliff Bizarre lotus vase, 'Cloyre', the mottled matt lilac and blue ground painted in vermilion, lime green and yellow, painted and printed marks, 11¾ in. high. **£1,900-2,200** *CSK*

A Clarice Cliff Bizarre lotus vase, painted in pink, green, yellow and blue, printed marks, 11½ in. high. **£650-750** *CSK*

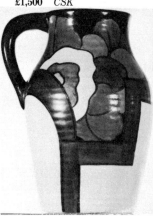

A Clarice Cliff Bizarre 'Latona' lotus vase, painted in pink, blue, purple and green, printed marks, 11¾ in. high. **£1,000-1,300** *CSK*

A Clarice Cliff Fantasque Bizarre tea-for-two set, painted in the 'Summer House' design, in multicolours with orange and black rims, printed marks. **£850-950** *CSK*

A Clarice Cliff Bizarre coffee set, in orange, yellow, green, brown and grey, comprising a coffee pot, 7 cups, 6 saucers, cream jug and sugar bowl, printed marks. **£200-£250** *CSK*

A Clarice Cliff Bizarre lotus vase painted in a rich chestnut, blue, purple and green, printed marks, 11½ in. high. **£600-700** *CSK*

A Clarice Cliff Bizarre 'Inspiration' vase, painted in brown and rust, and a blue zig-zag design, on a running turquoise glaze revealing the white body beneath, printed marks, 6¾ in. high. **£300-350** *CSK*

A large Clarice Cliff Fantasque wall plate, painted in vivid oranges, yellow, blue, red and green, factory marks and facsimile signature, 42 cm. diam. **£500-550** *P*

A Clarice Cliff Bizarre 'Golly' pencil holder, in green, orange and red, printed marks, 5¾ in. high. **£250-300** *CSK*

A Clarice Cliff Fantasque lotus vase, painted in orange, green, brown and black between wide orange and yellow borders, printed marks, 9½ in. high. **£500-550** *CSK*

A Clarice Cliff Fantasque plate, painted in black, orange, yellow, red and green, stamped marks, 22.7 cm. diam., 1931. **£250-300** *C*

The Fantasque series of designs include trees, foliage, hills and cottages painted in bright autumnal colours on cream bodies.

A rare Clarice Cliff Fantasque ginger jar and cover, painted in colours with cottages on stylised hills and with tall trees, printed marks and painted unique mark, 20 cm. high, 1932. **£1,000-1,200** *C*

Four Fantasque octagonal plates, painted in the 'Secrets' pattern with cottages on a hillside, in a coastal landscape, printed marks, 1931. **£250-300** *C*

A Fantasque conical bowl, on 4 flange feet painted in pure colours, with stylised trees and harebells, printed marks, hair crack to rim, 23.3 cm. diam., 1933. **£550-600** *C*

A Clarice Cliff plate, painted in colours with stylised trees and flowerheads, printed marks, 22.8 cm. diam., 1933. **£120-180** *C*

A Fantasque Bizarre centrepiece, by Clarice Cliff, painted in pink, blue, green, yellow and purple, mounted on 2 blue block feet and with separate flower holder, printed marks, 15¾ in. wide. **£450-£500** *CSK*

A Clarice Cliff coffee set, in orange, yellow, green, brown and blue, comprising: coffee pot, cream jug, sugar bowl and 6 cups and saucers, printed marks, 1936. **£400-500** *CSK*

A Clarice Cliff beer and sausage set, the 16 pieces painted with concentric coloured bands, printed marks, 47 cm. diam. of charger, 1934. **£450-500** *C*

A Clarice Cliff Fantasque Bizarre lotus vase, painted in red, yellow, green and black and large orange flowerheads, the neck painted orange, printed marks, 11½ in. high. **£650-750** *CSK*

MAKE THE MOST OF MILLER'S

Miller's is completely different each year. Each edition contains completely NEW photographs. This is not an updated publication. We never repeat the same photograph.

Two Clarice Cliff 'Crayon' plates, painted in pastel colours, printed marks, 23.2 cm. diam., 1934. **£200-£250** *C*

A Clarice Cliff coffee service for 6 on tray, painted in orange, yellow and brown, printed marks, chips to one saucer, 18.8 cm. height of teapot, 1935. **£700-850** *C*

A Clarice Cliff Fantasque single handled 'Isis' vase, painted with coloured foliage, printed marks, 24.2 cm. high, 1932. **£550-650** *C*

A Clarice Cliff breakfast set for one, painted in the 'Pansy Delicia' design with blue, pink and lilac flowerheads above a yellow, green and brown running glaze, printed marks, 11.2 cm. height of teapot, 1931. **£500-600**   *C*

A Clarice Cliff tea-for-two set, painted with the 'Canterbury Bells' design, with a spray of orange flowers before green foliage with coloured rim borders, printed marks, 11.6 cm. height of teapot, 1930. **£650-750**   *C*

A Clarice Cliff 'Sunshine' tea-for-two service, painted with hollyhocks on a cream ground within yellow and russet borders, 12 cm. height of teapot, 1934. **£450-£500**   *C*

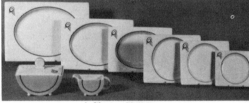

A Clarice Cliff 'Biarritz' 24-piece dinner service, decorated in 'Modern' design, with a black printed stylised scroll and painted silver borders, printed marks, 1932. **£1,000-1,300**   *C*

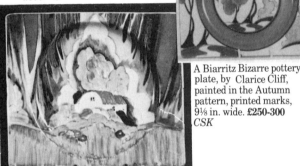

A Biarritz Bizarre pottery plate, by Clarice Cliff, painted in the Autumn pattern, printed marks, 9⅛ in. wide. **£250-300** *CSK*

A Biarritz Bizarre pottery plate, by Clarice Cliff, printed marks, 9 in. wide. **£300-350**   *CSK*

A Biarritz plate, painted with a cottage in stylised garden and with tall trees before a streaked amber, grey and brown sky, printed marks, 22.9 cm. wide, 1933. **£250-£300**   *C*

A Clarice Cliff 23-piece honeyglaze tea service, painted in moss green with bright orange handles outlined in black, printed marks, 11.1 cm. height of teapot, 1938. **£900-1,000**   *C*

A Clarice Cliff oviform ewer, painted in the 'Oriental' design, on a turquoise ground, printed marks, star crack, 27.4 cm. high. **£65-85** *C*

A Biarritz plate, painted with a cottage in stylised garden before a streaked amber, grey and brown sky, printed marks, 22.9 cm. wide, 1933. **£300-400**   *C*

'Biarritz' refers to the rectangular shaped design.

A Clarice Cliff coffee service for 6, painted with striped borders of yellow, russet and black, 18.8 cm. height of coffee pot, 1933. **£600-70** *C*

A Clarice Cliff tea service for four, painted in the 'Crocus' design, some pieces painted Crocus, 1935. **£200-300** *C*

A Clarice Cliff 'Lotus' vase, painted with the 'Crocus' design in orange, purple, blue, yellow and russet, between yellow and russet rim and foot borders, printed marks, painted Crocus, 29.7 cm. high. **£250-300** *C*

A Foley/Shelley 'Intarsio' pottery stick stand, printed marks, 27½ in. high. **£1,700-2,000** *CSK*

A Shelley white porcelain coffee set, painted in orange, black and silver, comprising a tapering cylindrical coffee pot, 6 cups with solid triangular handles, 6 saucers, cream jug and sugar bowl, printed marks. **£350-400** *CSK*

A Shelley white porcelain tea set, painted in grey, black and yellow with stylised butterfly wing motifs, comprising 12 cups, 12 saucers, 12 plates, milk jug and sugar basin, printed marks. **£750-850** *CSK*

The unusual stylish design and the production of a book on Shelley have led to a higher value than expected.

A Clarice Cliff 'Fantasque' single-handled 'Lotus' vase, painted in the 'Summer House' design, with stylised high-roofed cottages and tall trees, printed marks, 29 cm. high, 1932. **£1,100-1,400** *C*

A Clarice Cliff 'Gayday' 'Isis'-shaped vase, painted with a border of colourful daisies, between yellow rim and brown and green foot borders, printed marks, painted Gayday, 24.5 cm. high, 1936. **£200-£250** *C*

A Newport pottery 'Bizarre' candlestick, painted with formalised landscape in shades of yellow, blue and green, printed marks, 13.25 cm., 1930's. **£200-250** *S*

A Clarice Cliff honeyglaze breakfast service for 2, painted with clusters of stylised fruits between orange and blue rim borders, printed marks, small chip to spout of teapot, 13.6 cm. height of milk jug, 1930. **£400-500** *C*

A Ruskin high fire vase, covered in a streaked and mottled violet and sang-de-boeuf glaze, speckled with turquoise, impressed Ruskin, 9½ in. high, 1933. **£150-200** *CSK*

A Mintons Secessionist pottery jardinière, painted with stylised blue flowers, outlined in white slip and green foliage on a striped green and white ground, printed mark, 13 in. high. **£300-350** *CSK*

A large Newport pottery jug, painted with broad geometric band in bright green, orange, blue and yellow, gold printed marks, 29.15 cm., 1930's. **£200-250** *S*

(l.) A Royal Dux tazza, pink triangle mark, 16.5 cm. high. **£250-£300**

(c.) A Royal Dux candelabrum, with shaped framework outlined in pale green and pink, pink triangle mark, 35.5 cm. high. **£300-400**

(r.) A Royal Dux figure of a girl, partially covering her naked body with a puce and green robe that her pet dog tries to remove, pink triangle mark, 37 cm. high. **£400-£500**   *P*

A Carlton Ware lustre pottery vase, painted with a bold chequered and geometric design in vivid orange, yellow, tan and black, printed mark, 10¼ in. high. **£250-£300**   *CSK*

A Royal Dux Art Deco part bisque figure, 10 in. high. **£100-140**   *CDC*

A Jean Mayodon Art Deco faience vase, in blues and gold against a patterned ground in blue, green, gold and ochre, the underside with impressed monogram 'J.M.', 28.5 cm., c. 1925. **£100-125**   *S*

A pair of Theodore Deck peacock blue glazed vases, with cell diaper moulded panels, 13 in. **£250-300**   *DWB*

A Royal Dux figure of a dancing girl, in revealing blue dress, 12 ir high. **£120-150**   *Re*

An unusual Zsolnay lustre ewer, in the form of a bird, covered with a green/violet iridescent glaze, spires mark and 'Zsolnay Pecs', 33 cm. high. **£400-500**   *P*

A Goldscheider Art Deco pottery 'Bat Girl', in brown winged short costume, with amber veining, fingers of left hand glued, 1920's. **£500-600**   *CDC*

A Goldscheider figure of a semi-nude dancer, impressed marks, 16½ in. high. **£300-350**   *N*

An Art Deco pottery vase, incise and painted in brown with styli: flamingoes on turquoise mound on a cream ground, inscribed Simone Liarrieu, 12 in. high. **£2 £250**   *CSK*

An Art Deco Goldscheider pottery figure, by Claire Weiss, impressed marks, inscribed C. Weiss, 12¾ in. high. **£400-450**   *CSK*

A Hutschenreuther porcelain figure of Mephistopheles, by K. Tutler, factory marks, 29 cm. **£200-£300**   *P*

A Villeroy and Boch 'Mettlach' A Nouveau jardinière, impressed factory marks and number '2908' 22 cm. high. **£250-300**   *P*

An Augarten porcelain chocolate set, painted en grisaille with a nude figure reclining amid foliage, between thin orange banding and fluted butterscotch borders, comprising the pot and cover, milk jug, sugar bowl, four cups and saucers and four plates, underglaze blue shield and 'Wien' and in red 'Augarten Austria', height of pot, 16.75 cm. **£120-160** *P*

An Art Deco Limoges porcelain figural night light, modelled in a cubist manner, marked 'Halga, Limoges France', 18.5 cm. high. **£120-180** *P*

An unusual Italian Art Deco pottery wall lamp, marked 'Ariele' 'Torino-Italy, No 197', 29 cm. **£250-£300** *P*

An unusual Bing and Grondahl porcelain vase and cover, made by the late Countess Effie Hegermann Lidencrone in 1919, in browns, greys, blue and white, with factory marks, 'EHL' monogram and '1608/19', original fitted case, 30 cm. high. **£950-1,050** *P*

A Robj porcelain spirit flask, modelled as a jolly schoolmaster with a black gown trimmed in red, his mortar board with red tassel forming the stopper, marked on base, 'Robj Paris — Made in France', 26 cm. high. **£80-100** *P*

A small Royal Doulton character jug, 'Mephistopheles', designed by C. J. Noke and H. Fenton, c.m.l. & c., inscribed with verse, introduced 1937, withdrawn 1948, 8.5 cm. high. **£550-650** *P*

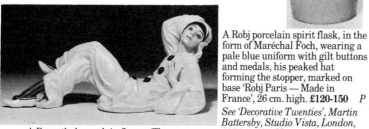

A Rosenthal porcelain figure, 'The Ash Wednesday Pierrot', by Constantin Holzer-Defanti, printed factory marks, impressed 'C. Holzer-Defanti' and 'K 459', 30 cm. long. **£500-600** *P*

A Robj porcelain spirit flask, in the form of Maréchal Foch, wearing a pale blue uniform with gilt buttons and medals, his peaked hat forming the stopper, marked on base 'Robj Paris — Made in France', 26 cm. high. **£120-150** *P*
See 'Decorative Twenties', Martin Battersby, Studio Vista, London, 1974, p. 180, No. 194, for a similar piece.

A Royal Doulton mask head jug, 'The Clown', Regd. No. 810520, having red hair with green and yellow tints, black and maroon facial markings and a multi-coloured handle, damaged, height 6½ in. **£1,500-2,000** *OL*

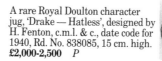

Five Royal Doulton character jugs, *(1.)* Capt. Hook, printed marks. **£200-250**
(2.) A Punch and Judy man, printed marks. **£300-400**
(3.) Dick Turpin, printed marks. **£60-80**
(4.) The Fortune Teller, printed marks. **£220-300**
(5.) Simple Simon, printed marks. **£250-350** *Bon*

A Royal Doulton character jug, 'Lord Nelson', designed by M. Henk, c.m.l. & c., introduced 1952, withdrawn 1969, 18.25 cm. high. **£150-200** *P*

A rare Royal Doulton character jug, 'Drake — Hatless', designed by H. Fenton, c.m.l. & c., date code for 1940, Rd. No. 838085, 15 cm. high. **£2,000-2,500** *P*

A Royal Doulton figure, 'Smuts', designed by H. Fenton, c.m.l. & c. introduced 1946, withdrawn 1948 17 cm. high. **£1,000-1,500**   *P*

DOULTON WARES
Doulton marks — abbreviations

o.u.m.	— oval undated mark
o.m.	— oval mark, dated
c.m.	— circular mark
r.m.	— rosette mark
r.m. & e.	— rosette mark and England
d.l.e.	— Doulton Lambeth England
d.s.l.	— Doulton Silicon Lambeth
d.s.p.	— Doulton & Slaters Patent
c.m.l. & c.	— circle mark, lion & crown
c.m. & l.	— circle mark and lion
r.d.e.	— Royal Doulton England
s.c.m.	— slip-cast mark
i.c.f.m.	— impressed circular faience mark
r.d.f.	— Royal Doulton Flambé

A pottery character jug of 'Johnny Appleseed', printed Royal Doulton marks, D 6372, 6½ in. high. **£150-£200**   *CSK*

A Royal Doulton figure, Marquise Silvestra, unrecorded, no details available, 24.5 cm., c. 1920. **£2,000-£3,000**   *Bon*

A Royal Doulton figure, 'The Lilac Shawl', after a model by C. J. Noke, printed mark and title, HN44, incised numerals probably as a date code for 1918, 8¾ in. **£400-500**   *S*

A Royal Doulton Kingsware Dewar's whisky flask, decorated with a figure of 'George the Guard', printed marks, 21.5 cm. **£90-120**   *Bon*

The shawl can be subject to flaking which reduces the value.

A Royal Doulton Kingsware Dewar's whisky flask, decorated with a 16th C. town-crier, the words 'Oyez! Oyez!' at the feet of the crier, printed marks, 22 cm. **£130-180**   *Bon*

A Royal Doulton figure, 'Robert Burns', designed by E. W. Light, HN42, c.m.l. & c., potted by Royal Doulton & Co., inscribed E. W. Light Sc. and No 5, introduced 1914, withdrawn 1938, 35.5 cm. high. **£1,400-1,700**   *P*

A Royal Doulton figure, 'Lady Ermine', green painted mark, H.N. 54, No. 15, 8¾ in. (22.3 cm.), incised date 2.18.1918. **£450-550**   *SC*

A Royal Doulton figure, 'Fruit Gathering', designed by L. Harradine, H.N. 562, c.m.l. & c., impressed date 9.23/8?, introduced 1923, withdrawn 1938, 20.5 cm. **£850-950**   *P*

A Royal Doulton figure, 'Pretty Lady', printed and painted marks, painted title and H.N. 70, 9¾ in., impressed date code for 1919. **£500-£600**   *S*

A Royal Doulton model of a fox, the creature lies curled with its tail around its head, having dark and light marking, H.N. 147, 9 cm. across, impressed date 2.1.36. **£100-£140**   *P*

In the 'Royal Doulton Figure Book' in the Animal Models appendix, H.N. 147 is entitled 'Fox on rock', the above model has no such rock.

A Royal Doulton model, 'Character Owl', H.N. 187, c.m.l. & c., No. 228, 19.5 cm. high. **£300-350**   *P*

A Royal Doulton figure, 'The Perfect Pair', designed by L. Harradine, HN 581, c.m. & l., impressed date 10.26, introduced 1923, withdrawn 1938, 18 cm. high. **£350-450**   *P*

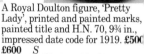

A Royal Doulton figure, 'Negligee', modelled as a young girl in a coloured slip and red turban, kneeling on a multi-coloured cushion, HN1219, printed and painted Royal Doulton marks, 5 in. high. **£300-400**   *CSK*

A Royal Doulton figure, 'Butterfly', printed and painted mark HN 1456, 6½ in. high. **£350-400**   *CSK*

A Royal Doulton figure, 'Angela', the young girl wearing a red and lilac dress, minor chip, printed and painted marks, painted title and HN1204, impressed date code for 1929, 7¼ in. **£350-400**   *S*

A Royal Doulton double-sided figure, of 'Mephistopheles and Marguerite', the Devil in long red robes and the young girl in a yellow dress, HN775, 8 in. high. **£600-700** *CSK*

A Royal Doulton figure, 'Negligee', designed by L. Harradine, HN 1272, c.m. & l., potted by Doulton & Co., impressed date 1.1.28, introduced 1928, withdrawn 1938, 12.5 cm. high. **£600-700**   *P*

ROYAL DOULTON FIGURES

- since 1913 2,000 different models have been produced by the Royal Doulton factory
- basically thought of as a modern day Staffordshire figure revival
- since 1920's figures mainly designed by Peggy Davies, Leslie Harradine and Mary Nicoll
- the HN numbering sequence was introduced with Charles Vyse 'Darling' HN 1 (which is still in production today)
- since 1938 new figures are introduced only to replace ones which are to be withdrawn and so at any one time there are only 200-300 figures in production
- any figure which is unsuccessful is withdrawn — and those are the ones most sought after by collectors
- this section is ordered in HN number sequence where possible.

A Royal Doulton figure, 'Columbine', designed by L. Harradine, HN 1296, c.m.l. & c., potted by Doulton & Co., impressed date 2.9.29, introduced 1928, withdrawn 1938, 15.5 cm. high. **£200-250**   *P*

A Royal Doulton figure, 'Geisha', designed by C. J. Noke, HN 1292, c.m. & l., potted by Doulton & Co., impressed date 4.1.28, introduced 1928, withdrawn 1938, 17.5 cm. high. **£500-600**   *P*

A Royal Doulton figure, 'Covent Garden', HN 1339, introduced 1929, withdrawn by 1938, 22.3 cm. high. **£250-300**   *Bea*

A Royal Doulton figure, of 'Pierrette', printed and painted marks, painted title and HN 731, impressed date code for 1927, 6¾ in. **£400-500**   *S*

A Royal Doulton figure, 'Marietta', HN 1341 printed Royal Doulton marks, 8¼ in. high. **£250-300** *CSK*

A Royal Doulton figure, 'Marion', HN 1583, introduced 1933, withdrawn 1938, 16.5 cm. high. **£150-200**   *Bea*

A Royal Doulton figure, 'Columbine', in pink and yellow dress seated on a low green column, printed and painted marks, HN1439, 6¼ in. high. **£350-400** *CSK*

Seven Royal Doulton figures:
1. 'Philippa of Hainault', HN 2008, introduced 1948, withdrawn 1953, 24.1 cm. **£400-450**
2. 'Matilda', HN 2011, introduced 1948, withdrawn 1953, 22.8 cm. **£450-500**
3. 'The Lady Anne Nevill', HN 2006, introduced 1948, withdrawn 1953, 24.1 cm. **£450-500**
4. 'Margaret of Anjou', HN 2012, introduced 1948, withdrawn 1953, 23.4 cm. **£300-350**

5. 'The Young Miss Nightingale', HN 2010, introduced 1948, withdrawn 1953, 22.8 cm. **£400-450**
6. 'Mrs. Fitzherbert', HN 2007, introduced 1948, withdrawn 1953, 22.8 cm. **£450-500**
7. 'Henrietta Maria', HN 2005, introduced 1948, withdrawn 1953, 23.4 cm. **£450-500** *EH*

A Royal Doulton figure, 'The Orange Lady', HN 1759, introduced 1936, withdrawn 1975, 22.2 cm. **£90-120** *TW*

A set of 8 Doulton Dickensian characters, picked out in colours, printed marks, 4 in. (10 cm.). **£180-£240** *SC*

1. A Royal Doulton flambé group, 'Polar Bears', covered in rich red glaze, r.d.e., 8.5 cm. high. **£150-200**
2. A Royal Doulton flambé model, 'Monkey', covered in a red and mottled blue and green glaze, c.m.l. & c., 8.5 cm. high. **£180-240**
3. A Royal Doulton flambé group, 'Pigs', covered in a rich red glaze shading to black, c.m.l. & c., date code for 1947, 17.75 cm. long. **£200-£250**
4. A Royal Doulton flambé animal, 'Polar Bear', in a red glaze shading to black, c.m.l. & c., incised '39', 9 cm. high. **£250-300**
5. A Royal Doulton flambé model, 'Lion', covered in a rich flambé glaze, r.d.e., 18.5 cm. long. **£230-£280** *P*

A Royal Doulton figure, 'Bonnie Lassie', HN 1626, introduced 1934, withdrawn 1953, 13.3 cm. **£120-150** *Bea*

A Royal Doulton figure, 'Rosebud', designed by L. Harradine, HN 1581, c.m.l. & c., potted by Doulton & Co., introduced 1933, withdrawn 1938, 8.25 cm. high. **£200-250** *P*

'The Gypsies', a Charles Vyse earthenware group, of a woman wearing a blue striped dress, turquoise shawl and black hat, the man wearing striped trousers, yellow striped waistcoat, painted artist's monogram, Chelsea 1925, 10½ in. high. **£650-750** *CSK*

Five Royal Doulton figures:
1. 'Wardrobe Mistress', HN 2145, introduced 1954, withdrawn 1967, 14.5 cm. **£180-240**

2. 'Spring Flowers', HN 1807, introduced 1937, withdrawn 1959, 18.5 cm. **£120-160**

3. 'Eleanor of Provence', HN 2009, introduced 1948, withdrawn 1953, 24 cm. **£200-250**

4. 'Deidre', HN 2020, introduced 1949, withdrawn 1955, 17.5 cm. **£150-180**

5. 'Ellen Terry as Queen Catherine', HN 379, introduced 1920, withdrawn 1949, badly cracked, 31.5 cm. **£200-250** *Bon*

A Royal Doulton figure, 'Bess', HN 2002, introduced 1947, withdrawn 1969, 18.4 cm. **£90-120** *TW*

A George II cake basket, engraved with a coat-of-arms within rococo and foliage cartouche, repair to handle, 14⅜ in. high (36.5 cm.), by Edward Aldridge, 1759, 40 oz. **£2,250-3,000** *C*

The arms are those of Mosley with Pulleine in pretence.

Value Points:

- Chinoiserie more popular than more straightforward rococo floral designs.
- Contemporary armorials.

A George III cake basket, 40.2 cm. (15¾ in.) wide, marked on body and handle, Robert Sharp, London, 1793, 962 gm. (30 oz. 19 dwt.). **£1,250-1,750** *S*

A George III cake basket, 12¼ in. wide, marked on base and handle, by Dorothy Langlands, Newcastle, 1809, 33 oz. 6 dwt. **£500-700** *SS*

A William IV fruit basket, 12½ in. (32 cm.) diam., London 1834, 35 oz. **£400-600** *LBP*

SILVER MARKET TRENDS

Prices realised during the last 12 months have underlined the trend which was set in 1981. Objects of rarity or in the top 10 with regard to quality, style and/or maker have brought a price which to those that observe only photographs, looks completely out of proportion. The collectors who are in the position where money is no object appear to be slightly on the increase, whilst the amount of these pieces available for sale is on the decrease. The prices are further boosted by the weakness of the pound against the dollar, and the flow across the Atlantic is once more approaching flood conditions. If the American economy continues to bump along without slipping then the prices will hold up.

There has been a steady increase in prices for leisure related items as well as pieces which will 'dress' the dining room and these should be areas to continue and watch. Traditional small collecting areas — vinaigrettes — wine labels — snuff boxes — appear to be losing out to new collecting fields. The exceptional examples will still bring buyers out of the woodwork, but the straightforward examples have remained steady, if they haven't in fact slackened.

The bullion price has been reasonably steady in the region of £5-6, and has therefore not been a factor to change prices in one direction or the other.

By Peter Waldron, Sotheby's

A George III cake basket, length 11¼ in. (29 cm.), London 1813, 17¾ oz. **£225-325** *LBP*

Minus Point:

- The chasing at centre was added later to probably cover armorials or inscription — hence lower price.

A Victorian cake basket, 33 cm. wide, probably by Martin Hall & Co., London 1881, 28 oz. **£550-750** *CEd*

A George III Irish cake basket, the centre with a contemporary coat-of-arms, some old repair, 12 in., by Robert Calderwood, Dublin, c. 1760, 24 oz. **£700-950** *WW*

A George III oval cake basket, 37.2 cm. (14⅝ in.) wide, Samuel Herbert & Co., London, 1762, 1,320 gm. (42 oz. 9 dwt.). **£1,500-£2,000** *S*

A pair of George III oval baskets and covers, the domed covers pierced and chased with vines, with flower handles, with tin liners to the baskets, 12½ in. (31.7 cm.) long, by William Pitts, 1803, 94 oz. **£4,500-5,500** *C*

Value Points:

- Unusual examples.
- Other baskets of this type do exist but it is unlikely that many have covers.

A George III cake basket, 12½ in. long, maker William Bateman (probably), London 1814, 30 oz. **£400-600** *HyD*

A George III cake basket, engraved with a crest and a coat-of-arms, 13¾ in. (35.2 cm.) diam., by S. Bergin, Dublin, 1819, 42 oz. 16 dwt. **£400-600** *SS*

A pair of silver baskets, London 1883, 31 oz. **£400-500** *BA*

An early George III sweetmeat basket, 6½ in. (16 cm.) wide, by William Plummer, London, 1764, 4 oz. 10 dwt. **£250-350** *SC*

A George IV cake basket, 12½ in. diam., marked on body and handle, by Joseph Angell, London, 1823, 39 oz. 4 dwt. **£400-600** *SS*

A pair of late Victorian small baskets, one damaged, maker's mark W. Comyns, London 1896, 28 oz. **£550-700** *HSS*

Value Points:

- Reproductions of Dutch baskets of c. 1770.
- Very good pierced and engraved decoration will demand strong competition and create a price 50% higher than the more simple copies of English Adam design.

A George III sugar basket, with blue glass liner, 14.7 cm., by Burrage Davenport, 1776. **£350-£450** *L*

A Charles II plain tumbler cup, 2¼ in. (5.6 cm.) high, maker's mark EG, 1681, 6 oz. 3 dwt. **£2,500-3,000** *C*

A pair of George I Provincial tumbler cups, 5.9 cm. diam., 4.5 cm. high, by Richard Richardson, Chester, 1722, 4.5 oz. **£1,400-1,600** *P*

A cake basket, in rococo taste, 15⅞ in. (40.3 cm.) wide, Mappin & Webb Ltd., London, 1929, engraved 'Reproduction after Paul Lamerie c.1739', 3,085 gm. (99 oz. 4 dwt.). **£2,500-3,000** *S*

Value Points:

- **This is silver-gilt.**
- Very good reproduction work is extremely expensive to make today.
- Manufacturing cost would create an unrealistic retail price which would begin to compete with the 1739 original!

A late 17th C. silver-gilt beaker, 3¼ in. (8.2 cm.) high, apparently unmarked, c. 1690, 97 gm. (3 oz. 3 dwt.). **£1,800-2,500** *S*

A pair of plain tapering beakers, one with two small repaired splits to the rim, 3⅜ in. (8 cm.) high, struck only with the Sterling mark, probably Cork or Limerick, 18th C., 12 oz. 18 dwt. **£750-1,000** *C*

Value Points:

- Note the repairs.
- Initials are later and will detract.
- If these had been positively identified with a maker the price would be doubled.

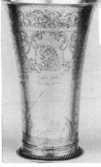

A late 17th C. silver-gilt beaker, 3¼ in. (8.2 cm.) high...

A set of 3 silver beakers, by Hancock & Co., London, 1909, 26 oz. 10 dwt. **£350-450** *BA*

A Dutch silver-gilt beaker, 6⅞ in. (17.4 cm.) high, maker's mark perhaps WF or WP conjoined, Dokkum, c. 1630, 9 oz. 16 dwt. **£3,000-4,000** *C*

A pair of German barrel-shaped double beakers, overall height 4½ in. (11.3 cm.), maker's mark perhaps IB for Johann Becker, Augsburg 1755/1757, 5 oz. **£1,000-£1,500** *C*

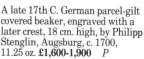

A late 17th C. German parcel-gilt covered beaker, 20 cm. high, by Johann Drentwett (I), Augsburg, c. 1690, 16 oz. **£1,500-2,000** *P*

A late 17th C. German parcel-gilt covered beaker, engraved with a later crest, 18 cm. high, by Philipp Stenglin, Augsburg, c. 1700, 11.25 oz. **£1,600-1,900** *P*

A late 17th/early 18th C. German parcel-gilt beaker, 10.2 cm. high, maker's mark untraced, Nuremburg, c. 1700, 4.5 oz. **£800-£1,000** *P*

An oval beaker, showing traces of gilding, 8.2 cm. high, by Johann Martin Satzger I, maker's mark, Augsburg, 1753-55, 135 gm. **£1,750-2,250** *S*

A German parcel-gilt beaker, 5¼ in. high, by Friedrich Schwertmuller II, Augsburg, 1745-47, 7 oz. (220 gm.). **£1,500- £2,000** *S*

An 18th C. German parcel-gilt beaker, with a later cover en suite, 13 cm. high, by Ehrenfried Schonberger, Berlin, c. 1730, 6 oz. **£900-1,100** *P*

A Swiss parcel-gilt écuelle and cover, 13.75 cm. diam., by Hans Jacob Fäsch, Basel, c. 1710, 11.5 oz. **£3,500-5,000** *P*

A Russian silver-gilt and niello beaker, 3¼ in., maker's initials, A.K., Moscow, 1837, 3½ oz. **£275-£325** *PWC*

A Fabergé circular two-handled caviar bowl, with cover and stand, gilt interior, the stand 17.5 cm. diam., signed with Imperial warrant mark, Moscow, 1899-1908. **£1,500-2,000** *C*

An oval Dutch brandy bowl, in earlier style, 10¼ in. (26 cm.) wide, maker's mark indistinct, 1840, and a sifter spoon, London, 1885, 7 oz. 7 dwt. **£150-200** *SC*

A punch bowl, 10½ in. (26.7 cm.) diam., by George Fox, London, 1893, 1,654 gm. (53 oz. 4 dwt.). **£750-900** *S*

A circular silver-coloured metal tcharka, the handle set with a rouble coin of Empress Elizabeth I, dated 1755, with gilt interior, 10.8 cm. long, maker's mark Cyrillic P.F., St. Petersburg 1908-17. **£200-300** *C*

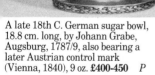

A presentation bowl, chased with scroll cartouches, one inscribed, 14 in. (35.5 cm.) diam., by E. Barnard & Sons, London, 1899, 4,016 gm. (129 oz. 3 dwt.). **£2,250-3,000** *S*

A late 18th C. German sugar bowl, 18.8 cm. long, by Johann Grabe, Augsburg, 1787/9, also bearing a later Austrian control mark (Vienna, 1840), 9 oz. **£400-450** *P*

A punch bowl, the wavy rim interrupted by masks, spreading base, 10¼ in. (26 cm.) diam., by Charles Stuart Harris, London, 1894, 1,236 gm. (39 oz. 15 dwt.). **£650-800** *S*

A hand raised Britannia standard stemmed punch bowl, of Queen Anne design, by Wm. Hutton & Sons Ltd., London 1906, Britannia High Standard, 44 oz. **£500-600** *WHL*

A circular parcel-gilt tcharka, with pellet border, 8.8 cm. long, maker's mark BOY (Postnikova No. 733), Moscow, 1704. **£700-900** *C*

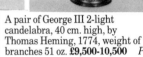

A pair of George III 2-light candelabra, 40 cm. high, by Thomas Heming, 1774, weight of branches 51 oz. **£9,500-10,500**   *P*

A covered sugar bowl, 16.8 cm. high, by Marthinus Lourens Smith, maker's mark (Cape), c. 1790, 366 gm. **£1,400-1,800**   *S*

An early Victorian 4-light candelabrum, 49 cm. high (19¼ in.), marked on base, branches and sconce, Joseph & John Angell, London, 1837, 2,528 gm. (81 oz. 6 dwt.). **£1,200-1,500**   *S*

A 5-light candelabrum, 23 in. high (58.2 cm.), the base and branches, Matthew Boulton, Birmingham, 1816, the remainder Robert Garrard, London, 1845, 5,868 gm. (188 oz. 14 dwt.). **£2,250-3,000**   *S*

A candelabrum is unlikely to sell for more than a quarter of the price of a pair of candelabra of same design, dimensions, date, etc.

A Victorian 10-light candelabrum, one branch broken, various mounts to the base missing, 38 in. high (96.5 cm.), by J. S. Hunt, 1845, 470 oz. **£5,500-6,500**   *C*

A pair of George III 3-light candelabra, 16¼ in. (41.2 cm.) high, by J. Wakelin and W. Taylor, 1786, 77 oz. **£4,500-5,500**   *C*

A Victorian centrepiece, 24 in. high (61 cm.), by Mortimer & Hunt, London, 1840, 5,349 gm. (172 oz.). **£2,000-2,500**   *S*

A pair of George III cast twin-branch candelabra, in the French style, 46 cm. high, 29 cm. span, by Thomas Henning, 1766, 145.5 oz. **£8,000-9,000** *P*

A pair of 3-branch candelabra, 19 in., by H.E. & Co., the branches Sheffield 1896, the bases London 1897. **£1,250-1,750**   *DWB*

Candelabra bases are often loaded from late 18th C. onwards. It is therefore difficult to make comparisons by weight.

For silver boxes, snuff boxes, vinaigrettes, etc., see the 'Boxes' section which follows Silver Plate.

A Victorian 3-light candelabrum and mirror plateau, 19 in. high (48 cm.), Cartwright & Woodward, Birmingham 1861, the candelabrum with P.O.D.R. mark for 2nd February 1861, 3,699 gm. (118 oz. 19 dwt.), excluding plateau. **£2,000-3,000**   *S*

A pair of Austrian 5-light candelabra, 22½ in. high (57 cm.), maker's mark of Max Gedlitzka for Josef B. Gedlitzka & Sohne, Vienna, c. 1895, 4,198 gm. (135 oz.). **£2,500-3,500**   *S*

A pair of Austrian 7-light candelabra, 27 in. high (68.5 cm.), by Schiffer, Vienna, 1858, 230 oz. **£2,500-3,500**   *C*

A rather clumsy design will achieve a lower price per ounce than something well balanced.

An Edwardian 5-light candelabrum, 52.5 cm. high, maker's mark JAF, Glasgow, 1902. **£700-900**   *CEd*

A pair of Danish 4-light candelabra, 22 in. high (56 cm.), Anton Michelsen, Copenhagen, 1885, 4,570 gm. (146 oz. 19 dwt.). **£1,800-£2,500** *S*

(l. & r.) A pair of 19th C. Portuguese 3-light candelabra, 43.5 cm. high, maker's mark IM (script), Oporto, c. 1840, 106.5 oz. **£1,000-1,200**

(c.) A Portuguese rose water dish or charger, profusely embossed with eagles and peacocks amidst foliage, 46.5 cm. diam., maker's mark Lara (script), Oporto, c. 1840, 37.5 oz. **£650-750** *P*

A pair of Dutch silver gilt 3-light candelabra, 26¼ in. (66 cm.) high, by Frans Simons, The Hague, 1800, weight of branches 144 oz. **£6,000-£7,000** *C*

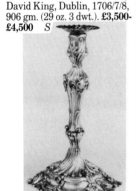

A pair of Queen Anne table candlesticks, 19.7 cm. high (7¾ in.), marked on bases and sconces, David King, Dublin, 1706/7/8, 906 gm. (29 oz. 3 dwt.). **£3,500-£4,500** *S*

A pair of George I octagonal candlesticks, 6½ in. high (17.2 cm.), by Joseph Clare, 1719, 18 oz. **£3,500-4,500** *S*

A pair of Polish silver candelabra, 54 cm. high, signed by Malcz, Warsaw, c. 1850. **£1,000-1,500** *C*

A pair of Queen Anne candlesticks, engraved with a coat-of-arms and a later monogram within baroque cartouches, 10 in. high (25.5 cm.), by John Barnard I, 1705, 29 oz. **£2,500-3,500** *C*

A pair of George III large candlesticks, 12 in. high (30.5 cm.), by L. P. and S. Courtauld II, 1778, 81 oz. **£5,500-6,500** *C*

A set of 4 George II table candlesticks, 34.5 cm. high (13½ in.), marked on bases and 2 nozzles, Elizabeth Godfrey, London, 1756/9, 3,365 gm. (108 oz. 4 dwt.). **£4,000-5,000** *S*

A pair of George II silver gilt table candlesticks, 9¾ in. high, by Ernest Sieber, London, 1747, 49 oz. **£3,000-£4,500** *SS*

A pair of George II candlesticks, 8¾ in. high (22.2 cm.), by James Warren, Dublin, c. 1755, 41 oz. **£1,500-2,000** *C*

A set of 4 George III table candlesticks, 9⅞ in. high, marked on bases and nozzles, Daniel Holy & Co. Sheffield, 1794 (loaded). **£1,200-1,600** *SS*

Two George III table candlesticks, 10 in. high (25.5 cm.), Ebenezer Coker, London, 1760/70, 1,139 gm. (36 oz. 13 dwt.). **£900-1,200** *S*

Even though 2 candlesticks look to be a pair in every respect if the date differs, the price will be 30% less than a straight pair.

A pair of George III silver neo-classical style candlesticks, 12⅝ in. high, maker's mark I.P. & Co. (John Parsons & Co.), Sheffield 1789, having later plated flambeaux finials. **£900-1,300** *GC*

A set of 4 George III candlesticks, engraved with the Royal Arms of George III, the nozzles with the Royal crest, Garter motto and Crown, 10½ in. high (26.7 cm.), by Eliza Godfrey, 1761, 94 oz. **£11,000-£13,000** *C*

A set of 4 George III silver candlesticks, 12¾ in. high, London 1773, maker's mark I.C. (John Carter II), one sconce differing with maker's mark I.P.E.W. (John Parker and Edward Wakelin), and once sconce later, London, 1861, maker's mark SW. **£1,500-2,200** *GC*

Four George IV table candlesticks, 11½ in. high (29 cm.), John & Thomas Settle, Sheffield, 1824 (loaded). **£1,500-2,000** *SC*

A set of 4 George IV candlesticks, 26.8 cm. high, by J. Staniforth & Co., Sheffield 1825 (loaded). **£1,000-£1,500** *L*

A pair of George III table candlesticks, 11½ in. high (29 cm.), John Carter, London, 1769 (loaded). **£900-1,300** *S*

A pair of Victorian candlesticks, 33.5 cm., maker's mark CB, 1892 and 1893 (loaded). **£350-450** *L*

A heavy set of 12 table candlesticks, in late 17th C. taste, 5¾ in. high (14.7 cm.), Britannia standard, Jones & Son, London, 1931, 11,259 gm. (362 oz.). **£4,000-4,500** *S*

A set of 4 George IV candlesticks, 12½ in. high (31.8 cm.), by John Fenton & Co. Sheffield, 1828, 2 converted for electricity and with plated bases. **£1,400-1,800** *C*

A George II silver taperstick, 4¼ in. high (11 cm.), by Humphrey Payne, London 1736, 2½ oz. **£400-500** *LBP*

A George II taperstick, 5⅜ in. high, Simon Jouet, London, 1753, 4 oz. 12 dwt. **£200-300** *SS*

A William III taperstick, 3¾ in. high, John Laughton Junior, London, 1700, 108 gm. (3 oz. 10 dwt.). **£1,750-2,000** *S*

A George III taperstick, 6 in. high (15 cm.), Robert Sharp, London, 1790, 194 gm. (6 oz. 5 dwt.). **£550-£650** *S*

A George III taperstick, 5¾ in. high (14.5 cm.), marked on base and nozzle, Nicholas Dumee, London, 1776, 125 gm. (4 oz. 1 dwt.). **£700-£800** *S*

A George III ship's chamberstick, with detachable circular cylindrical half stem, part missing, the underpart with striker, 18 cm. high, by Ebenezer Coker, 1768, also punched with a contemporary Patent Office mark, 14 oz. **£300-£400** *P*

Apparently the loose construction allows the chamberstick to adjust to the movement of a ship at sea.

A French silver-gilt and rock crystal chamber candlestick, 4½ in. (11.5 cm.) diam., unmarked, c. 1845. **£500-800** *S*

A figure candlestick, 8½ in. (21.5 cm.) wide, imported by Berthold Muller, London, 1911, 30 oz. 3 dwt. **£400-500** *SC*

A George III taperstick, by John Emes, London 1801. **£200-300** *WW*

A Victorian desk candlestick, 6¼ in. (16 cm.) high, by E. & J. Barnard, London, 1858, 13 oz. 10 dwt. **£800-1,000** *SC*

A set of 4 Italian table candlesticks, 6¾-7¼ in. (17.2-18.3 cm.) high, silver-coloured metal, stamped 'U. Bellini/Firenze', mid 20th C., 3,323 gm. (67 oz. 8 dwt.). **£900-£1,100** *S*

A George II snuffers stand, 20.8 cm., maker's mark probably struck and worn, 1742, 13.4 oz. **£400-500** *L*

A George II snuffers tray, 7¾ in. (19.5 cm.) long, by John Cafe, London, 1754, 267 gm. (8 oz. 12 dwt.). **£350-400** *S*

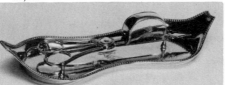

A pair of George III candle snuffers, London, 1787, maker's mark 'W B' probably William Bayley, and a snuffer tray, London 1781, length 9 in. (20 cm.). 8 oz. **£350-450** *LBP*

A Queen Anne snuffers stand and a pair of snuffers, by Matthew Cooper, 1704, gross 11 oz. 18 dwt. **£7,000-8,000** *C*

An early George III snuffers tray, 7½ in. (19 cm.) wide, by Elizabeth Cooke, London, 1764, 10 oz. **£350-£450** *SC*

A George III snuffers tray, 7½ in. (19 cm.) wide, by John Berthellot, London, 1765, 269 gm. (8 oz. 13 dwt.). **£350-450** *S*

A George I plain vase-shaped caster, 6⅞ in. (17.4 cm.) high, by Pierre Platel, 1714, 8 oz. 15 dwt. **£2,500-3,500** *C*

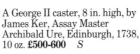

A Queen Anne baluster sugar dredger, 21 cm. high, by Charles Adam, 1708, 8.5 oz. **£750-900** *P*

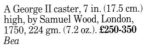

A George II caster, 7 in. (17.5 cm.) high, by Samuel Wood, London, 1750, 224 gm. (7.2 oz.). **£250-350** *Bea*

A fine George II caster, 8¼ in. (20.9 cm.) high, by Paul de Lamerie, 1732, the cover with lion passant, 17 oz. 13 dwt. **£11,000-£13,000** *C*

A George II caster, 8 in. high, by James Ker, Assay Master Archibald Ure, Edinburgh, 1738, 10 oz. **£500-600** *S*

(l.) A George III caster, by Peter, Ann and William Bateman, London, 1804. **£175-225**

(c.) A George II caster, by John Delmester, London, 1760. **£225-275**

(r.) A George III caster, by George Smith and Thomas Hayter, London, 1797. **£125-175** *FHF*

An unusual George III ovoid caster, 5 in. (12.5 cm.) high, marked on base and cover, by Emes & Barnard, London, 1808, 189 gm. (6 oz. 2 dwt.). **£450-575** *S*

A Danish caster, 6¾ in. (17.2 cm.) high, by Peder Pederson Ringsted of Faaborg, maker's mark only, c. 1715, 8 oz. **£2,000-2,500** *C*

A Victorian silver caster, 5½ in. high, maker's mark E.F. over H.T., London, 1889, 3.5 oz. **£70-100** *TW*

A George III silver-gilt epergne, with 4 cut glass bowls with silver-gilt vine tendril rims, one glass broken and one missing, 15½ in. (39.3 cm.) high, maker's mark WV IL possibly for W. Vere and J. Lutwyche, 1766, weighable silver 137 oz. **£10,000-12,000** *C*

A George IV circular mirror plateau, 11¼ in. (28.6 cm.) diam., by Philip Rundell, 1823, 31 oz. **£850-1,100** *C*

A Victorian sugar caster, 9 in. (22.5 cm.) high, by J. Wakley and F. C. Wheeler, London 1900, 342 gm. (10.9 oz.). **£200-300** *Bea*

A George III epergne, 13¾ in. (35 cm.) high, fully marked, by Thomas Pitts, London, 1773, 3,399 gm. (109 oz. 6 dwt.). **£8,000-£9,000** *S*

A William IV epergne and matching mirror plateau, 17¾ in. (45 cm.), maker's mark of Matthew Boulton Jnr., for M. Boulton & Plate Co., and obliterated marks of the Soho Plate Co., successors, Birmingham, 1834, 8,535 gm. (274 oz. 9 dwt.); the mirror plateau, 17½ in. (44.5 cm.) diam., by E. E. J. & W. Barnard for Edward Barnard & Sons, London, 1831 (4 cut-glass dishes). **£5,000-6,000** *S*

A table centrepiece, 13 in., by John S. Hunt, London, 1856, 83 oz. **£1,500-1,800** *Bon*

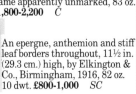

A Victorian centrepiece, with openwork frame, defective, with circular glass dish cut with a lozenge design, 17 in. (43.1 cm.) high, by J. S. Hunt, 1855, the dish-frame apparently unmarked, 83 oz. **£1,800-2,200** *C*

An epergne, anthemion and stiff leaf borders throughout, 11½ in. (29.3 cm.) high, by Elkington & Co., Birmingham, 1916, 82 oz. 10 dwt. **£800-1,000** *SC*

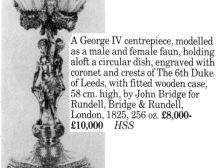

A George IV centrepiece, modelled as a male and female faun, holding aloft a circular dish, engraved with coronet and crests of The 6th Duke of Leeds, with fitted wooden case, 58 cm. high, by John Bridge for Rundell, Bridge & Rundell, London, 1825, 256 oz. **£8,000-£10,000** *HSS*

A fine George I plain octagonal coffee-pot, 9¾ in. (24.8 cm.) by Francis Plymley, 1715, gross 26 oz. **£10,000-13,000** *C*

The octagonal form is perhaps the most popular of all the plain designs. It is indicative of fine quality because of additional silver needed to withstand the stress at all the angles.

A George II plain tapering cylindrical coffee-pot, 9¼ in. (23.5 cm.) long, by James Manners, 1735, gross 28 oz. **£4,200-4,800** *C*

An attractive armorial can add considerably to the price of a piece in fine condition.

A George II plain tapering cylindrical chocolate-pot, 9 in. (22.9 cm.) high, maker's mark partly overstruck by date-letter but probably that of Samuel Walker, Dublin, 1736, gross 32 oz. **£2,500-£3,000** *C*

A mid 18th C. Irish baluster coffee-pot, 11 in. (28 cm.) high, marked on body and lid, by William Townsend, Dublin, c. 1755, 1,104 gm. (35 oz. 10 dwt.), all in. **£1,400-1,800** *S*

A George II coffee-pot, with later handle, 10¼ in. (26.5 cm.) high, by William Cripps, London, 1747, 1,026 gm. (33 oz.) all in. **£1,100-£1,300** *S*

A George III baluster coffee-pot, later initialled 'JEB', 10½ in. high, marked on body and cover, maker's mark rubbed, London, 1765, 28 oz. 16 dwt. **£900-1,100** *SS*

Lack of contemporary engraved crest or armorials may indicate something has been erased. Hence price would be lower.

(l.) A George III pear-shaped coffee-pot, 11¼ in. (28.6 cm.) high, maker's mark probably GG for George Gray, 1792, gross 31 oz. **£1,200-1,400**

(r.) A George III plain pear-shaped coffee-pot, engraved later with a crest, 11⅛ in. (28.2 cm.) high, by Samuel White, 1766, gross 28 oz. **£1,500-1,800** *C*

A George III baluster coffee-pot, 9¾ in. high, marked on body and cover, maker's mark rubbed, London, 1763, 23 oz. 18 dwt. all in. **£800-1,000** *SS*

A George II coffee-pot, 23 cm. high, by Fuller White, 1756, 19.5 oz. **£1,800-2,200** *P*

A George II baluster coffee-pot, with gadroon borders, 10¾ in. (27.2 cm.) high, marked on body and lid, by Whipham & Wright, London, 1759, 929 gm. (29 oz. 18 dwt.) all in. **£2,200-2,600** *S*

The gadroon bordered coffee-pot is the most sought after of all the mid 18th C. pots and commands a consequently higher price.

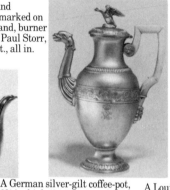

A George III baluster coffee-pot, 10½ in. high, by Walter Brind, 1773, 22 oz. gross. **£1,100-1,300** *N*

A George III coffee-pot, 11¾ in. (30 cm.) high, maker's mark W.F. or F.M., not traced, London, 1766, 924 gm. **£1,500-2,000** *Bea*

A Flemish baluster chocolate pot 32.5 cm. high, maker's mark P.C crowned, Ghent, 1758, 1200 gm., all in. **£2,250-2,750** *S*

A George III coffee jug and lampstand, 11 in. high, marked on base and cover, 1808, stand, burner and burner cover, 1809, Paul Storr, all London, 48 oz. 12 dwt., all in. **£3,000-4,000** *SS*

A Victorian pear-shaped coffee-pot, 7⅜ in. (18.7 cm.), by Mortimer and Hunt, 1841, gross 18 oz. 9 dwt. **£400-500** *C*

A German silver-gilt coffee-pot, 9¾ in. high (24.7 cm.), maker's mark H.C.W. in script, town mark crossed swords, c. 1795, 21 oz. 15 dwt. (675 gm.), all in. **£1,500-1,800** *S*

A Louis XV plain pear-shaped coffee-pot, 10¼ in. high (26 cm.), by Bertin Merger, Paris, 1728, with the charge and décharge marks of Jacques Cottin and Louis Gervais, gross 33 oz. **£5,000-6,000** *C*

The monogram is possibly that of Friedrich Wilhelm II, King of Prussia (1786-97).

A George IV baluster coffee-pot, 9¼ in. high, marked on body and cover, maker's mark I W, London, 1822, the handle Hayne & Cater, 28 oz. 12 dwt., all in. **£400-500** *SS*

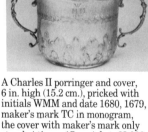

An Elizabeth I Communion cup, 6 in. high (15.3 cm.), maker's mark a stag's head, 1571, 6 oz. 8 dwt. **£2,000-2,500** *C*

A Charles II baluster porringer, pricked with the initials 'S/SS' and the date 1675, 3¼ in. high (8 cm.), T. Hutchinson, Great Yarmouth, 192 gm. (6 oz. 4 dwt.). **£1,600-2,000** *S*

A Charles II porringer and cover, 6 in. high (15.2 cm.), pricked with initials WMM and date 1680, 1679, maker's mark TC in monogram, the cover with maker's mark only struck 4 times, 17 oz. 4 dwt. **£2,000-3,000** *C*

Apart from a spoon, probably the most reasonably priced piece of Elizabethan silver available because practically every Parish Church ordered a new chalice at this time and a large number have survived.

Rare provincial pieces have an unpredictable demand dependent upon the number of collectors looking for a particular piece at any one time.

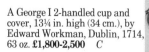

A George I 2-handled cup and cover, 13¼ in. high (34 cm.), by Edward Workman, Dublin, 1714, 63 oz. **£1,800-2,500** *C*

A James II porringer, 2¾ in. high (7 cm.), maker's mark DG and 2 fleur-de-lys, London, 1686, 132 gm. (4 oz. 5 dwt.). **£1,800-2,200** *S*

A Charles II cagework cup and cover, the cylindrical silver-gilt body with reeded borders, 7¼ in. high (18.5 cm.), maker's mark only Rc in a dotted circle, London, c. 1680, 965 gm. (31 oz. 3 dwt.). **£4,000-6,000** *S*

In May 1984, a particularly fine example of a cagework cup, the property of the Duke of Northumberland, sold for £28,600 at Sotheby's, Bond Street, underlining fine price for fine item from noted collection.

A George I chalice and paten, 8⅞ in. high (22.5 cm.), by Edward Workman, the paten without maker's mark, both Dublin, 1719, 709 gm. (22 oz. 16 dwt.). **£700-800** *S*

A George I 2-handled cup and cover, engraved later with a coat-of-arms and a crest, 12 in. high (30.5 cm.), by John Edwards, 1724, 84 oz. **£2,500-3,500** *C*

Value Points:

- A later coat-of-arms detracts from value.
- Strapwork is an indication of heavier than the average which adds to value.

A pair of George II 2-handled cups and covers, engraved with the Royal Crown, garter and motto, 38 cm. high, maker John Hugh Le Sage, London, 1744, 230 oz. **£10,000-15,000** *HSS*

Either a Royal christening gift or Ambassadorial silver. The Royal Provenance can quite easily double demand if the object is of note.

A George II cup and cover, 31 cm. high, by Gabriel Sleath, 1734, 62 oz. **£1,200-1,400** *P*

A pair of George III Irish 2-handled cups and covers, 37 cm. high, by Thomas Jones, Dublin, 1779, also stamped with the retailer's mark 'A. Fleming', 127.5 oz. **£3,000-3,500** *P*

A George III cup and cover, engraved with 3 saddled race-horses, names and dates, 14½ in. (36.9 cm.) high, by William Stroud, 1802, 75 oz. **£1,600-1,800** *C*

Even a small amount of good quality engraving can enhance value.

A George IV wine goblet, with gilt interior, 7⅝ in. high, by John Bridge, London, 1823, 14 oz. 16 dwt. **£300-400** *SS*

A Victorian presentation cup and cover, the design attributed to G. A. Carter, with gilt interior, 15¼ in. (38.6 cm.) high, by John Hunt & Robert Roskell 2,010 gm. **£1,100-1,300** *S*

With lacquered, oak box.

A George III silver-gilt race cup, 'Doncaster Races 1818', 38 cm. wide over handles, maker Benjamin Smith II, London, 1817, 136 oz. **£3,500-4,500** *HSS*

A George III bell-shaped goblet, engraved with the Prince of Wales feathers above the emblem of the Bath Harmonic Society, 6⅛ in. (15.5 cm.) high, by William Bennett, London, 1808, 216 gm. (8 oz. 8 dwt.). **£450-550** *S*

A George IV large silver-gilt trophy vase, height overall 30 cm., diam. of body 32 cm., by Paul Storr, 1821, 194 oz. **£6,000-6,500** *P*

A George IV race cup and cover, 'The Northallerton Races 1835', 39 cm. high, makers Rebecca Emes and Edward Barnard I, London, 1825, 82 oz. **£1,800-2,000** *HSS*

A presentation 2-handled cup, with contemporary inscription, 9½ in. high, by D. & C. Houle, London, 1862, 33 oz. **£350-400** *WW*

A pair of Victorian vase-shaped wine goblets, 5¾ in. high, fully marked, maker's mark JCS, London, 1865, 27 oz. 14 dwt. **£700-£900** *SS*

A Victorian silver-gilt cup and cover, in early 17th C. German taste, with a contemporary Bohemian faceted ruby glass beaker-shaped body, 13¼ in. (33.8 cm.) high, by Charles Fox, London, 1839. **£1,500-1,800** *S*

A pair of vases, 32 cm. high, by Carrington & Co., 1908, 160 oz. **£1,800-2,200** *L*

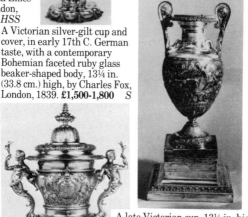

A silver-gilt 2-handled cup and cover, 24 in. (60.9 cm.) high, by Sebastian Garrard, 1905, 215 oz. **£4,000-4,500** *C*

A late Victorian cup, 13¼ in. high, by Hunt & Roskell, London, 1897/8, 48 oz. **£600-800** *DWB*

A large Victorian cup and cover, the formal-bordered pedestal base applied with the figures of Romulus and Remus, lacquered, 25½ in. (65 cm.) high, by John Hunt & Robert Roskell for Hunt & Roskell, London, 1875, stamped: 'Hunt & Roskell, late Storr & Mortimer 6848', 10,458 gm. (336 oz. 5 dwt.). **£5,500-6,500** *S*

A Spanish silver-gilt chalice, chased and enamelled in blue and white with the Instruments of the Passion, 8¼ in. (21 cm.) high, unmarked, probably early 16th C., gross 19 oz. 11 dwt. **£2,000-2,500** *C*

A Victorian silver-gilt presentation cup and cover and a shaped circular salver, 19½ in. (50 cm.) high, stamped: 390/E; the salver with pearl finish, 18¾ in. (47.4 cm.) diam., stamped: 141/Z, J., E., W. & J. Barnard for Edward Barnard & Sons, London, 1873, 6,915 gm. (222 oz. 7 dwt.). **£3,000-3,500** *S*

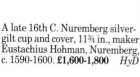

A late 16th C. Nuremberg silver-gilt cup and cover, 11¾ in., maker Eustachius Hohman, Nuremberg, c. 1590-1600. **£1,600-1,800** *HyD*

A Spanish silver-gilt ciborium and cover, with plain liner, 15 in. (38.1 cm.) high, unmarked, c. 1600, 49 oz. **£2,000-2,500** *C*

A Victorian yachting trophy, chased and engraved with the arms of the Corporation of Cowes and a portrait bust of Queen Victoria, 17 in. (43.5 cm.) high, marked on body and cover, W. & J. Barnard, London, 1887, 3,414 gm. (109 oz. 16 dwt.). **£1,400-1,800** *S*

A pair of Dutch chestnut vases and covers, 35 cm., by Hendrik Smidts, Amsterdam 1807, and with the retailer's mark of H. Diemond-Smith, 62 oz. **£1,300-1,600** *L*

A Flemish silver-gilt chalice, the underside inscribed PH. A. Quercu Renovavit et Auxit 1619, replaced bowl, 9 in. (23 cm.), 16th C., with later restorations, with silver-gilt spoon, in old case covered in red silk. **£600-800** *S*

A German silver-gilt standing cup, 16.4 cm. high, marked on bowl and foot, maker's mark AB conjoined, Augsburg, c. 1630, the underside dated 1632, 152 gm. **£1,000-1,300** *S*

A silver-gilt Akelei goblet, 18 cm. high, maker's mark Cyrillic A.G., Moscow, c. 1750. **£250-300** *C*

A German vase, 15½ in. (39.4 cm.), silver-coloured metal, c. 1895, engraved 'Made in Paris 1765', post-1893, French import marked, 2,169 gm. (69 oz. 15 dwt.). **£1,000-£1,300** *S*

(Left to Right)
1. An Elizabeth I silver-gilt baluster top spoon, 6¾ in. (17 cm.) long, marked on stem and bowl, maker's mark a bird's claw, London, 1560, 52 gm. (1 oz. 14 dwt.). **£700-900**

2. A Charles II Puritan spoon, the terminal pricked with the initials S.T., badly repaired, maker's mark I.I a mullet below, London, 1665. **£180-250**

3. An Apostle spoon, marked on bowl and stem, by Thomas Dare Sn., Taunton, c. 1632, dated 1632. **£600-700**

4. A pair of seal top spoons, with gilt knopped terminals, dated 1664, struck in the bowl and 3 times on the stem with maker's mark only TM conjoined, Provincial, c. 1664. **£800-1,000**

5. A Trefid spoon, with rat tail bowl, by Edward Mangy, Hull, c. 1670, 46 gm. (1 oz. 10 dwt.). **£600-£700** *S*

A Continental cup and cover, 15½ in. (39.4 cm.) high, late 19th C.; and a cup and cover of similar form, 15 in. (38.1 cm.) high, late 19th C., 39 oz. **£800-£1,000** *C*

(Left to Right)
1. A William III ascribed Provincial lace-back trefid spoon, 8¼ in. (21 cm.) long, the back of the stem punched thrice with the maker's initials RS, an anchor between, for Richard Sweet of Chard, West Country, c. 1700. **£350-400**

2. A pair of Charles II lace-back trefid spoons, of good gauge, 7½ in. (19 cm.) long, by John Smith, London, 1677. **£350-400**

3. A good James I seal-top spoon, 6¾ in. (17 cm.) long, maker's mark an anchor in a shaped shield, London, 1617. **£450-550**

4. A James I seal-top spoon, 6½ in. (16.5 cm.) long, by John Saunders, London, 1618. **£350-400**

5. A good Charles I Provincial-East Anglian (?) Apostle spoon — St. Thomas, the tapering hexagonal stem engraved on the back ST. Tho:, 6¼ in. (16 cm.) long, probably East Anglian (Norfolk or Suffolk), c. 1645. **£500-600**

6. A Charles I seal-top spoon, 7 in. (18 cm.) long, by Edward Hole, London, 1634. **£400-500** *P*

Two William III silver dognose teaspoons, 4¼ in., both marked with Britannia standard and one with the maker's mark of John Ladyman. **£150-200** *PWC*

A Charles II trefid basting spoon, the terminal reverse engraved with the initials 'DS', by Samuel Pantaine, Cork, c. 1680, 119 gm. (3 oz. 17 dwt.). **£1,500-2,000** *S*

A good Charles I seal-top spoon, 16.8 cm., by William Cary, probably 1638. **£400-450** *L*

A good Commonwealth Puritan spoon, 17.4 cm., by Jeremy Johnson, 1659. **£450-500** *L*

617

An important service of table ware, with husk and shell pattern handles, London, 1932, by Mappin & Webb, contained in mahogany bow-fronted chest, 35 in. wide, the service comprises 387 items, weighable items total 460 oz. **£6,500-7,500** *A*

A 67-piece canteen of silver cutlery, by James Dixon, Sheffield, 1937, 90 oz. excluding stainless steel knives. **£850-950** *BA*

(*l.*) A Russian parcel gilt and niello serving spoon, 18.9 cm., 1899-1901, silver coloured metal. **£100-130**

(*r.*) A set of 6 Russian parcel gilt and niello spoons, each 14.5 cm., Moscow 1908-17, 84 zolotniki, silver coloured metal. **£225-275** *L*

The Company of Morozov was founded in the Gostinniy Dvor in St. Petersburg in 1849 by Ivan Yevdokimovich Morozov. The business was principally mercantile, a house for the sale of goods made by other goldsmiths. The firm continued in existence until 1917 and was a purveyor to the Court.

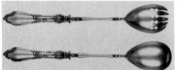

A pair of silver salad servers, 11⅞ in. (30 cm.), by Fabergé, maker's mark under Imperial warrant, Moscow, 1899-1908. **£500-£600** *S*

A fine composite silver gilt and niello table service, comprising: 12 dinner forks, 12 knives, 12 spoons, 12 dessert forks, 12 knives, 12 dessert spoons and 11 teaspoons, maker's marks Cyrillic M. Ch. possibly for M. Chulkov and P. Ya., Assay master I, Runov and others, Vologda, 1833, 1839, 1840, in a fitted case. **£2,200-2,600** *C*

A 2-handled circular dish, 6⅞ in. diam. (17.5 cm.), maker's mark RH only, c. 1660, 6 oz. 16 dwts. **£1,200-£1,500** *C*

A 6-place setting of Victorian 'Louis Philippe Pattern' cutlery, comprising: 6 tablespoons, 6 dinner forks, 6 dessert forks, 6 dessertspoons, by George Adam, 1864, 62 oz. **£500-700** *MN*

Minus Point:
• Sets for 6, when a slightly unusual pattern and therefore difficult to match, sometimes tend to sell for low prices.

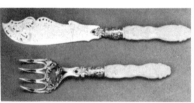

A pair of Victorian fish servers, by Hilliard and Thomason, Birmingham, 1856. **£250-350** *Bea*

Six George III plain circular dinner plates, with gadrooned borders, 9¾ in. diam. (25 cm.), by Robert Sharp, 1791, 110 oz. **£2,250-2,500** *C*

A pair of George III silver gilt serving dishes, 10 in. diam. (25 cm.), by Benjamin Smith, probably for Rundell, Bridge & Rundell, London, 1807, the undersides engraved: 'EA./FS', 55 oz. 7 dwt. (1721 gm.). **£5,000-£6,000** *S*

The arms are those of Ernest Augustus (1771-1851), fifth son of George III, created 1st Duke of Cumberland, later King of Hanover. He married, 1815, Frederica Sophia, daughter of the Grand Duke of Mecklenburg-Strelitz.

Twelve Regency Coburg pattern dessert spoons and 12 forks, by Paul Storr, 1818, 50 oz. **£2,600-£3,000** *C*

A Queen Anne circular strawberry dish, with repaired split, 8¾ in. diam. (22.2 cm.), maker's mark only partly visible but presumably that of David King, Dublin, 1710, 12 oz. 15 dwt. **£2,250-2,500** *C*

A George I dish, 7¼ in. diam. (18.5 cm.), by Thomas Walker, Dublin, 1715, 258 gm. (8 oz. 6 dwt.). **£1,400-1,600** *S*

A pair of George III silver gilt dishes, the raised centres inset with reliefs, probably cast from 17th C. originals, 16½ in. diam. (42 cm.), Britannia standard, Edward Cornelius Farrell, London, 1816, stamped: 'Lewis silversmith to HRH the Duke of York St. James's St London', 2,757 gm. (88 oz. 13 dwt.). **£2,750-3,000** *S*

A pair of George III dishes, 13 in. diam. (33 cm.), engraved later on the reverse with an inscription, 1774, maker's mark obliterated, 72 oz. **£1,400-1,600** *C*

These dishes originally formed part of a service presented to the Empress Elizabeth of Russia by the Governors of the province of Tulla around 1770. The service was sold by the Soviet government around 1934, at which time the maker's mark was obliterated.

A set of 6 Regency soup plates, with gadrooned, shell and foliage borders, 10½ in. diam. (26.7 cm.), by Paul Storr, 1811, 160 oz. **£4,500-£5,000** *C*

A Victorian meat dish, 19⅜ in. long (49.3 cm.), by J. S. Hunt, 1844, also stamped 'HUNT & ROSKELL LATE STORR MORTIMER AND HUNT', with traces of engraved cyphers, 68 oz. **£1,200-1,400** *C*

A pair of Victorian parcel gilt dessert stands, 8 in. diam. (20.5 cm.), Charles & George Fox, London, 1858, 33 oz. 18 dwt. **£700-£1,000** *SC*

A shell dessert dish, 12¼ in. across (31 cm.), by Richard Comyns, London, 1934, 57 oz. 19 dwt. **£1,750-2,000** *SC*

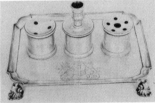

A George II ink stand, engraved with the arms of the 4th Duke of Leeds, maker Edward Faline, London 1740, 52 oz. **£7,000-9,000** *HSS*

A George II ink stand, engraved with the arms of the 4th Earl of Holdernesse, 28 cm. wide, maker George Methuen, London 1751, 45 oz. **£9,000-11,000** *HSS*

A silver fruit tazza, 11½ in. across, by Atkin Brothers, Sheffield 1937, 21.5 oz. **£225-275** *TW*

A George III ink stand, edged with gadrooning, engraved with the coronet and crest of the 4th Duke of Leeds, makers Charles Aldridge and Henry Green, London 1773, stand only marked, 31 oz. **£1,800-£2,200** *HSS*

A pair of silver bon-bon dishes, 7 in. diam., by Walker and Hall, Sheffield 1937, 17 oz. **£275-325** *TW*

An early Victorian ink stand, 26 cm. wide, maker's mark possibly for J and J Aldous, London, 1838, weight of silver 21 oz. **£500-700** *HSS*

A Victorian inkwell, in the form of a Roman oil lamp, 5¼ in. long (13.5 cm.), marked on base and lid, Robb & Whittet, Edinburgh, 1850, 136 gm. (4 oz. 8 dwt.). **£130-160** *S*

A Regency ink stand, 9 in. long (22.8 cm.), by Matthew Boulton, Birmingham, 1810, 21 oz. **£1,800-£2,200** *C*

A George III ink stand, the body in 2 parts and with an inset pounce-pot and inkwell, engraved with the monogram of Mary, the late Princess Royal 27 cm. wide by 8 cm. high, by John Parker I and Edward Wakelin, 1771, 60 oz. **£2,000-3,000** *P*

A Victorian shell-shaped ink stand, by Benjamin Smith II, 1838, 14 oz. 10 dwt. **£1,200-1,500**   *C*

A Victorian cast naturalistic ink stand, the youth with a hat at his feet reveals a wax box, 9.5 in., by H. Mason, Birmingham, 1859. **£275-350**   *WW*

A Victorian presentation silver ink stand, 11½ in. wide, makers Chas. T. Fox and George Fox, fully hallmarked for London 1857 and 1861, 33½ oz. **£700-900**   *PWC*

A Victorian ink stand, formed as a parrot on a perch, 8½ in. high (21.6 cm.), by J. C. Edgington, 1854, 17 oz. gross. **£1,000-1,200**   *C*

(*l.*) A George III ogee shaped cream jug, crested, 4 in. high (10 cm.), London, 1778, 3½ oz. **£80-120**

(*c.*) A George II cream jug, 3¼ in. high (9 cm.), hallmark indistinct but probably London 1755, 3¾ oz. **£80-120**

(*r.*) A Victorian pear-shaped cream jug, with gilt interior, 4¾ in. high (12 cm.), London 1850, 6 oz. **£80-£120**   *LBP*

A Victorian ink stand, 9½ in. wide (24.2 cm.), by Messrs. Barnard Bros., London, 1881, 24 oz. 7 dwt. of weighable silver. **£650-750**   *SC*

A late Victorian ink stand, in the Georgian style, 27 cm. wide, London, 1898, 32 oz. of weighable silver. **£500-650**   *HSS*

A George I-style cream jug, gilt interior, 10 cm. high overall, 19th C., 4 oz. **£700-800**   *P*

A fully marked example by David Willaume, London, 1719, 4½ in. high, 7 oz. 12 dwt., was sold by Sotheby's, in May 1984, for £9,350.

A George II baluster cream jug, 3¼ in. high, by George Greenhill Jones, London, 1738, 2 oz. 16 dwt. **£350-450**   *SS*

A George III vase-shaped jug, 12½ in. high (31.8 cm.), by John Scofield, 1781, 23 oz. gross. **£1,800-£2,200**   *C*

A George III ewer, 32.5 cm. high, by John Scofield, 1785, 26.75 oz. **£1,000-1,300**   *P*

Cartouche and crest later engraved.

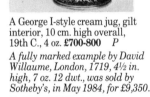

A George III cream jug, 4.5 in., maker Benjamin Bickerton, 1776. **£140-180**   *WW*

A George II beer jug, 8¼ in. high (20.7 cm.), maker's mark only partly visible, possibly that of William Townsend, Dublin, probably 1774, 32 oz. **£2,500-£3,000**   *C*

A Victorian racing trophy, formed as a large ewer, 24¾ in. high (62.8 cm.), by Robert Garrard, 1839, 144 oz. **£3,750-4,000**   *C*

A Victorian hot water jug, 12¼ in. high (30.8 cm.), fully marked Joseph & Albert Savory, for A.B. Savory & Sons, London, 1850, 942 gm. (30 oz. 6 dwt.), all in. **£650-£850** *S*

A Victorian Irish claret jug, 36.2 cm., maker's mark J.S., perhaps for John Smyth, Dublin 1877, 30 oz. **£900-1,100** *L*

A Victorian baluster ewer, 15¾ in. high, marked on body and lid, J. McKay, Edinburgh, 1846, loaded. **£850-950** *S*

An unusual Victorian ewer, 14¼ in. high (36.3 cm.), Richard Hennell, London, 1872, 26 oz. 9 dwt. **£700-800** *SC*

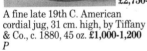

A cow creamer, 5¼ in. long (13.5 cm.), imported London, 1903, 5 oz. 8 dwt. **£300-325** *SC*

A hot water jug, on lamp stand, London, 1916, 46 oz. **£375-450** *SD*

A pair of late Victorian ewers, engraved with the Prince of Wales crest, 43.5 cm. high, by Elkington & Co., Birmingham, 1894, 110.5 oz. **£2,750-3,500** *P*

A fine late 19th C. American cordial jug, 31 cm. high, by Tiffany & Co., c. 1880, 45 oz. **£1,000-1,200** *P*

A French ewer and basin, height of ewer 11⅜ in. (29 cm.), length of basin 13 in. (33.1 cm.), maker's mark probably FAB, also bearing Turin town marks, Paris, 1819-38, 49 oz. **£1,900-2,100** *C*

A Spanish tapering cylindrical ewer, 6¼ in. high (15.8 cm.), maker's mark NOE, also struck with another mark, M, Cuenca, late 16th C., 22 oz. **£4,500-5,000** *C*

A Spanish parcel gilt ewer, old damage, 10⅝ in. high (27 cm.), unmarked late 16th C., 33 oz. **£4,800-5,200** *C*

A silver jug, partly painted with blue and green lacquer, 13.3 cm. high, signed with Imperial warrant mark of P. Ovchinnikov, Moscow, 1873. **£500-550** *C*

A Victorian model of a thoroughbred stallion, 20.2 cm. (8 in.) high, Robert Garrard, London, 1860, 1,205 gm. (38 oz. 15 dwt.). **£2,000-2,500** *S*

An equestrian statue of William III
as a Roman Emperor, 10¼ in. high
(26 cm.), struck on the tail with
sovereigns head and lion passant
only, c. 1835, 78 oz. 8 dwt. gross.
£800-900   *SC*

A Victorian ink stand, in the form
of a dragoon bandsman, 8½ in.
overall, London 1894, 18 oz. free.
£600-800   *CSK*

A figure of a hare, 12¼ in. (31 cm.)
high, imported London, 1902, 22 oz.
18 dwt. **£800-1,000**   *SC*

A German figure of a hare, 10⅝ in.
(27 cm.) high, B. Nieresheimer,
imported Berthold Muller, Chester,
1907, 18 oz. 19 dwt. **£600-800**   *SC*

An 'American Liberty' limited
edition silver and silver gilt chess
set, made to commemorate the
American War of Independence,
height of George III 4 in., stamped
with initials of the sculptor James
Goodbrand, each side in fitted wood
A parcel gilt nef, 15½ in. high, fully   case, London 1973, each inscribed
marked, Parsons of Tessier,   1837 of a limited edition of 2,000,
London, 1923, wood case, 50 oz.   290 oz. **£2,000-2,200**   *CSK*
18 dwt. **£2,000-2,500**   *SS*

A German silver gilt model of a
stork, with detachable head, 12 in.
high (30.4 cm.), 18 oz. 2 dwt.
(565 gm.). **£6,000-8,000**   *S*
*Provenance: Baron Carl Mayer de
Rothschild.*

A Continental paste set silver gilt
figure of a mediaeval knight,
11½ in. overall, import marks,
London 1924, 25 oz. **£750-900**
CSK

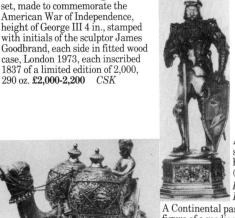

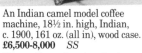

A Continental silver gilt and
enamel nef, with dark blue
enamelled sails, 34 cm. high by
28 cm. long, bearing English
import marks, 47 oz. **£1,400-1,800**
P

An Indian camel model coffee
machine, 18½ in. high, Indian,
c. 1900, 161 oz. (all in), wood case.
£6,500-8,000   *SS*

*The appliance functions in the
following manner: the neck is
lowered to cup delivery position by
turning the base plinth handle
which cranks the chain reins. Coffee
and milk are released from their
respective paniers by buttons located
at the back of the saddle and flow
into the body compartment just
above the neck. A small cord in
front of the saddle operates a valve
which dispenses the mixture, which
then issues from the camel's mouth.*

A Hungarian silver gilt model of a
peacock, with detachable head,
7¼ in. high (18.9 cm.), apparently
without a maker's mark, probably
by Munkacs, 1787, 13 oz. 11 dwt.
(424 gm.). **£1,500-2,000**   *S*

A George I small mug, 10.2 cm.,
Britannia standard, by Edward
Barnett, 1722. **£300-400**   *L*

A pair of French standing
cockerels, with detachable heads,
35 cm. high, Import Hallmark for
London 1896, 109 oz. **£1,500-2,000**   *CEd*

A Queen Anne cylindrical mug, 8.7 cm. (3½ in.) high, John Rand, London, 1703, 146 gm. (4 oz. 14 dwt.). **£300-400**   *S*

A pair of Queen Anne mugs, 9.7 cm. (3¾ in.) high, marked on bodies and handles, John Ruslen, London, 1713, 489 gm. (15 oz. 15 dwt.). **£4,000-5,000**   *S*

A George I mug, 9.1 cm. (3½ in.) high, Thomas Tearle, London, 1726, 214 gm. (6 oz. 18 dwt.). **£500-£600**   *S*

A set of 4 unusual George II plain tapering mugs, two 3⅞ in. (9.9 cm.) and two 3¼ in. (8.2 cm.) high, by Paul de Lamerie, 1746, 43 oz. **£22,000-25,000**   *C*

A pair of George II plain tapering cylindrical mugs, 3¾ in. (9.5 cm.) high, by Robert Calderwood, Dublin, c. 1740, 15 oz 4 dwt. **£1,400-1,600**   *G*

A George I tapered cylindrical mug, 10.8 cm. (4¼ in.) high, marked on body and handle, James Smith, London, 1718, 290 gm. (9 oz. 7 dwt.). **£550-650**   *S*

A George II baluster pint mug, by John Swift, London, 1747, 13.5 oz. **£500-600**   *WW*

A baluster mug, 12.5 cm. (5 in.) high, marked on base 3 times with maker's mark only IA crowned, the underside inscribed 'Isack De Lisle', Guernsey, c. 1750, 374 gm. (12 oz. 1 dwt.). **£700-800**   *S*

A George III baluster mug, 9 cm. (3½ in.) high, engraved with a later crest, Whipham & Wright, London, 1766, 239 gm. (7 oz. 14 dwt.). **£400-£500**   *S*

A George III baluster mug, 12.9 cm. by William Grundy, 1766, 13.5 oz. **£350-400**   *L*

A George III baluster mug, 9.3 cm. 3¾ in.) high, Richard Richardson, Chester, 1765, 200 gm. (6 oz. 9 dwt.). **£500-600**   *S*

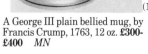

A George III plain bellied mug, by Francis Crump, 1763, 12 oz. **£300-£400**   *MN*

A George III mug, 11.5 cm. high, by Daniel Pontifex, 1809, 12.5 oz. **£250-300**   *P*

A George III tapered cylindrical mug, 14.5 cm. (5¾ in.) high, Isaac Cookson, Newcastle, 1772, 500 gm. (16 oz. 2 dwt.). **£600-700**   *S*

A George III tapered cylindrical mug, with gilt interior and glass bottom, 12 cm. (4¾ in.) high, John Emes, London, 1803. **£550-650**   *S*

A George III baluster christening mug, 9.5 cm. (3¾ in.) high, Rebecca Emes and Edward Barnard, London, 1819, 174 gm. (5.5 oz.). **£120-150** *Bea*

A Victorian christening mug, 9.6 cm., by Stephen Smith, also stamped The Goldsmiths Alliance Limited, Cornhill, London, 1872. **£90-120** *L*

A large child's mug, 4¼ in. (11 cm.) high, Carrington & Co., London, 1914 (excluding fitted case), 12 oz. **£240-280** *SC*

A William IV christening mug, 10 cm. high, by E.E.J. & W. Barnard, 6 oz. **£150-200** *P*

A set of 4 George III boat-shaped salt cellars, 14 cm. (5½ in.) wide, Henry Chawner, London, 1790, 17 oz. 8 dwt. **£800-900** *S*

A pair of George III salt cellars, maker William Pitts, London 1802, engraved with the crest of the 6th Duke of Leeds. 14 oz. **£500-600** *HSS*

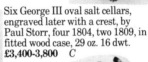

Six George III oval salt cellars, engraved later with a crest, by Paul Storr, four 1804, two 1809, in fitted wood case, 29 oz. 16 dwt. **£3,400-3,800** *C*

A set of 4 George III oblong salts, 12.5 cm. (5 in.) long, William Pitts, London, 1811, together with 4 salt spoons, crested, Thomas Willis and Jonathan Hayne, c. 1812, 714 gm. (22.9 oz.). **£550-650** *Bea*

A set of 4 William IV and early Victorian circular melon panelled salts, initialled with gilt interiors, one pair makers John Barber, George Cattle and William North 1831, the other 2 makers John Barber and William North 1838-40 (one with slight repair), 13 oz. **£450-550** *WW*

Four Victorian parcel gilt salt cellars, by J. S. Hunt, 1847, 16 oz. 8 dwt. **£1,400-1,600** *C*

A George V mustard pot with matching salt cellar, in 18th C. style, maker's mark H.A. and B., London, 1918, with contemporary spoons and blue glass liners, 572 gm., 18.3 oz. weight of silver. **£150-200** *Bea*

A pair of Victorian salt cellars, 6⅞ in. (17.5 cm.), 5¾ in. (14.6 cm.) high, by Robert Garrard, 1863 and 1865, also stamped R & S Garrard, Panton St. London, 28 oz. **£3,500-£4,000** *C*

A Victorian mustard pot, 3 in. high, fully marked, George Fox, with Old English pattern mustard spoon, George Adams, all London, 1867, 4 oz. 18 dwt. (liner). **£350-£400** *SS*

A George III drum mustard pot, 2¾ in. high, marked on base and cover, Edward Aldridge, London, 1764, 3 oz. 16 dwt. (liner). **£225-275** *SS*

A plain covered mustard pot, with fitted clear glass liner, by George Fox, London, 1861. **£140-180** *SS*

A pair of Victorian mustard pots, by Robert Garrard, 1851, 18 oz. 8 dwt. **£650-750** *C*

A George III preserve pot, 12.4 cm. (5 in.) high, Britannia standard, Edward Farrell, London, 1818, struck with the Paris import mark for 1819-39, 393 gm. (12 oz. 13 dwt.). **£700-800** *S*

The presence of a near-contemporary Paris import mark on this pot raises speculation as to a possible connection between Edward Farrell or more probably his chief retailer, Kensington Lewis, and French clients. This intriguing question is further complicated by the existence of a pair of silver gilt ewers of 1824, among Farrell's most astonishing achievements, bearing the arms of Charles X which for some reason were never presented to him but found their way instead into the Duke of York's collection.

A salt cellar, formed as a bull, 10 cm. high, by G & Co. Ltd., London, 1969, 10 oz. **£150-200** *CEd*

A pepperette, makers Charles & George Fox, London, 1860. **£90-120** *SS*

A Victorian pepper pot, 2¼ in. high (6 cm.), maker's mark E.C.B., London, 1868. **£100-130** *Bea*

A parcel gilt hexagonal trencher salt, 6.9 cm. high, maker's mark, also struck with a Dutch control mark, by Georg Wilhelm Fesenmayr, Augsburg, c. 1650, 166 gm. **£4,500-5,500** *S*

A rare Victorian pepper pot, in the form of Mr. Disraeli, 9 cm., by H. W. Dee of H. W. and L. Dee, 1878, and with design registration mark for 1st November 1878. **£1,000-2,000** *L*

Possibly the design for the pepper pot was inspired by satirical cartoons of Swain.

A Swedish silver oil and vinegar bottle stand, one bottle handle damaged, 12 oz. **£300-400** *PWC*

A rare Victorian novelty mustard pot, in the form of Mr. Punch, with blue glass liner, 10 cm., 1868 by Richard Hennell, and with design registration mark for 22nd February 1868, the spoon 1905, the original feather has probably been added to the replacement spoon. **£750-850** *L*

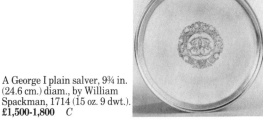

A Victorian soy frame, 1851, 24 oz. **£1,300-1,500** *C*

A George III cruet, of oval neo-classic form, the base engraved with the arms of the 6th Duke of Leeds, 30 cm. wide, maker Richard Cooke, London, 1800, bottles, London, 1877. **£1,500-1,800** *HSS*

Value Points:
● Larger than the normal.
● Engraved arms and provenance add to price.

A pair of silver shell-shaped salts, 3¼ in. (8.5 cm.), by Fabergé, maker's mark, workmaster J. Rappoport, St. Petersburg, late 19th C. **£750-850** *S*

Pieces from the Fabergé workshop will have a higher price than similar objects by other silversmiths.

A silver gilt mounted rock crystal standing salt, the mount and engraving on the bowl 19th C., 6¾ in. (17.2 cm.) high. **£1,800-2,200** *C*

A George I plain salver, 9¾ in. (24.6 cm.) diam., by William Spackman, 1714 (15 oz. 9 dwt.). **£1,500-1,800** *C*

A George I plain salver, 10¾ in. (27.4 cm.) diam., by Edward Cornock, 1726, 32 oz. **£3,500-4,000** *C*

A George II large shaped circular salver, 26¼ in. (66.6 cm.) diam., maker's mark probably JH in script overstriking another, 1759, 204 oz. **£4,750-5,250** *C*

In fitted wood case.

A George II salver, 11¼ in. diam., by John Tuite, London, 1739, 26 oz. 18 dwt. **£375-425** *SS*

A George II large plain shaped circular salver, 21⅝ in. (54.9 cm.) diam., by Robert Abercrombie, 1739, 129 oz. **£4,750-5,250** *C*

A George III tea pot stand, 18.6 cm., by Hester Bateman, 1788. **£225-275** *L*

A George III salver, 34.8 cm. diam., by John Swift or James Stamp, 1777, 39 oz. **£750-850** *L*

Jackson records that the mark is that of Swift, but Grimwade feels that Stamp seems a more likely attribution.

A George I salver, on 3 scroll bracket feet, with shaped border, 8½ in. (21.6 cm.) diam., by Paul de Lamerie, 1726, the border chased at a later date with rococo ornament, 13 oz. 4 dwt. **£2,750-£3,250** *C*

The later decoration at border and removal of arms from centre prevent this piece from selling for a true 'Lamerie' price. In good condition it would probably sell for between three and five times that shown.

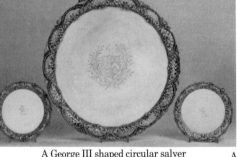

A George III shaped circular salver and 2 matching waiters, diam. of salver 16 in. (40.6 cm.), the salver and one waiter by F. Butty and N. Dumee, 1770, the other waiter by Samuel Courtauld, 1759, 95 oz. **£4,500-5,000** *C*

A large and heavy George III circular salver, 41.2 cm. diam., by Elizabeth Jones, 1787, 60 oz. **£650-£750** *L*

A George III salver, 9 in. diam., by Henry Chawner, London, 1793, 14 oz. **£275-325** *SS*

A George III salver, 14½ in. diam., maker's mark WB, London, 1796, 38½ oz. **£500-700** *PWC*

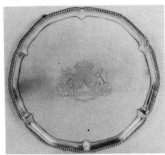

A George III salver, engraved with the Arms of the 5th Duke of Leeds, 41 cm. diam., by Robert Makepeace, London, 1795, 60 oz. 10 dwt. **£1,600-1,800** *HSS*

A pair of Regency salvers, 19 in. (48.3 cm.) diam., by William Bennett, 1817, 211 oz. **£4,500-£5,000** *C*

In fitted wood box.

A George III salver, 12 in. diam., by Story & Elliott, London, 1810, 27 oz. **£350-450**   *SS*

A Regency salver, 12½ in. (31.8 cm.) diam., by Paul Storr, 1818, 36 oz. **£3,500-4,000**   *C*
In fitted case.

A large and heavy William IV shaped circular salver, 24½ in. (57 cm.) diam., by Robert Garrard for R. & J. Garrard, London, 1832, 4,489 gm. (144 oz. 7 dwt.). **£2,000-£2,250**   *S*

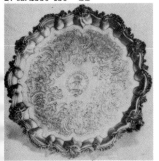

A William IV salver, 11 in. (28 cm.) diam., by W. K. Reid, London, 1836, 28 oz. **£350-450** *SC*

A Victorian shaped circular salver, 20⅜ in. diam., by Robert Garrard, London, 1845, 109 oz. 8 dwt. **£1,200-1,600**   *SS*

A salver, 15 in. diam., makers William Hutton & Sons, London, 1909, 47½ oz. **£275-325**   *PWC*
An inscription of no significance will detract from price.

A salver, 9¾ in. diam., maker's mark PFM, Sheffield, 1930, 18½ oz. **£140-200**   *PWC*

A salver, 12 in., maker's mark SB & S Ltd., Chester, 1930, 31½ oz. **£275-325**   *PWC*

An Indian Colonial waiter, 18 cm. diam., by George Gordon & Co., Madras, c. 1830, 12 oz. **£150-180** *CEd*

A pair of George I plain oval 2-handled double-lipped sauceboats, by Peter Archambo, 1724, 34 oz. **£10,000-13,000**   *C*
The earliest form of sauceboat and also the rarest.

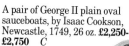

A pair of George II plain oval sauceboats, by Isaac Cookson, Newcastle, 1749, 26 oz. **£2,250-£2,750**   *C*

A pair of George II sauceboats, engraved with the Arms of the Duke of Leeds, and 3 subsidiary crests, 25 cm. wide, maker Peter Archambo I, London, 1736, 41 oz. **£4,500-5,500**   *HSS*

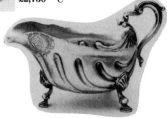

A George II oval sauceboat, 8½ in. (21.4 cm.), by Benjamin Gignac, London, 1746, 463 gm. (14 oz. 18 dwt.). **£800-1,200**   *S*

A pair of early George III oval sauceboats, maker William Sampel, London, 1763, 27 oz. **£1,000-1,400**   *WW*

A pair of George III plain oval sauceboats, by Thomas Johnston, Dublin, c. 1750, 36 oz. **£2,250-2,750**   *C*

A pair of George II oval sauceboats, 7¼ in. (18.5 cm.), by Robert Innes, London, 1750, 608 gm. (19 oz. 11 dwt.). **£1,200-1,400**   *S*

A pair of George III oval sauceboats, 7 in. (17.5 cm.) long, marks worn, c. 1750, 548 gm. (17.6 oz.). **£300-400**   *Bea*

Later decoration on the majority of items will halve or even quarter the price.

An American sauceboat, 20 cm. long, by Joseph Richardson (l) of Philadelphia, c. 1760, 12.5 oz. **£3,000-4,000**   *P*

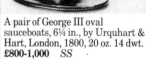

A pair of George III oval sauceboats, 6¼ in., by Urquhart & Hart, London, 1800, 20 oz. 14 dwt. **£800-1,000**   *SS*

A William IV sauceboat, 20 cm. long, 13 cm. high, by Paul Storr, 1836, 16.5 oz. **£1,300-1,600**   *P*

An unusual George IV silver gilt cast sauceboat, in the Renaissance manner, 23 cm. high overall, by Edward Cornelius Farrell, 1824, 30 oz. **£5,000-6,000**   *P*

Edward Farrell under the auspices of Kensington Lewis was probably the greatest exponent of copying and adapting the antique style. Now a much sought-after silversmith because of 'originality'.

A pair of George III oval sauceboats, 8¼ in., by William Burwash, London, 1812, 30 oz. 8 dwt. **£1,200-1,400**   *SS*

A pair of sauceboats, engraved with armorials, 8¾ in. (22.5 cm.), maker's mark obliterated, London, 1913, 1,088 gm. (35 oz.). **£600-700**   *S*

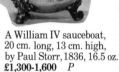

A pair of George III 2-handled boat-shaped sauce tureens, by J. Parker and E. Wakelin, 1767, 52 oz. **£4,000-4,500**   *C*

A pair of George III sauce tureens, covers lacking, 21.1 cm. across handles, possibly by Benjamin Mordecai or Benjamin Montigue, 1784, 26 oz. **£600-800**   *L*

Because the covers are missing price is a third.

A pair of George III sauce tureens and covers, by John Scofield, 1797, 37 oz. **£2,000-2,500**   *C*

A pair of George III 2-handled oval sauce tureens and covers, engraved slightly later with initial S, by D. Smith and R. Sharp, 1780, 41 oz. **£2,250-2,750**   *C*

A set of 4 George III sauce tureens and covers, each engraved on one side with contemporary armorials, 7¼ in. (18.3 cm.) wide, marked on bases and covers, by John Robins, London, 1802, 2,817 gm. (90 oz. 12 dwt.). **£4,500-5,500** *S*

A pair of sauce tureens, by William Foster, London, 1798, 43 oz. **£1,750-£2,250** *CEd*

A pair of George III 2-handled oval sauce tureens and covers, 7½ in. (19.1 cm.) long, by Thomas Robins, 1809, the finials by R. Smith, Dublin, c. 1810, 87 oz. **£3,000-3,750** *C*

A set of 4 George III silver gilt 2-handled shaped circular tureens, 9¼ in. (23.5 cm.) diam., by John Gwyn Holmes, 1805, 291 oz. **£5,500-6,000** *C*

A Charles II plain tapering cylindrical tankard, 6 in. (15.3 cm.) high, pricked on the handle with initials AMN, 1667, maker's mark WM a coronet above a mullet below, 21 oz. **£5,000-5,500** *C*

A Charles II plain tapering cylindrical tankard, the handle pricked with initials RES, old repairs to the cover and handle, 7¼ in. (18.4 cm.) high, maker's mark IA conjoined, 1683, 28 oz. **£2,000-2,500** *C*

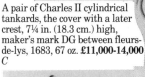

A Charles II plain tapering cylindrical tankard, 7⅛ in. (18.1 cm.) high, maker's mark M, 1672, 30 oz. **£3,500-4,500** *C*

A pair of Charles II cylindrical tankards, the cover with a later crest, 7¼ in. (18.3 cm.) high, maker's mark DG between fleurs-de-lys, 1683, 67 oz. **£11,000-14,000** *C*

A plain miniature tankard, on reeded rim foot, 2 in. (5 cm.) high, by David Clayton, c. 1700, maker's mark and lion's head erased only. **£700-900** *C*

A Queen Anne plain cylindrical flagon, 11¾ in. (29.8 cm.) high, by Benjamin Thraharne, 1704, 43 oz. **£1,750-2,250** *C*

A George II lidded tankard, contemporary marriage initials to handle 'B.T.M.', approx. 1⅔ pint capacity, by Edward Peacock, London, 1735, 21 oz. **£900-1,300** *MN*

A Queen Anne plain tapering cylindrical tankard, 7½ in. (19 cm.) high, by William Gamble, 1706, 30 oz. **£1,400-1,800** *C*

A George I tapered cylindrical tankard, 7¼ in. (18.5 cm.) high, marked on body, lid and handle, by Christopher Canner, London, 1718, 824 gm. (26 oz. 10 dwt.). **£1,250-£1,750** *S*

A William III cylindrical tankard, 8¼ in. (20.8 cm.) high, by Francis Singleton, 1700, 32 oz. **£3,200-4,000** *C*

A George III baluster lidded quart tankard, 8 in., by Thomas Chawner, London, 1786, 25 oz. **£800-1,200** *WW*

An unusual set of 3 George III tankards, gilt interiors, 6 and 4¾ in. (15 and 12 cm.) high, marked on bases and lids, by Sebastian & James Crespell, London, 1765, 1,928 gm. (62 oz.). **£2,500-3,000** *S*

Tankards simulating barrels are rarely found earlier than this date in silver.

A Victorian silver-mounted glass tankard, glass to cover cracked, 9 in. (22.8 cm.) high, by Elkington and Co., Birmingham, 1859. **£1,200-1,800** *C*

A George IV cylindrical tankard, 9½ in. (24.2 cm.) high, by Philip Rundell, 1820, 66 oz. **£4,000-5,000** *C*

The arms are those of Orme of Magdrum, co. Fyfe, impaling Bonsor of London and Polesden, co. Surrey.

A George III tankard, 7¾ in. high, marked on body and cover, Peter, Ann and William Bateman, London, 1804, 24 oz. 16 dwt. **£500-£700** *SS*

A heavy baluster tankard, 8¼ in. (20.5 cm.) high, marks erased, English, mid 18th C. with early 19th C. alterations, 1,461 gm. (47 oz.). **£500-700** *S*

A George IV tapering cylindrical tankard, 8 in. (20.3 cm.) high, by William Eaton, 1827, 62 oz. **£4,000-£5,000** *C*

A George III plain cylindrical tankard, in Scandinavian taste, engraved with a later crest and motto, 8 in. (20.3 cm.) high, by John Langlands, Newcastle, 1772, 26 oz. **£1,500-1,800** *C*

Silversmiths in Newcastle and York copied certain Scandinavian designs from the Restoration to c. 1800.

A tankard, by Robert Gordon, Madras, c. 1810. **£300-400** *CEd*

A late 19th C. Dutch silver-coloured metal tankard, 5¾ in., 8 oz. **£225-£325** *N*

A silver-mounted Japanese powder-blue porcelain tankard, gilding to the body worn, 9 in. (22.8 cm.) high, struck thrice with a mark IH, the porcelain Arita, c. 1700. **£1,000-1,200** *C*

A German silver gilt tankard, 6⅝ in. (17.4 cm.) high, maker's mark HR conjoined in a circle possibly for Hannss Reiff, Nuremberg, early 17th C., 10 oz. 15 dwt. **£2,500-3,500** *C*

A tapering cylindrical tankard, 27.4 cm. high, maker's mark, by Emidio Critien, Maltese, 1831, 1,530 gm. **£1,500-1,800** *S*

A miniature silver tankard, 5.8 cm. high, maker's initials of Grigory Serebryanikov, Moscow, 1751. £300-350 C

A silver tankard, 5¼ in. (13.4 cm.), maker's mark workmaster P.K., St. Petersburg, 1865, by Nicholls & Plinke. £700-1,000 S

A pair of George I plain octagonal tea caddies, the covers unmarked, by John Farnell, 1720, 12 oz. £2,000-2,500 C

A set of 3 early George II tea caddies, 4¾ in. (12 cm.) high, marked on bodies and 2 of the slide on covers, by James Smith I, London, 1730, 752 gm. (24 oz. 5 dwt.). £3,000-3,500 S

In unusual cut oak veneer case.

A set of 3 oblong tea caddies, each with sliding base, maker's mark of John Newton struck thrice and lion passant only, 30 oz. £1,200-1,500 C

Although the chasing suggests a date of about 1740, both the lion passant mark and Newton's own mark were changed in 1739 (cf. Grimwade, nos. 1544 and 1553).

A George II silver gilt rectangular tea caddy, by Edward Wakelin, 1747, 11 oz. 2 dwt. £1,750-2,250 C

A set of 3 George II oblong tea caddies, engraved with a crest, by Frederick Vonham, 1759, 25 oz. £1,400-1,800   C

A George III oblong tea caddy, after a model by Paul de Lamerie, with lead lining, by D. Smith and R. Sharp, 1762, gross 16 oz. 5 dwt. £2,250-2,750   C

A George III square tea caddy, 3⅞ in. (9.8 cm.) square, by J. Parker and E. Wakelin, 1769, 17 oz. 5 dwt. £1,500-1,800   C

A George II silver gilt rectangular tea caddy, or sugar box, by Edward Wakelin, 1747, 14 oz. 19 dwt. £2,750-3,250   C

A set of 3 George III rectangular tea caddies, in fitted silver-mounted shagreen case, by Pierre Gillois, 1768, 43 oz. £6,000-7,000   C

A George III square tea caddy, maker's mark SW probably for Samuel White, 1774, gross 11 oz. 19 dwt. £1,300-1,600   C

A George III oval tea caddy, by John Carter, 1776, 13 oz. 11 dwt. £1,300-1,600   C

A George III square tea caddy, the interior with lead lining, 4 in. (10.2 cm.) square, by W. and A. Lestourgeon, 1770, gross 18 oz. 17 dwt. £3,500-4,500   C

A George III oval tea caddy, maker's mark RH, London, 178? 11 oz. **£700-900**   *HGA*

A set of 3 George III tea caddies, in fitted South Indian ivory case, with silver handle cast and chased with scrolling foliage, maker's mark IP, 1774, 40 oz. **£5,500-6,500**   *C*

A George III oval tea caddy, maker's mark of Thomas Daniell overstriking another, possibly that of Robert Hennell, 1779, 12 oz. 7 dwt. **£1,000-1,300**   *C*

A set of 3 George III oval tea caddies, with bright cut borders, in fitted silver-mounted octagonal satinwood case, inlaid with oval panels of yew wood, maker's mark IP, 1777, 32 oz. **£4,500-5,500**   *C*

A George III tea caddy, 4½ in. high, marked on base and cover, by Robert Hennell, London, 1780, 16 oz. all in. **£800-1,200**   *SS*

A George III oval tea caddy, by William Plummer, 1783, 11 oz 6 dwt. **£1,500-2,000**   *C*

A William IV honey pot and cover, 7½ in., by Robert Garrard, London, 1836-37, 19 oz. **£350-500**   *HyD*

A George III silver tea caddy, maker Charles Aldridge, London, 1787, 13½ oz. **£750-1,000**   *PWC*

A George III oval 2-compartment tea caddy, 6½ in. (16.5 cm.) high, marked on base and lid, by John Emes, London, 1800, 426 gm. (13 oz. 14 dwt.), all in. **£700-1,000** *S*

A German rectangular tea caddy, on reeded sliding base, by Michel Stroht, Hamburg, dated 1789, town mark worn, mid 18th C., 6 oz. 10 dwt. **£700-1,000**   *C*

A George II Provincial plain bulle tea pot, by Joseph Collier, Exeter, 1731, 13.5 oz. **£750-1,250**   *P*

A Danish plain rectangular tea caddy, by Hendrich Reinicke, Copenhagen, 1710, Assay master Conrad Ludolf, 9 oz. 18 dwt. **£2,000-2,500**   *C*

A rectangular tea caddy, 13.4 cm. high, maker's mark, by Anthony Donker, Amsterdam, apparently 1700, 284 gm. **£700-1,000**   *S*

A George II tea pot later inscribed on the underside, 7 in. high, by James McKenzie, Assay Master Hugh Gordon, Edinburg 1755, 18 oz. 7 dwt. all in. **£1,500-1,85(** *S*

A George II bullet-shaped tea pot, maker's mark SB possibly for Samuel Blachford, Exeter, 1759, gross 19 oz. 2 dwt. **£2,750-3,250**　*C*

The petal motif on the spout is peculiar to Exeter and Plymouth silversmiths.

A George III tea pot and stand, 5 in. (12.7 cm.) high, marked on base, lid and stand, by Paul Storr, London, 1799, 556 gm. (17 oz. 18 dwt.), all in, excluding stand. **£1,200-1,400**　*S*

A George III tea pot and stand, 18 cm. high overall, by Hester Bateman, 1784, 18.5 oz. **£950-1,300**　*P*

A George II plain bullet-shaped tea pot, later ivory handle and finial, by Charles Martin, 1738, gross 15 oz. **£1,000-1,300**　*C*

An oval tea pot, 5¼ in. high, by Nathaniel Gillet, Aberdeen, c. 1790, NG; ABD; NG; NG; 20 oz. 4 dwt. all in. **£700-800**　*S*

A George III tea pot, by Robert and Samuel Hennell, London, 1806, 25.5 oz. **£350-450**　*WW*

A George III tea pot and stand, the oval stand with the same decoration and on 4 feet, 18 cm. high, by Alexander Field, 1799, 15 oz. **£450-600**　*P*

A Regency circular tea pot, by Paul Storr, 1811, gross 31 oz. **£2,000-£2,500**　*C*

A Regency circular tea pot, bearing traces of an engraved coat-of-arms, by Paul Storr, 1814, gross 26 oz. **£1,800-2,500**　*C*

A Regency circular tea pot, by Paul Storr, 1810, gross 35 oz. **£3,000-£3,500**　*C*

A George IV tea pot, makers R. Peppin, London, 1820, 18.5 oz. all in. **£250-350**　*WW*

A George IV oval tea pot, makers Rebecca Emes and Edward Barnard, London, 1825, 22.5 oz. all in. **£400-500**　*WW*

A crested melon fluted tea pot, by Paul Storr, stamped Storr & Mortimer 405, London, 1837, 27.5 oz. all in. **£1,000-1,300**　*WW*

A William IV silver tea pot, makers Joseph and John Angell, London, 1830, 25½ oz. **£250-350**　*PWC*

An early Victorian silver tea pot, 6⅝ in. high, maker's mark for Edward Barnard, Edward Barnard jnr., John Barnard, William Barnard, London, 1839, 26 oz. 10 dwt. **£300-400**　*GC*

An embossed and engraved silver tea pot, by Martin Hall & Co., Sheffield, 1856, 27 oz. **£300-400** *GM*

A George II tea kettle, stand and lamp, with draught-excluder, by Edward Wakelin, 1757, gross 160 oz. **£5,500-6,500** *C*

A George II plain inverted pear-shaped tea kettle, stand and lamp, by Thomas Heming, 1751, the stand and lamp unmarked, gross 39 oz. **£750-1,000** *C*

An 18th C. Dutch tea pot, 15 cm. high, by Obbe Ydema, Sneek, 1772, 11.75 oz. **£600-800** *P*

A George II 2-handled tea urn and cover, engraved later with a lozenge-of-arms, with plated internal fitment, 20¾ in. (52.7 cm.) high, by F. Butty and N. Dumee, 1767, gross 79 oz. **£1,250-1,750** *C*

A George IV compressed circular tea urn, 16¾ in. (42.5 cm.) high, fully marked, by E., E., J. & W. Barnard for Edward Barnard & Sons, London, 1828, 4,976 gm. (160 oz.). **£1,800-2,200** *S*

A George III tea urn, the body engraved at the back with a garlanded coat-of-arms, the base with spool-shaped section containing the heating iron, 19½ in. (49.5 cm.) high, marked on body and base and lid, by Charles Wright, London, 1779, 86 oz. all in, excluding heating iron. **£1,000-£1,500** *SC*

A Victorian tea kettle on stand, 13¼ in. (33.5 cm.) high, fully marked, by Joseph and John Angell, London, 1838, 1,744 gm. (56 oz.). **£700-1,000** *Bea*

A George III tea urn, engraved with the Arms of the 5th Duke of Leeds, the cover crested, complete with a cast-iron plug, 44.5 cm. high, maker Robert Sharp, London, 1792, gross 132 oz., excluding plug. **£1,500-2,000** *HSS*

A George III tea kettle, on lampstand, 38 cm. overall height, by Joseph Angell, 1817, the front hinge a later addition, with marks for 1858, 92 oz. **£1,800-2,200** *L*

A French tea urn, complete with detachable cover, lampstand and burner, silver-coloured metal, 19¾ in. (50 cm.) high, maker's mark P.G. & Cie above an anvil in a horizontal lozenge, 3,491 gm. (112 oz. 5 dwt.). **£1,500-2,000** *S*

A George III vase-shaped tea urn, engraved with a presentation inscription on one side and armorials on the other, 17¼ in. (43.5 cm.) high, by Henry Nutting, London, 1813, 3,943 gm. (126 oz. 16 dwt.) all in. **£1,500-2,000** *S*

A William IV campana-shaped 2-handled cup and cover, 16 in. (41 cm.) high, marked on body and cover, by Randall Cashell, Dublin, 1830, 3,389 gm. (109 oz.). **£1,400-£1,600** *S*

A George III oval tea pot and tea caddy, the tea caddy 1781, maker's mark worn but probably for A. Fogelberg and S. Gilbert; the tea pot c. 1781, date letter obliterated, maker's mark illegible, gross 27 oz. **£900-1,300** *C*

(*l.*) An early George III baluster chinoiserie decorated coffee pot, 11½ in., makers I.B. and W.B., London, 1764, 32.5 oz. all in. **£1,300-1,600**

(*r.*) A baluster hot milk jug, copied to match left-hand piece, 11½ in., maker R. Creighton, London, 1932, 28.5 oz. all in. **£400-500** *WW*

A George III miniature tea set, fully marked, by Edward Fernell, London, 1793, 363 gm. (11 oz. 14 dwt.) all in. **£3,750-4,500** *S*

A 3-piece crested and engraved silver tea set, by Thomas Wallis, London and George Fenwick, Edinburgh, c. 1810, 34 oz. **£550-750** *GM*

A George III 3-piece tea service with tea pot stand, 26.2 cm. across tea pot, 1804, the sugar bowl 1803, by John Emes, 37 oz. **£800-1,200** *L*

A George III tea and coffee service, by Thomas Robins, 1804, height of coffee pot 8 in. (20.3 cm.), by John Robins, 1805, gross 54 oz. **£1,750-£2,250** *C*

A George III tea pot and coffee pot en suite, 5¾ in. (14.7 cm.), and 9 in. (23 cm.) high respectively, marked on bases, covers and handles, by Urquhart & Hart, London, 1806-08, 48 oz. 9 dwt. all in. **£1,100-1,400** *SC*

A George III silver tea service, 54.7 oz. **£600-900** *DA*

A George III 4-piece tea and coffee service, William Burwash, London, 1813-14, together with a matching contemporary circular tea pot stand, 5¼ in. (13.5 cm.) diam., by William Brown, London, 1812, loaded, 2,295 gm. (73.7 oz.) all in, weighable. **£2,250-2,750** *Bea*

A George III 3-piece tea service, by A. & G. Burrows, 1815, 45 oz. **£600-£800** *N*

A matching 4-piece tea and coffee set, the tea pot and milk jug 1817, the sugar basin 1825, all William Elliott, the coffee pot Samuel Jackson, 1822, the tea pot and coffee pot handles and coffee pot finial John Figg,, c. 1840, 3,639 gm. (117 oz.) all in. **£3,250-4,000** *S*

A Regency tea service, by
G. McHattie, Edinburgh, 1816,
51 oz. gross. **£600-800**　*C*

A George IV tea urn and tea pot, by
Joseph Angell, London, 1827, and a
matching sugar bowl and cover,
probably Continental, 19th C.,
6,059 gm. (194 oz. 17 dwt.) all in.
£2,750-3,500　*S*

A George IV 3-piece tea service, by
Robert Gray & Son, Glasgow,
1820-21, 50 oz. **£600-800**　*CEd*

(*t.l.*) A George III water jug, marks
rubbed, maker probably G. and T.
Burrows, London, 1817, 25 oz. all
in. **£250-350**

(*t.r.*) A George III provincial
Scottish tea pot, maker's mark I.P.,
Canongate, Edinburgh, c. 1810,
23¼ oz. all in. **£900-1,200**

(*b.*) A George III 3-piece tea service,
the interiors gilded, marks rubbed,
possible maker Samuel Hennell,
London, 1816, 42 oz. all in. **£450-
£550**　*HSS*

A George IV 3-piece tea service, by
John Edward Terry, London, 1825,
1,708 gm. (54.9 oz.). **£550-650**
Bea

A George IV 3-piece tea service, by
Jonathan Hayne, London, 1827-29,
1,316 gm. (42.3 oz.). **£450-550**
Bea

A George III 4-piece silver tea and
coffee set, maker Thos. Watson,
Newcastle, 1809-10, 82¼ oz.
£1,250-1,750　*PWC*

A William IV coffee pot, by
Messrs. Barnard, 1834, 24.5 cm.,
30 oz. **£600-800**　*L*

A matching 4-piece tea and coffee
set, the tea and coffee pot by
Charles Fox, 1829-30, the basin
and jug by J. E. Terrey, 1822, all
London, 2,581 gm. (83 oz.) all in, in
fitted case with the trade card of
Salter, Widdowson & Tate, Strand,
in the cover, probably
contemporary. **£1,500-2,000**　*S*

A William IV 3-piece tea set, by
Richd. Hennell, London, 1831,
41 oz. **£550-650**　*A*

A William IV tea and coffee
service, some repairs to cream jug
and sugar basin, height of coffee
pot 11¼ in. (28.6 cm.), by Elder and
Co., Edinburgh, 1835, the tea pot
and coffee pot with the mark of
D.C. Rait as retailer, gross 99 oz.
£1,500-1,800　*C*

A good Victorian tea pot, by
Messrs. Barnard, 1839, 16.6 cm.,
27 oz. **£300-400**　*L*

A Victorian 3-piece melon pattern
tea set, J. & A. Savory, London,
1847, 42 oz. 5 dwt. all in. **£600-800**
SC

A Victorian silver cream jug,
maker Jas. Le Bass, Dublin, 1839,
11½ oz., and a Victorian plated tea
pot and sugar bowl to match,
makers Martin Hall & Co. **£200-
£300** *PWC*

A Victorian 4-piece tea and coffee
set, decorated in the manner of the
Ashburnham Dinner Service of
1836-37, John S. Hunt for Hunt &
Roskell, 1862, stamped '1847', the
coffee pot 1863, stamped '2134', all
stamped: 'Hunt & Roskell late
Storr & Mortimer', 2,421 gm.
(77 oz. 17 dwt.) all in. **£1,750-2,500**
S

A matched Victorian 4-piece tea
and coffee set, fully marked, the
kettle and stand, Martin, Hall &
Co., 1873, the tea and coffee pots,
John Angell, 1855, the basin,
maker's mark RD, 1852, all
London, 146 oz. 14 dwt. all in.
£2,250-3,000 *SS*

A Victorian 4-piece tea and coffee
service, by George Angel, London,
1852, 79 oz. **£1,400-2,000** *M*

A Victorian coffee pot and tea pot,
coffee pot 26.3 cm. high, by E. and
J. Barnard, 1856 and 1857, 44.5 oz.
£600-700 *L*

A Victorian 4-piece tea and coffee
service, E. J. and W. Barnard,
London, 1844, 2,493 gm. (80 oz.).
£1,750-2,250 *Bea*

A Victorian tea and coffee service,
with a plated shaped circular
salver, height of coffee pot 11½ in.
(29.2 cm.), diam. of salver 21½ in.
(54.6 cm.), by J. and J. Angell,
1847, gross 73 oz. **£1,850-2,350** *C*

An early Victorian Gothic 5-piece
tea and coffee service, maker's
mark S H over D C, London, 1852,
and a small tea pot, by Hyam
Hyams, London 1855, 95 oz. total
gross. **£2,000-3,000** *HSS*

A Victorian 4-piece baluster tea
and coffee set, fully marked, Joseph
Angell, London, 1854, 73 oz. 6 dwt.
all in. **£1,500-2,250** *SS*

A Victorian bachelor's 3-piece tea
set, maker's mark J.M. Dublin,
1870, 511 gm. (16 oz. 9 dwt.) all in.
£450-550   *S*

A Victorian 3-piece tea service,
each with a vacant quatrefoil
reserve, engraving removed, by
Thomas Smiley, 1879 and 1880, tea
pot 13.8 cm. high, 22 oz. all in.
£400-600   *L*

A Victorian 4-piece tea and coffee
set, fully marked, Martin, Hall &
Co., London, 1882, 2,603 gm. (84 oz.
14 dwt.) all in. **£1,250-1,750**   *S*

A silver tea service, London,
1902-06, 80 oz. **£600-800**   *CW*

A silver tea service, Sheffield, 1909,
67 oz. 14 dwt. gross. **£600-800**
DSH

A George V service,
W. Hutton & Sons
Ltd., Sheffield, 1911,
1,923 gm. **£600-800**
Bea

A tea set, the plain bodies applied
with a reeded girdle below everted
foliate shell and gadroon collars, by
Walker & Hall, Sheffield, 1938-39,
86 oz. 6 dwt. all n. **£700-1,000**   *SC*
In the manner of Paul Storr.

A Victorian tea service,
Birmingham, 1876, 51 oz. **£500-600**
CDC

A Martin, Hall and Co. silver
4-piece tea and coffee set, London,
1877-78, 70 oz. **£1,250-1,750**   *Bon*

A Victorian Adam-style tea and
coffee service, Sheffield, 1893,
48 oz. **£500-700**   *Re*

A silver tea service, Sheffield, 1903,
23 oz. **£200-300**   *CW*

An Edwardian silver tea set, by
Elkington & Co., Birmingham,
1903-05, No. 18847, 61¼ oz. all in.
£500-700   *O*

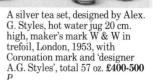

A silver tea set, designed by Alex.
G. Styles, hot water jug 20 cm.
high, maker's mark W & W in
trefoil, London, 1953, with
Coronation mark and 'designer
A.G. Styles', total 57 oz. **£400-500**
P

A 4-piece bullet-shaped tea service, by Crighton Brothers, London, 1938. **£600-800** *DWB*

The shape is of mid 18th C. Scottish origin, based on cannon balls occasionally referred to as skittle-ball shape.

A silver tea service, the tea pot 19.5 cm. long, maker's mark C.O. Moscow, 1888, and a tea strainer en suite, Moscow, late 19th C. **£400-500** *C*

A George III silver tray, 158 oz. **£3,750-4,500** *CW*

An American 5-piece tea set, by Reed & Barton, c. 1900, 101 oz. 7 dwt. all in. **£1,200-1,800** *SC*

A fine Queen Anne tray, on 4 bracket feet, 17 in. (43.1 cm.) long, by Simon Pantin, 1710, 57 oz. **£24,000-28,000** *C*

A George III tray, 20½ in. (52.1 cm.) long, by William Bennett, 1809, 81 oz. **£2,750-3,500** *C*

A Regency 2-handled shaped oval tray, 20¼ in. (51.4 cm.) long, by Paul Storr, 1818, engraved later with a crest, motto and inscription dated 1851, 110 oz. **£9,500-12,000** *C*

A Regency tea tray, 29 in., by Rebecca Emes and Edward Barnard, London, 1814, 128 oz. **£2,000-3,000** *WW*

A fine early George II soup tureen, cover and stand, height overall 34.5 cm., width of stand overall 48 cm., by Charles Kandler I, Britannia Standard, fully hallmarked, 1728, 215.5 oz. **£40,000-45,000** *P*

A George II oval soup tureen and cover, 16½ in. (43 cm.), overall, by George Wickes, London, fully marked on base and cover, 1741, 3,402 gm. (109 oz. 8 dwt.). **£17,500-£19,000** *S*

An early George III vegetable tureen, cover and liner, engraved with the Arms of The 4th Earl of Holdernesse and the D'Arcy motto, 41 cm. wide, by John Parker I. and Edward Wakelin, maker's marks only struck 3 times on base and once on cover, c. 1760, 134 oz. **£13,000-16,000** *HSS*

A George III plain oval 2-handled soup tureen and cover, 13½ in. (34.3 cm.) long, by J. Wakelin and R. Garrard, 1793, 85 oz. **£4,500-£5,500** *C*

A George III silver gilt 2-handled oval soup tureen and cover, 12½ in. (31.7 cm.) long, by Thomas Heming, 1776, with later plain liner, 108 oz. **£8,500-10,000** *C*

A Regency circular soup tureen and cover, engraved with a coat-of-arms and a crest, 12⅜ in. (31.5 cm.) diam., by Samuel Hennell, 1812, 178 oz. **£5,000-6,000** *C*

A 19th C. American soup tureen, 41 cm. long by 19 cm. high, by Frederick Marquand of New York, c. 1835, 91 oz. **£1,000-1,200** *P*

A George III oval soup tureen and cover, 19 in. (48.2 cm.), wide over handles, by Richard Sibley, London, marked on body, lid and liner, 1817-18, 5,600 gm. (180 oz.). **£6,000-6,500** *S*

A coursing trophy in the form of a tureen and cover, 43 cm. over handles, maker William Ker Reid, London 1833, 158 oz. (approximately). **£4,000-5,000** *HSS*

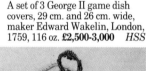

A set of 3 George II game dish covers, 29 cm. and 26 cm. wide, maker Edward Wakelin, London, 1759, 116 oz. **£2,500-3,000** *HSS*

A pair of George III game dish covers of oval form, 27 cm. wide, maker Andrew Fogelberg, London, 1773, 48 oz. **£2,250-2,750** *HSS*

A pair of George III oblong entree dishes and covers, 11¼ in. (28.5 cm.) wide, fully marked, Thomas Robins, London, 1810, 4,548 gm. (148 oz. 5 dwt.). **£2,500-3,000** *S*

Two George III entree dishes, with gadroon borders, by W. B., London, 1810 and 1811, 95 oz. **£1,250-1,750** *A*

A pair of George III entree dishes and covers, 29 cm. across, by Paul Storr, 1820, en suite with a pair of Old Sheffield plate liners and warmer stands, by Fenton Creswick, weight of entree dishes, 144 oz. **£5,500-7,000** *P*

A set of 4 William IV entree dishes, covers and handles, 27 cm. wide, by Joseph Hodgson, 1830, en suite, a set of 4 late period Old Sheffield plate warmers, overall height 23 cm., c. 1830, weighable silver 217 oz. **£3,000-3,750** *P*

A set of 4 George IV vegetable dishes and covers, 10½ in. (26.7 cm.) diam., by William Eaton, 1826, 226 oz. **£3,250-4,000** *C*

A pair of Danish circular vegetable dishes and covers, by F. C. V. Christensen, Copenhagen, 1872, 116 oz. **£1,300-1,600** *C*

A set of 4 William IV shaped oval entree dishes, covers and plated heater bases, 14 in. wide overall, marked on bases, covers, cover domes and finials, the heater bases struck with the crossed arrows mark, by Benjamin Smith, London, 1832, 215 oz. 10 dwt. **£7,500-8,500** *SS*

A George III argyle, 4½ in. (11.5 cm.) high, marked on base and lid, by Walter Brind, London, 1766, 332 gm. (10 oz. 14 dwt.) all in. **£900-1,200** *S*

A George III argyle, by J. E. Terry & Co., London, 1817. **£600-900** *FHF*

An early George II Chester brandy saucepan, 4.3 cm. high excluding handle, by Richard Richardson, Chester, 1728. **£500-600** *L*

A George IV large covered saucepan, 18 cm. high, by Emes and Barnard, 1822, 22.5 oz. **£600-£700** *P*

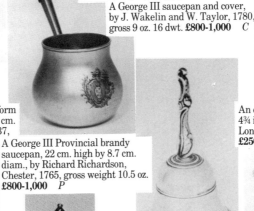

A George III saucepan and cover, by J. Wakelin and W. Taylor, 1780, gross 9 oz. 16 dwt. **£800-1,000** *C*

A Victorian wine ewer, in the form of a Pompeian jug or 'ascos', 23 cm. high overall, by Paul Storr, 1837, 32 oz. **£4,000-4,500** *P*

A George III Provincial brandy saucepan, 22 cm. high by 8.7 cm. diam., by Richard Richardson, Chester, 1765, gross weight 10.5 oz. **£800-1,000** *P*

An early Victorian invalid cup, 4¾ in. (12 cm.) high, by R. Hennell, London, 1837, 8 oz. 8 dwt. all in. **£250-350** *SC*

A George III dish ring, 8 in. (20.5 cm.) max. diam., maker's mark indistinct, by Joseph Jackson or John Laughlin, Dublin, 1789, 307 gm. (9 oz. 18 dwt.) (excluding later blue glass liner). **£1,300-1,500** *S*

A George III table bell, 10.5 cm. high, possible maker William Bayley, London, 1774, 5 oz. **£500-£800** *HSS*

A George III circular dish ring, maker's mark MB, Dublin, c. 1765, 14 oz. 8 dwt. **£1,500-1,800** *C*

A late Victorian replica of an Irish dish ring, 19.6 cm. diam., by George Nathan and Ridley Hayes, Chester, 1900, 12.8 oz. **£200-300** *L*

A George III cast hand bell, plain, with reeding, the baluster stem surmounted by bud terminal, by Thomas Daniel, 1776, 5.5 oz. **£500-£800** *P*

A Spanish table bell, with traces of gilding, repairs to handle, unmarked, 17th C., 9 oz. 14 dwt. **£450-600** *C*

A George II 3-handled vase and cover, the handles repaired, 8 in. (20.3 cm.) high, by Peter Taylor, 1751, 24 oz. **£350-500** *C*

An unusual set of 3 George II vases, 8 in. (20 cm.) and 6 in. (15.2 cm.) high, by Edward Wakelin, London, 1749, 50 oz. 8 dwt. **£2,200-2,500** *SC*

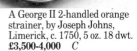

A George II 2-handled orange strainer, by Joseph Johns, Limerick, c. 1750, 5 oz. 18 dwt. **£3,500-4,000** *C*

A strawberry set, 8 in. (20.3 cm.) wide, by Martin Hall & Co., Sheffield, 1865, 16 oz. 11 dwt. of weighable silver. **£600-800**   *SC*

An Indian campaign service or compendium, contained in the original fitted case, 10.1 cm. height of beaker, by Hamilton and Co., c. 1860, 25 oz. of weighable silver. **£600-800**   *L*

A Queen Anne plain circular soap box, by Gabriel Sleath, 1711, the gilding to the interior later, 9 oz. 11 dwt. **£3,000-3,500**   *C*

A George III communion set, communion cup 7⅛ in. (18.1 cm.) high, flagon 11 in. (28 cm.) high, by Abraham Portal, 1763, 68 oz. **£2,500-3,000**   *C*

A pair of French silver gilt grape scissors, by Alexander Lefranc, Paris, 1819-38, 6 oz. 7 dwt. **£250-£300**   *C*

A silver Doncaster Corporation race common token, 1893. **£600-800** *HSS*

A rare and interesting William III badge of office, worn by the Town Waits (Musicians) of the Borough of Leicester, 15.7 cm. long by 13 cm. wide, maker's mark HC with 3 pellets, a mullet and 2 annulets, London, 1695, 4.75 oz. **£800-1,200**   *P*

A rare silver plaque, of oval convex form, engraved on the obverse with an allegory of the execution of King Charles I and on the reverse with the standing figure of King William III, 2¾ in. (7 cm.) long, English, c. 1698, in plain oval brass case. **£4,000-5,000**   *C*

Both its shape and convex form suggest that this plaque was originally intended to be the cover to a snuff box. It may never actually have been used as such, however, since its brass case appears to be approximately contemporary, and the condition of the engraving is exceptionally fine.

An unusual George III driving plate, the reign-rings formed as snakes and with horses' head, snake and fish-tail at the other angles, 12 in. (30.5 cm.) long, by W. Pitts and J. Preedy, 1792 and 1793, gross 53 oz. **£2,800-3,200**   *C*

A silver gilt book cover, 5⅔ in. (15 cm.) high, unmarked, German, second quarter 18th C. **£900-1,200** *S*

A lady's Victoria dressing table set, London, 1897, 11 oz. **£250-300** *CDC*

An unusual Victorian double letter clip, 8½ in. long, E.H.S., London, 1892. **£375-425**   *CSK*

An Imperial presentation silver cigarette case, set with a Nicholas II 25 Kopeck coin in gold mount, with sapphire set thumbpiece, in original red morocco case with applied Imperial eagle, 9.2 cm. long, maker's mark V T, St. Petersburg, late 19th C. **£650-750** *C*

A hanging paper clip, 4½ in. (11.5 cm.) overall, maker's mark SJ, London, 1893, 2 oz. 1 dwt. **£175-£225** *SC*

A George III silver gilt eye bath, 1⅝ in. wide, by Joseph Taconet, London, 1801, 5 dwt. **£750-850** *SS*

A German spherical pomander, covers lacking, 6.4 cm. high, unmarked, second quarter of 17th C., 80 gm. **£850-1,200** *S*

A silver-mounted ram's head table snuff-mull, with 4 chained implements including ivory hammer, rake, snuff-spoon and hare's paw, approx. 14¾ in. (37.5 cm.) wide, Edinburgh, 1872. **£1,300-1,600** *C*

A novelty scent flask, in the form of a parrot, with glass body, with realistically tooled silver feet and tail feathers, 3½ in. (9 cm.) high, by H. W. Curry, London, 1885. **£300-£400** *SC*

A Dutch silver shooting trophy, 4¾ in. (12 cm.) long, probably 17th C. **£500-600** *C*

A silver patent stamp applicator, 3⅛ in. high, maker's mark WH, London, 1902. **£120-160** *SS*

A Victorian novelty scent flask, in the form of an owl, 3¾ in. (9.5 cm.) high, by Charles & George Fox, London, 1846, 5 oz. 6 dwt. (all in, less bottle). **£550-650** *SC*

A Swedish parcel gilt silver pipe bowl, 4¾ in. (12 cm.) high, by Johan Wilhelm Ohlsson, Lidkoping, c. 1840, fitted with a contemporary turned wood stem, 23¾ in. (59 cm.) long. **£200-300** *S*

A German parcel gilt Torah shield, 24.8 cm. high, without a maker's mark, Hirshberg, second half 18th C., 415 gm. **£1,800-2,000** *S*

A pair of parcel gilt Torah finials, 31.5 cm. high, by J. Rimonim, Fürth, c. 1780, 840 gm. **£8,000-£10,000** *S*

An unusual Victorian stamping machine, with sprung mechanism and felt-covered roller, engraved 'Victoria de Bunsen, patent', the ivory handle engraved and painted with the motto and feathers of the Prince of Wales and monogram, in a fitted case, 9 in., by Sampson Mordan, London, 1884. **£1,600-£1,900** *CSK*

With a letter from the inventor to the Prince of Wales, later Edward VII, asking for his comments and opinions on her invention.

A Belgian censer, by Guillielmus Van Eesbeeck of Brussels, c. 1740, maker's mark only, 41 oz. **£850-950** *C*

An 18th C. wooden running footman's staff, with gilt metal rococo terminal, 65 in. (165 cm.) long. **£200-300** *L*

An unusual pair of silver lighters, by Dunhill, each with the Dunhill 'Unique' lighter mechanism, each 5.8 cm. high, one import marked London, 1928. **£250-300** *S*

A Sheffield plated 4-light candelabrum, 51.4 cm. **£500-600** *L*

A German parcel gilt and gilt metal reliquary, 4⅞ in. (12.4 cm.) high, unmarked, probably second half 17th C., gross 2 oz. 12 dwt. **£600-700** *C*

A set of 4 Sheffield plate cluster column candlesticks, 12½ in., c. 1775. **£200-300** *WW*

A silver gilt mounted whip, engraved 'Thorn, Maker, 185, Regent St. London', 45¼ in. (115 cm.) long, by William Forrester, London, 1840. **£2,000-£2,500** *S*

A set of 4 plated table candlesticks, 13¾ in. (35 cm.) high. **£350-400** *Bea*

A Sheffield plate centrepiece, 23 in. (58.5 cm.) high, by Walker, Knowles & Co., Sheffield, 1830. **£650-700** *S*

A pair of early electroplated candelabra, 24 in. **£400-500** *MN*

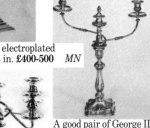

A good pair of George III 3-light candelabra, with Old Sheffield plate branches, 50 cm. high overall, branches 43 cm. wide, by Roberts, Clayton & Emary, Sheffield, 1809, loaded. **£1,300-1,500** *P*

A pair of Sheffield plate 5-light candelabra. **£200-250** *CDC*

An old Sheffield plate candelabrum, 27 in. high, mark 'Double Sun', Soho factory, by Matthew Boulton. **£300-400** *CDC*

A pair of electroplated 3-light candelabra, 22¼ in. (57 cm.) high. **£500-600** *Bea*

A 3-light candelabrum centrepiece, 22 in. (55.8 cm.) high, c. 1840. **£1,100-1,300** *C*

A pair of 3-light candelabra, each 59.9 cm. high, maker's mark of Elkington, Mason and Co. **£650-£750** *L*

A pair of Sheffield plate chambersticks and snuffers, 13 cm. high, c. 1815. **£150-250**

An electroplated table centrepiece, 15 in. high overall, c. 1860. **£250-£300** *Bon*

(c.) A Sheffield plate chamberstick, 12 cm. high, c. 1815. **£100-130** *P*

A Victorian 3-piece table centrepiece, to an 1869 registered design, on a mirror plateau in silver plate and gilt with figures of Britannia, lion, unicorn and the globe, complete with original box. **£500-600** *Bro*

An Edwardian Elkington's Corinthian oil lamp, 37 in. high overall, Birmingham, 1902. **£500-£600** *Re*

An electroplated epergne, 18½ in. (47 cm.) high, English, c. 1860. **£150-250** *S*

An electroplate 6-bottle cruet, Birmingham, 1872. **£100-150** *TW*

An unusual ink stand, 9 in. (23 cm.) diam., stamped 'Published as the Act directs by Henry Elkington, February 20th, 1851'. **£250-300** *SC*

A George III old Sheffield plate Argyle, c. 1810. **£200-250** *FHF*

A William Hutton & Sons Ltd. electroplated cruet, inspired by a design by Christopher Dresser, 16.75 cm. high, maker's mark, c. 1900. **£80-120** *S*

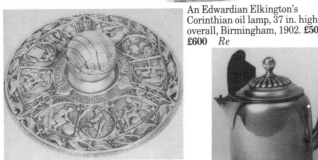

An electroplated Britannia metal 4-piece tea and coffee service, late 19th C. **£80-120** *TW*

A Sheffield plate Argyle, 13 cm. high, c. 1780. **£275-350** *P*

A George III old Sheffield plate Argyle, with later caned handle, c. 1790. **£120-150** *FHF*

An electroplated 4-piece tea set, Elkington & Co., 1850's, also struck with the PODR mark for the 30th June, 1855. **£250-350** *SC*

A Sheffield plated tea urn, complete with internal fittings, 48 cm. high overall. **£400-450** *L*

A Victorian plated kettle, on stand. **£250-300** *HGA*

A Victorian electroplated jug, 8½ in. (21.5 cm.) high, Martin Hall and Co. **£120-150** *Bea*

A pair of Regency cut glass sauce tureens, with Sheffield plate lids and bases. **£100-120**   *WW*

Three Sheffield plate graduated oval meat dish covers, 12 in. (30.5 cm.), 16 in. (40.5 cm.), and 20 in. (51 cm.) long. **£180-240** *Bea*

An electroplated 2-handled oval soup tureen and cover, 14 in. (36 cm.) over handles, Walker and Hall. **£260-300**   *Bea*

A pair of Sheffield plate circular breakfast dishes, and hot water stands. **£300-350**   *WW*

An electroplated soup tureen and cover, 12 in. (30.5 cm.) diam., T. Bradbury & Son, of Sheffield, c. 1855. **£700-800**   *S*

A Sheffield plate soup tureen and cover, 31 cm. high overall, c. 1820. **£900-1,100**   *P*

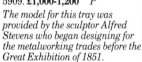

A Sheffield plate tray, 57 cm. long, c. 1820. **£400-500**   *P*

An early period cheese dish, 23 cm. wide, c. 1790. **£200-250**   *P*

An electroplated tea tray, 27 in. (68.7 cm.) wide over handles, by Thomas Bradbury & Sons, Sheffield, c. 1855, also stamped 5909. **£1,000-1,200**   *P*

The model for this tray was provided by the sculptor Alfred Stevens who began designing for the metalworking trades before the Great Exhibition of 1851.

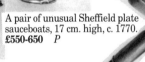

A pair of unusual Sheffield plate sauceboats, 17 cm. high, c. 1770. **£550-650**   *P*

A Sheffield plate salver, 25½ in. (65 cm.) diam., by T. & J. Creswick, c. 1830. **£550-650**   *S*

A patent brass cork extractor, 'The Rapid Cork Drawer', 22½ in. max., by Loftus of London. **£120-150** *HyD*

An unusual silver plate desk set, fitted with 3 carved and painted emu's eggs, 14½ in. (37 cm.) wide, probably Australian, glazed case, late 19th C. **£1,600-1,800**   *SC*

An unusual George III cork screw, with spirally fluted central shank and with plain wing nut, engraved twice with the same crest, 6¼ in., probably John Reilly, London, 1816. **£1,700-1,900**   *CSK*

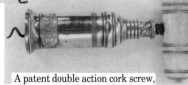

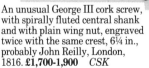

A plated novelty ink well, in the form of a watering can, containing integral well and small pen and pencil, 2¼ in. high, c. 1900. **£80-100** *SS*

A patent double action cork screw, 8½ in. extended, probably by Thomason, c. 1800. **£150-200** *HyD*

A double action brass cork screw, the central threaded shaft with open frame, Archimedean screw, probably Italian. **£100-140**   *BAC*

A Thomason 1902 patent cork screw, the brass barrel with patent tablet embossed with the lion and the unicorn and marked 'Dowler' & 'Patent', with remains of brush, Helix screw. **£100-130**   *BAC*

A German folding pocket cork screw, with a Helix screw. **£85-100** *BAC*

A ladies silver pocket roundlet or barrel-shape cork screw, 2¼ in. long, English, c 1800. **£100-130** *BAC*

A German pocket cork screw, the Archimedean screw marked 'Registered'. **£90-115**   *BAC*

A Farrow & Jackson's cork screw, with conventional wing nut. **£200-£230**   *BAC*

A Pullezi concertina cork screw, marked 'Heeley's Original Patent' and 'The Pullezi'. **£45-60**   *BAC*

Henry D. Armstrong of Maida Vale patented this design in 1902. It was manufactured by James Heeley.

A zig-zag cork screw, patented in Switzerland in 1919 by Jules Bart of France. Marked 'ZIG ZAG' and BTE S.G.D.G. **£45-50**   *BAC*

The cork screw is of the lazy tongs or concertina type but contains a spring mechamism.

A James Heeley's 'A1 Double Lever' cork screw, patented in 1888. **£30-£35**   *BAC*

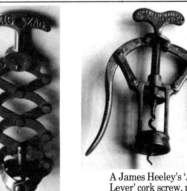

A bronzed concertina or lazy tongs cork screw. **£30-35**   *BAC*

One of the many inventions of Marshall Arthur Wier. The patent for this cork screw was taken out in 1884. An excellent working cork screw for the most stubborn corks.

A Colombus cork screw, manufactured in Germany, wooden handle with sprung shank and hinged with locking ring, this example marked 'original', centre worm. **£25-30**   *BAC*

A simple cork screw, with a turned wooden handle complete with brush and having the early form of ridged disc or flange following Henshall's patent. **£20-25**   *BAC*

A roundlet or barrel-shaped pocket screw, with grooved Helix screw. **£15-18** *BAC*

A cork screw, representative of an owl, similar to the Magic Lever Cork Drawer, marked 'BOJ'. **£15-£18** *BAC*

A simple cork screw, with an Archemedian screw, the handle incorporating an opener for bottles stopped with a glass marble following Hiram Codd's design of 1870. **£9-12** *BAC*

A simple cork screw, with a motif of Stokholm Town Hall, marked 'STOCKHOLM STADSHUSET'. **£13-16** *BAC*

A faceted round handled stirrup cork screw, with grooved tapered wire screw, 57 mm. long. **£7-10** *BAC*

A set of 4 George IV coasters, 16.5 cm. diam., by J. & T. Settle, Sheffield, 1816. **£1,000-1,500** *P*

A pair of Regency silver gilt wine coasters, marks partly worn, maker's mark on one illegible, by J. W. Story and W. Elliott, 1811. **£1,400-1,800** *C*

An open-framed female threaded lockable screw, probably by Perille. **£8-10** *BAC*

A pair of George III circular coasters, 5 in. (12.5 cm.) diam., by P. W. and W. Bateman, London, 1799. **£700-1,000** *Bea*

A pair of early Victorian wine coasters, 5¾ in. (14.5 cm.) diam., by Edward Farrell, London, 1837, also stamped 'C. Vaughan 39, Strand Fecit', loaded. **£1,400-1,800** *S*

A set of 4 George III wine coasters, maker John Harris III, London, 1787. **£3,000-4,000** *HSS*

A matched pair of George III coasters, 15.5 cm. diam., by Smith, Tate, Hoult & Tate, Sheffield, 1811-15. **£800-1,200** *P*

A pair of Regency coasters, with traces of gilding, by Paul Storr, 1815, also stamped 'Rundell Bridge Et Rundell Aurifices Regis Et Principis Walliae Regentis Britannias'. **£6,500-7,500** *C*

A wine coaster, 5¾ in., inset wood base with Tudor rose, by Omar Ramsden, London, 1935. **£400-600** *DWB*

This design of coaster is much heavier and of finer quality than the majority. It also lends itself to gilding and silver gilt objects are on the whole much more readily saleable. The maker's mark of Paul Storr allied with that of Rundell Bridge and Rundell at this date is indicative of quality and assuming good condition, a high price will be obtained.

A pair of electroplated Montieth bowls, 16 cm. high by 18 cm. diam., c. 1880. **£200-250** *P*

A silver campana shaped wine cooler of small size, with removable glass liner, 10½ in. high, maker Robinson, Edkins & Aston, Birmingham, 1833, 49½ oz. **£1,500-£1,800** *GSP*

A pair of plated wine coolers, first quarter 19th C. **£600-700**   *DWB*

The right hand cooler shows the oval silver inlet to take the engraved crest clearly. These silver inlays appear frequently on old Sheffield plate, without them the engraving would show the copper below.

A pair of Continental wine coolers, 11⅜ in. (28.9 cm.) high, London import marks for 1905, 206 oz. **£6,000-7,000**   *C*

A George III thread-edged wine funnel, 16.5 cm. high, by Solomon Hougham, 1804, 6 oz. **£250-350**   *P*

A wine syphon, of looped form, with shaped spigot, 15 in. (38 cm.), high overall, maker's mark only TH crowned, probably for Thomas Harache, c. 1750, 228 gm. (7 oz. 7 dwt.). **£2,000-2,300**   *S*

A Victorian champagne tap, apparently no maker's mark, Birmingham, 1875, case. **£250-300** *S*

A set of 4 George III wine coolers, 22 cm. high, 3 — London 1773, maker Andrew Fogelberg, 1 — London 1778, maker William Simons, 178 oz. **£12,000-15,000** *HSS*

A George III silver wine funnel, maker William Bock, London, 1796, 3¾ oz. **£300-375**   *PWC*

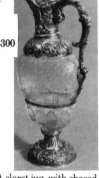

A claret jug, with chased silver gilt mounts, 14 in., by C.E., London, 1896. **£1,200-1,400**   *DWB*

A pair of silver plate wine wagons, with ivory casters, maker's mark HR, 1780. **£1,100-1,300**   *C*

A silver-mounted cut glass claret jug, Sheffield, 1890. **£550-650** *GSP*

A Victorian vase-shaped claret jug, 10¾ in. (27.5 cm.) high, by W. & G. Sissons, Sheffield, 1868, fitted case. **£600-900**   *SC*

A Victorian mounted glass claret jug, 33.5 cm. high, by Martin & Hall, Sheffield, 1865. **£600-900**   *P*

A wine taster, 4¾ in. (12 cm.) wide over handles, apparently unmarked, c. 1660, 51 gm. (1 oz. 13 dwt.). **£300-400**   *S*

A fully marked example would sell for double or more.

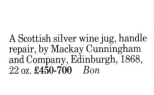

A Scottish silver wine jug, handle repair, by Mackay Cunningham and Company, Edinburgh, 1868, 22 oz. **£450-700**   *Bon*

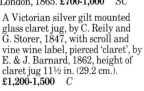

A silver-mounted wine jug, 14¼ in. (36 cm.) high, by E. & J. Barnard, London, 1865. **£700-1,000**   *SC*

A Victorian silver gilt mounted glass claret jug, by C. Reily and G. Storer, 1847, with scroll and vine wine label, pierced 'claret', by E. & J. Barnard, 1862, height of claret jug 11½ in. (29.2 cm.). **£1,200-1,500**   *C*

A Victorian silver-mounted claret jug, 10½ in. high, fully marked, by William Comyns, London, 1899. **£550-800** *SS*

A Victorian silver gilt wine service, 13½ in. high, London, 1869, and 4 matching goblets, 5 in. high, London, 1866, by Robert Harper, 46 oz. **£1,800-2,200** *DSH*

A Victorian claret jug, formed as a model of a kangaroo, 8⅜ in. high, marked on body and cover, by Edward Barnard & Sons, London, 1882, 19 oz. 4 dwt. **£2,000-2,500** *SS*

A George III fox head stirrup cup, gilt interior, 10 cm. long, by Henry Chawner, 1793, 6 oz. **£1,500-2,250** *P*

A Victorian parcel gilt wine set, jug 12¼ in. (31.2 cm.) high, by Richard Hennell, 1862 and 1863, gross 67 oz. **£2,000-2,500** *C*

A cut glass silver plate spirit barrel, 8¼ in. (21 cm.) high, early 20th C. **£450-500** *SC*

An ovoid spirit flask, 7¼ in. high, unmarked, c. 1865. **£550-650** *S*

A George II Irish spirit flask, with detachable gilt lined cup, 6¼ in. overall, Dublin, c. 1740. **£1,000-£1,400** *CSK*

An Asprey & Co. electroplated cocktail shaker, in the form of a pre-war fire extinguisher, with plaque inscribed 'The Thirst Extinguisher', 15 in. high overall. **£250-350** *Re*

A punch ladle, by R. & R. Keay, Perth, c. 1810, double-headed eagle; R & RK; double-headed eagle. **£275-350** *S*

A rare George III Provincial crescent-shaped wine label, 3.9 cm. long, titled 'Port', by William Twemlow of Liverpool and Chester, maker's mark only stamped twice, c. 1795. **£70-100** *P*

A set of 3 George III rectangular wine labels, 4.8 cm. long, pierced 'Port', 'Claret', and 'W. Wine', by Samuel Meriton (II), c. 1775. **£150-£200** *P*

A William IV scroll wine label, 6.5 cm. long, pierced 'Bucellas', by E., J., E. & W. Barnard, 1831. **£40-£60** *P*

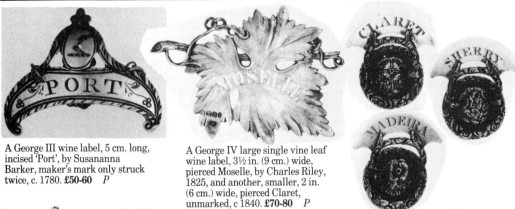

A George III wine label, 5 cm. long, incised 'Port', by Susananna Barker, maker's mark only struck twice, c. 1780. **£50-60**   *P*

A George IV large single vine leaf wine label, 3½ in. (9 cm.) wide, pierced Moselle, by Charles Riley, 1825, and another, smaller, 2 in. (6 cm.) wide, pierced Claret, unmarked, c 1840. **£70-80**   *P*

A rare set of 3 George IV stopper wine labels, 1¾ in. (4.5 cm.) high, by Ledsam, Vale & Wheeler, Birmingham, 1829. **£120-150**   *P*

A set of 3 unusual George III cast wine labels, pierced 'Claret' and 'Madeira', probably Benjamin Smith, London, 1807. **£300-400** *CSK*

Four Regency wine labels, by T. and J. Phipps and E. Robinson, 1813 and 1814, one with date-letter omitted, 4 oz. 12 dwt. **£350-450**   *C*

A pair of early Victorian wine labels, by Charles Reily and George Storer, London, 1839. **£60-90** *CSK*

The most common titles are Sherry, Madeira, Port and Claret which command a lower price.

A George III wine label, 1¾ in. (4.5 cm.) wide, by Matthew Linwood, Birmingham, 1811. **£70-£80**   *P*

A pair of George III heraldic and festoon wine labels, 2 in. (5 cm.) wide, Lisbon and Frontiniack, by William Smith, c. 1780. **£70-90**   *P*

A George IV sarcophagus-shaped nutmeg grater, 7.75 by 5.25 by 3.75 cm., by John Reily, 1825, 5.5 oz. **£300-400**   *P*

A George III horned crescent wine label, inscribed Hollands, 2 in. (5 cm.) wide, by Hester Bateman, c. 1775, also a George III wine label, inscribed Mountain, 2 in. (5 cm.) wide, c. 1780. **£80-100**   *P*

A George III oval patchbox, by Samuel Pemberton, Birmingham, 1807. **£60-80**   *HyD*

A snuff box, with gilt interior, Birmingham, 1844. **£200-250** *FHF*

A George III oval snuff box, dated 1774, the hinged engraved mother-of-pearl cover centred by an agate oval, traces of gilding, 3¼ in. (8.2 cm.) overall, by Stalker & Mitchison, Newcastle, c. 1774. **£350-450**   *SC*

A George III purse vinaigrette, decorated with fish-scale decoration, the grille marked with a lion passant on its edge, by Matthew Linwood, Birmingham, 1818. **£120-150**   *P*

A George III silver snuff box, 4¼ in. (10.8 cm.) wide, by Joseph Angell, London, 1817. **£900-1,000**   *C*

A George III snuff box, cast as a clenched fist, probably a prize for bare fist boxing, Sheffield, c. 1820. **£80-100**   *FHF*

A Victorian silver snuff box, 3¼ in., maker George Unite, Birmingham, 1888, 2¼ oz. **£80-100**   *PWC*

A snuff box, by Nathaniel Mills, Birmingham, 1850. **£200-250** *FHF*

A George III silver snuff box, 2¼ in., hallmarked London, 1808, maker's mark WW, 1 oz. **£90-110** *PWC*

A George III silver snuff box, gilt interior, 2¾ in., maker Joseph Willmore, Birmingham, 1810, 1¼ oz. **£80-100** *PWC*

A George III vinaigrette, maker's mark TB, London, 1802. **£100-150** *HGA*

A George III vinaigrette, 2.6 cm., by Matthew Linwood, Birmingham, 1811. **£90-110** *L*

A silver gilt vinaigrette, 2 in. (5 cm.) wide, by John Bettridge, Birmingham, 1828. **£350-400** *S*

A Victorian vinaigrette, gilt interior and floral grille, 2 in. (5 cm.) wide, by Wheeler & Cronin, Birmingham, 1843. **£150-200** *S*

A vinaigrette, with pricked basket pattern decoration, 1821. **£60-80** *HyD*

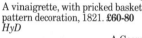

A Swiss 2-colour gold snuff box, 3⅝ in. (9.2 cm.) long, by Bautte & Cie, Geneva, c. 1820, in fitted case. **£1,300-1,600** *C*

A George IV silver gilt vinaigrette, 1¼ in. (3.5 cm.) wide, maker's mark 'R M', Birmingham, 1822. **£130-200** *LBP*

A fine gold-mounted tortoiseshell walking stick, the tapering shaft with metal tip, 36¼ in. (92 cm.) long, the plain collar with a Dutch control mark, c. 1760. **£2,000-2,300** *C*

A rare and macabre Victorian vinaigrette, realistically modelled as a skull, 3.7 cm. long, by Henry William Dee, 1872. **£350-450** *P*

An Austrian gold snuff box, mounted with a miniature of a gentleman, 3½ in. (9 cm.) long, 1802, maker's initials F.W., possibly for Friedrich Weyand, the miniature English School, c. 1775. **£2,200-2,500** *C*

A Victorian mounted claw vinaigrette, 4 cm. high, unmarked, c. 1865. **£70-80** *P*

A William IV silver gilt vinaigrette, 3.8 by 2.7 cm., by John Bettridge, Birmingham, 1830. **£70-80** *P*

A silver gilt vinaigrette, the cover with a die-stamped view of Windsor Castle, maker's mark of Nathaniel Mills for N. Mills & Son, Birmingham, 1837. **£450-550** *SS*

A Victorian silver vinaigrette, the gilt interior having pierced and engraved grille, 1½ by 1¼ in., by Nathaniel Mills, Birmingham, 1844. **£250-300** *TW*

A gilt metal topped ebony walking stick, 35½ in. (90 cm.) long, probably U.S.A., c. 1889. **£200-250** *S*

A Victorian Scottish vinaigrette, modelled as a thistle, 4.2 cm. high, Edinburgh, 1881. **£150-170** *P*

A George II gold-mounted grey agate snuff box, 4 in. (10 cm.) wide, in red leather case, c. 1760. **£2,300-£3,000** *C*

A gold and hardstone snuff box, inset with panels of orange-red agate with cloudy inclusions, lid panel cracked, 7.5 cm., by A. J. Strachan, maker's mark, London, 1833. **£1,400-1,800** *S*

A 19th C. French gold vinaigrette, enclosed by a lid inset with a carved bone-amber cameo, and with yellow amber base, 1½ in. long. **£700-800** *LBP*

A rare George III flexible fish vinaigrette, 7 cm. long, maker's mark rubbed, Birmingham, 1817. **£250-300**   *P*

An Imperial presentation gold cigarette case, set with a cabochon sapphire flanked by 2 circular-cut diamonds, 9.8 cm. long, maker's mark A H, St. Petersburg 1908-17, sold with an ivory plaque with engraved presentation inscription. **£3,000-3,500**   *C*

The inscription states that this case was presented by Tsar Nicholas II to Sir Arthur Trevor Dawson on March 7, 1911.

A George III 18 ct. gold oblong snuff box, 3¼ in. wide, marked on base and cover, by A. J. Strahan, London, 1818, 3 oz. 14 dwt. **£1,100-£1,500**   *SS*

An unusual English bonbonnière, the gold cagework mounts chased with flowered volutes and enclosing panels of striated coffee-coloured agate and plain and burgau mother-of-pearl, very slight damage, 1¼ in. (3 cm.), c. 1760. **£550-650**   *S*

A Victorian vinaigrette, cover decorated in low relief with St. Paul's Cathedral, hinge broken, inscribed in cover with later inscription, 4.1 cm. long, by Joseph Willmore, Birmingham, 1842. **£200-250**   *P*

A George IV vinaigrette, 3.3 cm., by John Shaw, Birmingham, 1821. **£100-150**   *L*

A George IV vinaigrette, Birmingham, 1823. **£100-150** *HyD*

A George IV small vinaigrette, 2.5 cm., by Thomas Shaw, Birmingham, 1826. **£100-150**   *L*

A George III vinaigrette, 3 cm., by Matthew Linwood, Birmingham, 1806. **£200-250**   *L*

An unmarked Victorian combined vinaigrette and pill box, modelled as a pendant gourd, 8.5 cm. long, c. 1865. **£140-160**   *P*

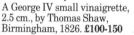

A Victorian vinaigrette, 5.4 cm., by Alfred Taylor, Birmingham, 1854. **£110-140**   *L*

A George IV small vinaigrette, engraved with foliage, by Joseph Taylor, Birmingham, 1825. **£55-65** *HGA*

A Swiss export gold and enamel snuff box, sides damaged, 3 in. (8 cm.), struck AM in a horizontal lozenge for Moulinié, Bautte, et Moynier, Geneva, c. 1820. **£2,100-£2,500**   *S*

A card case, die-stamped with a stag and 2 hinds, Birmingham, 1907. **£70-100**   *HGA*

A Swiss gold and enamel snuff box, in translucent blue over chevron turning, one side chipped, 3 in. (7.5 cm.), maker's mark M.C incuse, early 19th C. **£400-500**   *S*

A George IV vinaigrette, 2.6 cm., maker's mark T. & W. S., 1821. **£80-100**   *L*

An enamelled cigarette case, painted with a pair of borzois, 3½ in. (8.6 cm.), silver-coloured metal, probably German, c. 1910. **£350-400**   *S*

An enamelled oblong silver cigarette case, 3½ in. (9 cm.) wide, importer's mark M & C, Birmingham, 1912, probably German. **£350-400**   *S*

A Continental white metal cigarette case, 3¼ by 3¼ in. **£350-£400**   *CSK*

A Continental white metal cigarette case, the front enamelled with a naked young lady warming herself by a fire, 3½ by 3 in. **£600-£650**   *CSK*

A German enamelled cigarette case, 3¼ in. (8.7 cm.) high, by Louis Kuppenheim, Pforzheim, c. 1905. **£400-500**   *S*

The portrait has been identified from photographs by Reutlinger of Paris as being that of Lina Cavalieri, 'said to be the most beautiful woman in the whole world

An enamelled cigarette case, 3¼ in. (8.2 cm.) high, by George Unite, Birmingham, 1903. **£300-350**   *S*

A Victorian silver cigar box, with porcelain plaque of young lady on lid, 5 in. long. **£300-350**   *LRG*

An erotic cigarette case, the gilt interior with compartment hinged to reveal a scene depicting a young woman recently risen from her bed, 3⅝ in. high, c. 1920. **£350-400**   *SS*
Reputedly the gift of HRH the Maharajah of Patiala to a member of the MCC Indian tour of 1922.

A Viennese enamelled cigarette case, painted in translucent colours, with 'Musidora' after Gainsborough, 4 in. (10.2 cm.) high, silver-coloured metal, maker's mark apparently that of Carl Lustig, Vienna, c. 1920, stamped: 368. **£300-350**   *S*

A German enamelled cigarette case, painted with a portrait of Napoleon, 3½ in. (9 cm.) high, maker's mark rubbed, Louis Kuppenheim, Pforzheim, c. 1905. **£400-450**   *S*

A 2-colour gold-mounted nephrite paper knife, 27.7 cm. long, apparently unmarked, attributed to Fabergé, c. 1900. **£1,100-1,300**   *C*

A Continental electroplated cigarette case, 3½ by 3 in. **£250-300**   *CSK*

An enamel cigarette case, painted after Boucher, 3½ in. (9.1 cm.) wide, silver-coloured metal, unmarked, probably Austrian, c. 1930. **£600-650**   *S*

An enamelled cigarette case, painted with a beauty propped on cushions, gilt interior, some surface scratches to enamel, 4 in. (10.2 cm.) wide, probably German, importers' mark S & Co. in an oval, Birmingham, 1910. **£500-550**   *S*

A German enamelled electroplate cigarette case, painted with a beckoning wind-swept syren, scratched surface, 3¼ in. (8.4 cm.) high, stamped: 'Alpacca', c. 1910. **£650-700** *S*

A German silver cigarette case, having a secret inner lid, finely enamelled with an Eastern nude being displayed by her Arab master, 3¾ by 3¾ in., import marks for London, 1922. **£1,900-£2,100** *AGr*

An enamelled silver vesta case, 1¾ in. (4.7 cm.) high, probably German, importers' mark Simon & Alder, London, 1903. **£600-650** *S*

An enamelled curved oblong vesta case, 1½ in. (4.2 cm.) high, German or Austrian, importers' mark of Simon & Alder, London, 1903. **£300-350** *S*

An enamelled curved oblong vesta case, painted on one side with a naked girl, minor chip, 2 in. (5 cm.) high, probably German, importers' mark H & Co., London, 1908. **£700-£800** *S*

A rare gold vesta case, in the form of a portmanteau, with 2 hinged lids, a pill compartment at one end, 2 in. (5 cm.) long, unmarked, probably English, c. 1865. **£600-650** *S*

A rectangular nephrite vesta case, 2 in. (5.2 cm.) high, Austrian, c. 1905. **£150-180** *S*

An Austrian oblong vesta case, hinge slightly damaged, 2¼ in. (5.4 cm.) high, by Alois Blahuschek, Vienna, c. 1895, post 1882 Russian import marked. **£140-160** *S*

A Russian cloisonné enamel vesta case, minor chips, 2 in. (5.2 cm.) high, silver-coloured metal, unmarked, c. 1900. **£150-180** *S*

A Russian champlevé enamel vesta case, minor chips, 2¼ in. (5.5 cm.) high, maker's mark BP (Cyrillic), Moscow, 1877. **£150-180** *S*

A Russian niello boot-shaped vesta case, niello slightly imperfect, 2¾ in. (7 cm.) high, Novotshercasc, c. 1880. **£200-250** *S*

A gun metal vesta case, 1¾ in. (4.5 cm.) high, unmarked, probably French, c. 1905. **£45-55** *S*

A German gilt metal snuff box, 2¾ in. (7 cm.), c. 1760. **£400-450** *S*

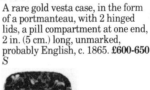

A Dutch reproduction of a late 18th C. oval snuff box, 6.6 cm. long, 1884. **£100-130** *P*

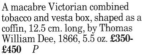

A George IV Irish toothpick box, with gold mounts. **£250-300** *HyD*

A macabre Victorian combined tobacco and vesta box, shaped as a coffin, 12.5 cm. long, by Thomas William Dee, 1866, 5.5 oz. **£350-£450** *P*

A blond tortoiseshell snuff box, with gold mounts, the lid decorated in gold piqué posé, damaged, 3¼ in. (8 cm.), apparently unmarked, c. 1725. **£350-400** *S*

A papier-mâché snuff box, the lid painted with: 'Persée delivre Andromède d'après C. Coypel', 3¾ in. (9.5 cm.), signed, inscribed and numbered: 6923, c. 1835. **£600-£650** *S*

A brass candlestick, German, 10½ in. (27.3 cm.) high, 16th C. **£1,200-1,600** *S*

A brass candlestick, fitted with two candle sockets, base cracked, restored, North German or Flemish, 12¾ in. (32.4 cm.) high, last quarter 15th C. **£1,800-2,400** *S*

A brass candlestick, 9½ in. (24 cm.); and a similar cast example, late 17th/early 18th C.; and a Flemish bronze candlestick, 7½ in. (19 cm.), early 17th C. **£420-450** *SC*

A pair of antique brass candlesticks, 5 in. **£120-140** *WW* *Where such sticks are made in sections either screwed or splayed to interlock it is possible to find marriages of each part.*

A pair of early Georgian brass candlesticks, 6¾ in. (17 cm.) high. **£400-450** *L*

A pair of brass candlesticks, having side pushers, 7 in., mid 18th C. **£260-300** *WW*

A pair of brass table candlesticks, probably French, 7¼ in. (18.5 cm.) high, mid 18th C. **£380-440** *S*

A pair of brass candlesticks, with ejectors, 7 in. (18 cm.). **£60-80** *L*

A pair of brass candlesticks, engraved with the arms of Parker of Arlington, 13 in. (33 cm.) high, early 18th C. **£2,600-3,000** *C*

A pair of George II brass table candlesticks, 8¼ in. **£400-450** *HyD*

A pair of brass candlesticks, one with solder repair, 10½ in., mid 18th C. **£700-800** *Bea*

A pair of brass table candlesticks, push-rod ejectors, 8 in. (20.4 cm.) high, mid 18th C. **£250-350** *S*

Two 17th C. German brass alms dishes, each 16 in. *(l.)* **£340-400**, *(r.)* **£180-220** *DWB*

A 16th C. German brass alms dish, centrally decorated with Adam and Eve, 16 in. **£380-42** *DWB*

A 16th C. German brass alms dish, 17½ in. **£300-350** *DWB*

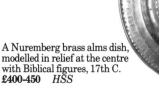

A Nuremberg brass alms dish, modelled in relief at the centre with Biblical figures, 17th C. **£400-450** *HSS*

A 16th C. German brass alms dish, 19 in. **£500-55** *DWB*

A bell metal alms dish, 10¼ in., 17th C. **£260-300**   *DWB*

Two Iserlöhn brass tobacco boxes, by Johann Heinrich Giese, the lids with portrait and battle medallions, stamped marks, 6 and 7½ in. wide, c. 1760. **£300-340**   *S*

A brass and copper tobacco box, engraved with perpetual almanac and lunar calendar, and a table for calculating the speed of a ship, 6½ in. (16.5 cm.) wide, Dutch, c. 1757. **£300-350**   *S*

A pair of late 18th C. chimney jamb hooks, with shaped brackets and urn shaped finials. **£140-160**   *DWB*

A Spanish brass inkstand, with an inkwell, sand pot, bell and quill pot, 10½ in. (27 cm.) wide, 18th C. **£500-600**   *C*

(l.) A copper and brass Iserlöhn tobacco box, 6½ in. (16 cm.) wide, mid 18th C. **£170-190**
(c.) A brass tobacco box, of oval form, engraved with genre scenes, 5½ in. (14 cm.), third quarter 18th C. **£140-160**
(r.) A copper and brass tobacco box, engraved with a scene of Daniel in the lion's den, 7 in. (18 cm.), late 18th C. **£120-140**   *SC*

A set of eight Nuremberg brass nesting weights, the mastersign of crossed key and arrow with initials G.M. and the number 4, 3¼ in. (82.3 mm.) diam., total weight 2 kilograms, third quarter 17th C. **£500-550**   *S*

A brass-bound loadstone, the magnetite mounted in two brass caps, marked N and S, 3⅛ in. (8.2 cm.) wide, 17th C. **£800-900**   *S*

Four brass imperial conical measures, No. 839, for London County Council, each with carrying handle, dated 1891. **£800-900**   *S*

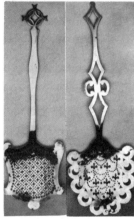

A set of eight De Grave and Co. cylindrical brass metric measures, No. 2509, each engraved London County Council, two litres to 0.01 litres, English, c. 1920. **£1,000-1,250**   *S*

Two brass skimmers, 23 in. (58 cm.) and 24 in. (61 cm.). **£150-180**   *L*

An antique brass kettle, with ceramic handle upon pierced brass stand upon paw feet. **£140-160**   *WM*

A Regency copper helmet shaped coal scuttle, and shovel, the handles of brass and turned wood. **£180-220**   *Re*

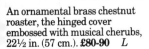

An ornamental brass chestnut roaster, the hinged cover embossed with musical cherubs, 22½ in. (57 cm.). **£80-90**   *L*

A brass footman, 16 in. wide, early 19th C. **£150-180**   *Re*

A late Regency copper samovar, the interior with case tube for iron warmer, 16 in. **£160-200**   *WW*

A collection of twenty-five horse brasses, some on martingales and face pieces. **£200-250**   *SS*

A pair of brass Powell and Hanmer brass motor car sidelamps, fitted with paraffin wicks, 13 in. (33 cm.) high. **£100-150**   *CSK*

A Scandinavian brass binnacle compass, inscribed Solver & Svarrer, Iverg Wellbach & Co. **£160-180**   *L*

A large brass ship's bell, 'Victoria', English, 15½ in. (39.5 cm.) diam., mid 19th C. **£600-700**   *S*

A 19th C. brass lectern. **£200-240**   *DA*

An engraved gilt-brass easel toilet mirror or picture frame, 3 ft. by 2 ft. ½ in. (92 by 62 cm.), c. 1870. **£1,000-1,250**   *S*

A suspended brass gas lamp, with original cranberry shades converted to electricity, 28 by 35 in. **£225-275**   *JT*

A large set of De Grave Short & Co. Ltd., brass beam scales, Class B to weight 500 oz. troy, English, 20th C. **£320-350**   *S*

A German steel balance, with brass pans contained in a box, 4⅞ in. (12.4 cm.) wide, enclosing compartments for weights, dated Anno 1736. **£320-350**   *P*

A brass corn balance, the beam signed Vandome, Filford & Co., Leadenhall St., London, the sliding weight engraved Lbs Per Bushel, 9⅝ in. (24.4 cm.) wide, 19th C. **£100-140**   *P*

A Florentine bronze mortar, by Giuliano di Mariotto de' Navi, signed and dated around the rim OPVS. IVLIANI. MARIOCTI. FLORENTINI. MCCCCC, 8 cm. high, 12 cm. diam., 16th C. **£1,800-2,400**   *C*

A Flemish bronze mortar, with traces of gilding, slightly rubbed, 10.5 cm. high, inscription for 1598. **£1,000-1,500**   *C*

A Paduan bronze casket, 7⅞ by 4¼ in. (20 by 10.7 cm.), c. 1500, interior now fitted as an inkwell, hinges later. **£4,000-5,000**   *S*

A Venetian bronze inkwell and lid, 20.5 cm. high, late 16th C. **£2,400-2,800**   *C*

A Venetian bronze incense burner, in Saracenic style, 9½ in. high (24.5 cm.), early 16th C. **£1,000-1,500**   *S*

A Californian copper and silver alloy bell, inscribed and dated STA. BARBARA 1761, 41 cm. high, mid 18th C. **£2,200-2,800**   *C*

A pair of Venetian bronze standing candlesticks, 58¾ in. high (149 cm.), c. 1600, one with later drip pan. **£14,000-16,000**   *S*

A pair of French bronze urns, after the antique, from the workshops of Thomire, one signed THOMIRE A PARIS on the base, 19 in. (48.2 cm.), c. 1815. **£1,200-1,600**   *S*

A late Victorian bronze chandelier, 78 cm. diam. **£650-850**   *Bon*

A Spanish bronze pestle and mortar, 5 in. diam., 17th C. **£200-250**   *SC*

An Italian bronze equestrian group of Marcus Aurelius, after the antique, rich dark brown patina, 14¾ in. (37.5 cm.), late 17th C., on white marble base. **£800-1,200**   *S*

A pair of Venetian bronze angels, each holding a candelabrum, 17 in. (43 cm.), late 17th C., on red marble stands, 18½ in. (47 cm.) overall. **£3,500-4,000**   *S*

A Paduan bronze statuette of a satyr, cast from a model by Severo da Ravenna, raised right hand repaired, hole in top of head, 20 cm. high, 16th C. **£6,000-8,000**   *C*

A Venetian gilt bronze lion sejant, 7½ in. (19 cm.), 17th C., marble base. **£3,000-4,000**   *S*

A Paduan bronze figure of a stallion, from the workshop of Severo da Ravenna, dark brown patina on reddish bronze, 5¾ in. high (15 cm.), 16th C., on elaborately inlaid yellow, black and white marble base. **£5,000-6,000**   *S*

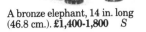

A Netherlandish bronze figure of a cow, copper brown patina, 5 in. (12.8 cm.), 17th C., rouge royale marble socle. **£3,000-4,000**   *S*

A bronze elephant, 14 in. long (46.8 cm.). **£1,400-1,800**   *S*

A French bronze statuette of the Farnese Hercules, after the antique, stamped with the 'C' couronné, 23.5 cm. high, early 18th C. **£1,400-1,800**   *C*

A pair of French bronze poodles, or Bologneser Hunde, 9 in. high (22.8 cm.), 18th C., French, Louis XVI style ormolu and marble bases. **£3,800-4,400** *S*

A bronze model of a Bacchanalian, entitled 'Improvisatore', after Duret, dark brown patination, Italian, 21½ in. (54.5 cm.) high, third quarter of the 19th C. **£700-800** *SC*

A pair of well patinated bronze groups, 19½ in. and 22½ in. high. **£900-1,400** *Re*

A bronze group of a young woman and child, black patination, 3 ft. ¾ in. (93 cm.), c. 1880. **£900-1,300** *S*

A bronze figure of a young woman, by Felix Maurice Charpentier, signed F. Charpentier and Colin et Cie, Paris, rich brown patination, 2 ft. 3¼ in. (69 cm.), c. 1870. **£550-750** *S*

A bronze figure of a water carrier, black patination, rich brown patination.

A bronze and gilt bronze figure of a water carrier, by Gazam, 26 in. **£1,400-1,800** *Bea*

A bronze figure of a cockerel, by Alfred Barye, signed A. Barye, rich dark green/black patination, 9 in. (23 cm.), c. 1880. **£300-400** *S*

A bronze casket, by August Cain, signed, 8 in. (20 cm.), c. 1860, with key. **£400-500** *S*

A bronze group of a retriever and a duck, by Paul Edouard Delabrierre, signed, rich brown patination, 7¼ in. (18.5 cm.), c. 1870. **£600-700** *S*

A late 19th C. French bronze group of a horse and jockey, signed A. E. Dubucand Fils, 42 cm. high. **£1,800-2,200** *C*

A bronze group of 'L'Accolade', after Mêne, signed 'P. J. Mêne', mid brown patination, 13 in. (33 cm.) high, late 19th/20th C. **£2,000-2,500** *SS*

The popularity of horse subjects has led to reproduction. Fresh bronzes keep a sulphurous metallic smell when rubbed or moistened. Cold cast bronze is a resin compound and does not have a metallic scratch.

A bronze group of two hunting dogs, by Pierre Jules Mêne, signed, light and dark brown patination, 9 in. (23 cm.), c. 1870. **£1,000-1,250** *S*

A Barbedienne gilt bronze equestrian group of Bertrand Duquesuin, by Emanuel Fremiet, signed, on a green veined marble base, 2 ft. 2¼ in. (66.5 cm.), c. 1880. **£1,100-1,300** *S*

A bronze figure of a rhinoceros, dark brown patina on yellowish bronze, 5¾ in. long (14.5 cm.), German. **£2,000-2,500** *S*

A bronze figure of a bear, by Christopher Fratin, rich brown patination, 7 in. (18 cm.), c. 1840. **£1,600-2,000** *S*

A bronze figure of an Irish setter, after P. J. Mêne, 15 in. long. **£200-300** *Re*

A rare bronze group of a ewe and a lamb, by Pierre Jules Mêne, signed and dated 1845, slightly rubbed brown patination, 6 in. (15 cm.). **£750-850** *S*

A bronze group of Napoleon on horseback, signed Morac, light brown patination, 1 ft. 7¾ in. (50 cm.), c. 1880. **£1,200-1,800** *S*

A Susse Freres bronze group of a mahout returning home on his elephant, by Roger Godchaux, signed, Susse Frs Edt. Cire Perdue and with the Susse Freres seal, rich chocolate brown patination, French, 1 ft. 10¾ in. (58 cm.), c. 1900. **£800-1,000** *S*

A French bronze bust of Nerina, after Emmanuele Villanis, and inscribed E. Villanis and stamped with the Société des Bronzes de Paris foundry stamp and AP and 7291, 45 cm. high. **£350-450** *C*

A bronze group of a Russian peasant couple, signed A. M. Bonegov, 1903, 38 cm. long. **£1,800-2,400** *C*

A bronze bust of Suzon, signed on the back A. Rodin, marked on the right side Cie des Bronzes a Bruxelles, 16⅛ in. (41 cm.) high, c. 1872. **£3,000-4,000** *C*

A large bronze figure of Mephistopheles, dark brown patination, signed, after Pierre Oge, 32½ in. (83 cm.), third quarter 19th C. **£800-1,200** *SC*

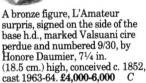

A bronze group cast with a farmer seated on a plough horse, by Edouard Drouot, signed, on a yellow marble base, rich brown patination, 1 ft. 2¼ in. (36 cm.), c. 1880. **£500-700** *S*

A bronze figure, L'Amateur surpris, signed on the side of the base h.d., marked Valsuani cire perdue and numbered 9/30, by Honore Daumier, 7¼ in. (18.5 cm.) high, conceived c. 1852, cast 1963-64. **£4,000-6,000** *C*

A bronze bust of 'Une Chinoise', by Jean Baptiste Carpeaux, signed B. Carpeaux and with Propriete Carpeaux, spread eagle seal, rich light and dark brown patinations, 13 in. (35 cm.), c. 1870. **£2,500-3,500** *S*

A bronze bust of Emmeline Pankhurst, mahogany plinth, later replacement, by W. Charles May, 13 in. (33 cm.), signed and dated 1895. **£150-200** *Bon*

An Austrian painted bronze model of a green parrot, stamped Geschotzt patent, 19th C. **£250-300** *WW*

An Amendola bronze study of a woman, the sitter thought to be the wife of the artist Sir Lawrence Alma-Tadema, signed 'G. B. Amendola', 28.5 cm. high. **£1,200-1,600** *P*

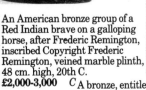

An American bronze group of a Red Indian brave on a galloping horse, after Frederic Remington, inscribed Copyright Frederic Remington, veined marble plinth, 48 cm. high, 20th C. **£2,000-3,000** *C*

A bronze, entitled L'Homme à la Fleur, signed and numbered on the base P. Gargallo, no. 4, by Pablo Gargallo, 24½ in. (62 cm.) high, conceived in 1907, cast before 1930. **£5,500-6,500** *C*

A bronze athlete, wrestling with a python, by Frederick Lord Leighton P.R.A., 10 in., on rectangular marble base. **£7,000-8,000** *HyD*

A bronze figure of a cougar, by John M. Swan, signed, 9¼ in. **£500-600** *HyD*

An English bronze statuette of Teucer, signed and dated Hamo Thornycroft R.A. 1907, cast by Singer Frome Somerset 1907, 43 cm. high. **£4,000-6,000** *C*

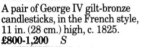

A pair of Louis XV gilt-bronze candlesticks, 12 in. (30.5 cm.) high, mid 18th C. **£5,500-6,500** *S*

A pair of Louis XV gilt-bronze wall candelabra, 1 ft. 7 in. (40 cm.), mid 18th C. **£5,500-6,500** *S*

A pair of Louis XVI gilt-bronze wall-lights, 22 in. (56 cm.), c. 1775. **£5,000-6,000** *S*

A pair of George IV gilt-bronze candlesticks, in the French style, 11 in. (28 cm.) high, c. 1825. **£800-1,200** *S*

A set of six French ormolu and glass wall-lights, 26 in. long, c. 1880. **£2,000-2,500** *AP*

A pair of ormolu two-branch wall brackets, late 19th C. **£550-650** *JD*

A pair of Louis XVI bronze, gilt-bronze and white marble candelabra, 16½ in. (42 cm.), c. 1780. **£1,500-2,000** *S*

A pair of early Louis XVI gilt-bronze candelabra, 15 in. (38 cm.) high, c. 1775. **£3,800-4,400** *S*

A pair of Empire gilt-bronze candelabra, 1 ft. 11½ in. (90 cm.) high, c. 1810. **£7,000-9,000** *S*
An almost identical pair at the Grand Trianon, are in the Salon de Musique.

A George III gilt-bronze hall lantern, with double-arched glazed panels with rococo clasps and with circular glass smoke dome, 2 ft. 2 in. (66 cm.), c. 1760. **£1,000-1,500** *S*

An ormolu chandelier, of Louis XIV-style, 32 in. (87.5 cm.) high, second quarter 19th C. **£2,500-3,500** *C*

A Charles X ormolu lamp-bouillotte, with green tôle shade, fitted for electricity, 27 in. (70 cm.) high. **£800-1,100** *C*

A pair of rococo revival gilt-bronze table candelabra, 1 ft. 9½ in. (55 cm.) high, mid 19th C. **£500-600** *S*

A pair of late Louis XV bronze and gilt-bronze chenets, 15 in. (38 cm.) high, c. 1770. **£3,000-3,500**   *S*

A pair of gilt-bronze chenets, signed Mottheau A Paris, 22 in. (55 cm.) high, late 18th/early 19th C. **£4,000-5,000**   *S*

A gilt-bronze glass standard oil lamp, the bowl, stem and base formed of sea-green glass decorated with gilt beads, 5 ft. 2 in. (157 cm.) high, c. 1870. **£1,800-2,400**   *S*

A pair of ormolu ice pails, attributed to Boulton and Fothergill, 9 in. (23 cm.) high, c. 1780. **£8,000-10,000**   *S*

A pair of porcelain-mounted gilt-bronze table lamps, the white porcelain painted with polychrome flowers, 2 ft. 8 in. (81 cm.) high, c. 1840. **£700-900**   *S*

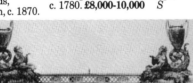

A Continental bronze and brass fire fender and dogs, 69 in. (175 cm.) wide, 19th C. **£600-800**   *SS*

A pair of Empire ormolu and cut-glass candlesticks, one slightly damaged, 12½ in. (32 cm.) high. **£700-800**   *C*

A large gilt-bronze table centre, signed Thomire à Paris, 2 ft. 7 in. high, 1 ft. 2 in. wide (79 by 36 cm.), early 19th C. **£3,500-4,500**   *S*

A pair of gilt-bronze and white marble lamps, in Louis XVI-style, fitted for electricity, 1 ft. 11 in. (58 cm.) high. **£1,200-1,600**   *S*

An Italian brass and iron faldistorio, 17th C. **£800-900**   *C*

A pair of cut-glass and gilt-brass two-branch moderator lamps, 33 in. high. **£700-800**   *AG*

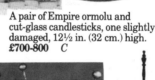

A cast iron adjustable taper stick on column and tripod, late 18th C. **£120-180**   *BA*

A German iron casket, applied with brass plaques decorated with cherubs and winged horses, 6 by 7½ in. (15.2 by 19 cm.), 17th C. **£600-800**   *S*

A wrought-iron strong box, concealed keyhole in the lid, with original key, South German, 15¼ in. (39.5 cm.) wide, 17th C. **£900-1,100**   *S*

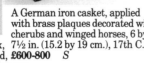

A polished steel and damascened snuff rasp, opening to reveal the rasp, and a pinch dispenser at one end, possibly Tüla, 6¼ in. (16 cm.), early 18th C. **£450-550**   *SC*

A cast-iron spring lever spiked man trap, c. 1880. **£300–350**   *CGC/FRM*

A wrought-iron door knocker, wrought with a 'Wildman' holding a snake, flanked by two monsters, 10½ in. (27 cm.) high, 18th C. **£400–500**   *S*

A Victorian cast metal lion door stop, 28 in. (71 cm.) long. **£60–90** *TW*

An architectural wire bird-cage, surmounted by the Royal Coat of Arms, 5 ft. 1 in. high, 2 ft. 9 in. wide (155 by 84 cm.), c. 1900. **£600-800** *S*

A pair of cast-iron campana-shaped garden urns, 39 in. high, early 19th C. **£550-750** *Re*

A pair of cast-iron garden urns, 33 in. (84 cm.), 19th C. **£450-650** *SC*

A set of six cast-iron garden or pub chairs, and a pair of circular cast-iron garden or pub tables, 2 ft. 3 in. high, 2 ft. 4½ in. diam. (69 cm. by 72 cm.), c. 1880. **£1,800-2,400** *S*
These are extensively reproduced conceivably from moulds taken from such as these.

A polished steel fire set, the grate 2 ft. 4 in. high, 2 ft. 9 in. wide (71 by 84 cm.), mainly 20th C. **£700-800** *S*

A cast-iron fire grate and surround, probably Coalbrookdale, 5 ft. 1 in. wide, 49 in. high, mid 19th C. **£1,000-1,500** *WIL*

A rare pair of Tudor candlesticks, old damage, 6⅜ in. (16.2 cm.) high, c. 1580. **£1,000-1,500** *C*

A Stuart candlestick, engraved with initials, 7 in. (17.8 cm.) high, c. 1675. **£180-220** *C*

A pewter flagon, the domed cover having twin-ball thumbpiece, patch at front, 8 in. (20.3 cm.) high, 15th/16th C. **£650-750** *S*

A rare candlestick, with touch NM in dotted circle struck twice, 10½ in. (26.5 cm.) high, c. 1600. **£3,200-3,600** *C*

A Stuart flagon, the domed cover with curved thumbpiece, stamped with initials TE, unmarked, 11¼ in. (28.6 cm.) high, c. 1610. **£800-1,000** *C*

A Charles II tankard, the flat raised cover with wrigglework stag, small holes in base, by Richard Dunne, 6½ in. (16.4 cm.) high, c. 1677. **£3,000-3,250** *C*

A Charles II circular charger, the centre with the Royal Arms of Charles II and dated 1671, by John Coursey, 18⅜ in. (46.7 cm.) diam., c. 1670. **£3,000-3,250** *C*

A beaker, engraved in wrigglework, the base with indistinct rose and crown touch and stamped owner's initials IA, 6⅝ in. (16.8 cm.) high, c. 1700. **£300-400** *S*

A Queen Anne tapering cylindrical tankard, engraved with wrigglework tulips and flowers, old repairs to cover, by Thomas Forde, Chester, 6 in. (15.3 cm.) high, c. 1710. **£1,800-2,200** *C*

A Stuart flagon, the handle punched with initials PEB, old repair to finial, unmarked, 9⅞ in. (25.2 cm.) high, c. 1630. **£1,100-1,300** *C*

A pewter bleeding basin, engraved on the inner wall with concentric rings measuring 8 to 32 fluid ounces, English, 6 in. (15 cm.) diam., late 18th C. **£350-400** *S*

See also under Medical.

A Hanse-Krug, in excavated condition, 'sealed' inside with a relief cast Crucifixion medallion, 8⅛ in. (20.6 cm.) overall, 14th/15th C. **£1,100-1,300** *S*

A German Tailor's Guild cup and cover, inscribed: Dis ist der Schneider Gesellen ihr Wilkommen, Anno 1697, three later sets of masters' initials all dated 1752 below, 24¾ in. (63 cm.) high, c. 1697. **£1,000-1,500** *S*

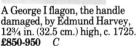

A George I flagon, the handle damaged, by Edmund Harvey, 12¾ in. (32.5 cm.) high, c. 1725. **£850-950** *C*

A pair of pewter candlesticks, with iron prickets, some repair, probably German, 17½ in. (44 cm.) high, 16th C. **£1,400-1,800** *S*

A pewter Schraubeflasche, engraved later with figures and floral panels, 10¼ in., 18th C. **£220-260** *S*

Four various French pewter flagons, 11½ in. to 13¾ in. high, probably 18th C. **£450-650** *GC*

A North German flagon or roerken, maker CAD dated 1680, the domed cover inscribed Thoms Appel 1683, 7¾ in. (19.7 cm.) high, c. 1683. **£1,100-1,300** *S*

An Austrian flagon, by the maker JS, 11¼ in. (28.8 cm.) high, 18th C. **£300-350** *S*

A composite set of three measures, each cover with hammer-head thumbpiece, 6½ in. (16.5 cm.), 5 in. (12.7 cm.) and 4½ in. (11.4 cm.) high overall, late 17th C. **£1,400-1,700** *C*

A lead garden fountain cistern, the back supporting a lead putto and dolphin fountain, the date 1764, 33 in. wide, 40 in. high overall. **£700-1,000**

Four Venetian keys, the bows wrought with gothic tracery, three with hexagonal ferrules over hollow shanks, one shaft replaced, the largest 6 in. (15.2 cm.) long, 16th C. **£350-450** *S*

A pair of lead garden urns, each moulded with putti, carrying vines and game, dolphin feet, 21 in. high. **£550-750** *PWC*

A pewter bullock, with a screw-off head, tail lacking, probably Dutch, 10 by 13 in. (26 by 33 cm.), 19th C. **£320-360** *SC*

Bristol Crown Fire Office, lead. **£600-700** *P*

A decorated steel tobacco box, with hinged lid engraved with the initial R.A. 1791 and View of Otaheite, the base engraved with five scenes, English, 4¾ in. (12 cm.) wide, dated 1791. **£350-450** *S*

A set of four Pontypool pictorial trays, painted with romantic English landscape views, with gilt scrollwork border, 2 ft. 6 in., 1 ft. 6 in. and 1 ft. 2 in., mid 19th C. **£700-900** *S*

Hand-in-Hand Fire Office, lead, clasped hands, small cuffs, above policy no. 58343 impressed on panel, c. 1730. **£400-500** *P*

London Assurance, lead, seated figure of Britannia, policy no. 40994 on panel below, traces of original paint, one hole. **£600-800** *P*

Licensed Victuallers and General Fire and Life Insurance, copper, some original gilding. **£220-280** *P*

Bristol Crown Fire Office, lead, crown raised above blank panel below with painted inscription, 'No. 15773', faded original paint (6Aii) (E), issued, c. 1808. **£1,000-1,500** *P*

Suffolk fire office, lead, raised 'Insured Suffolk Fire Office', some overpainting. **£120-180** *P*

Newcastle Fire Office, lead, border with arms of the city above, policy no. 6562. **£400-600** *P*

Norwich Union Fire Insurance, lead, pair of clasped hands above, 'Norwich' incised on decorative scroll and rectangular panel below. **£550-650** *P*

Norwich General Assurance, lead, arms of the city above Norwich and policy no. 1981 impressed on lower panel, some original gilding. **£350-450** *P*

Edinburgh Friendly Insurance, lead, a pair of clasped hands with lazy cuffs, raised with policy no. 10910 impressed on panel below. **£300-400** *P*

Union Fire Office, lead, four clasped hands, with 'Union' raised on panel above, policy no. 16594 impressed on panel below. **£1,400-1,800** *P*

Kent Insurance, lead, rampant horse above 'Invicta' and policy no., some splits, part overpainted. **£180-220** *P*

The General Insurance Company of Ireland, lead, raised phoenix, policy no. 3462 on panel below. **£1,000-1,500** *P*

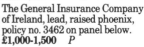

A lead garden figure, of putto and dolphin on sandstone base, 24 in. high. **£200-300** *BA*

An Italian bone marriage casket, possibly 15th C. in the style of the Embriachi, 31 by 32.5 by 23 cm. **£1,100-1,400**   *C*

A 19th C. Flemish or German ivory ewer, Christ Child's ankles repaired, stand slightly split, 26.5 cm. high. **£3,000-3,500**   *C*

An ivory tankard, probably German, 15½ in. (38 cm.), second half of the 19th C. **£5,000-6,000**   *SC*

An ivory mortar and pestle, the mortar 5¼ in. high (13.5 cm.), the pestle 7¼ in. (18.5 cm.), c. 1700. **£1,200-1,400**   *S*

An ivory oval plaque, French, 14 cm. by 9 cm., 18th C., on velvet mount. **£350-400**   *L*

A Dieppe ivory mirror, 183 by 126 cm., c. 1870. **£6,000-7,000**   *Bon*

A pair of Dieppe ivory mirrors, 2 ft. 9 in. high by 1 ft. 8 in. wide, 19th C. **£1,600-2,000**   *MMB*

A late 19th C. Dieppe ivory mirror, 34 in. high. **£500-600**   *Re*

A pair of French ivory and electrogilt white metal table candlesticks, by Pierre-Jacques-Theodore Blard, 8¾ in. high (22.4 cm.), c. 1855. **£1,500-2,000**   *S*

A whale-bone walking stick, 34 in. (86 cm.), 1810. **£650-750**   *S*

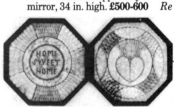

A pair of sailor's Valentine shell pictures, Barbadian, 9 in. wide (23 cm.), mid 19th C. **£650-750**   *S*

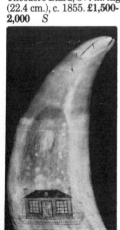

A scrimshawed whale's tooth, English, 7 in. high (18 cm.), mid 19th C. **£350-400**   *S*

A rare scrimshawed whale's tooth, decorated with Nelson's flagship 'Victory', English, 6 in. high (15 cm.), mid 19th C. **£1,100-1,200**   *S*

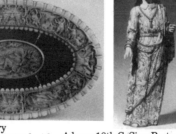

A 19th C. Dieppe ivory ornamental charger, centred with Venus riding on dolphins, piece of inner border chipped, 33.5 by 53.5 cm., oval. **£2,000-2,300**   *C*

A large 18th C. Sino-Portuguese ivory statue of Christ, gilding restored, 61 cm. high. **£6,000-7,000**   *C*

A French gothic ivory diptych leaf, representing the Adoration of the Magi, 3¼ in. (8.3 cm.), 14th C. **£2,000-2,500**   *S*

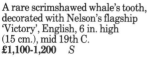

A sectional ivory group of a governess and four children, possibly of colonial origin, 7 cm. to 15 cm. **£1,100-1,200**   *Bon*

A large ivory crucifix figure, some fingers missing, now mounted on wooden cross, applied with the skull and crossbones and the Sacred Monogram, 21¾ in. high (55.2 cm.), 17th C.
£4,500-5,000   *S*

A South German ivory group of Christ at the Column, 7½ in. high (19 cm.), on ivory plinth with wood carcase, mid 17th C.
£5,000-6,000   *S*

An ivory figure of Cleopatra, her left hand holding drapery now missing, which formerly flowed across her loins, South German, both feet modern and detached, perspex base, 6⅛ in. high (15.5 cm.), first half 17th C.
£1,000-1,200   *S*

A 19th C. Dieppe ivory statuette of Charlemagne, 21.5 cm. high.
£900-1,000   *C*

A late 16th C. alabaster relief of a commander receiving the keys of a town, possibly Lepanto, chipped at corners, wooden frame with a gilt decorative border, 25.5 by 20 cm.
£550-650   *C*

(t.) A Meerschaum pipe, the stem carved as a gartered woman's leg, 4½ in., in a case. **£40–50**

(b.) A rare yew wood pipe holder, possibly Welsh, 12½ in. long, first half 18th C. **£200-250**   *SC*

A Meerschaum pipe carved as a flower bedecked maid, the stem silver mounted. **£90-120**   *CDC*

An Italian ivory double sided bust of a grotesque, one with a screaming warrior and the other with a monster with scaled chin, 2½ in. (6.5 cm.), 16th C.
£1,000-1,200   *S*

A pair of 19th C. alabaster urns on pedestals, 74 in. high (188 cm.).
£550–650   *SS*

A marble centre table, 2 ft. 5½ in. high (75 cm.), c. 1840.
£1,400-1,600   *S*

A Bluejohn urn, 13 in. high (33 cm.), 19th C. **£2,000-2,500**   *C*

A garniture of three George III Bluejohn vases, all damaged, 13½ in. high (34 cm.) and 10½ in. high (27 cm.). **£2,500-3,000**   *C*

A Nottingham alabaster panel of the Descent from the Cross, 15½ by 10 in. **£2,600-3000**   *GSP*

A 15th C. Nottingham alabaster relief of the Entombment, with traces of gilding and polychromy, missing corner and part of top edge, repaired crack, 36 by 26.5 cm. **£4,000-4,500**   *C*

A 19th C. English marble bust of a young girl, by Edward Onslow Ford, turned marble socle, 38 cm. high, 1877. **£500-600**   *C*

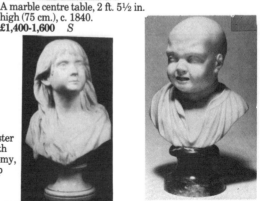

A white marble bust of a crying child, French or English, 11 in. high (28 cm.), late 18th C.
£400-500   *S*

A 19th C. French marble bust of a Breton girl, by Agathon Leonard (Van Weydeveldt), chipped edge behind, 46.5 cm. high. **£450-500**   *C*

A 16th C. Milanese marble lunette of the Resurrection, in the style of the Gaggini, his right arm loose, some chips and minor losses, 34 by 85.5 by 7 cm. **£3,500-4,500**   *C*

A pair of early 17th C. malines, alabaster reliefs of The Adoration of the Magi and The Circumcision, by Jasper de Hemeler or Hemeleers, with gilt ornamentation, one framed, both cracked, 11.5 by 9 cm. **£900-1,000**   *C*

A 15th C. Venetian Istrian stone decorative architectural relief of a putto-mask, surrounded by scrolling acanthus, some damage, 75 by 160 cm. **£1,600-2,000**   *C*

An early 19th C. Italian marble bust of an officer, edge of cloak damaged, 80 cm. high. **£400-500**   *C*

A fine 19th C. French marble bust of the Emperor Napoleon III, by Jean Auguste Barre, 61 cm. high. **£1,700-2,000**   *C*

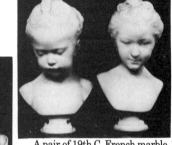

A pair of 19th C. French marble busts of young girls, by Henry Dasson, 49.5 cm. and 46.5 cm. high. **£2,000-2,500**   *C*

An early 19th C. Italian marble bust of Caroline Murat Bonaparte, after Canova, repaired crack in drapery, some chips on surface, part of right ear missing, 66 cm. high. **£900-1,000**   *C*

A pair of Italian black and coloured marble busts of Roman Emperors, 60 cm. high. **£5,000-6,000**   *C*

A white marble bust of a young woman smiling, by P... Giorgi, 1 ft. 11 in. (58.5 cm.), c. 1880. **£650-750**   *S*

A 19th C. Scottish marble bust of a man, by William Calder Marshall, veined reddish marble fluted half column on a moulded socle and square base with two large chips missing, 106 cm. high, 1849. **£350-450**   *C*

A white marble bust of the Duke of Bedford, by Joseph Nollekens, 46 in. overall (117.5 cm.). **£3,000-4,000**   *S*

A 19th C. Italian marble bust of a little girl, by Raffaello Monti, slightly weathered, socle damaged, 43.5 cm. high, dated 1858. **£550-650**   *C*

A 15th C. Tuscan marble bust of The Infant St. John The Baptist, attributed to the Master of the Marble Madonnas, 35.5 cm. high. **£19,000-22,000**   *C*

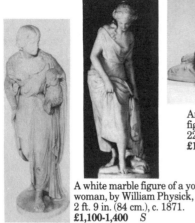

An Italo-Flemish white marble figure of a reclining female nude, 22¾ in. long (57.8 cm.), c. 1700. **£1,800-2,500** *S*

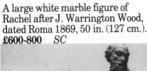

A white marble figure of a young woman, by William Physick, 2 ft. 9 in. (84 cm.), c. 1871. **£1,100-1,400** *S*

A large white marble figure of Rachel after J. Warrington Wood, dated Roma 1869, 50 in. (127 cm.). **£600-800** *SC*

An early 15th C. Sienese marble statuette of the Virgin Annunciate, attributed to Jacopo della Quercia, head replaced, joint of left index finger damaged, weathered, 55 cm. high. **£4,000-5,000** *C*

A carved marble statue by Giulio Tadolini, dated 1876, on rotating stand, 37 in. high (94 cm.). **£1,300-1,500** *SS*

A Netherlandish terracotta figure of St. Jerome, right foot missing, 17¼ in. long (43.8 cm.), second half 17th C. **£2,200-2,500** *S*

A 19th C. Italian white marble statuary figure, signed E. Caroni, 7 ft. 8 in. high. **£6,000-7,000** *PWC*

A small terracotta maquette, in the manner of Joseph Charles Marin, 4¼ in. high (14.5 cm.), c. 1800. **£500-600** *S*

An Italian white marble classical nude, signed D Barcaglia, Milano, 49½ in. high. **£1,800-2,000** *CSK*

A pair of terracotta Sphinxes, perhaps Piedmont, wood stand, 8¼ in. long (20 cm.), 18th C. **£1,200-1,400** *S*

A pair of Italian terracotta groups of Summer and Autumn, traces of original gilding, Bologna, 10¾ in. (27.3 cm.), late 18th C. **£1,200-1,500** *S*

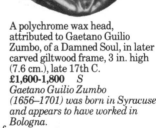

A polychrome wax head, attributed to Gaetano Guilio Zumbo, of a Damned Soul, in later carved giltwood frame, 3 in. high (7.6 cm.), late 17th C. **£1,600-1,800** *S*
Gaetano Guilio Zumbo (1656–1701) was born in Syracuse and appears to have worked in Bologna.

An early 16th C. South German or Austrian polychrome limewood relief of St. Joseph holding the Christ Child, damaged and repaired, 91.5 cm. high. **£3,000-3,400** *C*

A cold painted terracotta figure of an Arab Warrior, by J. Le Guluche, 2 ft. 5¼ in. (75.4 cm.), c. 1900. **£1,000-1,200** *S*

A set of four large Coades stone urns and covers, 37 in. (94 cm.), together with a damaged urn base, mid 19th C. **£1,500-2,000** *SC*

A South German boxwood plaquette of Adam and Eve, by the monogrammist A.L., signed A.L., 2⅛ in. (5.3 cm.), early 16th C. **£2,000-2,200** *S*

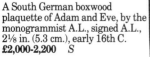

A pair of painted carved oak armorial wall appliques, German, repainted, 4 ft. 2 in. high by 2 ft. 2 in. (127 by 66 cm.), late 19th C. **£600-800** *S*

670

A good small German pearwood relief of the Washing of the Disciples' Feet (John 13: 1–20), 3 in. wide (7.7 cm.), 16th C. **£400-450** *S*

A set of 4 Allegorical panels, Flemish, 48 by 20 cm. each panel, c. 1530. **£1,100-1,300** *JB*

A German walnut figure of St. Stephen, traces of original colour, Middle Rhine, 35 in. (89 cm.), c. 1480. **£1,600-2,000** *S*

A Flemish oak relief depicting Sight, right hand corner inscribed Visus, probably from a set of the Five Senses, 8⅞ in. high (22.6 cm.), early 17th C. **£400-500** *S*

A 16th C. South German limewood polychrome ajoure relief of the execution of John The Baptist, sword missing, some repairs in plaster, 42.5 by 36.5 cm. **£1,200-1,400** *C*

A South German baroque carved and painted wood angel, the wings probably original but regilded, right arm and foot restored, 31 in. high (78.8 cm.), mid 18th C. **£1,000-1,200** *S*

A Netherlandish boxwood figure of the Farnese Hercules, 10¾ in. (27.3 cm.), 17th C. **£1,000-1,200** *S*

An early 16th C. South German limewood statuette of a Bishop Saint, left hand missing, re-cut in places, damages and restorations, 46 cm. high. **£400-450** *C*

A Swabian walnut figure of a king, probably one of the Magi, some restoration, 29 in. high (73.5 cm.), early 16th C. **£3,000-3,500** *S*

A 16th C. Spanish polychrome and gilt pinewood relief of the Nativity, restored, 86 by 70.5 cm. **£1,800-2,200** *C*

A pair of fine quality 16th C. Flemish oak carvings, possibly from a bed, with later stands and prickets, 12 in. high. **£600-800** *Hu*

A carved figure of St. Florian, S. German, 105 cm. high, c. 1520. **£1,400-1,600** *JB*

A late 15th or early 16th C. South German limewood statuette of the Virgin kneeling in Mourning, stripped of polychromy, some restorations. **£1,600-1,800** *C*

A walnut figure of St. John, Lorraine, 11¼ in. high (28.5 cm.), early 17th C. **£1,100-1,300** *S*

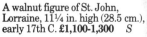

A 16th C. French polychrome oak bust of Christ, polychromy abraded, on a black wooden base, 25 cm. high. **£1,300-1,500** *C*

An early 16th C. South German or Swiss polychrome and giltwood bust of St. Nicholas, two fingers missing, polychromy abraded, wormeaten, 51 cm. high. **£1,400-1,600** *C*

A group of 8 Swabian limewood profile figures of Saints, from the wings of an Altar, 23 in. high (58.5 cm.), second quarter of 16th C. **£2,500-3,000** *S*

A fruitwood figure of Charity, Franco-Flemish, 13¾ in. high (35 cm.), c. 1600. **£1,500-1,700** *S*

A polychrome wood group of The Trinity, on carved giltwood bracket, 7¼ in. high (18.4 cm.), late 17th/early 18th C. **£300-400** *S*

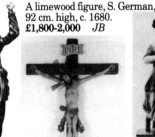

A limewood figure, S. German, 92 cm. high, c. 1680. **£1,800-2,000** *JB*

A fruitwood figure, probably English, 15¼ in. high (38.7 cm.), first half 17th C. **£600-700** *S*

A 17th C. Roman boxwood bozzetto for a Holy Water stoup, with traces of gilding, slight damage, 40.5 by 26 cm. **£1,500-1,700** *C*

A good German fruitwood figure of the Maria Immaculata, standing on an orb adorned with clouds, Bohemia or Lower Austria, minor damage, 14½ in. high (36.5 cm.), about 1725. **£1,400-1,600** *S*

A fine and large Tyrolean limewood polychrome crucifix, from the workshops of David Zurn, some repainting, much original colour and gilding beneath, 117 in. overall (297.2 cm.), mid 17th C. **£5,500-7,000** *S*

A ship's figurehead, 44 in. high (112 cm.), 20th C. **£600-700** *S*

A ship's figurehead, English, 20 in. high (51 cm.), 19th C. **£250-300** *S*

An 18th C. English oak statuette of William Shakespeare, by Salsbee, after Scheemaker's monument in Westminster Abbey of 1740, signed CUT BY SALSBEE Feb. ʸyᵉ9th 1762, minor chips, 23.5 cm. high. **£1,000-1,250** *C*

A German painted wooden and horn chandelier, carved with the bust of a 16th C. lady wearing a crown, fitted for electricity, 25 in. high (63 cm.). **£1,000-1,250** *C*

A Black Forest carved hardwood hall stand, in the form of a chained bear, 6 ft. 1 in. high. **£700-800** *AG*

A Spanish polychrome wood figure of Moses, probably Valladolid, toe broken, paint refreshed in the late 18th or early 19th C., 23½ in. long (29.8 cm.), late 16th C. **£2,600-3,000** *S*

A Swiss or German painted hat and umbrella stand, 6 ft. 9 in. high (206 cm.), c. 1880. **£1,000-1,200** *S*
Beware of 'glass fibre' imitations.

A carved walnut bellows, Italian, 72 m. long, c. 1650. **£700-800** *JB*

A painted wood group of three putti as acrobats, South German, 8¾ in. high (22.2 cm.), early 18th C. **£1,000-1,200** *S*

A good pair of Flemish oak figures, 17 in. (43 cm.), early 18th C. **£550-650** *SC*

Three Sialk type black painted
pottery cups, 5½ in. (14 cm.),
2¾ in. (7 cm.) and 4½ in.
(11.2 cm.) high, 3rd millennium
B.C. **£600-800**   *C*

(l.) An ovoid ewer, in bichrome
ware, 12 in., Archaic Period, 7th
Century B.C. **£300-400**
(r.) A small neck amphora, in
proto white painted ware, 5½ in.,
late Bronze Age, 12th Century
B.C. **£150-200**   *DWB*

A Phrygian red and black painted
rhyton, 10¾ in. (27.3 cm.) high,
mid 1st millennium B.C.
£1,800-2,200   *C*

A Cypriot white painted ware
oinochoe, with red and brown
concentric circles, 9 in. high
(23 cm.), 8th Century B.C.
£450-550   *C*

A heart-shaped baked clay corn
docket, 3.4 by 5 by 2.3 cm., c. 630
B.C., probably from a western
province such as Guzana.
£100-150   *C*

An Attic black figure little
masters band cup, 11 in. diam.
(28.2 cm.), 6th Century B.C.
£1,500-1,800   *C*

An Egyptian terracotta figure of a
crouching monkey, 2¾ in. high
(7.1 cm.), Dynasty XVIII.
£500-600   *C*

(l.) A green glazed composition
shabti, of the prophet of Neith,
Horudja, 7¾ in. high (19.7 cm.),
Dynasty XXVI. **£1,000-1,500**
(r.) A brilliant blue glazed
composition shabti, of the First
Concubine of Amun,
Est-em-khebi, 6 in. high
(15.1 cm.), Dynasty XXI.
£800-900   *C*

An Etruscan gesso-painted
terracotta female antefix, 7½ in.
high (19 cm.), 6th Century B.C.
£350-450   *C*

A pseudo-chalcidian black figure
amphora, from the Polyphemos
Group, incised and purple painted
detail, small repair at rim, 13 in.
high (33 cm.), 530–510 B.C.
£1,800-2,400   *C*

A Rhodian Herakles head vase,
2¾ in. high (7 cm.), late 6th
Century B.C. **£1,800-2,000**   *C*

An East Greek terracotta 'plastic'
flask, painted in red, minor repair
and restoration, 5½ in. high
(14 cm.), second half 6th Century
B.C. **£500-600**   *C*

A black glazed terracotta guttus,
repaired, handle damaged, 5⅛ in
(13 cm.) long, 4th Century B.C.
£400-500   *C*

An Apulian red figure bell krater,
by the Painter of Vatican V 50,
foot repaired, 12 in. high
(30.2 cm.), Middle Apulian.
£500-600   *C*

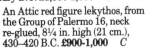

A Greek pottery askos, with
detailed black painting of the
wings and face, 3 in. high
(7.5 cm.), third quarter of 5th
Century B.C. **£1,500-1,600**   *C*

An Attic red figure lekythos, from
the Group of Palermo 16, neck
re-glued, 8¼ in. high (21 cm.),
430–420 B.C. **£900-1,000**   *C*

A Campanian Bail amphora, from
the Libation Group, 13½ in. high
(34.2 cm.), 4th Century B.C.
£450-550   *C*

A Romano-Egyptian turquoise
glazed frit vase, with moulded
frieze of birds and animals,
repaired and restored, 7 in. high
£1,800-2,200   *C*

An unusual East Roman yellow lead glazed terracotta lamp, 4¾ in. long (12 cm.), c. 1st Century A.D. **£500-600**   *C*

A figure of a soldier about to slay a prisoner, 7 in. high (17.8 cm.), Graeco-Roman. **£220-280**   *C*

A standing figure of Bes, wearing palmette head-dress, and carrying Harpocrates, 10¼ in. high (26 cm.), Graeco-Roman. **£250-300**   *C*

A Tarentine terracotta figure of Venus, repaired with minor restoration, 19 in. high (43.2 cm.), 3rd Century B.C. **£1,400-1,800**   *C*

A rare silver axe-head, in the form of a panther's head, 3½ in. long (8.8 cm.), early 1st millennium B.C. **£1,400-1,800**   *C*

Two Luristan bronze axe-heads, 8 in. long (20.2 cm.), and 4½ in. long (11.2 cm.), early 1st millennium B.C. **£400-450**   *C*

Two Celtic Bronze Age swords, 24 in. long (61 cm.), late 2nd millennium B.C. **£1,800-2,200**   *C*

An Egyptian bronze figure of the snake-headed god Nekhbeyet (or Nehebka), 6½ in. high (16.6 cm.), Ptolemaic Period. **£1,200-1,800**   *C*

A bronze figure of Neith, the rectangular base inscribed: 'May Neith give life, health and stability to Ptahusir, son of Amen-irru, born of' 3-wadjet, head, crown and base repaired, 15¾ in. high (40 cm.), Dynasty XXVI, late 7th/early 6th Century B.C. **£2,800-3,400**   *C*

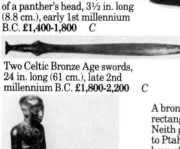

A bronze figure of Sekhmet, the lion-headed goddess, some restoration, 11½ in. high (29.3 cm.), Late Period. **£1,000-1,500**   *C*

An Egyptian bronze statue of Imhotep, the deified scribe seated on an openwork throne, 5¼ in. high (13.2 cm.), 6th-5th Century B.C. **£3,500-4,500**   *C*

A bronze figure of Osiris, wearing atef-crown, 6½ in. high (16.5 cm.), 4th-2nd Century B.C. **£650-850**   *C*

A bronze figure of a kneeling libation priest before a goddess, possibly Nekhbet, wearing a white crown and uraeus, on wooden rectangular base, 6 in. high (15.4 cm.), 6th-5th Century B.C. **£1,000-1,500**   *C*

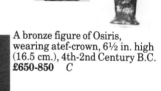

A seated bronze figure of Isis and Harpocrates, the goddess suckling Harpocrates, on wooden throne, 4¼ in. high (10.7 cm.), 6th-4th Century B.C. **£650-850**   *C*

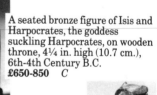

A bronze and wooden Ibis figure, 7 in. high (17.8 cm.), 4th-2nd Century B.C. **£1,400-1,800**   *C*

A Luristan bronze horse bit, each terminal cast in openwork relief with 'Master of Animals', 8 in. long (20.1 cm.), early 1st millennium B.C. **£2,500-3,500**   *C*

A bronze ichneumon, from a sceptre finial, 7½ in. (18.8 cm.), Late Period. **£4,000-5,000**   *C*

A Corinthian bronze 'spoiled'
helmet, 7 in. high (17.5 cm.), late
6th Century B.C.
£9,000-12,000   *C*
*The 'spoiled' helmet suggests that
the cheek-pieces were deliberately
turned outwards to ensure they
could not be re-used, either when
dedicated or when later removed
from the shrine.*

A bronze key, with cylindrical
and square body incised with an
Osiris, 5¾ in. high (13.5 cm.),
Ptolemaic or Roman Period.
£800-1,000   *C*

An Achaemenid silver phial,
10¾ in. diam. (27.5 cm.), c. 5th
Century B.C. **£3,500-4,000**   *C*

An Archaic Greek bronze female
statue, 4¼ in. high (10.8 cm.),
late 6th Century B.C.
£1,000-1,500   *C*

A Roman silver bowl, 4½ in.
diam. (11.2 cm.), 1st Century
B.C./A.D. **£1,000-1,500**   *C*

A 'pillar moulded' green glass
bowl, 4¾ in. diam. (12.4 cm.), 1st
Century A.D. **£400-500**   *C*

A Romano-Hungarian bronze
figure of Aphrodite, 5¼ in. high
(13.4 cm.), 2nd-3rd Century A.D.
£500-600   *C*

A translucent turquoise
mould-blown glass bowl, with
two wheel-cut bands around the
side, 3 in. diam. (7.6 cm.), 1st
Century A.D. **£150-200**   *C*

Three Babylonian haematite
trussed duck weights, 1st
millennium B.C. **£200-300**   *C*

A dark green translucent glass
flask, in the form of a snail,
6¼ in. long (16 cm.), c. 4th
Century A.D. **£1,000-1,500**   *C*

A grey schist upper part of a
statue of Osiris, 6 in. high
(15.5 cm.), Saite, c. 6th Century
B.C. **£700-900**   *C*

An olive green translucent glass
double balsamarium, 5 in. high
(12.9 cm.), c. 4th Century A.D.
£250-350   *C*

A translucent green glass double
balsamarium, 10 in. high
(25.4 cm.), 5th Century A.D.
£2,000-2,500   *C*

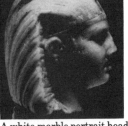

A white marble portrait head of a
Ptolemaic ruler, wearing
nemes-crown, recessed for a
bronze uraeus, the eyes recessed
for inlay, 3½ in. high (8.8 cm.),
2nd-1st Century B.C.
£3,500-4,000   *C*

The upper half of a sandstone
ushabti, 5½ in. high (14 cm.),
late Dynasty XVIII.
£2,000-2,500   *C*

An Egyptian limestone relief of
Rameses II, 30½ by 21½ in.
(75.7 by 49 cm.), Dynasty XIX,
c. 1290-1224 B.C. **£2,200-
2,800**   *C*

A Serpentine Royal Ushabti of
King Senkamenisken, 7½ in.
high (19.1 cm.), 643-623 B.C.
£6,000-8,000   *C*

Two Assyrian marble square
plaques, each carved with part of
a cuneiform text from the palace
of Ashurnasirpal, from Nimrud,
7¼ by 5½ in. (18.3 by 14.2 cm.),
Reign of Ashurnasirpal II
(883-859 B.C.). **£750-950**   *C*

An Egyptian basalt herm, 10¼ in. high (26 cm.), end 1st Century B.C./early 1st Century A.D. **£2,500-3,500** *C*

An alabaster pyxis, repaired with minor restoration, 5 in. diam. (12.7 cm.), Graeco-Roman. **£500-600** *C*

A limestone relief panel, carved on one side with the bearded head of Bacchus, the reverse with an erotic scene of Bacchus and a reclining female, 63 by 63 cm., Cypriot, 4th Century B.C. **£7,000-9,000** *P*

A South Arabian alabaster head of a female, the eyes inlaid with shell limestone, 8¼ in. high (21 cm.), 2nd-1st Century B.C. **£1,000-1,500** *C*

A Romano-British sandstone head of a young man, 9¼ in. high (23.5 cm.), 1st-2nd Century A.D. **£450-550** *C*

A Romano-Celtic red quartzite head of a river god, 8 in. high (20.3 cm.), 2nd Century A.D. **£550-750** *C*

A Roman marble statue of Sylvanus, head missing, 19½ in. high (49.5 cm.), late 2nd Century A.D. **£5,000-6,000** *C*

An East Roman limestone funerary banquet relief, depicting a reclining man, 19¼ by 29 in. (49 by 74 cm.), c. 150-200 A.D. **£1,800-2,200** *C*

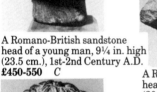

A porphyry head of Lucius Verus, on green marble stand, 9½ in. high (24.2 cm.). **£1,800-2,400** *C*

A Roman marble head of a young boy, possibly a member of the Imperial family, fragment of cheek, tip of nose and lip restored, 7½ in. high (19 cm.), early 3rd Century A.D. **£2,800-3,400** *C*

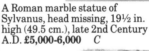

An East Roman limestone dyad relief, 6¼ in. high (15.8 cm.), 2nd-3rd Century A.D. **£650-750** *C*

A marble sarcophagus relief fragment of a running warrior, wearing a Phrygian type helmet, 19½ in. high (49.5 cm.), 3rd Century A.D. **£6,000-8,000** *C*

An Egyptian gesso-painted wooden upper half of an anthropoid sarcophagus, 23 in. high (58.5 cm.), Late Period. **£2,200-2,800** *C*

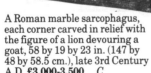

A Roman marble sarcophagus, each corner carved in relief with the figure of a lion devouring a goat, 58 by 19 by 23 in. (147 by 48 by 58.5 cm.), late 3rd Century A.D. **£3,000-3,500** *C*

A Coptic limestone frieze, 12¼ in. wide (30.8 cm.), 5th-6th Century A.D. **£150-200** *C*

A fragment of papyrus, bearing 6 lines of a hieratic inscription written in red and black ink, 30 in. long by 3½ in. (76.2 by 8.8 cm.), New Kingdom. **£1,800-2,400** *C*

An Egyptian wooden sarcophagus fragment, belonging to the Chantress of Amon-re, Gwr-iry, painted in black with red and blue detail, repaired, mounted behind glass, 13½ by 12½ in. (34.5 by 31.7 cm.), Dynasty XXX-early Ptolemaic. **£800-1,200** *C*

676

A fine and unusual Veramin carpet, the pale beige field with scalloped light brown spandrels, in a broad light beige border of palmettes and vine, between beige and medium brown flowering vine and blue stylised vine strips, minor repairs, 14 ft. 7 in. by 9 ft. 10 in. (444 by 299 cm.). **£7,000-8,000**   *C*

Debatable as to whether Veramin — but a good example.

A Malayer rug, the saffron field decorated with floral botehs, with a vine green floral border, 3 ft. 1 in. by 2 ft. 4 in. (94 by 71 cm.). **£300-£500**   *S*

A Veramin rug, the indigo field with an overall design of rosettes, flowerheads, palmettes and leaves, linked by vines, with madder border, 7 ft. 4 in. by 4 ft. 9 in. (223 by 145 cm.), c. 1900. **£4,000-5,000**   *S*

A Tabriz carpet, the ivory field with an indigo medallion and pale indigo spandrels, 13 by 9 ft. (396 by 274 cm.), c. 1880. **£2,500-4,000**   *S*

This carpet is of good quality, design and age.

A fine antique Tabriz Hadjijalili rug, the ivory field with large floral sprays and palmettes, around a shaded ice-blue scalloped arabesque floral vine medallion with pendants, with pale turquoise stripes, both ends re-woven, 5 ft. 7 in. by 3 ft. 9 in. (170 by 114 cm.). **£1,500-2,500**   *C*

'Hadjijalili' — master weaver in Tabriz.

A Teheran rug, the burgundy field with rows of flowering plants, trees and flower-vases, in a blue border of floral cartouches and roundels, 7 ft. by 4 ft. 5 in. (213 by 135 cm.). **£1,500-2,000**   *C*

A Sarough rug, the beige field with an indigo medallion and rose spandrels, 6 ft. 10 in. by 4 ft. 1 in. (208 by 124 cm.), c. 1900. **£800-£1,200**   *S*

A Sarough raised wool rug, the madder field with an indigo medallion, the indigo border with a design of palmettes and vines, triple guard stripes, 4 ft. 9 in. by 3 ft. 4 in. (148 by 102 cm.), c. 1920. **£1,000-2,000**   *S*

A fine Senneh pictorial prayer rug, with large columns supporting an indigo mehrab with floral sprays, in a rust red border of palmettes and vine between indigo shrub-motif stripes, 6 ft. 10 in. by 4 ft. 6 in. (208 by 137 cm.) **£1,500-2,500**   *C*

A Sarough rug, the ivory field with an indigo and madder pole medallion and peach spandrels, 6 ft. 5 in. by 4 ft. 3 in. (196 by 129 cm.), c. 1880. **£1,200-1,800**   *S*

A Nain rug, with pale indigo field, 5 ft. 5 in. by 3 ft. 8 in. (165 by 112 cm.), modern. **£500-600**   *S*

A fine Kirman carpet, the indigo field with a central burgundy and blue feathery ogival medallion, surrounded by scrolling vine and palmettes in a blood-red flowering spray border, between triple ivory and blue flowering vine stripes, one end small stain, 14 ft. 2 in. by 10 ft. (431 by 305 cm.). **£800-1,200**   *C*

A Nain rug, excellent condition, minor split, 7 ft. 4 in. by 5 ft. 1 in. (225 by 155 cm.). **£1,500-2,000**   *L*

Close to Esfahan — very similar weave.

A Kashan carpet, having a large floral figured dark blue and red-brown ground medallion on a figured beige field, 10 ft. 6 in. by 7 ft. 3 in. **£500-800**　*GC*

A Kashan Mohtasham carpet, the ivory field with palmettes and floral sprays, around a concentric medium blue and ivory similar medallion with pendants, very slight wear in places, 11 ft. 8 in. by 8 ft. 3 in. (354 by 251 cm.). **£5,000-£7,000**　*C*

Woven with soft, finely spun wool. 'Mohtasham' — a master weaver in Kashan — not all the carpets given this name are woven by him but his designs have continued to be used.

A Kashan rug, with indigo field, the madder border with floral sprays and arabesques, twin guard stripes, 6 ft. 8 in. by 4 ft. 3 in. **£500-£800**　*SC*

A fine antique Kurk Kashan rug, the ivory field with diagonal rows of flowering boteh, between golden-yellow angular vine stripes, 6 ft. 8 in. by 4 ft. 4 in. (202 by 130 cm.). **£1,200-1,800**　*C*

'Kurk', the softest wool taken from the chest of the sheep. Finely spun and good weave.

A Kerman pictorial rug, depicting Bahram-e-Gour out hunting, with a green floral border, 4 ft. 4 in. by 3 ft. (132 by 91 cm.), c. 1920. **£400-£600**　*S*

A Kashan silk prayer carpet, the ivory mehrab with a vase of flowers, flanked by flowering Trees of Life, birds and animals, indigo floral spandrels, with madder border, 10 ft. 6 in. by 6 ft. 10 in. (320 by 208 cm.), c. 1920. **£2,000-£3,000**　*S*

A silk Kashan prayer rug, with ivory field, the pale blue mehrab with palmettes and vine in a raspberry-red border, 6 ft. 8 in. by 4 ft. 3 in. (204 by 130 cm.). **£2,000-£3,000**　*C*

A Kerman carpet, the madder field with a circular medallion, and indigo floral border, 14 ft. 6 in. by 12 ft. 3 in. (442 by 373 cm.), c. 1930. **£800-1,200**　*S*

A Kashan carpet, indigo field, madder border with palmettes and vines, twin guard stripes, 9 ft. 9 in. by 7 ft. (297 by 213 cm.). **£800-£1,200**　*S*

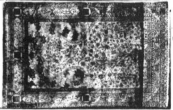

A fine silk Kashan prayer rug, the pale rose pink field with an inscribed mehrab with a variety of multi-coloured inscriptions above, in a blue palmette and flowering vine border, backed, slight damage to top, two minor repairs, 6 ft. 6 in. by 4 ft. (198 by 122 cm.). **£3,000-£5,000**　*C*

A Kashan carpet, with figured blue and red ground, the main border has a continuous design on a red field, one small hole, 10 ft. 8 in. by 7 ft. 4 in. **£500-800**　*GC*

A Kashan rug, with royal blue field, the rust-red indented spandrels with cloud-band and flowerheads, 6 ft. 7 in. by 4 ft. 3 in. (201 by 130 cm.). **£300-500**　*C*

A fine Kashan raised silk and metal thread prayer rug, with plain outer gold stripe, 6 ft. 8 in. by 4 ft. 4 in. (204 by 132 cm.). **£2,000-£4,000**　*C*

The mehrab is the arch at the top of the carpet only appearing in prayer rugs.

To find your way around the complex world of Oriental carpets and textiles you could attend auctions and exhibitions in five continents, visit galleries and museums in a score of cities, attend conferences, read books by the dozen, and talk to the world's leading experts…
or you could subscribe to

HALI

The International Journal of
Oriental Carpets and Textiles

A Kashan rug, the madder field with an indigo pole medallion and spandrels and indigo border, 6 ft. 10 in. by 4 ft. 5 in. (208 by 135 cm.), c. 1920. **£400-500** *S*

A pair of Kashan rugs, the ivory field of each with a variety of flowering trees in a blue border, each with areas of wear, 7 ft. 2 in. by 4 ft. 6 in. (218 by 137 cm.). **£1,500-3,000** *C*

A fine pair of Esfahan rugs, the ivory field decorated with scrolling foliage, within a wide ivory border and 2 outer guard stripes, 7 ft. by 4 ft. 6½ in. (214 by 139 cm.). **£3,000-5,000** *SS*

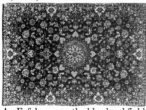

An Esfahan rug, the blood-red field with palmettes, floral sprays and perching birds, in a palmette and scrolling vine frame, 5 ft. by 3 ft. 4 in. (152 by 102 cm.). **£2,800-3,500** *C*

GLOSSARY

Abrash   Variations of density in a colour seen in a carpet by irregular horizontal washes, can greatly add to the value.

Aniline   Chemical dye, a derivative of coal-tar, first produced in the 1860's, most common in the red-blue-purple range, colours tend to fade (orange-pink, for instance can fade to walnut-brown).

Boteh   Widespread pattern of Persian origin (original meaning 'cluster of leaves'), used in Europe in the Paisley pattern.

Ch'ang   Chinese endless knot, the inextricable knot of destiny.

Chrome dye   A fast synthetic dye now used in all the major rug weaving areas, colours do not fade.

Gol Henai Pattern   Floral pattern associated with Persian rugs, mainly found on Hamadan rugs.

Hejira (or Hijra)   The beginning of the Muhammedan calendar, 16 July, A.D. 622.

Herati Pattern   Also called the mahi or fish pattern. This common pattern originated in East Persia.

Jufti   'False' knot, either Turkish or Persian, whereby the knots are tied to four, not two, warp threads.

Kelim   Also spelled kilim, gilim, gelim. Principally from Anatolia.

Madder   Deep red-brown dye.

Palas   Caucasian name for kelim.

Palmette   A flowerhead of heart-shape with many radiating lobes or petals.

Sileh   A corruption of a now lost Caucasian place name. A form of Soumak, sileh pieces tend to be woven with rows of large S-motifs.

Soumak   Sumak, Summak, Sumacq, Sumakh, thought to be a corruption of Shemaka, town in south east Caucasus.

Spandrels   Architectural term for the space between the curve of an arch and the enclosing mouldings.

Swastika   A hooked cross. Chinese symbol for 10,000 (wan) and happiness.

Tiraz   Official weaving factory usually set up under Royal patronage.

A pair of Esfahan rugs, the ivory field decorated with an oval madder medallion, within a madder border of palmettes and flowerheads and 2 outer guard stripes, 6 ft. 11 in. by 4 ft. 9¾ in. (209 by 137 cm.). **£2,000-3,000** *SS*

A Kashan rug, with ivory field and madder border, 6 ft. 7 in. by 4 ft. 3 in. (201 by 129 cm.), c. 1930. **£2,000-3,000** *S*

A good quality example.

A Kashan prayer carpet, the indigo mehrab with vases of flowers, with stylised trees and honeycomb flower spandrels, 14 ft. 4 in. by 10 ft. 3 in. (434 by 312 cm.), c. 1930. **£2,000-3,000** *S*

A pair of Kashan rugs, each with a magenta field and blue lobed pole medallion and spandrels, with green main border, 84 by 53 in. (214 by 135 cm.). **£500-800** *L*

These Kashans are of reasonably low quality.

A pair of Kashan rugs, the central terracotta, ivory and light blue medallion on a blue ground, the main border maroon, 84½ by 52 in. **£1,200-1,800** *Re*

Many similar rugs produced — varying in quality.

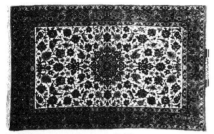

An Esfahan rug, the ivory field with palmettes and floral sprays around a radiating mole-grey medallion with pendants, an inscription at one end, 5 ft. 8 in. by 3 ft. 5 in. (173 by 104 cm.). £1,000-£1,500 *C*

A Ghashghai rug, the brick field with large finely hooked and stepped mid blue diamond medallion, with ivory centre diamond medallion, a turtle motif within, mid blue field and brick spandrels, kelim ends, 7 ft. 2 in. by 4 ft. 8 in. (218 by 142 cm.). £1,000-£2,000 *WW*

A Ghom part silk rug, the madder field with a central ivory pole medallion, with beige border, 4 ft. 4 in. by 7 ft. 9 in. £700-900 *SC*

An Esfahan rug, the madder field with an indigo medallion, with indigo spandrels, the indigo border with a design of palmettes, leaves and flowerheads, 7 ft. 8 in. by 4 ft. 11 in. (234 by 150 cm.), c. 1940. £2,000-3,000 *S*

A Ghom silk rug, the ivory field with an indigo medallion, ochre floral spandrels, indigo floral border, 5 ft. 7 in. by 3 ft. 6 in. (170 by 107 cm.). £1,000-1,500 *S*

Prolific rug-weaving area — many identical silk rugs produced — consequently there is a fairly set market price.

A Ghashghai rug, having an ivory central medallion on a dark blue ground and 4 red spandrels, 7 ft. 9 in. by 5 ft. 4 in. £600-900 *V*

A Ghashghai rug, the ivory field with large central madder ground lozenge, 6 ft. 2 in. by 5 ft. £400-800 *WHB*

A fine Esfahan Seirafian rug, the ivory field with palmettes, feathery leaves and vine around a burgundy concentric radiating floral medallion, an inscription cartouche at one end, 5 ft. 4 in. by 3 ft. 6 in. (163 by 107 cm.). £4,000-6,000 *C*

An Esfahan rug, with ivory field, pale indigo spandrels with vines and serrated leaves, 5 ft. 8 in. by 3 ft. 5 in. (173 by 104 cm.), c. 1930. £800-1,200 *S*

This is a medium quality rug from a prolific rug-producing centre.

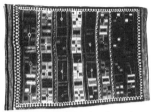

A Ghashghai gelim, in alternate shades of madder, ivory and indigo, 7 ft. 6 in. by 5 ft. (229 by 152 cm.), c. 1900. **£2,500-3,500** *S*

Value point
- Good vegetable colours helped this piece.

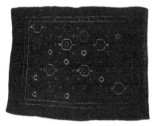

An Afshar rug, with indigo field, 3 inner and one outer guard stripe, geometric gelim ends, 5 ft. 3 in. by 3 ft. 11 in. (160 by 119 cm.), c. 1860. **£1,800-2,500** *S*

Finely woven rugs from this South Western area of Persia can be found but are not the norm.

A Heriz carpet, the ivory field with an indigo medallion, the madder border with rosette flowerheads and vines, 10 ft. 4 in. by 8 ft. (315 by 244 cm.). **£1,500-2,000** *S*
Ivory field always popular.

A large Heriz carpet, the tomato ground filled with stylised flowers and medallions, conforming indigo main border with ivory outer borders, condition low, 213 by 126 in. **£3,000-4,000** *SC*

Value Points
- Over the last 2½ years good 19th C. Heriz carpets have become extremely popular.
- An uncrowded design, pale madder, pale blue, ivory and saffron, are a plus factor.
- Also strongly designed border.
- Good Heriz are fetching up to 5 times as much as 3 years ago.

682

A Khamseh runner, the indigo field with 5 medallions, 9 ft. 5 in. by 2 ft. 11 in. (287 by 89 cm.), c. 1920. **£300-500** *S*

A fine and unusual Afshar flatweave, with a broad reciprocal arrow-head border between flowerhead and running-dog stripes, 6 ft. 10 in. by 4 ft. 6 in. (208 by 137 cm.). **£800-1,200** *C*

Value Points
- Flatweaves do wear relatively quickly, but are not common from this area.
- Good ivory reciprocal border.

A Mahal carpet, the indigo field with the herati pattern, the madder border with a palmette, 11 ft. 9 in. by 7 ft. 9 in. (358 by 236 cm.), c. 1930. **£600-900** *S*

A Serapi kelleh, the camel field with 2 columns of stepped guls, 4 geometric borders, 17 ft. 9 in. by 7 ft. 2 in. (541 by 218 cm.), modern. **£600-800** *S*

Value Point
- Difficult size to sell, although with popular camel field.

A Hamadan Maslaghan rug, the red field woven with a blue medallion and spandrels, 74 by 52 in. (188 by 132 cm.). **£150-250** *L*

Hamadans are mostly coarsely woven and consequently at the bottom end of the market.

A fine antique Afshar rug, the field with multi-coloured columns of boteh and floral motifs, the brown border between golden-yellow flowering vine and baton and lozenge stripes, a short kilim strip at each end, one side small repair, 8 ft. 8 in. by 4 ft. 8 in. (264 by 142 cm.). **£800-1,200** *C*

A large North West Persian kelleh, the indigo field with herati pattern around alternate brick-red similar stepped linked lozenges, containing the Persian royal cypher with lion and rising sun, an inscription panel at the top and inner stylised inscription border, dated AH 1253/1837 AD, areas of wear and damage, 19 ft. 2 in. by 7 ft. 8 in. (583 by 234 cm.). **£600-800** *C*

Value Points
- Carpets with relatively early dates will interest both dealer and collector
- Unfortunately this one is coarsely woven and the colours were not good — although the design is unusual.

A Heriz carpet, the pale indigo field with angular palmettes, vines and stylised flowerheads, a madder palmette and vine border, 13 ft. 3 in. by 9 ft. 8 in. (404 by 295 cm.), c. 1870. **£3,00-5,000** *S*

Value Point
- Good design and vegetable dyes — pale blue field adds to value.

A Garabagh runner, the black field with stylised sprays of flowers and leaves, 12 ft. 10 in. by 3 ft. 3 in. (391 by 99 cm.), c. 1900. **£500-800** *S*

Value Points
- There is a limit to the price of runners — not a great deal of demand for passage floor covering.
- Apart from the very fine and unusual pieces, most runners sell quite cheaply.
- This is a better example.

Two Soumac bag faces, with indigo hooked gul borders, 21½ by 20½ in., and 20 by 19½ in. **£400-£600** *Bea*

A Garabagh runner, the tomato field with green lobed pole medallions contained by a saffron band, all in a madder ground, some stains, part guards worn, 261 by 39 in. **£400-600** *SC*

A Shirvan runner, the indigo field with 6 medallions, enclosing guls within a saffron frame, 9 ft. 7 in. by 3 ft. 7 in. **£1,000-1,500** *SC*

Value Points
- Good age.
- Saffron, ivory and green good colours.
- Balanced border.
- With polychrome barber-pole guard stripes.

A Talysh runner, the pale indigo field with stylised plants, within an ivory rosette and dice border, 8 ft. 5 in. by 3 ft. 6 in. (257 by 107 cm.), c. 1860. **£1,500-2,500** *S*

Value Points
- Good Talysh.
- Typical well spaced ivory border and popular pale indigo field.
- Good vegetable dyes and age.

A Shirvan rug, the pale gold field with blue, white and pink geometric flowers, 5 ft. 2 in. by 4 ft. 3 in. **£400-600** *T*

A fine Shirvan carpet, in tones of rust-red, pink, blue and ivory on a dark blue field, small repairs, 10 ft. 1 in. by 5 ft. 8 in. **£700-900** *GC*

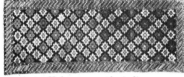

A Heriz runner, the madder field with 4 indigo medallions, 10 ft. 10 in. by 3 ft. 1 in. (330 by 94 cm.), c. 1880. **£500-800** *S*

A star Kuba runner, the indigo field with polychrome star guls, a barber-pole border, 9 ft. 3 in. by 3 ft. 7 in. (282 by 109 cm.). **£800-£1,200** *S*

A fine antique Mereze prayer rug, with indigo field, dated AH 1273/1856, areas of slight wear and damage, 4 ft. 2 in. by 3 ft. 5 in. (127 by 104 cm.). **£1,500-2,500** *C*

A Lenkoran rug, the indigo field with 2 crab medallions, 6 ft. 4 in. by 4 ft. 1 in. (193 by 124 cm.), c. 1930. **£500-800** *S*

Minus Point
- Mean narrow borders.

A Kazakh rug, with indigo field, the saffron border with rosettes, single reciprocal trefoil guard rails, 6 ft. 10 in. by 4 ft. 11 in., c. 1880. **£1,500-2,500** *SC*

A Kazakh Frachlo double ended prayer rug, with green field, 8 ft. 5 in. by 4 ft. 6 in. (257 by 137 cm.). **£600-800** *S*

A Fachralo Kazakh rug, the tomato-red field with floral motifs around a gabled blue lozenge, in a pale apricot border, areas of slight wear, 6 ft. by 4 ft. 2 in. (183 by 127 cm.). **£200-300** *C*

A Kazakh Bordjalou rug, the madder field with hooked medallions and double 'E' panels, the saffron border with half hooked guls, 7 ft. 10 in. by 5 ft. 7 in. (239 by 170 cm.), c. 1880. **£500-700** *S*

Value Points
- Good Bordjalou border.
- Strong reciprocal guard stripes.

A Moroccan carpet, with claret field around a hooked lime-green lozenge medallion, the shaded blue mehrabs with floral motifs, 10 ft. 1 in. by 6 ft. 1 in. (307 by 185 cm.). **£300-500** . *C*

A central Anatolian prayer kilim, the burgundy field with a pale pistachio green hooked prayer panel, in an apricot border of hooked lozenges, between indigo multiple motif stripes, one edge slight damage, 6 ft. 9 in. by 4 ft. (206 by 122 cm.). **£600-900** *C*

Value Points:
- soft shaded colours popular with private market —(gelims wear quite quickly.)

A Bessarabian gelim, depicting the Greek defeat of the Turks, after a painting by Dupresk, 8 ft. 10 in. by 7 ft. 2 in. (269 by 218 cm.), c. 1920. **£800-1,200** *S*

An Aubusson rug, with an ivory field, possibly Russian, 7 ft. 9 in. by 6 ft. (236 by 183 cm.), c. 1900. **£600-£900** *S*

A fine antique Melas rug, the field with a central brick-red panel of flowerheads, flanked by pale pistachio green panels of waisted lozenges, a short kilim strip at each end, 5 ft. 4 in. by 3 ft. 11 in. (163 by 119 cm.). **£800-1,200** *C*

A Bessarabian gelim, the ivory field with a design of medallions, in shades of green and ivory, 10 ft. 9 in. by 10 ft. 4 in. (328 by 315 cm.). **£800-1,500** *S*

Value Points:
- very unusual design for a Bessarabian — good soft light colours.

An early 15th C. orphrey, worked on linen with Christ on the Cross, in coloured silks against a ground worked in silver thread, perhaps South German, 48 by 21 in., c. 1400. **£3,000-5,000** *CSK*

An 18th C. Aubusson carpet, 20 ft. 5 in. by 19 ft. 6 in. (622 by 594 cm.). **£1,000-2,000** *S*

Value Points:
- A good carpet with a pale blue field but probably too big to make a very high price — quite coarsely woven.

An 18th C. Ghiordes prayer rug, with pale green mehrab, 6 ft. 10 in. by 5 ft. 1 in. (208 by 155 cm.). **£800-£1,200** *S*

Value Points:
- normally fairly worn but pretty rose madder, ivories and soft vine green.

A rare Sindh animal carpet, with madder field, a pale indigo border of flowers, 15 ft. 4 in. by 10 ft. 8 in. (467 by 325 cm.), c. 1880. **£500-800** *S*

A fine and large antique Bessarabian kilim, with beige field, a plain shaded pale indigo border, minor staining, 13 ft. 11 in. by 7 ft. 5 in. (425 by 226 cm.). **£3,500-4,500** *C*

Value Points:
- again decorators carpet
- very pretty soft colours

An Indian dhurry, the aubergine field with 9 rows of birds and 2 cows, 6 ft. 1 in. by 3 ft. 8 in. (185 by 112 cm.), 19th C. **£100-200** *S*

A fine Bessarabian rug, the sky blue field around an ivory scalloped panel, backed, 8 ft. by 5 ft. 5 in. (244 by 165 cm.). **£3,000-4,000** *C*

Value Points:
- decorators rugs
- good pastel colours

A late 19th C. Aubusson carpet, the champagne field with an oval floral medallion, 13 ft. 10 in. by 9 ft. 7 in. (422 by 292 cm.). **£2,000-4,000** *S*

Value Points:
- pastel colours popular with decorators
- a fine weave like this will wear less quickly than a coarse weave

An antique Tekke Turkman carpet, the brick-red field with 4 columns of linked Tekke guls, divided by cruciform secondary guls, areas of slight wear, ends reduced, new selvage, 7 ft. 8 in. by 5 ft. 8 in. (234 by 173 cm.). **£1,200-£1,800** *C*

Value Points
- Mixed gul and chevron border is a sign of earlier date (c. 1870-80).

A Baluchistan rug, the camel field with diagonal rows of alternately facing boteh, areas of corrosion and slight wear, 5 ft. 6 in. by 3 ft. 3 in. (168 by 99 cm.). **£500-800** *C*

Value Point
- Not very fine weave but good pale field with interesting botehs.

A coverlet or wall hanging, woven in blue and pink wool, with the date and the name of the embroideress, Carol(i)nia Pugliese 1830(?), Sardinian, 19th C. **£600-£900** *CSK*

An 18th C. hanging, with walnut silk field, Spanish or Portuguese, damaged and worn in places, 9 ft. 7 in. by 7 ft. 2 in. (292 by 218 cm.). **£300-500** *S*

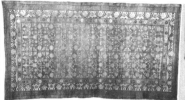

A Khotan carpet, with indigo field, 12 ft. 5 in. by 6 ft. 8 in. (378 by 203 cm.), c. 1880. **£1,500-2,000** *S*

Value Point
- Good quality pieces of this group from central Asia are relatively rare.

A rare 19th C. Lebanese fikie rug, with indigo field, with a madder pole medallion, a saffron gul border, 6 ft. 9 in. by 4 ft. 6 in. (206 by 107 cm.), c. 1860. **£600-900** *S*

Value Points:
- unusual but unattractive with medium coarse weave!

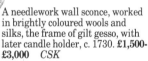

A large brightly coloured embroidered panel, in wool and silk, the black ground with a pair of yellow flowery shell cartouches outlined with blue scrollwork, all within a blue scarlet and green strapwork border, 2 ft. 9 in. high by 7 ft. 6½ in. wide (84 by 230 cm.), mounted on panel. **£3,000-4,000** *S*

A needlework wall sconce, worked in brightly coloured wools and silks, the frame of gilt gesso, with later candle holder, c. 1730. **£1,500-£3,000** *CSK*

Two cushions each worked with early 18th C. gros point, in green, blue and yellow silks and wools, 28 by 84 cm. **£250-300** *P*

A set of needlework hangings, in bargello work, with exotic leaves in shades of green and brown, the double panel 62 in. wide by 85 in., the narrow panel 43 in. wide, probably late 17th/early 18th C. **£3,000-4,000** *CSK*

A pair of orphrey panels, worked in coloured silks and gold thread, 15½ by 8 in., 16th C., framed and glazed. **£300-500** *CSK*

A Bible cushion cover, of ivory satin embroidered with flowers in brightly coloured silks and silver thread, enhanced with sequins, edged with pink satin trimmed with gold and silver lace, and trimmed with pink and silver ribbons at each corner, 10 by 13½ in., mid 17th C. **£1,500-2,500** *CSK*

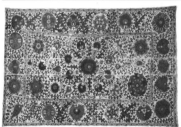

A Bokhara susani panel, with ivory field, 3 ft. by 5 ft. 10 in. (274 by 178 cm.), c. 1880. **£1,000-1,200** *S*

A late 17th C. embroidery, in polychrome silk, on a painted green linen ground, 2 ft. 4 in. by 1 ft. 11 in. (71 by 58 cm.), mounted. **£300-500** *S*

A Spanish silk and wool armorial hanging, on a dark blue background, 9 ft. 10 in. by 9 ft. 4 in. (299 by 283 cm.), 17th C. **£1,000-£1,500** *C*

A 17th C. stumpwork picture, with scenes from the 'Book of Esther', all in a variety of stitches with seed pearls, 1 ft. 2 in. by 9 in. (35 by 22 cm.), c. 1850, framed, and an embroidered picture, with David looking on as Bath-sheba bathes, mostly in satin stitch, 1 ft. 3 in. by 10 in. (38 by 25 cm.), c. 1850, framed. **£400-600** *S*

A late 17th C. stumpwork picture, of the Virgin, worked in a variety of colours and stitches on a cream silk ground, 14½ by 11½ in. (37 by 29 cm.), in a period cushion moulded walnut-veneered frame. **£800-1,200** *SS*

A Bokhara susani panel, the ivory ground embroidered with an unusual central tree, 5 ft. 10 in. by 3 ft. 8 in. (179 by 112 cm.), c. 1870. **£700-800** *S*

An early 18th C. panel of undyed linen, embroidered in blue, pink, yellow and ivory silks, in encroaching satin stitch and French knot, 67 by 87 cm., framed and glazed. **£300-450** *P*

An early 18th C. embroidered oval picture, 13 by 10 in. **£800-1,000** *Bea*

A mid 17th C. silkwork picture, the Goddess Minerva within a border of needlepoint lace and coiled silver thread, 30.5 by 40.5 cm., c. 1660's, framed and glazed. **£600-700** *P*

A pair of Jacobean crewel-work bed hangings, worked in brightly coloured wools, in Eastern style, 6 ft. 9 in. by 6 ft. 8 in. (206 by 203 cm.) and 2 narrow panels from the same set of hangings, 6 ft. 10 in. by 3 ft. (208 by 91.5 cm.). **£1,500-2,500** *L*

A silk worked picture of Jesus Christ, in a variety of stitches on a stained ivory silk ground, initialled M.P.? 1705, in a contemporary japanned frame, 18 by 19½ in. (46 by 50 cm.), late 17th/early 18th C. **£150-250** *SC*

Religious needlework is in less demand than other subjects.

A linen raised plush, applied silk and gross and petit point worked picture, in bright polychrome, initialled MO and dated 1849, contained in a gilt composition frame, 29 by 34 in. (74 by 86 cm.). **£150-200** *CS*

A pair of silk embroideries, the first inscribed in ink 'Marie G. D. e I R Pavlovski, 1799', gilt frames, 20.6 by 26.5 cm. **£800-1,000** *C*

A 17th C. stumpwork picture, the
ivory satin ground with Abraham
casting Hagar and Ishmael out into
the wilderness, in a variety of
stitches with seed pearls, the Will
and Testament of Thomas Hodkins,
1648, set into the back, 1 ft. 2 in. by
8 in. (36 by 21 cm.), c. 1650, framed.
£1,200-1,400   *S*

A beadwork panel, worked with a
lady and gentleman surrounded by
'the pelican in her piety', a stag, a
leopard and a dragon and large
sprays of flowers, inscribed in
beads along the upper and lower
border Anne Spielman, probably
for the base of a basket, framed and
glazed, English, mid 17th C., 10 by
13½ in. **£800-1,200**   *CSK*

A rare quilted patchwork coverlet,
of unbleached linen, the borders
worked in patchwork, edged with a
fringe, the central ground quilted
with a shell motif, the outer quilted
with chevron motifs, English, 68 by
88 in., c. 1780. **£1,000-1,500**   *CSK*

A late 18th C. Mexican needlework
sampler, the linen ground
embroidered in coloured floss silks
and gold thread worked mainly in
satin stitch, 40 by 60 cm. **£750-950**
P

A late 17th C. embroidered picture,
12¾ by 10 in., framed and glazed.
£750-950   *Bea*

An early 19th C. needlework
sampler by Charlotte Gregory,
1805, aged 13, the linen ground
worked in cross stitch with black
silk, 26 by 22 cm. **£150-200**   *P*

A stumpwork and needlework
picture, on an ivory silk ground,
signed S.C.H. 78, now contained in
a rosewood frame, 18½ by 22 in. (47
by 56 cm.), possibly third quarter of
the 17th C., framed later. **£1,200-
£1,600**   *SC*

A silk and woolwork picture, all on
an ivory ground contained by a gilt
frame, 13 by 16 in. (33 by 41 cm.),
the needlework third quarter of
17th C. **£400-800**   *SC*

A needlework portrait of King
Charles I, worked in coloured wools
and silks and embroidered at the
foot 'King Charles I worked by
? Anne Shore? in the 18 year of her
age', 10½ by 8½ in., 17th C., in
18th C. carved wooden frame.
£550-750   *CSK*

A late 17th C. silkwork picture,
embroidered in coloured silks with
tent stitch, 18 by 29 cm., c. 1690's.
£1,200-1,400   *P*

A needlework picture, worked in
coloured silks in petit point,
English, mid 17th C., 11 by 17 in.,
mounted on board. **£1,000-1,300**
CSK

A 17th C. English tent-stitch
picture of Solomon, 1 ft. 4 in. by
1 ft. (40 by 31 cm.), c. 1650,
mounted on wood. **£800-1,200**   *S*

A 17th C. stumpwork panel, 15 by
20½ in. **£1,200-1,500**   *HyD*

A silk and stumpwork picture,
framed, 10 by 16 in. (26 by 41 cm.),
late 17th C. **£300-400**   *SC*

A 17th C. stumpwork panel, 12½ by 17 in. **£2,500-3,500** *HyD*

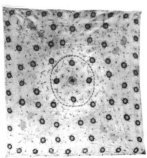

An 18th C. Ottoman bohca, the undyed linen lawn ground embroidered with silk and metal thread in pale madder, saffron and indigo, 5 ft. by 4 ft. 11 in. (153 by 150 cm.). **£500-700** *S*

An early 19th C. Persian wall hanging of printed cotton, kalamkar floral in mainly indigo and madder, lined, 1.3 by 0.86 m. **£100-140** *P*

A 19th C. Uzbek susani, the purple silk ground embroidered in mainly chain stitch, in coloured silks, lined, adapted as a curtain, probably Samarkand, 1.64 by 1.28 m. **£180-220** *P*

A late 19th C. Chinese panel, of ivory silk embroidered in satin stitch mainly with green, blue and brown silks, adapted as a curtain, 2.6 by 1.35 m. **£300-400** *P*

An early 18th C. Brussels cravat end, the surround with flower sprays worked with oeil de perdrix, lattice and a variety of other fillings, 32 by 34 cm., c. 1720's. **£450-500** *P*

A late 18th C. Swedish cushion, Skåne, with a central indigo octagonal medallion with ivory diamond medallions at each corner, a reciprocal indigo and madder border, rölakan weave, rosengång backing, 1 ft. 10 in. by 1 ft. 10 in. (56 by 56 cm.). **£150-250** *S*

A 19th C. Swedish cushion cover, Skåne, the walnut field with a floral design with a large parrot, flamskav weave, 3 ft. 3 in. by 1 ft. 8 in. (99 by 51 cm.). **£400-500** *S*

SWEDISH TEXTILES
These textiles have recently become popular. They all come from the Southern Province of Skåne.

A Gollu chi-chi rug, the ivory field with 3 cruciform medallions, with walnut border, dated 1320 AH, 1903 AD. **£800-1,200** *SC*

Value Point
• Ivory field always an advantage.

A Kutch embroidered shawl, the black cotton ground embroidered mainly in blue and purple silks, 1.6 m. square, c. 1900. **£80-120** *P*

A Polish silk sash, woven with blue and red flowers against canary yellow stripes, 25 in. wide by 78 in. long, late 18th C. **£2,000-2,500** *CSK*

A fine Yomut Hatchli ensi, with fox-brown field, 5 ft. 3 in. by 4 ft. 3 in. (160 by 130 cm.). **£700-900** *C*

An Antwerp classical tapestry, possibly from the Story of Zenobia and Aurelian, cut and joined down the middle, 10 ft. high by 15 ft. 2 in. wide (305 by 465 cm.), mid 17th C. **£3,500-4,000** *S*

An Aubusson tapestry overdoor, 4 ft. 1 in. by 7 ft. 6 in. (124 by 228 cm.). **£1,000-1,300** *L*

A fine Louis XV Beauvais tapestry, in pale verdure tones, signed J.B. Oudry 1736, in picture frame border, 8 ft. 7 in. by 13 ft. 8 in. **£10,000-12,000** *C*

Oudry designed cartoons for several of Aesop's fables that were woven at Beauvais under Nicholas Besaier who became Oudry's partner in 1734 and died in 1753.

A Flemish biblical tapestry, of the Meeting of Abraham and Melchizedek (Genesis 14.18), the border on a saffron ground, mainly in shades of blue and yellow, minor repairs, 10 ft. 9 in. high by 10 ft. 4 in. wide (330 by 315 cm.), late 16th C. **£2,500-3,000** *S*

A Franco-Flemish verdure tapestry, possibly Aubusson, 7 ft. 4 in. by 11 ft. 2 in. (225 by 340 cm.), early 18th C. **£5,000-6,000** *S*

A 19th C. flounce of Brussels point de gaze, 0.15 by 5.8 m., a length of edging similar, 0.04 by 6 m. **£200-250** *P*

A 19th C. Honiton appliqué bridal veil. **£250-300** *P*

A pair of Aubusson tapestry portières, on an ivory field with eau-de-nil border, each cut at the top, about 11 ft. high by 4 ft. 3 in. wide (335 by 130 cm.), c. 1860. **£700-800** *S*

Probably woven for Richard Grosvenor, 2nd Marquess of Westminster (d. 1869) for whom William Burn rebuilt Fonthill Abbey in the Scottish Baronial style in 1856. The house was demolished in the 1950's.

A Gobelins tapestry portrait, of the young Louis XIV, after Adam van der Meulen, 20 by 16 in. (51 by 41 cm.), third quarter 17th C. **£2,500-3,000** *S*

A Flemish verdure tapestry, extensive minor repairs, reduced in height, borders cut and joined, 6 ft. 5 in. high by 10 ft. 4 in. wide (210 by 315 cm.), early 18th C. **£4,000-5,000** *S*

A flounce of Honiton appliqué lace, 16 in. **£50-70** *CSK*

A Brussels tapestry, reduced, 9 ft. 7 in. by 10 ft. 6 in. (2 m. 91 cm. by 3 m. 20 cm.), early 18th C. **£19,000-£21,000** *C*

A Royal Windsor tapestry, after T. W. Hay, of Balmoral Castle, factory mark A Royal Windsor Tapestry 1884, 8 ft. 9 in. high by 5 ft. 3 in. wide (267 by 160 cm.). **£1,200-1,400** *S*

A Beauvais mythological tapestry fragment, from The Story of Cupid and Psyche, lower half of composition missing, lacking border, now with velvet surround, 5 ft. 2 in. high by 13 ft. 9 in. wide (158 by 420 cm.), c. 1680. **£1,500-£2,000** *S*

A late 19th C. Rasht wall hanging, of mainly red and blue worsted worked in chain stitch with coloured cottons and silks, lined, 2.26 by 1.4 m. **£450-550** *P*

An Antwerp tapestry, attributed to Michel Wauters, depicting the exercise Terre à Terre contre muraille à main gauche, extensive minor repairs, 11 ft. high by 9 ft. 8 in. wide (335 by 298.5 cm.), c. 1680. **£3,500-4,000** *S*

A blue ground Dragon robe, worked in gold thread and silk, 148 cm., 19th C. **£1,000-1,200** *Bon*

A mid 19th C. 2-piece gown, of Turkish terracotta velvet, the whole worked with gilt, red and metal strip embroidery, altered, c. 1860's. **£350-400** *P*

An early 17th C. woman's coif, the linen ground embroidered in stem stitch with black silk having silvered thread and sequin decoration, c. 1600's. **£2,000-2,500** *P*

A dress, printed in blue and mauve, c. 1835. **£650-750** *CSK*

A 19th C. flounce, of Brussels bobbin appliqué, 0.9 by 4.8 m. **£250-300** *P*

A pair of lappets, with 2 dress robings en suite of French needle lace, c. 1760. **£160-260** *CSK*

An early 19th C. bonnet veil, of Spanish blonde lace designed with flower sprays, c. 1820's. **£90-110** *P*

A black satin bonnet, c. 1810. **£400-£500** *CSK*

A pair of early 17th C. gentleman's gauntlets, of beige kid, embroidered with red and orange silk and gold thread appliqué having gold thread tassel trim, c. 1620's. **£280-340** *P*

An 18th C. tapestry cushion, having a modern velvet backing and fringe, restored, 15 by 14½ in. **£160-200** *WW*

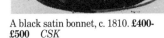

A Dragon robe, qifu, the blue ground embroidered with 8 dragons, picked out in gold file, 19th C. **£500-600** *S*

A mid 19th C. gown, of 18th C. brown silk brocaded in silk, c. 1840's. **£300-350** *P*

An open robe, and petticoat of ivory figured silk brocaded with sprays of blue and yellow, pink and red flowers, English, slightly altered, c. 1755. **£2,000-2,500** *CSK*

An open robe, and petticoat of yellow silk with vertical pink and green stripes, with English back, the front and petticoat trimmed with box pleated self-coloured silk, c. 1760. **£5,000-6,000** *CSK*

Miller's is a price GUIDE Not a price LIST
The price ranges given reflect the average price a purchaser should pay for similar items. Condition, rarity of design or pattern, size, colour, pedigree, restoration and many other factors must be taken into account when assessing values.

An open robe, with English back and petticoat of ivory figured silk brocaded in yellow, blue, pink and purple silks, trimmed with green and yellow braid and polychrome flybraid — c. 1755, with loops at the pockets for arranging the dress à la Polonaise. **£5,000-6,000** *CSK*
This was the wedding dress of Mary Dacre of Kirklington, Cumberland, wife of Sir John Clerk of Pennycuik, 5th Bart. (d. 1798).

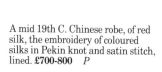

A mid 19th C. Chinese robe, of red silk, the embroidery of coloured silks in Pekin knot and satin stitch, lined. **£700-800** *P*

A mid 19th C. brown straw work
bonnet, c. 1840's. **£70-100**   *P*

An early 18th C. christening cap, of
white lawn, the crown, centre front
and back panels of hollie point lace,
c. 1730's. **£180-220**   *P*

A gentleman's nightcap, of linen
embroidered in brightly coloured
silks, enhanced with raised
woolwork, gold and silver thread,
English, c. 1600. **£3,000-4,000**
CSK

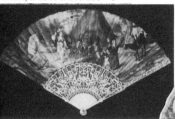

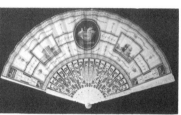

An Italian fan, with chinoiserie
sticks of carved and pierced ivory,
with chickenskin leaf, 29.5 cm.
long, c. 1760. **£250-300**   *P*

An important Cantonese
'Mandarin' fan, the black lacquer
sticks finely painted on each side in
2-colour gilt, 12½ in. (32 cm.),
c. 1870. **£1,200-1,500**   *S*

An Italian fan, with carved and
pierced Chinese sticks, the
chickenskin leaf of neo-classical
design, 27 cm. long, c. 1780's. **£300-
£350**   *P*

A fan, the chickenskin leaf painted
with classical ruins, with plain
ivory sticks, 11 in., Italian, c. 1780.
£200-250   *CSK*

A Canton fan, the feather leaf
painted with a view of Canton, the
bone sticks carved and pierced,
10½ in., c. 1840, in wooden fan box.
£500-600   *CSK*

A Canton parasol cockade fan, with
paper mount painted with figures
on a terrace, with lacquer sticks,
10¼ in. diam., including handles,
Canton, c. 1820; and a later lacquer
box. **£150-200**   *CSK*

A chinoiserie chromolithographic
fan, the wooden sticks also painted
with chinoiserie, c. 1860. **£105-135**
CSK

A tortoiseshell brisé fan, the
guardsticks decorated with
shubayama work, 12 in., Japanese,
c. 1880, in Chinese fitted lacquer
box. **£850-950**   *CSK*

A paper folding fan, lacquered in
various shades of grey and brown,
bamboo sticks, inscribed Zeshin,
red seal, late 19th C., fitted wood
box. **£1,000-1,200**   *C*

A fan, the paper leaf well-painted
with a Fête Champêtre, the ivory
sticks carved with serpents, gilt
and clouté with mother-of-pearl
birds, squirrels and houses, the

guardsticks of mother-of-pearl
carved and painted with mermaids,
11¾ in., German, c. 1730. **£2,300-
£2,600**   *CSK*

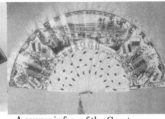

A fan, the leaf painted with a scene from a romance, the mother-of-pearl sticks carved with figures, pierced, silvered and gilt and backed with mother-of-pearl, 11½ in., c. 1730. **£250-300** *CSK*

A fan, with carved and pierced ivory sticks, the leaf a hand-coloured etching of figures strolling in a park, 27 cm. long, c. 1770's, in fan-shaped case. **£150-200** *P*

A souvenir fan, of the Great Exhibition, the bone sticks pierced and silvered, 10½ in., 1851. **£180-£220** *CSK*

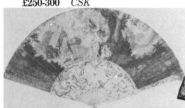

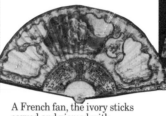

A fan, the leaf painted with an artist painting a Goddess, the ivory sticks carved with fairies and putti, pierced, painted and gilt, c. 1770. **£280-340** *CSK*

A French fan, the ivory sticks carved and pierced with shepherdesses, animals and landscape motifs and painted with flowers, with chickenskin leaf, 29 cm. long, c. 1760. **£300-350** *P*

A fan, the mother-of-pearl guards curved and engraved with warriors, the ivory sticks pierced and painted, 12 in. (30.3 cm.), possibly Dutch, mid 18th C. **£250-£300** *S*

An ivory brisé fan, French, Dieppe, c. 1870. **£250-300** *CSK*

An ivory brisé fan, painted with an oval portrait miniature after Gainsborough of Vice Admiral The Honourable George Cranfield Berkeley (1753-1818), one guardstick decorated with steel beads, the other guardstick replaced and the tips of several sticks replaced, 10½ in., English, 1784. **£650-750** *CSK*

An unmounted fan leaf, painted with classical ruins on chickenskin, 16 in. wide, in black glass mount, framed and glazed, with framer's label Thomas Fentham, 136 Strand, early 19th C. **£280-360** *CSK*

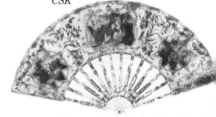

A dismounted fan, leaf painted with a classical procession, 14 in. wide, Italian, early 18th C., framed and glazed. **£350-400** *CSK*

A rare articulated fan, the silk leaf painted with cupid, the ivory sticks carved, pierced, silvered and gilt, the guardsticks set, 11 in., French, c. 1770, verso 19th C., in contemporary shagreen fan box. **£1,700-2,000** *CSK*

A fan, the leaf painted with a court scene, the mother-of-pearl sticks carved with putti and musicians pierced, silvered and gilt and backed with mother-of-pearl, 11 in., French, c. 1750, in glazed fan case. **£350-400** *CSK*

A paper fan, painted with classical figures in a landscape, ivory sticks, the guards with mother-of-pearl and piqué decoration, 10½ in., probably Italian, c. 1740. **£160-200** *WHB*

A Flemish fan, with carved and pierced ivory sticks, the paper leaf painted with a scene of merrymakers drinking, 28 cm. long, c. 1740's. **£400-450** *P*

A fine and rare early English wooden doll, with nailed-on auburn real hair on kid wig, the original clothes comprising a cardinal red silk bodice, one lower leg missing, one index finger missing, paint scuffed on head and shoulders, 16½ in. (42 cm.), English, c. 1770. **£1,500-1,800** *S*

Value Points:
• Clothes.
• Condition of paint on head.

A poured shoulder-wax doll, with blonde mohair and the hand-stitched stuffed body with poured wax lower limbs, unclothed, right arm broken at the top, 23 in. (58.5 cm.), English, c. 1860. **£350-400** *S*

A wedding group of 6 waxed shoulder composition dolls, 7⅛ in (18 cm.), English, late 19th C. **£400-450** *S*

A poured wax doll, blonde real hair, sparse, the stuffed body with wax lower limbs and blue stamp on chest, 'Hamley's-64-Regent Street W.Dolls Repaired', in original wool and cotton underclothing, left leg and foot distressed, 21 in. (53.5 cm.), English, c. 1860. **£300-350** *S*
This doll would be worth more in better condition.

A poured shoulder-wax doll, weighted blue glass eyes, with hair eyelashes and eyebrows, real long, reddish-brown hair, the hand-stitched and stuffed linen body with poured wax limbs, in original lace-panelled white dress with purple sash, some restoration, left little finger missing, right leg cracked, 23 in. (58.5 cm.), English, c. 1860. **£350-400** *S*

Value Points:
• Expression of face.
• Condition of clothes important.

An automaton tea drinker, the Jumeau head impressed tete Jumeau Bte S.G.D.G. indistinctly 4, composition body with bisque arms, holding in her hand a teapot and a cup in the other which she moves alternately while the music plays, left hand repaired, 20 in. (51 cm.) high overall, French, c. 1890. **£1,200-1,400** *S*

A rare walking/crying Bru Jeune R bisque doll, 24½ in. (62 cm.), French, c. 1895, in original Bebe Bru Marchant No. 9 box. **£3,000-3,500** *S*

A poured shoulder-wax doll, with a sad expression, fair real hair, the stuffed body with wax arms and composition legs, 31 in. (75 cm.), French, c. 1890. **£500-550** *S*

A Jumeau bisque doll, stamped in red 'TETE JUMEAU' and incised 9, jointed wood and composition body, with voice box, not working, Jumeau shoes marked 9, one finger missing, wig replaced, eyes broken off weight, 21 in. (53 cm.), French, c. 1895. **£800-900** *S*

A French Jumeau automaton of a young girl, in original pink silk dress, 48 cm. including base, marked 'Deposé Tete Jumeau Bte. S.G.D.G. 4'. **£2,500-2,800** *P*

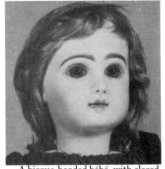

A poured shoulder-wax doll, inserted blonde real hair, with poured wax limbs, in original underclothing, small piece missing side of shoulder, 19 in. (48 cm.), English, c. 1880. **£250-300** *S*

A fine Bru Jeune bisque doll, impressed BRU Jne 8, fixed blue glass eyes, pierced ears, real blonde hair over cork pate and the leather body bearing paper label painted in red BEBE BRU Bte S.G.D.G., with bisque forearms and wooden lower legs, 21 in. (56 cm.), French, c. 1875. **£8,000-9,000** *S*

Bru dolls are rare.

A Jumeau bisque doll, stamped in red DEPOSE TETE JUMEAU Bte S.G.D.G. 4, with closed mouth, blonde real hair wig over cork pate, jointed wood and composition body, cracked back of head with 2 issuing hairlines, 13¾ in. (35 cm.), French, c. 1880. **£600-650** *S*

A Tête Jumeau bisque doll, stamped in red TETE JUMEAU and impressed 10, with open mouth, moulded blue glass eyes, cork pate with red-blonde real hair wig and jointed wood and composition body, 21½ in. (55 cm.) French, c. 1895. **£700-800** *S*

A bisque headed bébé, with closed mouth, mid brown hair wig and composition fixed wrist jointed body, with spare nightgown in case, 20 in. high, stamped Le Parisien bte SGDG A1 impressed Paris and stamped on the body Jumeau Medaille D'Or Paris. **£1,500-1,700** *CSK*

A bisque-headed bébé, with closed mouth, blonde wig and jointed composition body, 19 in. high, stamped in red Depose Tete Jumeau Bt. S.G.D.G. 9 and on the body Jumeau Medaille D'Or Paris. **£2,000-2,500** *CSK*

A bisque-headed bébé, with closed mouth, fixed wrist composition body, 25 in. high, marked E.J. A 10 and stamped on the body Jumeau Medaille D'Or Paris. **£4,000-4,500** *CSK*

An A. Lanternier bisque doll, with open/closed mouth and moulded upper teeth, curved limb composition body, 24 in. (61 cm.), French, c. 1925. **£150-200** *S*

A Jules Steiner bisque doll, with closed mouth, with jointed papier-mâché body, little finger missing, hands and toes scuffed, 17½ in. (44.5 cm.), French, c. 1885. **£1,200-£1,500** *S*

A Jumeau bisque doll, stamped in red DEPOSE TETE JUMEAU Bt S.G.D.G. 5, with closed mouth, blonde mohair wig over cork pate, the jointed composition body with straight wrists, in original red satin dress, 14 in. (36 cm.), French, c. 1880. **£1,800-2,000** *S*

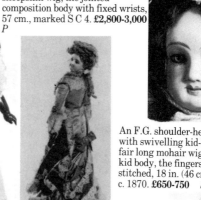

A Jules Steiner kicking/crying bisque doll, the cardboard torso containing the keywind mechanism activating her arms up and down, her head to turn from side to side and her 'voice' to cry Mama, Papa, with kicking legs, inoperative, several teeth missing, chip on left ear, 18½ in. (47 cm.), French, c. 1880. **£600-700**   *S*

A Jules Steiner crying doll, 18 in. (46 cm.), French, c. 1870. **£600-650** *S*

A good Henri Lioret phonograph Jumeau doll, impressed 11, the Lioret Merveilleux phonograph movement numbered 4775 and stamped ARQUE HL (in shield) DEPOSE, playing in English a nursery rhyme, 25 in. (63.5 cm.), French, c. 1893. **£2,000-2,500**   *S*

A fine bisque head bébé, by Steiner, with original blonde sheepskin wig, the jointed composition body with fixed wrists, 57 cm., marked S C 4. **£2,800-3,000** *P*

An F.G. shoulder-head bisque doll, with swivelling kid-based head, fair long mohair wig and gussetted kid body, the fingers separately stitched, 18 in. (46 cm.), French, c. 1870. **£650-750**   *S*

A fine and rare large Jules Steiner Bourgoin bisque doll, impressed Figure C No. 7, J. Steiner Bte. S.G.D.G., the eyes closing by means of a wire behind the left ear, with wood and composition body stamped in red on buttocks, Heinrich Handwerck, slight repainting to right eye, 33 in. (84 cm.), French, c. 1880. **£1,500-£1,800**   *S*

A rare black bisque doll, impressed 34-24, with jointed wood and composition body in original pink cotton dress, one finger broken, 14¼ in. (36 cm.), probably French, c. 1910. **£1,100-1,300**   *S*

A bisque swivel-head fashion doll, impressed C, long blonde real hair wig, one finger missing, another loose, 15 in. (38 cm.), French, c. 1870. **£1,000-1,200**   *S*

A fine and rare black bisque doll, probably by S.F.B.J. in association with Paris Bébé, the head impressed 634-30, with sleeping brown eyes, good jointed composition body, in original red and white spotted dress, combinations, petticoat, black socks and shoes marked 8, 23 in. (58 cm.) high, complete with original box, French, c. 1900. **£2,000-2,400**   *SC*

An S.F.B.J. bisque walking/talking doll, impressed DEPOSE S.F.B.J. 8, eyes moving from side to side as the legs are walked, composition and wood jointed body with straight legs which when moved backwards and forwards make her talk and turn her head, right hand distressed, eyes loose, left eye small chip, 23 in. (48.5 cm.), French, c. 1900. **£300-350**   *S*

A S.F.B.J. bisque doll, impressed 236 4, with open/closed mouth, with 5-piece composition bod, tiny chip to right eye socket, 12 in. (30.5 cm.), French, c. 1915. **£280-£320**   *S*

An extremely rare bisque-headed googly-eyed character doll, marked SFBJ 245 Paris 4, 13½ in. high. **£1,800-2,200**   *CSK*

A bisque-headed cymbal player, the wood body with press squeaker activating the arms to clash the cymbals, on wooden stick with whistle end, 15 in. (38 cm.), probably French, c. 1890. **£180-200**
S

A rare Schoenau & Hoffmeister bisque doll, impressed B/6, with chunky composition toddler body, 21 in. (53.5 cm.), German, c. 1915. **£900-1,000**   S

A Schoenau & Hoffmeister shoulder-bisque marotte doll, impressed 4700 10, the circular body turning playing a tune as the wooden handle is moved, in original white satin pointed outfit and hat with blue and white wool trim, 15 in. (38 cm.), German, c. 1900. **£250-280**   S

Value Points

- *condition of clothing is vital — this is in very good shape.*

An early Kathe Kruse cloth doll, with 5-piece stitched muslin head, pink well formed ears, seamstitch articulation at shoulders, swivel joints at hips, the legs stitched in 5 sections and stiffened, the arms in 2 stitched sections, in original blue, red, yellow and white checked dress and white pinafore, 17 in. (43 cm.), German, c. 1911. **£800-900**   S

These dolls are just coming into vogue.

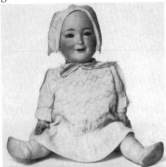

A fine Schoenau & Hoffmeister Princess Elizabeth bisque doll, with 5-piece chubby composition body, wig missing, 16 in. (40.5 cm.), German, c. 1938. **£800-900**   S

This doll would have fetched more if more sensitively clothed and wigged.

(*l.*) A Kathe Kruse cloth doll, the head stitched in 5 parts, the stuffed and stitched body jointed at hips, indistinctly marked on foot, tiny paint rub nose, 17 in. (43 cm.), German, c. 1928. **£500-600**

(*r.*) A fine Kathe Kruse cloth doll, impressed on left foot 18?5 and in red Kathe Kruse, the stuffed and stitched body with jointed hips, 17 in. (43 cm.), German, c. 1930, in original box. **£700-800**   S

A J. & D. Kestner bisque doll, impressed 1 192 4, with jointed wood and composition body in pink-flowered green dress, teeth missing, 15 in. (38 cm.), German, c. 1890. **£300-350**   S

A rare early Bahr & Proschild bisque doll, impressed B & P. 320.12 de, with 8 ball-jointed wood and composition body with straight wrists, firing mark behind right ear, 21 in. (53 cm.), German, c. 1885. **£800-900**   S

Bahr & Proschild are rare makers.

A rare Schoenau & Hoffmeister bisque 'My Dream Baby' doll, the moulded head and cloth body with voice box, not working, and composition hands, hands distressed, 10¾ in. (27.5 cm.), German, c. 1925. **£350-450**   S

A Schoenau & Hoffmeister baby is rarer than an Armand Marseille baby.

A J. D. Kestner bisque doll, impressed A 5 152, with ball-jointed wood and composition body, distressed, tiny firing hole on top lip, stringing loose, one little finger missing, 13 in. (33 cm.), German, c. 1880. **£250-300**   S

An Armand Marseille bisque Oriental doll, impressed ELLAR 4/o.K, 7½ in. (19 cm.), German, c. 1935. **£100-120**   S

A rare bisque character doll, impressed 154 4, probably by J. D Kestner, tiny white mark tip of nose, 13 in. (33 cm.), German, c. 1910. **£700-800**   S

This is similar to the 115A 'Philip mould of Kämmer & Reinhardt.

An Armand Marseille bisque googly-eyed doll, impressed 323 A.4/o.M., 9½ in. (24 cm.), German, c. 1912. **£500-550** *S*

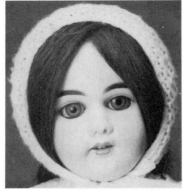

An Armand Marseille bisque doll, impressed AM 11 DEP, body repainted, 26 in. (66 cm.), German, c. 1900. **£180-240** *S*

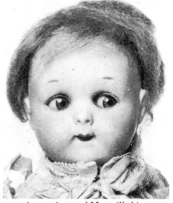

A rare Armand Marseille bisque character doll, impressed 200 A 3/o M D.R.G.N. 243/1, with 5-piece composition body, fine hairline on back of head, 9 in. (23 cm.), German, c. 1910. **£280-340** *S*

A large Gebruder Heubach all-bisque baby, 12½ in. (32 cm.) long, German, c. 1900. **£250-300** *S*

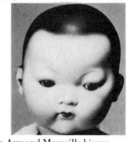

An Armand Marseille bisque Oriental 'My Dream Baby' doll, impressed A.M. 353/6K, with yellow composition 5-piece body, white dress, unstrung legs and arms distressed, 20 in. (51 cm.), German, c. 1925. **£400-500** *S*
This is a rare doll.

An Armand Marseille walking/talking bisque doll, impressed 390 A.6½M., with jointed wood and composition body, the legs activating the head to move from side to side, with voice box, arms associated, 24½ in. (62 cm.), German, c. 1905. **£300-350** *S*

A bisque-headed whistling doll, the straw filled body containing a bellows voice box and with composition hands, high marked with the square Heubach mark, 11½ in. high. **£350-400** *CSK*

A Gebruder Heubach bisque doll, impressed GEBRUDER HEUBACH, sunburst in a circle G.11.H., with ball-jointed wood and composition body, 30 in. (76 cm.), German, 1890. **£250-300** *S*

A Heubach googly-eyed doll, impressed indistinctly Einco 1, blue glass eyes moving from side to side by means of a wire at the back of the head, with 5-piece composition body, 9 in. (23 cm.), German, c. 1910. **£600-800** *S*
'Googly' dolls are very popular now.

A Gebruder Heubach bisque 'Whistling Jim' doll, impressed 1 87 74, the stuffed body with voice box, not working, which should give out a whistle when the chest is pressed, fingers chipped, 11 in. (28 cm.), German, c. 1910. **£400-500** *S*

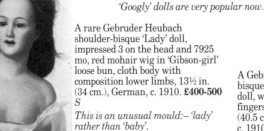

A rare Gebruder Heubach shoulder-bisque 'Lady' doll, impressed 3 on the head and 7925 mo, red mohair wig in 'Gibson-girl' loose bun, cloth body with composition lower limbs, 13½ in. (34 cm.), German, c. 1910. **£400-500** *S*
This is an unusual mould:– 'lady' rather than 'baby'.

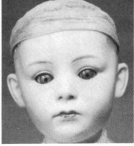

A Gebruder Heubach bisque character boy doll, wig missing, 2 fingers chipped, 16 in. (40.5 cm.), German, c. 1910. **£500-550** *S*

A Gebruder Heubach bisque googly
doll, impressed 9573 2/O, with
5-piece composition body, 8 in.
(20 cm.), German, c. 1915. **£500-550**
S

A good doll but small size.

(*l.*) A Schoenau & Hoffmeister
bisque-headed Oriental doll,
impressed '4900 3/O', with original
mohair wig, composition body with
ball-jointed limbs, 34 cm. high,
German, c. 1900. **£500-550**

(*r.*) A Simon & Halbig Oriental
doll, impressed '1329 6', with
composition body with ball-jointed
limbs, 36 cm. high, German,
c. 1900. **£1,100-1,300** *SS*

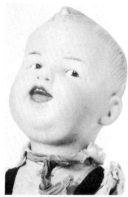

A Gebruder Heubach bisque-head
character doll, 31 cm., marked 5.
£500-700   *P*

*Rare character dolls are worth
considerably more.*

A Simon & Halbig bisque doll,
impressed S & H LL & S 10½, with
ball-jointed wood and composition
body, 23½ in. (60 cm.), German,
c. 1890. **£400-450** *S*

A rare Simon & Halbig bisque
Oriental doll, impressed S.H 1199
DEP 3½, the ball-jointed wood and
composition yellow body, toe
scuffed, 11½ in. (29 cm.), German,
c. 1900. **£800-850** *S*

A Simon & Halbig bisque character
doll, impressed 1428, with curved
limb composition body, 10 in.
(25.5 cm.), German, c. 1915. **£400-
450** *S*

A Simon & Halbig walking/talking
bisque doll, impressed 1039, with
jointed wood and composition body
containing voice box, the right arm
attached by stringing to the left leg
causing the doll to throw kisses, in
original pale turquoise silk dress
with French label, bonnet and
shoes impressed Paris depose, with
parasol, good restoration to left side
of face, 22 in. (56 cm.) German,
c. 1900. **£300-350** *S*

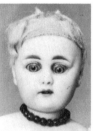

A Simon & Halbig shoulder-bisque
swivel-head doll, impressed S3H
939, with gussetted kid body with
bisque forearms, unclothed, 11½ in.
(29 cm.), German, c. 1880. **£250-350**
S

A large Kämmer and Reinhardt/
Simon and Halbig bisque doll,
impressed 117 80, with jointed
wood and composition body, in
original underclothing and pink on
white dress and muslin jacket, old
hairline above right eye, 30 in.
(76 cm.), German, c. 1915. **£2,500-
£3,000** *S*

A rare Kämmer and
Reinhardt bisque-head
character doll, marked
K * R 114 43, 43 cm.
£2,200-2,500
P

A Simon & Halbig/Kämmer &
Reinhardt bisque doll, stringing
loose, 30 in. (76 cm.), German,
c. 1890. **£400-450** *S*

A Simon & Halbig/Kämmer &
Reinhardt bisque doll, impressed
58, jointed wood and composition
body, stringing loose, some body
paint chipped, 24 in. (61 cm.),
German, c. 1900. **£350-400** *S*

A Simon &
Halbig/Kämmer
& Reinhardt
bisque doll,
stringing loose,
28 in. (71 cm.),
German, c. 1890.
£350-400 *S*

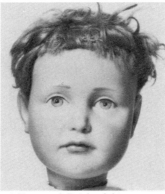

A Simon & Halbig/Kämmer & Reinhardt bisque walking doll, number hidden below, the ball-jointed composition and wood body with straight walking legs which move her head from side to side simultaneously, 16 in. (41 cm.), German, c. 1890. **£400-450** *S*

A Kämmer & Reinhardt bisque character doll, impressed 114 49, with ball-jointed wood and composition body, large crack back of head, unclothed, 19 in. (48 cm.), German, c. 1915. **£900-1,000** *S*

This is a rare character mould — in good condition worth **£1,300-1,600**

A Kämmer & Reinhardt/Simon & Halbig bisque doll, impressed 403 43, with ball-jointed wood and composition body, 18 in. (46 cm.), German, c. 1890. **£200-220** *S*

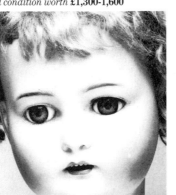

A Kämmer & Reinhardt/Simon & Halbig bisque doll, impressed 121 28, stringing loose, thumb missing, 14 in. (35.5 cm.), German, c. 1910. **£450-500** *S*

A large Kämmer & Reinhardt/ Simon & Halbig bisque doll, impressed 80, 3 fingers repaired, stringing loose, 31 in. (79 cm.), German, c. 1890. **£400-450** *S*

A fine large Kämmer & Reinhardt/ Simon & Halbig bisque doll, impressed 80, with 6 ball-jointed wood and composition body, index finger repaired, 32 in. (81 cm.), German, c. 1900. **£500-550** *S*

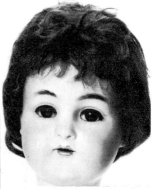

A brown bisque-headed character doll, marked K*R 100, 14¼ in. high. **£600-650** *CSK*

Brown is a rare colour.

A Kämmer & Reinhardt/Simon & Halbig bisque-head walking doll, marked on head, 25 in. high, c. 1920. **£400-500** *TW*

A Simon & Halbig/Kämmer & Reinhardt bisque doll, impressed 70, unstrung, missing lower left leg, torso scuffed, 27 in. (69 cm.), German, c. 1890. **£250-300** *S*

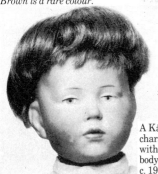

A Kämmer & Reinhardt bisque character doll, impressed 30 101, with jointed wood and composition body, 12 in. (30.5 cm.), German, c. 1910. **£700-750** *S*

Character dolls are more valuable.

A Kämmer & Reinhardt bisque-headed doll, impressed '114 46', with titian wig, having composition body with ball-jointed limbs, 46 cm. high. **£2,000-2,500** *SS*

A fine Lenci boy doll, marked on the sole of the left foot, 42 cm. **£450-£500** *P*

Condition of great importance with Lenci dolls as they are often affected by moth!

A painted cloth Lenci-type doll, wearing original red Indian costume, 16 in. high. **£250-300** *CSK*

An actual Lenci doll should be worth **£400-500**

A fine Lenci boy doll, 45 cm. **£400-£450** *P*

A poured shoulder-wax portrait lady doll, probably by Pierotti, the cloth lady body with wax limbs in the original 18th C. style, 20½ in. (52 cm.), c. 1900. **£350-450** *S*

Pierotti — good.

A rare large Lencidschanggo Oriental cloth doll, in original purple trouser suit with brightly coloured felt jacket in red, blue and yellow with silk embroidered dragon and foliage, left ear missing, hair sparse, some moth holes, 23 in. (58.5 cm.), c. 1925. **£450-550** *S*

See the identical doll in Dorothy S. Coleman's 'Lenci Dolls', page 32 and back cover.

A rare bisque character doll, impressed 1428 4, with curved limb composition body, stringing perished, 11 in. (28 cm.), German, c. 1910. **£500-600** *S*

A Heinrich Handwerck bisque doll, impressed DEP HANDWERCK 4½, with dark auburn real hair wig and jointed wood and composition body in cream blue-edged dress, black corduroy beret, 26 in. (66 cm.), German, c. 1905. **£450-£500** *S*

A bisque character doll, impressed F 3 B, composition body in long white christening robe and lacy bonnet, 22 in. (56 cm.), German, c. 1910. **£300-350** *S*

A good Pierotti poured shoulder-wax doll, inserted real blonde wisps of hair and the stuffed body with wax lower limbs in white long dress and cream silk cape and bonnet, fingers off left hand, 22½ in. (57 cm.), English, c. 1860. **£400-500** *S*

A Franz Schmidt bisque doll, impressed 1296 F. S. & C. SIMON & HALBIG X 36, 15 in. (38 cm.), German, c. 1911. **£250-300** *S*

An unusual bisque doll, impressed small K over large H 8, blonde mohair wig and ball-jointed wood and composition body in white pique dress, 25 in. (63.5 cm.), German, c. 1900. **£250-300** *S*

Two unusual dolls, one impressed with a clover leaf 5, the other W.D. 5, red mohair wig and 5-piece composition body, girl's legs cracked, both 13½ in. (34 cm.), German, c. 1900. **£800-900** *S*

A bisque doll, impressed AH 5½ Germany, red real hair wig and ball-jointed wood and composition body, 22½ in. (57 cm.), German, c. 1890. **£150-200** *S*

A papier-mâché headed
autoperipatetikos, 10 in. high.
£300-350   *CSK*

A Biedermeier shoulder-papier-
mâché doll, the stuffed body with
kid arms, in original brown striped
beige dress, cracked at neck and
sides of head, 22 in. (56 cm.),
German, c. 1830. £300-350   *S*

A composition articulated toy,
modelled as an old woman, as
levers are pressed, she nods her
head and raises the baby up and
down, 13 in. high, English, early
19th C. £350-400   *CSK*
The date makes this doll unusual.

A papier-mâché shoulder-headed
doll, the kid body with separated
fingers wearing contemporary
brown velvet frock and black shoe,
Sonneburg, 25 in. high, c. 1840.
£550-600   *CSK*
*These papier-mâché dolls are
increasingly popular and this is a
particularly big example.*

An unusual papier-mâché
shoulder-head doll, with finely
painted features and elaborately
moulded black hairstyle swept into
curls on the back of her head, tip of
nose rubbed, replacement arms,
17½ in. (44.5 cm.), German,
c. 1850. £400-500   *S*
*This doll has particularly good
moulding of her hair.*

An autoperipatetikos cloth-headed
doll, with the skirt hiding the
keywind mechanism activating her
metal feet to walk, with kid arms,
stamped in black under cardboard
Patented July 1862: also, Europe,
20 Dec. 1862, redressed, small
patches of face paint and one finger
missing, shoulderplate dented,
9 in. (23 cm.), American, c. 1862.
£350-400   *S*

A bisque Oriental doll, impressed
6/O, with 5-piece composition body
in original silk-backed cream
cotton dress with blue and metal-
thread flowers, olive-green velvet
coat, 10½ in. (26.5 cm.), German,
c. 1910. £400-450   *S*

An autoperipatetikos doll, with
parian bisque shoulder-head,
printed on base July 15th, 1862,
and containing the keywind
mechanism activating her metal
feet, kid arms and hands, in
original clothes, key missing, silk
distressed, 10½ in. (27 cm.),
German, c. 1865. £300-350   *S*

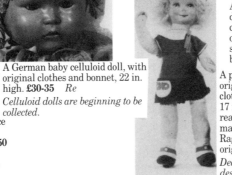

A German bisque-head googly-eyed
doll, water melon mouth and rigid
composition body dressed in
original pale blue and white striped
suit, marked 2410, 24 cm., with
box. £450-500   *P*

A good Biedermeier shoulder-
papier-mâché doll, with painted
face, blue eyes, the leather body
with wooden lower limbs, in
original white silk dress and
bloomers and purple velvet bodice
and bonnet, dress deteriorated,
10½ in. (27 cm.), c. 1825. £300-350
S
*These Biedermeier dolls are now
coming into vogue.*

A German baby celluloid doll, with
original clothes and bonnet, 22 in.
high. £30-35   *Re*
*Celluloid dolls are beginning to be
collected.*

A painted cloth advertising doll, in
original blue, white and orange
clothes with Oxo on the pocket,
17 in. high with swing ticket
reading Little Miss Oxo Specially
made for Oxo Ltd., by Deans
Ragbook Co. Ltd., London, in
original box. £200-250   *CSK*
*Dean's dolls are particularly
desirable.*

A wax-over-composition headed pedlar doll, in original chintz dress, her wares including baskets of vegetables, crab, shrimp, a chicken and various shellfish, 12 in. wide, under glass dome. **£650-750**   *CSK*

A fine and rare china half-doll, probably Meissen, in her original cream satin dress richly embroidered with metal thread and bands of filigree-edged pale green pique, little finger repaired, 9¼ in. (23.5 cm.) overall. **£300-350**   *S*

The fact that this doll was probably made in the Meissen factory adds considerably to the price. Without this attribution the price would be nearer £200-240

A china half-doll, incised 13752, in Art Deco style, 5¼ in. (13.5 cm.). **£120-135**   *S*

Highly stylised examples are worth more.

A William Goebels half-doll, marked 3, representing Jenny Lind, small chip on base, 3 in. (7.5 cm.); another similar but marked 4½ and larger, 4⅛ in. (10.5 cm.). **£150-200**   *S*

A shoulder-china pedlar doll, the body with china lower limbs attached to wooden body by peg joints, 39 cm. high overall, doll c. 1840. **£500-550**   *Bon*

Price depends on number of 'wares' on display.

A rare 3-faced doll, impressed Dep 450 2/o, hairline crack to forehead of crying face and chip to right eye socket, draw string to actuate the voice box, not working, 11½ in. (29 cm.), c. 1880. **£400-450**   *S*

A fine bisque-headed pulchinelle puppet, impressed 2, the stiffened cloth body with kid hands, 24 in. (61 cm.), French, c. 1870. **£1,000-£1,300**   *S*

A pre-war fur fabric teddy bear, 15 in. high. **£50-55**   *Re*

A Regency doll's spotted muslin cap; a doll's bed jacket and 2 pairs of pockets, c. 1770; a Regency drawstring bag; a pair of brown kid shoes and a smaller pair of pink kid slippers; and a silk brocade belt. **£400-500**   *CSK*

A doll's straw bonnet; another edged and trimmed with pink silk; and a straw bonnet trimmed with grey and cream striped ribbon, in a padded straw work box, c. 1820. **£400-450**   *CSK*

Accessories are very desirable.

A 19th C. French musical clockwork automaton, performing a conjuring trick with a dice and 3 coloured balls, 16 in. high. **£1,800-£2,000** *Bea*

A rare bisque-headed clown, standing on an accordian which plays when you press the base down and makes bells on the clown jingle, in original outfit, 26 in. (66 cm.) high overall, German, c. 1890. **£400-450** *S*

A Leopold Lambert automaton, when wound the girl raises the child to her face, turns her head, appearing to kiss the child while bouncing the ball in her left hand, 51 cm. high including base, with oval glass dome. **£1,300-1,500** *P*

A musical automaton of Miss Muffet, the bisque head impressed SFBJ60 Paris, the bisque hands moving alternately, when the music is activated she moves her head from side to side and up and down and her arms up and down, the key marked LB, probably by Lambert, 21 in. (53 cm.), French, c. 1900. **£1,000-1,100** *S*

A pedal-operated monkey guitarist, 13 in. (33 cm.) high, French, c. 1900. **£240-260** *S*

The Society lady musical automaton, she flutters her eyelashes while fanning herself and then slowly raises one hand to raise her veil and gaze across the room while her bosom gently heaves, 24 in. (61 cm.) wide, probably French, late 19th C. **£1,600-1,800** *S*

An organ grinder musical automaton, he nods his head while turning the handle to a street barrel organ, with a musical movement playing a single tune, 28 in. (71 cm.) high, 20th C. **£400-£450** *S*

An unusual advertising display automaton, the electrically operated and articulated figure with movements for mouth, eyebrows and head, 25 in. (64 cm.) wide, c. 1930. **£700-800** *S*

An automaton hand cart, with 2 dolls, the bisque Armand Marseille heads, both impressed 16/02, in original costume with clockwork mechanism, 19½ in. (49.5 cm.) long, German, c. 1910. **£700-800** *S*

A G. Vichy bisque-headed tricyclist automaton, the bisque head, probably F.G., hairline crack, lacking wig, with moving neck and legs, the carved wooden hands grasping the turned ivory handles, the tricycle with brass clockwork mechanism, stamped G. Vichy, 10½ in. (26.5 cm.) long, French, c. 1880's. **£450-500** *S*

A barrel organ grinder automaton, 17 in. (43 cm.) high, probably French, c. 1900. **£350-380** *S*

A bisque headed clockwork 3-wheeled toy, with original clothes, standing on a metal platform with moving head and arms, stamped on the clockwork G. Vichy Fils Paris, 6¼ in. high. **£250-280** *CSK*

A musical clockwork automaton group, in original 18th C. style clothes, woman's neck damaged, 12 in. high, with 2 brass plates marked A. Theroux Paris and Brevete SGDG. **£3,000-3,500** *CSK*

A hand-operated automaton musical tea party, the 3 bisque headed dolls impressed 'A 15/O M', the maid moves from side to side holding a tea pot, 29 by 21 by 31 cm. high overall. **£400-450** *SS*

A musical concert automaton, all figures with movement to their heads and right hands, beneath a glass dome, 18¼ in. (46.5 cm.), French, late 19th C. **£1,500-1,800** *S*

A keywind musical blacksmith forge automaton, 19½ in. (49.5 cm.), wide, French, c. 1900. **£350-400** *S*

A Decamps walking crouching tiger, with articulated legs and head, with clockwork mechanism, 15 in. (38 cm.) long, French, c. 1900. **£180-200** *S*

A printed paper dog orchestra picture automaton, with many movements, powered by clockwork mechanisms, framed, glazed, 13¾ in. (35 cm.), French, c. 1890. **£450-480** *S*

A musical seascape automaton, with ship model tossing in rough seas, the background with model train crossing a viaduct, 16 in. (40.5 cm.) high, French, late 19th C. **£400-450** *S*

A Decamps walking terrier, with articulated legs and neck and clockwork movement, 12 in. (30.5 cm.) long, French, c. 1900. **£250-300** *S*

An unusual German-made clockwork cloth covered parachutist toy, working parachute operated by clockwork driven ripcord release, 25.5 cm. high, c. 1938, together with non-original Technofix key. **£80-100** *SS*

An F. Martin cardboard box, 'Course de Taureau', containing tinplate horse-race toy, with jockey travelling around the central clockwork mechanism, marked 'JL', 7 in. (18 cm.) diam., c. 1896. **£200-250** *S*

A seated Mandarin toy, with nodding head, Brittains, c. 1890. **£150-180** *P*

A painted tinplate toy, of a cooper, fitted with clockwork motor causing the man to walk along pushing the barrels in front of him, 7½ in. long, by Fernand Martin, Paris, c. 1902. **£450-550** *CSK*

A singing birds automaton, one drinking from a simulated pond, another perched on a bough, turning its head from side to side, the third roosts in its nest and flaps its wings, with clockwork mechanism for the production of the realistic bird song, 25 in. (64 cm.) high, French, late 19th C. **£1,000-1,400** *S*

A singing birds automaton, probably by Bontems, the clockwork mechanism causes the birds to move their heads, tails and beaks, 22 in. (56 cm.) high, suspended on brass stand, 71 in. (180 cm.) high, French, c. 1880. **£1,000-1,500** *S*

An early violinist and harpist tinplate automaton, 9¾ in. (24.5 cm.) long, German, c. 1895.
£450-550 *S*

A tinplate 2 bears and see-saw, probably by Distler, with clockwork mechanism, 7¾ in. (19.5 cm.) wide, German, c. 1925.
£250-300 *S*

An early Bing tinplate open 4-seat tourer, with clockwork mechanism driving rear axle, paint on bonnet scorched, lacking 3 mudguards and umbrella holder, 10½ in. (26.5 cm.) long, German, c. 1902. **£1,500-£1,800** *S*

A Bing printed tinplate model, of a limousine, with clockwork motor, 11 in. (27 cm.) long, c. 1925, and an Astra Electric Traffic Light in original box. **£500-600** *CSK*

An American Kingsbury tinplate clockwork model, of a world speed record car, 'Bluebird', 18 in. long.
£100-120 *Re*

A Bing battleship 'H.M.S. Powerful', clockwork mechanism driving the 3-bladed propeller, some rust and flaking paint, 29 in. (74 cm.) long, German, c. 1912, in contemporary wooden box. **£800-£850** *S*

A small Bing tinplate De Dion, the clockwork mechanism driving the rear axle, 6 in. (15 cm.) long, German, c. 1910. **£350-400** *S*

Two pre-war German tinplate and clockwork limousines, 14 cm. long, with a Bing tinplate garage, 21 cm. wide, c. 1925. **£200-250** *SS*

A Carette lithographed tinplate and clockwork rear entrance 4-seater Tonneau automobile, roof twisted and detached, some chipping to paintwork, etc., 12¼ in. (31 cm.) long, German, c. 1907.
£2,000-2,200 *SS*

An Elastolin horse-drawn tinplate ambulance, 38 cm. overall, 2 Elastolin horses and stretcher party with casualty, damaged.
£120-150 *SS*

A Fishcer tinplate Toonerville Trolley, clockwork mechanism driving the rear axle and linked to driver's arm, 5¼ in. (13.5 cm.), German, c. 1925. **£200-280** *S*

A Carette printed tinplate model, of a 1910 Daimler Voyage limousine, fitted with clockwork motor with brake and reverse mechanism, 15½ in. (40.4 cm.) long, c. 1910. **£1,200-1,400** *CSK*

A J.E.P. tinplate Renault open tourer, the clockwork mechanism driving the rear axle, klaxon replaced, 13¼ in. (33.5 cm.) long, French, c. 1929. **£500-650** *S*

A good Marklin Constructor streamlined coupe, the clockwork mechanism linked to rear axle by drive shaft, 14½ in. (37 cm.) long, German, c. 1935. **£450-550** *S*

A large Tipp R100 tinplate Zeppelin, with rear propeller operated by clockwork mechanism, 25½ in. (65 cm.) long, German, c. 1930. **£600-800** *S*

An Alfa Romeo P2 clockwork tinplate racing car, with clockwork mechanism driving the rear axle, lacks radiator filler cap, 20½ in. (52 cm.) long, French, c. 1935.
£500-650 *S*

A Marklin tinplate constructor racing car, with clockwork mechanism, lacking drive shaft, 14¾ in. (37.5 cm.) long, German, c. 1935. **£250-300** *S*

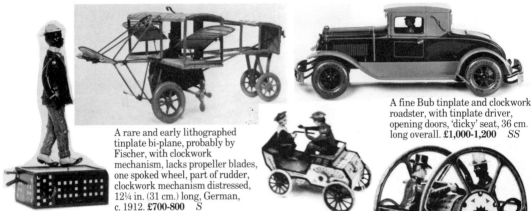

A rare and early lithographed tinplate bi-plane, probably by Fischer, with clockwork mechanism, lacks propeller blades, one spoked wheel, part of rudder, clockwork mechanism distressed, 12¼ in. (31 cm.) long, German, c. 1912. **£700-800** *S*

A fine Bub tinplate and clockwork roadster, with tinplate driver, opening doors, 'dicky' seat, 36 cm. long overall. **£1,000-1,200** *SS*

A Lehmann tinplate 'Oh-My', No. 690, with clockwork mechanism, 10½ in. (27 cm.) high, German, c. 1920. **£200-250** *S*

A Lehmann 'Naughty Nephew' tinplate and clockwork novelty toy, some damage, 12.5 cm. long, patent date May 12 1903. **£250-300** *SS*

A Lehmann zig-zag tinplate vehicle, No. 640, 5 in. (12 cm.) high, German, c. 1910. **£500-650** *S*

A Lehmann tinplate anxious bride, No. 470, contained in base of original cardboard box with operating instructions stuck to exterior of box, German, c. 1910. **£500-550** *S*

A Lehmann tinplate and clockwork 'Wild West Bucking Bronco', c. 1920. **£200-300** *SS*

A Gunthermann fire car, with clockwork mechanism driving the rear axle, lacking bell on bonnet, 6¾ in. (17 cm.) long, German, c. 1925. **£200-300** *S*

A Martin tinplate 'La Boule Mysterieuse', 13½ in. (34.5 cm.) high, French, c. 1910. **£300-350** *S*

A Lehmann tinplate 'Ampol' tricycle, No. 681, with revolving umbrella, the clockwork mechanism driving the rear axle, 5 in. (12.5 cm.) long, German, c. 1925. **£250-300** *S*

An unusual Lehmann Ikarus tinplate aeroplane, No. 653, the clockwork mechanism driving the propeller, lacking paper wings, 10½ in. (27 cm.) long, German, c. 1920. **£800-900** *S*

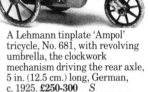

An S.M.J. tinplate pull-along train, in original cardboard box, 11 in. (28 cm.) wide, French, c. 1905. **£250-300** *S*

A Gunthermann tinplate pool player, the figure with articulated right arm holding a cue which propels a ball, with clockwork mechanism, 7½ in. (19 cm.) long, German, c. 1908. **£300-350** *S*

A good Dinky 28D Oxo van, English, c. 1934. **£400-550** *S*

An early Gunthermann tinplate vis-a-vis motor car, lacking side lamps, the vehicle 11 in. (28 cm.) long, bearing early knight and sword trademark, German, c. 1900. **£1,600-1,800** *S*

Poor condition.

An unusual Gunthermann tinplate 4-seat open tourer and passengers, paint scratched and chipped, 7½ in. (19 cm.) long, German, c. 1910. **£2,000-2,300** *S*

Three Dinky toys, original condition with chipped paint. **£170-200** *S*

A scarce Dinky supertoys No. 920 Guy Warrior van 'Heinz', practically mint condition, minor paint chipping on rear doors, 1960. **£150-200** *SS*

Fifteen Singer and Sunbeam. **£150-£180** *S*

Four spot-on vehicles, all boxed, all mint. **£400-500** *S*

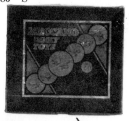

Fifteen Porsche sports racers. **£150-£180** *S*

A tinplate Paris-Tokio biplane, clockwork mechanism driving the wheels below, 9 in. (23 cm.) long, French, c. 1935. **£200-250** *S*

Eight Ferrari saloons. **£300-400** *S*

Meccano Dinky aeroplanes set 60, containing Imperial Airways low wing monoplane, DH Lepard Moth, General Monospar, Cierva Autogiro, Percival Gull and another, in original box; together with Dinky Singapore flying boat, fatigued, in original box. **£300-350** *S*

An early Issmayer tinplate fire pumper wagon, 6¾ in. (17 cm.) long, German, c. 1900. **£300-400** *S*

A J.E.P. tinplate and clockwork Renault saloon car, some rust damage, 3 wheels damaged, 33 cm. long. **£280-300** *SS*

A J.E.P. tinplate Paris bus, lithographed 'Madeleine . . .', with clockwork mechanism, 10¼ in. (26 cm.) long, French, c. 1925. **£300-350** *S*

A Distler lorry and trailer, with clockwork mechanism driving the rear axle, 19¾ in. (50 cm.) long, German, c. 1935. **£400-450** *S*

An 'Artillery Bank' cast-iron mechanical bank, slight repair, 8 in. (20.2 cm.) long, American, late 19th C. **£190-230** *S*

A 'Speaking Dog' cast-iron mechanical bank, by Shepard Hardware and J. & E. Stevens Co., 7 in. (18 cm.) long, American, late 19th C. **£300-350** *S*

A fine 'Always Did 'Spise a Mule' cast-iron mechanical bank, by J. & E. Stevens Co., in scarlet, yellow and light brown, 10 in. (25.5 cm.) long, American, late 19th C. **£900-1,100** *S*

These are particularly rare colours.

A cast-iron leap frog mechanical bank, by Shepard Hardware Co., paint chipped and movement inoperative, 7½ in. (19 cm.) wide, American, late 19th C. **£300-400** *S*

A cast-iron 'Dinah' mechanical bank, by John Harper & Co. Ltd., 6½ in. (16.5 cm.) high, English, 20th C. **£100-150** *S*

A Paddy and the Pig cast-iron mechanical bank, by J. & E. Stevens Co., in good original paint, 8 in. (20 cm.) high, American, late 19th C. **£550-650** *S*

A fine Zebra cart toy, with clockwork mechanism beneath moving the wheels and the figure, 10½ in. (26.5 cm.) long, probably French, c. 1900. **£250-300** *S*

A fine stump speaker cast-iron mechanical bank, in fine original paint, 9¾ in. (25 cm.) high, American, late 19th C. **£1,000-£1,300** *S*

A cast-iron 'Santa Claus' mechanical bank, chips to paint, 6 in. (15 cm.) high, American, late 19th C. **£450-550** *S*

A cast-iron clown on globe mechanical bank, lacks coin trap door, extended height, 11¼ in. (28.5 cm.), American, late 19th C. **£600-700** *S*

A small and decorative straw-work Noah's Ark, 12¾ in. (32.5 cm.) long, Bavarian, c. 1880. **£400-450** *S*

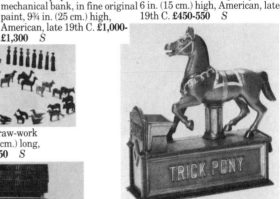

A good cast-iron 'Trick Pony' mechanical bank, by Shepard Hardware Co., 7 in. (18 cm.) wide, American, late 19th C. **£400-500** *S*

An unusual Noah's Ark, 23 in. (58.5 cm.) long, German, c. 1920. **£500-600** *S*

Figuren Alphabetspeil, a set of 25 printed paper on wood alphabet blocks, in original box, German, c. 1910. **£200-250** *CSK*

A painted wooden toy farm, all contained in a wooden box, probably Bavarian, c. 1900, together with a set of wooden building blocks and instruction leaflet. **£900-1,000** *SS*

A painted wooden doll's house, opening at the front to reveal 4 rooms with original wallpapers, floor coverings and with fireplaces, the kitchen with dresser and range, furniture including doll's house dolls, 25 in. high. **£250-300** *CSK*

A near mint Meccano non-constructional car, in original box, 8¾ in. (22 cm.) long, c. 1935. **£450-£500** *S*

A painted wood rocking horse, dapple grey with open mouth, paint flaked, saddle distressed, 41½ in. (105 cm.), English, 20th C. **£200-£250** *S*

A good Austin A40 pedal car, English, c. 1950. **£350-400** *S*

A mechanical walking crocodile, possibly by Decamps, the articulated papier-mâché and wooden beast with clockwork mechanism, 34 in. (86.5 cm.) long, French, c. 1915. **£500-600** *S*

A Victorian doll's house, 54 in. high, c. 1870. **£500-550** *S*

A Victorian doll's house, opening at the back to reveal 2 rooms and a further room of an attached small cottage to one side, 23 in. high by 23 in. wide (58.5 by 58.5 cm.), together with a sofa, armchair, 2 half-dolls, a china shoulder-head, a wooden doll, all English, c. 1890. **£280-350** *S*

A large Victorian doll's house, the 2 hinged front sections opening to reveal 9 rooms, 53 in. high by 40 in. wide (134.5 by 102 cm.), c. 1890's. **£600-700** *S*

A small papered wooden doll's house, the front opening in one to reveal 3 rooms each with fire surround, 27¼ in. high by 14¼ in. wide by 8½ in. deep (69 by 36.5 by 21.5 cm.), English, late 19th C. **£140-200** *S*

A wooden doll's house, the front removing to show 4 rooms with fireplaces and some original hall and floor coverings, 57 in. approximately, c. 1850. **£350-400** *CSK*

A late Victorian red-brick papered 2-storey doll's house, opening either side to reveal 4 rooms each with metal fireplace, 34 in. high by 26 in. wide (86 by 66 cm.), English, c. 1900. **£250-300** *S*

An interior of an open room, comprising approximately 51 items, including 2 composition dolls, overall height of room 20 in., English, late 19th C. **£500-£600** *S*

A miniature dresser, 11 by 8 in. **£80-120**

A set of 6 miniature Windsor chairs, 7¼ in. high. **£300-500**

A miniature doll pedestal table, 9½ in. diam., 4¾ in. high. **£90-120** *CSK*

A speaking picture book, with 8 colour plates of animals and accompanying rhyme, restored, quarto, German, c. 1900. **£250-300** *S*

Walt Disney original signed drawing of Minnie Mouse, denoted 'To Lady Southwood', and signed by the artist, 12 by 10 in. (30.5 by 25.5 cm.). This sold for £1,300 in May, 1984. *S*

Twelve rare and early Mickey Mouse stick pins, each marked 'Sterling Silver' on reverse, the stand 7¼ in. (18.5 cm.) high, the pins ⅞ in. (2.3 cm.) high, c. 1930. **£500-600** *S*

A large plush Felix the Cat, 17 in. (43 cm.) high, c. 1930. **£220-280** *S*

A rare Felix the Cat tea service, decorated with scenes of Felix the Cat and his friends, the teapot 3½ in. (9 cm.) high, c. 1929. **£200-£250** *S*

A plush covered Mickey Mouse, 51 cm. high. **£450-500** *SS*

A Britains' catalogue No. 33, 16th Lancers, early plug shoulder type, seven Lancers, Bugler and Officer with sword on galloping horses, 1894. **£450-550** *SS*

Seven Chad Valley-type stuffed felt dwarfs, 6½ in. (16.5 cm.) high, c. 1940. **£220-280** *S*

Britains' catalogue No. 7, Royal Fusiliers, 1st Type with plug-in rifles, (11), together with a further 4, lacking rifles, and 2 mounted Officers, damaged, c. 1895. **£350-£400** *SS*

Britains' catalogue No. 38, South African mounted Infantry, 4 with rifles on galloping horses and Officer with revolver, in original box. **£600-700** *SS*

*These are **very** rare.*

Britains' catalogue No. 37, Band of the Coldstream Guards, early type slotted arms, embossed plumes, together with a matching Drummer Boy with fixed arms, damaged, c. 1895. **£80-100** *SS*

*These are an early **date**, but poor condition.*

Britains' catalogue No. 101, Band of the 1st Life Guards, slotted arm type, with swords, no patent date, 6 from set of 12, 1 horse's leg broken, 1 tail broken, in box. **£200-300** *SS*

Britains' catalogue No. 79, R.N. Landing Party with gun, 8 sailors running, Petty Officer with sword, limber and gun, damaged, c. 1898. **£50-70** *SS*

Britains' catalogue No. 39, Royal Horse Artillery Gun Team, 6 horse team with mounted drivers, 2 seated gunners, gun with 2 gunners in bucket seats, traces incomplete, some chipping, c. 1898. **£300-350** *SS*

Britains' mounted Officer, dated 1.11.1902, possibly escort to Army Service supply column. **£60-70** *SS*

Britains' catalogue No. 113, East Yorkshire Regiment, 3rd edition, 20.1.1901, 7, one arm missing, 2 spikes broken, in original box, damaged. **£90-110** *SS*

Two good Whistock boxes of Britains' King's Royal Rifle Corps, No. 98, each box containing 8 figures, c. 1905. **£150-200** *S*

Two good Whistock boxes of Britains' Bluejackets, No. 78, each box containing 8 figures, c. 1905. **£150-200** *S*

Britains' catalogue No. 26, Boer Infantry, 2nd edition, 15.6.1906, 8 Privates, some slight paint damage, in original box. **£600-£700** *SS*

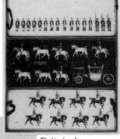

Britains' Coronation 'Sovereign's Escort' set, No. 2081, in original box, 23½ in. (60 cm.) wide, 1953. **£700-£800** *S*

An American ambulance, No. 781, comprising closed wagon, 2 soldiers on the driving seat, 4 horses with 2 outriders, 2 stretcher bearers, etc., in original box, Germany. **£180-200** *WIL*

An interesting lead elephant hunt set, probably by Heyde, comprising 9 elephants, 3 marksmen, 1 rearing riderless horse, 2 native bowmen, 6 bolas throwers, and 4 other figures, assorted vegetation and painted tinplate bases, early 20th C. **£400-450** *C*

Hornby gauge 'O' clockwork 4-4-0 locomotive 'Bramham Moor' No. 20, finished in L.N.E.R. green and black, **£200-250** *S*

(*l.*) Hornby gauge 'O' clockwork 4-4-2 tank locomotive, No. 2221, finished in G.W.R. green and black lined gold. **£70-90**

(*r.*) Hornby gauge 'O' clockwork 4-4-2 tank locomotive, No. 6954, finished in L.M.S. maroon and black lined in gold. **£70-90** *S*

A Hornby gauge 'O' 20-volt electric 4-6-2 Princess Elizabeth locomotive, No. 6201, with tender, some minor retouching to paintwork, in original fitted box. **£500-600**   *SS*

A Bing for Bassett-Lowke gauge '1' 4-4-2 clockwork tank locomotive, No. 11, L.B. & S.C.R. **£500-600**   *S*

An early Bing gauge 'III' hand-painted spirit-fired 4-4-0 locomotive, No. 1902, 'Black Prince', with tender, German, c. 1904. **£1,000-1,400** *S*

A Bing live steam spirit-fired Gauge II locomotive No. 593, 4-4-0, a 4 compartment 3rd class carriage and a 3 compartment guards van. **£800-900**   *EH*

A Bing early 20th C. German tinplate 'O' gauge railway. **£300-£400**   *DWB*

A 3½ in. gauge live steam model of a 2-6-4 tank locomotive, No. 42390, 34 in. (86 cm.) long. **£2,000-2,500** *S*

A good and early Bing gauge 'II' clockwork 4-4-0 locomotive, No. 2631, with tender, German, c. 1908. **£700-800**   *S*

A live steam coal-fired 5 in. gauge LNER Thompson Glass B1 4-6-0 locomotive, No. 61003, 'Gazelle', professionally built by Mr. F. West, Lea Green, London, 65½ in. (166.4 cm.) over buffers, and display track. **£2,000-2,500** *S*

A 3½ in. gauge copper and brass spirit-fired 2-4-0 locomotive, No. 715, 17¼ in. (43.5 cm.) long, English, c. 1880's. **£400-500** *S*

A 5-in. Welsh narrow gauge 0-6-0 coal-fired tank locomotive, No. 3. **£1,500-1,700**   *S*

A gauge I clockwork model, of an 0-4-0 Peckett saddle tank locomotive No. 810, by Carette for Bassett-Lowke. **£200-250** *CSK*

A rare gauge I clockwork model, by Marklin for Bassett-Lowke, of the Great Northern Railway 2-4-0 side tank locomotive No. TM 1020. **£300-400**   *CSK*

A 7¼ in. gauge live steam coal-fired 0-4-0 GWR tank locomotive, No. 1104, 38 in. (96.5 cm.). **£1,200-£1,500** *S*

Marklin for Bassett-Lowke gauge 'O' electric 4-4-0 Schools Class 'Merchant Taylor's locomotive, No. 17, with tender, c. 1935. **£400-450** *SS*

A 5 in. gauge model, of the Midland Railway Johnson 'Spinner' 4-2-2 locomotive and tender No. 2602, built by R. Glave, Barnstaple, 14 by 59 in. (35 by 150 cm.). **£1,800-£2,200** *C*

A 7 mm. scale 2-rail electric model, of the London Midland and Scottish Railway Class 7P 4-6-2 locomotive and tender No. 6207, 'Princess Arthur of Connaught', built by Bonds of Euston Road, 4 by 20¾ in. (10 by 52.5 cm.), c. 1938. **£600-700** *C*

A detailed Exhibition Standard 5 in. gauge model, of the Great Northern Railway Stirling 'Single' 4-2-2 locomotive and tender No. 47, built by R. Glave, Barnstaple, 14 by 56 in. (35.5 by 142 cm.). **£3,500-£4,000** *C*

A 5 in. gauge live steam coal-fired 0-4-0 Canterbury & Whitstable locomotive, 'Invicta', with sprung 4-wheeled tender, 33 in. (83.8 cm.) long. **£500-600** *S*

A 3½ in. gauge 0-4-0 locomotive, 'Tich', in dark green, 15½ in. **£300-£350** *GSP*

An exhibition standard 3½ in. gauge model, of the London and North Eastern Railway Ivatt Atlantic 4-4-2 locomotive and tender No. 4420, built by R. James, Basingstoke, 10¼ by 45 in. (26 by 114.5 cm.). **£1,800-2,200** *C*

A 5 in. gauge model, of the Great Western Railway King Class 4-6-0 locomotive and tender No. 6026, 'King John', built by C. C. May, Derby, 15 by 73½ in. (38 by 187 cm.). **£3,000-4,000** *C*

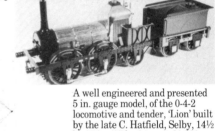

A well engineered and presented 5 in. gauge model, of the 0-4-2 locomotive and tender, 'Lion' built by the late C. Hatfield, Selby, 14½ by 37 in. (37 by 94 cm.). **£1,200-£1,300** *C*

A contemporary early 19th C. French Prisoner of War bone and horn model, of an 88-gun man-of-war, hull measurements, 11 by 2½ in. (28 by 6.5 cm.). **£2,000-2,600** *C*

A prisoner-of-war bone model, of an 88-gun third-rate ship-of-the-line, 20 by 27 in. (51 by 69 cm.), on wood and bone stand, early 19th C. **£1,600-1,800** *S*

A small prisoner-of-war model, replaced stern and figureheads, 8⅞ in. (22.5 cm.) long, French, early 19th C. **£400-500** *S*

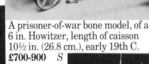

A prisoner-of-war bone model, of a 6 in. Howitzer, length of caisson 10½ in. (26.8 cm.), early 19th C. **£700-900** *S*

A half-block model of a brig, the laminated wooden hull mounted on mahogany wall plaque, 59 in. (150 cm.) long, English, mid 19th C. **£500-600** *S*

A rare mahogany Lovold's patent model deck seat and lifeboat, Patent No. 15462, 18 in. (46 cm.) long, with original patent specifications and drawings, in mahogany case, 1887. **£400-450** *S*

A finely detailed fully planked and rigged 1:32 scale model, of an Arabian Gulf pearling dhow, built by D. A. Brogden, Skegness, 16 by 16¾ in. (40.5 by 42.5 cm.). **£250-350** *C*

A bone prisoner-of-war ship model, of 'H.M.S. Nelson', lettered Lord Nelson, heavily restored, 13½ by 18½ in. (34 by 47 cm.), on modern ebonised base under perspex case, early 19th C. **£1,600-2,000** *S*

A model of a sectioned ship's hull, 17 in. (43 cm.) long, early 20th C. **£1,500-1,900** *S*

A rare wood and bone model of a galleon, lacking 3 top masts and bowsprit, 18 in. (46 cm.) long, probably English, early 19th C. **£300-400** *S*

A live-steam spirit-fired model, of an early steam ship, 31 in. (77 cm.) long, probably German, c. 1905. **£500-600** *CSK*

A bone and wood model of a man-of-war, 13½ by 12 in. (34.5 by 31.5 cm.), English, early 19th C. **£350-400** *S*

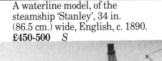

A waterline model, of the steamship 'Stanley', 34 in. (86.5 cm.) wide, English, c. 1890. **£450-500** *S*

A 1:48 scale model, of the Chebec 'L'Indiscret', and 5 members of the crew, on stand, 38 in. (96.5 cm.) long, English, modern. **£500-600** *S*

An extremely fine and detailed 1:48 scale fully rigged and planked model, of a Charles II sixth rate 26-gun man-of-war of c. 1686, built by D. A. Brogden, Skegness, 23 by 27 in. (58.5 by 68.5 cm.). **£2,000-£2,500** *C*

A half-block model, of the stern-wheeler steam river boat 'Richard Lander' by Kelso & Co., Model Makers, Glasgow, 11 by 38 in. (28 by 96.5 cm.), built by The Lytham Shipbuilding and Engineering Company Ltd., England, length B.P. 150 ft., beam moulded 30 ft., speed 11 knots, depth 6 ft. 6 in., 50 in. (127 cm.) long, Scottish, c. 1900. **£1,800-2,200** *S*

A 1:9½ in. scale model, of the Wallis WA-116 2-seater Autogyro Regn. letters G-AXAS, built by G. J. Izera, Bracknell, rota diameter, 26½ in. (67.5 cm.) overall length 13¼ in. (33.5 cm.). **£1,500-£1,800** *C*

An ⅛th scale wood and metal model, of a Lincolnshire corn wagon of c. 1900, 10 by 30 in. **£300-350** *C*

A model of the ocean liner 'Queen Mary', 66 in. (168 cm.) long, c. 1950. **£1,300-1,600** *S*

The model of the Queen Mary is very desirable.

A late 19th C. wooden model haywain, 26 in. (66 cm.) long overall. **£100-150** *S*

A 1:24 scale model, of the Hawker Hurricane Mk. 1 single-seater fighter of c. 1940, registration letters ALK, built by R. A. Burgess, Thornton Dale, wing span, 19½ in. (49.5 cm.), overall length 15¾ in. (40 cm.). **£800-850** *C*

A well-engineered 3 in. scale model, of a Wallis and Stevens 'Simplicity' Road Roller, built by D. G. Edwards, East Wittering, 1980, 24¾ by 35 in. (63 by 89 cm.). **£1,000-1,200** *C*

A wood and metal display model, of Sir Malcolm Campbell's World Land Speed Record 350 hp. Sunbeam, originally designed by L. Coatalen, 1920, the model commissioned by Sir Malcolm Campbell, c. 1924, 5½ by 23½ in. (14 by 59.5 cm.). **£1,000-1,500** *C*

An Exhibition Standard 2 in. scale model, of the Wallis and Stevens 'Advance' twin cylinder, 2 speed, 4 shaft Road Roller N. 7964, Regn. No. OT 7114, built by S. Jackson, Manchester, 18¼ by 30 in. (46.5 by 76.5 cm.). **£3,500-4,000** *C*

A finely engineered Exhibition Standard model, of a single cylinder overcrank stationary engine built to the designs of T. D. Walshaw by A. Mount, London, 9½ by 6¾ in. (24 by 17 cm.). **£300-£350**   *C*

A unique patent model, of a 3 cylinder horizontal reversing stationary engine, built by W. G. Duggan, Benton, and D. Ash, Leicester, c. 1920 to illustrate improvements relating to valve gears for reciprocating steam engines, patent no. 174667, 8⅜ by 18¾ in. (21.5 by 47.5 cm.). **£400-450** *C*

A full size single horizontal cylinder high speed stationary steam engine, built by Negelin and Hubner, Halle, 28 by 64 in. (71 by 162.5 cm.). **£500-550**   *C*

An early 20th C. tinplate and cast-iron model, single horizontal cylinder open crank gas engine, by Bing, 10 by 16 in. (25.5 by 40.5 cm.). **£600-650**   *C*

A 6-sided Allwin column, with 3 5-win machines, and 3 Allwin Deluxe, 66½ in. (169 cm.) high, English, c. 1925. **£600-700**   *S*

A 'Pussy Shooter' machine, 74 in. (188 cm.) high, English, c. 1935. **£350-450**   *S*

An electrically operated penny-in-the-slot clown gymnast automaton, 64 in. (162.5 cm.) high, English, c. 1925. **£700-1,000**   *S*

A Roland & Son 'Test Your Strength' machine, 58 in. (147 cm.) high, English, c. 1920. **£400-500**   *S*

The French execution coinslot automaton, 84 in. (214 cm.) high, c. 1935. **£500-600**   *S*

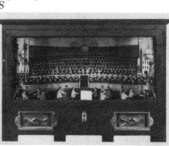

A large football machine, the football teams with articulated legs, 64 in. (163 cm.) high, English, c. 1935. **£350-550**   *S*

A mutoscope, by the International Mutoscope Reel Company, 74 in. (188 cm.) high, American, c. 1920. **£500-600**   *S*

A premium bond's 'Wheel of Fortune' machine, 24 in. (61 cm.) high, c. 1915. **£200-250**   *S*

An aeroplane Allwin-type machine, 33 in. (84 cm.) high, English, c. 1940. **£100-130**   *S*

A Klingsor gramophone, complete with 10 in. turntable, 39 in. (99 cm.) high, Swiss, c. 1925. **£500-£600**   *S*

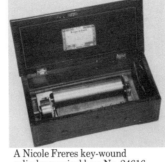

A rare Raymond Nicole key-wound cylinder musical box, No. 407, the 6 by 20 cm. cylinder playing 6 airs, spring to motor broken, 13½ in. (34.5 cm.) wide, Swiss, c. 1840. **£800-900** *S*

A Nicole Freres key-wound cylinder musical box, No. 24616, playing 3 overtures by Rossini, Weber and Meyerbeer, Gamme No. 906, 17½ in. (44.5 cm.) wide, Swiss, c. 1845. **£2,000-2,500** *S*

A Nicole Freres overture cylinder musical box, No. 43550, playing 4 overtures by Weber, Auber (2) and Boieldieu, in walnut-veneered case, 23 in. (58.5 cm.) wide, Swiss, c. 1870. **£2,200-2,500** *S*

A Nicole Freres cylinder musical box, No. 45617, playing 10 airs, in walnut-veneered case, 20½ in. (52 cm.) wide, Swiss, c. 1880. **£400-£450** *S*

A Bremond 'Bells-in-Sight' cylinder musical box, No. 3003, playing 8 airs, wings now missing, 23 in. (58.5 cm.) wide, Swiss, c. 1870. **£700-800** *S*

A late 19th C. Swiss cylinder musical box, on stand, by F. Conchon, playing 6 airs, 3 ft. 4 in. high. **£1,000-1,200** *MMB*

A Ducommun Girod 'Bells-Drum-and-Castanets-in-Sight' cylinder musical box, No. 5394, playing 8 airs, the comb with one broken tooth, 24 in. (61 cm.) wide, Swiss, c. 1890. **£1,000-1,200** *S*

A Société Junod bells and drum-in-sight interchangeable cylinder musical box, the 3 cylinders each playing 6 airs, 29 in. (74 cm.) long, Swiss, c. 1900. **£1,600-2,000** *SC*

A Mojon, Manger & Co. interchangeable cylinder musical box, each of the 4 18 cm. cylinders playing 6 airs, case distressed, 27½ in. (70 cm.) wide, Swiss, c. 1890. **£500-600** *S*

An elaborately carved cylinder musical box case, 25 in. (64 cm.) long, probably German, late 19th C. **£300-350** *S*

A 'Bells-in-Sight' cylinder musical box, No. 966, playing 6 airs, lacking tune sheet, 21 in. (53 cm.) wide, Swiss, c. 1880. **£800-900** *S*

A Charles Ullmann 'Bells, drums and castanets in sight' cylinder musical box, No. 6773, playing 8 popular airs, accompanied by 3 automated seated manderins each striking 2 bells, 28 in. (71 cm.) wide, Swiss, c. 1880. **£2,000-2,500** *S*

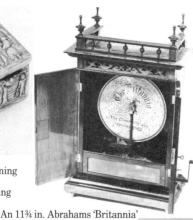

A singing bird box, the silver plated case with hinged lid opening to small singing bird, 3¾ in. (9.5 cm.) wide, in leather carrying case, c. 1900. **£650-750**   *S*

A 19th C. Continental burrwood musical box, the movement in base playing 1 air, 3½ in. **£200-300**   *O*

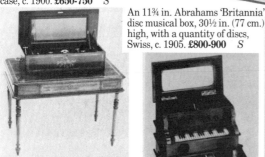

An 11¾ in. Abrahams 'Britannia' disc musical box, 30½ in. (77 cm.) high, with a quantity of discs, Swiss, c. 1905. **£800-900**   *S*

A Paillard & Co. 'Longue Marche' interchangeable cylinder musical box on stand, each of the 5 cylinders playing 8 airs, 42 in. (107 cm.) wide, Swiss, c. 1885. **£1,800-2,200**   *S*

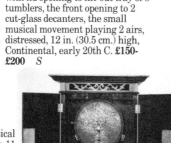

A 17¼ in. Stella disc musical box on stand, 29 in. (74 cm.) wide, Swiss, c. 1900. **£2,000-2,500**   *S*

A 15½ in. Polyphon disc musical box, No. 30899, bass dampers distressed, 22¾ in. (58 cm.) wide, with 39 discs, German, late 19th C. **£900-1,000**   *S*

A musical tantalus, the case in the form of a keyboard instrument with lid opening to lift-out tray of 8 tumblers, the front opening to 2 cut-glass decanters, the small musical movement playing 2 airs, distressed, 12 in. (30.5 cm.) high, Continental, early 20th C. **£150-£200**   *S*

A 25¼ in. Symphonion disc musical box, 57 in. high, German, c. 1900. **£2,000-2,500**   *S*

A 19⅝ in. Polyphon disc musical box, 36 in. (92 cm.) high, with 11 metal discs, German, c. 1900. **£1,300-1,500**   *S*

A 9 in. Abraham's 'Britannica' disc musical box, lacking pediment, 21½ in. (54.5 cm.) high, with 24 discs, Swiss, c. 1900. **£550-600**   *S*

A Theodore Bates 24-key dulcimer, playing 10 tunes on piano and 2 saucer bells, 39 in. (99 cm.) high, 2 spare barrels, English, c. 1840. **£1,500-2,000**   *S*

An 11¾ in. Symphonion disc musical box, 20 in. (51 cm.) wide, German, late 19th C. **£1,200-1,500**   *S*

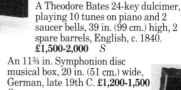

A 34-key Atlantic orchestrion, the coin-operated weight-driven movement playing on piano, xylophone, triangle and snare drum, the 2 39 cm. cylinders each playing 6 tunes, 77 by 30 by 24½ in. (196 by 76 by 62 cm.), c. 1925. **£2,500-3,000**   *S*

A good 11¾ in. Symphonion disc musical, 19½ in. (49.5 cm.) wide, with 12 metal discs, catalogue and tune list, German, c. 1895. **£900-£1,200**   *S*

A rare Ariston organette, for discs
and cardboard strip, 18 in. (46 cm.)
long, with 3 cardboard discs,
German, c. 1900. **£350-450** *S*

A Celestina paper-roll organette,
with 20-note instrument, 15 in.
(38 cm.) wide, with 18 paper rolls,
American, c. 1890. **£400-500** *S*

A serephone paper-roll organette,
with 20-note movement, 17 in.
(43 cm.) wide, with 6 paper rolls,
late 19th C. **£400-500** *S*

An A. Zuleger 'Tanzbar' player
concertina, with 28 reeds, and
4¼ in. wide paper roll drum, 10 in.
(26 cm.) long, German, c. 1910.
£550-650 *S*

A small 14-key barrel playing
organ, the 29 cm. pinned barrel 8
tunes, 16 in. (41 cm.) high, English,
mid 19th C. **£500-600** *S*

An Anderson piano-harpa, Patent
No. 2239, the 18-note instrument,
with one spare cylinder, 37 in.
(94 cm.) wide, Swedish, c. 1890.
£800-900 *S*

A Hupfeld automatic piano, the
electrically powered and coin-
operated movement with tracker
bar and rolls, 56 in. (142 cm.) wide,
English, c. 1900. **£3,000-4,000** *S*

An early 19th C. 14-key
chamber barrel organ, 47 in.
(119 cm.) high, not in
working order. **£800-900**
SS

A Faventia miniature barrel piano
on cart, the 38 cm. pinned cylinder
playing 6 tunes, 46 in. (117 cm.)
wide, Spanish, modern. **£450-500**
S

A Henry Brysceson chamber barrel
organ, with 3 cylinders, each
playing 10 tunes, 78 by 30 by
23 in., with mahogany cabinet for 3
further cylinders, English, c. 1810.
£2,000-2,200 *S*

A rare and early Kämmer
Reinhardt & Co. gramophone, the
5 in. turntable hand-driven by
wheel and pulley, with replacement
soundbox and horn, 11 in. (30 cm.)
long, with 3 Berliner discs,
German, c. 1895. **£900-1,000** *S*

A large horn gramophone, with
10 in. diam. turntable
Maestrophone soundbox, with
painted metal horn, the mouth
24 in. diam., Continental, c. 1910.
£650-750 *S*

A horn gramophone, with 10¾ in.
turntable, Imperator soundbox,
heavy metal trumpet horn,
Continental, c. 1910. **£400-500** *S*

A horn gramophone, with 12 in. turntable, Exhibition soundbox, with green and yellow painted petal horn, probably French, 1905. **£500-600** *S*

A salon pathephone, with 10 in. turntable, Mozart soundbox, white painted metal horn, 28 in. (71.5 cm.) high, French, c. 1910. **£250-300** *S*

An Edison fireside phonograph, Model A, Serial No. 13005, with 2 and 4 minute gearing, model C and model H reproducers, with 15 Edison cylinders, varying condition, 11½ in. wide. **£200-250** *Bea*

An Edison spring motor phonograph, with Bettini Type D reproducer, with a pair of blue painted card horns, American, c. 1903. **£1,000-1,200** *S*

An Aeolian orchestrelle, by the Aeolian Co., spreading 4⅝ octaves, and with 22 stops, 69½ in. high by 79½ in. wide, with 100 rolls, American, c. 1890. **£1,000-1,200** *Bea*

An English bentside spinet, the nameboard inscribed Gulielmus Rock Londini Fecit, third quarter 18th C., on a later stand with cabriole legs, 74¼ in. (189 cm.) wide. **£2,000-2,500** *C*

Compass: 5 octaves, FF-f3, chromatic. The ivory naturals with boxwood moulded fronts.

An overstrung boudoir grand pianoforte, 7 octave, by F. Kaim & Son, Kircheim Stuttgart, No. 6209. **£2,500-3,000** *CSK*

A square piano, by Patrick Butler, Dublin, 1798, the satinwood nameboard with holly and fruitwood stringing, the 5 octave keyboard, FF to f³, with ivory naturals and ebony accidentals, single action with overdampers, 5 ft. 2½ in. (158.7 cm.) long, 2 ft. 10⅝ in. (57.5 cm.) wide. **£1,600-2,000** *S*

A composite English spinet, the walnut nameboard with sycamore stringing inscribed on a boxwood plaque Johannes Ladyman Londini Fecit 1694, the keyboard, compass, AA to g³, with arcaded ivory naturals and ebony accidentals, 6 ft. ½ in. (184 cm.) long, second quarter of 18th C. **£1,300-2,000** *S*

A satinwood cased short grand piano, by John Broadwood & Sons, London, numbered 44541, 55 by 75 in. **£1,000-1,200** *PWC*

A mid Victorian burr-walnut cased cottage piano, by Henry Tolkien, King William Street, London Bridge, Serial No. 2181, 32½ by 26 in. **£450-600** *CGC*

A grand forte piano, by John Broadwood & Son, numbered inside 2524, 89½ by 42 in. (227.5 by 106.5 cm.). **£4,000-5,000** *C*

Compass: 5½ octaves, FF-c4; 2 pedals: una corda (with checkpiece) and forte.

An English violin, by a member of the Panormo family, length of back 13¹⁵/₁₆ in. (35.3 cm.), and a nickel-mounted violin bow, in case. **£2,000-2,500** *S*

An English violin, by Alfred Vincent, London, 1925, length of back 13¹⁵⁄₁₆ in. (35.4 cm.), in case. **£1,000-1,200**   *S*

A fine French violin, by Nicolas Lupot labelled Lupot et Gand . . . 1828 and Nicolas Lupot . . .1822, length of back 14⅛ in. (35.7 cm.), in case. **£9,000-10,000**   *C*

An Italian violin, by Leandro Bisiach, labelled Leandro Bisiach . . . Milano 1896 and signed by the maker, length of back 14³⁄₁₆ in. (36 cm.), in case. **£7,000-9,000**   *C*

An English violoncello, by Barak Norman & Nathaniel Cross, 1725, the back in 3 pieces, the scroll possibly of a later date, length of back 28³⁄₁₆ in. (71.7 cm.). **£2,300-£2,800**   *C*

A viola, labelled Jean Baptiste Vuillaume à Paris, length of back 15⁵⁄₁₆ in. (38.8 cm.), and a silver-mounted violin bow by W. E. Hill & Sons, London, 60 gm., in case with outer canvas cover. **£2,500-3,000**   *S*

An 18th C. French violin, by Claude Pierray, Paris 1747, the back 13⅞ in. (35.2 cm.), with 2 bows in a lined case. **£2,000-2,200**   *WHL*

A fine French violin, by Georges Chanot labelled Georges Chanot à Paris . . . 1835, length of back 13⅞ in. (35.3 cm.), in case. **£5,000-£6,000**   *C*

A French violin, ascribed to Pierre Silvestre labelled Pierre Silvestre/à Lyons 1848, length of back 14 in. (35.6 cm.). **£2,000-2,500**   *C*

A French violin, by Jean-Baptiste Vuillaume, Paris, 1867, length of back 14⅛ in. (35.9 cm.). **£9,000-£10,000**   *S*

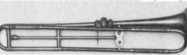

A silver-mounted violin bow, by François Nicolas Voirin, Paris, 50 gm. **£450-550**   *S*

An interesting silver-mounted violin bow, unstamped, 54 gm., c. 1830. **£700-800**   *S*

A fine French violin, by Jean-Baptiste Vuillaume, Paris, numbered 1945, the one piece back of medium to broad curl, the varnish of a red-brown colour, length of back 14⅛ in. (35.9 cm.). **£13,000-15,000**   *S*

A violin, labelled Bortolamio Obici, in Verona, 1684, length of back 14⅛ in. (35.9 cm.), and 2 violin bows, 1 silver-mounted, in shaped case. **£1,000-1,300**   *S*

An Italian violin, by Antonio Gragnani labelled Antonius Gragnani fecit/Liburni Anno 1751, length of back 14¹⁄₁₆ in. (35.7 cm.), in case with French silver-mounted violin bow. **£10,000-12,000**   *C*

An 8-keyed boxwood clarinet, in C by George Wood, London, length 23 in. (58.5 cm.), c. 1830. **£170-220**   *S*

A guitar, by Charles Boullangier, London, length of body 17½ in. (44.5 cm.), third quarter of 19th C., in wooden case. **£500-600**   *S*

A rare French 6-string pardessus de viole, by Nicolas Des Rousseaux, length of back 13 in. (33 cm.). **£4,000-5,000**   *C*

A Gothic double-action pedal harp, by Sebastian & Pierre Érard, London, with 46 strings, seven pedals and a louvre pedal, extreme height 5 ft. 9¾ in. (177.1 cm.), c. 1829. **£1,700-2,000**   *S*

A brass slide trumpet, by John Augustus Köhler, London, with 3 crooks and 3 shanks for C, D and Eb, c. 1850, in case. **£850-950**   *S*

An interesting and unusual double-action pedal harp, by Frederick Dizi, London, with 8 pedals including louvre pedal, 43 strings, extreme height 5 ft. 6¼ in. (168.3 cm.), c. 1820. **£550-650**   *S*

Dizi's patent for this harp mechanism was granted on 1st November 1817, No. 4171.

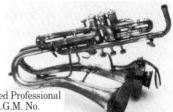

A jazzophone, stamped Professional and Jazzophone, D.R.G.M. No. 995.305, length 17⅝ in. (44.8 cm.), in leather case. **£550-650**   *S*

A pine secretaire bookcase, 77 in.
high by 39½ in. wide by 21 in. deep,
c. 1820. **£1,250-1,500**   *W*

A pine domed top box, with iron
straps, 41 in. wide by 19 in. high by
18 in. deep, c. 1840. **£65-80**   *AL*

A pine box, with trim round base,
29 in. wide by 12 in. high by 16 in.
deep. **£40-50**   *AL*

A pine small box, 24 in. wide by
10½ in. high by 12 in. deep, c. 1860.
£30-40   *AL*

A pine cutlery box, 12 in. long by
7½ in. wide, c. 1850. **£45-50**   *W*

A rocking chair, 43 in. high by
24 in. wide by 46 in. deep, c. 1880.
£225-250   *W*

A set of 4 smokers chairs, 31½ in.
high by 26 in. wide by 19 in. deep,
c. 1860. **£500-550**   *W*

A pine box settle, 44 in. high by
50 in. wide by 17½ in. deep, early
Victorian. **£425-475**   *W*

A kitchen chair. **£25-30**   *AL*

A pine settle, 67 in. high by 14 in.
deep, c. 1840. **£900-1,000**   *W*

A balloon-back cane seated chair.
£20-25   *AL*

A slat back chair. **£30-35**   *AL*

A pair of simulated bamboo chairs,
33 in. high by 17½ in. wide by
14 in. deep, c. 1840. **£110-125**   *W*

A Regency cane seat chair, 33 in.
high by 21 in. wide by 17 in. deep.
£175-200   *W*

A scroll back kitchen chair. **£25-30**
AL

An Arts & Crafts hall chair, 30 in.
high by 24 in. wide by 22 in. deep.
£140-150   *W*

An unusual carved pine rustic
bench, the back and arms in the
form of naturalistic branches,
carved with leaves and with a bear
seated in the branches, the plank
seat supported by standing carved
bears, probably Swiss, 4 ft. 2½ in.
wide (128 cm.), c. 1860. **£1,800-
£2,200**   *S*

A stick back chair. **£25-35**   *AL*

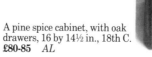

A cheese bench, 39 in. wide by 7 in.
deep by 21 in. high, c. 1840. **£20-25**
AL

A pine cane seated chair and a rush
seated chair, c. 1860. Between **£40-
£50** each   *AL*

A pine spice cabinet, with oak
drawers, 16 by 14½ in., 18th C.
£80-85   *AL*

A Scandinavian painted pine chest of drawers, 3 ft. high by 3 ft. 1 in. wide. **£120-140** *BEL*

A pine chest of drawers, 34 in. wide by 33 in. high by 18 in. deep, c. 1860. **£100-120** *AL*

An unusual Victorian chest of drawers. **£140-150** *AL*

A pine dressing chest, with replacement handles, c. 1900. **£130-140** *AL*

A pine collectors cabinet, with graduated drawers and compartment, painting of birds on top, 18 in. high by 15 in. wide by 8 in. deep, late Victorian. **£100-125** *W*

A flight of 18 grocery drawers, 2 ft. 7 in. high by 4 ft. 2 in. wide, c. 1890. **£375-425** *BEL*

A pine step commode, 26 in. high by 18 in. wide by 30 in. deep, early Victorian. **£250-275** *W*

A Scandinavian painted pine chest of drawers, recently painted, 3 ft. 1 in. high by 3 ft. 2 in. wide, c. 1890. **£140-160** *BEL*

MAKE THE MOST OF MILLER'S

Every care has been taken to ensure the accuracy of descriptions and estimated valuations.

Price ranges in this book reflect what one should expect to pay for a similar example. When selling one can obviously expect a figure below. This will fluctuate according to a dealer's stock, saleability at a particular

time, etc. It is always advisable to approach a reputable specialist dealer or an auction house which has specialist sales.

Unless otherwise stated, any description which refers to 'a set', or 'a pair' includes a valuation for the entire set or the pair, even though the illustration may show only a single item.

A Swedish pine dressing chest, with unusual carving, 6 ft. 6 in. high by 2 ft. 8 in. wide. **£180-200** *BEL*

A pine tray top commode, 31 in. high by 19 in. wide by 16½ in. deep, c. 1840. **£250-300** *W*

A pine 2-door cupboard, 33 in. wide by 36½ in. high by 17½ in. deep, c. 1860. **£90-110**   *AL*

A pine pot cupboard, 32 in. high by 15 in. wide by 12½ in. deep, late Victorian. **£75-85**   *W*

A pine tall cupboard, with shaped door, shelf inside, 18 in. wide by 0 in. high by 13 in. deep, c. 1860. **110-130**   *AL*

A tall cupboard, with adjustable shelves, with original lock and key, 19 in. wide by 11 in. deep by 51 in. high, c. 1840. **£110-130**   *AL*

A deep pine 2-door cupboard, 34 in. wide by 22 in. deep by 48 in. high, . 1840. **£110-120**   *AL*

A pine pot cupboard, with original porcelain handle, 14 in. wide by 0 in. high by 13½ in. deep. **£50-60**   *AL*

A pine cupboard, with drawer, 22 in. wide by 27 in. high by 17½ in. deep, c. 1840. **£30-40**   *AL*

A pine bedside cupboard, with lifting top, 2 ft. 6 in. high by 1 ft. 6 in. wide, c. 1890. **£60-70**   *BEL*

pine 2-door cupboard, with djustable shelves, 60 in. wide by 2 in. high by 13 in. deep. **£160-170**
L

A pine corner cupboard, 31½ in. high by 27 in. wide by 17½ in. deep, c. 1840. **£155-175**   *W*

A pine commode, with china pottery liner, 19 in. wide by 18 in. high by 18 in. deep, c. 1850. **£40-50**   *AL*

A pine display cabinet, 39 in. high by 27½ in. wide by 7½ in. deep, c. 1780. **£190-200** *W*

A finely panelled Scottish pine hanging cupboard, 6 ft. 1 in. high by 4 ft. 6 in. wide, c. 1800. **£350-400** *HG*

A press cupboard, with panelled sides, 6 ft. 8 in. high by 3 ft. 8 in. wide by 19 in. deep, c. 1840. **£375-£425** *PH*

A pine corner unit, 31 in. wide by 35 in. high by 18½ in. deep, c. 1860. **£50-60** *AL*

A North Wales housekeeper's cupboard, 6 ft. 3 in. long by 7 ft. 6 in. high by 20 in. deep, c. 1840. **£800-900** *PH*

A pine food cupboard, 72 in. high by 39 in. wide by 14½ in. deep, c. 1880. **£575-625** *W*

A Quicksey pine kitchen cabinet, complete with original fittings, glass storage jars and drawers, spice rack, flour bin and memoranda panels inside top doors, for shopping and useful household hints, enamel work top, 82 in. high by 48 in. wide by 22 in. deep, early 1920's. **£400-450** *OC*

A pine dresser, 83 in. high by 53 in. wide by 18 in. deep, late Victorian. **£725-775** *W*

A late Georgian pine dresser, painted with deep coloured varnish. **£1,800-2,000** *JF*

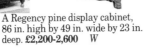

A Regency pine display cabinet, 86 in. high by 49 in. wide by 23 in. deep. **£2,200-2,600** *W*

A Scottish pitch pine dresser base, with 7 drawers and shaped back, 6 ft. 10 in. wide by 4 ft. 7 in. high, c. 1870. **£500-700** *LRG*

A North Wales dresser base, with a thick sycamore top, 33 in. high by 7 ft. 6 in. long by 20 in. deep, c. 1800. **£575-625** *PH*

A long pot board dresser base, 11 ft. 2 in. long by 37 in. high by 22 in. deep, c. 1830. **£625-675** *PH*

A small Scandinavian pine writing desk, with drawer with lifting top, 2 ft. 7 in. high by 2 ft. 5 in. wide, 19th C. **£125-150** *BEL*

A pine shelf unit, 20 in. wide by 31 in. high. **£30-£40** *AL*

An original pine secretaire, 58½ in. high by 40 in. wide by 17 in. deep. **£450-475** *W*

A pine bureau, 42 in. high by 41 in. wide by 17½ in. deep, c. 1830. **£675-£725** *W*

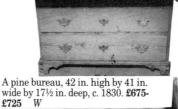

A pine hanging wall shelf, 27½ in. wide by 21½ in. high by 4½ in. deep, c. 1860. **£40-50** *AL*

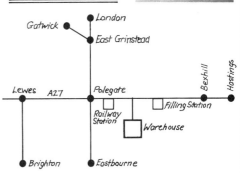

A pine breakfront kneehole desk, 47 in. wide by 33 in. high by 23 in. deep, c. 1860. **£355-370** *AL*

A pine flat top desk, 19 in. wide by 24 in. deep by 12 in. high, c. 1850. **£20-30** *AL*

A small Scandinavian pine sideboard, with 2 drawers, 3 ft. 1 in. high by 4 ft. 2 in. wide, c. 1875. **£140-160** *BEL*

A tall shelf unit, 41 in. wide by 45 in. high by 18 in. deep, c. 1860. **£40-50** *AL*

A drop-leaf table with drawer,
19 in. closed by 34 in. open by 35 in.
wide by 29 in. high, c. 1860. **£65-75**
AL

A pine stool, 15 in. wide
by 24 in. high by 12½ in.
deep. **£20-25** *AL*

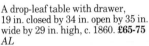

A beech and elm stool,
18 by 15 in., 19th C.
£21-23 *AL*

A bench table, 26 in. wide by 24 in.
high by 13 in. deep, c. 1860. **£40-50**
AL

An unusual Scandinavian pine
oval period table, 30 in. high by
34 in. wide by 51 in. long,
c. 1680-1720. **£425-475** *W*

A table, with 2 drawers, original
handles, 40 in. wide by 29 in. high
by 24 in. deep, c. 1840. **£90-100**
AL

A side table, 35½ in. wide by 28 in.
high by 18½ in. deep, c. 1860. **£55-
£65** *AL*

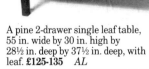

A pine 2-drawer single leaf table,
55 in. wide by 30 in. high by
28½ in. deep by 37½ in. deep, with
leaf. **£125-135** *AL*

A pine table, with turned legs,
33 in. wide by 28 in. high by 16 in.
deep, c. 1860. **£45-55** *AL*

An Edwardian pine writing table,
with 3 drawers, 30 in. high by
48 in. wide by 30 in. deep. **£275-300**
W

A pine single flap table, with
drawer, original porcelain handles,
22 in. deep by 28 in. high by 36 in.
wide, c. 1850. **£60-70** *AL*

A set of pine book shelves, 27 in. wide by 48 in. high by 6 in. deep, c. 1860. **£50-60**   *AL*

A pair of pine stools, 18 by 8½ by 18½ in., 19th C. **£58-62**   *AL*

A pine stool, 13 in. wide by 20 in. high. **£20-25**   *AL*

A Victorian sycamore stool. **£25-30** *W*

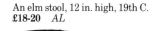

Pine library steps, restored, 71 in. high by 21 in. wide by 36 in. deep, 18th C. **£545-575** *W*

A pine stool, 12 in. high, 19th C. **£18-20**   *AL*

Pine steps, 28 in. high, early 20th C. **£18-20**   *AL*

An elm stool, 12 in. high, 19th C. **£18-20**   *AL*

A pine period table, 30 in. high by 36 in. wide by 21½ in. deep, c. 1720. **£300-350**   *W*

A Victorian pine table, 30 in. high by 19 in. wide. **£140-160** *W*

A pair of pine tables, with delicately turned legs, 42 in. wide by 29 in. high by 22 in. deep. **£50-£60** each *AL*

A Tyrolean pine centre table, with hinged moulded rectangular plank top, with later interior above the carved frieze on solid panelled and carved trestle supports, joined by stretchers and stepped feet, 41 in. wide (104 cm.), basically 18th C. **£2,000-2,500** *C*

A small pine side table, with original porcelain handles, 33 in. wide by 29 in. high by 17 in. deep, c. 1850. **£50-60** *AL*

A small pine drop-leaf table, 19 in. wide closed by 29 in. wide open by 29 in. high, c. 1840. **£60-70** *AL*

A pine gateleg table, 29½ in. high by 74 in. wide (flaps up), c. 1760. **£325-350** *W*

A pine washstand, 45 in. high by 42 in. wide by 20 in. deep, c. 1860. **£220-230** *W*

A small pine table, with 1 drawer, 35 in. wide by 29 in. high by 23 in. deep. **£50-60** *AL*

A double pine washstand, 39 in. wide by 35 in. high by 19 in. deep, c. 1840. **£60-70** *AL*

A pine washstand, 23 in. wide by 38 in. high by 16 in. deep, c. 1850. **£60-70** *AL*

A pine planter, 31 in. high by 32 in. wide by 19 in. deep, c. 1860. **£375-£400** *W*

A Scandinavian wardrobe, 2 ft. 9 in. wide by 6 ft. 4 in. high, 19th C. **£160-180** *BEL*

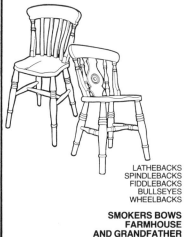

A pine washstand, with original brass handles, 29 in. wide by 46 in. high by 17 in. deep, c. 1860. **£110-£120** *AL*

A pine wardrobe, 43 in. wide by 78 in. high by 21 in. deep. **£210-220** *AL*

A Regency pine washstand, 38 in. high by 22 in. wide. **£150-170** *W*

A pine dressing table, 67 in. high by 42 in. wide by 19 in. deep, c. 1890. **£225-250** *W*

A pine dressing table, original handles, 38 in. wide by 57 in. high by 20 in. deep, c. 1860. **£170-180** *AL*

A pine dressing table, 65 in. high by 39 in. wide by 20 in. deep, c. 1870. **£225-250** *W*

A Georgian pine washstand, 29 in. high by 14 in. wide by 14 in. deep. **£115-130** *W*

An early 19th C. pine wardrobe, with panelled doors, 6 ft. 6 in. high by 3 ft. 10 in. wide. **£325-375** *BEL*

A pine 3-section wardrobe, 83 in. high by 70 in. wide by 21½ in. deep, c. 1880. **£600-650** *W*

A small pine wardrobe, 3 ft. 1 in. wide by 5 ft. 8 in. high. **£180-220** *BEL*

A German painted pine armoire, 6 ft. 4 in. high by 4 ft. 7 in. wide, c. 1840. **£450-500** *BEL*

A large wardrobe, with panelled doors, 5 ft. 4 in. wide by 7 ft. 2 in. high. **£450-500** *BEL*

A pine bread rack, 52 in. high by 28 in. wide by 15 in. deep, c. 1860. **£110-120** *W*

A pine towel rail, 25 in. wide by 31 in. high. **£25-30** *AL*

A pine towel rail. **£20-25** *AL*

A pine spinning wheel and spindle, late 19th C. **£160-190** *W*

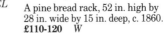

A 17th C. carved and panelled pine mule chest, 48 in. long by 30 in. high by 18 in. deep, c. 1680. **£300-£325** *PH*

A Scandinavian pine sledge, 38 in. long by 14 in. wide. **£45-50** *W*

A lacquer decorated bellows,
12½ in., 19th C. **£40-45** *AL*

A pair of glass candlesticks,
7½ in., early 20th C. **£7-8** *AL*

A green glass bottle, 18 in., late
19th C. **£9-10** *AL*

A Victorian picnic set, 8 by 7 in.,
19th C. **£36-38** *AL*

A glazed multi-brown jug, chipped,
12 in. high, late 19th C. **£7-8** *AL*

A rare Alexandra Inhaler, with
multi-colour decoration, glass tube
missing, 5 in., 19th C. **£19-20** *AL*

Three pottery Virol jars, 5 in., late
19th C. **£5-6** each *AL*

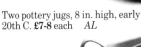

A Brown and Ponson's blancmange
mould, 5 in., late 19th C. **£22-26**
AL

A brown pottery drainer, 19th C.
£16-17 *AL*

Two pottery jugs, 8 in. high, early
20th C. **£7-8** each *AL*

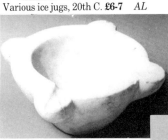

Various ice jugs, 20th C. **£6-7** *AL*

Two pestle and mortars, late
19th C. **£18-20** each *AL*

A marble mortar, 5½ by 13 in., mid
19th C. **£23-26** *AL*

Two pieces of Cornishware, early
20th C. **£8-9** each *AL*

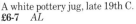

A white pottery shaving mug, 4 in.,
late 19th C. **£7-8** *AL*

A brown transfer-printed pottery
jug, 8 in., mid 19th C. **£11-13** *AL*

A white pottery jug, late 19th C.
£6-7 *AL*

A 2-handled pottery jug, 8½ in.,
19th C. **£11-12** *AL*

A brown and pale green crock, 11 in., mid 19th C. **£10-11** *AL*

A brown crock, glazed inside and outside, 12 in., mid 19th C. **£11-13** *AL*

A brown and cream crock, 10 in., mid 19th C. **£10-11** *AL*

A dark brown and cream bread crock, 10 by 10 in., 19th C. **£27-30** *AL*

A Zero Cool butter cooler, in red pottery with white china base, 11 by 5 in., early 20th C. **£7-9** *AL*

Two brown pottery jelly moulds, 4 in., 19th C. **£9-11** each *AL*

A brown and dark cream glazed jug and basin, 17 in. diam., early 20th C. **£35-38** *AL*

A brown and cream pottery casserole, 8 by 3 in., 19th C. **£5-6** *AL*

A brown and pale green crock, 14 in., mid 19th C. **£15-16** *AL*

Iron balance scales and weights, 16 by 22 in., late 19th C. **£50-60** *AL*

A tin and glass red painted candle lamp, with original decoration, 10 by 4 in., mid 19th C. **£10-11** *AL*

A set of Miller's beam scales, to weigh 4 bushel sack, fully restored and painted, complete with weights. **£550-750** *CGC/FRM*

A tin and glass Hurricane lamp, 16 in., early 20th C. **£5-6** *AL*

A pair of old platform scales, by W. & T. Avery, the tray of white porcelain, together with brass weights. **£180-220** *BHW*

An iron kettle, 13 by 12 in., 19th C. **£24-26** *AL*

A Kenrick brass and iron coffee mill, 6 by 6 in., 19th C. **£36-38** *AL*

An iron steelyard, 20 by 11 in., mid 19th C. **£24-26** *AL*

Brass spring scales, with tin pan, 17 in., early 20th C. **£15-16** *AL*

A brass blow lamp, 6 by 12 in., early 20th C. **£11-13** *AL*

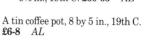

A brass kettle on stand, 13 by 9½ in., 19th C. **£60-65** *AL*

A tin coffee pot, 8 by 5 in., 19th C. **£6-8** *AL*

A tin watering can, 15 by 16 in., early 20th C. **£8-9** *AL*

A tin urn, with brass tap, 12 by 11 in., 19th C. **£11-13** *AL*

A tin watering can, 15 by 18 in., early 20th C. **£7-8** *AL*

A tin milk can, 18½ in., 19th C. **£11-13** *AL*

A blue enamel mug, 3 in., early 20th C. **£4.50-5** *AL*

A blue enamel mug, 3½ in., late 19th C. **£6-7** *AL*

Two tin cheese graters, 8 in., early 20th C. **£2-2.50** *AL*

A copper and brass rain gauge, 12 by 5 in., 19th C. **£14-16** *AL*

A brass bowl, 12 in., early 19th C. **£37-39** *AL*

An iron raisin pipper, 12 in., dated 7th Oct. 1897. **£8-9** *AL*

An iron and wood marmalade chopper, 16 in., late 19th C. **£6-7** *AL*

An iron and blue enamel tongue press, 10 by 10 in., 19th C. **£30-33** *AL*

Two iron string holders, 5 by 8 in., 19th C. **£10-11 each** *AL*

A wood and iron wallpaper roller, 8 in., 19th C. **£4-5** *AL*

Two-handled chopping knife, with boxwood handles, steel blade, 13 by 7 in., 19th C. **£11-13** *AL*

An iron trivet, 7 by 7 in., 19th C. **£7-9** *AL*

A selection of wood and iron chopping knives, 5 to 6 in., 19th C. **£7-8 each** *AL*

A red and white enamelled iron mincer, 12 in., late 19th C. **£5-6** *AL*

Wrought iron game hooks, 7 in., 19th C. **£11-13** *AL*

A copper ladle, 15 in. long, 18th C. **£18-19** *AL*

A tin and pine Bee Smoker, 11 by 6 in., early 20th C. **£4-5** *AL*

An iron keel, 21 in. long by 5 in., 19th C. **£14-16** *AL*

An iron Christmas tree stand, with boxwood handle, 6 by 6 in., 19th C. **£7-9** *AL*

An oyster opener, the silver-plated and ivory handled instrument bearing a plaque moulded 'Picault, Cout^ier...A Paris...Willm Lund Agent', London, 25.4 cm. long (10 in.), mid 19th C. **£200-250** *P*

A selection of tin scoops, 19th C. **£5-9** each *AL*

Two plated brass ice cream scoops, early 20th C. **£8-9** each *AL*

A pair of brass and iron fire dogs, 6 by 7 in., 19th C. **£18-20** *AL*

A pine and glass egg timer, 7 by 6 in., 19th C. **£7-8** *AL*

An iron foot last, 19th C. **£6-7** *AL*

A pair of brass candlesticks, 10 in., mid 19th C. **£40-45** *AL*

From top to bottom:
A 'Butter' knife, 8 in. **£7-8**
A 'Bread' knife, 15 in. **£10-11**
A Bread knife, 15 in. **£10-11**
A Bread knife with ivory handle, 15 in. **£19-20** All late 19th C. *AL*

An oak and iron bound pump action butter churn, c. 1880. **£200-£250** *CGC/FRM*

A wire sieve and mortar, 14 by 8 in., 19th C. **£9-11** *AL*

A brass and iron fire-guard, 19 by 19 in., early 20th C. **£31-33** *AL*

A wire cake stand, 14 by 10 in., 19th C. **£7-8** *AL*

A tin Cadbury's display stand, 9 by 13 in., early 20th C. **£7-8** *AL*

A wicker basket, 18 in., early 20th C. **£7-8** *AL*

A pine wooden tub, 14 by 16 in., early 20th C. **£9-11** *AL*

A wire waste paper basket, 23 by 15 in., early 20th C. **£11-13** *AL*

A wire egg basket, 14 by 10 in., 19th C. **£6-8** *AL*

A tin black and red painted housemaid's box, 12 by 10 in., 19th C. **£18-20** *AL*

A wicker basket, 18 by 10 in., early 20th C. **£7-9** *AL*

A wicker eel trap, 31 by 14 in., 19th C. **£24-25** *AL*

A wire mahogany bird cage, 16 by 14 in., 19th C. **£35-39** *AL*

A Sussex trug, 21 by 14 in., early
20th C. **£18-20** *AL*

A wicker basket, 14 in., early
20th C. **£6-7** *AL*

A wicker basket, 14 in., early
20th C. **£6-7** *AL*

A wicker basket, 16 in., early
20th C. **£6-7** *AL*

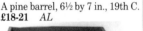

A pine barrel, 6½ by 7 in., 19th C.
£18-21 *AL*

A wood and hair sieve, 8 by 6 in.,
19th C. **£8-9** *AL*

A selection of wood and wire
garden sieves, 14 to 22 in., late
19th C. **£8-10 each** *AL*

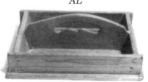

A basket shopping trolley, early
20th C. **£12-13** *AL*

A Nestle's pine wood packing case,
18 by 6½ by 13 in., early 20th C.
£10-11 *AL*

An elm and pine flax crusher, 25 by
34 by 7 in., early to mid 19th C.
£65-70 *AL*

Three elm grain measures, early
20th C. **£15-16** *AL*

A pine York County Hospital
money box, 9 by 9 in., 19th C. **£9-11**
AL

A mahogany knife box, with brass
handle, 14½ by 18½ in., mid
19th C. **£24-26** *AL*

A pine shoe cleaning box, 12 by
7½ in., 19th C. **£11-13** *AL*

A pine knife box, 14 by 10 in.,
19th C. **£12-13** *AL*

A pine letter rack, 14 by 9 in.,
19th C. **£11-13** *AL*

A pine knife box, 13 by 7½ in.,
19th C. **£8-9** *AL*

A sycamore bowl, 13 in., early
19th C. **£70-80** *AL*

Two small wooden rakes. **£5-7**
each *AL*

A sycamore bowl, 14½ in., early
19th C. **£70-80** *AL*

A pine duck board, with copper
nails, 26 by 15 in., 19th C. **£8-9**
AL

A wooden bath rack, 27 by 9 in.,
early 20th C. **£7-8** *AL*

A sycamore bowl, 18½ in., early
19th C. **£90-120** *AL*

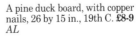

A pine apple tray, 39 by 19 in.,
19th C. **£12-13** *AL*

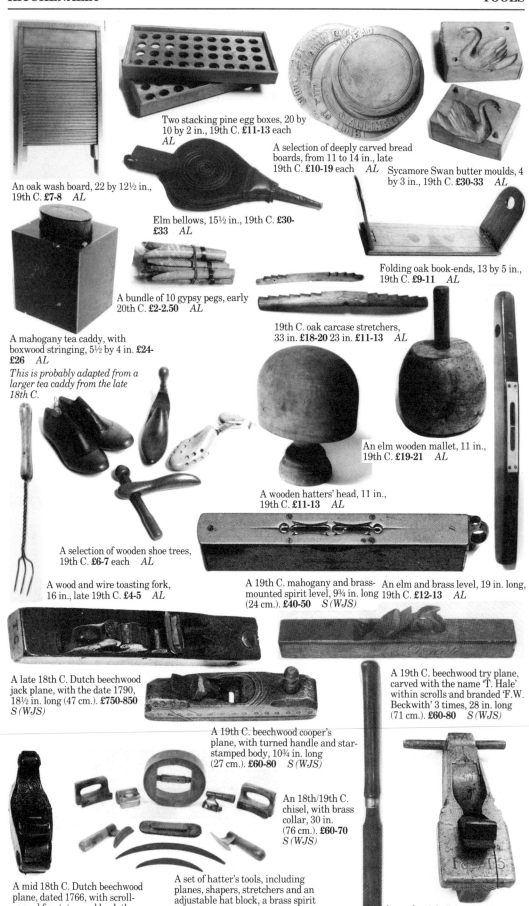

Two stacking pine egg boxes, 20 by 10 by 2 in., 19th C. **£11-13** each *AL*

A selection of deeply carved bread boards, from 11 to 14 in., late 19th C. **£10-19** each *AL*

Sycamore Swan butter moulds, 4 by 3 in., 19th C. **£30-33** *AL*

An oak wash board, 22 by 12½ in., 19th C. **£7-8** *AL*

Elm bellows, 15½ in., 19th C. **£30-£33** *AL*

Folding oak book-ends, 13 by 5 in., 19th C. **£9-11** *AL*

A bundle of 10 gypsy pegs, early 20th C. **£2-2.50** *AL*

19th C. oak carcase stretchers, 33 in. **£18-20** 23 in. **£11-13** *AL*

A mahogany tea caddy, with boxwood stringing, 5½ by 4 in. **£24-£26** *AL*

This is probably adapted from a larger tea caddy from the late 18th C.

An elm wooden mallet, 11 in., 19th C. **£19-21** *AL*

A wooden hatters' head, 11 in., 19th C. **£11-13** *AL*

A selection of wooden shoe trees, 19th C. **£6-7** each *AL*

A wood and wire toasting fork, 16 in., late 19th C. **£4-5** *AL*

A 19th C. mahogany and brass-mounted spirit level, 9¾ in. long (24 cm.). **£40-50** *S (WJS)*

An elm and brass level, 19 in. long, 19th C. **£12-13** *AL*

A late 18th C. Dutch beechwood jack plane, with the date 1790, 18½ in. long (47 cm.). **£750-850** *S (WJS)*

A 19th C. beechwood try plane, carved with the name 'T. Hale' within scrolls and branded 'F.W. Beckwith' 3 times, 28 in. long (71 cm.). **£60-80** *S (WJS)*

A 19th C. beechwood cooper's plane, with turned handle and star-stamped body, 10¾ in. long (27 cm.). **£60-80** *S (WJS)*

An 18th/19th C. chisel, with brass collar, 30 in. (76 cm.). **£60-70** *S (WJS)*

A mid 18th C. Dutch beechwood plane, dated 1766, with scroll-carved front, top and heel, the blade stamped 'Robert Moor', 8 in. long (20 cm.). **£800-900** *S (WJS)*

A set of hatter's tools, including planes, shapers, stretchers and an adjustable hat block, a brass spirit level and a hatter's saw, with hatched ebony handle and serrated steel blade. **£550-600** *S (WJS)*

An early 19th C. beechwood draw plane, dated 1815, 11½ in. long (29 cm.). **£180-200** *S (WJS)*

A box tantalus, with Boulle pattern to front and lid, with pair of ormolu handles and interior mirror to lid, with 4 cut glass decanters and 2 glasses. **£300-350** *JD*

An oak framed tantalus, with silver plated fittings containing 3 hobnail cut square bottles, cut ball stoppers, 16.5 cm. high, c. 1880. **£280-300** *Som*

The condition of the decanters is all important, any chips or cracks reduce the value dramatically.

A fine oak cased, 3 bottle tantalus, with cigar drawer and key, having brass mounts, etc. **£200-250** *BHW*

A George IV burr-walnut and ebonised liqueur set, with brass inlay, enclosing a gilt-mounted tray containing 4 decanters and 16 glasses, gilt painted with stars, 13 in. (33 cm.) wide. **£600-700** *SS*

A pair of tea caddies, one in applewood in the form of an apple, the other in pearwood in the form of a pear, the apple 4¼ in. (11 cm.) high, the pear 6½ in. (16 cm.). **£4,000-5,000** *S*

An 18th C. tea caddy, in the form of a canteloupe melon with segmented body, hinged lid and stalk finial, 5 in. (13 cm.) high. **£1,600-1,800** *S*

A tortoiseshell and mother-of-pearl tea caddy, enclosing 2 divisions, 5 by 7 in. (13 by 18 cm.), first quarter 19th C. **£200-225** *SC*

An 18th/19th C. tea caddy, in the form of a boxwood toadstool, 5 in. (13 cm.) high. **£750-850** *S (WJS)*

A pear-shaped tea caddy, of beech, blushed in crimson and applied with stalk finial, with steel lock and key, 6½ in. high, 19th C. **£650-£750** *T*

Many of these fruit-shaped tea caddies, often described as English early 19th C., are now thought to be of Dutch origin.

An 18th C. applewood tea caddy, in the form of an apple with brass stalk, traces of the original painted decoration, 5 in. (13 cm.) diam. **£1,600-1,700** *S (WJS)*

A George III inlaid satinwood tea caddy, 7½ in. high. **£375-425** *DWB*

A George III marble tea caddy, inlaid in geometric patterns, 11 in. (28 cm.) wide. **£1,400-1,600** *C*

A George III hexagonal mahogany tea caddy, inlaid with oval shell panels. **£325-350** *BHW*

A fine George III ivory decagonal tea caddy, with tortoiseshell stringing, inlaid with a mother-of-pearl star, the front with a gold shield, 4¼ in. (11 cm.) wide. **£500-£550** *C*

A George III burr-walnut tea caddy, inlaid with shells and fluting in a variety of woods, enclosing 2 divisions, 5½ by 7½ in. (13 by 19 cm.), third quarter 18th C. **£180-220** *SC*

A partridgewood and marquetry tea box, the interior fitted with 3 divisions, 6 by 12 in. (15 by 31 cm.), late 18th C. **£350-450** *SC*

A late 18th C. inlaid stinkwood and sycamore tea caddy, 7 in. (18 cm.) wide. **£150-180** *SC*

A late Georgian tortoiseshell tea caddy, with 2 lidded interior compartments, the front inlaid with mother-of-pearl, on 4 silver plated ball feet, 7 in. (18 cm.). **£300-£350** *L*

A rare George III mahogany tea caddy, inlaid with boxwood lines throughout, 10 in. (25 cm.), third quarter 18th C. **£475-525** *SC*

A George III satinwood and inlaid tea caddy, 6 in. (15 cm.). **£200-250** *L*

A late Georgian tortoiseshell tea caddy, inlaid with a bird perched on a branch in mother-of-pearl, with silvered ball finial and feet, 6½ in. (6.5 cm.). **£700-800** *L*

A Regency tortoiseshell-veneered tea caddy, with ivory ball finial and the ogee-shaped body on 4 ivory ball feet, 7¼ in. (18.5 cm.) high, c. 1820. **£425-475** *S*

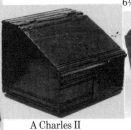

A Charles II small oak boarded desk box, 11 in. (28 cm.) wide, c. 1860. **£220-280** *SS*

A Georgian satinwood tea caddy, crossbanded in partridgewood. **£225-275** *JD*

A Regency paper scroll tea caddy, the interior with a mirror and lidded compartment, 7 in. (18 cm.) wide, c. 1810. **£220-300** *SS*

A 17th C. cedarwood writing desk, inlaid with scrollwork and the initials TG and the date 1622, interior fitted with an arrangement of moulded front drawers, 2 ft. 4 in. (71 cm.) wide. **£900-1,200** *S*

A silver-mounted Anglo-Indian ivory travelling bureau, enclosing a fitted interior, of 7 shaped drawers and 3 pigeonholes, formerly with a toilet mirror, Vizagapatam, 21¼ in. (54 cm.) wide, 18th C. **£700-800** *C*

An early 18th C. Goanese rosewood and ivory marquetry secretaire table cabinet, on a later stand, the whole inlaid with rows of engraved ivory naturalistic flowering plants, the fall front enclosing a fitted interior with 5 drawers, 55 cm. wide. **£2,000-2,500** *P*

A late Victorian walnut stationery box. **£40-60** *BHW*

A Boulle desk set. **£450-500** *SS*

A fine rosewood and ivory table cabinet, enclosing a well-fitted interior of 7 various-sized drawers, 23½ in. (60 cm.) high, early 18th C. **£2,200-2,500** *C*

A treen witch's box, the hinged lid mounted with bronze winged skull, the contents including a bisque head doll with human hair and stuffed body impaled with pins, a bone mortar, a treen jar and cover, a leather pin case stamped with scroll motif and with bone ojime, a wolf's paw, various bones and teeth, birds' feathers and stone and a bunch and a circle of dried flowers, includes photograph of an emaciated woman dressed in black — the original owner known as 'Auntie Bessie Benjamin' or 'Mad Bessie'. **£600-700** *Bon*

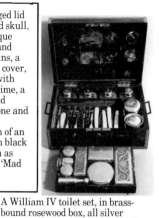

A rare papier-mâché writing box, the lower part opening to reveal a writing slope, the whole richly inlaid in mother-of-pearl with castle views and foliage, 1 ft. 4½ in. high by 1 ft. 3 in. wide (42 by 38 cm.), c. 1850. **£600-700** *S*

A William IV rosewood combined sewing and writing box, with reeded mouldings and mother-of-pearl inlay, 1 ft. 5 in. high by 1 ft. 6 in. wide (43 by 46 cm.), c. 1835. **£250-300** *SS*

A William IV toilet set, in brass-bound rosewood box, all silver items with 'S' and coronet for Duke of Sussex, London 1823 and 4, by (?) D/AD, approx. 56 oz. weighable silver. **£1,400-1,600** *DWB*

An Anglo-Indian ivory-veneered work box, the interior partly in sandalwood and with a removable tray of lidded compartments, on repoussé silver feet, 1 ft. 1 in. wide (33 cm.), early 19th C. **£600-650** *S*

A set of Reeves & Sons paints, contained in fitted brass bound mahogany box, c. 1910. **£100-125** *TW*

An Anglo-Indian ivory work box, of rectangular form, with sandalwood interior, inlay lifting and cracked, 21¾ by 12 in., 19th C. **£800-1,000** *HyD*

A rosewood and cut brass dressing box, enclosing a fitted interior with glass bottles and a manicure, above a secret jewel drawer, 6½ by 12 in. (16 by 31 cm.), second quarter of 19th C. **£120-150** *SC*

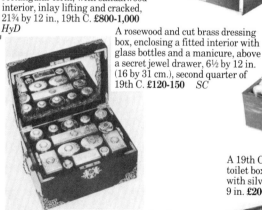

A Victorian dressing case, in burr-walnut. **£550-650** *RBB*

A Victorian rectangular ebonised dressing case, by Carrington and Co. 1961, 24 oz. gross weighable silver. **£1,500-1,800** *C*

A 19th C. brass-bound coromandel toilet box, by Aspreys, fully fitted with silver topped requisites, 12 by 9 in. **£200-250** *JD*

A late 17th C. Flemish brass-bound oyster walnut-veneered travelling strong box, with 2 small drawers and secret compartments, coaching bolts fitted to the sides, fitted carrying handles, 1 ft. 10½ in. by 1 ft. 1 in. high. **£2,400-2,800** *AG*

These boxes are often mounted on later stands.

A good Flemish brass-mounted oyster-veneered kingwood strong box, overlaid with fleur-de-lys strapwork and enclosing a well and 2 drawers, the lid with secret drawers in a panel, 10¾ in. high by 1 ft. 7 in. wide (27.5 by 48 cm.), c. 1700. **£800-1,000** *S*

A Malines ebonised wood and alabaster casket, the panels carved with shields and stylised foliage, one end sliding up to reveal 6 small drawers, 9¼ by 16¾ in. (23.5 by 42.5 cm.), early 17th C. **£550-650** *S*

A good Charles II walnut and marquetry lace box, with yew-wood banding and oval ebonised flower-filled centre, the frieze with panels of marquetry, 1 ft. 4½ in. wide (42 cm.), c. 1680. **£750-850** *S*

A late 17th C. box of red velvet, in silver thread, having silvered clasp, relined. **£150-175** *P*

A South German rosewood casket, inlaid with a geometric design, with repoussé silvered metal lockplate, 27 in. wide (69 cm.), mid 18th C. **£1,000-1,250** *C*

A Spanish polychrome and gilt pastiglia casket, bracket feet and with 1 swing handle on the lid, the pastiglia chipped in several places off the carcass, 6¾ in. high by 10½ in. wide (17 by 26.5 cm.), second half 14th C. **£2,000-2,200** *S*

A Spanish polychrome and gilt pastiglia casket, damaged, 8¼ by 9⅛ in. (21 by 23.2 cm.), 14th C. **£1,750-2,000** *S*

A late Louis XIV boulle casket, 5¼ in. high by 21 in. wide (13.5 by 53 cm.), early 18th C. **£1,200-1,400** *S*

An ivory-inlaid walnut box, inlaid with armorial beasts, elaborate strapwork and trailing foliage, the divided interior lined with green velvet, probably North Italian (Milanese), 13½ in. wide (43 cm.), late 16th/17th C. **£1,500-1,800** *C*

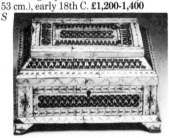

A bone casket, the pine body applied with pierced and coloured bone decoration, 9¼ in. wide (23 cm.), early 19th C. **£100-125** *S*

A Regency-period mahogany Masonic alms box, 10½ in. **£550-£650** *WW*

A prisoner-of-war bone casket, the pine case with fitted interior and applied with pierced bone decoration and with a love token, 9 in. wide (23 cm.), early 19th C. **£140-180** *S*

An early Victorian figured walnut rectangular book tray, 16 in. wide (40.5 cm.). **£200-250** *LBP*

A William IV ebony and cut brass jewel box, 5 by 12½ in. (13 by 32 cm.), second quarter of 19th C. **£200-240** *SC*

A mid 19th C. Anglo-Indian engraved ivory 2-compartment workbox, 16 in. wide. **£600-700** *SuB*

A rosewood specimen cabinet, the 8 drawers containing a collection of British butterflies, moths and neolithic flint fragments, on spherical feet, 20 by 21 in. (51 by 53.5 cm.), second quarter of the 19th C. **£350-400** *SC*

An 18th C. miniature casket, with brass loop carrying handles, 8 in. wide (20 cm.). **£180-220** *S (WJS)*

The form and construction of this piece indicates Flemish craftsmen of the late 17th/early 18th C. who constructed similar cabinets but raised on stands.

An Edwardian musical cigar holder, ebonised and with Chinese scenes painted on each door, 7½ in. high by 5 in. diam. of base (19 by 12½ cm.). **£80-100**   *LRG*

A George III oak candle box, 6 in. wide (15 cm.), c. 1770. **£40-50**   *SS*

A Sheraton-period mahogany serpentine slope-top knife box, interior adapted for stationery, 12½ in. high. **£200-250**   *N*

A Louis XV leather-covered cutlery box, tooled in gilt with foliate clasps and mounted with gilt metal carrying handle, 18 gilt metal knives, 18 spoons and 18 forks, 9¼ in. wide (23 cm.). **£1,600-1,800** *C*

A George III oak candle box, 8 in. wide (20 cm.), c. 1770. **£50-70**   *SS*

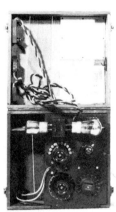

A 2-valve field set, Mark III with receiver, No. 1064, by the W/T factory, Soho, with two valves. **£300-350** *CSK*

A 3-valve receiver, in wood case with valves on top and control panel on front with pivoted coils. **£100-120** *CSK*

A rare B.T.H. valve-crystal receiver, type V.C., with B.B.C. approval mark, by the British Thomson-Houston Co. Ltd., in working order, 29 by 26 by 22 cm. high, 1924. **£115-130** *TKN*

An Atwater Kent 4-valve receiver, the tuners and other components mounted in individual circular bakelite and metal cases on mahogany baseboard. **£450-500** *CSK*

A Sterling type R1572 2-valve receiver, on walnut plinth, with hinged upper section and sloping top, two valves and B.B.C. transfer. **£180-200** *CSK*

A W.T. field set C.W. Mark III transmitter with single-valve, coupling and variometer controls, stud tuner, watch and circuit diagram in lid, 1918. **£250-280** *CSK*

A Fellophone Little Giant 4-valve receiver, No. 1137, with valves, loading coil, B.B.C. stamp 'Entirely British Manufacture' and leathercloth casing with Marconi licence plate. **£180-200** *CSK*

An A.J.S. type F6 4-valve receiver, in mahogany case with four valves, linked adjustable coils, reaction and two condenser knobs. **£300-350** *CSK*

A Marconi V2 2-valve receiver, in walnut case with two valves, two wave length plates, regenerator unit and B.B.C. transfer. **£220-250** *CSK*

A Telefunken type SRR2 2-valve receiver, on black stained oak plinth with two tuning knobs. **£50-70** *CSK*

A Revophone 2-valve amplifier, with valves, B.B.C. transfer and Marconi licence plate. **£60-80** *CSK*

An Armac 2-valve receiver, by R. McKellen & Co. Ltd., London WC2, with two condensers, pivoted coil mounting and mahogany case with control panel on top and B.B.C. stamp. **£80-100** *CSK*

A Wyvern 3-valve receiver, in mahogany case, three valves, three loading coils with one pivoted mount on side and Marconi licence plate, made by Fairfield & Co., Leicester, Reg. No. 3033. **£170-200** *CSK*

A spark gap transmitter and receiver, with sliding tuning coil, crystal detector, spiral coil, morse key and spark gap unit with 1907 patent date, in wood carrying case with headphones. **£200-220** *CSK*

(l.) A 3-valve battery amplifier, Model C Mark II, No. 388, by W/T Factory, Soho, in mahogany case with composition and front panels. **£140-160**
(c.) A Forward Spark 20 watt rear transmitter, Mark II, No. 682 by W/T Factory, Soho, in cloth-covered case. **£200-250**
(r.) A 50 watt H.T. unit, in cloth-covered case. **£80-100** *CSK*

A decorative table telephone, 16½ in. (42 cm.) high, c. 1892. **£200-225** *S*

A Mignon Model 2 typewriter, with red finish, gilt lines and lettering and crocodile-grained leather carrying case. **£1,400-1,600** *CSK*
This is a rare early model and the fact that it is red adds considerably to the price.

A Schreibmachine Picht braille machine, German, c. 1910. **£425-475** *S*

An Edelmann typewriter, the three-row type-wheel mechanism with curved enamel index operated by key, inking by roller, two shift and one space levers, German, 10½ in. (26.5 cm.) wide, c. 1897. **£250-275** *S*

A Telefunken 3-valve battery amplifier, in black stained wood case with three valves concealed by flap. **£150-170** *CSK*

A good Merritt typewriter, No. 12107, 1234, the letter index mechanism with sliding letter selection lever, rubber typeface and inking by pad, instruction leaflet, contained in original wooden case, American, c. 1900. **£275-325** *S*

A Hall typewriter, No. 2498, the index machine, lacking rubber type and inking pad, with letter index above and selection lever, mahogany case, 15¼ in. (38.5 cm.) wide, American, c. 1885. **£220-250** *S*

A short wave tuner, Mark III* 3459, by the W/T Factory, Southgate, with two condenser knobs, two stud tuners, two crystal detectors with change-over switch and spare crystals in lid. **£350-400** *CSK*

A Williams No. 2 typewriter, the grasshopper action type bars mounted on either side of the platen, double shift, and three-row keyboard, metal cover, American, c. 1893. **£125-150** *S*

A James Watt portable copying machine, with sloping writing surface and a drawer in the base with wetting tank, lacking inkwell, English, 18 in. (45.8 cm.) wide, late 18th C. **£300-350** *S*

A Hammond No. 1 typewriter, the swinging sector type-class mechanism with inking by ribbon, two-row keyboard with piano-type ebony keys, American, c. 1888. **£350-380** *S*

A black enamelled 'penny farthing' (ordinary) bicycle, for a child, a replica built pre-war period, the front wheel approximately 21 in. (54 cm.). **£95-120** *P*

A Victorian perambulator, 43 in. wide. **£150-180** *WHL*

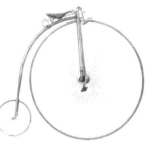

A 'penny farthing' bicycle. **£1,300-1,600** *Re*

A good Victorian baby carriage, c. 1880. **£1,000-1,200** *CGC/FRM*

A Surrey, with black painted wood body and iron shod wheels, complete with shafts. **£700-800** *DSH*

An early 'penny farthing' bicycle, in original condition, but repainted and with a new large wheel tyre, c. 1870. **£1,400-1,600** *CGC/FRM*

A child's scooter, approx. 79 cm. tall, wheels approx. 25 cm. diam. **£55-65** *P*

A lady's four-wheel Phaeton, with adjustable hood and button back upholstered seat. **£800-900** *JF*

A Landau, with black and cream painted exterior, the brass hub caps stamped 'Atkinson & Philipson Newcastle'. **£5,000-6,000** *DSH*

A Brougham, with blue painted wood body, the hub caps stamped 'Wilson & Sons Ltd., Sheffield'. **£1,600-2,000** *DSH*

A horse-drawn omnibus, with blue and red painted exterior. **£1,600-2,000** *DSH*

An estate two-man hand firepump, on a two-wheel sprung hand cart, complete with stirrup pumps, buckets, brass hose nozzle, etc.. **£350-450** *CGC/FRM*

A good Irish jaunting cart. **£1,000-1,500** *CGC/FRM* *This cart is said to have been used by John Wayne in the film 'The Quiet Man'.*

A fine gentleman's Brougham, on a four wheel C sprung suspension and chassis, restored and painted in dark green livery, maker Rippon Bros., Huddersfield, Bradford, c. 1890. **£3,000-3,500** *CGC/FRM*

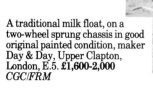

A traditional milk float, on a two-wheel sprung chassis in good original painted condition, maker Day & Day, Upper Clapton, London, E.5. **£1,600-2,000** *CGC/FRM*

A four-wheel Yorkshire road pole wagon, restored and painted in red and blue livery, c. 1912. **£800-900** *CGC/FRM*

A patent improved four-furrow seeding plough, by Pierce, Wexford. **£400-450** *CGC/FRM*

A rare early 1930's period stylized Minerva mascot, chrome plated, approx. 10.5 cm. tall. **£200-250** *P*

A baker's delivery hand cart, restored and painted with contemporary logo designs. **£850-950** *CGC/FRM*

A good early brass Royal Automobile Club member's car badge, No. B2185, approx. 17.5 cm. tall. **£200-300** *P*

A plated brass Isotta-Fraschini 'Spirit of Triumph' mascot, approx. 15 cm. tall. **£200-300** *P*

A replated rearward-leaning winged 'Flying-B' mascot, for the '3½/4¼' range of Bentley cars. **£40-50** *P*

A Lalique frosted glass ram's head, 9.5 cm., 1930's. **£1,400-1,600** *S*

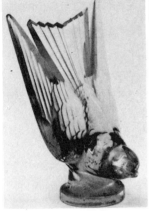

A plated brass... A Lalique pink tinted glass swallow mascot, 15.25 cm., 1930's. **£500-600** *S*

A Lalique cockerel head mascot, 18 cm., 1930's. **£350-400** *S*

A Lalique eagle head mascot, in original chromed metal Rolls Royce base, 10 cm. height of mascot, 1920's. **£800-900** *S*

A chromium-plated brass Automobile Association badge, the badge inscribed Stenson Cooke Secretary and no. 3, 4½ in. (12 cm.). **£200-250** *CSK*

'The M E Rear Screen', a nickel-plated motor car Auster screen, in two parts with black canvas leg cover, 46 in. (117 cm.) wide. **£180-220** *CSK*

A Lalique: 'Chrysis', nude, mascot, frosted glass, approx. 13 cm. tall. **£160-200** *P*

A chromium-plated and enamelled Brooklands Flying Club badge, inscribed 6, 4 in. (10 cm.) high. **£750-950** *CSK*

A chromium-plated and enamelled Brooklands 130 m.p.h. badge, damage to enamelling, 3¾ in. (10 cm.) high. **£700-900** *CSK*

A chromium-plated and enamel Brooklands Automobile Racing Club badge, inscribed 1285, 4 in. (10 cm.) high. **£120-150** *CSK*

Norton. A c. 1922 Model 1611, in above average condition.
£3,000-3,500   *PW*

Triumph. A c. 1920 unrestored example, with three-speed gearbox, chain driven, the crankcase stamped 83 HRR.
£900-1,000   *PW*

Autoped, c. 1916, the maker's plate stamped D.1840, this motorised scooter is powered by a single-cylinder four-stroke engine of 155 c.c. **£450-550**   *PW*

Norton. A 1923 Model 1611, hand gear change, also featured are early internal expanding front brakes. **£2,500-3,000**   *PW*

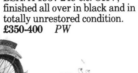

BSA. A 1937 249 c.c. OHV, finished all over in black and in totally unrestored condition.
£350-400   *PW*

A 1926 model A.J.S., H.9 498 c.c., de luxe tourer motorcycle, poor condition. **£400-450**   *JF*

BSA. A c. 1940 M20.
£650-750   *PW*

A 1957 Ariel motor cycle combination, comprising Ariel Model FH 650 c.c. Huntmaster Twin. **£550-600**   *CDC*

A 1928 Rolls-Royce 40/50 H.P. Phantom I Sedanca De Ville, engine, six-cylinder, overhead-valve, bi-block, capacity 7,668 c.c., four-speed gearbox. **£30,000-35,000**   *CSK*

An Ariel Huntmaster motor cycle combination. **£550-600**   *CDC*

A Rolls-Royce Phantom II limousine. **£13,000-14,000**   *PW*

A 1928 Ford Model-AF 14.9 H.P. sport coupe, engine, four-cylinder, side-valve, monoblock, capacity 2,003 c.c., three-speed gearbox, with comprehensive restoration.
£3,000-4,000   *CSK*

A 1932 M.G. Midget J2-type sports, engine, four-cylinder, OHC, capacity 847 c.c., four-speed gearbox, good condition.
£14,000-16,000   *CSK*

A 1929 M.G. 14/40 H.P. Mk. IV sports two-seater, engine, four-cylinder, side-valve, monoblock, capacity 1,802 c.c., three-speed gearbox, in good condition. **£7,500-8,500**   *CSK*

A 1931 Austin seven saloon, in nearly original condition.
£2,500-3,000   *A*

A 1937 M.G. (T.A.), 2-seater sports car, 1292 c.c., 99,380 recorded miles. **£3,000-3,500**   *FHF*

A 1933 Maserati 4CM-2000 2-litre racing car, engine, four-cylinder, twin overhead camshafts, supercharged, four-speed gearbox.
£35,000-40,000   *CSK*

A 1937 Aston Martin 'International', H.P. 15, this 4-seater touring car is finished in dark blue, wire wheels, and has coachwork by Aston Martin, sound condition throughout. **£6,000-7,000** *PW*

A 1936 M.G. Midget TA sports two-seater, engine, four-cylinder, OHV, monobloc, capacity 1,292 c.c., four-speed synchromesh gearbox, in good order. **£9,500-10,500**   *CSK*

A 1934 Morris 8 Minor, brown and cream bodywork in restored condition. **£2,500-3,000**   *A*

A 1950 Jaguar XK120 3.4-litre roadster, engine, 6-cylinder, twin overhead camshafts, 4-speed synchromesh gearbox. **£12,500-£13,500**   *CSK*

A 1939 Morgan super sports MX4 sports 2-seater, engine, 2-cylinder, overhead-valve, capacity 990 c.c., 3-speed gearbox, restored. **£7,000-£8,000**   *CSK*

A 1938 S.S. 100 3½-litre sports 2-seater, engine, 6-cylinder, overhead-vale, monobloc, 4-speed synchromesh gearbox, in good condition, mileage estimated 100,000 miles. **£25,000-30,000** *CSK*

A Daimler Dart, SP.250, 2½-litre, V.8 sports car, approximate year of manufacture 1961, in dark blue, recorded mileage 85,000. **£3,000-£3,500**   *PWC*

A 1950 Bristol 401 2-litre 2-door sports saloon, engine, 6-cylinder, 4-speed synchromesh gearbox. **£4,000-5,000**   *CSK*

A 1948 Rolls-Royce 'Silver Wraith', supplied originally by H. A. Fox Limited, front-opening sun roof, is finished in metallic pale bronze, odometer indicates 51,363 miles. **£9,000-10,000**   *PW*

A Jensen Interceptor Mk. III, 1973. **£3,000-4,000**   *DLJ*

A 1953 Alvis 4.3-litre single-seater racing special, engine, 6-cylinder, overhead-valve, 4-speed gearbox, central change. **£12,000-14,000** *CSK*

A 1960 M.G. A-1600 Mk. I sports 2-seater, engine, 4-cylinder, overhead valve, monobloc. **£3,500-£4,000**   *CSK*

A 1976-77 McLaren M23 Formula I single-seater racing car, engine, 8-cylinder, 4 overhead camshafts, vee, bore, capacity 2993 c.c., 6-speed gearbox. **£18,000-20,000** *CSK*

A 1966 Austin-Healey 3000 Mk. III sports 2-4 seater, engine, 6-cylinder, capacity 2912 c.c., 4-speed synchromesh gearbox with overdrive. **£4,500-5,000**   *CSK*

A 1961 Bentley Continental S2 Flying Spur 4-door sports saloon, engine, 8-cylinder, overhead-valve, vee, 6230 c.c., 4-speed Hydramatic automatic gearbox, steering column selection. **£10,500-12,500** *CSK*

Two hundred and eighty-eight Continental S2s were built, these featuring the latest V-8 engine, power steering, and automatic transmission.

A 1938/39 Leyland 'FTK I' fire engine, engine, 6-cylinder petrol type. **£5,000-6,000**   *P*

One of only 6 built. Believed to be a sole survivor.

A 1969 Jaguar E-type roadster '4.2', in pale yellow with black leather interior, low mileage, sound condition. **£4,500-5,000**   *PW*

A good stuffed trout in bow-fronted glass case, gilt edges and lettering 'caught in Lough Mask June 5th 1903', 24 in. long by 12 in. high. **£130-160** *NML*

An unusual case of mounted brown trout, in bow-fronted glass case, inscribed 'Loch Monar', 21 in. long by 15 in. high, c. 1900. **£120-150** *NML*

A fine stuffed perch by J. Cooper & Sons, caught by T. W. Theedom, H.B.A.S. competitions 1946, wt. 2 lb. 3 oz. in bow-fronted glass case, gilt edges and lettering, 19 in. long by 13 in. high. **£80-100** *NML*

A good case of 6 mixed fish, set against a background of reeds, carp, roach, rudd, perch, pike and trout, caught by Edward J. Powell 1895, gilt edges, 30 in. long by 24 in. high. **£350-450** *NML*

A stuffed roach caught by W. G. Charman at Amberley, August 18th, 1926, wt. 2 lb., in bow-fronted glass case, 19 in. long by 12 in. high. **£70-100** *NML*

An early 19th C. painted tin creel, hinged lid with clasp and sliding fish hole, 10 in. long by 7 in. high. **£75-100** *NML*

A carved wooden model of a salmon, inscribed 'caught by Dorothy Blacklock, with a 'Dallas' in Cragganmore, Dalchroy 7th September 1926'. **£200-250** *CEd*

A large leather-bound wicker creel, with leather shoulder straps and brass buckle, 15 in. long by 12 in. high, c. 1910. **£30-50** *NML*

Two Milwards & Sons, Redditch tackle and bait cases, 'The Zealand' and 'The Palliser', green and gold enamelled finish, 6½ by 3 by 2 in. **£2-5** each *NML*

As described in the 'Fishermans list' by Milwards 1910. P.177.

A good Hardy Brothers brown English willow creel, with leather shoulder and coat straps, marked 'Hardy Brothers, makers Alnwick England', 14 in. long by 13 in. high, c. 1915. **£40-60** *NML*

A good mahogany fly cabinet by J. Bernard & Son, containing about 140 gut-eyed salmon flies, door chipped by lock, 12 by 8 by 5½ in. **£400-500** *S*

A Hardy trace-making and repairing outfit, 3 matching tools in black japanned box, with compartment for wire and another for swivels, etc., 5 by 3½ in., c. 1935. **£30-50** *JMG*

A C. Farlow & Co. trout fly cabinet 'The Meakin', black japanned tin, with fall front revealing 6 drawers, each compartmented with see through lids, holding a collection of 500 flies, 8½ by 7 by 4¾ in., c. 1925. **£130-160** *NML*

A Hardys anglers knife No. 3, with tweezers, disgorger, file, scissors stiletto and screwdriver with chamois clip case, 4 in. long, c. 1930. **£25-40** *NML*

A black painted tin 5 division fly box, containing approximately 250 gut-eyed salmon flies, 12 in. wide, c. 1910. **£350-400** *CEd*

A Victorian galvanised bellied bait kettle, oblong body with convex sides and recessed, hinged ventilated lid, 14 in. long by 9 in. wide. **£30-50** *NML*

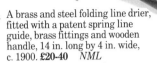

A brass and steel folding line drier, fitted with a patent spring line guide, brass fittings and wooden handle, 14 in. long by 4 in. wide, c. 1900. **£20-40** *NML*

A large brass and iron Farlows line drier, 16 in. long by 3 in. wide, c 1890. **£30-50** *NML*

A late 19th C. crocodile skin fly wallet, by G. Little & Co., Haymarket, London, containing 100 gut-eyed salmon flies in 15 vellum pages, some with pockets and others faced with wool, 7½ by 5 by 3½ in. **£80-100** *NML*

Various vintage fishing floats, including the 'Zephyr' patent float, celluloid and luminous floats. **£2-5** *NML*

Two 19th C. bone disgorgers, 5 and 6 in. long. **£2-5 each** *NML*

Various early fishing floats and pike bungs, some with sliding dowels, 1890-1920's. **£2-5** *NML*

A collapsible steel framed landing net with decorated burnt cane handle, 65 in. long, c. 1920. **£10-15** *NML*

A bamboo shafted extending landing net, with brass fittings and curved metal frame, no makers name, 39 in. long by 60 in. extended, c. 1870. **£35-45** *NML*

An early 19th C. line clearing ring of brass, hinged opposite its locking latch, 2½ in. diam. **£30-50** *NML*

A late 19th C. small hand fly tying vice, with octagonal hollow handle and sprung steel jaws. **£30-40** *NML*

A black japanned 'gentle shoot' with ventilated lid and wire clip, c. 1910. **£20-30** *NML*

A gentle shoot was fixed to the waist and contained maggots which could be obtained by using one hand only and without spillage.

A boxwood cast and tackle winder, the 4 sections with sliding compartment between, with leather box, 8 in. long, c. 1890. **£15-£25** *NML*

A Hardys anglers guide 1917, 42nd edition, 403 pp., with ochre and gold covers with red cloth spine. **£80-100** *NML*

A Hardy Brothers 'Bethune' line drier, of bronzed brass with 4 dismountable A-frames, wooden handle with 'W' reel fitting, brass winding arm with bone handle, c. 1910. **£60-70** *JMG*

A Hardy catalogue of 1900, 304 pp., with worn and faded red cover showing the Hardy factory in Alnwick, many illus., 8½ by 5½ in. **£100-125** *JMG*

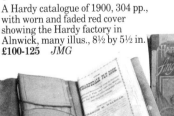

The 'Wharfedale' fly book, by Francis M. Walbran, giving names and directions for using 48 standard fly patterns, the wallet containing 10 leaves and pockets for casts and tackle, 1888. **£40-50** *NML*

A P. D. Malloch's of Perth, Scotland, tackle catalogue, 136 pp., 1923. **£20-30**   *NML*

'The Art of Angling' by Thomas Best, the 10th edition including 'Nobbs' complete troller, 260 pp., contemporary full calf binding, 1814. **£35-45**   *NML*

A tackle catalogue 'The Fishermans List', by Hy. Milward & Sons Ltd., Redditch, 350 pp., 1910. **£50-60**   *NML*

A Scottish leister salmon spear, of wrought iron, with 5 barbed prongs, 13 by 8 in., 19th C. **£20-30**   *JMG*

The 'Hardy-Zane Grey' 6 in. big game multiplying reel, in its leather case with brass grease gun. **£550-650**   *S*

A fine 12 ft. 3-piece greenheart trout fly rod, with typical 19th C. tapered wooden butt, fitted with brass spear and reel fittings, scroll engraved on the butt 'Benetfink and Co., Cheapside, London', spare top and a brass crank handled fly winch, 3 in. diam., 1⅝ in. wide. **£90-140**   *Bon*

A rare Hardys 5 in. ebonite 'silex' spinning reel, of 'starback' form with 'Bickerdyke' line guide, with slight wear, the star stamped Hardy's Pat. The 'Silex', c. 1912. **£200-300**   *S*

A Hardy Bros. Ltd. the 'Longstone' alloy reel, leather case, 4¼ in. diam., c. 1925. **£35-45**   *NML*

A Hardy Bros. 'perfect' trout fly reel, silent mechanism perforated drum, marked 'Hardy's Alnwick Patent', dismounted to show mechanism, diam. 2⅞ in., c. 1920. **£90-140**   *NML*

A rare Hardy Bros. 'Bougle' trout reel, of alloy with nickel-plated smooth brass foot, the inside struck W, finish worn, diam. 2⅝ in., c. 1915. **£400-600**   *Pea*

HARDY 'PERFECT' FLY REELS

First patented in 1888. A complete set of all ages and sizes numbers about 160 reels. There were many design changes.

- All brass with wire lineguard, before 1895
- All brass with cast cage, c. 1895-1900
- Alloy with brass face, c. 1900-10
- Alloy with white handle, c. 1910-22
- Alloy, black handle, smooth foot, c. 1922-28
- Alloy, black handle, notched foot, 1928-c. 1948
- Alloy, curved logo, black handle, notched foot, straight-line logo, c. 1948-67
- Alloy, black handle, straight-line logo, black cone in centre of face, 1976-current

JMG

A Hardy Bros. Ltd. 'Fortuna' alloy sea reel, with 'ship's wheel' tension nut and double handle with ebonite knobs, 7 in. diam. **£200-250**   *CEd*

A Hardy Bros. alloy salmon reel 'The Uniqua', fixed check brass foot, ivory handle, 2 in. wide by 4½ in. diam., c. 1917. **£30-50**   *NML*

A fine late 19th C. walking stick rod, hollowed bamboo butt section with silver-plated screw cap, engraved W. Osborn maker, 26 North St, Exeter, rod comprises bamboo butt 3 greenheart sections and 6 split cane tops, 12½ ft. long, ivory ferrule caps and drop rings. **£110-160**   *Bon*

A Hardy Bros. Ltd. 'super silex' reel, cardboard case, 3¾ in. wide, c. 1937. **£60-85**   *NML*

A rare Hardy 'Perfect' trout fly reel, of brass, with ivorine handle, rod-in-hand trademark, brass ball-bearings, large and small perforations in drum, 1896 check, extra fine condition, 2½ in. diam., c. 1898. **£350-450** *JMG*

A dismounted brass faced Hardy Bros. salmon fly reel, rod-in-hand trade mark Hardy Logo, 1896, check mechanism, 2¼ in. wide by 4½ in. diam. **£100-130** *NML*

An Illingworth casting reel, second model stamped OIL ME PLEASE and with grey finish, in leather plush-lined case, 6 by 3½ in., c. 1908. **£150-200** *JMG*

A rare Hardy Bros. 4 in. 1891 pattern all brass perfect, No. 141, the regulator with guard and 4-pillar nickel silver line guide, the face and core with large and small ventilations and the plate with Rod-in-Hand mark, retaining most original finish. **£1,000-1,200** *S*

A C. Farlows aluminium salmon reel, ventilated drum, brass foot strapped tension screw, 'Holofast' logo, 2⅜ in. wide by 4½ in. diam., c. 1925. **£50-70** *NML*

An Edward Vom Hofe New York salmon fly reel, No. 6-0, nickel silver and ebonite, counter balanced 'S' crank, antifoul and ebonite handle, marked Edward Vom Hofe maker N.Y. Pat. July 14 '96, 1⅝ in. wide by 4¼ in. diam., fine condition. **£45-90** *NML*

A walnut, brass and aluminium starback 'Aerial' reel, perforated drum, ivorine handles optional check and drag mechanism, smooth brass foot, 1¾ in. wide by 3 in. diam., c. 1910. **£60-80** *NML*

An S. Allcock's Redditch 'Aerial' reel, aluminium construction with perforated front plate, optional check and variable drag and brass foot, fitted line guard, 1⅞ in. wide by 4 in. diam., c. 1930. **£40-50** *NML*

A large Malloch's patent sun and planet reel, bronzing worn on plates, 5½ in. **£200-240** *S*

A Julius Vom Hofe New York ebonite and nickel-plated multiplying reel, counter balanced crank, optional check, adjustable end float, patent Nov. 17th 1885, and Oct. 8 1889, 2¼ in. wide by 2¾ in. diam. **£35-55** *NML*

A brass pole winch, the side plate engraved 'HAYWOOD-MAKER', **£160-200** *Bon*

James and Mary Haywood, Birmingham Reelsmiths, c. 1825-52.

A good early 19th C. brass multiplying reel clamp rod fitting locking mechanism, ivory handle, ratio 2:75 to 1, 1⅞ in. wide by 1⅝ in. diam. **£160-180** *NML*

A rare Scottish vintage fishing tackle dealer, c. 1924, with a deep knowledge of old reels, grey beard, ruddy-ish patina, and a most generous nature towards owners of fine tackle; buys up to £300 *JMG*

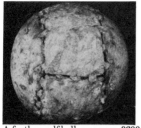

A feather golf ball, no name. **£600-£700**   *CEd*

A white painted feather golf ball, name indistinct. **£700-800**   *CEd*

Two almost mint Tom Morris feather golf balls, stamped 'T. Morris' and inscribed '27' in ink, c. 1840. **£1,500-1,800** each   *S*

A Forgan brass dye stamp, with stained baluster handle, 4½ in. long, c. 1870. **£80-100**   *CEd*

A Royal Doulton stoneware whisky jug, lettered 'Col. Bogey Whisky' in relief, with golfing transfers, English, 7½ in. high (19 cm.), c. 1910. **£300-350**   *S*

A Royal Doulton golfing plate, 10½ in. diam. (26.5 cm.), c. 1925. **£120-140**   *S*

A good and large Doulton Lambeth golfing jug, English, 9½ in. high (24 cm.), c. 1910. **£525-575**   *S*

A silver gilt Open Championship medal presented to Jack Simpson for winning the 1884 Golf Championship at St. Andrews, 2¾ in. **£5,000-5,500**   *CEd*

A Royal Doulton kingsware tankard, showing golfers and caddies in 17th C. dress, the rims edged in brown, printed marks, 14 cm. **£220-280**   *Bon*

A Royal Doulton 2-handled vase, 5 in. long. **£150-170**   *CEd*

A Royal Doulton golfing jug, decorated with raised figures of golfers in the style of Charles Crombie, English, 9 in. high (23 cm.), c. 1910. **£300-350**   *S*

Two golfing bronzes, woman lacking golf ball and club, 8 in. high (20 cm.), c. 1910. **£300-350**   *S*

A Royal Doulton vase. **£180-220**   *CEd*

A Royal Doulton bowl, printed and coloured, 8¼ in. high. **£200-220**   *CEd*

A trophy labelled 'ACTUAL HAGEN BALL, USED BY WALTER HAGEN, IN RECORD ROUND OF 67 DURING OPEN CHAMPIONSHIP 1929 AT MUIRFIELD', mounted on silver tripod fashioned as 2 cleeks, 6½ in. high. **£300-350**   *CEd*

A pair of blue and white pottery vases, printed with golfing scenes by Mitchell entitled 'The Drive off', and 'Through the Green', 1 with signature and dated 1910, 27 cm. tall. **£1,200-1,400**   *P*

A Royal Doulton kingsware golfing jug, 22.5 cm. high. **£300-350**   *P*

A bronze figure of Harry Vardon, by H.S. Ludlow, cast by Elkington & Co., 7½ in. overall, c. 1900. **£800-£900**   *CEd*

A scarred head long-nosed short spoon, by Tom Morris, c. 1875. **£700-800** *CEd*

A Hugh Philp brassed driver, the scarred head, 5½ in. long (14 cm.), c. 1840. **£600-700** *S*

An early spoon, probably by Philp, scarred head with indistinct stamp on head 'H...LP', bearing Royal and Ancient tie-on label, 39¾ in. long (1.1 m.), c. 1856. **£900-1,000** *S*

A good and early Forgan putter, scarred head, 38½ in. long (98 cm.), c. 1860. **£350-450** *S*

A scarred head wooden putter, by Tom Morris, regripped. **£450-500** *CEd*

A scarred head long-nosed baffing spoon, by Jackson of Perth. **£1,800-£2,200** *CEd*

John Jackson 1805-78 — A master club maker. A fine example in good condition.

A scarred head long-nosed driver, by Andrew Forgan, c. 1880. **£300-£325** *CEd*

Andrew Forgan 1846-1926, Greenkeeper to the Royal Perth Golfing Society, c. 1878.

A scarred head long-nosed play club, by T. Morris, c. 1875. **£750-£900** *CEd*

A scarred head long-nosed driver, by Jack Morris, greenheart shaft. **£550-600** *CEd*

Jack Morris, nephew of Tom Morris, Professional at Hoylake, a span of 60 years 1869-1929.

A brass gutta golf ball mould, for the Trophy golf ball, Bramble Pattern No. 11917, by John White & Co., Edinburgh. **£300-340** *CEd*

Two cleeks, 1 left-handed by John Gray, stamped J.N. Gray, c. 1875, and a right-handed cleek by Nicholson of Pittenweem, c. 1890. **£250-300** *CEd*

A scarred head putter by T. Morris, c. 1880. **£400-450** *CEd*

A Schoenhut golfing game in original box, containing male and female figures with articulated arms, American, 36 in. long (93 cm.), c. 1935. **£220-240** *S*

A composition painted caricature figure, of an early golfer advertising the Penfold golf ball, 21½ in. high. **£300-350** *CEd*

(*l.*) An electroplate golfing ink stand, 9½ in. wide (24 cm.), c. 1903. **£350-400**

(*r.*) A golfing pipe rest, the leather covered pipe rests with nickled figure of a golfer between them, 6½ in. wide (16.5 cm.), c. 1930. **£40-£50** *S*

Reminiscences of Golf on St. Andrews Links, by James Balfour, published by David Douglas, Edinburgh, spine damaged, 1887. **£300-400** *CEd*

Golf, a weekly record of 'Ye Royal and Ancient Game', No. 25 Vol. I, Friday March 6th 1891, in red covers. **£20-25**

Another edition of golf, similar to above, dated No. 25 Vol. I, Friday March 13th 1891, in red covers. **£20-25** *S*

A Robinson and Leadbetter Parian ware bust of W. G. Grace, 29 cm. tall. **£450-500** *P*

A Henry Cotton golf match display, comprising a signed score card for a match between T. H. Cotton, and S. I. King versus A. H. Padgham and W. J. Cox held on the 21st April, 1940, together with the golf balls used by Cotton and Padgham, 2 photographs of the match, the presentation cheque and 2 press cuttings, in glazed case, 12 in. (30.5 cm.) square, 1940. **£275-325** *S*

A composition painted caricature figure, carrying a golf bag of clubs advertising the Dunlop golf balls, 17 in. high. **£200-220** *CEd*

A cold-cast bronze figure of a 19th C. cricketer, 61 cm. tall. **£800-£900** *P*

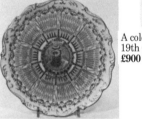

A blue ground pottery jug, printed in colours, with a portrait of W. A. Woodfall and facsimile signature, 13.5 cm. tall. **£140-160** *P*

A pottery plaque, printed in colours, with a portrait of Don Bradman and facsimile signature, 17 cm. tall. **£120-140** *P*

A Coalport porcelain plate, commemorating W. G. Grace's century of centuries, 22 cm. diam. **£300-350** *P*

A blue ground pottery jug, printed in colours, with a portrait of Herbert Sutcliffe and facsimile signature, slight chips to handle, 13.5 cm. tall. **£110-130** *P*

A cricketing jug, with 3 cricketers, in white on a stoneware ground between blue flowerheads and brown foliage outlined in white on a green ground, impressed Doulton Lambeth England, 8¾ in. high. **£100-140** *CSK*

A Doulton stoneware cricketers mug, sprigged with a bowler, wicket keeper and batsman, impressed marks, restored chip, 15.5 cm., 1890's. **£180-220** *SS*

A Lambeth Doulton jug, printed in black with portraits of W. G. Grace, Geo. Giffin and K. S. Ranjitsinhji, impressed mark, hairline crack to handle, 17.5 cm. tall. **£150-175** *P*

A Norah Braden stoneware vase, with light potting rings, ashen-white glaze falling short of the foot, brushed in deep brown, impressed NB seal, incised and painted numerals, 16.3 cm., early 1930's. **£350-400** *S*

A large tin-glazed earthenware flared bowl, by Alan Caiger-Smith, decorated in gold, copper and ruby lustres on a white ground, painted blue and red monogram and glaze type marks, 42 cm. diam. **£110-140** *C*

A large stoneware crock and cover, by Michael Cardew, the vessel covered in a mottled medium brown glaze and deeply incised, impressed MC and Wenford Bridge seals, 36.5 cm. high, c. 1975. **£350-450** *C*

A Hans Coper stoneware bowl, thickly glazed in a pitted ashen-white speckled in pale olive and brown, impressed HC seal, 27.8 cm. diam., 1950's. **£700-800** *S*

A Joanna Constantinidis stoneware vase, finely incised and speckled in charcoal-brown, the foot faintly lustrous, impressed seal, 43.2 cm., 1970's. **£120-150** *S*

A black stoneware vase, by Hans Coper, covered in a burnished matt black manganese glaze, impressed HC seal, 11 cm. high, c. 1972. **£1,200-1,500** *C*

A black stoneware vase, by Hans Coper, covered in a matt black manganese glaze, impressed HC seal, 17.7 cm. high, c. 1970. **£1,500-1,700** *C*

A Michael Cardew Winchcombe pottery cider jar, the red earthenware vessel decorated in dark brown, covered in an amber glaze, impressed monogram and pottery seal, 32.5 cm. high. **£200-250** *P*

A stoneware vase, by Hans Coper, with inlaid matt manganese lines radiating from the unglazed rim, the shoulders with a further covering of manganese over a shiny iron-rich 'treacle' glaze, impressed HC seal, 12.8 cm. high, c. 1953. **£450-550** *C*

A porcelain bowl, by Dorothy Feibleman, hand-built in white, blue and greyish-blue clays with marquetry millefiore, the interior covered in a clear glaze and the exterior unglazed, 10 cm. diam., 1976. **£300-400** *C*

A Ruth Duckworth stoneware vase, part-glazed in deep brown, the interior glazed ashen-white, the rim banded in green, 24.8 cm., early 1960's. **£500-600** *S*

An inlaid porcelain bowl with cut rim, by Ruth Franklin, decorated in pink, blue, green and yellow, on a matt white ground, signed R. Franklin, 10.5 cm. high, c. 1978. **£60-80** *C*

A Hans Coper stoneware vase, rubbed with a dark brown stain beneath an ashen-white glaze, impressed HC seal, rim repaired, 31.3 cm., 1970's. **£300-400** *S*

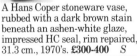

A stoneware bowl, by Ian Godfrey, covered in a slate-brown and pale ash glaze with a streaked khaki high fired glaze to the rim, 14.4 cm. high, c. 1972. **£40-50** *C*

A Marion Gaunce porcelain bowl, laminated in panels of blue, cream, lavender and pink, incised MG, 18 cm., c. 1982. **£250-350** *S*

A Sam Haile slipware trophy cup, decorated in cream and deep brown slips against an olive ground, impressed SH monogram and seal, 19.9 cm., 1940's. **£200-250** *S*

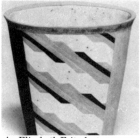

An Elizabeth Fritsch stoneware vase, painted in lilac, ochre, pale blue and black against a speckled ashen-white ground, 17.1 cm., c. 1979. **£1,200-1,500** *S*

A Sam Haile stoneware vase, impressed SH monogram, 38.2 cm., c. 1938. **£250-300** *S*

A Sam Haile stoneware vase, the lightly-ribbed body brushed in brown against a speckled mushroom glaze shaded at one side to grey-green, incised SH monogram, 16.9 cm., c. 1940. **£200-£250** *S*

A large stoneware vase, by Ewen Henderson, the hand-built grey grained body laminated with white and streaked with cobalt-blue and olive-green, 58 cm., c. 1980. **£200-£250** *C*

A polished porcelain bowl, by Nicholas Homoky, the rounded form inlaid with black, impressed NH seal, 8.8 cm. high, c. 1980. **£100-150** *C*

A Japanese stoneware bowl and cover, probably Kanjiro Kawai, the body banded in pale and dark olive speckled in rust, the cover in similar glazes against a rust and black tenmoku ground, 10.4 cm., 1940's. **£150-200** *S*

A Bernard Leach stoneware vase, impressed BL and St. Ives seals, 28 cm., 1960's. **£250-350** *S*

A large and deep stoneware dish, by Bernard Leach, decorated in an iron-red and black tenmoku glaze with a wax resist design, impressed BL and St. Ives seals, 34.2 cm. diam., c. 1964. **£1,000-1,500** *C*

A Bernard Leach stoneware pilgrim bottle, covered with a tenmoku glaze fired to a metallic copper finish with dark brown mottling, impressed St. Ives seal and 'B.L.' monogram, 32.5 cm. high. **£500-700** *P*

An important stoneware punch-bowl and cover, by Bernard Leach, the interior covered in an iron-red glaze stopping short of the unglazed rims and the outer surfaces covered in a rich tenmoku glaze with traces of iron-red, impressed BL and St. Ives seals, slight restoration to the cover, minor old chips to the base, 30.4 cm. diam., c. 1960. **£2,000-£2,500** *C*

A stoneware pilgrim plate, by Bernard Leach, covered in a rich black tenmoku and shaded iron-brown glaze and decorated in wax resist, BL and St. Ives seals, minor restoration to underside of rim, 32.4 cm. diam., c. 1970. **£700-900** *C*

A Bernard Leach stoneware 'Leaping Salmon' vase, painted in rust against a speckled mushroom ground, impressed BL and St. Ives seals, 40.1 cm., 1960's. **£1,000-1,500** *S*

A Bernard Leach stoneware vase, 39.2 cm., 1960's. **£900-1,200** *S*

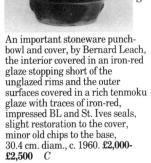

A Bernard Leach stoneware bottle-vase, combed with a wave motif through an orange peel textured tenmoku glaze, impressed BL and St. Ives seals, 18.6 cm., late 1950's. **£500-700** *S*

A Bernard Leach stoneware vase, glazed in running olive falling short of the foot to reveal the speckled rust body, impressed BL and St. Ives seals, 28.3 cm., 1960's. **£800-1,000** *S*

A Bernard Leach stoneware pilgrim dish, glazed in a rich cinnamon and deep blue-green, impressed BL and St. Ives seals, 31.6 cm., 1960's. **£1,500-1,750** *S*

An early David Leach, St. Ives stoneware vase, impressed St. Ives seal, 44.3 cm., c. 1939. **£300-400** *S*

A tall stoneware vase, by Bernard Leach, covered in a rich tenmoku glaze with traces of iron-red and deep olive-green at the shoulders, impressed BL and St. Ives seals, 37.5 cm. high, c. 1960. **£400-500** *C*

A Mashiko Kiln stoneware bottle-vase, glazed in a rich black tenmoku, the neck and shoulders with a thin nuka glaze, 17.5 cm., c. 1965. **£200-250** *S*

A William Marshall St. Ives stoneware vase, washed in a creamy glaze over the speckled buff ground and brushed in lustrous deep brown, impressed WM and St. Ives seals, minor flake to rim, 35 cm., 1970's. **£200-250** *S*

A Jane Osborn-Smith porcelain vase, painted in pastel shades, the rim pierced and threaded with a plaited silk cord, painted initials, 7.6 cm., c. 1978. **£300-400** *S*

An early Katharine Pleydell-Bouverie stoneware vase, carved and glazed in pale celadon against the biscuit, impressed KPB seal and Cole, 7.5 cm., c. 1928. **£200-250** *S*

An early Katharine Pleydell-Bouverie stoneware vase, with an ashen-green glaze falling short of the foot and brushed in blue on 1 face, impressed KPB and Cole seals, rim restored, 18.2 cm., 1930's. **£150-250** *S*

A Lucie Rie stoneware bowl, glazed in ashen-white and banded at the rim in a lustrous bronze-brown, impressed LR seal, 31 cm. max. width, c. 1970. **£600-800** *S*

A Lucie Rie porcelain bowl, incised through a chocolate brown glaze with bronze/mother-of-pearl lustre, between unglazed bands, impressed LR seal, 13.7 cm., 1970's. **£2,000-2,500** *S*

USE THE INDEX!

Because certain items might fit easily into any of a number of categories, the quickest and surest method of locating any entry is by reference to the fully cross-referenced index at the back of the book. This is particularly true this year when certain sections, e.g. Worcester Porcelain and Oak Furniture have been featured in isolation.

A stoneware vase, by Lucie Rie, with slate-grey body covered in a pitted thick white glaze, streaked with blue and brown, impressed LR seal, 12.2 cm. high, c. 1960. **£400-500** *C*

A rare stoneware salad bowl, with pulled rim, by Lucie Rie and Hans Coper, the white glaze with a profusion of brown specks and with a narrow brown border to the rim, recessed foot with LR and HC seals, slight restoration to the rim, 30.8 cm. wide, c. 1958. **£300-400** *C*

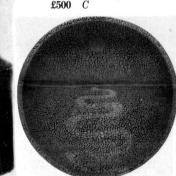

A porcelain bottle, by Lucie Rie, covered in a bronze manganese glaze, thinning in places to reveal pale brown beneath, with sgraffito decoration, impressed relief LR seal, restoration to the rim, 30 cm. high, c. 1960. **£1,400-1,800** *C*

A Lucie Rie porcelain vase, incised through a lustrous bronze-brown glaze, impressed LR seal, 24.5 cm., 1970's. **£700-800** *S*

A Mary Rogers stoneware bowl, the deep brown body brushed with buff, beneath a pale blue and pale green vermiform glaze, impressed MER seal, 38.5 cm., 1970's. **£250-300** *S*

A Hamada Shoji earthenware bowl, glazed in a speckled blue-grey and brown, with brush strokes of olive-black and ashen-white, 8.9 cm., c. 1950. **£200-250** *S*

A stoneware jar, by Hamada Shoji, covered in a thin brushed nuka glaze over a sand-coloured pigment and with stylised characters in trailed tenmoku, base with impressed spur marks of small shells, paper lablels, 'Made in Japan', and 'no. 56', 22 cm. high, c. 1959. **£1,000-1,200** *C*

A Hamada Shoji stoneware vase, 24.9 cm., c. 1960. **£300-500** *S*

A Hamada Shoji stoneware vase, splashed with kaki against an orange peel textured tenmoku ground, bearing labels 'Made in Japan' and numbered 27, 23 cm., c. 1960. **£600-700** *S*

A Japanese stoneware tea pot and cover, possibly by Hamada Shoji, the body decorated in resist against a speckled lustrous brown ground, the glaze falling short of the foot, minor chip to spout, 13.5 cm., c. 1940. **£180-250** *S*

A stoneware salt-glazed vase, by Hamada Shoji, covered in a brushed white slip, with running manganese and cobalt brushwork, 25.8 cm. high, c. 1959. **£1,000-1,500** *C*

A Martin Smith Raku bowl, glazed in a veined ashen-white against a black stained ground, the interior glazed, impressed MS, 13.2 cm., c. 1978. **£500-600** *S*

A William Staite Murray stoneware vase, with a mottled deep brown and black glaze, impressed pentagon seal, minor restoration to rim, 43.5 cm., 1930's. **£300-350** *S*

A Martin Smith Raku 'pocket' vase, glazed in a veined ashen-white against a black stained ground, the interior glazed, 20.5 cm., c. 1978. **£400-500** *S*

(*l.*) A Judith Trim sawdust-fired vase, mottled in grey against the terracotta body, 22.7 cm., c. 1980. **£130-160**

(*r.*) A similar Judith Trim vase, 17.5 cm., c. 1980. **£80-100** *S*

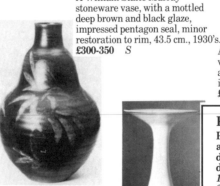

A Charles Vyse stoneware vase, with a shaded cinnamon and mirror-black tenmoku glaze, brushed in ochre with stylised bamboo leaves, incised Vyse 1934, 29.2 cm. **£250-300** *S*

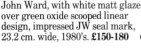

A stoneware hand-built bowl, by John Ward, with white matt glaze over green oxide scooped linear design, impressed JW seal mark, 23.2 cm. wide, 1980's. **£150-180** *C*

A stoneware bottle, by Lucie Rie, covered in a white glaze stopping short of the foot, impressed LR seal, 26.5 cm. high, c. 1975. **£600-700** *C*

A Jokwe axe, carved on each side with a mask, a further mask below at the rear, with steel blade, 21 in. long (48 cm.). **£225-250**   *C*

A North Nigerian wood maternity group, the caryatid of a stool from which the seat is missing, cross-hatched scarification on the breast and back, devices on the abdomen, probably Afo, 19¾ in. high (50 cm.), early 20th C. **£160-180**   *C*

A Dan wood mask, bagle or bugle, with reddened features, 8 in. high (20.5 cm.). **£100-125**   *C*

A Baule wood mask, surmounted by the figure of a cockerel partially coloured blue and red, 15 in. high (35.5 cm.). **£450-500**   *C*

A very fine Ganda wood drum, probably for royal use, the hide membrane fixed with wood pegs, pierced truncated conical lug for suspension, glossy brown patina, base repaired, 42 in. high (107 cm.). **£250-300**   *C*

A baule wood heddle pulley, the head finial with incised coiffure, scarification on neck, temples and between brows, 7½ in. high (19 cm.). **£175-225**   *C*

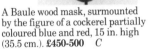

A fine male Ibeji, incised scarification on the chest and back of the neck, scorched eyes, inscription on base: ILORIN 2 Sept 1912, probably from Ilorin, 8½ in. high (21.5 cm.). **£80-120**   *C*

A rare Kongo wood figure of a seated chief, with glass inlay eyes and painted black brows, carved ear pendants, the cape and elaborate headgear each carved with snakes which have glass and red bead eyes respectively, traces of green and black paint, kaolin on the body of the principal figure, 20 in. high (51 cm.), c. 1860. **£1,200-1,400**   *C*

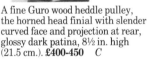

A fine Guro wood heddle pulley, the horned head finial with slender curved face and projection at rear, glossy dark patina, 8½ in. high (21.5 cm.). **£400-450**   *C*

A pair of Ibeji, male and female, with carved triangular pendants and high-soled sandals, beads about the neck and cowries at the wrists, from eastern Igbomina, about Omu Aran, each about 10¼ in. high (26 cm.). **£150-200**   *C*

A very rare Yoruba wood staff for the cult of Shopono, the god of smallpox, the carved kneeling male figure with lenticular cicatrice on each shoulder, holding a wood phallus in both hands, from Ogbomosho, 24¼ in. long (61.5 cm.). **£225-275**   *C*

Woodcarvings for the cult of Shopono are seldom found in collections, partly no doubt because few were made, but especially because of the secrecy which shrouded its activities. It was for many years proscribed by the British administration on the grounds that it was spreading the disease and operating a protection racket.

A Yoruba wood group of a British District Officer and 5 men in a boat, extensive traces of kaolin embellishments, by Thomas Ona of Ijebu-Ode, 12½ in. long (32 cm.). **£1,400-1,600**   *C*

A very fine and rare Benin bronze cylindrical armlet, cast in low relief with 2 horsemen alternating with 2 standing figures, brown patina, 5 in. high (12.8 cm.). **£1,800-2,200** *C*

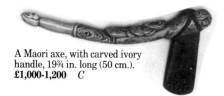

A Maori axe, with carved ivory handle, 19¾ in. long (50 cm.). **£1,000-1,200** *C*

A Yoruba wood figure, wearing a whitened suit with carved lapels incorporating the initials NP, detachable sola topi, the base inscribed: Pilot Flack, by Thomas Ona of Ijebu-Ode, 10 in. high (25.5 cm.). **£650-750** *C*

The famous carver Thomas Ona flourished from about the turn of the century and into the 50's, first at Ijebu Ode (whence his carving style was derived) and later at Lagos, where he was well known for his gently satirical carvings of colonial administrators, lawyers, missionaries and occasionally Yoruba, made for the British.

A rare Shira-Puna wood female figure, face with darkened brows and high incised coiffure, the remainder covered with kaolin, the legs held wide apart with the large feet forming a single base, cracks, 11¾ in. high (30 cm.). **£500-600** *C*

A Luba wood stool, with keloid and incised scarification on the breasts and about the protuberant navel, the coiffure incised and quartered at the back glossy reddish-brown patina, with scorched ornament, the base damaged, 21½ in. high (55 cm.). **£1,400-1,600** *C*

A rare Luntu wood male figure, glossy brown patina, minor cracks, 14¾ in. high (37 cm.). **£4,500-5,000** *C*

A fine Makonde wood helmet mask, the geometric scarification marks applied with beeswax, the coiffure recessed and set with human hair, coloured black, 9 in. high (23 cm.), c. 1920. **£1,700-2,000** *C*

A Maori nephrite figure neck pendant, hei tiki, the top of the head pierced for suspension, minor damages, 5⅛ in. (13 cm.) high. **£700-800** *C*

A Maori tiki of typical embryonic form, with 1 original and 1 replaced shell eye and pierced cord hole, behind, 1 foot clearly stuck, 3¾ in. **£400-450** *GSP*

A New Guinea wood fishing charm figure, male, neatly carved back with rings about the neck, incised tapering headgear, red patina, with No. 6787, 6½ in. high (16.5 cm.). **£300-350** *C*

A rare Zambia or Malawi chief's knife, bound with copper wire, iron blade, 19 in. long (48 cm.). **£1,800-£2,200** *C*

A fine Fiji wood oil dish, dari no waiwai ni bete, glossy dark patina, with label: King Coffey of Abysinnia, Platter and Fork, 14 in. (35.5 cm.) long. **£650-750** *C*

These dishes were used by priests to anoint themselves with coconut oil before entering a trance on behalf of a petitioner who would have offered suitable gifts. The session would take place in a sacred building (bure kalou).

A fine Fiji wood headrest, on 4 sq. ft., 2 repaired, chips, glossy brown patina, traces of 2 old labels, 17¼ in. (44 cm.) long. **£400-450** *C*

A fine Fiji wood headrest, on 4 square feet, 2 repaired, chips, glossy brown patina, traces of 2 old labels, 17¼ in. (44 cm.) long. **£400-£450** *C*

A Solomon Islands wood canoe prow ornament, musumusu, 9 in. (23 cm.) high. **£1,500-1,750** *C*

John Lennon self-portrait with
Yoko Ono, in black felt tip, signed
John Lennon 1969, 19 by 14 in. (48
by 36 cm.), mounted in card.
£2,500-3,000 *S*

The Silver Beatles, a rare original
print of John Lennon, Paul
McCartney, Stuart Sutcliffe,
George Harrison and Johnny
Hutch, 4¾ by 6½ in. (12 by
16.5 cm.), June/July, 1960. **£400-
£450** *S*

*The name of the group was changed
from 'Johnny and the Moondogs' to
'Long John and the Silver Beatles'
and thence to 'The Silver Beatles'
especially for this important
audition. The silver braid edging to
their shirt lapels can just be seen in
this print.*

A 'Presentation' 'Gold'
disc for a Beatles
single, c. 1964. **£1,000-
£1,200** *S*

'Imagine', hand-written lyrics by
John Lennon in black ink on paper
from The New York Hilton, 5½ by
4½ in. (14 by 11 cm.), c. 1971.
£6,000-7,000 *S*

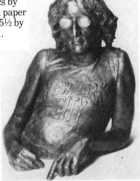

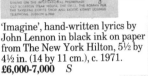

John Lennon, bronze by K. Carter,
numbered 6/15, exhibited at the
Royal Academy, 15 in. (38 cm.)
high, 1981. **£1,500-2,000** *S*

Two original John Lennon
drawings, dated May, 68, each on
card, 8 by 12¾ in. (20 by 32.5 cm.).
£2,500-3,000 *S*

An autographed pencil sketch of
Ringo Starr, signed by all 4
members of The Beatles, together
with 2 photographs showing the
sketch being signed, 3 additional
photographs and a newspaper
article, and a programme for their
concert at the Regal Theatre, Hull,
1964. **£650-750** *S*

John Lennon in
the 'Top Ten
Club', 1961,
photograph by
Jurgen Vollmer,
13¾ by 10¼ in.
£400-500 *S*

'Help' premier, comprising 2 tickets
to the London premier and
programme leaflet, 1965. **£120-140**
S

Autographed Two Virgins LP,
signed on back outside cover by
John Lennon for himself and Yoko
Ono, c. 1968. **£200-250** *S*

An autographed Beatle concert
programme, signed by all 4
members of the group, c. 1964.
£300-350 *S*

Two photographs of M.P. Bessie
Braddock with the Beatles, sold
with negative and copyright, 1965.
£120-140 *S*

John Lennon in Hamburg, 1961,
photograph by Jurgen Vollmer,
signed by him, 14 by 10½ in. (35.5
by 26.5 cm.). **£400-500** *S*

*This photograph is widely known
as the cover for John Lennon's LP
'Rock 'n Roll', released in 1975.*

George Harrison in Hamburg,
1961, photograph by Jurgen
Vollmer, signed by him on the
cardboard mount, 14 by 10½ in.
(35.5 by 26.5 cm.). **£600-700** *S*

A collection of photographs relating to John Lennon 1975, comprising 52 35 mm. colour transparencies and approximately 78 black and white negatives, sold with copyright. **£1,000-1,200** *S*

John Lennon 'Mind Games', 4-colour separation for the album cover, with signature of John with stylised portraits of himself and Yoko, framed and glazed, c. 1973. **£1,000-1,200** *S*

Paul McCartney and George Harrison in the 'Top Ten Club', Hamburg 1961, photograph by Jurgen Vollmer, signed, 14 by 10½ in. (35.5 by 26.5 cm.). **£400-£500** *S*

Apple, a sign of brushed stainless steel inset with word 'Apple' in bright green, 9 by 12 in. (23 by 30.5 cm.). **£300-350** *S*

The Eagles 'Hotel California', original airbrush art work for the lettering panel used on the album cover, 22 by 24 in. (56 by 61 cm.), 1975. **£350-400** *S*

A Beatle bubble gum machine, by Oak Mfg. Co. Inc., the upper portion containing bubble gum balls and gifts, 16 in. (40.5 cm.) high, American, c. 1965. **£350-400** *S*

A Beatles Toy 'n Joy bubble gum machine, containing bubble gum balls and gifts with glazed window at front, 14 in. (35.5 cm.) high, American, c. 1965. **£450-500** *S*

Jimi Hendrix 'Presentation' 'Gold' record, 'The Cry of Love'. **£3,000-£4,000** *S*

Marc Bolan's custom-built polished aluminium electric guitar, by Valeno Inst. Co., Florida. **£2,000-£2,500** *S*

It is believed that this instrument was custom-made for Marc Bolan in America, 2 others were ordered at the same time which he gave to Eric Clapton and Jeff Lynne.

'That's the way it was and is', original pencil drawing of Elvis Presley, signed and dated '75, mounted, framed and glazed, 24¾ by 28½ in. (63 by 72 cm.). **£450-500** *S*

Keith Richards' 'Framus' acoustic guitar, lettered 'Rolling Stones' with photograph of Richards playing the instrument, with a letter of authenticity, c. 1965. **£750-£850** *S*

A woven silk card, 1915. **£13-£15** *MS*

Cards of this type generally fall into a £10-20 price range.

A 'Presentation' 'Gold' disc of '(I can't get no) satisfaction' by The Rolling Stones. **£1,100-1,200** *S*

A novelty card which, when held to the light reveals a man pouring water over the band from the window above, c. 1907. **£8-10** *MS*

Three embroidered silk cards, c. 1914-18. **£2.50-3.50** each *MS*

These cards were extensively made by French and Belgian peasants during World War I for sale to British and Allied troops.

Two brilliantly coloured 'Kaleidoscope' cards, c. 1906. **£15-20** each *MS*

A rotating disc set inside the cards causes patterns to change.

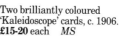

Two French 'fantasy head' cards, c. 1910. **£8-11** each *MS*

'Fantasy head' cards vary from £5-20

Three 'local view' photographic postcards. **£15-£18** each   *MS*

Views of windmills are widely collected and may vary in price from £1-25. These, being clear 'close up' photographs, fall into the upper price bracket.

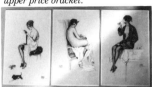

Three glamour cards, by Leonnec, c. 1914-18. **£5-7** each   *MS*

Cards such as these were normally issued in sets of 6-7. They carry no premium for complete sets. Widely bought by troops during World War I.

A coloured set of 6 aircraft postcards, published by Raphael Tuck, c. 1912. **£20-£25** the set   *MS*

Individual cards £2-3

Scott 1901 Antarctic Expedition, 4 cards posted from ports of call. **£150-180** *S*

Two map cards, 1905-15. **£1-£10**

(t.) An unusual and rare advertising card. **£7-9**

(b.) Value reduced because someone has marked a tour route on it in ink. **£2.50-3.50** *MS*

A set of 6 chromo cards, by Mailick (Hope and Innocence not shown), c. 1910. **£23-25** *MS*

Sets of three subjects are more common: £8-12
Photographic sets not so desirable: three £1-1.50 six £2-3.50

Three Exhibition souvenir cards, 1911, 1918, 1909. **50p-£2** each   *MS*

Smaller exhibitions tended to produce fewer cards — these are more sought after than those from larger exhibitions. So, too, are those bearing the exhibition's own postmark.

Three shipping cards:
(t.) A signed advertising card, by Cassiers, chromo printed, c. 1904. **£8-12**
(c.) A typical Company issue, c. 1908-15. **£2-4**
(b.) From the 'Celebrated Liners' set, c. 1912. **£3-4** *MS*

A set of 3 Bamforth song cards, 1908-18. **£1-2**   *MS*

There were approximately 2,000 different song sets issued in this manner. Although very collectable, they are also very common.

A boxing educational card, 1 of a set of 12, 1908-20. **£2-4** each   *MS*

Two 'large alphabet' chromo cards, c. 1905. **£2-3** each *MS*

Similar photographic cards: **50p-£1**

A set of the whole alphabet will carry a premium of 15% on top of the individual values of the cards.

Two very rare early commemorative postcards, issued for Queen Victoria's Diamond Jubilee 1897.
(top) Coloured, used. **£150-£180**
(bottom) Plain sepia, unused. **£50-70** *MS*

The date of posting affects values, those posted on the actual day being commemorated carrying considerably higher values. The world record price for a card of this type was £355.

Three postcards of views painted on commission, by A. R. Quintin, 1915-25. **50p-£1** each   *MS*

These cards are as common as they are popular and are being reproduced today.

A set of 6 comic sports cards, by Kinsella, c. 1912. **£12-18** the set   *MS*

A typically French glamour card, by Rocher, c. 1900. **£7-9** *MS*

Glamour cards may vary from £5-20 depending on the artist.

Four early semi-erotic glamour cards, c. 1903. **£4-6** each   *MS*

A set of 6 would carry a 10% premium.

Two early Nazi propaganda postcards, c. 1937. **£5-7** each *MS*

Nazi cards are extremely collectable, with the rarer examples selling for as much as £200.

Three coloured postcards for children:
(l. to r.) English, German, Dutch, 1908-30. **50p-£1** each   *MS*

Two 'Gruss aus' (greetings from) cards, 1885-1900. **£2-£10** each   *MS*

Greetings cards of this type and period were mostly produced on the Continent.

A local interest/transport photographic card, c. 1910. **£30-35** *MS*

Deterioration of the photographic image makes very little difference to value, provided clarity remains.

A 'card on card' card, an unusual but popular theme issued c. 1905-20. This example dated 1915. **£1-3** *MS*

An interesting photographic Railway card, commemorating the closure of the 'only one-horse railway in the world', the Dandy of Port Carlisle, c. 1915. **£8-12** *MS*

A railway official advertising card. **£8-12** *MS*

All private railway companies issued similar cards. Small companies tended to issue fewer, some of which are now highly priced. Overall range **£1-100**

A post World War I 'Event' card, commemorating the visit of a Tank to Hastings on July 15-16, 1918. **£5-10** *MS*

Tanks, often German, were commonly displayed in English towns at this time. Most were melted for scrap during World War II.

Three of a set of 48 'Queen Victoria's Dolls' House' cards, c. 1908, at £1 per card   *MS*

Complete set in original album **£50-100**

A French Art Nouveau card, showing the Japanese influence on the movement. **£8-12** *MS*

W. D. & H. O. Wills Musical Celebrities, 8 cards, the original set, condition mint. **£800-900** *S*

W. D. & H. O. Wills Ships, 86 cards from this rare set of 100, condition mint. **£1,000-£1,200** *S*

An art reproduction card, from the Wallace Collection, of the kind still sold in galleries today, c. 1905-15. **50p-£1** *MS*

A trade card, the back printed with details of the front subject matter, presented to children for good attendance or achievement at School or Sunday School, c. 1902-05. **£1-3** *MS*

Allen & Ginter 'Pirates of the Spanish Main', 31 cards from a set of 50. **£100-150** *S*

Allen & Ginter 'Parasol Drill', 34 cards from a set of 50 and 18 duplicates, condition of majority good/fine. **£140-180** *S*

Consolidated Cig. Co. 'Consols and Paxi' double-image revolving cards, 21 cigarette cards and 20 duplicates, condition good to poor. **£180-200** *S*

(*l.*) Allen & Ginter 'General Government & State Capital Buildings of the United States', 14 cigarette cards from a set of 50, condition of majority good. **£100-150**

(*c.*) Thirty Allen & Ginter cigarette cards from various sets. **£70-80**

(*r.*) Allen & Ginter 'Great Generals', 13 cigarette cards from a set of 50. **£60-80** *S*

A collection of 180 glamour and other postcards, in 2 albums. **£300-350** *S*

W. Duke & Sons, 'Coins of all Nations' cigarette cards, 20 from a set of 50. **£40-50** *S*

A good and early album of 360 postcards, dating from c. 1899. **£400-500** *S*

(*t.l.*) Allen & Ginter 'Celebrated American Indian Chiefs', 38 from a set of 50 with 1 duplicate, condition of majority fine/excellent. **£120-£150**

(*t.r.*) Allen & Ginter 'The World's Champion', 26 from a set of 50 with duplicates, condition of majority fine/excellent. **£80-90**

(*b.l.*) Allen & Ginter 'World's Smokers', 30 from a set of 50, condition of majority fine/excellent. **£80-90**

(*b.r.*) Allen & Ginter 'Quadrupeds', 25 from a set of 50, condition of majority fine/excellent. **£80-90** *S*

A collection of 95 risque postcards, the majority undivided back, most depicting ladies in stages of undress or erotic situations, all contained in one small album. **£180-220** *S*

A good 'disaster' card, 1921. **£8-12** *MS*

An exceptional early album of 480 postcards, the majority undivided back, all contained in album, dating from c. 1901. **£600-700** *S*

A sports postcard, showing Preston North End football team. Photographs of this kind date mainly from 1908-20.

League Teams **£5-8**

Amateur Teams **£1-3**   *MS*

A sports card — cricket. **£2-8** *MS*

All sports cards are collectable, but cricket is easily the most popular subject.

A comic fantasy sports card, 1905-20. **£4-6**   *MS*

Two 'real photographic' motor cycling cards, 1905-25. **£4-8** each   *MS*

The world's first postcard, published in Austria, in October 1869, postmarked October 1869. **£200-300**

Any other date (this one Feb. 1870. **£3-5**   *MS*

Two film star cards, 1910-50. **50p-£3** each   *MS*

The general rule is: the bigger the star, the higher the price. Autographs can increase the value by as much as 10 times.

First U.K. aerial post, from London to Windsor (1), printed in sepia, and Windsor to London (2), printed in grey, 1911. **£30-£40**   *S*

An early 'poster' advertising card, c. 1905-10. **£30-35** *MS*

Postcards of this type vary from £20-50. Identical subjects in the form of advertising leaflets £1-2

These cards were legitimately reproduced by Shell, c. 1950-70 and, suitably distressed, are sometimes passed off as originals. Reproductions have a glossy finish and this is the simplest way of recognising them. Although they also have the word 'copyright' on the reverse, this can be removed, and it is not unknown for a cheap, but old, card to be split and the reverse pasted in place, complete with stamp and early postmark.

Two local interest photographic cards, 1902-20.

(*t.*) **£8-10**

(*b.*) **£18-24**   *MS*

The interest in these cards lies in their reflection of social history. The horse-drawn van is a more precise comment than the general view of a station platform, hence its higher price. Collectors of local interest cards tend to specialise in aspects of their home towns.

Two very early English postcards of 'Court' size, approx. 1½ in. shorter than standard, 1898-1901. **£5-15** *MS*

Earliest postmarks command highest prices. Those postmarked 1894-95. £200-£300. None known pre-1894.

A German satirical chess card, showing notables of the period, c. 1914-15. **£12-15** *MS*

Chess is an uncommon, but well collected, subject.

A rare and early German postcard, c. 1888. **£25-35** *MS*

An Irish Anti-Home Rule propaganda card. **£8-10** *MS*

Such cards are datable by the events and characters shown. Normally £5-15

An embossed 'coin' card, issued for many countries giving rates of exchange for other principal currencies, 1905-15. **£3-5**   *MS*

A Victory celebration card, 1918. **£24-26**   *MS*

A very collectable card combining local interest and special event value.

A typical Edwardian Valentine's greetings card. **£1-3**   *MS*

A rhinoceros horn libation cup, carved in relief with a continuous scene of figures in a landscape, 2⅞ in. (7.4 cm.) high, 17th C. **£1,800-2,200** *S*

A bronze ritual vessel, the sides cast with a frieze of U motifs, the patina of greyish colour with some green areas and patches of azurite, a pictogram on the interior, 15 in. (38.1 cm.), middle Zhou Dynasty. **£1,800-2,400** *S*

A gilt-bronze figure of Avalokitesvara, waisted base, an ambrosia vase held in the right arm lowered at the side, 5 in. (12.7 cm.), Tang Dynasty. **£850-1,250** *S*

A rootwood brush pot, the gnarled exterior of yellowish-brown colour, 7¼ in. (18.3 cm.), 19th C. **£350-450** *S*

A pair of Pekin blue glass bowls, 8¾ in. (22.3 cm.), engraved four character mark for Qianlong and period. **£450-550** *SC*

A Chinese carved wood figure, of a dignitary, decorated in gesso and lacquer, 10 in. high, 19th C. **£280-320** *MMB*

A stained boxwood okimono, of a group of terrapins, their eye pupils inlaid in black, signed Masakatsu and kao, late 19th C. **£700-800** *C*

An ivory netsuke, of a baku, unsigned, 19th C. **£2,500-3,000** *C*

Soten: a tsuba, decorated in gold, silver, shakudo and copper, signed, 7.6 cm. **£500-600** *S*

A turquoise Pekin glass bowl, the exterior carved in relief with a phoenix and a large peony, 6½ in. (16.5 cm.), 19th C. **£350-400** *S*

A Sino-Tibetan gilt-bronze figure of Avalokitesvara, in his sadaksari form, 9⅛ in. (23.2 cm.), 18th C. **£550-650** *S*

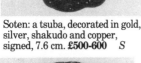

Omori Tokinobu: a Shibuichi tsuba, details in copper, silver, sentoku and shakudo, signed, 6.9 cm. **£800-900** *S*

An ivory netsuke, carved as a karashishi, unsigned, late 18th/early 19th C. **£550-600** *C*

Tomotada: a study of a wolf with a crab, in well patinated ivory, the eye pupils inlaid with dark horn, one replaced, signed, 18th C. **£2,200-2,800** *S*

A rare gilt-bronze figure of a boy, his right hand clasping a lotus bud resting on his right knee, lightly encrusted in places, 1¾ in. (4.5 cm.), Tang Dynasty, wood stand. **£3,800-4,400** *S*

A model of a hatching tengu, the pupils inlaid, the ivory lightly worn and well patinated, late 18th C. **£550-650** *S*

A spherical group of masks, lightly stained in brown. **£80-120** *Bon*

A Korean gilt-bronze figure of Buddha, the left hand raised in vitarkamudra and the right lowered in veradamudra, 3¼ in. (8.3 cm.). **£2,500-3,000** *S*

A Sino-Tibetan gilt-bronze figure of a standing Bodhisattva, the arched ungilt lotus base with engraved decoration, the mandala assembled from twelve sections, 106 cm., mid 19th C. **£4,000-5,000** *Bon*

Three noh masks, one with the hairwork stained in chocolate-brown, 6.5 cm. and 7 cm., all signed Tamatoshi. **£100-150** *Bon*

A bronze censer and cover, cast in low relief on the sides with key fret and taotie, 12.5 cm., late Ming Dynasty. **£100–150** *Bon*

Dosho: a manju of square shape, carved in ivory, signed. **£900-1,100** *S*

A rectangular bronze Kodansu, decorated in iroe hirazogan and takazogan and nikubori, the hinged outer door enclosing three wood drawers with silver and gilt handles, signed Kyoto Inoue sei, 19.7 cm. high, late 19th C. **£4,500-5,500** *C*

A rare cameo scent bottle, simulating the Chinese, the opaque-white body speckled in red and applied with two sprays of lotus in dark blue, 6 cm., by Daniel and Lionel Pearce at Thomas Webb & Sons, late 19th C. **£350-400** *S*
In that the stoppers of these bottles are often fitted with spoons, it is likely that they were made to take powder of some form. The use of snuff itself has largely disappeared in the Orient. It must be considered probable that other inhalent powders or incense were originally put in them.

A jade vase and cover, of flattened baluster shape, the stone of 'sodden snow' tone, 8¾ in. (22.3 cm.), 18th C., wood stand. **£1,200-1,600** *S*

A pair of jade bowls, of sombre dark green colour, 13.5 cm., wood stand and fitted case. **£300-350** *Bon*

A pair of green jade figures of phoenix, 9½ in. (24.2 cm.), 19th C. **£600-700** *S*

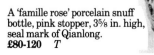

A spinach-green jade bowl, the sides carved with a floral frieze, the stone of rich tones with mottling and flecks, 9 in. (22.8 cm.), 19th C. **£1,200-1,600** *S*

A group of two quail, well carved in ivory, the eyes inlaid with horn, unsigned, late 18th C. **£600-700** *S*

A 'famille rose' porcelain snuff bottle, pink stopper, 3⅝ in. high, seal mark of Qianlong. **£80-120** *T*

A pale green jade censer and cover, carved around the sides with two large taotie motifs, 6⅝ in. (16.8 cm.), Qianlong, wood stand. **£2,000-2,500** *S*

An important sword of Viking type, in excavated condition, the double-edged blade slightly tapering with 'wurmbunt' pattern-welding, the oval quillon and pommel inlaid with brass bands with stamped linear decoration, 37½ in. long (95.3 cm.), 9th C. **£5,000-7,000**   S

An important sword of Viking type, in excavated condition, with 'wurmbunt', pattern-welding, short oval quillons with silver studs through the tips and finely inlaid with vertical silver lines, 37¼ in. long (94.5 cm.), 9th C. **£7,000-£10,000**   S

The term 'wurmbunt' refers to a type of welding which came into use in the late 3rd or early 4th C., although the particular German word (Wurm-=worm, bunt=many coloured) appears some hundred years later and refers to the rippled pattern. This pattern was achieved by tightly winding alternate steel and iron wires of different hardness (carbon content) around one or more metal cores: the separately forged steel edges were fitted either side and the whole was then welded together; the final touches consisted of polishing the surfaces to a smooth finish and in sharpening the edges. This complicated technique which required great skill from the craftsmen came to a peak in the 9th C. but disappeared gradually over the next 200 years and finally survived only in the welded inscriptions on blades of 13th and 14th C. swords.

A mediaeval sword, with cord-bound leather-covered wooden grip, the surface acid cleaned, 34 in. blade, probably early 15th C. **£1,000-1,500**   C

A fine mediaeval sword, with central fuller between 2 inlaid brass fillets, struck with a mark, a star and P, half of the original wooden grip, and typical Thames patination, probably English, 27¾ in. blade, 15th C. **£6,000-9,000** C

From the Thames near Bull Wharf. This form of hilt was used from the late 14th C. until the end of the Middle Ages, and illustrations are found on many English church monuments of this period. The inlaid brass fillets in the blade are unusual.

A German rondel dagger, in excavated condition, hilt entirely of brass, pommel incised with a cross, sun, moon, triangle and star, 9¾ in., early 16th C. **£300-500**   C

A Flemish ballock dagger, 13¼ in., early 16th C. **£1,000-£1,500**   C

An unusual Scottish basket hilted back-sword, replacement wood grip, corroded overall, c. 1620. **£650-850**   P

An Italian dagger, of cinquedea type, with broad triangular blade with narrow central fuller, later wooden grip, 16½ in., late 15th C. **£1,500-2,250**   C

A fine quality gilt bronze romantic style dagger, tapering diamond section blade, the quillon bloc set and scattered with garnets, probably French, a few garnets missing, 19 cm., c. 1860. **£200-400** P

A good silver gilt mounted Scottish dirk, hilt set with gilt studs, agate pommel surmounted by a small stone, the ferrule overlaid with silver thistles and a crown, the leather covered scabbard with silver gilt mounts, the reverse with a plaque signed Hunter Boyd & Co., Army Contractor to His Majesty, Edinburgh, complete with companion knife and fork mounted en suite, tip of blade broken and agate pommel of dirk cracked, 35.5 cm., c. 1810. **£700-800**   P

The crest is that of Fraser.

A post-'02 Scottish Highland dirk, by Kirkwood, Edinburgh, single-edged 29 cm. blade, carved hardwood grip with brass pique work, brass mounts, cut-glass pommel, in leather covered sheath with companion knife and fork. **£250-350**   SS

A good Victorian naval officer's dirk, blade 17½ in., retaining nearly all original polish, by Seagrove & Co., The Hard, Portsea, gilt wire bound white fish-skin covered grip, spring button catch, in its gilt mounted leather sheath, very good condition. **£175-250** Wal

A Nazi German Red Cross Officer's dagger, 25 cm. blade. **£130-170**   P

A Nazi German Land Customs dagger, by Eickhorn, Solingen, 25 cm. blade. **£160-220**   P

A good Nazi German S.S. Officer's dagger, 22 cm. blade etched with motto Meine Ehre Heisst Trueu, Holbein hilt. **£400-500**   *P*

A 2nd pattern commando FS fighting knife, by 'Wilkinson Sword', retaining most original darkened finish, in its leather sheath, blade 6½ in. **£200-225** *Wal*

A Continental silver-mounted plug bayonet, the blade from a backsword, pitted, ebony hilt with silver mounts, 17½ in., mid 18th C. **£100-150**   *C*

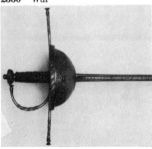

A fine, large gold-mounted Sumatran kris, watered blade 15 in. with scrolled top, one piece carved ivory hilt, the ivory probably hippopotamus tusk. **£250-£350**   *Wal*

An Indian gold-mounted dagger, with tapering single-edged watered blade damascened in gold, and with tiger's head pommel set with chrysoberyl eyes, one missing, in original velvet-covered wooden scabbard, velvet worn, with heavy pierced gold locket and chape, tip slightly damaged, 12½ in., late 18th C. **£2,000-2,500**   *C*

A scarce wooden hilted commando knife, with darkened finish overall, blade 6½ in. **£120-160**   *Wal*

A rare 1st pattern FS commando fighting knife, etched 'Wilkinson Sword', 'The F.S. Fighting Knife', leather sheath, blade 6¾ in. **£350-£400**   *Wal*

A plug bayonet, with earlier rapier blade, later turned figured wooden hilt, and brass mounts, in associated cloth-covered wooden scabbard, split, 15⅞ in., the blade early 17th C., the hilt mounts late 17th C. **£200-250**   *C*

An early socket bayonet, double-edged blade, short shank and long socket with simple '2' shaped locking slot, worn, pitted, but a collector's item as early bayonets have a low survival rate, blade 17½ in., c. 1700. **£80-120**   *WD*

A swept-hilt rapier, with slender tapering blade of flattened hexagonal section struck with the inscription 'Andrea' and 'Ferara' and with the maker's mark 'ST' monogram in a crowned shield, for Stantler?, and original wire-bound grip, 40¼ in. blade, early 17th C. **£750-1,250**   *C*

A Pappenheimer rapier, the tapering blade of flattened hexagonal section with a central inscribed fuller on each face of the forte, inscription illegible, crowned ST mark, for Stantler, struck on the tang, decoration with slight traces of silvering, 40 in. blade, early 17th C. **£700-1,000**   *C*

A Spanish cup-hilt rapier, with blade stamped with the spurious date 1553, the ricasso struck with the crowned swan mark of Clemens Dinger, 43 in. blade, late 17th C. **£1,500-1,800**   *C*

An Italian cup-hilt rapier, with blade of flattened diamond section, with the signature 'Clemens Dinger' twice, the ricasso stamped twice on each side with his mark, a standing swan, 42½ in. blade, mid 17th C. **£3,000-4,000**   *C*

A small sword, with tapering blade of hollow triangular section etched with scrollwork and a sun, worn, at the forte, French or English, 32¼ in. blade, c. 1750-60. **£300-500** *C*

An ivory hilted hunting sword, slightly curved blade, with 'Running Wolf' mark and Cit Salin Gen, hilt with brass shell and knuckle bow, ivory grip, 30¼ in., early 18th C. **£250-350**   *S*

A rare Irish cruciform-hilted dress sword, of the Knights of the Order of St. Patrick, in original velvet-covered leather scabbard, damaged, with engraved gilt brass mounts, chape missing, the locket signed Brady, 43 Dame St., Dublin, and retaining most of its original gilt finish, 29 in. blade, late 18th C. **£500-900**   *C*

An English or German cross-hilted sword, blade of flattened hollow diamond section changing to flattened hexagonal at the forte, partly inlaid in brass, the hilt entirely of iron, the whole encrusted in silver, rubbed, 35½ in. blade, early 17th C. **£400-700**   *C*

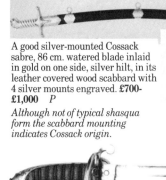

A good silver-mounted Cossack sabre, 86 cm. watered blade inlaid in gold on one side, silver hilt, in its leather covered wood scabbard with 4 silver mounts engraved. **£700-£1,000** *P*

Although not of typical shasqua form the scabbard mounting indicates Cossack origin.

A Russian sword of honour, with straight double-edged blade fluted almost to the point, inscribed 'Fabrica De Toledo Ano De 1864', gilt copper hilt and with double shell guard inscribed in Russian 'For Valour', original leather scabbard, incomplete, 35¼ in. blade, c. 1865. **£500-700** *C*

By tradition presented to Sergei de Wesselitsky Bojidarovitch, 1805-66, from whom it descended to the present owner.

A presentation sabre, the 31½ in. Persian watered steel blade with damascened calligraphy, ebony chequered grip and copper gilt backstrap, inscribed George. Prince. Of. Wales. To. Henry. Lord. Paget. in leather covered scabbard with profusely decorated gilt mounts. **£2,500-3,000** *CSK*

A Victorian 1822 pattern militia infantry officer's sword, slightly curved blade 32½ in., retaining much original polish, original wash leather dress knot, in its steel scabbard. **£50-90** *Wal*

A good Georgian sabre, of a Grenadier Company officer, blade 30 in., by Dawes, Birmingham, in its tooled leather scabbard, c. 1800. **£350-450** *Wal*

A Georgian officer's light cavalry sabre, curved single-edged blade 29½ in., with clipped back tip, retaining nearly all original blued and gilt etched decoration of: crown, 'G.R' 1801-16 Royal Arms, Military Trophies and foliage and maker, within scroll 'King & Bradford', plain copper gilt hilt retaining much original gilding, copper wire bound ribbed ivory grip, in its leather scabbard, very good condition. **£450-550** *Wal*

A good Georgian officer's light cavalry sabre, blade 31 in., copper gilt hilt, diced ivory grip, in its leather scabbard. **£800-900** *Wal*

A George V 1857 pattern Coldstream Guards officer's sword. **£80-100** *Wal*

A steel javelin head, in excavated condition, 13½ in. (34 cm.) long, 9th C. **£100-120** *S*

A Carolingian thrusting spear head, in excavated condition, vertically grooved socket retaining the stump of the original haft, 18¾ in. (47.5 cm.) long, 9th C. **£300-500** *S*

A winged lance head, of Frankish type in excavated condition, socket and wings with deeply cut vertical grooves, cleaned, 24¾ in. (63 cm.) long, 9/10th C. **£400-600** *S*

An Austrian or Italian armour piercing spike, in excavated condition, fitted into the remains of the original haft, length of spike 11¼ in. (28.3 cm.), late 15th C. **£120-150** *S*

Two steel javelin heads, in excavated condition, 20 in. and 18¼ in. long (51 and 46.3 cm.), 11th C. **£150-200** *S*

An Italian glaive (fauchard), 33 in. head, mid 16th C. **£300-400** *C*

A German halberd, the fluke stamped with the maker's mark, a fleurette, studded haft restored, 25 in. long (63.5 cm.), late 16th C. **£1,000-1,500** *S*

Provenance: Joe Kindig Collection.

A German woodknife, broad double-edged blade both sides with long pious inscriptions in Latin and German, some wear, 27¼ in., late 17th C. **£400-600** *S*

A German or Swiss halberd, with later wooden staff, 19½ in., head, early 16th C. **£400-500** *C*

A rare Dutch combination sword-pistol, slightly curved single-edged blade, the left side fitted with 6 in. 2-stage barrel (with muzzle ring), the right side with small swan-neck cock, pan and steel and trigger, 31⅛ in. long overall (79 cm.), mid 17th C. **£2,500-3,500** *S*

A German 7-flanged mace, entirely of steel, the hollow shaft fitted with later suspension rings above the central moulding, 24½ in., probably mid 16th C. **£1,500-2,500** *C*

A German 7 flanged mace, entirely of steel, with round hollow shaft pierced for a thong, 25½ in., 16th C. **£1,000-1,200** *C*

A scarce small size Victorian belt axe, by 'Thornhill London', bearing Crown V.R., the haft of steel, complete with its leather belt pouch, some wear and light pitting, minor crack in one grip and some wear to leather, 11 in. overall. **£80-£120** *WD*

An extremely rare U.S. model 1912 fencing bayonet, with leather covered flexible blade, twisted at the top to give horizontal stiffness and terminating in a bulbous tip, the leather stamped 'R.I.A. 1914 H.E.K.'. **£40-60** *WD*

A Chinese sword, inscription on both sides of blade, 42 in., mid 19th C. **£250-300** *S*

The inscription gives Emperor's name Daoguang and the date 1840.

A mounted wakizashi, by Kanetaka, the blade 54.5 cm. **£1,000-1,500** *S*

A mounted tanto, blade 26.6 cm. **£1,000-1,500** *S*

A rifled flintlock pistol, signed A. Dam, swan-neck cock with some chiselled decoration, walnut stock with steel furniture, pierced silver butt cap engraved with foliage and ornate figures, 15½ in., mid 17th C. **£1,000-1,500** *S*

A pair of flintlock cannon barrel pocket pistols, the breeches engraved 'London', border engraved locks signed 'Paillov', some worm to stocks and damaged overall, c. 1680. **£1,500-2,500** *P*

A pair of 12 bore Spanish miquelet percussion belt pistols, barrels 5 in., with traces of blueing, locks engraved TORRENTO, foliate engraved brass furniture, ramrods and 1 belt hook restored. **£350-400** *Wal*

A Koto Tachi, ascribed to Yukimitsu, blade 72.7 cm. **£1,000-1,500** *S*

A Shinto Tachi, ascribed to Kozuke Daijo Sukesada, blade 67.8 cm. **£800-1,200** *S*

A very fine Japanese sword wakizashi, blade 40 cm., signed 'Heianjo Noju — Yoshihira Saku', inscribed 'Ikkawsih Tadatsona Chokore'. 'Toshikatsu-Shige?' Owner's Name? (Yoshihira working 1681), with 2 mekugi ana, very good condition. **£1,000-1,500** *Wal*

A fine Cossack miquelet-lock holster pistol, with earlier slender twist barrel, inlaid with gold, with gold-filled mark at the breech, gold-damascened lock struck with a mark, 19th C., the barrel probably 17th C., 18 in. **£600-800** *C*

A pair of Central European flintlock pistols, ramrods restored, both stocks cracked and partially restored, 18½ in. long (46 cm.), late 17th C. **£1,800-2,200** *S*

A fine pair of flintlock holster pistols, barrels inscribed 'Londini', engraved flat locks signed 'J. Willowes Fecit', engraved brass mounts including spurred pommels, by John Willowes, London, London proof marks, 16¼ in., c. 1710-15. **£3,000-4,000** *C*

A pair of Brescian flintlock belt pistols, with shortened 2-stage barrels numbered 1 and 2 on the tang, stamped 'Lazarino Cominazzo' on the breech, later silver fore-sights, steel mounts chiselled in relief in the Brescian manner, 17 in., c. 1700. **£3,000-£3,500** *C*

A fine pair of 22 bore German double barrelled flintlock holster pistols, by I. V. Kell, barrels 9½ in., engraved 'I·V·KELL' beneath pans, stocks nicely carved around furniture, horn tipped wooden ramrods and horn fore-caps, good working order and condition, c. 1740. **£2,500-3,000** *Wal*

A Continental flintlock double barrelled over and under pocket pistol, with turn-off canon barrels, push-on safety catches, and silver butt, possibly Russian, 1 top jaw screw and safety catch missing, action faulty, 6¼ in. (16 cm.), mid 18th C. **£680-720** *SC*

A pair of silver-mounted flintlock turn-off pistols, the barrels engraved at the breech and signed below the steel springs, silver mounts cast and chased in relief, engraved with owner's crest, by Richard King, London proof marks, 12¼ in., c. 1740. **£600-800** *C*

A rare pair of flintlock duelling pistols, breeches with platinum-lined maker's stamp, silver escutcheons, original brass-tipped wooden ramrods, in original case with trade label and some accessories, by Thos. Manton, 144 Long Acre, London, No. 198, the barrels forged by William Fullerd, 14¾ in., c. 1820. **£3,500-4,000** *C*

A pair of 28 bore flintlock duelling pistols, by W. Parker, octagonal 10 in. barrels with platinum touch holes and gold lines to breeches, mahogany case with maker's label, pincer mould, flask, cleaning rod, etc. **£1,500-2,000** *SS*

An unusual German miquelet-lock holster pistol, barrel signed 'Georg Hartl' on the fluted breech, wooden trigger guard and ramrod pipes, 1 loose, forn fore-end cap, and later wooden ramrod, stock rubbed and slightly bruised, 13¼ in. barrel, mid 18th C. **£450-550** *C*

The complete absence of metal mounts is a highly unusual feature.

A pair of Turkish percussion cap rifled pistols, chequered butts inlaid with silver wire, gold inlaid trigger guards, 16 in., mid 19th C. **£1,000-1,200** *S*

An unusual over-and-under flintlock pistol, barrels drilled into single block of metal, top flat signed W. Jackson London, struck with London proof marks, 9¾ in., c. 1825. **£1,000-1,300** *S*

A 6 self-shot cocking bar hammer percussion pepperbox revolver, fluted barrel block 3 in., Birmingham proved, 2-piece wooden grips, very good condition. **£375-450** *Wal*

A good 9 mm. Belgian double-barrelled percussion knife pistol, 6 in., damascus barrels 4 in., Liège proved, ribbed hammer spurs, folding triggers and 5 in. shallow diamond section blade, good working order and condition. **£550-£625** *Wal*

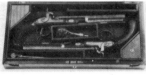

A pair of 26 bore percussion duelling pistols, by Beckwith, octagonal 9¾ in. barrels, stepped locks, converted from flint, some damage, 15 in. overall, in their re-lined mahogany case with label, pincer mould, cleaning rod and replacement flask. **£800-1,000** *SS*

A cased pair of percussion cap travelling pistols, signed J. Lang, Haymarket London, recessed breech with twin platinum lines and plug, London proof marks, iron furniture, in green baize-lined case, cap tin, bullet mould, cleaning rod, lid with trade label of Lang No. 7 Haymarket, 11¾ in., c. 1840. **£800-£1,200** *S*

A pair of metal percussion cap travelling pistols, with Birmingham proof marks, nickel silver frames and saw handle butts, 9 in., c. 1850. **£500-600** *S*

A pair of percussion duelling pistols, with signed barrels, some minor pitting, platinum plugs, signed case-hardened bolted locks, German silver fore-end caps, silver escutcheons, original brass-tipped wooden ramrods, and traces of original finish, in original case, minor wear, with trade label and some accessories, by James Wilkinson & Son, 27 Pall Mall, London, No. 4428 for 1835 15½ in. **£1,500-1,700** *C*

A pair of French percussion duelling or target pistols, 24 cm. barrels, signed on the top flat Gosset à Paris, locks signed in gold within an oval cartouche, close fitted case with some accessories, the pistols retaining much original colour, c. 1850. **£800-1,000**   *P*

A percussion cap Scottish pistol, under side of butt scratched T. Frice, belt hook, ball trigger, ramshorn butt, hammer and nipple lacking, pricker associated, 10¾ in., c. 1840. **£300-500**   *S*

A cased Tranter percussion cap revolver, barrel struck with London proof marks, top strap signed 'Jno Rigby & Co. St. James St. London', 5 chambered cylinder with London proof marks, in green baize-lined mahogany case with bullet mould, powder flask, nipple key, turnscrew, tins and key, 9¾ in., c. 1860. **£600-900**   *S*

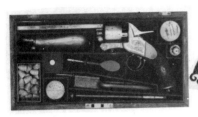

A cased .45 long spur Webley percussion cap revolver, struck with Birmingham proof marks and signed on top flat 'William Henry Fairfax, Birmingham', inscribed 'Webley's Patent', the back strap inscribed 'By Her Majesty's Royal Letters Patent 77¹ˈ, in case with powder flask, cap tin, oil bottle, nipple key, double bullet mould, cleaning rod, spare nipples, 12½ in., c. 1855. **£700-900**   *S*

A Scottish pistol, lock plate signed 'Alexr Campbell', metal stock decorated overall, ramshorn butt with pricker, butt inset with silver ovals with coat-of-arms, 12½ in., mid 19th C. **£1,400-1,700**   *S*

A Turkish flintlock holster pistol, with engraved barrel inlaid with silver and brass, stamped with counterfeit proof marks and the inscription 'L. Lazarino', full stock entirely encased in silver filigree set with corals, 19 in., 19th C. **£300-400**   *C*

A pair of 20 bore French silver-mounted percussion holster pistols, converted from flintlock, barrels 8 in., silver furniture chiselled with flowers, foliage, rocaille and trophies, all struck with an antler control mark, well worn overall. **£450-500**   *Wal*

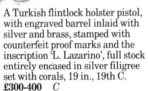

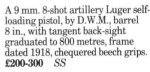

A miquelet flintlock hand mortar, probably a Victorian composite, double diameter brass barrel, bearing a poincon of a coronet over 'UO', 18th C. Italian lock signed inside 'GIACOMO LVCIANI', and walnut stock with brass capped flared butt and iron trigger guard, some bruising and light pitting, 18½ in. overall, 2⅝ in. bore **£1,000-1,500**   *Wal*

A very rare 12 shot .36 in. Walch Navy SA percussion revolver, octagonal barrel 6 in., No. 48, iron frame with side plate to left side, double hammers and triggers. **£450-550**   *Wal*

A 9 mm. 8-shot artillery Luger self-loading pistol, by D.W.M., barrel 8 in., with tangent back-sight graduated to 800 metres, frame dated 1918, chequered beech grips. **£200-300**   *SS*

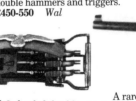

A .22 R.F. 3-shot belt buckle pistol No. 4, the hinged front cover bearing a Nazi Party Eagle, near new, barrels 1¾ in. **£500-600**   *WD*

A rare 7.63 mm. Mauser 'Late Flatside' M.1896 auto pistol, serial No. 22274, with large ring hammer, barrel 5½ in. **£240-280**   *WD*

A rare Nazi black leather carrying case and holster for the 27 mm. Heeres signal pistol or the Kampf pistol, with spaces for 10 cartridges and pocket for pistol, complete with shoulder strap, 13 by 8 in. **£130-160**   *WD*

An unusual needle-fire knife pistol, 2½ in. circular barrel .22 calibre, knife body with single edged 4½ in. blade, central fuller, signed 'Fy Berthod 39 & 41 Passage Jouferoy Paris', a hinged corkscrew serves to release blade and trigger, body with panels of mother-of-pearl, 6½ in., mid 19th C. **£1,000-1,300**   *S*

A rare Nazi 27 mm. hammerless double-barrelled signal pistol, serial No. 6874, dated '44, with maker's code 'EEU', top selector switch for left, right or double shot, barrels 9 in. **£350-500**   *WD*

A German wheel lock gun, fitted
with fore and rear sights, plain lock
with engraved brass wheel cover,
walnut full stock, inlaid with horn
plaques, 39½ in., early 17th C.
£2,000-3,000 *S*

A rare miquelet-lock folding stock
carbine, brass butt plate, original
ramrod with steel and brass tip,
and exposed trigger without guard,
Spanish or Italian, late 17th C.
£750-1,000 *C*

A Japanese matchlock carbine,
with brass action and iron trigger
guard, lacking ramrod, 38 in. long
(96.5 cm.). **£250-300** *SC*

(*t.*) A flintlock sporting gun, signed
rounded lock, later iron-capped
ramrod, the cast and chased silver
escutcheon with traces of a coronet
and double monogram, iron parts
lightly pitted, barrel 36⅛ in., late
17th C., by Thomas Wornall. **£700-
£900**

(*b.*) A rare English dog-lock fowling
piece, with sighted barrel of great
length, iron mounts, single barrel
band, later, and wooden ramrod,
broken, 61½ in. barrel, c. 1640-50.
£1,200-1,600 *C*

A very rare Dutch snap matchlock
target gun, with 2-stage barrel,
struck at the breech with a
standing halberdier mark twice,
similar to the Copenhagen mark,
pan cover missing, in worn
condition throughout, barrel
51½ in., late 17th C. **£500-1,000**
C

*Only about 30 examples of this
distinctive type of gun have
survived.*

A German wheel-lock target rifle,
struck on the underside of the
breech with the mark of Cornelius
Klett of Salzburg, lock struck with
maker's mark 'HKM' on the inside
(for Hans Kaspar Maler?), and
finely engraved, walnut full stock
inlaid with staghorn lines
enclosing engraved staghorn
panels, ramrod replaced, fore-end
incomplete, barrel 45¼ in., late
17th C. **£3,500-4,500** *C*

A Dutch boy's gun, trigger guard
and curved butt cap with grotesque
monster masks and foliage cast and
chiselled in high relief, horn-tipped
ramrod, fore-end of stock restored,
29¼ in. long (74.5 cm.), 18th C.
£800-1,200 *S*

A flintlock blunderbuss, with
3-stage belled brass barrel, spring
bayonet, full brass mounts, and
original horn-tipped wooden
ramrod, unsigned, London proof
marks, steel parts pitted, 29½ in.,
early 19th C. **£450-500** *C*

A rare Prussian military flintlock
musket, by Daun Splittgerber's
Erben, Potsdam, with sighted
barrel, lock inscribed 'Potzdam
Magaz' and signed with initials
'DSE', escutcheon engraved with
the cypher of Frederick the Great,
ramrod missing, varnished
throughout, 41¼ in. barrel, c. 1775.
£750-1,000 *C*

An Italian flintlock blunderbuss,
with belled 3-stage barrel, folding
butt, brass mounts, steel belt hook
and wooden ramrod, probably
Brescian, 32 in., c. 1740. **£500-700**
C

A steel barrel flintlock blunderbuss,
barrel belling at muzzle, lock with
H.E.I.C. mark and date 1776, stock
damaged, 25¾ in., late 18th C.
£300-400 *S*

A flintlock blunderbuss, by
Beckwith, the brass barrel stamped
'London', and with a sprung
bayonet, the lock engraved
'Beckwith', overall minor corrosion
and the cock defective, 78 cm. long
overall. **£500-600** *L*

A flintlock blunderbuss, brass
barrel belling at muzzle, breech
struck with London proof marks,
top flat inscribed 'London', signed
'Taylor', 31 in., late 18th C. **£500-
£1,000** *C*

A muzzle loading percussion cap
gun, 16 in. barrel with bell shape
muzzle, engraved lockplate, walnut
stock and ramrod, 19th C. **£100-150**
BD

A percussion cap sporting gun, by
D. Egg, London, 36 in. barrel,
engraved lockplate and trigger
guard, the walnut stock with
carved chequered grip, ramrod.
£250-350 *BD*

A percussion cap musket, by Fred. Barnes, Tower Hill, London with 30 in. barrel, walnut stock with brass trigger guard and butt cap, ramrod. **£150-200** *BD*

A 22 bore Continental percussion rifle, converted from wheel-lock 44 in., engraved 'Hans Winckler', with brass maker's mark, full-stocked, well worn, some pieces of bone missing or replaced, ramrod missing, some stock cracks. **£400-£450** *Wal*

An 11 bore percussion shot gun, with barrels, shortened, signed on the rib, locks, minor light rust spots throughout, in original fitted veneered case, inscribed 'Fabrique De Lepage à Paris', and with some accessories, Liége proof, barrelsmith's marks of Le Clerc (?), 29¾ in. barrels, c. 1840. **£600-800** *C*

A 16 bore percussion sporting gun, with barrels signed, signature worn, platinum plugs, signed locks, silver escutcheon and brass-tipped ramrod, in pigskin-lined case stamped 'Rampling's', with nearly all accessories including 4 steel chargers, trade label removed, by Joseph Harkom, Edinburgh, London proof marks, No. 130, 29¾ in. barrels, c. 1840. **£450-600** *C*

A double-barrelled percussion cap rifle, the barrels struck beneath breech with London proof marks and numbered 3735, central rib, engraved J. Purdey 314 Oxford Street, London, platinum lines and plugs, ramrod lacking, 44½ in., c. 1840. **£700-1,200** *S*

An 11 bore percussion pigeon gun, of fine quality, engraved platinum plugs, vacant silver escutcheon, no provision for ramrod, in lined and fitted oak and leather 2-tier double case, with trade label, powder flask, and 2 shot flasks, by Joseph Lang & Sons, 22 Cockspur Street, London, No. 3875, 30⅞ in. barrels, c. 1869. **£1,000-1,500** *C*

A German percussion target rifle, signed in gold and with 4 gold breech lines, foliate engraved lock, by G. Camphausen in Crefeld, aperture back-sight, ramrod and 1 pipe missing, 31 in. barrel, c. 1860. **£1,000-1,500** *C*

A Brunswick rifle, signed Clough & Son Bath, full walnut stock with detachable fore-end, brass furniture, hinged brass lid for 2 compartment patch box set in the butt, iron ramrod, bayonet bar mounted at side of muzzle, 46½ in., mid 19th C. **£400-600** *S*

A Henry Atkin 12 bore self-opening side-lock ejector sporting gun. **£3,800-4,200** *S*

A W. W. Greener 12 bore 'Grade L90' sidelock ejector sporting gun, the 27 in. barrels with 2½ in. chambers, serial No. 68810, right bore worn and with slight dents, in leather case with many accessories. **£2,500-3,000** *S*
The gun was completed in 1936.

A pair of 16 bore sidelock ejector guns, by J. Woodward, No. 6148/9, replacement stocks, rebarrelled, chopper-lump, 28 in. barrels, in an oak and leather case. **£8,000-12,000** *C* *Rebarrelled by J. Purdey, c. 1973.*

A Westley Richards 12 bore selective single trigger sidelock ejector sporting gun, 28 in. barrels, locks with gold cocking indicators, serial No. 18264, in a canvas case. **£3,800-4,200** *S*

A pair of John Dickson & Son 12 bore assisted-opening 'round action' ejector sporting guns, 28 in. barrels, serial Nos. 4705/6 in oak and leather case. **£4,700-5,200** *S*
Rebarrelled by the makers, c. 1978.

A J. Woodward & Sons 12 bore sidelock ejector sporting gun, 29 in. barrels, serial No. 5974. **£3,200-£3,400** *S*

A 12 bore sidelock ejector gun, by C. Hellis, No. 4069, stock with recoil pad, 26 in. barrels, in a leather case. **£1,800-2,500** *C* *Sleeved by Hellis in 1979.*

A pair of 12 bore sidelock ejector guns, by W. Powell, No. 13702/3, signed and numbered in gold, 29 in. barrels, triggers set left, in their leather case with canvas cover. **£6,500-7,500** *C*

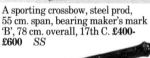

A 12 bore sidelock ejector gun, by J. Purdey, No. 13350, 30 in. barrels. **£4,500-5,500** *C* *Built c. 1889, the gun relatively little used.*

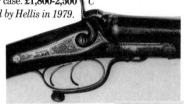

A fine matched pair of John Blissett & Son 12 bore hammer non-ejector sporting guns, 30 in. damascus barrels, serial Nos. 4372 and 4413, No. 1 right bore worn, rechequered, in a leather case. **£2,500-3,500** *S*

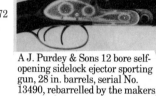

A J. Purdey & Sons 12 bore self-opening sidelock ejector sporting gun, 28 in. barrels, serial No. 13490, rebarrelled by the makers, restocked, in a canvas case. **£4,000-£5,000** *S*

A pump-up air gun, top flat inscribed London, double platinum lines, stepped lockplate, signed Boston, ball reservoir engraved Bullard 37 High Holborn London, wooden ramrod, with spare unsigned reservoir and foot pump with turned wooden handles 19½ in., 49 in., late 18th C. **£1,200-£1,400** *S*

A rare Tudor light sporting crossbow, with steelbow, later string, with later pommel of ivory and wood, inlaid all over with bone or ivory, all replacements, iron lugs for bender, small pierced belt hook with traces of gold damascened scrollwork, and later long trigger lever, trigger safety-stop missing, English, 27 in., mid 16th C. **£1,500-£2,000** *C*

A sporting crossbow, steel prod, 55 cm. span, bearing maker's mark 'B', 78 cm. overall, 17th C. **£400-£600** *SS*

A sporting stone bow, with steel arm and integral spanning lever, struck with maker's mark H.B. above a bird, mechanism slightly defective, 24¾ in. long, 18th C. **£500-800** *S*

A model bronze cannon, on solid walnut carriage with bronze wheels, 21 in. (53.25 cm.) long overall, 19th C. **£300-350** *LBP*

An important bronze rampart gun, 38½ in. long, mid 16th C. **£3,000-£4,000** *CEd*

A Victorian signal cannon, 74 cm. bronze barrel of good form mounted on its oak carriage with brass fittings and brass wheels. **£1,500-£2,000** *P*

A 4-pounder iron carronade, stamped at the breech with B(ailey) P(egg) & Co., and 322 (lb. weight), now mounted on iron bound naval type carriage, the piece 42½ in. long. **£300-400** *CEd*

A Brescian morion, 12 in. (31 cm.) high, late 16th C. **£1,200-1,600** *S*

An impressive pair of bronze barrelled signalling or saluting cannon, on their original carriages, barrels 19¼ in., bore diameter 1⅛ in., 4 bore, early 19th C. **£600-£800** *Wal*

A Cabasset, formed in 1 piece, c. 1600. **£100-150** *Wal*

A fine German close helmet, with 1-piece skull, plume-holder missing, South German, 12 in. high, c. 1560. **£3,500-4,500** *C*

A Cuirassier helmet, with 2-piece skull, later decoration, and later single gorget-plate front and rear, plume-holder missing, 13 in. high, mid 16th C. **£800-1,200** *C*

An Italian siege close helmet and cuirass, of Savoyard type, the helmet and cuirass extensively damaged and pitted throughout, 10¼ in. and 18 in. high, early 17th C. **£1,000-1,400**　*C*

A Cuirassier helmet, minor damage throughout, 12¾ in. high, c. 1630. **£750-1,000**　*C*

(*l.*) A Prussian guard dragoon officer's pickelhaube, printed 'Dodkins Collection' label. **£500-£550**

(*r.*) A Prussian officer's pickelhaube, of the 1st Grenadiers, applied iron cross dated 1813. **£400-450**　*Wal*

An 1834 pattern officer's helmet, of the Inniskillin Dragoons, copper skull, gilt lion, coat of arms missing from helmet plate, gilding worn from skull and slight damage to scrolls. **£800-1,200**　*P*

(*l.*) A Prussian guard infantry officer's pickelhaube, skull age lining overall, some concealing minor gilding wear, silk lining missing. **£300-325**

(*r.*) A Prussian other rank's helmet of the 6th Cuirassier Regiment, chinscales short, and leather repaired, lining worn and loose, inside of skull painted black with minor solder repairs. **£350-450** *Wal*

A fine post-1902 officer's blue cloth ball-topped helmet, of the Royal Artillery, in its tin case, fastener damaged, with engraved brass plate, 'G. L. de la C. Fuller, Esq.' R.G.A. **£225-275**　*Wal*

A very fine Victorian officer's gilt helmet, of the 4th Royal Irish Dragoon Guards, 1871 pattern, gilt fittings throughout, red leather backed gilt ring chinchain and rose bosses, falling white horsehair plume, cloth lining, very good condition. **£600-675**　*Wal*

A scarce Victorian officer's lance cap, of the 12th, Prince of Wales's Royal Lancers, chinchain backing and leather sweat-band in lining restored, good condition for age, c. 1856. **£750-1,000**　*Wal*

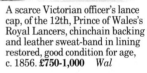

A good officer's lance cap, of the 16th Lancers, plume holder with bullion surround, c. 1905. **£600-800** *S*

(*l.*) A Bavarian infantry officer's pickelhaube, leather backed brass chinscales, silk lining. **£240-280**

(*r.*) A Prussian officer's pickelhaube, of the 16th Dragoons silvered 'Dragon' eagle HP with 'Waterloo' battle honour, skull age crazed and congealed overall, lining some wear, neck guard slightly mis-shapen. **£275-300**　*Wal*

A fine post-1902 officer's uniform, of the 21st (Empress of India's) Lancers, the whole in good condition, the gilt generally sound overall, silk lining to inside of cap damaged, lining to inside of collar worn, reverse of pouch leather scuffed. **£2,000-2,500**　*Wal*

A very fine post-1902 officer's silvered helmet, of the Life Guards, old tailor's label inside reads: '25/6/25 Lord Allenby 7⅜ full.', very good condition, silk lining worn in parts. **£1,500-2,250**　*Wal*

(*l.*) A scarce Edward VII other ranks helmet, of the King's Own Norfolk Imperial Yeomanry. **£300-£350**

(*r.*) A Victorian officer's helmet, of the Fife Light Horse. **£450-550** *Wal*

A very fine post-1902 officer's silvered helmet, of the Sussex Yeomanry. **£1,250-1,500**　*Wal*

A duelling gauntlet, of blackened
steel, wrist of articulates lames and
fingers of small scales overlapping
in the reverse way to normal,
14½ in., c. 1630. **£750-1,000**   C

A rare white metal parade eagle,
from a Prussian Garde du Corps
other ranks parade helmet, 8½ in.
£250-350   *Wal*

A fine late Victorian other ranks
silvered helmet, of the Derbyshire
Yeomanry, in very good condition.
£425-500   *Wal*

*It is unusual to find other ranks
helmets in such good condition. The
skull is almost perfect.*

A buff coat, sleeveless and made of
sections of leather stitched
together, cloth-lined, mid 17th C.,
and a pair of buff-leather gauntlets
with flared cuffs, 17th C., coat
29½ in. high. **£600-800**   C

A composite shot-proof half-armour,
cuirass struck with the Nuremberg
mark, on a wooden stand,
comprehensively German, 17th C.
£2,500-3,500   C

A composite full armour, of bright
steel, close helmet perhaps
Innsbruck, gorget perhaps
Greenwich, struck with the
Nuremberg mark, on wooden
dummy, comprehensively German,
mid to late 16th C., the helmet
c. 1550. **£6,000-8,000**   C

A German composite half-armour,
of bright steel, helmet probably
Brunswick, full arm defences
including mitten gauntlet for the
left hand only struck with the
Nuremberg mark, cuirass struck
with the Augsburg mark, retaining
many original leathers, on wooden
stand, comprehensively late
16th C., the helmet c. 1560. **£3,500-
£4,500**   C

A Hungarian shield, of painted
leather-covered wood,
probably South German, 36¾ in.,
mid 16th C. **£10,000-12,000**   C

*This is a shield of a type used in the
Hussar tournaments that became
popular at the Habsburg Court in
the middle of the 16th C. The arms
are those of the Barons Dufenbach
of Austria.*

A composite half-armour, all the
main edges turned, on a wooden
stand, probably German, early
17th C. **£800-1,200**   C

A German composite black and
white half-armour, fingered
gauntlets with long cuffs, retaining
original buff leather gloves, on
wooden stand, comprehensively
late 16th C. **£4,000-5,000**   C

A rare Italian steel buckler,
engraved Monce Rigo, Doge,
Venezia and dated 1566 in Roman
numerals, 33.5 cm. diam. **£1,200-
£1,600**   P

A scarce Imperial German
cavalryman's parade uniform,
believed of the Garde du Corps,
white tunic with scarlet piping and
cuffs, with silver bullion cloth
facings, with plain, silver-plated
buttons, very slight surface
mothing to tunic, overalls some
stitching repairs at seams, some
surface moth and minor stains.
£750-1,000   *Wal*

A Saxon powder-flask, with blued
iron mounts including belt hook,
with original silk cords and silver-
net covered tassels, worn, 9¼ in.
high, early 17th C. **£1,000-1,250**
C

*The inscription refers to the Elector
Christian II of Saxony, 1591-1611.*

An Italian powder-flask, entirely of
steel, 8½ in. high, early 17th C.
£500-900   C

A horn powder-flask, engraved with a hunter, his dog, birds and trees and the name S John Mason 1613, 9 in. (23 cm.) long, early 17th C. **£450-500**   *S (WJS)*

A pear-shaped common top Hawksley gun flask, the telescopic nozzle graduated 2¼-3 drams, minor dents, 8 in. overall. **£20-30**   *WD*

An Indian ivory powder-flask, silver hanging rings and chain, late 18th C. **£150-250**   *P*

A fine French stiffened leather shot or powder-flask, in the manner of Bagard à Nancy, 11 in. (28 cm.) wide, early 18th C. **£1,200-1,800**   *S*

A good quality 18th C. eprouvette, with turned rosewood handle, and a sleeper with good age patina, 9 in. overall. **£80-120**   *WD*

A brass side drum, of the 1st. Battalion Grenadier Guards, maker's name Potter, Aldershot, and a pair of drumsticks. **£250-300**   *Wal*

A copper 3-way powder-flask, with hinged cavity for 12 bore balls, 4¼ in. **£75-100**   *Wal*

A flintlock eprouvette, plain brass barrel with attached brass wheel numbered I to XII, 6¾ in., c. 1770. **£300-350**   *S*

An Indo-Portuguese powder-horn, 18th C. **£250-450**   *SS*

A clay pigeon thrower, 31 in. cocked, early 20th C. **£40-60**   *S*

A pair of gunner's callipers, iron-tipped brass arms, signed Elliott Bros., 30, Strand, London, 21¼ in. (54 cm.), mid 19th C. **£300-400**   *S*

A George III oval Masonic medal, engraved on 1 side with 2 bare-breasted angels, Masonic emblems and the motto 'Holiness to the Lord', the other with Masonic emblems and motto 'Sit Lux et Lux Fuit', by Thomas Harper II, 1817. **£50-60** *P*

A large mahogany Masonic chair, with demi-lune crest inlaid with square and compass, mid 19th C. **£170-200** *Bon*

An opaque twist wine glass, with Beilby-style enamelling, decorated with the jewels of the Master and Senior Warden and other emblems in white enamels edged in pink, on multi-spiral and double thread stem, chip to foot-rim, 15 cm., 18th C. **£500-600** *Bon*

A Georgian silver past masters collar jewel, of Gallows type, by Thomas Harper. **£100-140** *Bon*

A good Masonic glass jug, engraved with 2 windows of Masonic emblems and a ribboned circular monogram, 18 cm., c. 1780. **£200-£250** *Bon*

A Liverpool porcelain tankard, the body printed with entwining various Masonic symbols and incorporating 3 emblematic figures in 18th C. dress, 12.2 cm. **£300-350** *Bon*

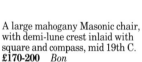

A rare Georgian Masonic plate jewel, engraved at each side with various emblems including those of rank, 6.5 cm., late 18th/early 19th C. **£85-115** *Bon*

A Georgian silver gilt Royal arch breast jewel, by Thomas Harper, pierced with the ark of the covenant flanked by columns and below the arch and 'all seeing eye', 6.8 cm., dated 1820. **£100-130** *Bon*

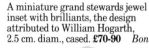

A miniature grand stewards jewel inset with brilliants, the design attributed to William Hogarth, 2.5 cm. diam., cased. **£70-90** *Bon*

A Georgian silver gilt Royal arch breast jewel, by Thomas Harper, dated 1803, and a further engraved No. 244, Thomas Harper Fleet Street Fecit, 7 cm. **£90-120** *Bon*

A rare Georgian plate jewel of pierced type, with an 'all seeing eye' and ribboned motto 'Amor Honor et Justitia' reversed by similar decoration and motto 'Sit Lux et Lux Fuit', 6 cm., late 18th/early 19th C. **£130-160** *Bon*

A sheet brass hanging lantern, the sides pierced in the form of square and compass within a roundel, the base with travel motifs, all within border of star and half-moons, the hood engraved with Masonic emblems and Latin script, the windows glazed with panels of sheet horn, 40 cm. high. **£300-350** *Bon*

A rare Georgian silver plate jewel, engraved with Masonic emblems and Lodge No. 7 E.L., 4.5 cm. diam. **£120-160** *Bon*

Lodge No. 7, the Tuscan Lodge, is now No. 14, E.L. are the initials of Edward Lloyd. This name appears in registers for 1795 and again in 1797 together with the Trade of Poulterer.

WINE

London is, and always has been, the world market place for fine wine; the two main auction houses involved with the sale of wines being Christies and, since 1970, Sotheby's. Both of these auctioneers have departments specialising in the valuation and sale of wines and spirits.

Amongst the wines regularly sold at auction there are some which actually qualify as 'antique' if the word is defined as meaning an item at least 100 years old. These are understandably extremely rare and the majority of wines sold are from more recent vintages!

Prices of fine wines have increased steadily during the 1984 season. The attractive exchange rate between the U.S. dollar and sterling has brought large numbers of American buyers to London and purchases for the American market have done much to ensure high, and in some cases record, prices for rare items. Demand for mature vintages of Claret and Burgundy has remained strong with most wines selling over their estimated price.

Château Lafite — 1899. Vintage Pauillac, 1er cru classé. Château-bottled. Perfect capsule, label and level.
I bottle. **£600-650**   C

Imperial Tokay — c. 1840. Contemporary clear glass straight-sided bottle with baluster neck and prominent string lip. Height 21 cm. Remains of wax seal. Good level. Bright amber colour and natural light flaky sediment.
I half-bottle. **£150-160**   C
From the collection of the late Dennis Wheatley sold at Christie's in November, 1968.

The wines listed below provide an illustration of the levels of price increases since 1980. The wines quoted represent the top level of the market and the vintages shown are amongst those recognised as the finest of the last 20 years.

RED BORDEAUX

	Price in 1980	Price in 1984
Château Lafite		
Pauillac. 1er Cru Classé		
1961 1 dozen bottles	£750-800	£2,200-2,500
1966 1 dozen bottles	£450-500	£1,100-1,200
1970 1 dozen bottles	£275-325	£850-900
Château Latour		
Pauillac. 1er Cru Classé		
1961 1 dozen bottles	£550-600	£1,800-2,200
1966 1 dozen bottles	£250-275	£900-1,100
1970 1 dozen bottles	£250-325	£650-750
Château Margaux		
Margaux. 1er Cru Classé		
1961 1 dozen bottles	£500-600	£1,800-2,100
1966 1 dozen bottles	£225-275	£750-850
1970 1 dozen bottles	£225-275	£550-650
Château Mouton-Rothschild		
Pauillac. 1er Cru Classé		
1961 1 dozen bottles	£650-850	£2,000-2,250
1966 1 dozen bottles	£250-350	£800-900
1970 1 dozen bottles	£225-350	£700-750
Château Haut-Brion		
Pessac (Graves). 1er Cru Classé		
1961 1 dozen bottles	£550-650	£1,550-1,650
1966 1 dozen bottles	£250-300	£700-800
1970 1 dozen bottles	£150-225	£500-600

	Price in 1980	Price in 1984
Château Cheval-Blanc		
St. Emilion. 1er Grand Cru Classé		
1961 1 dozen bottles	£525-625	£1,450-1,550
1966 1 dozen bottles	£225-275	£675-725
1970 1 dozen bottles	£200-300	£525-550
Château Petrus		
Pomerol. Cru Exceptionnel		
1961 1 dozen bottles	£1,600-1,700	£4,500-5,500
1966 1 dozen bottles	£600-700	£2,000-2,750
1970 1 dozen bottles	£475-550	£2,000-2,200
Château Palmer		
Cantenac (Margaux). 3me Cru Classé		
1961 1 dozen bottles	£550-650	£1,500-2,000
1966 1 dozen bottles	£200-300	£600-700
1970 1 dozen bottles	£175-250	£550-650

WHITE BORDEAUX

	Price in 1980	Price in 1984
Château d'Yquem		
Sauternes. 1er Grand Cru Classé		
1961 1 dozen bottles	£450-500	£950-1,150
1967 1 dozen bottles	£350-450	£1,100-1,200
1970 1 dozen bottles	£225-275	£375-475

PORT

	Price in 1980	Price in 1984
Cockburn		
1963 1 dozen bottles	£80-100	£190-230
1967 1 dozen bottles	£65-85	£100-150
1970 1 dozen bottles	£65-80	£90-130
Dow		
1963 1 dozen bottles	£90-120	£200-240
1966 1 dozen bottles	£70-100	£175-200
1970 1 dozen bottles	£60-80	£110-130
Graham		
1963 1 dozen bottles	£80-120	£250-300
1966 1 dozen bottles	£70-90	£180-220
1970 1 dozen bottles	£65-90	£125-145

Liebfraumilch Auslese —
Vintage 1921.
H. Sichel Sohne. Excellent
lead capsule. Pictorial body
label in good condition apart
from slight tear in one corner,
depicting nuns gathering
grapes. Neck label. Excellent
level.
I half-bottle. **£50-60**   *C*

*An unusually rare and
interesting label of what is now
the famous 'Blue Nun' brand
first registered in Germany in
1925. 1921 was of course the
greatest vintage of the period,
probably the best between 1865
and 1949.*

Napoléon, Grande Fine
Champagne Réserve Cognac
— 1811. Glass shoulder button
embossed 'N'. Plain lead
capsule, slightly damaged.
I bottle. **£175-200**   *C*

Château Lafite — Vintage
1961.
Pauillac Ier cru classé.
Château-bottled Impeccable
label. Level excellent.
I impériale, in original case.
£3,300-3,500   *C*
Very rare in this size.

Tokay Aszu, 6 putts —
Vintage 1866.
Tokay Hegyaluavideki
Borkereskedelmi, Madi
Pinceszet. Very good label and
excellent level.
I half-litre. **£120-130**   *C*

La Tâche — Vintage 1945.
Domaine de la Romanée-Conti.
I bottle. **£450-500**   *C*

*Magnificent. Rare. Still
remarkably deep coloured and
youthful looking.*

Salignac, Grande Fine
Champagne — 1929.
Embossed lead capsule.
Labelled, 'Shipped by L. de
Salignac & Co., Cognac'. Good
appearance.
I bottle. **£45-50**   *C*

Believed Château Lafite —
Vintage 1864.
Lead capsule embossed
'Cockburn & Campbell, Claret
1864'. Christie's slip-label
only. Level top-shoulder, very
good for age.
I magnum. **£500-550**   *C*

Château d'Yquem — Vintage
1900.
Label slightly torn. Level
upper-shoulder, very good for
age. Excellent colour.
I bottle. **£600-650**   *C*

Imperial Tokay — 1711.
Reputed to have originally
come from the cellar of
Napoléon Bonaparte. In old
dark-coloured handblown
bottle with slight seepage from
cork. Wax seal disintegrated.
Level to bottom-shoulder.
I small bottle.   **£280-350**   *C*

Château Lafite — Vintage
1854.
In original slender, tapering
necked mid 19th C. Bordeaux
bottle with embossed château
capsule. Label in excellent
condition. Level very good for
age, 2 in. (5 cm.) below cork.
Colour normal for vintage and
age. 'Rebouche fait au château
en Mars 1953' on slip-label.
I bottle. **£1,600-1,700**   *C*

Château d'Arche, Crème de
Tête — Vintage 1920.
Sauternes, 2 me cru classé.
Fournufrères, Kappelhoff &
Co., Bordeaux.
Branded corks, rare.
2 bottles. **£575-625**   *C*

DIRECTORY OF SPECIALISTS

This directory is in no way complete. If you wish to be included in next year's directory, or you have a change of address or telephone number, please could you inform us before April 1st, 1985. Finally we would advise readers to make contact by telephone before a visit is made, therefore avoiding a wasted journey, which nowadays is both time consuming and expensive.

Any entry followed by (R) denotes a specialist who undertakes restoration work.

ART DECO & ART NOUVEAU

LONDON

Antique Emporium
965 Fulham Rd., S.W.5
Tel: 01-731 2814

Baptista Arts
Stand D3/4, Chenil Galleries
183 King's Rd., S.W.3
Tel: 01-581 2231

Butler & Wilson
189 Fulham Rd., S.W.3
Tel: 01-352 3045

Chilton
Stand A11/12, Chenil Galleries
181-183 King's Rd., S.W.3
No tel.

T. Coakley
Stand D13, Chenil Galleries
181-183 King's Rd., S.W.3
Tel: 01-351 2914

Cobra & Bellamy
149 Sloane St., S.W.1
Tel: 01-730 2823

Cobweb
2 Englands Lane, N.W.3
Tel: 01-586 4605

Ebury
89 Ebury St., S.W.1
Tel: 01-730 3341

Editions Graphiques Gallery
3 Clifford St., W.1
Tel: 01-734 3944

The Facade
196 Westbourne Grove, W.11
Tel: 01-727 2159

Galerie 1900
267 Camden High St., N.W.1
(*also at* 80 Grosvenor St., W.1)
Tel: 01-485 1001

Galerie Moderne
8 Halkin Arcade
Motcombe St., S.W.1
Tel: 01-235 8353

Gallery '25
4 Halkin Arcade, Motcomb St., S.W.1
Tel: 01-235 5178

David Gill (appointment only)
25 Palace Gate, W.8
Tel: 01-584 9184

Jones
194 Westbourne Grove, W.11
Tel: 01-229 6866

Lewis M. Kaplan Associates Ltd.
50 Fulham Rd., S.W.3
Tel: 01-589 3108

Dan Klein Ltd.
11-12 Halkin Arcade
Motcomb St., S.W.1
Tel: 01-245 9868

Lighting Lee (Antique Forum Ltd.)
Stand 324/5 Alfie's Antique Market
13-25 Church St., N.W.8
Tel: 01-286 0859

John & Diana Lyons Gallery
47-49 Mill Lane, West Hampstead
N.W.6
Tel: 01-794 3537

Pruskin Gallery
183 King's Road, S.W.3
Tel: 01-352 9095

BERKS.

Lupin Antiques
134 Peascod St., Windsor
Tel: (07535) 56244

LANCS.

A. S. Antiques
26 Broad St., Salford
Tel: (061737) 5938

LEICS.

Birches Antique Shop
15 Francis St., Stoneygate, Leicester
Tel: (0533) 703235

SURREY

Galerie 39
39 Kew Road, Richmond
Tel: 01-948 1633 & 3337

Peter & Debbie Gooday
20 Richmond Hill, Richmond
Tel: 01-940 8652

SUSSEX

Armstrong-Davis Gallery
The Square, Arundel
Tel: (0903) 882752

WARWICKSHIRE

Studio
Warwick Antique Centre
High St., Warwick
Tel: (0926) 41382

YORKS.

Dragon Antiques
10 Dragon Rd., Harrogate
Tel: (0423) 62037

SCOTLAND

The Rendezvous Gallery
100 Forest Ave., Aberdeen
Tel: (0224) 323247

ARMS & MILITARIA

LONDON

Nimrod Dix & Co.
17 Piccadilly Arcade, W.1
Tel: 01-493 5082

Tradition
5a Shepherd Street, W.1
Tel: 01-493 7452

GLOS.

The Curiosity Shop
80-84 Southgate St., Gloucester
Tel: (0452) 27716

SUSSEX

J. R. Barrett
63 Spences Lane, Lewes
Tel: (079 16) 3268

Military Antiques (by appt. only)
42 Janes Lane, Burgess Hill
Tel: (04446) 3516 & 43088

YORKS.

The Antiques Shop
226 Harrogate Rd., Leeds
Tel: (0532) 681785

Andrew Spencer Bottomley
32 Rotcher Hill, Holmfirth
Tel: (0484) 685234

WALES

Hermitage Antiques
10 West St., Fishguard
Tel: (0348) 873037

BOXES, TREEN & WOODEN OBJECTS

LONDON

Simon Castle
38B Kensington Church St., W.8
Tel: 01-937 2268

Halcyon Days
14 Brook St., W.1
Tel: 01-629 8811

AVON

Andrew Dando
4 Wood St., Queen Sq., Bath
Tel: (0225) 22702

BERKS.

Charles Toller
20 High St., Datchet
Tel: (0753) 42903

BUCKS.

A. & E. Foster
Little Heysham, Forge Rd., Naphill
Tel: (024024) 2024

HANTS.

House of Antiques
4 College St., Petersfield
Tel: (0730) 62172

KENT

Imogen Nichols Antiques
The Farriers Cottage
St. Nicholas-at-Wade, Nr. Birchington
Tel: (0843) 81237

LEICS.

Stable Antiques
14 Loughborough Rd., Hoton
Nr. Loughborough
Tel: (0509) 880208

CAMERAS

LONDON

Sean Sexton
Stand 606, Alfie's Antique Market
13-25 Church St., N.W.8
Tel: 01-723 1370

Vintage Cameras Ltd.
254/256 Kirkdale, Sydenham, S.E.26
Tel: 01-778 5416

CARPETS

LONDON

David Black Oriental Carpets
96 Portland Rd., Holland Park, W.11
Tel: 01-727 2566

Hindustan Carpets Ltd.
B. Block, 53/79 Highgate Rd., N.W.5
Tel: 01-485 7766

Mayfair Carpet Gallery
6-8 Old Bond St., W.1
Tel: 01-493 0126/7

Vigo Sternberg Galleries
37 South Audley St., W.1
Tel: 01-629 8307

BUCKS.

Swillet Rug Restorations (R)
22 Lodge Lane, Chalfont-St.-Giles
Tel: (02404) 4776

DORSET

J. L. Arditti
88 Bargates, Christchurch
Tel: (0202) 485414

SOM.

M. & A. Lewis
Oriental Carpets & Rugs
8 North St., Wellington
Tel: (082347) 7430

SUSSEX

Lindfield Galleries Ltd.
59 High St., Lindfield
Tel: (04447) 3817

YORKS.

Omar (Harrogate) Ltd.
8-10 Crescent Rd., Harrogate
Tel: (0423) 503675/69587

SCOTLAND

Whytock & Reid
Sunbury House, Belford Mews
Edinburgh
Tel: 031-226 4911

CLOCKS & BAROMETERS

LONDON

Asprey & Co. PLC
165-169 New Bond St., W.1
Tel: 01-493 6767

Bobinet Ltd.
102 Mount St., W.1
Tel: 01-408 0333/4

Aubrey Brocklehurst
124 Cromwell Rd., S.W.7
Tel: 01-373 0319

Camerer Cuss & Co.
17 Ryder St., St. James's, S.W.1
Tel: 01-930 1941

J. Carlton Smith
17 Ryder St., St. James's, S.W.1
Tel: 01-930 6622

Chelsea Clocks
Antiquarius, 135 King's Rd., S.W.3
Tel: 01-352 8646

The Clock Clinic Ltd.
85 Lower Richmond Rd., S.W.15
Tel: 01-788 1407

John Craggs Ltd.
15/17 King St., St. James's, S.W.1
Tel: 01-930 3817

Philip & Bernard Dombey
174 Kensington Church St., W.8
Tel: 01-229 7100

Garner & Marney Ltd.
41/43 Southgate Rd., N.1
Tel: 01-226 1535

Keith Harding, F.B.H.I. (R)
93 Hornsey Rd., N.7
Tel: 01-607 6181/2672

E. Hollander Ltd.
80 Fulham Rd., S.W.3
Tel: 01-589 7239

Gerald Mathias (R)
R5/6 Antiquarius
135 King's Rd., S.W.3
Tel: 01-351 0484

North London Clock Shop Ltd. (R)
72 Highbury Park, N.5
Tel: 01-226 1609

R. E. Rose, F.B.H.I.
731 Sidcup Rd., Eltham, S.E.9
Tel: 01-859 4754

Strike One (Islington) Ltd.
51 Camden Passage, N.1
Tel: 01-226 9709

Temple Brooks
12 Mill Lane, N.W.6
Tel: 01-452 9696

Volpone
12 Wynyatt St., Clerkenwell, E.C.1
Tel: 01-837 5686

AVON

The Clock Shop
9 Walcot St., Bath
Tel: (0225) 62756

Smith & Bottrill
The Clock House, 17 George St., Bath
Tel: (0225) 22809

BERKS.

Medalcrest Ltd.
Charnham House, Charnham St.
Hungerford
Tel: (0488) 84157

The Old Malthouse
15 Bridge St., Hungerford
Tel: (04886) 2209

Times Past Antiques Ltd.
59 High St., Eton
Tel: (07535) 57018

BUCKS.

The Guild Room, The Lee
Great Missenden
Tel: (024020) 463

CAMBS.

Rodney T. Firmin
16 Magdalene St., Cambridge
Tel: (0223) 67372

CHESHIRE

Peter Bosson Antiques
10B Swan St., Wilmslow
Tel: (0625) 525250/527857

Coppelia Antiques
Holford Lodge, Plumley Moor Rd.
Plumley
Tel: (056581) 2197

CORNWALL

Charles Jackson Antiques
48, 49 & 50 Market Jew St., Penzance
Tel: (0736) 4388/3774

Ian Tuck (R)
The Friary, Trethurgy, St. Austell
Tel: (0726) 850039

CUMBRIA

Don Burns
The Square, Ireby, Carlisle
Tel: (09657) 477

The Old Man Antiques
Coniston
Tel: (09664) 389

DERBYS.

Derby Clocks
974 London Rd., Derby
Tel: (0332) 74996

D. J. Mitchell, Temple Antiques
Glenwood Lodge, Temple Walk
Matlock, Bath
Tel: (0629) 4253

DORSET

Good Hope Antiques
2 Hogshill Street, Beaminster
Tel: (0308) 862119

Tom Tribe & Son
Bridge St., Sturminster Newton
Tel: (0258) 72311

ESSEX

It's About Time (R)
863 London Rd., Westcliff-on-Sea
Tel: (0702) 72574/205204

Littlebury Antiques
58/60 Fairycroft Rd., Saffron Walden
Tel: (0799) 27961

Simpson Antiques
44 Lower St., Stanstead Mountfichet
Tel: (0279) 813388

Tempus Fugit (appointment only)
c/o Trinity House, Trinity St.
Halstead
Tel: (0787) 475409

Trinity Clocks
26 Trinity St., Colchester
Tel: (0206) 46458

GLOS.

J. & M. Bristow Antiques
28 Long St., Tetbury
Tel: (0666) 52222

Michael G. Cox (appointment only)
Avon House, Market Place, Tetbury
Tel: (0666) 52201

George Curtis
14 Suffolk Parade, Cheltenham
Tel: (0242) 513828

Colin Elliott
4 Great Norwood St., Cheltenham
Tel: (0242) 528590

Saxton House Gallery
High St., Chipping Camden
Tel: (0386) 840278

HANTS.

Charles Antiques
101 The Hundred, Romsey
Tel: (0794) 512885

E. F. P. Dobson
6 Valley Rd., Chandlers Ford
Tel: (04215) 2335

Evans & Evans
40 West St., Alresford
Tel: (096273) 2170

Gerald E. Marsh
32A The Square, Winchester
Tel: (0962) 54505

HEREFORD

G. & V. Taylor Antiques
Winforton Court, Winforton
Tel: (05446) 226

HERTS.

Country Clocks (R)
3 Pendley Bridge Cottages
Tring Station, Tring
Tel: (044282) 5090

John de Haan
12A Seaforth Drive, Waltham Cross
Tel: (0992) 763111 & (0920) 2534

ISLE OF WIGHT

Museum of Clocks
Alum Bay
Tel: (0983) 754193

KENT

Nigel Coleman Antiques
High St., Brasted
Tel: (0959) 64042

Hadlow Antiques
No. 1 The Pantiles, Tunbridge Wells
Tel: (0892) 29858

Henry Hall Antique Clocks
19 Market Square, Westerham
Tel: (0959) 62200

Imperial Antiques
1 Royal Parade, Chislehurst
Tel: 01-467 8020

The Old Clock Shop
63 High St., West Malling
Tel: (0732) 843246

Derek Roberts Antiques
24 Shipbourne Rd., Tonbridge
Tel: (0732) 358986

Malcolm G. Styles (R)
66 Culverden Park Rd.
Tunbridge Wells
Tel: (0892) 30699

LANCS.

Ken Weigh (R)
Signwriting & Numbering
9 Links Rd., Blackpool
Tel: (0253) 52097

LEICS.

G. K. Hadfield
Blackbrook Hill House, Tickow Lane
Shepshed
Tel: (05095) 3014

C. Lowe & Sons Ltd. (R)
37-40 Churchgate, Loughborough
Tel: (0509) 217876

MERSEYSIDE

T. Brown, Horological Restorers (R)
12 London Rd., Liverpool 3
Tel: (051709) 4048

MIDDX.

Court House Antiques
19 Market Place, Brentford
Tel: 01-560 7074 & (09322) 27186

Onslow Clocks
36 Church St., Twickenham
Tel: 01-892 7632

NORFOLK

Delawood Antiques & Clock
Restoration (R)
10 Westgate, Hunstanton
Tel: (04853) 2903

NORTHUMBERLAND

Prudhoe Cottage Antiques
15 St. Mary's Chare, Hexham
Tel: (0434) 605522 & (0661) 33421

OXON.

Peter Fell of Thame
81 High St., Thame
Tel: (084421) 4487

Laurie Leigh Antiques
36 High St., Oxford
Tel: (0865) 244197

Telling Time
57 North St., Thame
Tel: (084421) 3007

Witney Antiques
96-98 Corn St., Witney
Tel: (0993) 3902

SOMERSET

Bernard G. House, Mitre Antiques
13 Market Place, Wells
Tel: (0749) 72607

Edward A. Nowell
21-23 Market Place, Wells
Tel: (0749) 72415

Matthew Willis, Antique Clocks
22 Silver St., Glastonbury
Tel: (0458) 32103

SUFFOLK

Bullivant Antiques (R)
White Gates, Elmswell Rd.
Great Ashfield
Tel: (0359) 40040

Score Antiques
1 & 2 The Score, Beccles
Tel: (0473) 2927

SURREY

Abbott Antiques (appointment only)
158 Ember Lane, Esher
Tel: 01-398 2984

The Clock Shop
64 Church St., Weybridge
Tel: (0932) 40407/55503

Roger A. Davis
Antiquarian Horologist
19 Dorking Rd., Great Bookham
Tel: (0372) 57655/53167

Horological Workshops
204 Worplesdon Rd., Guildford
Tel: (0483) 576496

Geoffrey Stevens
26-28 Church Road, Guildford
Tel: (0483) 504075

Surrey Clock Centre
3 Lower St., Haslemere
Tel: (0428) 4547

SUSSEX

Adrian Alan Ltd.
4 Frederick Place, Brighton
Tel: (0273) 25277

Bay Tree House Ltd.
19 Middle St., Brighton
Tel: (0273) 24688

The Clock Shop
51 London Rd., St. Leonards-on-Sea
Tel: (0424) 436984

Dean House Antiques
Bepton Rd., Midhurst
Tel: (073081) 2277

WEST MIDLANDS

Osborne's (R)
91 Chester Rd., New Oscott
Sutton Coldfield
Tel: (021355) 6667

WILTS.

Andre Davis Ltd.
Church House, 26 High St.
Bromham, Chippenham
Tel: (0380) 850347

P. A. Oxley
The Old Rectory, Cherhill, Nr. Calne
Tel: (0249) 812742

YORKS.

The Clock Shop
Hilltop House, Bellerby, Nr. Leyburn
Tel: (0969) 22596

The Dusty Miller Gallery
Low Laithe, Pateley Bridge
Tel: (0423) 780515

Haworth Antiques (R)
Harrogate Rd., Huby, Nr. Leeds
Tel: (0423) 74293

and at

West Park Antiques Pavilion
20 West Park, Harrogate
Tel: (0423) 61758

Windsor House Antiques (Leeds) Ltd.
18-20 Benson St., Leeds
Tel: (0532) 444666

SCOTLAND

Browns of Argyle St. Ltd.
1060 Argyle St., Glasgow
Tel: (041) 248 6760

Dareau Antique Clocks
66 Cumberland St., Edinburgh
Tel: (031) 556 0352

Christopher Wood
(appointment only)
Harlaw House, Kelso
Tel: (05737) 321

WALES

Derek Rayment Antiques (R)
42 Alyn Drive, Rossett
Nr. Wrexham, Clwyd
Tel: (0244) 570869

Swansea County & W.P. Ltd.
49 St. Helen's Rd., Swansea
Tel: (0792) 53334

DOLLS, TOYS & GAMES

LONDON

Stuart Cropper
Gray's Mews, 1-7 Davies Mews, W.1
Tel: 01-499 6600

Donay Antiques
12 Pierrepont Row, N.1
Tel: 01-359 1880

Engine 'n' Tender
19 Spring Lane, Woodside, S.E.25
Tel: 01-654 0386

Glenlea Gallery
109 Thurlow Park Rd., S.E.21
Tel: 01-670 3161

Lead Soldier, Antiquarius
135 King's Rd., S.W.3
Tel: 01-352 8734

Pete McAskie
Stand D10-12, Basement, Grays
Mews Antiques, 1-7 Davies Mews
W.1
Tel: 01-629 2813

The Dolls House Toys Ltd.
29 The Market, Covent Gdn., W.C.2
Tel: 01-379 7243

The Singing Tree
69 New King's Road, S.W.6
Tel: 01-736 4527

CORNWALL

Mrs. Margaret Chesterton
33 Pentewan Rd., St. Austell
Tel: (0726) 2926

DORSET

Hobby Horse Antiques
29 & 5 (at Bridge) West Allington
Bridport
Tel: (0308) 22801

GLOS.

Antique Dolls' Shop & Dolls' Hospital
Days Stable, Sheep St.
Stow-on-the-Wold
Tel: (0451) 30381

China Doll
31 Suffolk Parade, Cheltenham
Tel: (0242) 33164

KENT

Hadlow Antiques
1 The Pantiles, Tunbridge Wells
Tel: (0892) 29858

SOMERSET

Min Lewis Antiques
Southfield House, Rode
Tel: (0373) 830531

STAFFS.

Multro Ltd.
10 Madeley St., Tunstall,
Stoke-on-Trent
Tel: (0782) 813621

SURREY

Curiosity Shop
72 Stafford Rd., Wallington
Tel: 01-647 5267

Doll Shop (appointment only)
18 Richmond Hill, Richmond
Tel: 01-940 6774

Past & Presents
52 High St., Thames Ditton
Tel: 01-398 0962

W. MIDLANDS

Meriden House Antiques
75 Market St., Stourbridge
Tel: (03843) 5384

YORKS.

Tim Armitage
Vintage Toyshop, 498 Bradford Rd.
Batley
Tel: (0924) 471386

SCOTLAND

The Workshop
38 Union Place, Dundee
Tel: (0382) 644950

WALES

Museum of Childhood Toys &
Gift Shop
Water St., Menai Bridge, Gwynedd
Tel: (0248) 712498

EPHEMERA

LONDON

Bayly's Gallery
8 Princes Arcade, Piccadilly, W.1
Tel: 01-734 0180

Gilda Conrich Antiques
12 The Mall, 359 Upper St.
Camden Passage, N.1
Tel: 01-226 5319

Dodo
185 Westbourne Grove, W.11
Tel: 01-229 3132

Follies
Stalls M5, M6 and M7, Antiquarius
135 King's Rd., S.W.3
Tel: 01-352 7989

M. & R. Glendale
121 Gray's Antique Market
58 Davies St., W.1
Tel: 01-629 2851

David Godfrey
37 Kinnerton St., S.W.1
Tel: 01-235 7788

Pleasures of Past Times
11 Cecil Crt., Charing Cross Rd.
W.C.2
Tel: 01-836 1142

Danny Posner
The Vintage Magazine Shop
39/41 Brewer St., W.1
Tel: 01-439 8525

Quadrille Antiques
27 Craven Terrace, W.2
Tel: 01-262 7824

Peter Stockham at Images
16 Cecil Crt., Charing Cross Rd.
W.C.2
Tel: 01-836 8661

BUCKS.

Omniphil Ltd.
Germains Lodge, Fullers Hill
Chesham
Tel: (0494) 771851

Also at

Stand 110, Gray's Antique Market
Davies St., W.1
Tel: 01-629 1309

KENT

Mike Sturge
17 Market Buildings Arcade
Maidstone
Tel: (0622) 54702

SURREY

Richmond Antiquary
28 Hill Rise, Richmond
Tel: 01-948 0583/01-727 4745

FISHING TACKLE

DORSET

Yesterday Tackle
67 Jumpers Rd., Christchurch
Tel: (0202) 476586

HANTS.

Nick Marchant-Lane
Salters Cottage, Bramshott, Liphook
Tel: (0428) 723990

KENT
Alan Clout
36 Nunnery Fields, Canterbury
Tel: (0227) 55162

SURREY
Gary Brooker
Wintershall, Dunsfold
Tel: (048649) 478

SCOTLAND
Jamie Maxtone Graham
Nithside, Closeburn, Thornhill
Tel: (08484) 382

FURNITURE

LONDON
Asprey & Co. PLC
165-169 New Bond St., W.1
Tel: 01-493 6767
F. E. A. Briggs Ltd.
73 Ledbury Rd., W.11
Tel: 01-727 0909/01-221 4950
C. W. Buckingham
301-303 Munster Rd., S.W.6
Tel: 01-385 2657
(See also under HANTS.)
John Creed Antiques Ltd.
3 & 5A Camden Passage, N.1
Tel: 01-226 8867
Zal Davar Antiques
26A Munster Rd., S.W.6
Tel: 01-736 1405/2559
John Keil Ltd.
154 Brompton Rd., S.W.3
Tel: 01-589 6454
Lee & Stacey
5 Pond St., N.W.3
Tel: 01-794 7904/452 0056
C. H. Major (Antiques) Ltd
154 Kensington Church St., W.8
Tel: 01-229 1162
Mallett & Son (Antiques) Ltd.
40 New Bond St., W.1
Tel: 01-499 7411
M. & D. Seligmann
37 Kensington Church St., W.8
Tel: 01-937 0400
Murray Thomson Ltd.
141 Kensington Church St., W.8
Tel: 01-727 1727
Phelps Ltd.
129-235 St. Margaret's Rd.
E. Twickenham
Tel: 01-892 1778/7129
William Tillman
30 St. James's St., S.W.1
Tel: 01-839 2500
O. F. Wilson Ltd.
Queen's Elm Parade, Old Church St.
S.W.3
Tel: 01-352 9554
Windsor House Antiques (Leeds) Ltd.
298 Westbourne Grove, W.11
Tel: 01-221 4883

AVON
Cottage Antiques
The Old Post Office, Langford Place
Langford, Nr. Bristol
Tel: (0934) 862597

BERKS.
Mary Bellis Antiques
Charnham Close, Hungerford
Tel: (0488) 82620
Biggs of Maidenhead
Hare Hatch Grange, Twyford
Tel: (073522) 3281
The Old Malthouse, Hungerford
Tel: (04886) 2209
Medalcrest Ltd.
Charnham House, Charnham St.
Hungerford
Tel: (0488) 84157
Charles Toller
20 High St., Datchet
Tel: (0753) 42903

BUCKS.
Jeanne Temple Antiques
Stockwell House, 1 Stockwell Lane,
Wavendon, Milton Keynes
Tel: (0908) 583597
Bishop (Marlow) Ltd.
8 & 10 West St., Marlow
Tel: (06284) 3936

CAMBS.
W. Stockbridge & Sons Ltd.
25/26 Bridge St., Cambridge
Tel: (0223) 353500

CHESHIRE
Coppelia Antiques
Holford Lodge, Plumley Moor Rd.
Plumley
Tel: (056581) 2197

John King Antiques
157-159 London Rd. South, Poynton
Tel: (0625) 873110

Townwell House Antiques
52 Welsh Row, Nantwich
Tel: (0270) 625953

CLEVELAND
Margaret Bedi Antiques
5 Station Rd., Billingham
Tel: (0642) 554483

CUMBRIA
Haughey Antiques
Market St., Kirkby Stephen
Tel: (0930) 71302
Townhead Antiques
Newby Bridge
Tel: (0448) 31321
Jonathan Wood Antiques
Broughton Hall, Cartmel
Grange-over-Sands
Tel: (044854) 234

DERBYS.
Spurrier-Smith Antiques
28B & 41 Church St., Ashbourne
Tel: (0335) 43669 and
      (home) (077389) 368

DEVON
Old Store Antiques
St. Marychurch Rd., Newton Abbot
Tel: (0626) 4690

DORSET
Johnsons of Sherborne Ltd.
South St., Sherborne
Tel: (0935) 812585

ESSEX
Templar Antiques
4 & 6 Stoneham St., Coggeshall
Tel: (0376) 61220
Stone Hall Antiques
Down Hall Road
Matching Green, Harlow
Tel: (0279) 731440

GLOS.
Baggott Church Street Ltd.
Church St., Stow-on-the-Wold
Tel: (0451) 30370
W. R. Cambridge & Son
14 Rotunda Terrace, Cheltenham
Tel: (0242) 514502
Huntington Antiques Ltd.
The Old Forge, Church St.
Stow-on-the Wold
Tel: (0451) 30842
Painswick Antiques & Interiors
Beacon House, Painswick
Tel: (0452) 812578
Anthony Preston Antiques Ltd.
The Square, Stow-on-the-Wold
Tel: (0451) 31586
Studio Antiques Ltd.
Bourton-on-the-Water
Tel: (0451) 20352

HANTS.
Barlow Antiques
Bridge House, Stockbridge
Tel: (026481) 744
Binsted Place Antiques
Binsted, Nr. Alton
Tel: (04204) 3146
C. W. Buckingham
Twin Firs, Southampton Rd., Cadnam
Tel: (0703) 812122
Cedar Antiques
High St., Hartley Wintney
Tel: (025126) 3252
Mark Collier Antiques
1-3 Bridge St., Fordingbridge
Tel: (0425) 52555
House of Antiques
4 College St., Petersfield
Tel: (0730) 62172
Lita Kaye of Lyndhurst
13 High St., Lyndhurst
Tel: (042128) 2337
St. Peter's Gallery
Chesil St., Winchester
Tel: (0962) 68901
Elizabeth Viney
Jacob's House, High St., Stockbridge
Tel: (026481) 761

HEREFORDS.
Great Brampton House Antiques
Madley
Tel: (0981) 250244
Leominster Antiques
87 Etnam St., Leominster
Tel: (0568) 3217

HERTS.
C. Bellinger Antiques
91 Wood St., Barnet
Tel: 01-449 3467
Phillips of Hitchin (Antiques) Ltd.
The Manor House, Hitchin
Tel: (0462) 32067

HUMBERSIDE
Geoffrey Mole
400 Wincolmlee, Hull
Tel: (0482) 27858

KENT
Chislehurst Antiques
7 Royal Parade, Chislehurst
Tel: 01-467 1530

LANCS.
West Lancs. Exports
Black Horse Farm, 123 Liverpool Rd.
South Burscough, Nr. Ormskirk
Tel: (0704) 894634

LINCS.
Kirkby Antiques Ltd.
Kirkby-on-Bain, Woodhall Spa
Tel: (0526) 52119/53461
also at:
Kirkby Antiques Ltd.
Clifton Cottage, 19 Market Place
Tattershall
Tel: (0526) 42225
Geoff Parker Antiques Ltd.
Haltoft End
Freiston, Nr. Boston
Tel: (0205) 760444

MIDDLESEX
J. W. Crisp Antiques
166 High Street, Teddington
Tel: 01-977 4309
Phelps Ltd.
129-135 St. Margaret's Rd.
E. Twickenham
Tel: 01-892 1778

NORFOLK
Arthur Brett & Sons Ltd.
40-44 St. Giles St., Norwich
Tel: (0603) 28171
Pearse Lukies
Bayfield House, White Hart St.
Aylesham
Tel: (026373) 4137

NORTHANTS.
Nick's Antiques
47 Bath Road, Kettering
Tel: (0536) 521824

NORTHUMBERLAND
Prudhoe Cottage Antiques
15 St. Mary's Chare, Hexham
Tel: (0434) 605522 & (0661) 33421

NOTTS.
Matsell Antiques Ltd.
Nottingham Antique Centre
James Alexander Building
London Rd., Nottingham
Tel: (0602) 55548/54504 & 288267

OXON.
Elizabethan House Antiques
28 & 55 High St.
Dorchester-on-Thames
Tel: (0865) 340079
Peter Norden Antiques
High St., Burford
Tel: (099382) 2121
Zene Walker
The Bull House, High St., Burford
Tel: (099382) 3284
Witney Antiques
96-98 Corn St., Witney
Tel: (0993) 3902

SHROPSHIRE
R. C. Cave & Sons Ltd.
17 Broad St., Ludlow
Tel: (0584) 3568
Feathers Antiques Ltd
20-22 Bull Ring, Ludlow
Tel: (0584) 2884
Paul Smith
10 Church St., Ludlow
Tel: (0584) 2666
M. & R. Taylor (Antiques)
1 Church St., Ludlow
Tel: (0584) 4169
White Cottage Antiques
Tern Hill, Nr. Market Drayton
Tel: (063083) 222
Stanley Woolston
29 Broad St., Ludlow
Tel: (0584) 3554
and also at
Tamberlane House, The Buttercross
Ludlow

SOMERSET
Colin Dyte Antiques
Huntspill Rd., Highbridge
Tel: (0278) 788590
Grange Court Antiques
Corfe, Nr. Taunton
Tel: (082342) 498
Trevor Micklem Antiques Ltd.
Gateway House, North St., Milverton
Tel: (0823) 400404

Edward A. Nowell
21-23 Market Place, Wells
Tel: (0749) 72415

SUFFOLK
David Gibbins Antiques
21 Market Hill, Woodbridge
Tel: (03943) 3531
Michael Moore Antiques
The Old Court, Nethergate St., Clare
Tel: (0787) 277510
Peppers Period Pieces (R)
29 Guildhall St., Bury St. Edmunds
Tel: (0284) 68786
Randolph
99 High St., Hadleigh
Tel: (0473) 823789

SURREY
Keith Atkinson
59 Brighton Rd., South Croydon
Tel: 01-688 5559
Dovetail Antique Restoration (R)
Riverdale Farm, Broadmead Rd.
Old Woking
Tel: (04862) 22925
Heath-Bullock
8 Meadrow, Godalming
Tel: (04868) 22562
Rayne Antiques
332 Brighton Rd., South Croydon
Tel: 01-680 8395
Anthony Welling Antiques
Broadway Barn, High St., Ripley
Tel: (0483) 225384

SUSSEX
A27 Antiques Warehouse
Dittons Rd., Industrial Estate,
Polegate
Tel: (03212) 7167
Bursig of Arundel
63-65 Tarrant St., Arundel
Tel: (0903) 883846
Humphry Antiques
East Street, Petworth
Tel: (0798) 43053
Richard Davidson
Lombard St., Petworth
Tel: (0798) 42508
The Grange Antiques
High St., Robertsbridge
Tel: (0580) 880577
The Old Mint House
High St., Pevensey, Eastbourne
Tel: (0323) 762337
John G. Morris Ltd.
Market Square, Petworth
Tel: (0798) 42305
Village Antiques
2 & 4 Cooden Sea Rd., Little Common
Bexhill-on-Sea
Tel: (04243) 5214

WEST MIDLANDS
Rock House Antiques &
Management Services
Rock House, The Rock, Tettenhall
Wolverhampton
Tel: (0902) 755882

WILTS.
Avon Antiques
26-27 Market St., Bradford-on-Avon
Tel: (02216) 2052
Robert Bradley
71 Brown St., Salisbury
Tel: (0722) 3677
Combe Cottage Antiques
Castle Combe, Nr. Chippenham
Tel: (0249) 782250
Michael Gray Antiques
1 St. John's Alley, Devizes
Tel: (0380) 6719
Ian G. Hastie
46 St. Ann St., Salisbury
Tel: (0722) 22957
Robert Kime Antiques
Dene House, Lockeridge
Tel: (067286) 250
Monkton Galleries
Hindon
Tel: (074789) 235
Paul Wansbrough
Seend Lodge, Seend, Nr. Melksham
Tel: (038082) 213
K. A. Welch
1a Church St., Warminster
Tel: (0985) 214687

YORKS.
Robert Aagaard Ltd.
Frogmire House, Stockwell Rd.
Knaresborough
Tel: (0423) 864805
(Specialises in fireplaces)
Barmouth Court Antiques
Abbeydale House, Barmouth Rd.
Sheffield
Tel: (0742) 582160/582672

Bernard Dickinson
88 High St., Gargrave
Tel: (075678) 285

Jeremy A. Fearn
The Old Rectory, Winksley, Ripon
Tel: (076583) 625

W. F. Greenwood & Sons Ltd.
2 & 3 Crown Place, Harrogate
Tel: (0423) 504467

Old Rectory Antiques
The Old Rectory, West Heslerton
Malton
Tel: (09445) 364

SCOTLAND

John Bell of Aberdeen Ltd.
Balbrogie, By Blackburn, Kinellar
Aberdeenshire
Tel: (0224) 79209

Paul Coutts Ltd.
101–107 West Bow, Edinburgh
Tel: 031-225 3238

Letham Antiques
45 Cumberland St., Edinburgh
Tel: 031-556 6565

Nicholson Antiques
3 Cranston St., Edinburgh
Tel: 031-556 1842

Roy Sim Antiques
21 Allan St., Blairgowrie, Perthshire
Tel: (0250) 3860/3700

Unicorn Antiques
65 Dundas St., Edinburgh
Tel: 031-556 7176

FURNITURE – PINE

LONDON

Adams Antiques
47 Chalk Farm Rd., N.W.1
Tel: 01-267 9241

Olwen Carthew
109 Kirkdale, S.E.26
Tel: 01-699 1363

Princedale Antiques
70 Princedale Rd., W.11
Tel: 01-727 0868

Scallywag
The Old Church, Wren Rd.,
Camberwell Green, S.E.5
Tel: 01-701 5353

This & That
50 & 51 Chalk Farm Rd., N.W.1
Tel: 01-267 5433

AVON

Abbas Combe Pine
4 Upper Maudlin St., Bristol 2
Tel: (0272) 299023

BEDS.

Country Primitives
Ampthill Antiques Centre, Ampthill
Tel: (0296) 668294

BUCKS.

The Pine Merchants
52 High St., Gt. Missenden
Tel: (02406) 2002

CO. DURHAM

Horsemarket Antiques
27 Horsemarket, Barnard Castle
Tel: (0833) 37881

DERBYS.

Old Farm Furniture
Parwick Lees Farm, Ashbourne
Tel: (0335) 25473

DEVON

Country Cottage Furniture
Yealmbury Hill, Yealmpton
Plymouth
Tel: (0752) 880525

Fine Pine
Woodland Rd., Harbertonford
Tel: (080423) 465

GLOS.

Bed of Roses Antiques
12 Prestbury Rd., Cheltenham
Tel: (0242) 31918

Gloucester House Antiques
Market Place, Fairford
Tel: (0285) 712790

Huntington Antiques
The Old Forge, Church St.
Stow-on-the-Wold
Tel: (0451) 30842

HANTS.

C. W. Buckingham
Twin Firs, Southampton Rd., Cadnam
Tel: (0703) 812122

The Pine Cellars
38 Jewry St., Winchester
Tel: (09626) 7014

The Pine Co.
104 Christchurch Rd., Ringwood
Tel: (04254) 3932

HEREFORD

The Hay Galleries Ltd.
4 High Town, Hay-on-Wye
Tel: (049782) 0356

HERTS.

Romic
4 Evron Place (off Market Place)
Hertford
Tel: (0992) 552880

HUMBERSIDE

Bell Antiques
68 Harold St., Grimsby
Tel: (0472) 695110

Keith Miles Marketing Ltd.
Milbourne Sandhome Landing
Newport, Brough
Tel: (0430) 40210

Paul Wilson Pine Furniture
Perth St. West, Hull
Tel: (0482) 447923

LANCS.

Cardwell & Sheriff
Moss Hey Garages, Chapel Rd.
Marton Moss, Blackpool
Tel: (0253) 696324

Enloc Antiques
Old Corporation Yard, Knotts Lane
Colne
Tel: (0282) 861417

Utopia Pine
Holme Mills, Carnforth
Tel: (0524) 781739

LEICS.

Lowe of Loughborough
37-40 Church Gate, Loughborough
LE11 1UE
Tel: (0509) 212554

LINCS.

Allens Antiques
Moor Farm, Stapleford
Tel: (052285) 392

Stowaway (UK) Ltd.
2 Langton Hill, Horncastle
Tel: (06582) 7445

NORTHANTS.

Acorn Antiques
The Old Mill, Moat Lane, Towcester
Tel: (0327) 52788

NOTTS.

Vintage Pine
113 Ilkeston Rd., Nottingham
Tel: (0602) 702571

OXON.

Market Place Antiques
35 Market Place, Henley-on-Thames
Tel: (04915) 7287

SOMERSET

Chez Chalons
Old Hambridge Mill, Hambridge
Nr. Curry Rivel, Langport
Tel: (0458) 252374

Domus
Woodcock St., Castle Cary
Tel: (0963) 50912

Herald House Antiques
Herald House, North St., Langport
Tel: (0458) 250587

Grange Court Antiques
Corfe, Taunton
Tel: (0823) 42498

Pennard House
East Pennard, Shepton Mallet
Tel: (074986) 266

STAFFS.

Anvil Antiques
41 St. Edwards St., Leek
Tel: (0538) 371657

Aspleys Antiques
Compton Mill, Compton, Leek
Tel: (0538) 373396

SUFFOLK

Michael Moore Antiques
The Old Court, Nethergate St., Clare
Tel: (0787) 27751

SUSSEX

Hillside Antiques
Balcombe Rd., Pound Hill, Crawley
Tel: (0293) 884018

Graham Price Antiques
A27 Antiques Warehouse
Dittons Rd. Industrial Estate
Polegate
Tel: (03212) 7167/7166

Rope Walk Antiques
Rope Walk, Rye
Tel: (0797) 223486

SURREY

Odiham Antiques
High St., Compton, Guildford
Tel: (0483) 810215

F. & L. Warren
The Sawmills, Firgrove Hill, Farnham
Tel: (0252) 726713

Wych House Antiques
Wych Hill, Woking
Tel: (04862) 64636

YORKS.

Daleside Antiques
St. Peter's Square, Cold Bath Rd.
Harrogate
Tel: (0423) 60286

Manor Barn Pine
Burnside Mill, Main St., Addinham
Ilkley
Tel: (0943) 830176

Pine Finds
Shippen Bower, Marton-cum-Grafton,
Nr. York
Tel: (09012) 3133

GLASS

LONDON

Asprey & Co. PLC
165-169 New Bond St., W.1
Tel: 01-493 6767

Phyllis Bedford Antiques
3 The Galleries, Camden Passage, N.1
Tel: 01-882 3189, home: 01-354 1332

W. G. T. Burne (Antique Glass) Ltd.
11 Elystan St., S.W.3
Tel: 01-589 6074

Delomosne & Son Ltd.
4 Campden Hill Rd., W.8
Tel: 01-937 1804

Eila Grahame
97A Kensington Church St., W.8
Tel: 01-727 4132

Lloyds of Westminster
51 Kinnerton St., S.W.1
Tel: 01-235 1010

S. W. Parry
113 Portobello Rd., W.11
(Sat. only)
Tel: 01-740 0248 (Sun. to Fri.)

J. F. Poore
5 Wellington Terrace, W.2
Tel: 01-229 4166

R. Wilkinson & Son (R)
43-45 Wastdale Rd., Forest Hill
S.E.23
Tel: 01-699 4420

AVON

Somervale Antiques
6 Radstock Rd., Midsomer Norton
Bath
Tel: (0761) 412686

CAMBS.

Hilton Gallery
3 St. Mary's Passage, Cambridge
Tel: (0223) 356886

DORSET

A & D Antiques
21 East St., Blandford Forum
Tel: (0258) 55643

Quarter Jack Antiques
The Quarter Jack, Bridge St.
Sturminster Newton
Tel: (0258) 72558

HANTS.

Todd & Austin Antiques & Fine Art
2 Andover Rd., Winchester
Tel: (0962) 69824

SOMERSET

Abbey Antiques
52-54 High St., Glastonbury
Tel: (0458) 31694

STAFFS.

The Old House, 47 High St., Kinver
Tel: (0384) 872985

SUFFOLK

Maureen Thompson
Sun House, Long Melford
Tel: (0787) 78252

SURREY

A. Henning
48 Walton St., Walton-on-the-Hill
Tadworth
Tel: (073781) 3337

WORCS.

Gavina Ewart
60-62 High St., Broadway
Tel: (0386) 853371

SCOTLAND

Janet Lumsden
51A George St., Edinburgh
Tel: 031-225 2911

William MacAdam (appointment only)
86 Pilrig St., Edinburgh
Tel: 031-553 1364

AVON

The Vintage Wireless Company
Tudor House, Cossham St.
Mangotsfield, Bristol
Tel: (0272) 565474

KENT

York House Antiques
37 High St., Seal
Tel: (0732) 62811

SOMERSET

Philip Knighton (R)
The Wellington Workshop
14 South St., Wellington
Tel: (082347) 7332

METALWARE

LONDON

Jack Casimir Ltd.
The Brass Shop, 23 Pembridge Rd.
W.11
Tel: 01-727 8643

Arthur Davidson Ltd.
78-79 Jermyn St., S.W.1
Tel: 01-930 6687

Gee Bee Antiques
201 Brompton Rd., S.W.3
Tel: 01-589 3317

Robert Preston
1 Campden St., W.8
Tel: 01-727 4872

Alistair Sampson Antiques
156 Brompton Rd., S.W.3
Tel: 01-589 5272

BEDS.

Christopher Sykes Antiques
The Old Parsonage, Woburn
Milton Keynes
Tel: (052525) 259/467

BERKS.

Rye Galleries
60-61 High St., Eton
Tel: (07535) 62837

BUCKS.

Albert Bartram
177 Hivings Hill, Chesham
Tel: (0494) 783271

CLEVELAND

Margaret Bedi Antiques
5 Station Rd., Billingham
Tel: (0642) 554483

CUMBRIA

Stable Antiques
Oakdene Country Hotel
Garsdale Rd., Sedbergh
Tel: (0587) 20280

GLOS.

Key Antiques
11 Horsefair, Chipping Norton
Tel: (0608) 3777

Country Life Antiques
Sheep St., Stow-on-the-Wold
Tel: (0451) 30776

Peter Norden Antiques
Kingshead, Birdlip
Tel: (045282) 2299

OXON.

Robin Bellamy Ltd.
97 Corn St., Witney
Tel: (0993) 4793

Elizabethan House Antiques
28 & 55 High St.
Dorchester-on-Thames
Tel: (0865) 340079

Lloyd & Greenwood Antiques
Chapel House, High St., Burford
Tel: (099382) 2359

SUFFOLK

Brookes Forge (R)
Flempton, Bury St. Edmunds
Tel: (0284) 84473
home: (0449) 781376

WILTS.

Combe Cottage Antiques
Castle Combe, Chippenham
Tel: (0249) 782250

Rupert Gentus Antiques
The Manor House, Milton Lilbourne
Nr. Pewsey
Tel: (06726) 3344

YORKS.

Windsor House Antiques (Leeds) Ltd.
18-20 Benson St., Leeds
Tel: (0532) 444666

PORCELAIN

LONDON

Albert Amor Ltd.
37 Bury St., St. James's, S.W.1
Tel: 01-930 2444

Antique Porcelain Co. Ltd.
149 New Bond St., W.1
Tel: 01-629 1254

Susan Becker
18 Lower Richmond Rd., S.W.15
Tel: 01-788 9082

David Brower Antiques
113 Kensington Church St., W.8
Tel: 01-221 4155

Cale Antiques
24 Cale St., Chelsea Green, S.W.3
Tel: 01-589 6146

Cathay Antiques
12 Thackeray St., W.8
Tel: 01-937 6066

Chester Antiques
97 Mount St., W.1
Tel: 01-499 5315

China Choice
New Cavendish St., W.1
Tel: 01-935 0184

Craven Antiques
17 Garson House, Gloucester Terrace
W.2
Tel: 01-262 4176

Delomosne & Son Ltd.
4 Campden Hill Rd., W.8
Tel: 01-937 1804

H. & W. Deutsch Antiques
111 Kensington Church St., W.8
Tel: 01-727 5984

Miss Fowler
1A Duke St., Manchester Square, W.1
Tel: 01-935 5187

Gay Antiques
1 Beauchamp Place, S.W.3
Tel: 01-584 9615

Graham & Oxley (Antiques) Ltd.
101 Kensington Church St., W.8
Tel: 01-229 1850

Grosvenor Antiques Ltd.
27 Holland St., Kensington, W.8
Tel: 01-937 8649

Harcourt Antiques
5 Harcourt St., W.1
Tel: 01-723 5919

Heirloom & Howard Ltd.
1 Hay Hill, Berkeley Square, W.1
Tel: 01-493 5868

Hoff Antiques Ltd.
66A Kensington Church St., W.8
Tel: 01-229 5516

Klaber & Klaber
2A Bedford Gardens, Kensington
Church St., W.8
Tel: 01-727 4573

Mercury Antiques
1 Ladbroke Rd., W.11
Tel: 01-727 5106

Raven Antiques
256 Lee High Rd., S.E.13
Tel: 01-852 5066

Edward Salti
43 Davies St., W.1
Tel: 01-629 2141

Gerald Sattin Ltd.
25 Burlington Arcade, Piccadilly, W.1
Tel: 01-493 6557

Jean Sewell (Antiques) Ltd.
3 Campden St., Kensington Church
St., W.8
Tel: 01-727 3122

Simon Spero
109 Kensington Church St., W.8
Tel: 01-727 7413

Aubrey Spiers Antiques
Shop C5, Chenil Galleries
183 King's Rd., S.W.3
Tel: 01-352 2123

Betty & Vera Vandekar at 'Walbrook'
101B Kensington Church St., W.8
Tel: 01-727 2471

Earle D. Vandekar of
Knightsbridge Ltd.
138 Brompton Rd., S.W.3
Tel: 01-589 8481/3398

Venner's Antiques
7 New Cavendish St., W.1
Tel: 01-935 0184

Joanna Warrand
99 Kensington Church St., W.8
Tel: 01-727 2333

Winifred Williams
3 Bury St., St. James's, S.W.1
Tel: 01-930 4732

AVON

Andrew Dando
4 Wood St., Queen Square, Bath
Tel: (0225) 22702

BERKS.

Len's Crested China
Twyford Antiques Centre
Nr. Reading
Tel: (0753) 35162

The Old School Antiques
Dorney, Windsor
Tel: (06286) 3247

CHESHIRE

Monogram Studios (R)
25 Kinsey St., Congleton
Tel: (02602) 3957

CORNWALL

London Apprentice Antiques
Pentewan Rd., St. Austell
Tel: (0726) 63780

DERBYS.

P. W. Gottschald Antiques
Sandyford Farm, Nr. Belper
Tel: (077382) 3305

C. B. Sheppard Antiques
(appointment only)
Hurst Lodge, Chesterfield Rd.
Tibshelf
Tel: (0773) 872419

DEVON

David J. Thorn
2 High St., Budleigh Salterton
Tel: (03954) 2448

ESSEX

Constance & Anthony Chiswell
1 Market Place, Dunmow
Tel: (0371) 2388

GLOS.

Aldbury Antiques
High St., Blockley
Nr. Moreton-in-Marsh
Tel: (0386) 700280

Hamand Antiques
Friday St., Painswick
Tel: (0452) 812310

Studio Antiques Ltd.
Bourton-on-the-Water
Tel: (0451) 20352

HANTS.

Gerald Austin Antiques
2A Andover Rd., Winchester
Tel: (0962) 69824 Ext. 2

Goss & Crested China Ltd.
62 Murray Rd., Horndean
Tel: (0705) 597440

HEREFORD & WORCS.

Sabina Jennings
Newcourt Park, Lugwardine
Tel: (0432) 850752

M. Lees & Sons
Tower House, Severn St., Worcester
Tel: (0905) 26620

KENT

The Antique Porcelain Collector
High St., Shoreham Village
Nr. Sevenoaks
Tel: (09592) 3416

Bygones
Peirce Cottage, Charing, Ashford
Tel: (023371) 2494

Dunsdale Lodge Antiques
Brasted Rd., Westerham
Tel: (0959) 62160

Hop Pole Antiques
41 Pound Rd., E. Peckham
Tonbridge
Tel: (0622) 871993

Steppes Hill Farm Antiques
Stockbury, Sittingbourne
Tel: (0795) 842205

W. W. Warner (Antiques) Ltd.
The Green, Brasted
Tel: (0959) 63698

LANCS.

Burnley Antiques & Fine Arts Ltd.
336A Colne Rd., Burnley
Tel: (0282) 20143/65172

LEICS.

Charnwood Antiques
54 Sparrow Hill, Loughborough
Tel: (0509) 231750

NORFOLK

T. C. S. Brooke
The Grange, Wroxham
Tel: (06053) 2644

Cromer Antiques Gallery
Church St., Cromer
Tel: (0263) 512355

OXON.

Castle Antiques
Lamb Arcade, Wallingford, Oxon.
Tel: (0491) 35166

David John Ceramics
25 Oxford St., Woodstock
Tel: (0993) 812649

SHROPS.

Castle Gate Antiques
15 Castle Gate, Shrewsbury
Tel: (0743) 61011 (eves)

Tudor House Antiques
33 High St., Ironbridge
Tel: (095245) 3237

STAFFS.

As Found (R)
5 Averill Drive, Western Springs
Rugeley, Staffs.
Tel: (08894) 3824

SURREY

Elias Clark Antiques Ltd.
1 The Cobbles, Bletchingley
Tel: (0883) 843714

William Hockley Antiques
Kent House, High St., Cranleigh
Tel: (0483) 276197

J. P. Raison (appointment only)
Sturt House, Sturt's Lane, Tadworth
Tel: (073781) 3663/3557

SUSSEX

Barclay Antiques
7 Village Mews, Little Common
Bexhill-on-Sea
Tel: (0797) 222734 (home)

Geoffrey Godden, Chinaman
17-19 Crescent Rd., Worthing
Tel: (0903) 35958

Magpie House Antiques
27 Kemp St., Brighton
Tel: (0273) 683892

McPherson & Wood
80A St. George's Rd., Kemp Town
Brighton
Tel: (0273) 681661

David Morfee Antiques
St. Aubyn, Willingdon Lane
Jevington, Nr. Polegate
Tel: (03212) 6997

Leonard Russell
21 King's Avenue, Newhaven
Tel: (0273) 515153

WILTS.

The China Hen
9 Woolley St., Bradford-on-Avon
Tel: (02216) 3369

Mark Collier Antiques
High St., Downton
Tel: (0725) 21068

Marjorie Whitworth (Antiques)
20 West St., Wilton
Tel: (072274) 2165

YORKS.

Brian Bowden
199 Carr House Rd., Doncaster
Tel: (0302) 65353

David Love
10 Royal Parade, Harrogate
Tel: (0423) 65797

Nanbooks
Undercliffe Cottage, Duke St., Settle
Tel: (07292) 3324 or (04685) 551

SCOTLAND

David G. M. Jones
Broombank Antiques
Culloden Moor, Inverness-shire
Tel: (0463) 790569

WALES

Gwalia Antiques
Main St., Goodwick, Fishguard
Dyfed
Tel: (0348) 872634

POTTERY

LONDON

Britannia
Gray's Market, 58 Davies St., W.1
Tel: 01-629 6772

Cale Antiques
24 Cale St., Chelsea Green, S.W.3
Tel: 01-589 6146

Gerald Clark Antiques
1 High St., Mill Hill Village, N.W.7
Tel: 01-906 0342

Richard Dennis
144 Kensington Church St., W.8
Tel: 01-727 2061

Graham & Oxley (Antiques) Ltd.
101 Kensington Church St., W.8
Tel: 01-229 1850

Jonathan Horne
66C Kensington Church St., W.8
Tel: 01-221 5658

D. M. & P. Manheim Ltd.
69 Upper Berkeley St., Portman Sq.
W.1
Tel: 01-723 6595

J. & J. May
40 Kensington Church St., W.8
Tel: 01-937 3575

Mercury Antiques
1 Ladbroke Rd., W.11
Tel: 01-727 5106

Oliver-Sutton Antiques
34C Kensington Church St., W.8
Tel: 01-937 0633

Rogers
76 Royal Hospital Rd., S.W.3
Tel: 01-352 9007

Alistair Sampson Antiques
156 Brompton Rd., S.W.3
Tel: 01-589 5272

CUMBRIA

Kendal Studio Pottery
2-3 Wildman St., Kendal
Tel: (0539) 23291

DEVON

David J. Thorn
2 High St., Budleigh Salterton
Tel: (03954) 2448

KENT

Bygones
Peirce Cottage, Charing, Ashford
Tel: (023371) 2494

Dunsdale Lodge Antiques
Brasted Rd., Westerham
Tel: (0959) 62160

W. W. Warner (Antiques) Ltd.
The Green, Brasted
Tel: (0959) 63698

LANCS.

Burnley Antiques & Fine Arts Ltd.
336A Colne Rd., Burnley
Tel: (0282) 20143/65172

SURREY

Elias Clark Antiques Ltd.
1 The Cobbles, Bletchingley
Tel: (0883) 843714

SUSSEX

Magpie House Antiques
27 Kemp St., Brighton
Tel: (0273) 683892

Leonard Russell
21 King's Avenue, Newhaven
Tel: (0273) 515153

WILTS.

Bratton Antiques
Market Place, Westbury
Tel: (0373) 823021

Marjorie Whitworth (Antiques)
20 West St., Wilton
Tel: (072274) 2165

YORKS.

Nanbooks
Undercliffe Cottage, Duke St., Settle
Tel: (07292) 3324 or (04685) 551

SCIENTIFIC INSTRUMENTS

LONDON

Arthur Davidson Ltd.
78-79 Jermyn St., S.W.1
Tel: 01-930 6687

Mariner Antiques Ltd.
55 Curzon St., W.1
Tel: 01-499 0171

Mayfair Microscopes Ltd.
64 Burlington Arcade, W.1
Tel: 01-629 2616

Arthur Middleton Ltd.
12 New Row, Covent Garden, W.C.2
Tel: 01-836 7042/7062

Harriet Wynter Ltd.
50 Redcliffe Rd., S.W.10
Tel: 01-352 6494

BEDS.

Christopher Sykes Antique
The Old Parsonage, Woburn
Milton Keynes
Tel: (052525) 259/467

DEVON

Galaxy Arts
38 New St., Barbican, Plymouth
Tel: (0752) 667842

ESSEX

Mayflower Antiques
180-182 High St., Dovercourt
Harwich
Tel: (02555) 4079

GLOS.

Country Life Antiques
Sheep St., Stow-on-the-Wold
Tel: (0451) 30776

NORFOLK

Humbleyard Fine Art
Waterfall Cottage, Mill St.
Swanton Morley
Tel: (036283) 793

Also at

Coltishall Antiques Centre
Coltishall, Norfolk

Turret House
Wymondham
Tel: (0953) 603462

SUSSEX

Trevor Philip & Sons
2 Prince Albert St., Brighton
Tel: (0273) 202119

SILVER

LONDON

Asprey & Co. Ltd.
165-169 New Bond St., W.1
Tel: 01-493 6767

N. Bloom & Son (Antiques) Ltd.
40-41 Conduit St., W.1
Tel: 01-629 5060

Bond Street Galleries
111-112 New Bond St., W.1
Tel: 01-493 6180

Howard Jones
43 Kensington Church St., W.8
Tel: 01-937 4359

London International Silver Co.
82 Portobello Road, W.11
Tel: 01-979 6523

S. J. Phillips Ltd.
139 New Bond St., W.1
Tel: 01-629 6261/2

HANTS.

St. Peter's Gallery
Chesil St., Winchester
Tel: (0962) 68901

KENT

Bygones
Peirce Cottage, Charing, Ashford
Tel: (023371) 2494

Steppes Hill Farm Antiques
Stockbury, Sittingbourne
Tel: (0795) 842205

Ralph Antiques
40A Sandwich Industrial Estate
Sandwich
Tel: (0304) 611949/612882

SOMERSET

Edward A. Nowell
21-23 Market Place, Wells
Tel: (0749) 72415

YORKS.

Georgian House
88 Main St., Bingley
Tel: (0274) 568883

WINE ANTIQUES

LONDON

Brian Beat
36 Burlington Gardens, W.1
Tel: 01-437 4975

Eximious Ltd.
10 West Halkin St., W.1
Tel: 01-235 7222

Richard Kihl
164 Regent's Park Rd., N.W.1
Tel: 01-586 3838/0873

AVON

Robin Butler
9 St. Stephen's St., Bristol
Tel: (0272) 276586

CHESHIRE

Bacchus Antiques
27 Grange Avenue, Hale
Nr. Altrincham
Tel: (061980) 4747

FAIR ORGANISERS

LONDON

Century Antique Fairs
57 Mill Lane, N.W.6
Tel: 01-794 3551

Philbeach Events Ltd.
Earl's Court Exhibition Centre
Warwick Rd., S.W.5
Tel: 01-385 1200

BERKS.

Granny's Attic Fairs
Dean House, Cookham Dean
Tel: (06284) 3658

Silhouette Fairs (inc. Newbury
Antique & Collectors' Fairs)
25 Donnington Sq., Newbury
Tel: (0635) 44338

CHESHIRE

Susan Brownson, Antique Fairs
North West
Brownslow House, Gt. Budworth
Northwich
Tel: (0606) 891267 & (061962) 5629

Pamela Robertson
8 St. George's Crescent, Queen's Park
Chester
Tel: (0244) 678106

CORNWALL

West Country Antiques & Collectors'
Fairs (Gerry Mosdell)
Hillside, St. Issey, Wadebridge
Tel: (08414) 666

ESSEX

Stephen Charles Fairs
3 Leigh Hill, Leigh-on-Sea
Tel: (0702) 714649/556745 and
(0268) 774977

Emporium Fairs
13 Abbeygate St., Colchester
Tel: (0206) 66975

Heirloom Markets
11 Wellfields, Writtle, Chelmsford
Tel: (0245) 422208

HERTS.

Bartholomew Fayres
Herts. & Essex Antiques Centre
The Maltings, Station Rd.
Sawbridgeworth
Tel: (0279) 725809 or 36603

Also in: Essex

Lima Antiques
(Mavis & George Camm)
North House, 8 Danesbury Pk. Rd.
Welwyn
Tel: (043871) 4744

HUMBERSIDE

Seaclef Fairs Ltd.
78 Humberston Ave., Humberston
Grimsby
Tel: (0472) 813858

KENT

C. & A.J. Barmby
68 Judd Rd., Tonbridge
Tel: (0732) 356479

Darent Fairs
Whitestacks Cottage, Crockenhill
Lane, Eynsford
Tel: (0322) 863383

LINCS.

J.P. Antiques Fairs
286 High St., Lincoln
Tel: (0522) 29022

NOTTS.

Top Hat Exhibitions Ltd.
66-72 Derby Rd., Nottingham
Tel: (0602) 419143

OXON.

Portcullis Fairs
6 St. Peter's St., Wallingford
Tel: (0491) 39345

SHROPS.

Middleton Fairs (Stephen Middleton)
31 Ludlow Heights, Bridgnorth
Tel: (07462) 4114

SUFFOLK

Camfair (Ros Coltman)
Longlands, Kedington, Haverhill
Tel: (0440) 704632

Lorna Quick Fairs
St. John's Antique Centre
31 & 32 St. John's St.
Bury St. Edmunds
Tel: (0284) 3024

SURREY

Antiques & Collectors' Club
No. 1 Warehouse, Horley Row
Horley
Tel: (02934) 72206

Joan Braganza
76 Holmesdale Rd., Reigate
Tel: (07372) 45587

Cultural Exhibitions Ltd.
8 Meadrow, Godalming
Tel: (04868) 22562

Historic and Heritage Fayres
The Moorings, Molember Rd.
East Molesey
Tel: 01-398 5324

SUSSEX

Brenda Lay
Dyke Farm, West Chiltington Rd.
Pulborough
Tel: (07982) 2447

Shirley Mostyn
Mostyn Fairs
Mostyn's Antiques Centre
64 Brighton Rd., Lancing
Tel: (0903) 752961

YORKS.

Bowman Antique Fairs
7 Church Hill, Bramhope, Leeds
Tel: (0532) 843333

*Also in: Cheshire, Cleveland
Lincolnshire, Staffordshire and
Yorkshire*

Castle Galleries & Fairs
31 Castlegate, York
Tel: (0904) 27222

SHIPPERS

LONDON

Featherstone Freight Services
274 Queenstown Rd., S.W.8
Tel: 01-720 0422

Stephen Morris Shipping
89 Upper St., N.1
Tel: 01-359 3159

Phelps Ltd.
129-135 St. Margaret's Rd.
E. Twickenham
Tel: 01-892 1778/7129

DORSET

Allan Franklin Transport
5 Brunel Close
Ebblake Industrial Estate, Verwood
Tel: (0202) 826539/871354

HANTS.

Canadia Exports Ltd.
Canadiana
139 Goldsmith Ave., Hants.
Tel: (0705) 816278

HUMBERSIDE

Geoffrey Mole
400 Wincolmlee, Hull
Tel: (0482) 27858

LANCS.

West Lancs. Antique Exports
Black Horse Farm, 123 Liverpool Rd.
South Burscough, Nr. Ormskirk
Tel: (0704) 894634/35720

SOMERSET

Colin Dyte Antiques
Huntspill Rd., Highbridge
Tel: (0278) 788590

SUSSEX

A27 Antiques Warehouse
Dittons Road Industrial Estate
Polegate
Tel: (03212) 7167

British Antiques Exporters Ltd.
Queen Elizabeth Avenue
Burgess Hill
Tel: (04446) 45577

Peter Semus Antiques
The Warehouse, Gladstone Rd.
Portslade
Tel: (0273) 420154/202989

YORKS.

Micheal Bishop
Breeze Farm, Main Rd., Haisthorpe
Driffield
Tel: (0262) 89393

SCOTLAND

Mini-Move Maxi-Move (Euro) Ltd.
27 Jock's Lodge, London Rd.
Edinburgh
Tel: 031-652 1255

TRADE SUPPLIERS

Green & Stone of Chelsea
259 King's Rd., London, S.W.3
Tel: 01-352 6521/0837

C. & A.J. Barmby
Fine Art Accessories
68 Judd Rd., Tonbridge, Kent
Tel: (0732) 356479

Air Improvement Centre Ltd.
23 Denbigh St., London, S.W.1
Tel: 01-834 2834

Stanley Tools Ltd.
Woodside, Sheffield, S. Yorkshire
Tel: (0742) 78678

ANTIQUE CENTRES AND MARKETS

LONDON

A.B.C. Antique Centres
15 Flood St., S.W.3
Tel: 01-351 5353

Alfies Antique Market
13-25 Church St., N.W.8
Tel: 01-723 6066

Antiquarius Antique Market
135/141 King's Rd., S.W.3
Tel: 01-351 5353

The Antique Hypermarket
104a Kensington Church St., W.8
Tel: 01-229 5892

Bermondsey Antique Market &
Warehouse
173 Bermondsey St., S.E.1
Tel: 01-407 2040

Bond Street Antique Centre
124 New Bond St., W.1
Tel: 01-351 5353

Chenil Galleries
181-183 King's Rd., S.W.3
Tel: 01-351 5353

Hampstead Antique Emporium
12 Heath St., N.W.3
Tel: 01-794 3297

London Silver Vaults
Chancery House, 53-65 Chancery
Lane, W.C.2
Tel: 01-242 3844

AVON

Bath Antique Market
Guinea Lane, Paragon, Bath
Tel: (0225) 22510

Clifton Antiques Market
26/28 The Mall, Clifton
Tel: (0272) 741627

Great Western Antique Centre
Bartlett St., Bath
Tel: (0225) 24243

BEDFORDSHIRE

Woburn Abbey Antiques Centre
Woburn Abbey
Tel: (052525) 350

BERKSHIRE

Twyford Antiques Centre
1 High St., Twyford
Tel: (0734) 342161

BUCKINGHAMSHIRE

Antique Collectors' & Craft Market
Buckingham Town Hall

The Antiques Market
The Scout Hall, Silver Hill
Chalfont St. Giles
Tel: (02407) 4083

Great Missenden Antique Arcade
76 High St., Gt. Missenden
Tel: (02406) 2819

CAMBRIDGESHIRE

Collectors' Market
Dales Brewery, Swydir St. (off Mill
Rd.), Cambridge
Tel: (0223) 311047

CHESHIRE

Chester Antique Hypermarket
41 Lower Bridge St.
(Antique Forum Ltd.), Chester
Tel: (0244) 314991

The City of Chester Antiques Market
Guildhall, Watergate St., Chester
Tel: ((0244) 314208

Stancie Cutler Antique & Collectors
Fairs
Nantwich Civic Hall, Nantwich
Tel: (0270) 665841

CLEVELAND

Mother Hubbard's Antiques Arcade
140 Norton Rd., Stockton-on-Tees
Tel: (0642) 615603

CUMBRIA

Cockermouth Antiques Market
Main St., Cockermouth
Tel: (0900) 824346

J. W. Thornton Antiques
Supermarket
North Terrace, Bowness-on-
Windermere
Tel: (0229) 88745

DEVONSHIRE

Antique & Collectors' Fair
The Commodore Hotel, Instow
Tel: (0271) 860347

Antique Centre
19 Broad St., Town Square
South Molton
Tel: (07695) 3599

Barbican Antique Market
82-84 Vauxhall St., Plymouth
Tel: (0752) 667990/266927

New Street Antique Centre
27 New St., The Barbican, Plymouth
Tel: (0752) 661165

Torquay Antique Centre
177 Union St., Torquay
Tel: (0803) 26621

DORSET

Antique Market
Town Hall/Corn Exchange
Dorchester
Tel: (0963) 62478

Antique Market
Digby Hall, Sherborne
Tel: (0963) 62478

Antiques Trade Warehouse
28 Lorne Park Rd., Bournemouth
Tel: (0202) 292944

Barnes House Antiques Centre
West Row, Wimborne Minster
Tel: (0202) 886275

ESSEX

Antique Centre
Doubleday Corner, Coggeshall
Tel: (0376) 62646

Baddow Antiques & Craft Centre
The Bringy, Church St.
Great Baddow
Tel: (0245) 71137

Boston Hall Antiques Fair
Boston Hall Hotel, The Leas,
Westcliff-on-Sea
Tel: (0702) 714649

Maldon Antiques & Collectors'
Market
United Reformed Church Hall
Market Hill, Maldon
Tel: (07875) 2826

Orsett Antiques Fair
Orsett Hall, Prince Charles Ave.
Orsett
Tel: (0702) 714649

Trinity Antiques Centre
7 Trinity St., Colchester
Tel: (0206) 577775

GLOUCESTERSHIRE

Antique Centre
London House, High St.
Moreton-in-Marsh
Tel: (0608) 51084

Cheltenham Antique Market
54 Suffolk Rd., Cheltenham
Tel: (0242) 29812/32615/20139

Cirencester Antique Market
Market Place (Antique Forum Ltd.)
Cirencester
Tel: 01-262 1168

Gloucester Antique Centre
Severn Road, Gloucester
Tel: (0452) 29716

Tewkesbury Antique Centre
78 Church St., Tewkesbury
Tel: (0684) 294091

HAMPSHIRE

Winchester Craft & Antique Market
King's Walk, Winchester
Tel: (0962) 62277

HEREFORD & WORCESTER

Brook Farm Antiques Centre
Brook Farm, Abbot's Salford,
Nr. Evesham
Tel: (0386) 870244

Leominster Antiques Market
14 Broad St., Leominster
Tel: (0568) 2189/2155

HERTFORDSHIRE

The Herts. & Essex Antiques Centre
The Maltings, Station Rd.
Sawbridgeworth
Tel: (0279) 725809

St. Albans Antique Market
Town Hall, Chequer St., St. Albans
Tel: (0727) 66100

KENT

The Antiques Centre
120 London Rd., Sevenoaks
Tel: (0732) 452104

Canterbury Weekly Antique Market
Sidney Cooper Centre, Canterbury
(No telephone No.)

Hoodeners Antiques & Collectors'
Market
Red Cross Centre, Lower Chantry
Lane, Canterbury
Tel: (022770) 437

Hythe Antique Centre
The Old Post Office, 5 High St., Hythe
Tel: (0303) 69643

Noah's Ark Antique Centre
King St., Sandwich
Tel: (0304) 611144

The Old Rose Gallery (Antique
Market)
152 High St., Sandgate
Tel: (0303) 39173

Rochester Antiques & Flea Market
Rochester Market, Corporation St.,
Rochester
Tel: 01-262 1168

Rusthall Antique Centre
32 High St., Rusthall
Tel: (0892) 21225

Sandgate Antiques Centre
61-63 High St., Sandgate
Tel: (0303) 38987

Westerham Antique Centre
18 Market Sq., Westerham
Tel: (0959) 62080

LANCASHIRE

Accrington Antique Centre
7 Abbey St., Accrington
Tel: (0254) 35820

Bolton Thursday Antique Market
St. Paul's Parochial Hall
Tel: (0204) 51257 (Thurs. only)

Butter Lane Antique Centre
40a King St. West, Manchester
Tel: 061-834 1809

Eccles Used Furniture & Antique
Centre
325/7 Liverpool Rd., Patricroft Bridge
Eccles
Tel: 061-789 4467

Manchester Antique Hypermarket
Levenshulme Town Hall
965 Stockport Rd., Levenshulme
Tel: 061-224 2410

North Western Antique Centre
New Preston Mill (Horrockses Yard),
New Hall Lane, Preston
Tel: (0772) 798159

LEICESTERSHIRE

The Kibworth Antique Centre
5 Weir Rd., Kibworth
Tel: (053753) 2761

Leicester Antique Centre Ltd.
16-26 Oxford St., Leicester
Tel: (0533) 553006

LINCOLNSHIRE

The Antique Centre
1 Spilsby Rd., Wainfleet
Tel: (0754) 880489

Castlegate Antique Centre
23 Castlegate, Grantham
Tel: (0476) 68596

Stamford Antiques Centre
32a St. Peter's St., Stamford
Tel: (0780) 51188/54489

MERSEYSIDE

Southport Antique Centre
1 King St., Southport
Tel: (0704) 37831

NORFOLK

Coltishall Antiques Centre
High St., Coltishall
Tel: (0603) 738306

Holt Antiques Centre
Albert Hall, Albert St., Holt
Tel: (0362) 5509

The Old Granary Antique &
Collectors' Centre
King Staithe Lane, off Queen's St.
King's Lynn
Tel: (0553) 5509

Norwich Antique & Collectors' Centre
Quayside, Fye Bridge, Norwich
Tel: (0603) 612582

NORTHAMPTONSHIRE

Finedon Antiques Centre
3 Church St., Finedon
Tel: (0933) 680316

The Village Antique Market
62 High Street, Weedon
Tel: (0326) 42015

NORTHUMBERLAND

Colmans of Hexham
(Saleroom & Antique Fair)
15 St. Mary's Chare, Hexham
Tel: (0434) 603812/605522

NOTTINGHAMSHIRE

East Bridgford Antiques Centre
Main St., East Bridgford
Tel: (0949) 20540

Newark Art & Antiques Centre
The Market Place, Chain Lane
Newark
Tel: (0636) 703959

Nottingham Antique Centre
British Rail Goods Yard
London Rd., Nottingham
Tel: (0602) 54504/55548

Top Hat Antiques Centre
66-72 Derby Road, Nottingham
Tel: (0602) 49143

OXFORDSHIRE

The Antique Centre
Laurel House, Bull Ring
Market Place, Deddington
Tel: (0869) 38968

SHROPSHIRE

Ironbridge Antique Centre
Dale End, Ironbridge
Tel: (095245) 3784

Ludlow Antiques Centre
29 Corve St., Ludlow
Tel: (0584) 5157

Shrewsbury Antique Market
Frankwell Quay Warehouse
(Vintagevale Ltd.), Shrewsbury
Tel: (0734) 50916

SOMERSET

Taunton Antiques Centre
27/29 Silver St., Taunton
Tel: (0823) 89327

STAFFORDSHIRE

The Antique Centre
Royal Hotel, Walsall
Tel: (0922) 24555

Aspleys Antique Market
Compton Mill, Compton
Tel: (0538) 373396

Bridge House Antiques & Collectors'
Centre
56 Newcastle Rd., Stone
Tel: (0785) 818218

Rugeley Antique Centre
161/3 Main Rd., Rugeley
Tel: (08894) 77166

SUFFOLK

Old Town Hall Antique Centre
High St., Needham Market
Tel: (0449) 720773

St. John's Antique Centre
31-32 St. John's St.
Bury St. Edmunds
Tel: (0284) 3024

Waveney Antiques Centre
Saltgate, Beccles
Tel: (0502) 716147

SURREY

Antique Centre (East Molesey)
46 Bridge Rd., East Molesey
Tel: 01-979 4969

Antique Centre
22 Haydon Place
Corner of Martyr Rd., Guildford
Tel: (0483) 67817

Farnham Antique Centre
27 South St., Farnham
Tel: (0252) 724475

The Godalming Antiques Gallery
Church St., Godalming
Tel: (04868) 4758

Maltings Market
Bridge Sq. (Farnham Maltings
Association Ltd.)
Tel: (0252) 726234

The Old Forge Antiques Centre
The Green, Godstone
Tel: (0883) 843230

The Old Smithy Antique Centre
7 High St., Merstham
Tel: (07374) 2306

Victoria & Edward Antiques
61 West St., Dorking
Tel: (0306) 880455

SUSSEX – EAST

Antiques Centre
176 High St., Uckfield
Tel: (0825) 4948

Antique Market
Leaf Hall, Seaside, Eastbourne
Tel: (0323) 27530

Heathfield Antiques Centre
Heathfield Market, Heathfield
Tel: (042482) 387

Lewes Antiques Centre
20 Cliffe High St., Lewes
Tel: (07916) 6148

Newhaven Antique Market
28 South Way, Newhaven
Tel: (07912) 7207

Seaford's "Barn Collectors' Market"
The Barn, Church Lane, Seaford
Tel: (0323) 890010

Strand Antiques
Strand House, Rye
Tel: (0797) 222653

SUSSEX – WEST

Antiques Market
Parish Hall, South St., Lancing
Tel: (0903) 32414

Arundel Antiques Market
5 River Road, Arundel
Tel: (0903) 882012

Midhurst Antiques Market
Knockhundred Row, Midhurst
Tel: (073081) 4231

Mostyn Antiques Centre
64 Brighton Rd., Lancing
Tel: (0903) 752961

Petworth Antiques Market
East St., Petworth
Tel: (0798) 42073

Snoopers Paradise Bric-a-Brac
Market
Robert Warner & Son Ltd.
South Farm Rd., Worthing
Tel: (0903) 32710

Treasure House Antiques Market
Rear of High St., in Crown Yard,
Arundel
Tel: (0903) 883101/882908

TYNE & WEAR

Newcastle Antiques Centre
64-80 Newgate St.
Newcastle-upon-Tyne
Tel: (0632) 614577

WARWICKSHIRE

Antiques Etc.
22 Railway Terrace, Rugby
Tel: (0788) 62837

Kenilworth Monthly Antique Market
Greville Suite, De Montfort Hotel
Kenilworth
Tel: (0926) 55253

Vintage Antique Market
36 Market Place, Warwick
Tel: (0926) 491527

Warwick Antique Centre
20-22 High St., Warwick
Tel: (0962) 495704/494494/491382

WEST MIDLANDS

Birmingham Thursday Antique
Market
141 Bromsgrove St., Birmingham
Tel: 021-692 1414

The City of Birmingham Antique
Market
St. Martins Market, Edgbaston St.
Tel: 01-267 4636

WILTSHIRE

Marlborough Antiques Centre
Cavendish House, High St.
Marlborough
Tel: (0672) 2912/3570

YORKSHIRE – NORTH

Grove Collectors' Centre
Grove Road, Harrogate
Tel: (0423) 61680

West Park Antiques Pavilion
20 West Park, Harrogate
Tel: (0423) 61758

YORKSHIRE – SOUTH

Treasure House Antiques Centre
8-10 Swan Street, Bawtry
Tel: (0302) 710621

YORKSHIRE – WEST

Yorkshire Antique Centre
Queen's Rd. Mills, Queen's Rd.
Halifax
Tel: (9422) 62940)

SCOTLAND

Corner House Antiques
217 St. Vincent St., Glasgow
Tel: 041-221 1000

The Victorian Village
57 West Regent St., Glasgow
Tel: 041-332 0703

INDEX TO ADVERTISERS

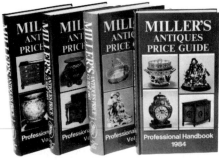